Campii and Motor Caravan Site Guide 2012

Compiled and Edited by
Reg Cade

Published by
Cade's Guides Limited,
Fairbourne Drive, Atterbury, Milton Keynes, MK10 9RG
Tel: 0844 504 9500
Email: enquiries@cades.co.uk
Website: www.cades.co.uk

Design and Administration
Mary Soper

Advertisement Manager
Malcolm Johnson

Printed by
Acorn Web Offset, Normanton, West Yorkshire

Distribution (Booktrade)
Kuperard
59 Hutton Grove, London, N12 8DS

(Camping and Caravan Trade)
Cade's Guides Limited (address above)

ISBN 1 - 905963 - 10 - 6

Dear Reader

Welcome to the 2012 edition of 'Cade's Camping, Touring & Motor Caravan Site Guide', our 41st Edition. Cade's truly were the pioneers in 'Campsite' guides back in 1971, and despite many immitators, still today remain the best selling, most accurate and up to date guides available. Of course we have a website too these days, but we know that you can't beat a hand held book for ease of use when comparing sites throughout different regions and this is confirmed by the thousands of readers buying Cade's each year.

In this publication you will find details on over 1,800 Touring Parks. The information we feature has been provided to us by the owners or operators of each park and has been updated, as always. So popular is Cade's, that we have had to add even more pages this year to accommodate all the information.

We are not agents for the parks, nor they of us, and we publish only such information as is supplied to us by them, in good faith. The Trade Descriptions Act binds Park owners and operators to accurately describe their facilities, however you should always check directly with the Park that any particular facility which is important to you during your stay, would be available at that time. Certain things such as entertainment, site shops, swimming pools etc. are often only available during peak season and obviously our publication cannot allow for every eventuality. Most parks produce a brochure or leaflet of their own describing them in greater detail, and they are happy to send them out on request.

Do remember to use the Discount Vouchers worth £40 which you will find at the back of this guide. They entitle you you to a one pound per night reduction on pitch fees at certain Parks throughout the guide. Look out for the voucher symbol ⬛ on the facilities line in the Park descriptions. Use of the vouchers can save you over three times the cover price of this guide.

Towards the back of the guide there is a useful Classified Section, providing information on suppliers of various products and services throughout the caravan and camping trade.

If you have a Touring Caravan, you may like to know Cade's now insure them. Visit our website www.cadesinsurance.co.uk or call us FREE on 0800 090 1660 for the same great price. You have trusted Cade's to provide the best in touring park information for over 40 years, why not trust us to insure your van? Thousands do.

All that remains now is for us to thank you for choosing Cade's and to wish you all the very best for your touring holidays in 2012.

The Cade's Team

Foreword 3
Symbols 6

ENGLAND
Berkshire 12
Bristol 12
Buckinghamshire 13
Cambridgeshire 14
Channel Islands 16
Cheshire 17
Cornwall 18
Cumbria 43
Derbyshire 53
Devon 58
Dorset 79
Durham 90
Essex 91
Gloucestershire 94
Hampshire 97
Herefordshire 100
Hertfordshire 102
Isle of Man 102
Isle of Wight 102
Kent 104
Lancashire 109
Leicestershire 112
Lincolnshire 112
London 118
Manchester 119
Merseyside 119
Norfolk 119
Northamptonshire 130
Northumberland 130
Nottinghamshire 133
Oxfordshire 135
Shropshire 136
Somerset 138
Staffordshire 151
Suffolk 152
Surrey 155
Sussex (East) 155
Sussex (West) 157
Warwickshire 160
West Midlands 160
Wiltshire 161
Worcestershire 163
York (County of) 164
Yorkshire, East 165
Yorkshire, North 166

Yorkshire, South 178
Yorkshire, West 178

WALES
Anglesey 180
Bridgend 182
Caerphilly 182
Carmarthenshire 182
Ceredigion
(Cardiganshire) 184
Conwy 187
Denbighshire 188
Flintshire 189
Gwynedd 189
Merthyr Tydfil 198
Monmouthshire 198
Newport 198
Pembrokeshire 198
Powys 203
Swansea 206
Vale of Glamorgan 206
Wrexham 206

SCOTLAND
Aberdeenshire 207
Angus 208
Argyll & Bute 209
Ayrshire, North 210
Ayrshire, South 210
Dumfries & Galloway.. 212
Edinburgh 215
Fife 215
Highland 216
Lanarkshire, North 222
Lanarkshire, South 222
Lothian, East 222
Lothian, West 223
Morayshire 223
Orkney Islands 224
Perth & Kinross 224
Scottish Borders 225
Stirlingshire 226
Western Isles 227

NORTHERN IRELAND
Antrim 228
Armagh 229
Belfast 229
Down 229
Fermanagh 230
Londonderry 230
Tyrone 231

REPUBLIC OF IRELAND
Cavan 231
Clare 231
Cork 232
Donegal 233
Dublin 233
Galway 233
Kerry 233
Kilkenny 234
Leitrim 235
Limerick 235
Louth 235
Mayo 235
Roscommon 236
Sligo 236
Tipperary 236
Waterford 237
Westmeath 237
Wexford 237
Wicklow 237

Sites Open All Year ... 238

Adult Only Parks 242

Fishing on Site 244

Classified Ads 249

Map Section 255

Pitch Fee Discount Vouchers 265

ENGLAND

⋏ Tents	⋏ Tentes
⌂ Motor Caravans	⌂ Auto-Caravanes
⌂ Touring Caravans	⌂ Caravanes
⌂ U.S. R.V.'s	⌂ Auto-Caravanes (Etats Unis)
≢ Nearest Station	≢ Gare Locale
♿ Facilities for Disabled	♿ Handicapés
⚠ No Motorcycles	⚡ Branchments Electrique Pour Caravanes
⚡ Electricity Hook-ups	▣ Emplacement Service Complet
▣ Fully Serviced Pitches	▣ Emplacement Surface Dure
▣ Hard Standings	⚠ Motorcyclettes Non-Admises
▥ Flush Toilets	▥ Toilettes
⚲ Water	⚲ Eau
↑ Showers	↑ Douches
☉ Shaver Points	☉ Prises Electrique pour Rasoirs
⌐ Washing Facilities	⌐ Bains
▬ Ironing Facilities	▬ Repassage
▣ Launderette	▣ Laverie Automatique
♟ Chem. Toilet Disposal	♟ Décharge pour W.C. Chemique
S⚑ Site Shop	S⚑ Magasin du Terrain
M⚑ Mobile Shop	M⚑ Magasin Mobile
I⚑ Local Shop	I⚑ Magasin du Quartier
⌀ Gas	⌀ Gaz
☎ Public Telephone	☎ Cabines Téléphoniques
✗ Café Restaurant	✗ Café
⚐ Licensed Club	⚐ Club/Bar Patenté
⛶ T.V.	⛶ Salle de Télévision
♣ Games Room	♣ Salle de Jeux
⋒ Childs Play Area	⋒ Terrain de Jeux Enfants
⤳ Outdoor Pool	⤳ Piscine du Terrain
⤳ Indoor Pool	⤳ Piscine a l'interieur
❀ Sports Area	❀ Terrain de Sports et de Jeux
⋈ Pets Welcome	✐ Pêche sur place
✐ Fishing on Site	▣ Stationment à côté de la caravane permis
▣ Parking by Unit	▣ Carte Credit Accepter
▣ Credit Cards Accepted	▣ Bon Remise 'Cades' Accepter
▣ Money-Off Vouchers	A Camping Seulment Adulte
A Adults Only Park	⚘ Emplacements pour La Saison
⚘ Seasonal Pitches	⚲ Gardiennage
⚲ Secure Storage	📶 Wi-Fi
📶 Wi-Fi Access	
Nearby Facilities	Nearby Facilities
⌐ Golf	⌐ Golf
✐ Fishing	✐ Pêche
⚓ Sailing	⚓ Voile
⤳ Boating	⤳ Canotage
∪ Riding	∪ Equitation
⤳ Water Ski-ing	⤳ Ski Nautique
℘ Tennis	℘ Tennis
⤳ Climbing	⤳ Ascension

6

Enjoy your holiday
Choose Best of British

A group of **five star** privately owned prestigious
Touring and Holiday Parks to suit all tastes with
a warm and friendly welcome wherever you go

the
Bestof
British
quality touring and holiday parks

www.bob.org.uk

PO Box 28249 Edinburgh EH9 2YZ

VISIT **www.cades.co.uk** TO SEE OUR MONTHLY COMPETITION

Where good times come naturally

Whether it's a back to nature experience you're looking for or a range of on-site facilities, we have a site that will suit you down to the ground. Set up camp in the seclusion of the trees or on a heathland clearing; sleep under canvas in a leafy glade or by the shore of a loch or stream.

A Forest Holiday is about taking time to do the things you enjoy the most, whether that's discovering something new, getting active or simply relaxing in beautiful woodland surroundings. It's all about choice... and whatever you choose, our sites are the perfect place.

Scotland
Ardgartan
Cashel
Cobleland

Wales
Beddgelert

Forest of Dean
Bracelands
Christchurch

New Forest
Aldridge Hill, Ashurst
Denny Wood & Matley Wood
Hollands Wood, Holmsley
Ocknell & Longbeech
Roundhill, Setthorns

Scotland
Glenmore

Yorkshire
Spiers House

Norfolk
Thorpe

Wiltshire
Postern Hill

For more information call
0845 130 8224 / 024 7642 3008
www.campingintheforest.com

forestholidays
Caravan & Camping

ENGLAND

BERKSHIRE

DORNEY REACH
Amerden Caravan Site, Off Old Marsh Lane, Dorney Reach, Nr Maidenhead, Berkshire, SL6 0EE
Tel: 01628 627461
Email:
beverly@amerdencaravanpark.co.uk
www.amerdencaravanpark.webs.com
Pitches For Å 🚐 🚃
Acreage 3 **Open** April **to** October
Access Good **Site** Level
Nearest Bus Stop (Miles) 1¼
Near River Thames.
Facilities 🛁 ⃒ 🎇 🕈 ⌐ ☉ ⌐ ⊿ 🗑 🚽
🎇 🛆 ⏸ 🖳
Nearby Facilities ⌐ ✓ ⏚ 🗲 ∪ ♪ ♫
Nearest Town Maidenhead
Directions Leave M4 junc 7, Slough West, then A4 towards Maidenhead. Turn left at second set of traffic lights signposted Dorney Reach and caravan site, then first turn right.
🚆 Taplow

HURLEY
Hurley Riverside Park, Hurley, Nr Maidenhead, Berkshire, SL6 5NE
Tel: 01628 824493/823501
Email: info@hurleyriversidepark.co.uk
www.hurleyriversidepark.co.uk
Pitches For Å 🚐 🚃 **Total** 200
Acreage 15 **Open** March **to** October
Access Good **Site** Level
Nearest Bus Stop (Miles) Outside
Family-run Park alongside the River Thames with access to the Thames Path. Ideal for visiting Legoland® Windsor, Oxford and Henley. Discounted tickets for Legoland available to purchase. Disabled toilets. Slipway, nature trail and riverside picnic ground. David Bellamy Gold and Special Distinction Awards. Fully serviced Caravan Holiday Homes and ReadyTents for hire.
Facilities 🛁 ⃒ 🗲 🎇 🕈 ⌐ ☉ ⌐ 🗑 🖳 🚽
🌡 🎇 🛆 🚿 ✹ ⌐ ⏸ 🖳 🛜
Nearby Facilities ⌐ ✓ ⌖ ∪
Nearest Town Henley-on-Thames

Directions Maidenhead, A4130 west towards Henley. After 3¼ miles turn right, ¾ mile past Hurley Village, into Shepherds Lane. Entrance 200 yards on left.
🚆 Maidenhead/Henley-on-Thames

NEWBURY
Oakley Farm Caravan Park, Oakley Farm House, Penwood Road, Wash Water, Newbury, Berkshire, RG20 0LP
Tel: 01635 36581
Email: info@oakleyfarm.co.uk
www.oakleyfarm.co.uk
Pitches For Å 🚐 🚃 **Total** 30
Acreage 3 **Open** March **to** October
Access Good **Site** Gentle Slope
Nearest Bus Stop (Miles) ½
Not suitable for caravans over 22 foot long.
Facilities ⃒ 🎇 🕈 ⌐ ☉ 🚽 🖳 🖳
Nearby Facilities ⌐
Nearest Town Newbury
Directions From the A34 south of Newbury take the exit marked Highclere and Wash Common. Turn left onto the A343 towards Newbury, turn right after ¼ mile (by car sales garage) into Penwood Road. Site is then 400 metres on your left.
🚆 Newbury

RISELEY
Wellington Country Park, Odiham Road, Riseley, Berkshire, RG7 1SP
Tel: 01189 326444
Email: info@wellington-country-park.co.uk
www.www.wellington-country-park.co.uk
Pitches For Å 🚐 🚃 **Total** 72
Acreage 6 **Open** Mid March **to** Nov
Access Good **Site** Level
Nearest Bus Stop (Miles) ¼
Set within a country park with childrens play areas and nature walks. Ideal base for touring.
Facilities ⃒ 🗇 🎇 🕈 ⌐ ☉ ⌐ 🗑 🖳 🚽
🌡 🛆 🖳 ✕ 🗇 🖳 🖳
Nearby Facilities ⌐ ∪
Nearest Town Reading
Directions From the M4 junction 11 follow the A33 south towards Basingstoke. The park is signposted from the roundabout at the end of the dual carriageway.
🚆 Mortimer

BRISTOL (County of)

BRISTOL
Baltic Wharf Caravan Club Site, Cumberland Road, Bristol, BS1 6XG
Tel: 0117 926 8030
www.caravanclub.co.uk
Pitches For 🚐 🚃 **Total** 55
Acreage 2½ **Open** All Year
Access Good **Site** Level
Nearest Bus Stop (Miles) Outside
Quiet waterside site ½ mile from the town centre. River ferry service to the city centre in Summer. Near to Bristol Zoo, SS Great Britain and museums. Non members welcome. Booking essential.
Facilities 🛁 ⃒ 🎇 🕈 ⌐ ⌐ ⊿ 🗑 🚽
🌡 🛆 🖳 ⏸ 🖳 🛜
Nearby Facilities ⌐
Directions Leave the M5 at junction 18 and take the A4. After Clifton Suspension Bridge keep in left lane and follow signs to harbour. At lights stay in right lane through Hotwells, go over the crossing and move to left lane, go over bridge following signs for SS Great Britain. Site is 500yds on left.
🚆 Bristol Temple Meads

BRISTOL
Brook Lodge Touring Caravan & Camping Park, Cowslip Green, Bristol, BS40 5RB
Tel: 01934 862311
Email: info@brooklodgefarm.com
www.brooklodgefarm.com
Pitches For Å 🚐 🚃 **Total** 29
Acreage 4½ **Open** 18-Mar **to** 01-Nov
Access Good **Site** Mostly Level
Beautiful grounds with mature trees, lawns and garden, nestled in view of the nearby Mendip Hills. Trout fishing at Blagdon Lake 2 miles. Bird life and walks. Graded 3 Stars, AA 3 Pennants, ANWB Approved, Green Business Bronze Award, ETC and Welcome International.
Facilities ⃒ 🗇 🎇 🕈 ⌐ ☉ ⌐ 🗑
🌡 🛆 🖳 ⏸ 🖳
Nearby Facilities ⌐ ✓ ⌖ ∪ ♪ ⌖
Directions From Bristol take A38 south west for 9 miles, Park is signposted on the left. Or from the M5 junc 18 take A4 then A370, turn left to Barrow Gurney on B3130 to A38. After

Bristol Airport Park is 3 miles. 1 mile from the Darlington Arms to the bottom of the hill, opposite the Holiday Inn..

BUCKINGHAMSHIRE
BEACONSFIELD
Highclere Farm Country Touring Park, Newbarn Lane, Seer Green, Nr Beaconsfield, Buckinghamshire, HP9 2QZ
Tel: 01494 874505
Email: highclerepark@aol.com
www.highclerefarmpark.co.uk
Pitches For Å ⊕ ⊕ **Total** 100
Acreage 6 **Open** March **to** January
Access Good **Site** Level
Nearest Bus Stop (Miles) Outside
Near to Legoland, Chiltern Air Museum, Miltons Cottage, Odds Farm (Rare Breeds), Bekonscot, Amersham and London.
Facilities ᕼ ╏ ⊟ ⊞ ⚑ ʆ ⌐ ⊙ ↲ ⌂ ⧄ ☎
🕻 🛈 ◉ ⊖ ⚑ ⊬ ⊟ ⊡
Nearby Facilities ⌐ ⌰ ∪ ℛ
Nearest Town Beaconsfield
Directions Leave the M40 at junction 2, go into Beaconsfield and take the A355 towards Amersham. After 1 mile turn right to Seer Green and follow tourist signs.
⇞ Seer Green

MILTON KEYNES
Gulliver's Milton Keynes Camping & Caravanning Club Site, Livingstone Drive, Milton Keynes, Buckinghamshire, MK15 0DT
Tel: 02476 475580
www.campingandcaravanningclub.co.uk/gullivers
Pitches For Å ⊕ ⊕ **Total** 90
Open 29-Mar **to** 05-Nov

Access Good **Site** Level
Nearest Bus Stop (Miles) ½
Adjacent to Gulliver's Land Theme Park and near a lake. Just a short drive to Central Milton Keynes. Pods for Glamping. Excellent location for footpaths and cycle routes. Non members welcome. You can also call us on 0845 130 7633.
Facilities ᕼ ╏ ⊟ ⊞ ⚑ ʆ ⌐ ⊙ ↲ ⌂ ☎
⊟ ◉ ⚑ ⊬ ⊟ ⊡ ⊚
Nearby Facilities ⌐ ⌰ ⊥ ⊀ ∪ ∂ ℛ ↂ
Nearest Town Milton Keynes
Directions From the M1 take the A509 towards Central Milton Keynes and follow signs for Gullivers Theme Park (on the V10 Brickhill Street).
⇞ Milton Keynes

NEWPORT PAGNELL
Lovat Meadow Touring Caravan Park, c/o Middleton Pool, Tickford Street, Newport Pagnell, Buckinghamshire, MK16 9BG
Tel: 01908 610477
Email: middletonpool@newport-pagnell.org.uk
www.newport-pagnell.org.uk
Pitches For ⊕ ⊕ **Total** 40
Open 05-Apr **to** 31-Oct
Access Good **Site** Lev/Slope
Nearest Bus Stop (Miles) ¼
Situated by a small river. Ideal for Central Milton Keynes with its shopping centre and Xscape, also for the MK Bowl.
Facilities ╏ ☎ ⊡ 🏊 ⊟ ⊡ ⊡
Nearby Facilities ⌐ ⌰ ⊥ ⊀ ∪ ∂ ℛ ↂ
Nearest Town Newport Pagnell
Directions 1½ miles from the M1 junction 14. From Newport Pagnell town centre, turn into St Johns Street, go over the iron bridge onto London Road and the Park entrance is on the right after the BP Garage.
⇞ Milton Keynes

STONY STRATFORD
Cosgrove Park, Cosgrove, Milton Keynes, Buckinghamshire, MK19 7JP
Tel: 01908 563360
Email: enquiries@cosgrovepark.co.uk
www.cosgrovepark.co.uk
Pitches For ⊕ ⊕ **Total** 400
Acreage 180 **Open** 01-Apr **to** 01-Nov
Access Good **Site** Lev/Slope
Nearest Bus Stop (Miles) ¼
180 acres of parkland featuring twelve lakes and two rivers. **See our advertisement on the next page.**
Facilities ᕼ ╏ ⊞ ⚑ ʆ ⌐ ⊖ ⊡ ☎
🕻 🛈 ◉ ◈ ✕ ⊓ ↘ ⊬ ⊟ ⊡ ⊡ ⌰ ⚡ ⊚
Nearby Facilities ⌐ ⌰ ⊥ ⊀ ∪ ↂ
Nearest Town Stony Stratford
Directions From the A5 roundabout at Old Stratford in Milton Keynes, take the A508 then turn second right and go through Cosgrove Village.
⇞ Wolverton

CAMBRIDGESHIRE

CAMBRIDGE

Appleacre Park, London Road, Fowlmere, Cambridgeshire, SG8 7RU
Tel: 01763 208354
Email: ajbearpark@aol.com
www.appleacrepark.co.uk
Pitches For A ⬚ ⬚ **Total** 23
Acreage 3 **Open** All Year
Access Good **Site** Level
Nearest Bus Stop (Miles) Entrance
A small pleasant Park at the southern end of the village. Only 3 miles from Duxford Imperial War Museum. RSPB Nature Reserve just a 20 minute walk away.
Facilities ⌁ ⊡ ⬚ ⬚ ⬚ ⬚ ⬚ ⬚ ⬚ ⬚
⬚ ⬚ ⬚ ⬚
Nearby Facilities ⬚ ⬚ ⬚ ⬚
Nearest Town Cambridge
Directions 9 miles south of Cambridge on the B1368 through Fowlmere Village on the left hand side.
⬚ Foxton

CAMBRIDGE

Cherry Hinton Caravan Club Site, Lime Kiln Road, Cherry Hinton, Cambridgeshire, CB1 8NQ
Tel: 01223 244088
www.caravanclub.co.uk
Pitches For A ⬚ ⬚ **Total** 60

Acreage 5½ **Open** All Year
Access Good **Site** Level
Nearest Bus Stop (Miles) ½
Set in old quarry works with imaginative landscaping. Only ½ a mile from Cambridge town centre. Close to the American War Cemetary, Duxford Imperial War Museum, Wicken Fen Nature Reserve, Wimpole Hall and Audley End House & Gardens. Non members welcome. Booking essential.
Facilities ⬚ ⌁ ⊡ ⬚ ⬚ ⬚ ⬚ ⬚ ⬚ ⬚
⬚ ⬚ ⬚ ⬚ ⬚ ⬚
Nearby Facilities ⬚ ⬚
Nearest Town Cambridge
Directions From south west on A10, pass over M11 junc 11 and continue onto A1309 sp Cambridge. At the fifth set of traffic lights turn right into Long Road (A1134). After 1½ miles at the roundabout continue to Queen Ediths Way, after 1 mile turn right into Lime Kiln Road.
⬚ Cambridge

CAMBRIDGE

Highfield Farm Touring Park, Highfield Farm, Long Road, Comberton, Cambridge, Cambridgeshire, CB23 7DG
Tel: 01223 262308
Email: enquiries@highfieldfarmtouringpark.co.uk
www.highfieldfarmtouringpark.co.uk
Pitches For A ⬚ ⬚ **Total** 120

Acreage 8 **Open** April to October
Access Good **Site** Level
Nearest Bus Stop (Miles) ½
Well maintained, long established family run Touring Park. 1½ miles of farmland walks. Close to the historic University City of Cambridge, and the Imperial War Museum, Duxford. Calor Caravan Park Awards 2002, Best Park in England (Finalist).
Facilities ⌁ ⊡ ⬚ ⬚ ⬚ ⬚ ⬚ ⬚ ⬚ ⬚ ⬚
⬚ ⬚ ⬚ ⬚ ⬚ ⬚ ⬚ ⬚ ⬚
Nearby Facilities ⬚ ⬚ ⬚
Nearest Town Cambridge
Directions From Cambridge - Leave A1303/A428 (Bedford) after 3 miles, follow camping signs to Comberton. From M11 - Leave junction 12, take A603 (Sandy) for ½ mile then B1046 to Comberton (2 miles).
⬚ Cambridge

EARITH

Westview Marina, High Street, Earith, Huntingdon, Cambridgeshire, PE28 3PN
Tel: 01487 841627
Email: elainefidler@homecall.co.uk
Pitches For A ⬚ ⬚ **Total** 28
Acreage 2 **Open** March to October
Access Good **Site** Level
Nearest Bus Stop (Miles) Outside
River frontage. Ideal touring.
Facilities ⌁ ⬚ ⬚ ⬚ ⬚ ⬚ ⬚ ⬚ ⬚
Nearby Facilities ⬚ ⬚ ⬚ ⬚ ⬚

Nearest Town St. Ives (Cambs)
Directions 5 miles from St. Ives and 12 miles from Cambridge.
☞ Huntingdon

ELY

Riverside Caravan & Camping Park, 21 New River Bank, Littleport, Ely, Cambridgeshire, CB7 4TA
Tel: 01353 860255
Email: riversideccp@btopenworld.com
www.riversideccp.co.uk
Pitches For Å ⊞ ⊞ **Total** 49
Acreage 4½ **Open** All Year
Access Good **Site** Level
Nearest Bus Stop (Miles) ¼
ADULTS ONLY site alongside the River Ouse for fishing and boating. 5 miles from the historic city and cathedral of Ely.
Facilities ∮ ⊞ ⊞ ⌂ ⊙ ⊖ ⊿ ♣
⌷ ⊙ ⊟ ⊞ Å ⊁ ⊚
Nearby Facilities ⌐ ✓ ⊥ ⊾ ∪ ♞ ⚡
Nearest Town Ely
Directions On the A10, 5 miles north of Ely, cross the River Ouse and turn right at the roundabout.
☞ Littleport

GRAFHAM

Grafham Water Caravan Club Site, Church Road, Grafham, Huntingdon, Cambridgeshire, PE28 0BB
Tel: 01480 810264
www.caravanclub.co.uk
Pitches For ⊞ ⊞ **Total** 87
Acreage 6½ **Open** All Year
Access Good **Site** Level
Nearest Bus Stop (Miles) ½
Near to Grafham Water. Refurbished amenity block. David Bellamy Gold Award for Conservation 2005. Non members welcome. Booking essential.
Facilities ⅙ ∮ ⊞ ⊞ ⌂ ⊙ ⊖ ⊿ ⊞ ⊙ ⊚
⌷ ⊙ ⊟ ⊞ Å ⊸ ⊞ ⊟ ⊚
Nearby Facilities ⌐ ✓ ⊥ ⊾ ∪ ♞
Nearest Town Huntingdon
Directions From the A1 at Buckden roundabout follow caravan park signs. From the A14 leave at Ellington and follow caravan park signs from the village.
☞ Huntingdon

GREAT SHELFORD

Cambridge Camping & Caravanning Club Site, 19 Cabbage Moor, Great Shelford, Cambridgeshire, CB22 5NB
Tel: 01223 841185
www.campingandcaravanningclub.co.uk/cambridge
Pitches For Å ⊞ ⊞ **Total** 120
Open 29-Mar **to** 05-Nov
Site Level
Nearest Bus Stop (Miles) ¼
On the outskirts of the city of Cambridge. 6 miles from Duxford Imperial War Museum and the American Cemetery. Boat launching. Dog Walk. 4 Star Graded and AA 3 Pennants. Non members welcome. You can also call us on 0845 130 7633.
Facilities ⅙ ∮ ⊞ ⊞ ⌂ ⊙ ⊖ ⊿ ⊞ ⊙ ⊚
⌷ ⊙ ⊟ ⊞ ⊟ ⊞ ⊚
Nearby Facilities ⌐ ✓ ∪

Directions Leave the M11 at junction 11 onto the B1309 signposted Cambridge. At the first set of traffic lights turn right, after ½ mile you will see the site sign on the left hand side pointing down the lane.
☞ Great Shelford

HUNTINGDON

Burliegh Hill Farm, Somersham Road, St Ives, Huntingdon, Cambs., PE27 3LY
Tel: 01480 462173
Email: mschwier@talk21.com
Pitches For Å ⊞ ⊞ ⊞ **Total** 40
Acreage 8 **Open** All Year
Access Good **Site** Level
Nearest Bus Stop (Miles) ½
Relaxing picturesque parkland area. Walkways and trees around the farm with information plaques and environmental projects to see. Ideal for nature lovers and walkers. You can also call us on Mobile: 07855 286238.
Facilities ⅙ ⊞ ⌂ ⊙ ⊖ ⊿ ⌷ ⊞ ♞
Nearby Facilities ⌐ ✓ ⊥ ⊾ ∪ ♗ ♞
Nearest Town St Ives
Directions From the M11 north of Cambridge (which becomes the A14 to Huntingdon), take the A1096 to St. Ives, cross the river bridge and roundabout and follow the B1040 towards Somersham. Go past St. Ives Industrial Estate on the left, at the mini roundabout turn le
☞ Huntingdon

HUNTINGDON

Houghton Mill Caravan Club Site, Mill Street, Houghton, Huntingdon, Cambridgeshire, PE28 2AZ
Tel: 01480 466716
www.caravanclub.co.uk
Pitches For ⊞ ⊞ **Total** 65
Acreage 8½ **Open** March **to** Nov
Access Good **Site** Level
Nearest Bus Stop (Miles) ½
On the banks of the River Great Ouse. Adjacent to Houghton Mill working watermill. Ideal for walkers, bird watchers and wildlife enthusiasts. Non members welcome. Booking essential.
Facilities ⅙ ∮ ⊞ ⌂ ⊙ ⌷ ⊙ ⊟ ⊸ ⊞
Nearby Facilities ⌐ ✓ ⊥ ⊾
Nearest Town Huntingdon
Directions From the A1(M)/A1 turn onto the A14 sp Huntingdon, then take the A141. At Texaco roundabout turn onto the A1123 sp Houghton, after 1¼ miles turn right sp Houghton, continue into Mill Street, pass the church and site is on the left.
☞ Huntingdon

HUNTINGDON

Huntingdon Boathaven & Caravan Park, The Avenue, Godmanchester, Huntingdon, Cambridgeshire, PE18 8AF
Tel: 01480 411977
Email: boathaven.hunts@virgin.net
www.huntingdonboathaven.co.uk
Pitches For Å ⊞ ⊞ **Total** 35
Acreage 2 **Open** March **to** October
Access Good **Site** Level
Nearest Bus Stop (Miles) ¼
Marina and caravan park situated on the

Great River Ouse. Near to many tourist attractions. Limited fishing on site.
Facilities ⅙ ∮ ⊞ ⊞ ⌂ ⊙ ⊖ ⊟
⌷ ⊙ ⊸ ⊟ ⊿ ♣
Nearby Facilities ⌐ ✓ ⊥ ♞
Nearest Town Cambridge
Directions From the A14 turn off to Godmanchester and travel towards Huntingdon. Turn left before the fly-over to Huntingdon Boathaven.
☞ Huntingdon

HUNTINGDON

Quiet Waters Caravan Park, Hemingford Abbots, Huntingdon, Cambridgeshire, PE28 9AJ
Tel: 01480 463405
Email: quietwaters.park@btopenworld.com
www.quietwaterscaravanpark.co.uk
Pitches For Å ⊞ ⊞ **Total** 20
Acreage ½ **Open** April **to** October
Access Good **Site** Level
Nearest Bus Stop (Miles) Outside
In the centre of a riverside village, good for fishing and boating.
Facilities ⅙ ⊞ ⌂ ⊙ ⊖ ⊿ ⊞ ⊙ ⊚
⌷ ⊙ ⊟ ⊸ ⊟ ⊞ ⊿ ♣ ⊚
Nearby Facilities ⌐ ✓ ⊾ ∪
Nearest Town St Ives/Huntingdon
Directions Junction 25 off the A14. West of Cambridge on the A14, after 12 miles look for Hemingford Abbots, we are 1 mile into the village. 3 miles east of Huntingdon on the A14.
☞ Huntingdon

HUNTINGDON

Stroud Hill Park, Fen Road, Pidley, Huntingdon, Cambridgeshire, PE28 3DE
Tel: 01487 741333
Email: stroudhillpark@btconnect.com
www.stroudhillpark.co.uk
Pitches For Å ⊞ ⊞ **Total** 60
Open All Year
Access Good **Site** Lev/Slope
Nearest Bus Stop (Miles) ½
Quiet, attractive, rural, ADULTS ONLY site. Set in ancient bluebell woodland on a 150 acre family farm. Tennis on site. 18 hole golf course next door.
Facilities ⅙ ∮ ⊞ ⊞ ⌂ ⊙ ⊖ ⊿ ⊞ ⊙ ⊚
⌷ ⊙ ⊚ ✗ ♈ ⊸ ⊟ ⊞ ⊿ ⊚
Nearby Facilities ⌐
Nearest Town St. Ives
Directions Take the A141 signposted March, 4 miles from St Ives and 7 miles from Huntingdon.
☞ Huntingdon

HUNTINGDON

The Willows Caravan Park, Bromholme Lane, Brampton, Huntingdon, Cambridgeshire, PE18 8NE
Tel: 01480 437566
Email: willows@willows33.freeserve.co.uk
www.thewillowscaravanpark.com
Pitches For Å ⊞ ⊞ ⊞ **Total** 70
Acreage 4 **Open** All Year
Access Good **Site** Level
Nearest Bus Stop (Miles) ¼

CAMBRIDGESHIRE, CHANNEL ISLANDS

Situated on Ouse Valley Way, attractive walks. Launching area for boats and canoes. Fishing and boating available. Separate tent field. No groundsheets. Heated toilet block. Resident wardens on site. Country park, Grafham Water and sports facilities nearby. Site is Caravan Club, Camping & Caravanning Club and AA Listed.
Facilities ♿ ⚡ 🚽 ♨ ⛐ 🔌 ☉ ⌂ 🗑 🛁
🍴 🗙 🛖 📖 ♨
Nearby Facilities ┍ ╱ ⚓ ⚐ ⅃
Nearest Town Huntingdon
Directions Brampton is situated between the A1 and the A14 (formerly A604). Follow the B1514 through Brampton towards Huntingdon, taking right hand signposted turning into Bromholme Lane.
⚏ Huntingdon

HUNTINGDON

Wyton Lakes Holiday Park, Banks End, Wyton, Huntingdon, Cambridgeshire, PE28 2AA
Tel: 01480 412715
Email: loupeter@supanet.com
www.wytonlakes.com
Pitches For ⚑ 🚐 🚌 **Total** 80
Acreage 12½ **Open** April **to** Oct
Access Good **Site** Level
Nearest Bus Stop (Miles) ¼
ADULTS ONLY site situated alongside a river with four fishing lakes on site.
Facilities ♿ ⚡ 🚽 🔌 ♨ ⛐ ☉ ⌂ 🗑 🛁
🍴 ☉ ♨ 🛖 📖 ╱ ♨ ♨ 🌣 ≋
Nearby Facilities ┍ ╱
Nearest Town Huntingdon
Directions Leave the A14 at junction 23 and follow signs for the A141 March. On the 4th roundabout take the A1123 for St. Ives, park is approx. 1 mile on the right.
⚏ Huntingdon

MARCH

Floods Ferry Marina Park, Staffurths Bridge, March, Cambridgeshire, PE15 0YP
Tel: 01354 677302
www.floodsferrymarina.co.uk
Pitches For ⚑ 🚐 🚌 **Total** 7
Open All Year
Access Good **Site** Level
ADULTS ONLY PARK in a relaxed, remote location adjacent to the Old Nene River for fishing. Marina and a ramp for disabled access. Long/short term moorings. Occasional live music in the clubhouse. Ideal for walking and bird watching. You can also contact us on Mobile: 07795 525644.
Facilities ♿ ⚡ 🚽 🔌 ♨ ⛐ ☉ ⌂ 🛁
☉ ♈ 🛖 📖 ╱ ♨ 🌣
Nearby Facilities ┍ ╱ ♨
Nearest Town March
Directions 4 miles from March. Take the A141 from March towards Chatteris, look for Floods Ferry and golf course sign and take this turn, continue for 3 miles and look for park sign on the right, single lane road to the park.
⚏ March

PETERBOROUGH

Ferry Meadows Caravan Club Site, Ham Lane, Peterborough, Cambridgeshire, PE2 5UU
Tel: 01733 233526
www.caravanclub.co.uk
Pitches For ⚑ 🚐 🚌 **Total** 265
Acreage 30 **Open** All Year
Access Good **Site** Level
Nearest Bus Stop (Miles) ½
Set in a country park with plenty of activities available nearby, and a 6 acre shopping complex. Near to Nene Valley Steam Railway. Non members welcome. Booking essential.

Facilities ♿ ⚡ 🚽 ♨ ⛐ 🔌 ☉ ⌂ 🗑 🛁
🍴 ☉ 🛖 📖 ≋
Nearby Facilities ┍ ╱ ⚓ ⚐ ⅃
Nearest Town Peterborough
Directions From South on the A1, do not turn onto the A1139, instead turn left at next junction just past the service station sp Showground. At the T-junction turn left, continue and turn left sp Nene Park, continue and site is on the left.
⚏ Peterborough

ST. IVES

Crystal Lakes Leisure Park, Low Road, Fenstanton, Cambridgeshire, PE28 9HU
Tel: 01480 497728
Email: info@crystallakesleisure.com
www.crystallakesleisure.com
Pitches For ⚑ 🚐 🚌 **Total** 110
Acreage 32 **Open** March **to** Oct
Access Good **Site** Level
Nearest Bus Stop (Miles) ¼
Excellent fishing on site. Childrens indoor play centre.
Facilities ♿ ⚡ 🚽 🔌 🅵 🕀 ♨ ⛐ ☉ ⌂ 🗑 🛁
🍴 ☉ ♨ 🗙 🛖 ♨ 🛖 📖 ╱ 🌣 ≋
Nearby Facilities ┍ ╱ ⚓ ♨ ⅃
Nearest Town St Ives
Directions Turn off the A14 at junction 27 and follow caravan park signs.
⚏ Huntingdon

ST. NEOTS

Camping & Caravanning Club Site, Hardwick Road, Eynesbury, St. Neots, Cambridgeshire, PE19 2PR
Tel: 01480 474404
www.campingandcaravanningclub.co.uk/stneots
Pitches For ⚑ 🚐 🚌 **Total** 180
Acreage 11 **Open** 29-Mar **to** 05-Nov
Access Good **Site** Level
Nearest Bus Stop (Miles) ½
On the banks of the River Ouse for boating, fishing and walking. Plenty of sports facilities in the area. Non members welcome. You can also call us on 0845 130 7633.
Facilities ♿ ⚡ 🚽 🔌 ♨ ⛐ ☉ ⌂ 🗑 🛁
🍴 ☉ ♨ 🛖 📖 ☉ 🛁
Nearby Facilities ┍ ╱ ♨ ⅃
Nearest Town Cambridge
Directions From the A1 take the A428 to Cambridge, at the second roundabout turn left to Tescos, go past the sports centre and follow the international signs to the site.
⚏ Cambridge

WISBECH

Virginia Lake Caravan Park, Smeeth Road, St Johns Fen End, Wisbech, Cambridgeshire, PE14 8JF
Tel: 01945 430167/430585
Email: louise@virginialake.co.uk
www.virginialake.co.uk
Pitches For ⚑ 🚐 🚌 **Total** 98
Acreage 7 **Open** All Year
Access Good **Site** Level
Nearest Bus Stop (Miles) ½
Set in Fenland countryside with a fishing lake and clubhouse. 30 minutes from the beach.
Facilities ♿ ⚡ 🚽 🔌 🅵 🕀 ♨ ⛐ ☉ ⌂ 🗑 🛁
🍴 🍴 ☉ ♨ 🗙 🛖 ♨ 🛖 📖 ☉ ╱ 🌣 ♨
Nearby Facilities ┍ ╱ ⚓ ⅃
Nearest Town Wisbech/Kings Lynn
Directions From either direction, turn off the A47 halfway between Wisbech and Kings Lynn at the junction to Terrington St John.
⚏ Kings Lynn

CHANNEL ISLES

GUERNSEY

Fauxquets Valley Campsite, Candie Road, Castel, Guernsey, Channel Isles, GY5 7QL
Tel: 01481 255460
Email: info@fauxquets.co.uk
www.fauxquets.co.uk
Pitches For ⚑ 🚌 **Total** 120
Acreage 8 **Open** 22-Apr **to** 15-Sep
Access Poor **Site** Level
Nearest Bus Stop (Miles) ½
Situated in the middle of Guernseys beautiful countryside. Ideal for exploring beaches, other islands, towns and villages.
Facilities ♿ ⚡ 🅵 ♨ ⛐ ☉ ⌂ 🚌 🗑 🛁 🕀
🛒 ☉ 🗙 🛖 ♨ ♨ 🛖 📖 🕀
Nearby Facilities ┍ ╱ ♨ ⚓ U ⅃
Nearest Town St Peter Port
Directions From the ferry, go to the big roundabout and go straight up the hill, turn left at the top into Queens Road. Turn right at sign 'Filter In Turn', go straight through three sets of lights and turn second right after the speed bumps.

JERSEY

Beuvelande Camp Site, Beuvelande, St Martin, Jersey, Channel Isles, JE3 6EZ
Tel: 01534 853575
Email: info@campingjersey.com
www.campingjersey.com
Pitches For ⚑ 🚌 **Total** 150
Acreage 6 **Open** 01-Apr **to** 30-Sep
Site Level
Nearest Bus Stop (Miles) ¼
Caravans are now allowed on the Channel Islands by permit from Jersey Tourism. AA 5 Pennant Premier Park and listed under Best Parks in Britain.
Facilities ♿ ⚡ 🅵 ♨ ⛐ ☉ ⌂ 🚌 🗑 🛁 🕀
🛒 ☉ 🗙 🛖 ♨ ♨ 🛖 📖 🕀
Nearby Facilities
Nearest Town St. Martin
Directions From the harbour take the A6 to St. Martin Church then follow signs to camp site.

JERSEY

Rozel Camping Park, La Grande Route De Rozel, Rozel, St Martin, Jersey, Channel Isles, JE3 6AX
Tel: 01534 855200
Email: rozelcampingpark@jerseymail.co.uk
www.rozelcamping.co.uk
Pitches For ⚑ 🚌 **Total** 200
Open Mid May **to** Mid Sept
Access Good **Site** Level
Nearest Bus Stop (Miles) Entrance
Ideal for coastal walks and beaches. Take-Away food available.
Facilities ♿ ⚡ 🅵 ♨ ⛐ ☉ ⌂ 🚌 🗑 🛁
🛒 🍴 ☉ ♨ 🗙 🛖 ♨ 🛖 📖 ☉ ╱ 🌣 ≋
Nearby Facilities ┍ ╱ ⚓ ♨ U ♨ ♨ ⅃
Directions On leaving Elizabeth Harbour by La Route du Port Elizabeth, take the A1 to the east, then the A17, go to the 4th set of traffic lights and turn left onto the A6. Stay in the middle lane and continue on the A6 to Five Oaks, then St Martins Church. Take the B38 to Rozel and the park is on the right.

CHESHIRE
CHESTER

Chester Fairoaks Caravan Club Site, Rake Lane, Little Stanney, Chester, Cheshire, CH2 4HS
Tel: 0151 355 1600
www.caravanclub.co.uk
Pitches For ▲ ⊕ ⊜ **Total** 100
Acreage 8 **Open** All Year
Access Good **Site** Level
Nearest Bus Stop (Miles) ½
Pleasant open and level site with oak tree boundaries. Close to the delightful city of Chester. Non members welcome. Booking essential.
Facilities ⚬ ⵏ ⊡ ⅏ ⏃ ⌐ ⌁ ⇌ ⌿ ⊜
⅏ ⊙ ⏚ ⚓ ⊞ ⊟ ⊡ �⚷
Nearby Facilities ⌐ ⌿
Nearest Town Chester
Directions Leave the M53 at junction 10 and take the A5117 signposted Queensferry. After ¼ mile in Little Stanney turn left signposted Chorlton. Site is ¼ mile on the left.
⇌ Chester

CHESTER

Chester Southerly Holiday Park, Balderton Lane, Marlston-cum-Lache, Chester, Cheshire, CH4 9LB
Tel: 01244 671308
Email: stay@chestersoutherly.co.uk
www.chestersoutherly.co.uk
Pitches For ▲ ⊕ ⊜ **Total** 90
Acreage 8 **Open** All Year
Access Good **Site** Level
Nearest Bus Stop (Miles) ¼
Easy access to North Wales and the coast. Ideal for visiting Chester city and zoo.
Facilities ⚬ ⵏ ⊡ ⏃ ⏚ ⌐ ⌁ ⇌ ⌁ ⊡ ⊜
⅏ ⊙ ⚓ ⏚ ⊞ ⊟ ⊡ ⌿ ⌖
Nearby Facilities ⌐ ⌿ ⌖ ∪ ⌯
Nearest Town Chester
Directions Leave the A55 at exit 36 and follow caravan symbols. Just 2 mins off the A55.
⇌ Chester

CHESTER

Manor Wood Country Caravan Park, Manor Wood, Coddington, Chester, Cheshire, CH3 9EN
Tel: 01829 782990
Email: info@manorwoodcaravans.co.uk
www.manorwoodcaravans.co.uk
Pitches For ▲ ⊕ ⊜ **Total** 25
Acreage 8 **Open** All Year
Access Good **Site** Level
Nearest Bus Stop (Miles) ¼
Excellent views. Only 15 minutes from Chester City. Fishing on site. Fantastic walks and cycleways. Golf courses within 5 minutes drive.
Facilities ⚬ ⵏ ⊡ ⏃ ⏚ ⌐ ⌁ ⊙ ⌁ ⇌ ⊡ ⊜
⅏ ⅏ ⊙ ⚓ ⚓ ⏚ ⌇ ⊞ ⊟ ⊡ ⌿ ⌖ ⌃ ⏚
Nearby Facilities ⌐ ⌿ ⌯
Nearest Town Chester
Directions From the A41 Whitchurch to Chester road, at Broxton roundabout take the A534 signposted Wrexham. Turn opposite the Cock O Barton Pub and the Park is 500 yards on the left.
⇌ Chester

CHESTER

Netherwood Touring Site, Netherwood House, Whitchurch Road, Nr Chester, Cheshire, CH3 6AF
Tel: 01244 335583
Email:
netherwood.chester@btinternet.com
www.netherwoodtouringsite.co.uk
Pitches For ⊕ ⊜ **Total** 15
Acreage 1½ **Open** March to 31-Oct
Access Good **Site** Level
Nearest Bus Stop (Miles) Outside
ADULTS ONLY site on the Shropshire Union Canal. 5 miles from a Zoo.
Facilities ⵏ ⏚ ⏃ ⊙ ⊜ ⅏ ⊙ ⌁ ⊡ ⌿ ⎍
Nearby Facilities ⌐ ⌿ ⏃ ⌖
Nearest Town Chester
Directions On A41, approx. 1 mile from Chester bypass.
⇌ Chester

KNUTSFORD

Royal Vale Caravan Park, London Road, Allostock, Knutsford, Cheshire, WA16 9JD
Tel: 01565 722355
Email: canistay@royalvale.co.uk
www.royalvale.co.uk
Pitches For ▲ ⊕ ⊜ ⊜ **Total** 52
Access Good **Site** Level
ADULTS ONLY PARK situated in the heart of Cheshire countryside, 3 miles south of the historic market town of Knutsford, which has an excellent shopping centre, fine restaurants and old inns. Country walks direct from the Park. Historic homes nearby including Tatton Park, Gawsworth Hall and Little Moreton Hall.
Facilities ⚬ ⵏ ⊟ ⊡ ⏚ ⏃ ⌐ ⊙ ⌁ ⇌ ⊡ ⊜
⊙ ⌇ ⊟ ⊡ ⚓ ⌖ ⏚
Nearby Facilities ⌐ ⌿ ∪
Nearest Town Knutsford
Directions Just off the A50 midway between Knutsford and Holmes Chapel.
⇌ Knutsford

MACCLESFIELD

Strawberry Wood Caravan Park, Home Farm, Farm Lane, Lower Withington, Macclesfield, Cheshire, SK11 9DU
Tel: 01477 571407
Email:
info@strawberrywoodcaravanpark.co.uk
www.strawberrywoodcaravanpark.co.uk
Pitches For ⊕ ⊜ **Total** 25
Acreage 5 **Open** March to October
Access Good **Site** Level
Unique site set amongst mature woodland. Large coarse fishing pond adjacent to the site.
Facilities ⵏ ⊡ ⏚ ⏃ ⌐ ⊙ ⊜ ⊡ ⌿ ⌖ ⚓
Nearby Facilities ⌐ ⌿
Nearest Town Macclesfield
Directions Leave the M6 at junction 18 and take the A54 to Holmes Chapel. Then take the A535 to Macclesfield, after 4 miles turn right onto the B5392 (Farm Lane). The site entrance is 700 yards on the right hand side.
⇌ Goostrey

NORTHWICH

Delamere Forest Camping & Caravanning Club Site, Station Road, Delamere, Northwich, Cheshire, CW8 2HZ
Tel: 01606 889231
www.campingandcaravanningclub.co.uk/delamere
Pitches For ▲ ⊕ ⊜ **Total** 80
Acreage 6 **Open** All Year
Access Good **Site** Level
Ideal for walking and cycling (bike hire). Near to Chester Zoo, Go Ape Adventure Playground, Oulton Park Raceway, Railway Age Museum and Beeston Castle. Non members welcome. You can also call us on 0845 130 7633.
Facilities ⚬ ⵏ ⊡ ⏚ ⏃ ⌐ ⊙ ⌁ ⌁ ⊡ ⊜
⊙ ⚓ ⏚ ⊞ ⊡ ⏚ ⏚
Nearest Town Frodsham
Directions From the A556 in Delamere turn into Station Road and the Site is located on the opposite side of the train tracks.
⇌ Northwich

NORTHWICH

Woodbine Cottage Caravan Park, Warrington Road, Acton Bridge, Northwich, Cheshire, CW8 3QB
Tel: 01606 852319
Email: jjdone@woodbinecottage-caravanpark.co.uk
Pitches For ▲ ⊕ ⊜ **Total** 55
Acreage 2½ **Open** March to Oct
Access Good **Site** Lev/Slope
Situated on the banks of the River Weaver. Nearby attractions including Blakemore Crafts and Anderton Boat Lift. Within easy reach of Chester, Liverpool, Manchester and the North Wales coast. Static caravans for hire. You can also contact us on Mobile: 07747 175327.
Facilities ⵏ ⊡ ⏚ ⏃ ⌐ ⊙ ⌁ ⌁ ⊡ ⊜
⊙ ⚓ ⏚ ⌖ ⚓
Nearby Facilities ⌐ ⌿ ∪ ⌯
Nearest Town Northwich
Directions Leave the M56 at Junction 10 and take the A49 towards Whitchurch. Continue across Acton Swing Bridge and the Park entrance is on the left after the Riverside Inn.
⇌ Acton Bridge

WINSFORD

Lamb Cottage Caravan Park, Dalefords Lane, Whitegate, Northwich, Cheshire, CW8 2BN
Tel: 01606 882302
Email: info@lambcottage.co.uk
www.lambcottage.co.uk
Pitches For ⊕ ⊜
Open March to October
Access Good **Site** Level
Peaceful retreat for Adults only. Ideal for touring the heart of Cheshire.
Facilities ⚬ ⵏ ⊟ ⊡ ⏚ ⏃ ⌐ ⊙ ⌁ ⌁ ⊡ ⊜
⊙ ⚓ ⏚ ⌖ ⏚ ⏚
Nearby Facilities ⌐ ⌿ ∪ ⌯
Nearest Town Winsford
Directions 1 mile from the A556.
⇌ Cuddington

ENGLAND

CORNWALL

CORNWALL

BODMIN

Camping & Caravanning Club Site, Old Callywith Road, Bodmin, Cornwall, PL31 2DZ
Tel: 01208 73834
www.campingandcaravanningclub.co.uk/bodmin
Pitches For Å ♛ ♟ **Total** 130
Acreage 11 **Open** 14-Apr **to** 31-Oct
Site Lev/Slope
Nearest Bus Stop (Miles) 1
On the edge of Bodmin Moor. Within easy reach of the coast and close to many places of interest. BTB 4 Star Graded and AA 3 Pennants. Non members welcome. You can also call us on 0845 130 7633.
Facilities ƒ ▥ ♠ ↾ ⊙ ⌐ ◨ ◘ ☻
▯ ▣ ◐ ◭ ↤ ▣ ◱ ⚘ ✧
Nearby Facilities ↾ ✔ ∪
Directions From the north stay on the A30 until signpost Bodmin, turn right crossing over the dual carriageway in front of industrial estate, then turn immediately left at international sign. Site is on the left down Old Callywith Road.
⇻ Bodmin Parkway

BODMIN

Lanarth Hotel & Caravan Park, St Kew Highway, Bodmin, Cornwall, PL30 3EE
Tel: 01208 841215
Email: lanarthhotel@live.co.uk
www.lanarthhotel.co.uk
Pitches For Å ♛ ♟ **Total** 86
Acreage 10 **Open** April to October
Access Good **Site** Level
Nearest Bus Stop (Miles) Entrance
Beautiful rural setting, conveniently situated for beaches and moors. Ideal for touring Cornwall and Devon.
Facilities ƒ ▥ ♠ ↾ ◨ ☻
▯ ▣ ▽ ↾ ↤ ▣ ☙
Nearby Facilities ↾ ✔ ⊥ ↘ ∪ ♪ ♪
Nearest Town Wadebridge
Directions On the A39 at St. Kew Highway, approx 4 miles east of Wadebridge and 8 miles west of Camelford.
⇻ Bodmin

BODMIN

Ruthern Valley Holidays, Ruthernbridge, Bodmin, Cornwall, PL30 5LU
Tel: 01208 831395
Email: info@ruthernvalley.com
www.ruthernvalley.com
Pitches For Å ♛ ♟ **Total** 26
Acreage 8½ **Open** All Year
Access Good **Site** Level
Quiet, rural, wooded location with farm animals. Glamping wigwams and pods.

Facilities ⚿ ƒ ▥ ▦ ♠ ↾ ⊙ ⌐ ◨ ◘ ☻
▯ ▣ ◐ ◭ ▯ ▣ ◱ ☙ ✧
Nearby Facilities ↾ ✔ ⊥ ↘ ∪ ♪ ♪ ✧
Nearest Town Bodmin/Wadebridge
Directions Take the A389 to Bodmin, turn off to Nanstallon and follow brown tourism signs and signs to Ruthernbridge. In Ruthernbridge, just before Stone Bridge turn left and the Park is 300 metres on the left.
⇻ Bodmin Parkway

BODMIN

South Penquite Farm, South Penquite, Blisland, Bodmin, Cornwall, PL30 4LH
Tel: 01208 850491
Email: thefarm@bodminmoor.co.uk
www.southpenquite.co.uk
Pitches For Å ♟ **Total** 40
Acreage 5 **Open** Mid April **to** October
Access Good **Site** Level
South Penquite is a 200 acre organic sheep farm set high on Bodmin Moor. Interesting farm walk.
Facilities ⚿ ▥ ♠ ↾ ⌐ ◨ ◘ ▯ ◭ ✔
Nearby Facilities ↾ ✔ ⊥ ↘ ∪
Nearest Town Bodmin
Directions Enter Cornwall on the A30 and drive for approx. 18 miles, take right turn signposted St. Breward, farm lane will be on the right after 3 miles.
⇻ Bodmin Parkway

BOSCASTLE

Lower Pennycrocker Farm, St Juliot, Boscastle, Cornwall, PL35 0BY
Tel: 01840 250257
www.pennycrocker.com
Pitches For Å ♛ ♟ ♟ **Total** 40
Acreage 4 **Open** Easter **to** Oct
Access Good **Site** Level
Nearest Bus Stop (Miles) ½
Scenic views, ideal touring.
Facilities ⚿ ƒ ▥ ♠ ↾ ⊙ ⌐ ◨ ▯ ↤ ▣
Nearby Facilities ↾ ✔ ⊥ ∪
Nearest Town Boscastle
Directions 2½ miles north of Boscastle on B3263, turn left signposted Pennycrocker.
⇻ Bodmin

BOSCASTLE

St. Tinney Farm Holidays, Otterham, Cornwall, PL32 9TA
Tel: 01840 261274
Email: info@st-tinney.co.uk
www.st-tinney.co.uk
Pitches For Å ♛ ♟ **Total** 20
Acreage 34 **Open** 27-Mar **to** 01-Oct
Nearest Bus Stop (Miles)
Own country pub with an outdoor heated swimming pool, fishing and childrens pony rides. David Bellamy Gold Award for Conservation.

Facilities ƒ ▥ ♠ ↾ ⊙ ⌐ ◨ ◘ ☻
▯ ▣ ◐ ☻ ▯ ▦ ↾ ↘ ✦ ↤ ▣ ◱ ⚘ ✧
Nearby Facilities ↾ ✔ ⊥ ↘ ∪ ♪ ♪
Nearest Town Boscastle
Directions Bypass Launceston on the A30 then take the A395 for 8 miles to Hallworthy. Turn second right onto the B3262 to the junction with the A39, turn right for Bude, after 1 mile turn right for Otterham.
⇻ Bodmin

BUDE

Budemeadows Touring Park, Widemouth Bay, Bude, Cornwall, EX23 0NA
Tel: 01288 361646
Email: holiday@budemeadows.com
www.budemeadows.com
Pitches For Å ♛ ♟ **Total** 145
Acreage 9 **Open** All Year
Access Good **Site** Level
Nearest Bus Stop (Miles) Outside
1 mile from sandy beaches, cliff walks and the rolling surf of Widemouth Bay. Spectacular coastal scenery. Licenced Bar and heated pool.
Facilities ⚿ ƒ ▥ ▤ ♠ ↾ ⊙ ⌐ ◨ ◘ ☻
▯ ▣ ◐ ☻ ▯ ▦ ↾ ↘ ✦ ↤ ▣ ◱ ⚘ ✧
Nearby Facilities ↾ ✔ ⊥ ↘ ∪ ♪ ♪
Nearest Town Bude
Directions From Bude take the A39 south for 3 miles.
⇻ Exeter

BUDE

Camping & Caravanning Club Site, Gillards Moor, St Gennys, Bude, Cornwall, EX23 0BG
Tel: 01840 230650
www.campingandcaravanningclub.co.uk/bude
Pitches For Å ♛ ♟ **Total** 100
Acreage 6 **Open** 23-Apr **to** 24-Sep
Site Lev/Slope
Nearest Bus Stop (Miles) 1
Near the coastal paths in the heart of King Arthurs Country. Table tennis on site. BTB 4 Star Graded and AA 3 Pennants. Non members welcome. You can also call us on 0845 130 7633.
Facilities ⚿ ƒ ▥ ♠ ↾ ⊙ ⌐ ◨ ◘ ☻
▯ ▣ ◐ ☻ ▯ ▦ ↾ ↤ ▣ ◱
Nearby Facilities ↾ ✔ ∪ ♪ ♪
Directions Going south on the A39 the site is on the right in lay-by 9 miles from Bude. Going north on the A39 the site is on the left in lay-by 9 miles from Camelford, approx. 3 miles off the B3262 junction. Brown camping signs ½ mile either side of the site, als
⇻ Bodmin

BUDE
Cornish Coasts Caravan & Camping Park, Middle Penlean, Poundstock, Bude, Cornwall, EX23 0EE
Tel: 01288 361380
www.cornishcoasts.co.uk
Pitches For ▲ ⌂ ⇔ **Total** 66
Acreage 3½ **Open** April **to** October
Access Good **Site** Level
Nearest Bus Stop (Miles) Outside
Small, friendly park in a designated Area of Outstanding Natural Beauty. Superb views of the sea across to Lundy Island. Statics available for hire.
Facilities ✦ ▯ ⌨ ☂ ┌ ⊙ ⌿ ⛴ ◨ ☎
⅏ ⌁ ⚑ ✿ ♨ ▣
Nearby Facilities ┌ ✔ ⚓ ♫
Nearest Town Bude
Directions Leave the M3 at junction 27 and take the A361 until the A39 junction at Barnstaple. Continue on the A39 towards Bude to Poundstock (approx 5 miles south of Bude). Set back from the road in the layby on the right hand side.
⇌ Bodmin

BUDE
Coxford Meadow Campsite, St Gennys, Bude, Cornwall, EX23 0NS
Tel: 01840 230707
Email: sladebraydon@supanet.com
Pitches For ▲ ⌂ ⇔ **Total** 25
Acreage 1¼ **Open** Easter **to** October
Site Lev/Slope
Nearest Bus Stop (Miles) ½
Quiet site with sea views. 1 mile from Crackington Haven beach and coastal path. Near Boscastle and Tintagel. Ideal for walking and touring. 3 hard standings available.
Facilities ✦ ┌ ┌ ⊙ ⌿ ⛴ ◨ ☎
⌁ ▯ ♨ ▣
Nearby Facilities ┌ ✔ ⚓ ∪
Nearest Town Bude
Directions Take the A39 south from Bude to Wainhouse Corner and turn right to St Gennys. After 1½ miles turn right at the crossroads, Coxford is first on the right.
⇌ Bodmin

BUDE
Penhalt Farm Holiday Park, Widemouth Bay, Bude, Cornwall, EX23 0DG
Tel: 01288 361210
Pitches For ▲ ⌂ ⇔ **Total** 100
Acreage 7 **Open** Easter **to** Oct
Access Good **Site** Lev/Slope
Nearest Bus Stop (Miles) 1
2 miles from Widemouth Bay, ideal for surfing and swimming. 5 miles from Bude.
Facilities ✦ ▯ ⌨ ☂ ┌ ⊙ ⌿ ⛴ ◨ ☎
⅏ ⌁ ⚑ ♨ ▣

Nearby Facilities ┌ ✔ ⚓ ∪ ♫
Nearest Town Bude
Directions On the A39 about 4 miles south of Bude, take the second turn right for Widemouth Bay. Turn left by Widemouth Manor Hotel and the site is two thirds of a mile on the left.
⇌ Exeter

BUDE
Red Post Inn, Launcells, Bude, Cornwall, EX23 9NW
Tel: 01288 381305
Email: gills17@hotmail.co.uk
www.redpostinn.co.uk
Pitches For ▲ ⌂ ⇔ **Total** 36
Acreage 2 **Open** March **to** Oct
Access Good **Site** Level
Nearest Bus Stop (Miles) Park Entrance
Quiet, family run park near the beach. Centrally located for exploring the coast and towns.
Facilities ✦ ▯ ⌨ ☂ ┌ ⊙ ⌿ ⛴ ☎
⌁ ✕ ▯ ♨ ▣
Nearby Facilities ┌ ✔ ⚓ ∪ ♫ ☇
Nearest Town Bude
Directions 4 miles from Bude on the A3702. 14 miles from the A30.

BUDE
Sandymouth Holiday Park, Stibb, Bude, Cornwall, EX23 9HW
Tel: 0844 272 9530
Email: enquiries@sandymouthbay.co.uk
www.sandymouthbay.co.uk
Pitches For ▲ ⌂ ⇔ **Total** 219
Acreage 24 **Open** 13-Mar **to** 25-Nov
Access Good **Site** Sloping
Nearest Bus Stop (Miles) ¼
Set in immaculately maintained parkland on North Cornwalls Atlantic coast. Within 1 mile of the beach and ideally placed for sightseeing and tourist attractions.
Facilities ✦ ▯ ⌨ ☂ ┌ ⊙ ⌿ ☎
⅏ ⌁ ✕ ▯ ♨ ♨ ⚑ ✿ ▣
Nearby Facilities ┌ ✔ ⚓ ∪ ♫
Nearest Town Bude
Directions Take the A39 from Bude to Kilkhampton, then follow signs for Sandymouth Beach. The Park is on the left ¾ miles from the beach.
⇌ Exeter

BUDE
Upper Lynstone Camping & Caravan Park, Upper Lynstone Farm, Bude, Cornwall, EX23 0LP
Tel: 01288 352017
Email: reception@upperlynstone.co.uk
www.upperlynstone.co.uk
Pitches For ▲ ⌂ ⇔ **Total** 65
Acreage 5 **Open** Easter **to** October

Access Good **Site** Lev/Slope
Nearest Bus Stop (Miles) ¼
Within easy reach of good surfing beaches. Access to cliff walks. Families and couples only, no groups.
Facilities ⅎ ✦ ⌨ ☂ ┌ ⊙ ⌿ ◨ ☎
⅏ ⌁ ♨ ⚑ ▯ ▣
Nearby Facilities ┌ ✔ ⚓ ∪ ♫
Directions ½ mile south of Bude on Widemouth Bay road.
⇌ Exeter

BUDE
Widemouth Bay Caravan Park, John Fowler Holidays, Widemouth Bay, Bude, Cornwall, EX23 0DF
Tel: 01271 866766
Email: stay@johnfowlerholidays.com
www.johnfowlerholidays.com
Pitches For ▲ ⌂ ⇔ **Total** 200
Acreage 50 **Open** March **to** October
Access Good **Site** Level
Close to one of Cornwalls finest surfing beaches. Perfect location for touring both Devon and Cornwall.
Facilities ⅎ ✦ ▯ ⌨ ☂ ┌ ⊙ ⌿ ⛴ ◨ ☎
⅏ ⌁ ⚐ ✕ ▯ ▯ ⚑ ♨ ⚑ ▯ ▣ ▣ ☀ ❄ ☇
Nearby Facilities ┌ ✔ ⚓ ∪ ♫
Directions From the M5 take the A361 then the A39 to Bude. Widemouth Bay is 4 miles west of Bude, clearly signposted.
⇌ Exeter

BUDE
Widemouth Fields Caravan & Camping Park, Park Farm, Poundstock, Bude, Cornwall, EX23 0NA
Tel: 01288 361351
Email:
enquiries@widemouthbaytouring.co.uk
www.widemouthbaytouring.co.uk
Pitches For ▲ ⌂ ⇔ **Total** 180
Acreage 10 **Open** 31-Mar **to** 30-Sep
Access Good **Site** Level
Just a mile from the sands of Widemouth Bay, set in glorious Cornish countryside with panoramic views. Ideal base for touring Cornwall, Dartmoor and South West Devon. New for 2012 - Seasonal Pitches available.
Facilities ⅎ ✦ ▯ ⌨ ☂ ┌ ⊙ ⌿ ⛴ ◨ ☎
⅏ ⌁ ⚐ ✕ ▯ ▯ ⚑ ♨ ⚑ ▯ ▣ ▣ ☀ ❄ ☇
Nearby Facilities ┌ ✔ ⚓ ∪ ♫
Nearest Town Bude
Directions Take the A39 Atlantic Highway south from Bude for 3 miles, look for a layby and sign on the left just past the junction for Widemouth Bay, entrance is on the left.
⇌ Barnstaple

CORNWALL

BUDE
Willow Valley Holiday Park, Dye House, Bush, Bude, Cornwall, EX23 9LB
Tel: 01288 353104
Email: willowvalley@talk21.com
www.willowvalley.co.uk
Pitches For 𝗔 ⌗ ⌗
Open Easter **to** End Oct
Access Good **Site** Level
Nearest Bus Stop (Miles) ½
Beaches and lovely walks nearby.
Facilities ⚒ ⚭ 🎅⚑☂⊙⟿◢◪◻☕
♺ ◉ ♨⊠⋈
Nearby Facilities ┌ 🏊⟂⭢∪ℛ⚲
Nearest Town Bude
Directions Just off the A39 between Bude and Kilkhampton.

BUDE
Wooda Farm Holiday Park, Poughill, Bude, Cornwall, EX23 9HJ
Tel: 01288 352069
Email: enquiries@wooda.co.uk
www.wooda.co.uk
Pitches For 𝗔 ⌗ ⌗ **Total** 200
Acreage 12 **Open** April **to** October
Access Good **Site** Lev/Slope
Nearest Bus Stop (Miles) Outside
Overlooks sea and coastline. Woodland walks, coarse fishing, large childrens play area, tennis court, badminton court, gym, dog exercise field and short golf course. Sandy beaches 1½ miles. Licensed bar and take-away. Off License on site.
Facilities ⚒ ⎍ ⎀ ⊞⚑☂⊙⟿◢◪◻☕
♺ ⫙◉ ⚘✗⊠⋈◭✿✲⊞☐◪✐⚲
Nearby Facilities ┌ 🏊⟂⭢∪ℛ⚲
Nearest Town Bude
Directions Take road to Poughill 1¼ miles, go through village. At crossroads turn left. Site 200yds along on right hand side.
⇌ Exeter

CAMELFORD
Lakefield Caravan Park, Lower Pendavey Farm, Camelford, Cornwall, PL32 9TX
Tel: 01840 213279
Email:
lakefieldequestriancentre@btconnect.com
Pitches For 𝗔 ⌗ ⌗ **Total** 40
Acreage 5 **Open** April **to** Sept
Access Good **Site** Level
Nearest Bus Stop (Miles) ½
3 miles from the beach and 1 mile from local amenities. Full equestrian facilities providing lessons, site rides and hacks for all the family. Close to the Moors and 2 miles form a golf course.
Facilities ⚒ ⚭ ⚑☂⊙⟿◢◪◻☕
♺ ⫙◉ ✗⊠◭✿✲⊞☐◪⚲
Nearby Facilities ┌ 🏊⟂⭢∪ℛ⚲⚲
Nearest Town Camelford
Directions 1 miles north of Camelford on the B3266 Boscastle road.
⇌ Bodmin

COVERACK
Little Trevothan Caravan Park, Coverack, Helston, Cornwall, TR12 6SD
Tel: 01326 280260
Email: sales@littletrevothan.co.uk
www.littletrevothan.co.uk
Pitches For 𝗔 ⌗ ⌗
Acreage 10½ **Open** March **to** Dec
Access Good **Site** Level
Nearest Bus Stop (Miles) ½
¾ miles from the beach in an area of outstanding natural beauty.
Facilities ⚒ ⚭ ⚑☂⊙⟿◢◪◻☕
♺ ◉ ⫙◭✿✲⊞☐◪✲⚲
Nearby Facilities ┌ 🏊⟂⭢∪ℛ⚲
Nearest Town Helston

Directions Take the A39 to Helston, then follow the B3083 to Culdrose, turn left onto the B3293 signposted Coverack. Go past BT Goonhilly, turn right before Zoar Garage, third turning on the left, site is 300yds on the right.
⇌ Redruth

COVERACK
Penmarth Farm Camp Site, Coverack, Helston, Cornwall,
Tel: 01326 280389
Pitches For 𝗔 ⌗ ⌗ **Total** 28
Acreage 2 **Open** March **to** October
Access Good **Site** Level
Nearest Bus Stop (Miles) ¼
¼ mile woodland walk to the sea and beach.
Facilities ✗⚭⚑☂⊙⟿ ⫙◉⚑
Nearby Facilities ┌ 🏊⟂⭢∪
Nearest Town Helston
Directions From Helston take the B3293 for approx. 10 miles.
⇌ Camborne

CRACKINGTON HAVEN
Hentervene Park, Crackington Haven, Bude, Cornwall, EX23 0LF
Tel: 01840 230365
Email: contact@hentervene.co.uk
www.hentervene.co.uk
Pitches For ⌗ ⌗ **Total** 9
Acreage 8 **Open** March **to** October
Access Good **Site** Level
Nearest Bus Stop (Miles) Entrance
Beautiful and peaceful Park situated in North Cornish countryside. 2 miles from the beach for sands, swimming and surfing. Self catering accommodation also available.
Facilities ⚒ ⎍ ⚭⚑☂⊙⟿◢◪◻☕
◉◭✿⫙⊞☐◪⚲
Nearby Facilities ┌ 🏊⟂⭢∪ℛ
Nearest Town Bude
Directions From Bude take the A39 Wadebridge road. Approx 1½ miles after Wainhouse Corner, turn left sp Crackington Haven. At the junction in ¾ miles turn right and see the Hentervene sign, Park is ½ a mile on the right.
⇌ Bodmin Parkway

CRANTOCK
Quarryfield Holiday Park, Crantock, Newquay, Cornwall, TR8 5RJ
Tel: 01637 830338
Email:
quarryfield@crantockcaravans.orangehome.co.uk
www.quarryfield.co.uk
Pitches For 𝗔 ⌗ ⌗ **Total** 125
Acreage 4½ **Open** Easter **to** End Oct
Access Good **Site** Lev/Slope
Nearest Bus Stop (Miles) ¼
Just a 10 minute walk to the village, Crantock beach and the River Gannel.
Facilities ⚒ ⚭⚑☂⊙⟿◢◪◻☕
♺ ⫙◉ ⚘◭✿⊞☐◪◻☕
Nearby Facilities ┌ 🏊⭢∪ℛ
Nearest Town Newquay
Directions From the A3075 Newquay to Redruth road, turn off signposted Crantock Village, site is approx. 2½ miles.
⇌ Newquay

CRANTOCK
Treago Farm Caravan & Camping Site, Treago Farm, Crantock, Nr Newquay, Cornwall, TR8 5QS
Tel: 01637 830277
Email: info@treagofarm.co.uk
www.treagofarm.co.uk
Pitches For 𝗔 ⌗ ⌗ **Total** 90
Open Easter **to** Oct
Access Good **Site** Level
Nearest Bus Stop (Miles) ½

Peaceful, rural setting, away form it all! Footpath to two lovely beaches. Surrounded by National Trust land.
Facilities ⚒ ⚭⚑☂⊙⟿◢◪◻☕
♺ ◉ ⫙◭✿⊞☐◪✐
Nearby Facilities ┌ 🏊⟂⭢∪ℛ
Nearest Town Newquay
Directions 2 miles south west of Newquay. Turn right off the A3075 and follow signs to Crantock, the follow signs to West Pentire.
⇌ Newquay

FALMOUTH
Retanna Holiday Park, Edgcumbe, Helston, Cornwall, TR13 0EJ
Tel: 01326 340643
Email: retannaholpark@btconnect.com
www.retanna.co.uk
Pitches For 𝗔 ⌗ ⌗ **Total** 24
Acreage 8 **Open** March **to** Nov
Access Good **Site** Lev/Slope
Nearest Bus Stop (Miles) Entrance
Just a short drive to The Flambards Experience, Gweek Seal Sanctuary and Poldark Mine.
Facilities ⚒ ⎍ ⚭⚑☂⊙⟿◢◪◻☕
♺ ◉ ⚘♨⫙◭✿⊞☐◪
Nearby Facilities ┌ 🏊⟂⭢∪⚲ℛ⚲
Nearest Town Falmouth
Directions Midway between Falmouth and Helston on the A394, on the right hand side after passing through Edgcumbe.
⇌ Falmouth/Truro

FALMOUTH
Tregedna Farm Touring Caravan & Camping Park, Maenporth, Falmouth, Cornwall, TR11 5HL
Tel: 01326 250529
www.tregednafarmholidays.co.uk
Pitches For 𝗔 ⌗ ⌗ **Total** 40
Acreage 12 **Open** Easter **to** End Sept
Access Good **Site** Sloping
Nearest Bus Stop (Miles) ¼
Situated in the beautiful Maen Valley, just minutes from the beach and surrounded by wooded countryside.
Facilities ⚭⚑☂⊙⟿◢◪◻☕
♺ ◉ ⫙◭✿⊞☐
Nearby Facilities ┌ 🏊⟂⭢∪ℛ
Nearest Town Falmouth
Directions Take the A39 from Truro to Falmouth, 2½ miles to Falmouth on the Maenporth to Mawnan Smith road.
⇌ Penmere

FOWEY
Penhale Caravan & Camping Park, Fowey, Cornwall, PL23 1JU
Tel: 01726 833425
Email: info@penhale-fowey.co.uk
www.penhale-fowey.co.uk
Pitches For 𝗔 ⌗ ⌗ **Total** 56
Acreage 5 **Open** April **to** October
Access Good **Site** Lev/Slope
Splendid views, close to sandy beaches with many lovely walks nearby. Central for touring.
Facilities ⚒ ⎍ ⚭⚑☂⊙⟿◢◪◻☕
♺ ⫙◉ ⚘♨⊠⋈◭✿⊞☐◪⚲
Nearby Facilities ┌ 🏊⟂⭢∪ℛ⚲ℛ⚲
Nearest Town Fowey
Directions 1 mile west of Lostwithiel on the A390, turn left onto the B3269. After 3 miles turn right at the roundabout onto the A3082. Penhale is 500yds on the left.
⇌ Par

A Private, Quiet, Pretty Park recommended for young families & the mature

ROSEVILLE HOLIDAY PARK 01872 572448
Goonhavern, Perranporth, Nr. Truro, Cornwall TR4 9LA   www.rosevilleholidaypark.co.uk

✳ Suits young families and the mature ✳ Outdoor Pool ✳ Children's Play Area
✳ Disabled Room ✳ Electric Hook-ups ✳ Launderette ✳ Dog Walk ✳ Toilet & Shower Block

FOWEY
Penmarlam Caravan & Camping Park, Bodinnick-by-Fowey, Fowey, Cornwall, PL23 1LZ
Tel: 01726 870088
Email: info@penmarlampark.co.uk
www.penmarlampark.co.uk
Pitches For ⚠ ⛺ ⛗ **Total** 65
Acreage 4 **Open** Easter **to** Oct
Access Good **Site** Lev/Slope
Quiet site with two areas, one sheltered and one with stunning views. Near the Eden Project. Boat launching and storage.
Facilities ⚅ ⚇ ⚈ ⚉ ⚊ ⚋ ⚌ ⚍ ⚎
⚏ ☖ ☗ ☘ ☙ ⚐
Nearby Facilities ☇ ☈ ☉ ☊ ☋ ☌
Nearest Town Fowey
Directions From the A38 eastbound, pass Liskeard and turn left onto the A390 sp St. Austell. In East Taphouse turn left onto the B3359 sp Polperro & Looe. After 5 miles turn right sp Bodinnick. Site is on the right in 5 miles.
⚟ Liskeard/Par/Looe

FOWEY
Polruan Holidays - Camping & Caravanning, Polruan-by-Fowey, Cornwall, PL23 1QH
Tel: 01726 870263
Email: polholiday@aol.com
www.polruanholidays.co.uk
Pitches For ⚠ ⛺ ⛗ **Total** 47
Acreage 2 **Open** Easter **to** 1st October
Access Good **Site** Lev/Slope
Nearest Bus Stop (Miles) Outside
Coastal park surrounded by sea, river and National Trust farmland.
Facilities ⚇ ⚈ ⚉ ⚊ ⚋ ⚌ ⚍ ⚎
⚏ ☖ ☗ ☘ ⚐
Nearby Facilities ☈ ☉ ☊ ☋
Nearest Town Fowey
Directions From Plymouth A38 to Dobwalls, left onto A390 to East Taphouse, then left onto B3359. After 4¼ miles turn right signposted Polruan.
⚟ Par

GOONHAVERN
Roseville Holiday Park, Goonhavern, Nr Truro, Cornwall, TR4 9LA
Tel: 01872 572448
Email: roseville.park@btconnect.com
www.rosevilleholidaypark.co.uk
Pitches For ⚠ ⛺ ⛗ **Total** 90
Acreage 8 **Open** Easter **to** October
Access Good **Site** Level
Nearest Bus Stop (Miles) ¼
Ideal for North Cornwall. Quiet, private site. Families and mature persons only.
Facilities ⚅ ⚇ ⚈ ⚉ ⚊ ⚋ ⚌ ⚍ ⚎
⚏ ☖ ☗ ☘ ☙ ⚐
Nearby Facilities ☇ ☈ ☉ ☊ ☋ ☌
Nearest Town Truro
Directions 6 miles from Newquay on the A3075.
⚟ Truro

GORRAN HAVEN
Trelispen Caravan & Camping Park, Gorran Haven, St Austell, Cornwall, PL26 6NT
Tel: 01726 843501
Email: trelispen@care4free.net
www.trelispen.co.uk
Pitches For ⚠ ⛺ ⛗
Acreage 1½ **Open** April **to** Oct
Access Good **Site** Level
Nearest Bus Stop (Miles) ¼
Within walking distance of Gorran Haven with its beach and fine cliff scenery.
Facilities ⚇ ⚈ ⚉ ⚊ ⚋ ⚌ ⚍
Nearby Facilities ☈ ☉ ☊ ☋ ☌
Nearest Town Mevagissey
Directions From St. Austell take the B3273 south following signs for Gorran Haven. Nearing Gorran Haven look for brown tourism signs to Trelispen.
⚟ St. Austell

HAYLE
Beachside Holiday Park, Hayle, Cornwall, TR27 5AW
Tel: 01736 753080
Email: reception@beachside.co.uk
www.beachside.co.uk
Pitches For ⚠ ⛺ ⛗ **Total** 83
Acreage 20 **Open** Easter **to** 30-Sep
Access Good **Site** Sloping
Nearest Bus Stop (Miles) Outside
Right beside a golden sandy beach. Sea fishing from site.
Facilities ⚇ ⚈ ⚉ ⚊ ⚋ ⚌ ⚍ ⚎
⚏ ☖ ☗ ☘ ☙ ☖ ⚐ ☗ ⚐
Nearby Facilities ☇ ☈ ☉ ☊ ☋
Nearest Town Hayle
Directions Leave the A30 at roundabout signed Hayle, turn right opposite the Jet Petrol Station and the entrance is ½ mile on the right.
⚟ Hayle

HAYLE
Higher Trevaskis Caravan & Camping Park, Gwinear Road, Connor Downs, Hayle, Cornwall, TR27 5JQ
Tel: 01209 831736
www.highertrevaskiscaravanpark.co.uk
Pitches For ⚠ ⛺ ⛗ **Total** 75
Acreage 5¼ **Open** April **to** October
Access Good **Site** Level
Nearest Bus Stop (Miles) ½
Friendly, secluded, family run, countryside park. Spacious, level pitches in small enclosures. Designated play areas and our renowned spotlessly clean facilities.
Facilities ⚇ ⚈ ⚉ ⚊ ⚋ ⚌ ⚍ ⚎
⚏ ☖ ☗ ☘ ☙ ⚐
Nearby Facilities ☇ ☈ ☉ ☊ ☋ ☌
Nearest Town Hayle
Directions From the A30 at the Hayle roundabout (McDonalds) take the first exit signposted Connor Downs. After 1 mile turn right to Carnhell Green. Park is on the right in ¾ miles.
⚟ Hayle

HAYLE
Lavender Fields Touring Park, Penhale Road, Carnhell Green, Hayle, Cornwall, TR14 0LU
Tel: 01209 832188
Email: info@lavenderfieldstouring.co.uk
www.lavenderfieldstouring.co.uk
Pitches For ⚠ ⛺ ⛗ **Total** 60
Acreage 5 **Open** All Year
Access Good **Site** Level
Nearest Bus Stop (Miles) Outside
10 minutes from Gwithian Beach with excellent surfing. Near to St Ives, Truro and Penzance for all your shopping.
Facilities ⚇ ⚈ ⚉ ⚊ ⚋ ⚌ ⚍ ⚎
⚏ ☖ ☗ ☘ ☙ ⚐
Nearby Facilities ☇ ☈ ☉ ☊ ☋ ☌ ☍
Nearest Town Hayle
Directions Leave the A30 at Hayle roundabout taking the first exit sp Conner Downs, after 1 mile turn right sp Carnhell Green. Go across the level crossing to the T-Junction, turn left and the site is 750 yards on the right.
⚟ Hayle

HAYLE
Parbola Holiday Park, Wall, Gwinear, Cornwall, TR27 5LE
Tel: 01209 831503
Email: bookings@parbola.co.uk
www.parbola.co.uk
Pitches For ⚠ ⛺ ⛗ **Total** 110
Acreage 14 **Open** April **to** September
Access Good **Site** Level
Nearest Bus Stop (Miles) Outside
No dogs allowed during July and August. Hair and make-up room.
Facilities ⚅ ⚇ ⚈ ⚉ ⚊ ⚋ ⚌ ⚍ ⚎
⚏ ☖ ☗ ☘ ☙ ☖ ⚐ ☗
Nearby Facilities ☇ ☈ ☉ ☊ ☋ ☌ ☍
Nearest Town Hayle
Directions Travel on A30 to Hayle, at roundabout leave first exit to Connor Downs. At end of village turn right to Carnhell Green, right at T-Junction, Parbola is 1 mile on the left.

HAYLE
Sunny Meadow Holiday Park, Lelant Downs, Hayle, Cornwall, TR27 6LL
Tel: 01736 752243
Email: sunnymeadow@tiscali.co.uk
www.sunnymeadowholidaypark.co.uk
Pitches For ⚠ ⛺ ⛗ **Total** 3
Open All Year
Access Good **Site** Level
Nearest Bus Stop (Miles) ¼
Quiet, safe site in the countryside, only 3 miles from St Ives. Rural walks and coastal paths nearby.
Facilities ⚇ ⚈ ⚉ ⚊ ⚋ ⚌ ⚍ ⚎
Nearby Facilities ☈ ☉
Nearest Town St Ives
Directions Stay on the A30 until you reach the Penzance/St Ives roundabout, then take the A3074 for St Ives. At the second mini roundabout turn left, and the site is 2/3rds of a mile.
⚟ St Erth

HAYLE

Treglisson Touring Park, Wheal Alfred Road, Hayle, Cornwall, TR27 5JT
Tel: 01736 753141
Email: steve@treglisson.co.uk
www.treglisson.co.uk
Pitches For Å ⬛ ➤ **Total** 26
Acreage 2½ **Open** Easter **to** Oct
Access Good Site Lev/Slope
Nearest Bus Stop (Miles) 1
Just 5 minutes from the beaches of St Ives Bay. Centrally situated, ideal for touring West Cornwall.
Facilities ⬛ symbols
Nearby Facilities symbols
Nearest Town Hayle/St. Ives
Directions Take the A30 to roundabout outside Hayle and take the 4th exit to Hayle. At the first mini roundabout turn left, after a mile (past the golf course) theres a sign on the left.
⚡ Hayle

HELSTON

Boscrege Caravan & Camping Park, Ashton, Helston, Cornwall, TR13 9TG
Tel: 01736 762231
Email: enquiries@caravanparkcornwall.com
www.caravanparkcornwall.com
Pitches For Å ⬛ ➤ **Total** 50
Acreage 7 **Open** Easter/1 April **to** Oct
Access Good Site Level
Quiet family park in a garden setting. No club. Near sandy beaches. Ideal for exploring West Cornwall. Newly refurbished toilets/showers for 2010. Microwave for campers.
Facilities symbols
Nearby Facilities symbols
Nearest Town Praa Sands
Directions From Helston follow Penzance road (A394) to Ashton, turn right by post office along road signposted to Godolphin and continue about 1½ miles to Boscrege Park.
⚡ Penzance

HELSTON

Gunwalloe Caravan Park, Gunwalloe, Helston, Cornwall, TR12 7QP
Tel: 01326 572668
Pitches For Å ⬛ ➤ **Total** 40
Acreage 3½ **Open** April **to** October
Access Good Site Level
Nearest Bus Stop (Miles) 1
One mile form the beach. Ideal for touring the Lizard Peninsula.
Facilities symbols
Nearby Facilities symbols

Nearest Town Helston
Directions From Helston take the A3082 towards The Lizard, after 2 miles turn right to Gunwalloe for 1 mile, site is signposted.
⚡ Redruth

HELSTON

Lower Polladras Touring Park, Carleen, Helston, Cornwall, TR13 9NX
Tel: 01736 762220
Email: lowerpolladras@btinternet.com
www.lower-polladras.co.uk
Pitches For Å ⬛ ➤ **Total** 60
Acreage 4 **Open** Easter/1 Apr **to** Early Jan
Access Good Site Level
Nearest Bus Stop (Miles) ¼
A family run park in an area of outstanding natural beauty, overlooking classic Cornish countryside. Centrally located for exploring Cornwall and The Lizard. 10 minutes away from safe, sandy, lifeguarded beaches. Low season special deals. Year round storage.
Facilities symbols
Nearby Facilities symbols
Nearest Town Helston/Praa Sands
Directions From Helston take the A394 to Penzance and turn right at the Hilltop Garage onto the B3302. After ½ a mile turn left to Carleen Village and follow signs to the park. From the A30 take the exit to Camborne West, turn left at the first roundabout then right at the next three mini roundabouts, take the B3303 for 6 miles, turn left at the junction with the B3302, turn first right and follow signs to Carleen.
⚡ Penzance/Camborne

HELSTON

Poldown Caravan & Camping Site, Carleen, Breage, Helston, Cornwall, TR13 9NN
Tel: 01326 574560
Email: stay@poldown.co.uk
www.poldown.co.uk
Pitches For Å ⬛ ➤ **Total** 13
Acreage 1¼ **Open** April **to** Sept
Access Good Site Level
Nearest Bus Stop (Miles) Outside
Small, secluded, pretty site. 2 hard standings and 6 fully serviced pitches available. Ideal for touring West Cornwall. ETB 4 Star Graded.
Facilities symbols
Nearby Facilities symbols
Directions Take A394 (signed Penzance) from Helston. At top of the hill on outskirts of Helston take the B3303 signed Hayle/St Ives. Take the second left on this road and we are ¼ mile along.
⚡ Penzance

INDIAN QUEENS

Gnome World Holiday Park, Moorland Road, Indian Queens, Cornwall, TR9 6HN
Tel: 01726 860812
Email: gnomesworld@btconnect.com
Pitches For Å ⬛ ➤ **Total** 50
Acreage 8 **Open** March **to** Dec
Access Good Site Level
Nearest Bus Stop (Miles) ¼
Many camping pitches with lots of space. Goss Moor Cycle Trail and the Eden Project nearby.
Facilities symbols
Nearby Facilities symbols
Nearest Town Newquay
Directions Approx. 1 mile from the A30, signposted.
⚡ Newquay/St Austell

ISLES OF SCILLY

Bryher Campsite, Bryher, Isles of Scilly, Cornwall, TR23 0PR
Tel: 01720 422559
Email: relax@bryhercampsite.co.uk
www.bryhercampsite.co.uk
Pitches For Å
Open April **to** October **Site** Level
Near the beach.
Facilities symbols
Nearby Facilities symbols
Nearest Town St Mary's
Directions Can be reached by boat from the main island to St Marys.
⚡ Penzance

ISLES OF SCILLY

Garrison Holidays, Tower Cottage, The Garrison, St Marys, Isles of Scilly, Cornwall, TR21 0LS
Tel: 01720 422670
Email: tedmoulson@aol.com
www.garrisonholidays.com
Pitches For Å **Total** 120
Acreage 9½ **Open** Easter **to** October **Site** Level
Small, family orientated campsite. Electric hook-ups (10) on marked pitches, rest of site is not formally marked. Small fields, mostly sheltered. No vehicles on site. Transport for luggage is available from the ferry to the site for a small charge. Childrens play area adjacent to site.
Facilities symbols
Nearby Facilities symbols
Nearest Town St Mary's
Directions From Penzance take a boat, skybus or helicopter to Isles of Scilly. Park is 10 minutes walk from Hugh Town, St Marys.
⚡ Penzance

ISLES OF SCILLY

St. Martins Campsite, Middle Town, St Martins, Isles of Scilly, Cornwall, TR25 0QN
Tel: 01720 422888
Email: camping@stmartinscampsite.co.uk
www.stmartinscampsite.co.uk
Pitches For 🏕 **Total** 50
Acreage 2½ **Open** Easter **to** End Oct
Site Level
Sheltered site adjacent to a south facing white sandy beach on a peaceful, idyllic island.
Facilities ⚷ 🅱🕭🏳⊙🍴🔌🔥🏪⚑
Nearby Facilities 🏊🚤⏛🎣∪
Directions Take a ferry, plane or helicopter from Penzance to St. Marys. Launch from St. Marys to St. Martins.
🚆 Penzance

ISLES OF SCILLY

Troytown Farm Campsite, Troytown Farm, St Agnes, Isles of Scilly, Cornwall, TR22 0PL
Tel: 01720 422360
Email: enquiries@troytown.co.uk
www.troytown.co.uk
Pitches For 🏕 **Total** 36
Open March **to** Nov
Site Lev/Slope
Spectacular views across the western rocks towards Bishop Rock Lighthouse. It also has its own sandy beach.
Facilities 🅱🕭🏳⊙🍴🔥
⊡🏪🔥⊙🔌🔥🏳🌙⚑
Nearby Facilities 🏊🚤⏛🎣∪ 🎣⚡
Nearest Town St. Agnes
Directions Take the ferry from Penzance or fly from south west airports. NB: It is not possible to bring your car to Scilly.
🚆 Penzance

JACOBSTOW

Edmore Tourist Park, Edgar Road, Wainhouse Corner, Jacobstow, Bude, Cornwall, EX23 0BJ
Tel: 01840 230467
Email: enquiries@cornwallvisited.co.uk
www.cornwallvisited.co.uk
Pitches For 🏕 🚐 🚎 **Total** 28
Acreage 3 **Open** 1 week before Easter **to** 1st Week Oct
Access Good **Site** Level
Nearest Bus Stop (Miles) ¼
Rural area with coastal walks. 2½ miles from the beach. Good touring base.
Facilities ⨍🅱🏳⊙🍴🔌🔥
🏪⚷🛋🔥⊡
Nearby Facilities 🏊🚤∪
Nearest Town Bude
Directions On the A39 Bude to Camelford road, 9 miles west of Bude.
🚆 Exeter

LANDS END

Cardinney Caravan & Caravan Park, Main A30, Lands End Road, Crows-an-Wra, Lands End, Cornwall, TR19 6HX
Tel: 01736 810880
Email: cardinney@btinternet.com
www.cardinney-camping-park.co.uk
Pitches For 🏕 🚐 🚎 **Total** 90
Acreage 5 **Open** All Year
Access Good **Site** Level
Nearest Bus Stop (Miles) Outside
Sennen Cove Blue Flag, scenic coastal walks, ancient monuments, scenic flights, Minack Ampitheatre, trips to the Isles of Scilly. Ideal for touring Lands End Peninsula. ETB 4 Star Graded.
Facilities ⨍🔥🅱🅱🏳⊙🍴🔌🔥
🟊⊙✗🔥🔥⊡🔥
Nearby Facilities 🏳🚤⏛∪🎣⚡

Nearest Town Sennen Cove
Directions From Penzance follow Main A30 to Lands End, approx 5¼ miles. Entrance on right hand side on Main A30, large name board at entrance.
🚆 Penzance

LANDS END

Lower Treave Caravan & Camping Park, Crows-an-Wra, St Buryan, Penzance, Cornwall, TR19 6HZ
Tel: 01736 810559
Email: camping@lowertreave.co.uk
www.lowertreave.co.uk
Pitches For 🏕 🚐 🚎 **Total** 56
Acreage 5 **Open** Easter **to** Oct
Access Good **Site** Level
Nearest Bus Stop (Miles) Entrance
Quiet family site in the heart of Lands End peninsular with panoramic rural views to the sea. Sheltered, level grass terraces. 2 miles from the Blue Flag beach of Sennen Cove, and close to The Minack Theatre and St Michaels Mount.
Facilities ⨍🅱🏳⊙🍴🔌🔥
🟊⊙🔥⊡🔥
Nearby Facilities 🏳🚤⏛🎣∪🎣⚡
Nearest Town Lands End
Directions On A30 midway between Penzance and Lands End, a mile beyond the village of Crows-an-Wra.
🚆 Penzance

LISKEARD

Colliford Tavern Camp Site, Colliford Lake, St Neot, Liskeard, Cornwall, PL14 6PZ
Tel: 01208 821335
Email: info@colliford.com
www.colliford.com
Pitches For 🏕 🚐 🚎 **Total** 40
Acreage 5 **Open** All Year
Access Good **Site** Lev/Slope
Situated on Bodmin Moor next to Colliford Lake.
Facilities ♿⨍🅱🏳⊙🍴🔥
🟊✗🔥🔥⊡🔥🔥
Nearby Facilities 🚤⏛∪
Nearest Town Bodmin
Directions On the A30, 10 miles east of Bodmin and 12 miles west of Launceston.
🚆 Bodmin Parkway

LISKEARD

Pine Valley Park, Double Bois, Liskeard, Cornwall, PL14 6LE
Tel: 01579 320183
Email: relax@pinevalleypark.co.uk
www.pinevalleypark.co.uk
Pitches For 🏕 🚐 🚎 **Total** 45
Acreage 3 **Open** All Year
Access Good **Site** Level
Overlooking beautiful wooded valley and open countryside.
Facilities ⨍🅱🏳⊙🍴🔌🔥
🔥🟊🔥⊡🌙
Nearby Facilities 🏳🚤⏛🎣∪🎣⚡
Nearest Town Liskeard
Directions 3 miles from Liskeard towards Bodmin. Just off the main A38 at Double Bois.
🚆 Liskeard

LISKEARD

Trenant Chapel House, Trenant Caravan Park, St Neot, Liskeard, Cornwall, PL14 6RZ
Tel: 01579 320896
Pitches For 🏕 🚐 🚎 **Total** 8
Acreage 1 **Open** April **to** October
Site Level

Close to Siblyback and Colliford Reservoirs for fishing, boardsailing and bird watching. Situated in a sheltered corner of Upper Fowey Valley and bounded by tributary of Fowey river. Close to Bodmin moor, ideal for walking and touring.
Facilities ⨍🅱🏳⊙🍴🔌🔥🏪⊡⚑
Nearby Facilities 🏳⏛∪
Nearest Town Liskeard
Directions Take St Cleer road off the A38 at Dobwalls, after 1 mile turn left signposted St. Neot, after 1 mile turn right signposted Trenant, ½ mile turn right signposted Trenant.
🚆 Liskeard

LIZARD

Henrys Campsite, Caerthillian Farm, The Lizard, Cornwall, TR12 7NX
Tel: 01326 290596
www.henryscampsite.co.uk
Pitches For 🏕 🚐 🚎 **Total** 45
Acreage 1½ **Open** All Year
Access Good **Site** Level
Nearest Bus Stop (Miles) ¼
Spectacular sea views. Close to secluded or popular beaches and near coastal footpaths. Just a short walk to the village.
Facilities ⨍🅱🅱🏳⊙🍴🔥
🟊🏪⊙🔥🔥⊡
Nearby Facilities 🏳🚤⏛🎣∪🎣⚡
Nearest Town Helston
Directions Take the main A3083 Helston to Lizard road, enter the village and take the first turn right opposite Regent Cafe, then turn second right at the bottom of the hill.
🚆 Redrut

LIZARD

Silver Sands Holiday Park, Gwendreath, Nr Kennack Sands, Ruan Minor, Helston, Cornwall, TR12 7LZ
Tel: 01326 290631
Email: info@silversandsholidaypark.co.uk
www.silversandsholidaypark.co.uk
Pitches For 🏕 🚐 🚎 **Total** 50
Acreage 9 **Open** March **to** October
Access Good **Site** Level
Quiet, family site in area of outstanding natural beauty. 800 metres from a sandy beach. Ideal for touring and walking.
Facilities ⨍🅱🏳⊙🍴🔌🔥
🏪⊙🔥🔥⊡🔥
Nearby Facilities 🏳🚤⏛∪
Nearest Town Helston
Directions From Helston take the A3083 Lizard road, pass RNAS Culdrose then turn left onto the B3293 sp St Keverne. Follow for 4 miles passing Future World @ Goonhilly, turn right at the next crossroads to Kennack Sands. After 1½ miles turn left sp Gwendreath and the Park is 1 mile down the lane.
🚆 Redruth

LOOE

Bay View Farm, St Martins, Looe, Cornwall, PL13 1NZ
Tel: 01503 265922
Email: mike@looebaycaravans.co.uk
www.looebaycaravans.co.uk
Pitches For 🏕 🚐 🚎 **Total** 25
Acreage 3 **Open** All Year
Access Good **Site** Lev/Slope
Nearest Bus Stop (Miles) 1
Near to the beach, The Eden Project and many National Trust properties. We have eight shire horses on the farm. You can also contact us on mobile: 07967 267312.
Facilities ♿⨍🔥🅱🏳⊙🍴🔌🔥
🔥⊡🔥🔥
Nearby Facilities 🏳🚤⏛🎣∪🎣⚡
Nearest Town Looe

CORNWALL

Directions From Plymouth or Liskeard take the A38 to Trerulefoot roundabout, then take the (A387) B3253 to No-Mans-Land. Follow signs for the Monkey Sanctuary and Bay View Farm is at the end of the lane.
⇌ Looe

LOOE

Camping Caradon Touring Park, Trelawne, Looe, Cornwall, PL13 2NA
Tel: 01503 272388
Email: enquiries@campingcaradon.co.uk
www.campingcaradon.co.uk
Pitches For ▲ ⊞ ⊟ **Total** 85
Acreage 3 **Open** All Year
Access Good **Site** Level
Nearest Bus Stop (Miles) Site Entrance
In a rural location, within easy reach of all of Cornwall. The Eden Project is only 20 miles away. 2½ miles from Looe and 2 miles from Polperro. Free Wi-Fi. Family/disabled facilities. On local bus route. November to March by prior booking only.
Facilities ⬥ ⚡ 🖬 🖾 🛢 🏪 🗘 🞋 🔌 ▣ 🛢
⚽ 🕙 ⊙ ▽ 🕮 ♣ 🖾 ⬆ 🔳 🖎 ⬟ 🤏 🛜
Nearby Facilities ⌐ ✗ ⏚ ⤢ U ⇗ ♫
Nearest Town Looe/Polperro
Directions From Looe take the A387 towards Polperro. After 2 miles turn right onto the B3359. Take the next turning right, and Camping Caradon is clearly signposted.
⇌ Looe

LOOE

Highertown Farm Campsite, Highertown Farm, Lansallos, Looe, Cornwall, PL13 2PX
Tel: 01208 265211
Email: highertownfarmcampsite@nationaltrust.org.uk
www.nationaltrust.org.uk
Pitches For ▲ ⊞ ⊟
Open Easter **to** Oct
Access Good **Site** Sloping
Nearest Bus Stop (Miles) ¼
Facilities ⬥ ⚡ 🛢 🔳 🞋 📱🖎 ▣
Nearby Facilities ⌐ ✗ ⏚ ⤢ U ♫ ⤢
Nearest Town Looe/Fowey
Directions From the A38, at Dobwalls take the A390, at East Taphouse take the B3359 and travel east for 4½ miles, follow signs for Lansallos.
⇌ Looe

LOOE

Polborder House Caravan & Camping Park, Bucklawren Road, St Martin, Looe, Cornwall, PL13 1QS
Tel: 01503 240265
Email: reception@polborderhouse.co.uk
www.polborderhouse.co.uk
Pitches For ▲ ⊞ ⊟ **Total** 36
Acreage 3 **Open** All Year
Access Good **Site** Level
Nearest Bus Stop (Miles) ½
Small, select, award winning park set in beautiful countryside, 1¼ miles from the sea. Holiday caravans also available for rent. Top 100 UK Parks Finalists.
Facilities ⬥ ⚡ ⚡ 🖬 🖾 🛢 🏪 🗘 🞋 ⬅ ▣ 🛢
⚽ 🕙 ⊙ 🛢 🞋 🔳 🖎 ⬟ 🤏 🛜
Nearby Facilities ⌐ ✗ ⏚ ⤢ ♫
Nearest Town Looe

Directions 2¼ miles east of Looe off B3253, follow signs for Polborder and Monkey Sanctuary.
⇌ Looe

LOOE

Tencreek Holiday Park, Polperro Road, Looe, Cornwall, PL13 2JR
Tel: 01503 262447
Email: reception@tencreek.co.uk
www.dolphinholidays.co.uk
Pitches For ▲ ⊞ ⊟
Acreage 20 **Open** All Year
Access Good **Site** Lev/Slope
Nearest Bus Stop (Miles) ¼
Excellent coastal and countryside views. Good park facilities including indoor pool and a large modern club house with entertainment.
Facilities ⬥ ⚡ 🖬 🖾 🛢 🏪 🗘 🞋 ⊙ ⬅ ▣ 🛢
⚽ 🕙 ⊙ ✗ ▽ 🕮 ♣ 🖾 ⬆ 🔳 🖎 ⬟ 🤏
🛜
Nearby Facilities ⌐ ✗ ⏚ ⤢ U ♫
Nearest Town Looe
Directions 1¼ miles west of Looe on the A387 Looe to Polperro road.
⇌ Looe

LOOE

Tregoad Park, St Martins, Looe, Cornwall, PL13 1PB
Tel: 01503 262718
Email: info@tregoad.co.uk
www.tregoad.co.uk
Pitches For ▲ ⊞ ⊟
Acreage 55 **Open** All Year
Nearest Bus Stop (Miles) ¼
Ideal for touring.
Facilities ⬥ ⚡ 🖬 🖾 🛢 🏪 🗘 🞋 ⊙ ⬅ ▣ 🛢
⚽ 🕙 ⊙ ✗ ▽ 🕮 ♣ 🖾 🞋 ⬆ 🔳 🖎 ⬟ 🤏
🛜
Nearby Facilities ⌐ ✗ ⏚ ⤢ U ♫ ⤢
Nearest Town Looe
Directions From Looe take the B3253 and follow signs to St Martins and Hessenford. Stay on this road until you go down a steep hill, Tregoad is on the right.
⇌ Looe

LOOE

Trelay Farmpark, Pelynt, Nr Looe, Cornwall, PL13 2JX
Tel: 01503 220900
Email: stay@trelay.co.uk
www.trelay.co.uk
Pitches For ▲ ⊞ ⊟ **Total** 70
Acreage 4½ **Open** 01-Apr **to** 31-Oct
Access Good **Site** Sloping
Nearest Bus Stop (Miles) ¼
A small, uncommercialised Park surrounded by farmland, with a friendly, family atmosphere. Good sized grass pitches. 3 miles from Looe and the pretty fishing village of Polperro.
Facilities ⬥ ⚡ 🖬 🖾 🛢 🏪 🗘 🞋 ⊙ ⬅ ▣ 🛢
⚽ 🕙 ⊙ 🛢 ✗ 🕮 🞋 ⬆ 🔳 🖎 ⬟ 🤏 🛜
Nearby Facilities ⌐ ✗ ⏚ ⤢ U ♫ ⤢
Nearest Town Looe
Directions From Looe take the A387 over the bridge towards Polperro. After 2 miles turn right onto the B3359 towards Pelynt and Trelay Farmpark is exactly 1 mile on the right.
⇌ Looe

LOSTWITHIEL

Eden Valley Holiday Park, Lanlivery, Bodmin, Cornwall, PL30 5BU
Tel: 01208 872277
Email: enquiries@edenvalleyholidaypark.co.uk
www.edenvalleyholidaypark.co.uk
Pitches For ▲ ⊞ ⊟
Acreage 12 **Open** Easter **to** End Oct
Access Good **Site** Level
Nearest Bus Stop (Miles) 3
Stream runs through the park. Woodland and river walks.
Facilities ⬥ ⚡ ⚡ 🖬 🖾 🛢 🏪 🗘 🞋 ⊙ ⬅ ▣ 🛢
⚽ 🕙 ⊙ 🛢 🕮 ♣ 🕮 ⬆ 🔳 🖎 🖎 ⬟ ⤢ 🤏
Nearby Facilities ⌐ ✗ ⏚ ⤢ U ⇗ ♫
Nearest Town Fowey
Directions From Lostwithiel take the A390 for 1½ miles.
⇌ Lostwithiel

MARAZION

Trevair Touring Site, South Treveneague Farm, St Hilary, Penzance, Cornwall, TR20 9BY
Tel: 01736 740647
Email: info@trevairtouringpark.co.uk
www.trevairtouringpark.co.uk
Pitches For ▲ ⊞ ⊟ **Total** 35
Acreage 3½ **Open** End March **to** October
Access Good **Site** Level
Nearest Bus Stop (Miles) 1
Everyone is welcome at our clean and friendly site. Set in the peace and quiet of the countryside, yet within 2 to 3 miles of beaches, shops and pubs.
Facilities ⚡ 🖾 🛢 🗘 🞋 ⊙ ⬅ ▣ 🛢 ⬆ 🞋 🔳
Nearby Facilities ⌐ ✗ ⏚ U
Nearest Town Marazion
Directions 3 miles from Marazion, B3280 through Goldsithney signposted South Treveneague.
⇌ St. Erth

MARAZION

Wheal Rodney Holiday Park, Gwallon Lane, Marazion, Cornwall, TR17 0HL
Tel: 01736 710605
Email: reception@whealrodney.co.uk
www.whealrodney.co.uk
Pitches For ▲ ⊞ ⊟ **Total** 30
Acreage 2 **Open** March **to** October
Access Good **Site** Level
Nearest Bus Stop (Miles) ¼
The nearest touring park to St. Michaels Mount.
Facilities ⚡ 🖾 🛢 🗘 🞋 ⊙ ⬅ ▣ 🛢
⚽ 🞋 ⬆ 🞋 🔳 🖎 ⬟ 🛜
Nearby Facilities ⌐ ✗ ⏚ ⤢ U ♫
Nearest Town Marazion
Directions On the A30 towards Penzance, at Crowlas turn left signposted Rospeath, 1½ miles on the right. Or from Marazion on the A30 turn opposite the Fire Engine Inn, site is 500 metres on the left.
⇌ Penzance

MAWGAN PORTH

Magic Cove Touring Park, Mawgan Porth, Newquay, Cornwall, TR8 4BD
Tel: 01637 860263
Email: magic@magiccove.co.uk
www.magiccove.co.uk
Pitches For ⚠ 🚐 🚓 **Total** 25
Acreage 1 **Open** Easter **to** Oct
Access Good **Site** Level
Nearest Bus Stop (Miles) ¼
300yds from a sandy beach. Ideal centre for North Cornwall coast. Water adjacent to each pitch and TV points.
Facilities ⨍ 🕼 🞉 🏱 ☉ ♨ 🍽 ☕🗙🖃 🗗 🛜
Nearby Facilities 🏌 ✔ ∪ 🎠
Nearest Town Newquay
Directions Exit the A30 at Highgate Hill Junction (A39) sp Newquay & Airport. Follow Airport signs to Trekenning roundabout and take the first exit. Continue to follow Airport signs, go past the Airport, at the T-Junction turn right to Mawgan Porth. Turn right by Pitch n Putt. Campsite is 300 yards on the left.
🚏 Newquay

MAWGAN PORTH

Marver Touring Park, Marver Chalets, Mawgan Porth, Nr Newquay, Cornwall, TR8 4BB
Tel: 01637 860493
Email: familyholidays@aol.com
www.marverholidaypark.co.uk
Pitches For ⚠ 🚐 🚓 **Total** 15
Acreage 2½ **Open** April **to** Oct
Access Good **Site** Level
Nearest Bus Stop (Miles) Outside
Peaceful location in a valley with superb views. 300 yards to the beach, excellent coastal walks. Ideal base for touring Cornwall.
Facilities ⨍ 🕼 🏱 ☉ ♨ 🗙🖃 🗗
Nearby Facilities 🏌 ✔ ⚓ ☇ ∪ 🎠
Nearest Town Newquay
Directions From Newquay take the B3276 coast road to Padstow. After 6 miles, on entering Mawgan Porth, turn right at the Mawgan Porth Stores, park is 300 yards on the left.
🚏 Newquay

MAWGAN PORTH

Sun Haven Valley Holiday Park, Mawgan Porth, Cornwall, TR8 4BQ
Tel: 0800 634 6744
Email: sunhaven@sunhavenvalley.com
www.sunhavenvalley.com
Pitches For ⚠ 🚐 🚓 **Total** 109
Acreage 7 **Open** Easter **to** Oct
Access Good **Site** Level
Nearest Bus Stop (Miles) Outside
A 10 minute walk from the large sandy beach.
Facilities ⨍ 🕼 🏱 ☉ ♨ 🍽 🖃 🞉
🗙 🎱 🞉 🗙 🛢 🞉 🗗 🛜

Nearby Facilities 🏌 ✔ ⚓ ☇ ∪ 🎠 🎣 ✕
Nearest Town Padstow
Directions Leave the A30 at Highgate Hill for Newquay and follow signs for the airport. Go past the airport and turn right at the T-Junction for Mawgan Porth. At the beach turn right on the only road inland (with crazy golf on the left), ¼ mile to the s-bend and the Park is ½ a mile further on.
🚏 Newquay

MEVAGISSEY

Seaview International, Boswinger, Gorran, St Austell, Cornwall, PL26 6LL
Tel: 01726 843425
Email: holidays@seaviewinternational.com
www.seaviewinternational.com
Pitches For ⚠ 🚐 🚓 🚖 **Total** 189
Acreage 15 **Open** March **to** Oct
Access Good **Site** Level
Nearest Bus Stop (Miles) ½
Englands TOP PARK. Beautiful park with panoramic coastline views. Surrounded by sandy beaches, nearest ½ mile. New alfresco dining area. Free sports and pastimes on site. Holiday caravans also for hire, all have Rose Award. Holiday home caravans to buy. Full sub-letting scheme available. AA Best Campsite of the Year 2007 and AA 5 Pennant Premier Park.
Facilities ⚕ ⨍ 🖃 🕼 🞉 🏱 ☉ ♨ 🍽 🞉 🞉
🗙 🎱 🞉 🗙 🞉 🞉 ♨ 🞉 ⚓ ☇ ✚ 🖃 🗗 🞉
Nearby Facilities 🏌 ✔ ⚓ ☇ ∪ 🎠 🎣 ✕
Nearest Town Mevagissey/St Austell
Directions From St Austell take the B3273 to Mevagissey, prior to village turn right. Then follow signs to Gorran.
🚏 St Austell

MEVAGISSEY

Tregarton Park, Gorran, Nr Mevagissey, St Austell, Cornwall, PL26 6NF
Tel: 01726 843666
Email: reception@tregarton.co.uk
www.tregarton.co.uk
Pitches For ⚠ 🚐 🚓 **Total** 125
Acreage 12 **Open** April **to** October
Access Good **Site** Lev/Terraced
Nearest Bus Stop (Miles) Outside
Beautiful sheltered park with glimpses of the sea through the valley. 1½ miles to the nearest beach, 2½ miles from the Lost Garden of Heligan and 9 miles from The Eden Project.
Facilities ⚕ ⨍ 🖃 🕼 🞉 🏱 ☉ ♨ 🖃 🞉 🞉
🗙 🎱 🞉 🗙 🞉 ⚓ ☇ ✚ 🖃 🗗 🛜
Nearby Facilities 🏌 ✔ ⚓ ☇ ∪ 🎠
Directions From St Austell take the B3273 signposted Mevagissey. After 4 miles, at the top of Pentewan Hill turn right signposted Gorran Haven. Park is 3 miles on the right .
🚏 St. Austell

MULLION

Franchis, Cury Cross Lanes, Mullion, Helston, Cornwall, TR12 7AZ
Tel: 01326 240301
Email: enquiries@franchis.co.uk
www.franchis.co.uk
Pitches For ⚠ 🚐 🚓 **Total** 70
Acreage 4 **Open** Easter **to** Oct
Access Good **Site** Lev/Slope
Nearest Bus Stop (Miles) ½
Set in 17 acres of woodland and fields. Near to beaches and Helford River.
Facilities ⨍ 🕼 🏱 ☉ ♨ 🖃 🞉 🗙 🎱🗗
Nearby Facilities 🏌 ✔ ⚓ ∪ 🎠
Directions On the A3083, 5 miles south of Helston and 2 miles north of Mullion.
🚏 Redruth

MULLION

Mullion Holiday Park, Ruan Minor, Nr Helston, Cornwall, TR12 7LJ
Tel: 0844 335 3732
Email:
touringandcamping@parkdeanholidays.com
www.parkdeantouring.com
Pitches For ⚠ 🚐 🚓 **Total** 150
Acreage 49 **Open** March **to** Oct
Access Good **Site** Level
Nearest Bus Stop (Miles) Outside
Award winning family holiday park situated in an area of outstanding natural beauty, surrounded by Blue Flag Beaches, hidden coves and superb coastal walks.
Facilities ⨍ 🖃 🕼 🏱 ☉ ♨ 🖃 🞉 🞉
🗙 🎱 🞉 🗙 🞉 🞉 ⚓ ☇ ✚ 🖃 🗗 ⛄
🛜
Nearby Facilities 🏌 ✔ ⚓ ☇ ∪ 🎠 🎣
Nearest Town Helston
Directions From the A30 take the A39 through Truro towards Falmouth. Then take the A394 to Helston then the A3083 for The Lizard. Park is 7 miles on the left.
🚏 Redruth

NEWQUAY

Camping & Caravanning Club Site, Tregurrian, Nr Newquay, Cornwall, TR8 4AE
Tel: 01637 860448
www.campingandcaravanningclub.co.uk/tregurrian
Pitches For ⚠ 🚐 🚓 **Total** 90
Acreage 4½ **Open** 29-Mar **to** 05-Nov
Access Good **Site** Level
Nearest Bus Stop (Miles) ¼
The glorious sandy beach of Watergate Bay is just ¾ miles away. There is a pretty coastal walk from the site to the beach. BTB 4 Star Graded, AA 3 Pennants and Loo of the Year Award. Non members welcome. You can also call us on 0845 130 7633.

Facilities 👤 ⚏ 🔥 🚿 🅿 ☺ 🍴 🛒 🔌 📞
📺 🚻 🔋 ➕ 🅿 🔌
Nearby Facilities ⌐ 🚴 ⚓ ∪ ♪
Nearest Town Newquay
Directions Leave the A30 after a prominent railway bridge by turning right signposted Newquay Airport, St Columb Major at roundabout on the A39. Join the A3059 to Newquay, after 1½ miles turn right signposted Newquay Airport and follow signs to Watergate Bay.
🚆 Newquay

NEWQUAY
Carvynick Country Club Summercourt, Newquay, Cornwall, TR8 5AF
Tel: 01872 510716
Email: info@carvynick.co.uk
www.carvynick.co.uk
Pitches For 🚐 🚙 🚌
Open All Year
Nearest Bus Stop (Miles) ¼
Situated in the heart of Cornwall amidst the rolling hills of the beautiful South West, Carvynick Holiday Park in Newquay extends a warm welcome to those seeking tranquil family holidays in Cornwall. Located only 10 minutes from the stunning Newquay beaches, dramatic Cornish coastline and only 14 miles from the world famous Eden Project. Our central location provides easy access to all of Cornwall's many attractions.
Facilities ⚏ 🔥 🚿 🅿 ☺ 🍴 🛒 🔌 📞
✕ ♨ 🔋 ➕ 🔌 🅿
Nearby Facilities ⌐ 🚴 ⚓ ∪ ♪
Nearest Town Newquay
Directions From the A30 heading west, take the Summercourt exit signposted A3058 Newquay. Travel into Summercourt, at the traffic lights turn right and the Park is first on the left.
🚆 Newquay

NEWQUAY
Cottage Farm Touring Park, Treworgans, Cubert, Newquay, Cornwall, TR8 5HH
Tel: 01637 831083
Email: info@cottagefarmpark.co.uk
www.cottagefarmpark.co.uk
Pitches For ⛺ 🚐 🚙 **Total** 45
Acreage 2 **Open** April to End Sept
Access Good **Site** Level
Nearest Bus Stop (Miles) ¼
Within easy reach of three National Trust beaches. Small, family site, peaceful and in a rural location.
Facilities ⚏ 🔥 🚿 🅿 ☺ 🍴 🛒 🔌 📞
🚻 ➕ 🔌
Nearby Facilities ⌐ 🚴 ⚓ ∪ ♪ 🏇
Nearest Town Newquay

Directions Newqauy to Redruth road A3075, turn right onto High Lanes, follow signs to Cubert, at Cubert Village turn right at the mini roundabout sp Crantock-Wesley road. Continue for ½ a mile passing Cubert Primary School on your left, then look for Blue Cottage Farm sign on the left hand side.
🚆 Newquay

NEWQUAY
Crantock Plains Touring Park, Crantock, Newquay, Cornwall, TR8 5PH
Tel: 01637 830955
Email: crantockplainstp@btinternet.co.uk
www.crantock-plains.co.uk
Pitches For ⛺ 🚐 🚙 **Total** 60
Acreage 4 **Open** April to Sept
Access Good **Site** Level
Nearest Bus Stop (Miles) ¼
Spacious park set in peaceful countryside. 2½ miles from Newquay.
Facilities 👤 ⚏ 🔥 🚿 🅿 ☺ 🍴 🛒 🔌 📞
🚻 🚻 🔋 ➕ 🔌
Nearby Facilities ⌐ 🚴 ⚓ ∪ ♪ 🏇
Nearest Town Newquay
Directions Turn off the A30 onto the A392. Approx. 9 miles past Morrisons turn onto the A3075, after 1 mile follow signs.
🚆 Newquay

NEWQUAY
Hendra Holiday Park, Newquay, Cornwall, TR8 4NY
Tel: 01637 875778
Email: enquiries@hendra-holidays.com
www.http://www.hendra-holidays.com
Pitches For ⛺ 🚐 🚙 **Total** 548
Open Easter to October
Access Good **Site** Level
Nearest Bus Stop (Miles) Outside
Country views. Only 1½ miles from beaches. Indoor and outdoor Oasis Fun Pools.
Facilities 👤 ⚏ 🔥 🚿 🅿 ☺ 🍴 🛒 🔌 📞
🚻 🚻 🔋 🔋 ✕ ♨ 🍴 🔥 🏪 ➕ 🛒 🔌 📞 🔌
📶
Nearby Facilities ⌐ 🚴 ⚓ ∪ ♪
Nearest Town Newquay
Directions 1½ miles from Newquay on the A392.
🚆 Newquay

NEWQUAY
Holywell Bay Holiday Park, Holywell Bay, Cornwall, TR8 5PR
Tel: 0844 335 3732
Email: touringandcamping@parkdeanholidays.com
www.parkdeantouring.com
Pitches For ⛺ 🚐 🚙 **Total** 40
Acreage 40 **Open** Mar to Oct
Access Good **Site** Level
Nearest Bus Stop (Miles) Outside

Beach is a short stroll from the park, with Newquay town centre only 5 miles away. Heated outdoor pool, bar and restaurant on Park. FREE kids clubs and live family entertainment.
Facilities ⚏ 🔥 🚿 🅿 🛒
🔋 🚻 🔋 ✕ 🍴 🏪 🔥 🏪 ➕ 🛒 🔌 📞 📶
Nearby Facilities ⌐ 🚴 ∪ ♪
Nearest Town Newquay
Directions Follow the M4 to Exeter and take the A30 to Okehampton. Turn off at the first slip road to Newquay (A39), continue over the roundabout to the A3075 towards Redruth, the park is 2 miles.
🚆 Newquay

NEWQUAY
Monkey Tree Holiday Park, Scotland Road, Rejerrah, Newquay, Cornwall, TR8 5QR
Tel: 01872 572032
Email: enquiries@monkeytreeholidaypark.co.uk
www.monkeytreeholidaypark.co.uk
Pitches For ⛺ 🚐 🚙 **Total** 750
Acreage 56 **Open** 01-Apr to 31-Oct
Access Excellent **Site** Level
Nearest Bus Stop (Miles) Outside
Monkey Tree Holiday Park is located just 4 miles from Perranporth and only 8 miles from Truro, Cornwall's main shopping town. The park is easily accessible to all parts of Cornwall with its excellent location adjacent to the A30. The central location means that most of Cornwall's main attractions are easy and quick to reach.
Facilities 👤 ⚏ 🔥 🚿 🅿 ☺ 🍴 🛒 🔌 📞
🚻 🚻 🔋 🔋 ✕ 🍴 🏪 🔥 🏪 ➕ 🌀 🛒 🔌 📞 🚴 🌀
🏪 📶
Nearby Facilities ⌐ 🚴 ⚓ ∪ ♪ 🏇
Nearest Town Newquay
Directions From the A30 at the Carland Cross roundabout, take the turning onto the B3285 to Perranporth at Boxheater Junction. Take the second turning on the right signposted Monkey Tree Holiday Park. The park can be found 1 mile on the left hand side.
🚆 Newquay

NEWQUAY
Newperran Holiday Park, Rejerrah, Newquay, Cornwall, TR8 5QJ
Tel: 01872 572407
Email: holidays@newperran.co.uk
www.newperran.co.uk
Pitches For ⛺ 🚐 🚙 **Total** 400
Acreage 25 **Open** Easter to Oct
Access Good **Site** Level
Nearest Bus Stop (Miles) ¼

cornwall's finest parks

independent, top graded parks, offering fabulous facilities, superb locations and superior service - especially for families and couples - choose a great holiday from cornwall's finest quality pa

ESCAPE
EXPLORE
DISCOVER

CORNWALL'S
FINEST FIVE STAR
HOLIDAY PARK

trevornick
holiday park

DOG FRIENDLY

HOLIDAY PARK

www.trevornick.co.uk - 0843 453 5531
Holywell Bay Nr. Newquay Cornwall TR8 5PW

•• **TOURING** •• **CAMPING** •• **EUROTENTS** ••

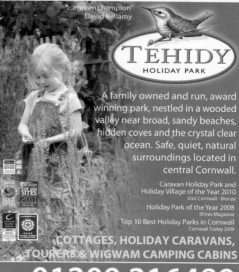

Concessionary green fees, scenic views and central to nine golden beaches. Quality in Tourism 5 Stars, AA 4 Pennants and BH&HPA.
Facilities ⚓
Nearby Facilities
Nearest Town Newquay
Directions Take the A30 towards Redruth, turn right onto the B3285 signposted Perranporth and Goodhavern. At the junction at Goodhavern turn right onto the A3075 and turn left at the Newperran sign.
≠ Newquay

NEWQUAY
Newquay Holiday Park, Newquay, Cornwall, TR8 4HS
Tel: 0844 335 3732
Email: touringandcamping@parkdeanholidays.com
www.parkdeantouring.com
Pitches For Å ⚓ ⚓ **Total** 50
Acreage 60 **Open** March **to** Oct
Access Good **Site** Sloping
Nearest Bus Stop (Miles) Outside
Set in rolling Cornish countryside, only 2 miles from a choice of 11 beaches. Three heated outdoor pools. FREE kids clubs and live family entertainment.
Facilities ⚓
Nearby Facilities
Nearest Town Newquay
Directions Follow the M4 to Exeter and take the A30 to Okehampton. Continue until you see the turn off for St. Mawgan, go along the road and take the A3059 to Newquay.
≠ Newquay

NEWQUAY
Perran-Quay Touring Park, Hendra Croft, Rejerrah, Nr Newquay, Cornwall, TR8 5QP
Tel: 01872 572561
Email: rose@perran-quay.co.uk
www.perran-quay.co.uk
Pitches For Å ⚓ ⚓ ⚓ **Total** 100
Acreage 7½ **Open** All Year
Access Good **Site** Level
Nearest Bus Stop (Miles) Outside
5 minutes from Holywell Bay. Licensed bar on site. Ideal touring. You can also contact us on Mobile: 07867 872031.
Facilities ⚓
Nearby Facilities
Nearest Town Newquay/Perranporth
Directions On the A3075 midway between Perranporth and Newquay (approx 3 miles to each).
≠ Newquay

NEWQUAY
Riverside Holiday Park, Lane, Newquay, Cornwall, TR8 4PE
Tel: 01637 873617
Email: info@riversideholidaypark.co.uk
www.riversideholidaypark.co.uk
Pitches For Å ⚓ ⚓ **Total** 60
Acreage 7 **Open** Easter **to** October
Access Good **Site** Level
Nearest Bus Stop (Miles) ½
In a peaceful position, beside the River Gannel. Only 2½ miles from the spectacular coastline and sandy beaches.
Facilities ⚓
Nearby Facilities
Directions Approx. 2½ miles from Newquay town centre, situated 1 mile off the A392 Newquay road.
≠ Newquay

NEWQUAY
Rosecliston Park, Trevemper, Newquay, Cornwall, TR8 5JT
Tel: 01637 830326
Email: info@rosecliston.co.uk
www.rosecliston.co.uk
Pitches For Å **Total** 126
Acreage 12 **Open** Late May **to** Sept
Access Good **Site** Lev/Slope
Nearest Bus Stop (Miles) Entrance
ADULTS ONLY PARK. 18 to 30s camping site. Close to Newquay with its nightlife, shopping and excellent surfing beaches.
Facilities ⚓
Nearby Facilities
Nearest Town Newquay
Directions On the A3075 Newquay to Redruth road, 1 mile from Newquay Boating Lake.
≠ Newquay

NEWQUAY
Summer Lodge Holiday Park, Whitecross, Newquay, Cornwall, TR8 4LW
Tel: 0844 272 1138
Email: enquiries@summerlodge.co.uk
www.summerlodge.co.uk
Pitches For Å ⚓ ⚓
Open 31-Mar **to** 31-Oct
Access Good **Site** Sloping
Nearest Bus Stop (Miles) ¼
Set in beautiful countryside and ideally situated for touring. Short distance from beach and main town of Newquay.
Facilities ⚓
Nearby Facilities
Directions From the A30 take the A39 Newquay road to Halloon roundabout, go straight over and follow signs for the A392. After approx 3 miles the Park is on the left.
≠ Newquay

NEWQUAY
Trebarber Farm, St Columb Minor, Newquay, Cornwall, TR8 4JT
Tel: 01637 873007
Email: trebarberfarm@talktalk.net
www.trebarberfarmholidays.com
Pitches For ▲ ⊞ ⊟
Acreage 5 Open May to October
Access Good Site Level
Quiet, ideal family centre for touring and beaches. Within walking distance of Porth Reservoir (coarse fishing) and a golf course.
Facilities ⬥ ♿ ⌂ ⊙↵⌨ ◻ ☎⊞
Nearby Facilities ⌿ ✦ ⚓ ⌇ ∪ ⚲
Nearest Town Newquay
Directions 3 miles from Newquay on A3059, Newquay to St. Columb Major road.
⇌ Newquay

NEWQUAY
Trekenning Tourist Park, Trekenning, Newquay, Cornwall, TR8 4JF
Tel: 01637 880462
Email: holidays@trekenning.co.uk
www.trekenning.co.uk
Pitches For ▲ ⊞ ⊟ Total 75
Acreage 6½ Open All Year
Access Good Site Sloping
Nearest Bus Stop (Miles) ½
Family site, family run. Holiday homes for sale.
Facilities ⨍ ♿ ⌂☏⌂⊙↵
◻ ☎ ⍾ ◻ ⊙ ✕ ▯ ♦ ♨ ⚒ ✿ ⌨ ▣ ◻ ☼
☂
Nearby Facilities ⌿ ✦ ⚓ ⌇ ∪ ⚲
Directions From Newquay take the A3059 to the Trekenning roundabout, site entrance is 20 yds on the right before the roundabout.
⇌ Newquay

NEWQUAY
Treloy Touring Park, Newquay, Cornwall, TR8 4JN
Tel: 01637 872063/876279
Email: treloy.tp@btconnect.com
www.treloy.co.uk
Pitches For ▲ ⊞ ⊟ ⊞ Total 223
Acreage 12 Open Easter to Mid Sept
Access Good Site Lev/Slope
Nearest Bus Stop (Miles) Outside
Ideal site for touring the whole of Cornwall. Coarse fishing nearby. Own golf course close by with concessionary Green Fees. Free entertainment.
Facilities ⬥ ⨍ ▣ ♿ ☏⌂⊙↵ ◻ ☎
◻ ⍾ ◻ ⊙ ✕ ▯ ♦ ♨ ⚒ ✿ ⌨ ▣ ◻ ☼
Nearby Facilities ⌿ ✦ ⚓ ⌇ ∪ ⚲
Nearest Town Newquay
Directions 3 miles from Newquay off the A3059 Newquay to St Columb Major Road.
⇌ Newquay

NEWQUAY
Trenance Holiday Park, Edgcumbe Avenue, Newquay, Cornwall, TR7 2JY
Tel: 01637 873447
Email: enquiries@trenanceholidaypark.co.uk
www.trenanceholidaypark.co.uk
Pitches For ▲ ⊞ ⊟ Total 134
Acreage 15 Open April to Oct
Access Good Site Sloping
Nearest Bus Stop (Miles) Outside
1 mile from Newquay town centre and next door to Newquay Zoo.
Facilities ⨍ ♿⌂⌂⊙↵⌨ ◻ ☎
◻ ⍾ ◻ ⊙ ✕ ♦ ▯ ▣ ◻
Nearby Facilities ⌿ ✦ ⚓ ⌇ ∪ ⚲ ⚲
Nearest Town Newquay
Directions On the main A3075 Newquay to Truro road, approx 1 mile from Newquay town centre.
⇌ Newquay

NEWQUAY
Trencreek Holiday Park, Trencreek, Newquay, Cornwall, TR8 4NS
Tel: 01637 874210
Email: trencreek@btconnect.com
www.trencreekholidaypark.co.uk
Pitches For ▲ ⊞ ⊟ Total 150
Acreage 10 Open April to September
Access Good Site Level
Nearest Bus Stop (Miles) Outside
Coarse fishing on site, 15 minutes footpath walk to Newquay, 1 mile by road.
Facilities ⨍ ▣ ♿⌂⌂⊙↵⌨ ◻ ☎
◻ ⍾ ◻ ⊙ ✕ ▯ ♦ ♨ ⌇ ▯ ✦ ◻
Nearby Facilities ⌿ ✦ ⚓ ⌇ ∪ ⚲ ⚲ ✗
Nearest Town Newquay
Directions A392 to Quintrell Downs, turn right Newquay East/Porth, at Porth crossroads, ¾ miles outside Newquay, turn left to Trencreek.
⇌ Newquay

NEWQUAY
Trethiggey Touring Park, Quintrell Downs, Newquay, Cornwall, TR8 4QR
Tel: 01637 877672
Email: enquiries@trethiggey.co.uk
www.trethiggey.co.uk
Pitches For ▲ ⊞ ⊟ ⊞ Total 157
Acreage 16 Open 02-Mar to 02-Jan
Access Good Site Lev/Slope
Nearest Bus Stop (Miles) ¼
Close to beaches and central for Cornwalls attractions. Licensed Bar on site. Ideal touring.
Facilities ⬥ ⨍ ▣ ♿⌂⌂⊙↵ ◻ ☎
◻ ⍾ ◻ ⊙ ✕ ▯ ♦ ♨ ⌨ ▣ ◻ ☼ ☂ ✗
Nearby Facilities ⌿ ✦ ⚓ ⌇ ∪ ⚲ ⚲
Nearest Town Newquay
Directions 2 miles north west of Newquay on the A3058.
⇌ Quintrell Downs

NEWQUAY
Trevarrian Holiday Park, Trevarrian, Mawgan Porth, Newquay, Cornwall, TR8 4AQ
Tel: 01637 860381
Email: holiday@trevarrian.co.uk
www.trevarrian.co.uk
Pitches For ▲ ⊞ ⊟ Total 180
Acreage 8 Open Easter to 01-Oct
Access Good Site Level
Near the beach. Ideal for families and couples. First class facilities. Always a friendly welcome.
Facilities ⬥ ⨍ ▣ ♿⌂⌂⊙↵ ◻ ☎
◻ ⍾ ◻ ⊙ ✕ ▯ ▯ ♦ ♨ ⌇ ✿ ▣ ◻ ☼ ✦
Nearby Facilities ⌿ ✦ ⚓ ⌇ ∪ ⚲ ⚲
Nearest Town Newquay
Directions Take A30 west at Exeter. At Indian Queens, take the Newquay turning. At the rbt take third exit sp Newquay and Wadebridge, at next rbt take third exit for Wadebridge and St Columb, next rbt take first exit sp Newquay Airport. Continue past petrol station and turn right through the woods. Go past the airport and turn rt at the T-Jct, Trevarrian is ½ a mile on left.

NEWQUAY
Trevornick Holiday Park, Holywell Bay, Newquay, Cornwall, TR8 5PW
Tel: 01637 830531
Email: bookings@trevornick.co.uk
www.trevornick.co.uk
Pitches For ▲ ⊞ ⊟ Total 600
Acreage 30 Open 31-Mar to 15-Sep
Access Good Site Level
Right next to the beach with stunning sea views. On site 18 hole golf course and 18 hole pitch n putt. Tourers and static tents.
Facilities ⬥ ⨍ ▣ ♿⌂⌂⊙↵⌨ ◻ ☎
◻ ⍾ ◻ ⊙ ✕ ▯ ♦ ♨ ⌇ ✿ ⌨ ▣ ◻ ☼ ✗
☂
Nearby Facilities ⌿ ✦ ⚓ ⌇ ∪ ⚲ ⚲
Nearest Town Newquay
Directions Take Newquay to Perrenporth A3075 road. Take turning for Cubert/Holywell.
⇌ Newquay

NEWQUAY
Watergate Bay Touring Park, Watergate Bay, Newquay, Cornwall, TR8 4AD
Tel: 01637 860387
email@watergatebaytouringpark.co.uk
www.watergatebaytouringpark.co.uk
Pitches For ▲ ⊞ ⊟ Total 171
Acreage 30 Open March to End Oct
Access Good Site Level
Nearest Bus Stop (Miles) Outside
½ mile from Watergate Bay in a rural location in an area of outstanding natural beauty.
Facilities ⬥ ⨍ ▣ ♿⌂⌂⊙↵ ◻ ☎
◻ ⍾ ◻ ⊙ ✕ ▯ ♦ ♨ ⌇ ✿ ⌨ ▣ ◻ ☼
✦ ☂

HARLYN SANDS HOLIDAY PARK
family owned, family run for families

Bucket and Spade holidays at their very best! Located within a few minutes walk of Harlyn Bay, and with facilities on site including our Super Splash Indoor Fun Pool, Showtime Entertainment Room and Snack Shack there's no where better for you and your young family to come and enjoy the best Cornwall has to offer!

T: 01841 520720
E: enquiries@harlynsands.co.uk

www.harlynsands.co.uk
Lighthouse Road, Trevose Head, Padstow, Cornwall PL28 8SQ

AA HOLIDAY CENTRE

Nearby Facilities ┌ ✦ ♨ ∪ ♪
Nearest Town Newquay
Directions 4 miles north of Newquay on the B3276 Coast Road to Padstow. Follow directions shown from Watergate Bay.
⇌ Newquay

PADSTOW

Carnevas Farm Holiday Park, Carnevas Farm, St Merryn, Padstow, Cornwall, PL28 8PN
Tel: 01841 520230
Email: carnevascampsite@aol.com
www.carnevasholidaypark.co.uk
Pitches For ▲ ⊞ ⊟ **Total** 198
Acreage 8 **Open** April **to** October
Access Good **Site** Lev/Slope
Nearest Bus Stop (Miles) ½
Well run family park in a lovely rural position, near to numerous sandy beaches. Ideal touring. AA 4 Pennants and ETB 4 Star Park.
Facilities ♿ ∮ ◫ ⛽ ┌ ⊙ ╝ ▄ ◎ ⌷ ☎
♨ ℀ ☐ ⊗ ✗ ♀ ♨ ♠ ⊞ ⬢ ▣ ☂
Nearby Facilities ┌ ✦ ⚓ ♨ ∪ ♪ ♪
Nearest Town Padstow
Directions From Padstow take the B3726 Newquay coast road, turn right at Tredrea Inn just before getting to Porthcothan Bay. Site ¼ mile up road on right.
⇌ Newquay

PADSTOW

Dennis Cove Camping Ltd., Dennis Cove, Padstow, Cornwall, PL28 8DR
Tel: 01841 532349
Email: denniscove@freeuk.com
www.denniscove.co.uk
Pitches For ▲ ⊞ ⊟ **Total** 42
Acreage 5 **Open** April **to** September
Access Fair **Site** Lev/Slope
Nearest Bus Stop (Miles) ¼

Scenic views. Site adjoins Camel Trail cycle track. 10 minute walk to Padstow centre. 5 electric hook-ups. Groups by permission only. Reservation essential.
Facilities ∮ ◫⛽┌⊙╝▄◎⌷♨⊙⬢⊡
Nearby Facilities ┌ ✦ ⚓ ♨ ∪ ♪ ♪
Nearest Town Padstow
Directions Signposted off A389 on outskirts of Padstow Town.
⇌ Bodmin Parkway

PADSTOW

Dennis Farm, Padstow, Cornwall, PL28 8DR
Tel: 01841 533513
www.wix.com/dennisfarm/campsite
Pitches For ▲ **Total** 24
Acreage 1 **Open** June **to** Sept
Site Lev/Slope
Nearest Bus Stop (Miles) ¼
Tent only site by the River Camel, ten minutes walk to Padstow. Own slipway and moorings.
ALSO OPEN Spring Bank Holiday week.
Facilities ◫⛽┌⊙╝▄◎⌷
♨☐⊗⬢⊡
Nearby Facilities ┌ ✦ ⚓ ♨ ∪ ♪ ♪
Nearest Town Padstow
Directions Take the A389 to Padstow. Take first turning on the right by Tesco, then turn second right into Dennis Lane, continue to the end of the lane.
⇌ Bodmin Parkway

PADSTOW

Harlyn Sands Holiday Park, Lighthouse Road, Trevose Head, Padstow, Cornwall, PL28 8SQ
Tel: 01841 520720
Email: enquiries@harlynsands.co.uk
www.harlynsands.co.uk
Pitches For ▲ ⊞ ⊟
Open Easter **to** Oct

Access Good **Site** Level
Nearest Bus Stop (Miles) ¼
Near the beach. Fun pool on site.
Facilities ♿ ∮ ◫⛽┌⊙╝▄◎⌷☎
♨ ℀ ☐ ⊗ ✗ ♀ ♠ ⊞ ⬢ ▣ ☂
Nearby Facilities ┌ ∪
Nearest Town Padstow
Directions From Padstow take the B3276 Newquay coast road. After 1 mile follow signs for Harlyn Sands.
⇌ Bodmin

PADSTOW

Higher Harlyn Park, St Merryn, Padstow, Cornwall, PL28 8SG
Tel: 01841 520022
Email: pbharlyn@aol.com
www.higherharlynpark.co.uk
Pitches For ▲ ⊞ ⊟ **Total** 200
Acreage 8 **Open** Easter **to** End Sept
Access Good **Site** Level
Nearest Bus Stop (Miles) Entrance
Near the beach and within walking distance of the village. Outdoor pool, bar, shop, restaurant, pizzeria, breakfasts and childrens play area.
Facilities ♿ ∮ ◫⛽┌⊙╝▄◎⌷
♨ ℀ ☐ ⊗ ✗ ♀ ♠ ⊞ ⬢ ▣ ☂
Nearby Facilities ┌ ✦ ⚓ ∪
Nearest Town Padstow
Directions 3 miles south of Padstow on the Newquay road in St Merryn Village.
⇌ Bodmin Parkway

PADSTOW

Mother Ivey's Bay Holiday Park, Trevose Head, Padstow, Cornwall, PL28 8SL
Tel: 01841 520990
Email: info@motheriveysbay.com
www.motheriveysbay.com
Pitches For ▲ ⊞ ⊟ **Total** 100

Acreage 10 **Open** April **to** October
Access Good **Site** Level
Nearest Bus Stop (Miles) ¼
Own private sandy beach. Beautiful coastal walks.
Facilities
Nearby Facilities
Nearest Town Padstow
Directions 4 miles from Padstow. Signposted off the B3276 Padstow to Newquay coastal road (Trevose Head).
⇌ Bodmin

PADSTOW

Music Water Touring Park, Rumford, Wadebridge, Cornwall, PL27 7SJ
Tel: 01841 540257
www.wix.com/musicwater/touringpark
Pitches For Å ⊞ ⊞ **Total** 140
Acreage 8 **Open** April **to** Oct
Access Good **Site** Lev/Slope
5 miles from beaches. Cafe/restaurant nearby. Ideal touring base.
Facilities
Nearby Facilities
Nearest Town Wadebridge
Directions From Wadebridge take the A39 to Winnards Perch roundabout, then take the B3274. Turn first left and site is on the right.
⇌ Bodmin

PADSTOW

Old MacDonalds Farm, Porthcothan Bay, Padstow, Cornwall, PL28 8LW
Tel: 01841 540809
Email: enquiries@oldmacdonalds.co.uk
www.oldmacdonalds.co.uk
Pitches For Å ⊞ ⊞ **Total** 50
Acreage 3½ **Open** All Year
Access Good **Site** Level
Nearest Bus Stop (Miles) Outside
½ a mile to the beach. Campers have free access to old MacDonalds Farm Park and can help feed the animals. Pony rides, crazy golf and a miniature railway on site. Dutch speaking owners.
Facilities
Nearby Facilities
Nearest Town Padstow/Newquay
Directions Just off the B3276 coast road. 5 miles south of Padstow and 9 miles north of Newquay.

PADSTOW

Padstow Holiday Park, Cliffdowne, Padstow, Cornwall, PL28 8LB
Tel: 01841 532289
Email: mail@padstowholidaypark.co.uk
www.padstowholidaypark.co.uk
Pitches For Å ⊞ ⊞ **Total** 50
Acreage 7 **Open** March **to** Dec
Site Level
Nearest Bus Stop (Miles) Outside
Quiet location in open countryside with no club or bar. Near to several sandy beaches. Footpath to Padstow (1 mile). 1 mile from a Tesco store.
Facilities
Nearby Facilities
Nearest Town Padstow
Directions From Wadebridge take the A389 to Padstow, site is on the right hand side 1½ miles before Padstow.
⇌ Bodmin

PADSTOW

Padstow Touring Park, Padstow, Cornwall, PL28 8LE
Tel: 01841 532061
Email: mail@padstowtouringpark.co.uk
www.padstowtouringpark.co.uk
Pitches For Å ⊞ ⊞ ⊞ **Total** 180
Acreage 13¼ **Open** All Year
Access Good **Site** Level
Nearest Bus Stop (Miles) Outside
Quiet family park with panoramic views. Several sandy beaches within 3 miles. Footpath to padstow. Three amenity blocks. Free brochure.
Facilities
Nearby Facilities
Nearest Town Padstow
Directions On A389 1 mile south south west of Padstow.

PADSTOW

Seagull Tourist Park, St Merryn, Padstow, Cornwall, PL28 8PT
Tel: 01841 520117
Pitches For Å ⊞ ⊞ **Total** 100
Acreage 4 **Open** Easter/1 April **to** End Oct
Access Good **Site** Level
Nearest Bus Stop (Miles) ½
Quiet family site near the fishing port of Padstow, and with seven golden sandy beaches, cliff walks and surfing all within a 15 minute drive.
Facilities
Nearby Facilities
Nearest Town Padstow
Directions From St Columb take the B3274 towards Padstow, head for St Merryn and go past the old airfield.
⇌ Bodmin Parkway

PENRYN

Menallack Farm, Treverva, Penryn, Cornwall, TR10 9BP
Tel: 01326 340333
Email: cheese@menallack.co.uk
Pitches For Å ⊞ ⊞ **Total** 30
Acreage 1½ **Open** Easter **to** Oct
Access Good **Site** Lev/Slope
Nearest Bus Stop (Miles) ½
Secluded site with lovely views.
Facilities
Nearby Facilities
Nearest Town Falmouth
Directions From take the A39 "Asda" roundabout turn right up the hill to Mabe Burnthouse. At the crossroads turn left and follow the road, at crossroads turn right to Gweek, site is signposted 1½ miles.
⇌ Penryn

PENZANCE

Bone Valley Caravan & Camping Park, Heamoor, Penzance, Cornwall, TR20 8UJ
Tel: 01736 360313
Email: wardmandie@yahoo.co.uk
www.bonevalleyholidaypark.co.uk
Pitches For Å ⊞ ⊞ **Total** 17
Acreage 1 **Open** All Year
Access Good **Site** Level
Nearest Bus Stop (Miles) ¼
1 mile from Penzance, 3 miles from St Michaels Mount and 10 miles from Lands End. Coastal footpaths.
Facilities
Nearby Facilities
Nearest Town Penzance

Directions Follow the A30 (Penzance Bypass) to roundabout and turn right signposted Heamoor. Follow road through the village to camping/caravan sign and turn right, continue to next camping/caravan sign, signposted Bone Valley.
⇌ Penzance

PENZANCE

Garris Farm, Gulval, Penzance, Cornwall, TR20 8XD
Tel: 01736 365806
Pitches For Å ⊞ ⊞
Acreage 8 **Open** May **to** October
Access Good **Site** Sloping
Nearest Bus Stop (Miles) ¼
Facilities
Nearby Facilities
Nearest Town Penzance
Directions Leave A30 turning right at Growlas on road to Luogvan B3309 to Castlegate. Follow road to Chysauster ancient village.
⇌ Penzance

PENZANCE

Kenneggy Cove Holiday Park, Higher Kenneggy, Rosudgeon, Penzance, Cornwall, TR20 9AU
Tel: 01736 763453
Email: enquiries@kenneggycove.co.uk
www.kenneggycove.co.uk
Pitches For Å ⊞ ⊞ **Total** 45
Acreage 8 **Open** Mid May **to** End of Sept
Access Good **Site** Level
Nearest Bus Stop (Miles) ¼
A quiet site which operates a policy of no noise after 10pm. 12 minutes walk to the stunning beach and S.W. Coastal Path. Quality take-away food service.
Facilities
Nearby Facilities
Nearest Town Penzance
Directions Midway between Penzance and Helston on the A394. Take turn into lane signposted Higher Kenneggy towards the sea.
⇌ Penzance

PENZANCE

River Valley Country Park, Relubbus, Penzance, Cornwall, TR20 9ER
Tel: 01736 763398
Email: rivervalley@surfbay.co.uk
www.surfbayholidays.co.uk
Pitches For ⊞ **Total** 40
Acreage 18 **Open** 26-Feb **to** 06-Jan
Access Good **Site** Sloping
Nearest Bus Stop (Miles) ¼
Tranquil, partly wooded park, along the banks of a clear shallow stream. Near to beaches, pubs, golf course and St Michaels Mount.
Facilities
Nearby Facilities
Nearest Town Penzance
Directions From the A30 at St. Michaels Mount roundabout, take the A394 towards Helston. At the next roundabout turn left onto the B3280 to Relubbus, after 3 miles go over the bridge and River Valley is on the left.
⇌ Penzance

PENZANCE

Sennen Cove Camping & Caravanning Club Site, Higher Tregiffian Farm, St Buryan, Penzance, Cornwall, TR19 6JB
Tel: 01736 871588
www.campingandcaravanningclub.co.uk/ sennencove
Pitches For Å ⊞ ⊞ **Total** 75
Acreage 4 **Open** 23-Apr **to** 24-Sep

Access Good **Site** Level
Nearest Bus Stop (Miles) ¼
Situated on a farm in peaceful countryside. 2½ miles from the beach at Sennen Cove which has won numerous awards. BTB 4 Star Graded and AA 3 Pennants. Non members welcome. You can also call us on 0845 130 7633.
Facilities ⬚
Nearby Facilities ⬚
Nearest Town Penzance
Directions Follow the A30 towards Lands End, turn right onto the A3306 St. Just to Pendeen road, site is 50 yards on the left.
⚡ Penzance

PENZANCE
Wayfarers Caravan & Camping Park, St Hilary, Penzance, Cornwall, TR20 9EF
Tel: 01736 Penzance 763326
Email: elaine@wayfarerspark.co.uk
www.wayfarerspark.co.uk
Pitches For Ⓐ 🏠 🚐 **Total** 39
Acreage 4 **Open** May to Sept
Access Good **Site** Level
Nearest Bus Stop (Miles) Outside
ADULTS ONLY PARK. Tranquil, landscaped surroundings. Graded Excellent by the English Tourist Board. Pitches with 16amp hook-ups and awnings from £86 per week. Four luxury holiday homes for hire.
Facilities ⬚
Nearby Facilities ⬚
Nearest Town Marazion
Directions 2 miles east of Marazion on the B3280.
⚡ Penzance

PERRANPORTH
Perran Sands Holiday Park, Perranporth, Cornwall, TR6 0AQ
Tel: 01872 573551
Email: perransands@haven.com
www.haventouring.com/toperransands
Pitches For Ⓐ 🏠 🚐 **Total** 350
Open 23-Mar to 05-Oct
Access Good **Site** Level
Nearest Bus Stop (Miles) Entrance
A lively and popular Holiday Park with access to a surfing beach. On-Park family entertainment, kids clubs and a wide choice of sports and leisure facilities.
Facilities ⬚
Nearby Facilities ⬚
Nearest Town Perranporth

Directions From Exeter take the A30 through Devon and Cornwall. 1 mile beyond the Wind Farm roundabout turn right onto the B3285 towards Perranporth. Perran Sands is on the right after the village of Goonhavern and before you go down the hill into Perranporth.
⚡ Truro

PERRANPORTH
Perran Springs Holiday Park, Goonhavern, Truro, Cornwall, TR4 9QG
Tel: 01872 540568
Email: info@perransprings.co.uk
www.perransprings.co.uk
Pitches For Ⓐ 🏠 🚐
Acreage 21 **Open** Easter to October
Access Good **Site** Level
Nearest Bus Stop (Miles) ½
Award winning, friendly, quiet family park offering: Coarse Fishing Lakes, Nature Trail and Pond, Spacious Level Pitches, Electric Hook-ups, Caravan Holiday Homes to buy and hire, Eurotents, Shop, Launderette, Childrens Play Area and Panoramic Countryside Views. 4 Star Park and Bellamy Gold Award.
Facilities ⬚
Nearby Facilities ⬚
Nearest Town Perranporth
Directions Leave the A30 and turn right onto the B3285 signposted Perranporth. Follow the brown tourism signs marked Perran Springs for 1½ miles. Entrance will then be clearly seen.
⚡ Truro

PERRANPORTH
Perranporth Camping & Touring Park, Budnick Road, Perranporth, Cornwall, TR6 0DB
Tel: 01872 572174
Pitches For Ⓐ 🏠 🚐 **Total** 150
Acreage 6 **Open** Easter to 30-Sep
Access Good **Site** Lev/Slope
Nearest Bus Stop (Miles) ¼
½ a mile from the town and beach. Adjoining a golf course and 300 metres from stables.
Facilities ⬚
Nearby Facilities ⬚
Nearest Town Perranporth
Directions ½ a mile north east of Perranporth town centre, off the B3285 Perranporth to Newquay road.
⚡ Truro

PERRANPORTH
Tollgate Farm Caravan & Camping Park, Budnick Hill, Perranporth, Cornwall, TR6 0AD
Tel: 01872 572130
Email: enquiries@tollgatefarm.co.uk
www.tollgatefarm.co.uk
Pitches For Ⓐ 🏠 🚐 **Total** 110
Acreage 10 **Open** Easter to 30-Sep
Access Good **Site** Lev/Slope
Nearest Bus Stop (Miles) Entrance
Fantastic views from this quiet, friendly, family run site, less than 1 mile from the beach. Help feed the animals. Great for walking. Take-away food bar (peak season). Ideal base for touring.
Facilities ⬚
Nearby Facilities ⬚
Nearest Town Perranporth
Directions From the A30 take the B3285 signposted Perranporth, site is 1½ miles after Goonhavern on the right.
⚡ Newquay

POLZEATH
South Winds Camping & Caravan Park, Old Polzeath Road, Polzeath, Nr Wadebridge, Cornwall, PL27 6QU
Tel: 01208 863267
Email: info@southwindscampsite.co.uk
www.polzeathcamping.co.uk
Pitches For Ⓐ 🏠 🚐 **Total** 100
Acreage 7 **Open** May to September
Access Good **Site** Level
Nearest Bus Stop (Miles) ¼
Outstanding views of countryside and sea. ½ a mile from Polzeath Beach.
Facilities ⬚
Nearby Facilities ⬚
⚡ Bodmin Road

POLZEATH
Tristram Camping & Caravan Park, Polzeath, Nr Wadebridge, Cornwall, PL27 6TD
Tel: 01208 862215
Email: info@tristramcampsite.co.uk
www.polzeathcamping.co.uk
Pitches For Ⓐ 🏠 🚐 **Total** 150
Acreage 10 **Open** March to Nov
Access Good **Site** Level
Nearest Bus Stop (Miles) ¼
Set on a cliff top overlooking Polzeath beach. Private access onto the beach.
Facilities ⬚
Nearby Facilities ⬚
Nearest Town Polzeath
Directions From Wadebridge take the B3314 and follow signs to Polzeath.
⚡ Bodmin

PORTHTOWAN

Porthtowan Tourist Park, Mile Hill, Porthtowan, Truro, Cornwall, TR4 8TY
Tel: 01209 890256
Email: admin@porthtowantouristpark.co.uk
www.porthtowantouristpark.co.uk
Pitches For Å ⊕ ⊜ **Total** 80
Acreage 5½ **Open** Easter to Sept
Access Good **Site** Level
Nearest Bus Stop (Miles) 1
A level site with spacious pitches in an area of outstanding natural beauty. Close to a sandy surfing beach, cycle trail and coastal path. Superb toilet/laundry facilities with free showers and family rooms. Ideal touring base.
Facilities ᕲ ∮ ⊞ ⊞ ᵣ ⊙ ⊸ ◢ ◻ ☂
🖫 ⊙ ◒ ♠ 𝄢 ♣ ✦ ⊟ ⊡
Nearby Facilities ⌐ ✔ 𝕃 ⊁ ∪ ♪
Nearest Town Porthtowan/Truro
Directions Take signpost off A30 Redruth/Porthtowan. Cross the A30, through north country to T-Junction, right up the hill, park is ½ a mile on the left.
⇌ Redruth

PORTREATH

Cambrose Touring Park, Portreath Road, Redruth, Cornwall, TR16 4HT
Tel: 01209 890747
Email: cambrosetouringpark@supanet.com
www.cambrosetouringpark.co.uk
Pitches For Å ⊕ ⊜ **Total** 60
Acreage 7 **Open** April to Oct
Access Good **Site** Level
Nearest Bus Stop (Miles) ½
1½ miles from the beach. Near to tramway. Ideal for walking and touring.
Facilities ᕲ ∮ ⊞ ᵣ ⊙ ⊸ ◢ ◻ ☂
🖫 ⊙ ◒ ♠ 𝄢 ♣ ✦ ⊟
Nearby Facilities ⌐ ✔ ∪ ⊁
Nearest Town Portreath
Directions From Redruth take the B3300 to Portreath, pass the Treasure Park on the left and after ¼ mile turn right signposted Porthtowan, Cambrose is 100 yards on the left.
⇌ Redruth

PORTREATH

Tehidy Holiday Park, Harris Mill, Illogan, Portreath, Cornwall, TR16 4JQ
Tel: 01209 216489
Email: holiday@tehidy.co.uk
www.tehidy.co.uk
Pitches For Å ⊕ ⊜ ⊜ **Total** 28
Acreage 4½ **Open** March to November
Access Good **Site** Level
Nearest Bus Stop (Miles) Outside
Multi Award winning Holiday Park set in a wooded valley, close to beautiful sandy beaches and coves.
Facilities ᕲ ∮ ⊞ ᵣ ⊙ ⊸ ◢ ◻ ☂
🖫 ⊟ ◒ ⊡ ♠ 𝄢 ⊟ ✦ 🛜
Nearby Facilities ⌐ ✔ 𝕃 ⊁ ∪
Nearest Town Portreath
Directions From the A30, exit to Portreath and Porthtowan and follow signs for Portreath. Turn left at the crossroads, go straight over next crossroads, Park is 300 metres after the Cornish Arms.
⇌ Redruth

PORTSCATHO

Trewince Farm Touring Park, Trewince Farm, Portscatho, Truro, Cornwall, TR2 5ET
Tel: 01872 580430
Email: bookings@trewincefarm.co.uk
www.trewincefarm.co.uk
Pitches For Å ⊕ ⊜ **Total** 25
Acreage 3 **Open** May to Sept
Access Good **Site** Lev/Slope
Nearest Bus Stop (Miles) ½
Near the beach in an area of outstanding natural beauty. Horse and pony riding on site.
Facilities ∮ ⊞ ᵣ ⊙ ⊸ ☂
🖫 ⌿ ⊠ 𝄢 ✦ ⊟ ✦ ✦
Nearby Facilities ⌐ ✔ 𝕃 ⊁ ∪ ♪
Nearest Town Truro
Directions From St. Austell take the A390, then turn left onto the B3287 to Tregony, then the A3078 to St. Mawes. Leave at Trewitian and follow the road to St. Anthony.
⇌ Truro

PRAA SANDS

The Old Farm, Lower Pentreath, Praa Sands, Penzance, Cornwall, TR20 9TL
Tel: 01736 763221
Email: info@theoldfarmpraasands.co.uk
www.theoldfarmpraasands.co.uk
Pitches For Å ⊕ ⊜ **Total** 15
Acreage 1 **Open** April to October
Access Good **Site** Level
Nearest Bus Stop (Miles) Outside
Small friendly site, 400 yards from the beach.
Facilities ⊞ ᵣ ⊙ ⊸ ☂ 🖫 ⊟
Nearby Facilities ⌐ ✔ 𝕃 ⊁ ∪
Nearest Town Penzance
Directions We are on the A394, 6 miles from both Helston and Penzance. Take the turning to Praa Sands and follow this road right down to the car parks where you will come to a junction, turn right and The Old Farm sign will be in front of you.
⇌ Penzance

REDRUTH

Chiverton Park, East Hill, Blackwater, Truro, Cornwall, TR4 8HS
Tel: 01872 560667
Email: chivertonpark@btopenworld.com
www.chivertonpark.co.uk
Pitches For Å ⊕ ⊜ **Total** 12
Acreage 4 **Open** 01-Mar to 01-Nov
Access Good **Site** Level
Nearest Bus Stop (Miles) ½
Quiet park, close to beaches. Easy access to the north and south coast.
Facilities ᕲ ∮ ⊞ ⊞ ᵣ ⊙ ⊸ ◢ ◻ ☂
🖫 ◒ ♠ 𝄢 ✦ ⊟ 🛜
Nearby Facilities ⌐ ✔ ∪ ♪
Nearest Town St Agnes
Directions Travel along the A30 to Chiverton Cross roundabout 4 miles north of Redruth. Take the B3277 St. Agnes road, after 500 yards turn left and the park is 200 yards down on the left.
⇌ Truro

REDRUTH

Globe Vale Holiday Park, Radnor, Redruth, Cornwall, TR16 4BH
Tel: 01209 891183
Email: info@globevale.co.uk
www.globevale.co.uk
Pitches For Å ⊕ ⊜ **Total** 138
Acreage 9 **Open** All Year
Access Good **Site** Level
A 10 minute drive from Portreath and Porthtowan beaches. Good access from the A30, ideal for visiting St. Ives, Penzance and Truro.
Facilities ∮ ⊞ ⊞ ᵣ ⊙ ⊸ ◢ ◻ ☂
🖫 ⊙ ✕ ♀ ♠ 𝄢 ✦ ⊟ ⊟ ✦ ✦
Nearby Facilities ⌐ ∪
Directions From Redruth follow signs to Portreath and Porthtowan from the A30 roundabout. At the double roundabout take the third exit to North Country. At the crossroads turn right signposted Radnor and follow signs. Approx. 4 miles from Redruth.
⇌ Redruth

REDRUTH

Lakeside Camping, The Golden Lion Inn, Stithians Lake, Menherion, Redruth, Cornwall, TR16 6NW
Tel: 01209 860332
Email: enquiries@golden-lion-inn.co.uk
www.golden-lion-inn.co.uk
Pitches For Å ⊕ ⊜ ⊜ **Total** 12
Open All Year **Access** Good **Site** Level
Nearest Bus Stop (Miles) ½
Set behind the gardens of an award winning pub and restaurant. 20 yards from a lake for windsurfing, sailing and kayaking. Fly fishing permits.
Facilities ∮ ⊞ ᵣ ⊟
🖫 ✕ 𝄢 ✦ ⊟ ⊟ 🛜
Nearby Facilities ⌐ ✔ 𝕃 ⊁ ∪ ♪ ♪ ⊁
Nearest Town Redruth
Directions Leave the A30 at Redruth and take the B3297 signposted Four Lanes and Helston. At the brow of the hill turn left signposted Stithians Lake, site is 2½ miles.
⇌ Redruth

REDRUTH

Lanyon Holiday Park, Loscombe Lane, Four Lanes, Redruth, Cornwall, TR16 6LP
Tel: 01209 313474
Email: lanyonadmin@btconnect.com
www.lanyonholidaypark.co.uk
Pitches For Å ⊕ ⊜ ⊜ **Total** 50
Acreage 14 **Open** April to Oct
Access Good **Site** Level
Nearest Bus Stop (Miles) ¼
Surrounded by open countryside. 6 miles to Portreath surfing beach. 3¼ miles from Stithians Lake and close to the Great Flat Lode Trail.
Facilities ∮ ⊞ ᵣ ⊙ ⊸ ◢ ◻ ☂
🖫 ✕ ♀ ⊟ ♠ 𝄢 ✦ ⊟ ⊟ ✦ ✦ 🛜
Nearby Facilities ⌐ ✔ 𝕃 ⊁ ∪
Directions Leave A30 at Camborne/Pool A3047 exit, keep to the left hand lane and drive straight through the next two sets of traffic lights. Pass Tesco Extra and turn next right over railway bridge (sp Four Lanes). Follow this road up hill [approx 1½ miles], at T-Jct turn rt, take 2nd right at Pencoys Village Hall. Park is on the left.

CORNWALL

REDRUTH
St Day Touring Park, Church Hill, St Day, Redruth, Cornwall, TR16 5LE
Tel: 01209 821086
Email: jo@stdaytouringpark.co.uk
www.stdaytouringpark.co.uk
Pitches For ▲ ⚎ ⚎ ⚎ **Total** 32
Acreage 4 **Open** All Year
Access Good **Site** Level/Sloping
Nearest Bus Stop (Miles) Entrance
ADULTS ONLY small, peaceful Park in rural surroundings. Central location.
Facilities ⚏ ⌇ 🐾⚏✉🛈 🅿︎☉⚊ ⚊ 🖥 ☎
🎱 ⚏⚏🖥🖥⚊🌣
Nearby Facilities ⌇ ⚲ ⚓ ⚓ 🔱 U ♪ ♫ ✗
Nearest Town Redruth
Directions 1½ miles from the A30 at Scorrier.
🚲 Redruth

REDRUTH
Stithians Lake Country Park, Stithians Lake, Menherion, Redruth, Cornwall, TR16 6NW
Tel: 01209 860301
Email: stithianswatersports@swlaketrust.org.uk
www.swlaketrust.org.uk
Pitches For ▲ ⚎ ⚎ **Total** 40
Acreage 2 **Open** 30-Mar **to** 30-Nov
Access Good **Site** Level
Nearest Bus Stop (Miles) ½
By a lake with a watersports and angling centre.
Facilities ⚏ ⌇ 🐾✉🛈 🅿︎ 🖥 ☎
🎱 🅿︎Ⓧ🖥⚊🌣⌇🌣
Nearby Facilities ⚲ ⚓ 🔱 U ♪ ✗
Nearest Town Falmouth
Directions From Redruth take the B3297 towards Helston. Stithians Lake is signposted, follow the brown tourism signs to the entrance which is by The Golden Lion Inn.
🚲 Redruth

REDRUTH
Wheal Rose Caravan & Camping Park, Wheal Rose, Scorrier, Redruth, Cornwall, TR16 5DD
Tel: 01209 891496
Email: whealrose@aol.com
www.whealrosecaravanpark.co.uk
Pitches For ▲ ⚎ ⚎ **Total** 50
Acreage 6½ **Open** March **to** Dec
Access Good **Site** Level
Nearest Bus Stop (Miles) Outside
Adjacent to a mineral tramway. Cenral for all of West Cornwalls attractions. AA 4 Pennants.
Facilities ⚏ ⌇ 🐾⚏✉🛈 🅿︎☉⚊ ⚊ 🖥 ☎
🎱 🅿︎☉⚊🖥🅿︎⚊ ⌇🌣⚏🖥🖥🐾🌣
Nearby Facilities ⌇ ⚲ ⚓ 🔱 U ♪ ♫
Nearest Town Redruth

Directions From the A30 take the Scorrier slip road and turn right at the Plume of Feathers, follow signs to park.
🚲 Redruth

SALTASH
Dolbeare Park, Landrake, Saltash, Cornwall, PL12 5AF
Tel: 01752 851332
Email: reception@dolbeare.co.uk
www.dolbeare.co.uk
Pitches For ▲ ⚎ ⚎ ⚎ **Total** 60
Acreage 9 **Open** All Year
Access Good **Site** Level
Nearest Bus Stop (Miles) ¾
Centrally located between beaches and the moors, ideal for exploring both Cornwall and Devon. Easy access. Close to Looe, Polperro and Plymouth. Take-away on site.
Facilities ⚏ ⌇ 🐾⚏✉🛈 🅿︎☉⚊ ⚊ 🖥 ☎
🎱 🅿︎☉⚊🖥🅿︎⚊🌣 ⚊🌣
Nearby Facilities ⌇ ⚲ ⚓ 🔱 U ♪ ♫ ✗
Directions From Saltash take the A38 west for 4 miles to Landrake. At the footbridge turn right and follow signs to the site. ¾ miles from the A38.
🚲 Saltash

SENNEN
Seaview Holiday Park, Sennen, Lands End, Cornwall, TR19 7AD
Tel: 01736 871266
Email: bookings@seaview.org.uk
www.seaview.org.uk
Pitches For ▲ ⚎ ⚎ **Total** 160
Acreage 11 **Open** All Year
Access Good **Site** Level
Nearest Bus Stop (Miles) Outside
½ mile to Whitesands Bay Blue Flag beach with surfing. Sennen Cove, Lands End and coastal walks.
Facilities ⚏ ⌇ 🐾⚏✉🛈 🅿︎☉⚊ ⚊ 🖥 ☎
🎱 🅿︎☉Ⓧ🖥🅿︎⚊🌣 ⚊🌣✗🖥🅿︎⚊🌣
Nearby Facilities ⌇ ⚲ ⚓ 🔱 U ♪ ✗
Nearest Town Penzance
Directions From Penzance take the A30 signposted Lands End. Stay on the A30 and Sennen Village just before Lands End.
🚲 Penzance

ST. AGNES
Beacon Cottage Farm Touring Park, Beacon Drive, St Agnes, Cornwall, TR5 0NU
Tel: 01872 552347
Email: beaconcottagefarm@lineone.net
www.beaconcottagefarmholidays.co.uk
Pitches For ▲ ⚎ ⚎ **Total** 70
Acreage 4 **Open** 01-Apr **to** 30-Sep
Access Good **Site** Level
Nearest Bus Stop (Miles) ½
On a working farm, surrounded by National Trust land. Sandy beach 1 mile, beautiful sea views.

Facilities ⌇ 🐾⚏✉🛈 🅿︎☉⚊ ⚊ 🖥 ☎
🎱 🅿︎☉⚊🖥🅿︎⚊🌣 ⚊🌣
Nearby Facilities ⌇ ⚲ ⚓ 🔱 U ♪ ♫ ✗
Directions From the A30, take the B3277 to St. Agnes, take road to the Beacon and follow signs to the site.
🚲 Truro

ST. AGNES
Presingoll Farm Caravan & Camping Park, St Agnes, Cornwall, TR5 0PB
Tel: 01872 552333
Email: pam@presingollfarm.co.uk
www.presingollfarm.co.uk
Pitches For ▲ ⚎ ⚎ **Total** 90
Acreage 5 **Open** Easter **to** End October
Access Good **Site** Level
Nearest Bus Stop (Miles) Outside
Working farm overlooking the North Cornwall coastline. Near the Cornish Coastal Path and surf beaches within 2 miles. Ideal for walking. Dogs must be kept on a lead.
Facilities ⚏ ⌇ 🐾⚏✉🛈 🅿︎☉⚊ ⚊ 🖥 ☎
🅿︎ 🅿︎☉⚊🖥🅿︎⚊🌣 ⌇🌣
Nearby Facilities ⌇ ⚲ U ♪ ✗
Nearest Town St Agnes
Directions Leave the A30 at Chiverton Cross roundabout and take the B3277 for St. Agnes. Site is 3 miles on the right.
🚲 Truro

ST. AUSTELL
Croft Farm Holiday Park, Luxulyan, Bodmin, Cornwall, PL30 5EQ
Tel: 01726 850228
Email: enquiries@croftfarm.co.uk
www.croftfarm.co.uk
Pitches For ▲ ⚎ ⚎ **Total** 52
Acreage 5 **Open** 21-Mar **to** 21-Jan
Access Good **Site** Lev/Slope
1 mile from the Eden Project.
Facilities ⌇ 🐾⚏✉🛈 🅿︎☉⚊ ⚊ 🖥 ☎
🎱 🅿︎☉⚊🖥🅿︎⚊🌣 ⚊🌣
Nearby Facilities ⌇ ⚲ ⚓ 🔱 U
Nearest Town St Austell
Directions From St Austell follow signs for the Eden Project, Croft Farm is 1 mile from the main entrance.
🚲 Luxulyan

ST. AUSTELL
River Valley Holiday Park, London Apprentice, St Austell, Cornwall, PL26 7AP
Tel: 01726 73533
Email: mail@cornwall-holidays.co.uk
www.rivervalleyholidaypark.co.uk
Pitches For ▲ ⚎ ⚎ **Total** 40
Acreage 9 **Open** April **to** Oct
Access Good **Site** Level
Nearest Bus Stop (Miles) Outside
Alongside a river with woodland walk and cycle trail to the beach.

VISIT **www.cades.co.uk** TO SEE OUR MONTHLY COMPETITION

ENGLAND

Facilities ⌀ ▢ ▥ ♒ ⌂ ☺ ⊿ ▣ ☕
▦ ⚑ ♒ ▣ ⚡ ✦ ⊞ ◲ ❅ ⚲ 🛜
Nearby Facilities ↾ ✒ ⚓ ↘ ♞ ♪
Nearest Town St Austell
Directions Take the B3273 from St Austell
to Mevagissey, 1 mile to London Apprentice,
site is on the left hand side.
➤ St Austell

ST. AUSTELL
Treveor Farm Caravan & Camping Site,
Gorran, St Austell, Cornwall, PL26 6LW
Tel: 01726 842387
Email: info@treveorfarm.co.uk
www.treveorfarm.co.uk
Pitches For ⛺ ▢ ➡ **Total** 50
Acreage 4 **Open** April **to** Oct
Access Good **Site** Level
1 mile to the beach and coastal path. 3 miles
from the Lost Gardens of Heligan and only
15 miles from the Eden Project.
Facilities ⌀ ▥ ♒ ⌂ ☺ ⊿ ▣ ☕
▦ ⚑ ♒ ▣ ⊞ ◲
Nearby Facilities ↾ ⚓ ↘ ♪
Nearest Town St Austell/Gorran Haven
Directions Take the B3273 from St Austell
towards Mevagissey. After Pentewan at top
of the hill turn right to Gorran. After approx 4
miles turn right into the park at the signboard.
➤ St Austell

ST. BURYAN
Tower Park Caravans & Camping, St
Buryan, Penzance, Cornwall, TR19 6BZ
Tel: 01736 810286
Email: enquiries@towerparkcamping.co.uk
www.towerparkcamping.co.uk
Pitches For ⛺ ▢ ➡ **Total** 102
Acreage 12 **Open** March **to** October
Access Good **Site** Level
Nearest Bus Stop (Miles) ¼

Peaceful, family run campsite in West
Cornwall. Short walk to the village pub and
shop. Holiday caravans for hire.
Facilities ♿ ⌀ ▥ ♒ ⌂ ☺ ⊿ ▣ ☕
▣ ▦ ◲ ▢ ⚑ ♒ ⚲ ⊞ ◲ 🛜
Nearby Facilities ↾ ✒ ⚓ ↘ ∪ ♪ ♞
Nearest Town Penzance
Directions From the A30 Lands End road
turn left onto the B3283 towards St. Buryan.
In the village turn right then right again and
the park is 300 yards on the right.
➤ Penzance

ST. BURYAN
Treverven Caravan & Camping Park, St
Buryan, Penzance, Cornwall, TR19 6DL
Tel: 01736 810200
Email: trevervenpark@btconnect.com
Pitches For ⛺ ▢ ➡ ➡ **Total** 120
Acreage 6 **Open** Easter **to** End Oct
Access Good **Site** Level
Nearest Bus Stop (Miles) ½
Situated in an area of outstanding natural
beauty with direct access onto the South
West Coastal Path. Many sandy beaches
and coves in the area.
Facilities ♿ ⌀ ▥ ♒ ⌂ ☺ ⊿ ▣ ☕
▣ ▦ ⚑ ♒ ⚲ ▣ ⊞ ◲ ❅ 🛜
Nearby Facilities ↾ ✒ ⚓ ↘ ∪ ♪ ♞
Nearest Town Porthcurno
Directions From Penzance take the A30
Lands End road, after approx 3 miles turn
left onto the B3283 to St Buryan. Proceed
through the village and turn left onto the
B3315 Lamorna road, Park is 1½ miles.
➤ Penzance

ST. IVES
Ayr Holiday Park, Ayr, St Ives, Cornwall,
TR26 1EJ
Tel: 01736 795855
Email: recept@ayrholidaypark.co.uk
www.ayrholidaypark.co.uk
Pitches For ⛺ ▢ ➡ ➡ **Total** 80
Acreage 6 **Open** All Year
Access Good **Site** Level/Sloping
Nearest Bus Stop (Miles) Entrance
Beautiful coastal views. Just a 10 minute walk
to the town centre, harbour and beaches of
St Ives.
Facilities ♿ ⌀ ▢ ▥ ▥ ♒ ⌂ ☺ ⊿ ▣ ☕
▣ ▦ ⚑ ♒ ⚲ ▣ ⊞ ◲ 🛜
Nearby Facilities ↾ ✒ ⚓ ∪ ♪
Nearest Town St Ives
Directions From the A30 take the St Ives
exit following signs to St Ives for heavy
vehicles, day visitors and Tate Gallery. Join
the B3311 then the B3306 and follow brown
tourism signs to the Park.
➤ St Ives

ST. IVES
Balnoon Camping Site, Balnoon, Nr
Halsetown, St Ives, Cornwall, TR26 3JA
Tel: 01736 795431
Email: nat@balnoon.fsnet.co.uk
Pitches For ⛺ ▢ ➡ **Total** 23
Acreage 1 **Open** Easter **to** October
Access Good **Site** Level
Nearest Bus Stop (Miles) Outside
Situated in the countryside with views of
adjacent rolling hills. Equidistant from the
beautiful beaches of Carbis Bay and St. Ives,
approx. 2 miles.
Facilities ▥ ♒ ⌂ ☺ ▣ ⚲ ⊞ ☕ ◲ ▣
Nearby Facilities ↾ ✒ ∪ ♪
Nearest Town St. Ives

CORNWALL

Directions From the A30 take the A3074 for St. Ives, at the second mini-roundabout turn first left signposted Tate St. Ives (B3311), turn second right signposted Balnoon. Approx. 3 miles from the A30.
⇌ St. Ives

ST. IVES

Higher Chellew, Nancledra, Penzance, Cornwall, TR20 8BD
Tel: 01736 364532
Email: higherchellew@btinternet.com
www.higherchellewcamping.co.uk
Pitches For ⋏ ⌂ ⊟ **Total** 30
Acreage 1½ **Open** Easter **to** End Sept
Access Good **Site** Level
Nearest Bus Stop (Miles) Outside
Peaceful and private small site with views of Trencrom and glimpses of the sea. Spectacular walks in the area. Near St Michaels Mount. A few fully serviced pitches available.
Facilities ⛱ ⨍ ⧫⌂⊙⊿⊟⚑ 🍴
Nearby Facilities ┌ ⋌ ⚓ ⌇ U ⚡
Nearest Town St Ives/Penzance
Directions On the B3311 in between Penzance and St Ives.
⇌ St Ives/Penzance

ST. IVES

Little Trevarrack Holiday Park, Laity Lane, Carbis Bay, St Ives, Cornwall, TR26 3HW
Tel: 01736 797580
Email: info@littletrevarrack.co.uk
www.littletrevarrack.co.uk
Pitches For ⋏ ⌂ ⊟ **Total** 200
Acreage 20 **Open** April **to** Sept
Access Good **Site** Lev/Slope
Nearest Bus Stop (Miles) ½

1 mile from Carbis Bay beach. 2 miles to St Ives (bus service in high season only). Heated swimming pool and paddling pool. Ideal for touring West Cornwall. 2 dogs allowed per pitch.
Facilities ⛱ ⨍ ⧫⏕⌂⊙⊿⊟◻ 🍴
⚑⊙⛊⊠⩇⨸⌇⧗⊞◻🌻 ☼ ⋒
Nearby Facilities ┌ ⋌ ⚓ ⌇ U ⚡ ⚡ ⊁
Nearest Town St Ives
Directions Turn off the A30 onto the A3074 towards St Ives. At Carbis Bay the site is signposted left opposite the junc to the beach, turn left and follow for 150 yards to the crossroads, go straight across and the site is second on the right.
⇌ Carbis Bay

ST. IVES

Penderleath Caravan & Camping Park, Towednack, St Ives, Cornwall, TR26 3AF
Tel: 01736 798403
Email: holidays@penderleath.co.uk
www.penderleath.co.uk
Pitches For ⋏ ⌂ ⊟ **Total** 75
Acreage 10 **Open** Easter **to** Oct
Access Good **Site** Lev/Slope
Nearest Bus Stop (Miles) Outside
Set in a classified area of outstanding natural beauty, with fabulous views over countryside to the sea. Very peaceful and tranquil. Outside the main season we offer an Adults Only Camping Area. You can also contact us on Mobile: 07840 208542.
Facilities ⛱ ⨍ ⏕⌂⊙⊿⊟◻ 🍴
⊙⛊⊠⩇⨸⌇⧗⊞◻
Nearby Facilities ┌ ⋌ ⚓ ⌇ U ⚡ ⊁
Nearest Town St Ives
Directions From the A30 take the A3074 signposted St. Ives. At the second mini roundabout turn left, at the end of the road turn left then immediately right, turn left at next fork.
⇌ St. Ives

ST. IVES

Polmanter Touring Park, Halsetown, St Ives, Cornwall, TR26 3LX
Tel: 01736 795640
Email: reception@polmanter.co.uk
www.polmanter.co.uk
Pitches For ⋏ ⌂ ⊟ **Total** 250
Acreage 20 **Open** 01-Apr **to** 03-Nov
Access Good **Site** Level
Nearest Bus Stop (Miles) Entrance
Within walking distance of St Ives and beaches.
Facilities ⛱ ⨍ ⧫⏕⌂⊙⊿⊟◻ 🍴
⊙⛊⊠⩇⨸⌇⧗⊞◻ ⋒
Nearby Facilities ┌ ⋌ ⚓ ⌇ U ⚡ ⊁
Nearest Town St Ives
Directions From the A30 take the A3074 to St Ives, turn left at the second mini-roundabout via Halsetown. Turn right at the B3311 and turn right at the Halsetown Inn, then first left.
⇌ St Ives

ST. IVES

St Ives Bay Holiday Park, Upton Towans, Hayle, Cornwall, TR27 5BH
Tel: 01736 Hayle 752274
Email: stivesbay@btconnect.com
www.stivesbay.co.uk
Pitches For ⋏ ⌂ ⊟ **Total** 200
Acreage 12 **Open** May **to** September
Access Good **Site** Lev/Slope
Nearest Bus Stop (Miles) ½
Park adjoining own sandy beach, onto St. Ives Bay. Children very welcome. Sea views. Dogs no longer accepted. Dial-a-Brochure 24 hours, Mr R. White. (See our display advertisement).
Facilities ⏕⌂⊙⊿⊟
◻⛊⊙⊠⨸⚑⏁⩇⌇⊞⋌
Nearby Facilities ┌ ⋌ ⚓ ⌇ U ⚡
Nearest Town Hayle

Directions A30 from Camborne to Hayle, at roundabout take Hayle turn-off and then turn right onto B3301, 600yds on left enter park.
⚐ Hayle

ST. IVES
Trevalgan Touring Park, Trevalgan, St. Ives, Cornwall, TR26 3BJ
Tel: 01736 792048
Email: recept@trevalgantouringpark.co.uk
www.trevalgantouringpark.co.uk
Pitches For ⚑ ⚑ ⚑ **Total** 130
Acreage 5 **Open** April **to** End Sept
Access Poor **Site** Level
Nearest Bus Stop (Miles) Entrance
A delightful rural setting near the coastal path and in an area of outstanding natural beauty.
Facilities ⚙ ⚙ ⚙ ⚙ ⚙ ⚙ ⚙ ⚙ ⚙
Nearby Facilities ⚙ ⚙ ⚙ ⚙
Nearest Town St Ives
Directions From the A30 take the St Ives exit and follow directions to St Ives for heavy vehicles and Tate Gallery. Join the B3311 then the B3306, at the next junction turn left signposted Trevalgan.
⚐ St Ives

ST. JUST
Kelynack Caravan & Camping Park, Kelynack, St Just, Penzance, Cornwall, TR19 7RE
Tel: 01736 787633
Email: enquiries@kelynackholidays.co.uk
www.kelynackholidays.co.uk
Pitches For ⚑ ⚑ ⚑ **Total** 30
Acreage 2 **Open** All Year
Access Good **Site** Level
Nearest Bus Stop (Miles) ¼
Small and secluded site nestling alongside a stream. Just 1 mile from the coast in the beautiful Cot Valley.
Facilities ⚙ ⚙ ⚙ ⚙ ⚙ ⚙ ⚙
Nearby Facilities ⚙ ⚙ ⚙ ⚙ ⚙
Nearest Town Penzance
Directions From Penzance take the A3071 to St Just. Just before reaching St Just turn left onto the B3306, follow road down the hill for 1 mile then turn left, after 200 yards turn left again.
⚐ Penzance

ST. JUST
Roselands Caravan Park, Dowran, St Just, Penzance, Cornwall, TR19 7RS
Tel: 01736 788571
Email: info@roselands.co.uk
www.roselands.co.uk
Pitches For ⚑ ⚑ ⚑ **Total** 30
Acreage 4 **Open** All Year
Access Good **Site** Level
Nearest Bus Stop (Miles) ¼
Close to the sea. Ideal for walking and bird watching. All attractions nearby. 5 miles from Lands End. Cycle hire on site.
Facilities ⚙ ⚙ ⚙ ⚙ ⚙ ⚙ ⚙
Nearby Facilities ⚙ ⚙ ⚙ ⚙ ⚙
Nearest Town Penzance
Directions From the A30 Penzance by-pass take the A3071 to St Just for 5 miles, turn left at sign and park is 800 yards.
⚐ Penzance

ST. JUST
Secret Garden Caravan Park, Bosavern House, St Just, Penzance, Cornwall, TR19 7RD
Tel: 01736 788301
Email: mail@bosavern.com
www.secretbosavern.com
Pitches For ⚑ ⚑ ⚑ **Total** 12
Acreage 1 **Open** March **to** October
Access Good **Site** Level
Nearest Bus Stop (Miles) ½
Walled garden site surrounded by trees and flowers. Excellent walking country, good beaches nearby. Local authorities licensed site.
Facilities ⚙ ⚙ ⚙ ⚙ ⚙ ⚙ ⚙ ⚙ ⚙
Nearby Facilities ⚙ ⚙ ⚙ ⚙ ⚙
Nearest Town St Just/Penzance
Directions Take the A3071 from Penzance towards St. Just. Approximately 550yds before St. Just turn left onto the B3306 signposted Lands End and airport. Secret Garden Caravan Park is 500yds from the turn off, behind Bosavern House.
⚐ Penzance

ST. JUST
Trevaylor Caravan & Camping Park, Botallack, St Just, Cornwall, TR19 7PU
Tel: 01736 787016
Email: trevaylor@cornishcamping.co.uk
www.cornishcamping.co.uk
Pitches For ⚑ ⚑ **Total** 79
Acreage 5 **Open** Mid March **to** October
Access Good **Site** Level
Nearest Bus Stop (Miles) Outside
Easy access to the golden sands, rugged cliffs and white surf of the Atlantic Ocean. 500 metres from the coastal path and Crown Mines. Bar serving real ale and good food (during high season) on site.
Facilities ⚙ ⚙ ⚙ ⚙ ⚙ ⚙ ⚙ ⚙ ⚙
Nearby Facilities ⚙ ⚙ ⚙ ⚙ ⚙
Nearest Town Sennen Cove/St Just
Directions On the B3306 Lands End to St Ives road, approx 1 mile to the north of St Just.
⚐ Penzance

ST. MAWES
Trethem Mill Touring Park, St Just-in-Roseland, Truro, Cornwall, TR2 5JF
Tel: 01872 580504
Email: reception@trethem.com
www.trethem.com
Pitches For ⚑ ⚑ **Total** 84
Acreage 4 **Open** April **to** Mid Oct
Access Good **Site** Lev/Slope
Nearest Bus Stop (Miles) ¼
Discover the unexplored Roseland, staying on the only 5 Star Park on the Peninsula. Family owned and run, we offer a relaxing and tranquil setting. Ideally located for walking, sailing, beaches and gardens. National Caravan Park of the Year 2010, England in Excellence Awards.
Facilities ⚙ ⚙ ⚙ ⚙ ⚙ ⚙ ⚙ ⚙ ⚙
Nearby Facilities ⚙ ⚙ ⚙ ⚙ ⚙
Nearest Town St Mawes
Directions From Tregony follow the A3078 to St. Mawes. Approx. 2 miles after passing through Trewithian look out for caravan and camping sign.
⚐ Truro

ST. MERRYN
Tregavone Farm Touring Park, St Merryn, Padstow, Cornwall, PL28 8JZ
Tel: 01841 520148
Email: info@tregavone.co.uk
www.tregavonefarm.co.uk
Pitches For ⚑ ⚑ **Total** 40
Acreage 4 **Open** March **to** October
Access Good **Site** Level
Quiet family run site situated near sandy surfing beaches, country views, well maintained and grassy. AA 2 Pennants.
Facilities ⚙ ⚙ ⚙ ⚙ ⚙ ⚙ ⚙ ⚙ ⚙
Nearby Facilities ⚙ ⚙ ⚙ ⚙ ⚙
Nearest Town Padstow
Directions Turn right off A39 (Wadebridge-St. Columb) onto A389 (Padstow) come to a T-junction and turn right, in 1 mile turn left, entrance on left after 1 mile.
⚐ Newquay

ST. MERRYN
Trethias Farm Caravan Park, St Merryn, Padstow, Cornwall, PL28 8PL
Tel: 01841 520323
Email: trethiasfarm@btconnect.com
Pitches For ⚑ ⚑ **Total** 63
Acreage 12 **Open** April **to** September
Access Good **Site** Level
Nearest Bus Stop (Miles) 1
Near beach, scenic views. Couples and family groups only. ETB 3 Star Graded and David Bellamy Gold Award for Conservation 2010.
Facilities ⚙ ⚙ ⚙ ⚙ ⚙ ⚙ ⚙
Nearby Facilities ⚙ ⚙ ⚙ ⚙ ⚙
Nearest Town Padstow
Directions From Wadebridge follow signs to St. Merryn, go past Farmers Arms, third turning right (our signs from here).
⚐ Bodmin Parkway

ST. MERRYN
Trevean Farm Caravan & Camping Park, St Merryn, Padstow, Cornwall, PL28 8PR
Tel: 01841 520772
Email: trevean.info@virgin.net
www.treveancaravanandcamping.net
Pitches For ⚑ ⚑ **Total** 68
Acreage 2 **Open** April **to** October
Access Good **Site** Level
Nearest Bus Stop (Miles) ½
Situated near several sandy, surfing beaches. ETC 4 Star Grading.
Facilities ⚙ ⚙ ⚙ ⚙ ⚙ ⚙ ⚙ ⚙ ⚙
Nearby Facilities ⚙ ⚙ ⚙ ⚙ ⚙
Nearest Town Padstow
Directions From St. Merryn village take the B3276 Newquay road for 1 mile. Turn left for Rumford, site ¼ mile on the right.
⚐ Newquay

ST. MERRYN
Treyarnon Bay Caravan Park, Treyarnon Bay, Padstow, Cornwall, PL28 8JR
Tel: 01841 520681
www.treyarnonbay.co.uk
Pitches For ⚑ ⚑ **Total** 55
Acreage 6 **Open** April **to** Sept
Access Poor **Site** Level/Sloping
Nearest Bus Stop (Miles) Entrance
Family park overlooking Treyarnon Bay and only 200 yards from the beach. Great for surfing and walking.
Facilities ⚙ ⚙ ⚙ ⚙ ⚙ ⚙ ⚙ ⚙
Nearby Facilities ⚙ ⚙ ⚙ ⚙ ⚙
Nearest Town Padstow
Directions From Wadebridge take the A389 west and follow signs to St. Merryn and Treyarnon Bay. 3 miles from Padstow.
⚐ Bodmin/Newquay

Whitsand Bay Holiday Park

Relaxing Luxurious
01752 822597

In a stunning location with 5 miles of beach on the Rame Peninsula, south east Cornwall, our Holiday Park offers various pitches for Tourers, Camper Vans, Caravans & Tents. A heated swimming pool, cafe, shop and restaurant/bar provide fun for all the family.

www.whitsandbayholidays.co.uk   *enquiries@whitsandbayholidays.co.uk*

AA ▶▶▶

TINTAGEL

The Headland Caravan & Camping Park, Atlantic Road, Tintagel, Cornwall, PL34 0DE
Tel: 01840 770239
Email: headland.caravan@talktalkbusiness.net
www.headlandcaravanpark.co.uk
Pitches For Å ⚏ ⚏ Total 60
Acreage 4 **Open** Easter **to** October
Access Good **Site** Lev/Slope
Nearest Bus Stop (Miles) ¼
Three beaches within walking distance. Scenic views. Ideal touring centre.
Facilities ⌁ 🔲 ⚏⚏ ⌁ ⊙ ⌐ ⚋ ▣ ☎
🌡 🏦 🛠️🚻🅿🖃
Nearby Facilities ⌐ ✒ ⚓ ⤢ ↘ Ụ ৎ
Directions Follow camping/caravan signs from B3263 through village to Headland.
≇ Bodmin Parkway

TINTAGEL

Trewethett Farm Caravan Club Site, Trethevy, Tintagel, Cornwall, PL34 0BQ
Tel: 01840 770222
www.caravanclub.co.uk
Pitches For Å ⚏ ⚏ Total 141
Acreage 15 **Open** March **to** Nov
Access Good **Site** Level
Breathtaking views overlooking Bossiney Cove. ½ a mile from a sandy beach. Spectacular clifftop walks. Near Tintagel Castle, picturesque ports and harbours. Non members welcome. Booking essential.
Facilities ⌁ 🔲 ⚏⚏ ⌁ ⌐ ▣ ☎ 🛠️🚻🅿🖃
Nearby Facilities ⌐ ✒
Nearest Town Tintagel
Directions From NE on the A30, turn onto the A395 via slip road. After 11 miles at the T-junction turn right onto the A39, after 1 mile just before the transmitter turn left, at T-junction turn right onto the B3266. After 2½ miles at the junction on the bend turn left on to the B3263. Site is on the right.
≇ Tintagel

TORPOINT

Whitsand Bay Holiday Park, Millbrook, Torpoint, Cornwall, PL10 1JZ
Tel: 01752 822597
Email: enquiries@whitsandbayholidays.co.uk
www.whitsandbayholidays.co.uk
Pitches For ⚏ ⚏ ⚏ Total 49
Acreage 27 **Open** All Year
Access Good **Site** Level
Nearest Bus Stop (Miles) Outside
On the Devon/Cornwall border with a designated ancient monument. Overlooking the sandy beaches of Whitsand Bay. Near Plymouth.
Facilities ⚷ ⌁ 🔲 ⚏⚏ ⌁ ⌐ ⊙ ⌐ ⚋ ▣ ☎
🌡 ✕ 🏦 🛒 ♨ 🛠️🚻🅿🖃 ╳ ☕ 🛜
Nearby Facilities ⌐ ✒ ⚓ ↘ Ụ ⚓ ৎ
Nearest Town Plymouth
Directions Take the A38 to Plymouth and follow signs to Torpoint Ferry. From Ferry continue for 3 miles and at Antony turn left for Whitsand Bay. After 2 miles turn left at the T-Junction, 1 mile to Whitsand Bay. Follow the road for 2 miles then turn left into the Park.
≇ Plymouth

TRURO

Carnon Downs Caravan & Camping Park, Carnon Downs, Truro, Cornwall, TR3 6JJ
Tel: 01872 862283
Email: info@carnon-downs-caravanpark.co.uk
www.carnon-downs-caravanpark.co.uk
Pitches For Å ⚏ ⚏ Total 150
Acreage 20 **Open** All Year
Access Good **Site** Level
Nearest Bus Stop (Miles) Outside
Quiet, family run park with good quality facilities. Ideally central for touring. Excellent location for sailing and water sports. David Bellamy Gold Award for Conservation and ETB 5 Star Exceptional Graded.
Facilities ⚷ ⌁ 🔲 ⚏⚏ ⌁ ⌐ ⊙ ⌐ ⚋ ▣ ☎
🌡 🏦 🛒🛠️🚻🅿🖃 ☕
Nearby Facilities ⌐ ✒ ⚓ ↘ Ụ ⚓ ৎ
Nearest Town Truro
Directions On the A39 Falmouth road, 3 miles West of Truro.
≇ Truro

TRURO

Chacewater Camping & Caravan Park, Coxhill, Chacewater, Truro, Cornwall, TR4 8LY
Tel: 01209 820762
Email: chacewaterpark@aol.com
www.chacewaterpark.co.uk
Pitches For Å ⚏ ⚏ Total 100
Acreage 6 **Open** May **to** End September
Access Good **Site** Level
Nearest Bus Stop (Miles) Outside
Exclusively for Adults. The ideal holiday base for the Over 30s.
Facilities ⚷ ⌁ 🔲 ⚏⚏ ⌁ ⌐ ⊙ ⌐ ⚋ ▣ ☎
🌡 🏦 🛠️🚻🅿 ▣Å
Nearby Facilities ⌐ ✒ Ụ
Nearest Town Truro
Directions From A30 take the A3047 to Scorrier. Turn left at Crossroads Hotel onto the B3298. 1½ miles turn left to Chacewater, ½ mile sign directs you to the park.
≇ Truro

TRURO

Cosawes Park, Cosawes Park Homes, Perranarworthal, Truro, Cornwall, TR3 7QS
Tel: 01872 863724
Email: info@cosawes.com
www.cosawestouringandcamping.co.uk
Pitches For Å ⚏ ⚏ Total 50
Acreage 4 **Open** All Year
Access Good **Site** Lev/Slope
Nearest Bus Stop (Miles) ¼
Situated in a 100 acre wooded valley, an area of outstanding natural beauty. New toilet and shower facilities with disabled/family rooms. Fully serviced hard standing pitches. Near to local beaches, Flambards and the city of Truro.
Facilities ⚷ ⌁ 🔲 ⚏⚏ ⌁ ⌐ ⊙ ⌐ ⚋ ▣ ☎
🌡 🏦 🛒🛠️🚻🅿🖃 ╳ ✎ ☕ ⚋ ▣ ☎
Nearby Facilities ⌐ ✒ ⚓ ↘ Ụ ⚓ ৎ ✗
Nearest Town Truro/Falmouth
Directions From Truro take the A39, as you exit the village of Perranarworthal take signposted turning on the right.
≇ Truro/Perranwell

TRURO

Summer Valley Touring Park, Shortlanesend, Truro, Cornwall, TR4 9DW
Tel: 01872 277878
Email: james@summervalley.co.uk
www.summervalley.co.uk
Pitches For Å ⚏ ⚏ Total 50
Acreage 3 **Open** April **to** October
Access Good **Site** Sloping
Nearest Bus Stop (Miles) ¼
Ideal touring centre for all of Cornwall.
Facilities ⌁ 🔲 ⚏⚏ ⌁ ⌐ ⊙ ⌐ ⚋ ▣ ☎
🌡 🏦 🛒🛠️🚻🅿🖃 🛜
Nearby Facilities ⌐ ✒ Ụ ৎ
Nearest Town Truro
Directions 2½ miles north of Truro on the B3284 Perranporth road.
≇ Truro

TRURO

Veryan Camping & Caravanning Club Site, Tretheake Manor, Veryan, Truro, Cornwall, TR2 5PP
Tel: 01872 501658
www.campingandcaravanningclub.co.uk/veryan
Pitches For Å ⚏ ⚏ Total 150
Acreage 9 **Open** 29-Mar **to** 05-Nov
Access Good **Site** Sloping
Nearest Bus Stop (Miles) ¼
Ideal for exploring the beaches and coves of the Cornish Coast. BTB 4 Star Graded and AA 3 Pennants. Non members welcome. You can also call us on 0845 130 7633.
Facilities ⚷ ⌁ 🔲 ⚏⚏ ⌁ ⌐ ⊙ ⌐ ⚋ ▣ ☎
🌡 🏦 🛒🛠️🚻🅿🖃 ╳ ৎ
Nearby Facilities ✒ Ụ ৎ
Nearest Town Veryan
Directions Take the A390 from St. Austell, leave at the A3078 sign on the left, turn left at the filling station and follow international signs.
≇ Truro

WADEBRIDGE

Little Bodieve Holiday Park, Bodieve Road, Wadebridge, Cornwall, PL27 6EG
Tel: 01208 812323
Email: info@littlebodieve.co.uk
www.littlebodieve.co.uk
Pitches For Å ⚏ ⚏ Total 195
Acreage 22 **Open** April **to** October
Access Good **Site** Lev/Slope
Nearest Bus Stop (Miles) ¼
Just a few minutes from superb beaches and golf courses. 5 minutes from The Camel Trail, 10 minutes from Padstow and Crealy Adventure Park and 25 minutes from The Eden Project.
Facilities ⌁ 🔲 ⚏⚏ ⌁ ⌐ ⊙ ⌐ ⚋ ▣ ☎
🌡 🍺 🎱 ✕ 🏦 🛒 ♨ 🛠️🚻🅿🖃 ╳ ♨
Nearby Facilities ⌐ ✒ ⚓ ↘ Ụ ⚓ ৎ
Nearest Town Wadebridge
Directions 1 mile north of Wadebridge Town centre turn off the A39 and take the B3314 towards Rock, Portreath and Port Isaac.
≇ Bodmin Parkway

WADEBRIDGE
St. Mabyn Holiday Park, Longstone Road, St Mabyn, Nr Wadebridge, Cornwall, PL30 3BY
Tel: 01208 841677
Email: info@stmabyn.co.uk
www.stmabynholidaypark.co.uk
Pitches For Å ♠ ♠ ♠ **Total** 120
Acreage 12 **Open** 15-Mar **to** 31-Oct
Access Good **Site** Level/Sloping
Nearest Bus Stop (Miles) ¼
Situated near Bodmin Moor. Ideal for exploring the whole of Cornwall. Easy access to Eden Project, Truro, Wadebridge, Padstow and many other places of interest.
Facilities (icons)
Nearby Facilities ┌ ✓ ⅄ ∪ ⊋
Nearest Town Wadebridge
Directions Take the B3266 from either Camelford or Bodmin. Site is at Longstone crossroads. From Wadebridge take the A389 to Bodmin then the B3266.
⇌ Bodmin Parkway

WADEBRIDGE
The Laurels Holiday Park, Padstow Road, Whitecross, Wadebridge, Cornwall, PL27 7JQ
Tel: 01209 313474
Email: lanyonadmin@btconnect.com
www.thelaurelsholidaypark.co.uk
Pitches For Å ♠ ♠ **Total** 35
Acreage 2 **Open** April **to** Oct
Access Good **Site** Level
Nearest Bus Stop (Miles) Entrance
6 miles from Padstow, and close to Rock and Port Isaac. Ideal for touring north and south Cornwall.
Facilities (icons)
Nearby Facilities ┌ ✓ ⅄ ∪ ⊋ ℛ ✗
Nearest Town Padstow
Directions On the crossroads of the A39 and the A389 Wadebridge/Padstow junction, close to the Royal Cornwall Showground.
⇌ Bodmin

WADEBRIDGE
Trewince Farm Holiday Park, St Issey, Wadebridge, Cornwall, PL27 7RL
Tel: 01208 812830
Email: enquiries@trewincefarm-holidaypark.co.uk
www.trewincefarm-holiday-park.co.uk
Pitches For Å ♠ ♠ **Total** 120
Acreage 15 **Open** Easter **to** End Oct
Access Good **Site** Level
Nearest Bus Stop (Miles) ¼
Only 4 miles from picturesque Padstow and the Camel Trail. Ideal for cycling and walking.
Facilities (icons)
Nearby Facilities ┌ ✓ ⅄ ∪ ⊋ ℛ ✗
Nearest Town Padstow
Directions Take the A39 from Wadebridge towards Padstow, turn right onto the A389, site is signposted 1 mile on the left.
⇌ Bodmin Parkway

CUMBRIA
AMBLESIDE
Low Wray National Trust Campsite, Low Wray, Near Ambleside, Cumbria, LA22 0JA
Tel: 015394 63862
Email: campsite.bookings@nationaltrust.org.uk
www.ntlakescampsites.org.uk
Pitches For Å ♠ **Total** 140
Open Week Before Easter **to** End Oct
Site Lev/Slope
Nearest Bus Stop (Miles) 1
Beautiful lakeside location with spectacular views. Centrally based for visiting all parts of the Lake District.
Facilities (icons)
Nearby Facilities ┌ ✓ ⅄ ∪ ℛ ✗
Nearest Town Ambleside
Directions From Ambleside take the A593, turn left at Clappersgate onto the B5286, turn left at sign for Wray. Site is less than 1 mile on the left.
⇌ Windermere

APPLEBY
Silverband Park, Silverband, Knock, Nr Appleby, Cumbria, CA16 6DL
Tel: 01768 361218
Pitches For ♠ ♠ **Total** 12
Acreage ½ **Open** All Year
Access Good **Site** Sloping
Nearest Bus Stop (Miles) Outside
Ideal for touring the Lakes and Fells. Only two fully serviced pitches available. Bus service only once a week.
Facilities (icons)
Nearby Facilities ┌ ✓ ⅄ ∪
Nearest Town Appleby/Penrith
Directions Turn left off the A66 Penrith to Scotch Corner road at Kirkby Thore. After 2 miles at T-Junction turn left, after 100 yards take the first turn right, site is 1 mile on the right.
⇌ Appleby/Penrith

APPLEBY
Wild Rose Park, Ormside, Appleby, Cumbria, CA16 6EJ
Tel: 017683 51077
Email: reception@wildrose.co.uk
www.wildrose.co.uk
Pitches For Å ♠ ♠ **Total** 226
Acreage 40 **Open** All Year
Access Good **Site** Lev/Slope
Quiet park in the unspoilt Eden Valley with superb views. Midway between Lakes and Yorkshire Dales. Secure Storage from Nov to March.
Facilities (icons)
Nearby Facilities ┌ ✓
Nearest Town Appleby
Directions Centre Appleby take B6260 Kendal for 1½ miles. Left Ormside and Soulby 1½ miles left, ½ mile turn right.
⇌ Appleby

ARNSIDE/SILVERDALE
Fell End Caravan Park, Slackhead Road, Hale, Nr Milnthorpe, Cumbria, LA7 7BS
Tel: 01524 781453
Email: enquiries@pureleisure-holidays.co.uk
www.fellendcaravanpark.co.uk
Pitches For ♠ ♠ **Total** 80
Acreage 12 **Open** All Year
Access Good **Site** Lev/Slope
Nearest Bus Stop (Miles) Outside
In an area of outstanding natural beauty, Fell End is a meticulously kept site with mature gardens and a country inn. Leisure Club with pool, gym, steam room and soft play. Close to Lakes and Dales. Open all year to tourers.
Facilities (icons)
Nearby Facilities ┌ ✓ ⅄ ∪ ⊋ ℛ ✗
Nearest Town Arnside/Silverdale
Directions Leave the M6 at junction 35, take the A6 north and turn left at Wildlife Oasis (after passing Esso fuel station). Follow signs to Fell End Caravan Park.
⇌ Arnside

ARNSIDE/SILVERDALE
Hall More Caravan Park, Hale, Nr Milnthorpe, Cumbria, LA7 7BP
Tel: 01524 781453
Email: enquiries@pureleisure-holidays.co.uk
www.hallmorecaravanpark.co.uk
Pitches For Å ♠ ♠ **Total** 52
Acreage 5 **Open** March **to** January
Access Good **Site** Level
Nearest Bus Stop (Miles) ¼
Rural location, excellent for walking, rambling, etc.. Camping Pods. Own coarse fishery and trout fishery adjacent. Nearby Leisure Club. Easy access to the Lake District.
Facilities (icons)
Nearby Facilities ┌ ✓ ⅄ ∪ ⊋ ℛ ✗
Nearest Town Arnside/Milnthorpe
Directions Leave the M6 at junction 35, take the A6 north and turn left at Wildlife Oasis (after passing Esso fuel station). Follow signs to Fell End Caravan Park and Hall More is signposted from there.
⇌ Arnside

ARNSIDE/SILVERDALE
Silverdale Caravan Park, Cove Road, Silverdale, Nr Carnforth, Lancashire, LA5 0SH
Tel: 01524 701508
Email: reception@holgates.co.uk
www.holgates.co.uk
Pitches For Å ♠ ♠ **Total** 70
Acreage 10 **Open** 22-Dec **to** 06-Nov
Access Good **Site** Lev/Slope
Nearest Bus Stop (Miles) Outside
On Morecambe Bay. In area of outstanding natural beauty. Indoor swimming pool, gym, spa bath, sauna and steam room. Restaurant and bar. Finalist for Cumbria Tourism Awards 2009 Holiday Park of the Year.

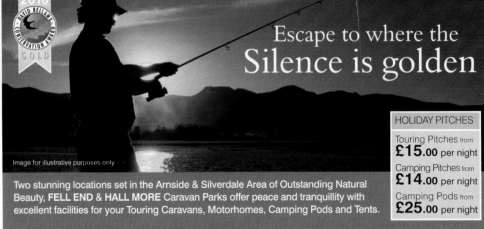

2010 DAVID BELLAMY CONSERVATION AWARD GOLD

Image for illustrative purposes only

Escape to where the Silence is golden

Facilities ⬚
Nearby Facilities ⬚ ⬚ ⬚ ⬚ ⬚ ⬚
Nearest Town Morecambe
Directions 5 miles northwest of Carnforth, between Silverdale and Arnside.
⬚ Silverdale

BROUGHTON IN FURNESS
Birchbank Farm, Birchbank, Blawith, Ulverston, Cumbria, LA12 8EW
Tel: 01229 885277
Email: info@birchbank.co.uk
www.birchbank.co.uk
Pitches For ⬚ ⬚ ⬚ **Total** 20
Acreage 1 **Open** May to October
Access Good **Site** Mostly Level
Small farm site. Next to open Fell, good walking area.
Facilities ⬚ ⬚ ⬚ ⬚ ⬚ ⬚ ⬚ ⬚
Nearby Facilities ⬚ ⬚ ⬚ ⬚ ⬚
Nearest Town Coniston Water
Directions A5092 ¼ mile west of Gawthwaite turn for Woodland. Site is 2 miles on the right along an unfenced road.
⬚ Kirkby in Furness

CARLISLE
Dalston Hall Caravan Park, Dalston, Carlisle, Cumbria, CA5 7JX
Tel: 01228 710165
Email: info@dalstonholidaypark.com
www.dalstonhallholidaypark.com
Pitches For ⬚ ⬚ ⬚ **Total** 71
Acreage 3½ **Open** March to End Jan
Access Good **Site** Level
Nearest Bus Stop (Miles) Outside
Adjacent to a golf course (same ownership). Fishing rights on the adjacent river.
Facilities ⬚ ⬚ ⬚ ⬚ ⬚ ⬚ ⬚ ⬚ ⬚ ⬚ ⬚ ⬚ ⬚ ⬚ ⬚ ⬚ ⬚

Nearby Facilities ⬚ ⬚ ⬚ ⬚ ⬚ ⬚
Nearest Town Carlisle
Directions Leave the M6 at junction 42 and take the road to Dalston. At Dalston take the B5299 towards Carlisle, site is on the right after 1 mile.
⬚ Dalston

CARLISLE
Dandy Dinmont Caravan & Camping Site, Blackford, Carlisle, Cumbria, CA6 4EA
Tel: 01228 674611
Email: dandydinmont@btopenworld.com
www.caravan-camping-carlisle.itgo.com
Pitches For ⬚ ⬚ ⬚ **Total** 47
Acreage 4 **Open** March to October
Access Good **Site** Level
Nearest Bus Stop (Miles) ¼
Now a mainly Adult Park, children are accepted, but there are no ball games or play area. Ideal for historic Carlisle Castle, Cathedral, Roman Wall, Border Country, and only 45 minutes from the Lake District.
Facilities ⬚ ⬚ ⬚ ⬚ ⬚ ⬚ ⬚ ⬚ ⬚ ⬚
Nearby Facilities ⬚ ⬚ ⬚
Nearest Town Carlisle
Directions On A7 at Blackford, 4¼ miles north of Carlisle. Leave M6 at intersection 44, and take the A7 north (Galashiels road), site approx 1½ miles on the right. After Blackford sign, follow road directional signs to site.
⬚ Carlisle

CARLISLE
Englethwaite Hall Caravan Club Site, Armathwaite, Carlisle, Cumbria, CA4 9SY
Tel: 01228 560202
www.caravanclub.co.uk
Pitches For ⬚ ⬚ **Total** 63
Acreage 5 **Open** March to Nov

Access Good **Site** Lev/Slope
Tranquil 15 acre estate in the Eden Valley with lovely views and Inglewood Forest as a backdrop. Riverside walks. Near the Lake District, Yorkshire Dales and Hadrians Wall. Own sanitation required. Non members welcome. Booking essential.
Facilities ⬚ ⬚ ⬚ ⬚ ⬚ ⬚ ⬚ ⬚
Nearby Facilities ⬚
Nearest Town Carlisle
Directions Leave the M6 or A6 at junction 42 and take the B6263 signposted Wetheral, after 1¾ miles turn right signposted Armathwaite. Site is approx. 2¾ miles on the right. Warning! - Bumpy road, recommended max speed 35mph.
⬚ Carlisle

CARLISLE
Green Acres Caravan Park, High Knells, Houghton, Carlisle, Cumbria, CA6 4JW
Tel: 01228 675418
Email: info@caravanpark-cumbria.com
www.caravanpark-cumbria.com
Pitches For ⬚ ⬚ **Total** 30
Acreage 3 **Open** Easter to October
Access Good **Site** Level
ADULT ONLY PARK. Ideal touring base for Hadrians Wall, Carlisle City, the Lake District and the Scottish Borders. AA 3 Pennant Graded.
Facilities ⬚ ⬚ ⬚ ⬚ ⬚ ⬚ ⬚ ⬚ ⬚ ⬚ ⬚ ⬚ ⬚ ⬚ ⬚
Nearby Facilities ⬚ ⬚ ⬚ ⬚
Nearest Town Carlisle
Directions Leave the M6 at junction 44 (North Carlisle). Take the A689 for 1 mile, turn left signposted Scaleby. Site is 1 mile on the left.
⬚ Carlisle

COCKERMOUTH
Wheatsheaf Inn, Low Lorton, Cockermouth, Cumbria, CA13 9UW
Tel: 01900 85199
Email: j.williams53@sky.com
www.wheatsheafinnlorton.co.uk
Pitches For ▲ ⛺ ⛟ **Total** 40
Open March **to** 15-Nov
Access Good **Site** Level
In the town of Cockermouth (Wordsworth) and close to five lakes (osprey), Whinlatter and Go Ape.
Facilities ...
Nearby Facilities ...
Nearest Town Cockermouth
Directions From Keswick take the A66, turn left at Embleton sign onto the B5292, then take the B5289.
⚏ Workington

COCKERMOUTH
Whinfell Camping, Lorton, Nr Cockermouth, Cumbria, CA13 0RQ
Tel: 01900 85260/85057
Email: ramcclellan@tiscali.co.uk
Pitches For ▲ ⛺ ⛟ **Total** 40
Acreage 5 **Open** 15-Mar **to** 15-Nov
Access Good **Site** Level
Ideal touring and walking. Near to many attractions including Whinlatter Visitor Centre, Sellafield Visitor Centre, Ravenglass Miniature Steam Railway, Muncaster Castle & Gardens and an Owl centre.
Facilities ...
Nearby Facilities ...
Nearest Town Cockermouth
Directions Take the A66 then the B5292 at Braithwaite into Low Lorton, follow caravan and camping signs. Or take the 5289 from Cockermouth.
⚏ Workington

CONISTON
Coniston Hall Camping Site, Coniston, Cumbria, LA21 8AS
Tel: 015394 41223
Pitches For ▲ ⛺
Acreage 200 **Open** March **to** October
Site Level
Nearest Bus Stop (Miles) ½
Lake access. Dogs to be kept on leads.
Facilities ...
Nearby Facilities ...
Nearest Town Coniston
Directions 1 mile south of Coniston.
⚏ Windermere

CONISTON
Park Coppice Caravan Club Site, Coniston, Cumbria, LA21 8LA
Tel: 01539 441555
www.caravanclub.co.uk
Pitches For ▲ ⛺ ⛟ **Total** 280
Acreage 20 **Open** March **to** Nov
Access Good **Site** Lev/Slope
Nearest Bus Stop (Miles) Outside
Situated between Coniston Water and mountains in 63 acres of National Trust woodland. Ideal for walking and bird watching, especially in Grizedale Forest. Post Office, junior orienteering course and Red Squirrel Nature Trail on site. Non members welcome. Booking essential.
Facilities ...
Nearby Facilities ...
Nearest Town Coniston
Directions On the A593, 1 miles south of Coniston Village, just past the A5084 junction in Torver. NB: Approach is narrow in places.
⚏ Ulverston

CONISTON
Pier Cottage Caravan Park, Pier Cottage, Coniston, Cumbria, LA21 8AJ
Tel: 01539 441497/441252
Pitches For ⛺ ⛟ **Total** 10
Acreage 1 **Open** March **to** October
Access Good **Site** Level
Nearest Bus Stop (Miles) ¼
Lakeside site with boating, fishing and fellwalking.
Facilities ...
Nearby Facilities ...
Nearest Town Coniston
Directions 1 mile east of Coniston off the B5285 Hawkshead road.
⚏ Windermere

CUMWHITTON
Cairndale Caravan Park, Cumwhitton, Headsnook, Brampton, Nr Carlisle, Cumbria, CA8 9BZ
Tel: 01768 896280
Pitches For ⛺ ⛟ **Total** 5
Acreage 2 **Open** March **to** October
Access Good **Site** Level
Scenic views, ideal touring, quiet site, water and electricity to individual touring sites. Windsurfing nearby.
Facilities ...
Nearby Facilities ...
Nearest Town Carlisle
Directions Follow A69 to Warwick Bridge and then follow unclassified road through Great Corby to Cumwhitton, approx. 9 miles.
⚏ Carlisle

DENT
Conder Farm Campsite, Deepdale Road, Dent, Sedbergh, Cumbria, LA10 5QT
Tel: 01539 625277
Email: conderfarm@aol.com
Pitches For ▲ ⛺ ⛟ **Total** 47
Acreage 1½ **Open** March **to** Oct
Site Sloping
Nearest Bus Stop (Miles) ¼
Quiet scenic location. Ideal for touring, fell walking and caving. Buses on Wednesdays and Saturdays only.
Facilities ...
Nearby Facilities ...
Nearest Town Sedbergh
Directions Leave the M6 at junction 37 and take the road for Sedbergh following signs for Dent for approx. 10 miles. At the George & Dragon take the right hand fork to Dent.
⚏ Dent

DENT
Ewegales Farm, Dent, Sedbergh, Cumbria, LA10 5RH
Tel: 01539 625440
Pitches For ▲ ⛺ ⛟ **Total** 60
Acreage 5½ **Open** All Year
Access Good **Site** Level
Nearest Bus Stop (Miles) Outside
Alongside a river for fishing.
Facilities ...
Nearby Facilities ...
Nearest Town Dent
Directions Leave the M6 at junction 37 and head towards Sedbergh then Dent, park is 3½ miles east of Dent Village.
⚏ Dent

EGREMONT
Tarnside Caravan Park, Braystones, Egremont, Cumbria, CA21 2YL
Tel: 01946 822777
Email: reception@seacote.com
www.tarnsidepark.co.uk
Pitches For ▲ ⛺ ⛟ ⛟ **Total** 20
Acreage 2 **Open** March **to** October
Access Good **Site** Level
Nearest Bus Stop (Miles) Entrance
Beside a lovely beach and tarn. Ideal for walking.
Facilities ...
Nearby Facilities ...
Nearest Town Egremont
Directions From the A595 3 miles south of Egremont, take the B5345 and follow signs for Tarnside Park.
⚏ Braystones

ESKDALE
Eskdale Camping & Caravanning Club Site, Boot, Holmrook, Cumbria, CA19 1TH
Tel: 01946 723263
www.campingandcaravanningclub.co.uk/eskdale
Pitches For ▲ ⛟ **Total** 80
Acreage 8 **Open** 01-Mar **to** 14-Jan
Access Good **Site** Level
Close to Scafell Pike, Wastwater, the River Esk, Hardknott Fort, Eskdale Mill and Muncaster Castle. Camping Pods available for hire. Camping barn available. Non members welcome. You can also call us on 0845 130 7633.
Facilities ...
Nearest Town Ravenglass
Directions From the A595 turn right onto local road signposted Birkby, continue on to Eskdale.
⚏ Dalegarth

ESKDALE
Fisherground Campsite, Fisherground, Eskdale, Cumbria, CA19 1TF
Tel: 01946 723349
Email: camping@fishergroundcampsite.co.uk
www.fishergroundcampsite.co.uk
Pitches For ▲ ⛟ **Total** 215
Acreage 12 **Open** March **to** October
Site Level/Sloping
Quiet family site in the heart of the Lake District. Near the beach, a river and a waterfall. Plenty of good walks in the area. 7 mile miniature railway with our own private station. Childrens adventure play area.
Facilities ...
Nearby Facilities ...
Nearest Town Eskdale
Directions Turn right ¾ miles past Broughton on A595 and go up Duddon Valley (signed Ulpha). 4 miles to Ulpha, then turn left (sp Eskdale). 6 miles over Birker Moor, descend to Eskdale and turn right at the King George IV Inn. Site is the first turning on the left.
⚏ Ravenglass

GOSFORTH
Seven Acres Caravan Park, Holmrook, Cumbria, CA19 1YD
Tel: 01946 822777
Email: reception@seacote.com
www.sevenacrespark.co.uk
Pitches For ▲ ⛺ ⛟ ⛟ **Total** 37
Acreage 4 **Open** March **to** October
Access Good **Site** Level
Nearest Bus Stop (Miles) Entrance
2 miles from the beach and close to the Lake District, Wasdale and some of Englands finest mountains.
Facilities ...
Nearby Facilities ...
Nearest Town Egremont
Directions On the A595 4 miles south of Egremont.
⚏ Seascale

CUMBRIA

GRANGE-OVER-SANDS

Cartmel Caravan & Camping Park, Wells House Farm, Cartmel, Grange-Over-Sands, Cumbria, LA11 6PN
Tel: 015395 36270
Email: info@cartmelcamping.co.uk
www.cartmelcamping.co.uk
Pitches For 𝗔 **Total** 59
Acreage 5 **Open** March to October
Site Level
Nearest Bus Stop (Miles) Outside
Tranquil park set in picturesque surroundings, yet only 2 minutes from the village square. Cartmel, one of South Lakelands oldest and prettiest villages, has grown up around its famous 12th Century Priory.
Facilities ⚷ ∮ ⅏ 🛒 🖨 🅿️ ⊙ ⇨ ⛽ ⬛
🏋️ ⊙ ⚲ 🅰️ ⭐ 🅿️ 🖳
Nearby Facilities 🏌️ ✓ U
Nearest Town Grange-over-Sands
Directions Enter Cartmel from the A590, turn right at the Pig & Whistle, turn next left and the entrance is shortly on the right hand side.
⇌ Grange-over-Sands

GRANGE-OVER-SANDS

Greaves Farm Caravan Park, c/o Prospect House, Barber Green, Grange-over-Sands, Cumbria, LA11 6HU
Tel: 015395 36329/36587
www.greavesfarmcaravanpark.co.uk
Pitches For 𝗔 ⚏ ⛟ **Total** 20
Acreage 3 **Open** March to October
Access Good **Site** Level
Quiet, select, family run park. Ideal base for exploring the Lake District.
Facilities ⚷ ∮ ⅏ 🛒 🖨 ⊙ ⚲ 🅰️ ⭐ 🅿️ 🖳
Nearby Facilities 🏌️ ✓ ⚓ ⚲ U 🏇
Nearest Town Grange-over-Sands
Directions Come off the A590 approx 1 mile south of Newby Bridge at the sign "Cartmel 4 miles". Proceed 1½ miles to sign for caravan park.
⇌ Grange-over-Sands

GRANGE-OVER-SANDS

Lakeland Leisure Park, Moor Lane, Flookburgh, Nr Grange-over-Sands, Cumbria, LA11 7LT
Tel: 01539 558556
Email: lakeland@haven.com
www.haventouring.com/tolakeland
Pitches For 𝗔 ⚏ ⛟ **Total** 185
Open Mid March to End Oct
Access Good **Site** Level
Nearest Bus Stop (Miles) 1
A relaxed and easy going Holiday Park ideally situated for touring and exploring. Less than 20 miles from Lake Windermere. Enjoy a wide choice of on-park facilities including a 9 hole golf course, tennis and much more.

Facilities ⚷ ∮ ⅏ 🛒 🖨 ⊙ ⇨ ⛽ ⬛ 🏋️ 🎱 ⚷ ⊙ ⚲ 🍴 🖳 🎾 🅰️ ⭐ 🅿️ 🖳 🛈
Nearby Facilities 🏌️ ∪ 🏇
Nearest Town Grange-over-Sands
Directions Leave the M6 at junction 36 onto the A590, turn left onto the A6/A590 for Barrow-in-Furness. Then take the B5277 through Grange-over-Sands, then Allithwaite and into Flookburgh. Turn left at the village square and travel 1 mile down this road to the Park.
⇌ Cark-in-Cartmel

GRANGE-OVER-SANDS

Meathop Fell Caravan Club Site, Grange-over-Sands, Cumbria, LA11 6RB
Tel: 01539 532912
www.caravanclub.co.uk
Pitches For ⚏ ⛟ **Total** 131
Acreage 10 **Open** All Year
Access Good **Site** Lev/Slope
Peaceful site. Ideal base to explore North Lancashire and Southern Lake District. Close to Brockhole National Park Visitor Centre. Non members welcome. Booking essential.
Facilities ⚷ ∮ ⅏ 🛒 🖨 ⊙ ⚲ 🅰️ ⭐ 🅿️ 🖳
Nearby Facilities 🏌️ ⚓
Nearest Town Grange-over-Sands
Directions Leave M6 at junc 36. Take the A590 sp South Lakes. After 3¼ miles turn left via slip road sp Barrow, at roundabout turn left onto B5277 and immediately turn left sp Meathop. Within ¾ miles turn right up incline and keep right at the top, in 200 yards fork left at green notice board, site is on the left in 150 yards. NB: Steep approach.

HAWKSHEAD

Hawkshead Hall Farm, Hawkshead, Nr Ambleside, Cumbria, LA22 0NN
Tel: 015394 36221
Email: enquiries@hawksheadhall-campsite.com
www.hawksheadhall-campsite.com
Pitches For 𝗔 ⚏ **Total** 55
Acreage 5 **Open** March to Nov
Access Good **Site** Sloping
Nearest Bus Stop (Miles) ¼
Surrounded by Lakeland fells with superb views. ¼ of a mile from Hawkshead Village.
Facilities ∮ ⅏ 🛒 🖨 ⊙ ⚲ 🅰️ ⭐ 🅿️ 🖳
Nearby Facilities 🏌️ ✓ ⚓ ⚲ U 🏇 🏇
Nearest Town Hawkshead
Directions From Ambleside take the B5286 to Hawkshead, we are ¼ of a mile before the village on the left.
⇌ Windermere

HAWKSHEAD

The Croft Caravan & Camp Site, North Lonsdale Road, Hawkshead, Nr Ambleside, Cumbria, LA22 0NX
Tel: 015394 36374

Email: enquiries@hawkshead-croft.com
www.hawkshead-croft.com
Pitches For 𝗔 ⚏ ⛟ **Total** 100
Acreage 5 **Open** March to November
Access Good **Site** Level
Sheltered site surrounded by the hills and fells of the Lake District. Across the road from Hawkshead Village. Self catering flats and caravans also available.
Facilities ⚷ ∮ ⅏ 🛒 🖨 ⊙ ⇨ ⛽ ⬛ 🏋️ 🎱 ⊙ ⚲ 🍴 🅰️ ⭐ 🅿️ 🖳
Nearby Facilities 🏌️ ✓ ⚓ ⚲ U 🏇 🏇
Nearest Town Hawkshead
Directions From Ambleside take the B5286 to Hawkshead Village.
⇌ Windermere

KENDAL

Ashes Exclusively Adult Caravan Park, The Ashes, New Hutton, Kendal, Cumbria, LA8 0AS
Tel: 01539 731833
Email: info@ashescaravanpark.co.uk
www.ashescaravanpark.co.uk
Pitches For ⚏ ⛟ **Total** 25
Acreage 1½ **Open** 01-Mar to 07-Nov
Access Good **Site** Lev/Slope
Nearest Bus Stop (Miles) ½
ADULTS ONLY SITE in a countryside setting with views of the Cumbrian Fells. Popular with walkers and ideal for visiting many local attractions. Close to the Lakes and the Yorkshire Dales.
Facilities ⚷ ⚷ ∮ ⅏ 🛒 🖨 ⊙ ⚲ 🖨 ⭐ 🅿️ 🖳 🛈
Nearby Facilities 🏌️ ✓ ⚓ ⚲ U 🏇 🏇
Nearest Town Kendal
Directions Leave the M6 at junction 37 and take the A684 towards Kendal. In 2 miles at the crossroads turn left signposted New Hutton, site is in ¾ miles on the right.
⇌ Oxenholme

KENDAL

Camping & Caravanning Club Site, Millcrest, Shap Road, Kendal, Cumbria, LA9 6NY
Tel: 01539 741363
www.campingandcaravanningclub.co.uk/kendal
Pitches For 𝗔 ⚏ ⛟ **Total** 50
Acreage 3 **Open** 29-Mar to 05-Nov
Site Lev/Slope
Nearest Bus Stop (Miles) ½
Right in the middle of the Lake District. Tumble drier and spin drier on site. BTB 4 Star Graded and AA 3 Pennants. Non members welcome. You can also call us on 0845 130 7633.
Facilities ∮ ⅏ 🛒 🖨 ⊙ ⇨ ⛽ ⬛ 🏋️ ⊙ ⚲ 🅰️ ⭐ 🅿️ 🖳 🛈
Nearby Facilities 🏌️ ✓ ⚲ U 🏇 🏇

Directions On the A6, 1½ miles north of Kendal, site entrance is 100 yards north of the nameplate Skelsmergh.
⊭ Kendal

KENDAL
Lambhowe Caravan Park, Crosthwaite, Nr Kendal, Cumbria, LA8 8JE
Tel: 015395 68483
Email: lynda9@tiscali.co.uk
Pitches For 🚐 🚗 **Total** 14
Acreage 20 **Open** 01-Mar **to** 16-Nov
Access Good **Site** Level
Nearest Bus Stop (Miles) ¼
Set in the delightful Lyth Valley. Just a 15 minute drive to Lake Windermere.
Facilities ⨍ 🖪 🖽 🖉 🖛 ⊙ ⌷ ⌇
🖪 🗓 ⚲ 🖛🖭 ⚡
Nearby Facilities ⌐ ⌊ ⚓ ⅋
Nearest Town Bowness on Windermere
Directions Leave the M6 at junction 36 and take the A590, then take the A5074 towards Bowness. Lambhowe is opposite the Damson Dene Hotel.
⊭ Windermere

KENDAL
Low Park Wood Caravan Club Site, Sedgwick, Kendal, Cumbria, LA8 0JZ
Tel: 01539 560186
www.caravanclub.co.uk
Pitches For 🚐 🚗 **Total** 141
Acreage 20 **Open** March **to** Nov
Nearest Bus Stop (Miles) ½
Peaceful site with varied bird life and wild flowers. River fishing. Non members welcome. Booking essential.
Facilities ⚲ ⨍ 🖪 🖽 🖉 🖵 🖲 ⚡
🖪 🗓 🛆 🖛🖭 🖭 ⚡
Nearby Facilities ⌐ ⌊
Nearest Town Kendal
Directions Leave the M6 at jct 36, take A590 sp South Lakes, after 3¼ miles leave via slip road signposted Barrow. At roundabout follow brown signs and turn into road sp Sedgwick, After 150 yds turn left onto road running parallel with the River Kent. Fork right at the junction, site is on left after ½ a mile.
⊭ Kendal

KENDAL
Pound Farm, Crook, Cumbria, LA8 8JZ
Tel: 01539 821220
Email: poundfarm@northdales.co.uk
www.northdales.co.uk
Pitches For Å 🚐 🚗 **Total** 20
Open Mar **to** Jan
Access Good **Site** Lev/Slope
Nearest Bus Stop (Miles) 1
6 miles from Lake Windermere.
Facilities ⨍ 🖪 🖽 🖉 🖵 ⊙ ⌷ 🖭 ⚲
Nearby Facilities ⌐ ⌊ ⚓ U ⅋ ⚓ ⅋

Nearest Town Stavely
Directions From the A591 turn into Rather Heath Lane, turn onto the B5284, site is 3¼ miles.
⊭ Stavely

KENDAL
Waters Edge Caravan Park, Crooklands, Nr Kendal, Cumbria, LA7 7NN
Tel: 015395 67708
Email: info@watersedgecaravanpark.co.uk
www.watersedgecaravanpark.co.uk
Pitches For Å 🚐 🚗 **Total** 32
Acreage 3 **Open** March **to** November
Access Good **Site** Level
Nearest Bus Stop (Miles) ¼
Set in quiet and pleasant countryside. Lakes, Yorkshire Dales and Morecambe Bay within easy reach.
Facilities ⚲ ⨍ 🖪 🖽 🖉 🖵 ⊙ ⌷ 🖭 ⚡
🖪 🗓 ⊙ ⚲ 🛆 🖛🖭 🖭 ⚡
Nearby Facilities ⌐ ⌊ ⚓ U ⅋ ⚓ ⅋
Nearest Town Kendal
Directions A65 Crooklands, ¾ mile from M6 motorway junction 36.
⊭ Oxenholme

KESWICK
Burns Farm Caravan Site, St Johns-in-the-Vale, Keswick, Cumbria, CA12 4RR
Tel: 017687 79225
Email: info@burns-farm.co.uk
www.burns-farm.co.uk
Pitches For Å 🚐 🚗 **Total** 40
Acreage 1¼ **Open** Easter **to** October
Access Good **Site** Level
Nearest Bus Stop (Miles) Outside
Quiet family site with beautiful views. Small charge for use of WiFi. Ideal touring, walking and climbing. AA Graded.
Facilities ⚲ ⨍ 🖪 🖽 🖉 🖵 ⌷ 🖭 ⚡
🖪 🗓 🖛🖭 🖭 ⨍ ⚲ ⚡
Nearby Facilities ⌐ ⌊ ⚓ U ⅋ ⚓ ⅋
Nearest Town Keswick
Directions Turn left off the A66 (Penrith to Keswick road) ½ mile past B5322 junction signposted Castlerigg Stone Circle and Burns Farm. Site is on the right, farm is on the left. 2¼ miles from Keswick.
⊭ Penrith

KESWICK
Camping & Caravanning Club Site, Crow Park Road, Keswick, Cumbria, CA12 5EP
Tel: 01768 772392
www.campingandcaravanningclub.co.uk/keswick
Pitches For Å 🚐 🚗 **Total** 250
Acreage 14 **Open** 02-Feb **to** 26-Nov
Access Good **Site** Level
Nearest Bus Stop (Miles) ½
Situated on the banks of Derwentwater, ideal

for fishing and water sports. Boat launching for small boats. Good hillwalking area. Close to the centre of Keswick. All units must have towing vehicle on site overnight. One vehicle per pitch. BTB 4 Star Graded, David Bellamy Gold Award and AA 3 Pennants. Non members welcome. You can also call us on 0845 130 7633.
Facilities ⨍ 🖪 🖽 🖉 🖵 ⊙ ⌷ 🖭 ⚡
🖪 🗓 ⊙ ⚲ 🛆 🖛🖭 🖭 ⚡
Nearby Facilities ⌐ ⌊ ⚓ U ⅋ ⚓
Nearest Town Keswick
Directions From Penrith take the A5271, turn left into Main Street (Keswick), turn right to pass Lakes Bus Station, pass the rugby club and turn right, site is on the right.
⊭ Penrith

KESWICK
Camping & Caravanning Club Site, Derwentwater Caravan Park, Crow Park Road, Keswick, Cumbria, CA12 5EN
Tel: 01768 772579
www.campingandcaravanningclub.co.uk/derwentwater
Pitches For 🚐 🚗 **Total** 44
Acreage 16 **Open** 01-Mar **to** 05-Jan
Access Good **Site** Level
Nearest Bus Stop (Miles) ½
Within the heart of the Lake District National Park. BTB 4 Star Graded, David Bellamy Gold Award and AA 3 Pennants. Non members welcome. You can also call us on 0845 130 7633.
Facilities ⚲ ⨍ 🖪 🖽 🖉 🖵 ⊙ ⌷ 🖭 ⚡
🖪 🗓 ⚡
Nearby Facilities ⌐ ⌊ ⚓ U
Nearest Town Keswick
Directions Leave the M6 at junction 40 and take the A66 signposted Keswick and Workington for 13 miles. Do not take the A591, stay on the A66. At the roundabout turn left signposted Keswick Town Centre, follow signs for caravan park to Derwentwater.
⊭ Penrith

KESWICK
Castlerigg Farm Camping & Caravan Site, Keswick, Cumbria, CA12 4TE
Tel: 01768 772479
Email: info@castleriggfarm.com
www.castleriggfarm.com
Pitches For Å 🚐 🚗
Acreage 3 **Open** March **to** Nov
Access Good **Site** Sloping
Exceptional panoramic views in a quiet area. Ideal for walking. 25 minute walk to Keswick town. Couples and families only. No noise after 10.30pm.

CUMBRIA

Facilities
Nearby Facilities
Nearest Town Keswick
Directions From Keswick take the A591 towards Windermere, after approx. 1½ miles turn right at the top of the hill following camping sign and the Site is on the left.
≠ Penrith

KESWICK

Castlerigg Hall Caravan & Camping Park, Castlerigg Hall, Keswick, Cumbria, CA12 4TE
Tel: 01768 774499
Email: info@castlerigg.co.uk
www.castlerigg.co.uk
Pitches For ▲ ⊞ ⊟ **Total** 193
Open 20-Mar **to** 09-Nov
Access Good **Site** Lev/Slope
Nearest Bus Stop (Miles) ¼
Stunning views and superb walking country, in the heart of the English Lakes.
Facilities
Nearby Facilities
Nearest Town Keswick
Directions 1½ miles south east of Keswick off the A591, turn right past Heights Hotel.
≠ Penrith

KESWICK

Dalebottom Farm Caravan & Camping Park, Naddle, Keswick, Cumbria, CA12 4TF
Tel: 017687 72176
Email: dalebottomfarm@yahoo.co.uk
www.dalebottomfarm.co.uk
Pitches For ▲ ⊞ ⊟ **Total** 60
Acreage 7 **Open** 01-Mar **to** 01-Nov
Access Good **Site** Lev/Slope
Nearest Bus Stop (Miles) Outside
In the heart of lakeland.
Facilities
Nearby Facilities
Nearest Town Keswick
Directions 2 miles south of Keswick on the A591 Windermere road.
≠ Penrith

KESWICK

Gill Head Farm Caravan & Camping Park, Troutbeck, Penrith, Cumbria, CA11 0ST
Tel: 017687 79652
Email: enquiries@gillheadfarm.co.uk
www.gillheadfarm.co.uk
Pitches For ▲ ⊞ ⊟ **Total** 40
Acreage 10 **Open** March **to** November
Access Good **Site** Sloping
Nearest Bus Stop (Miles) ¼
Situated on a working hill farm in a great location within the Lake District National Park providing superb views. Ideal for families and walkers.
Facilities
Nearby Facilities
Nearest Town Keswick
Directions Leave the M6 at junction 40 (Penrith), take the A66 west for 9 miles. Then take the A5091 (left) and after 100 yards turn first right.
≠ Penrith

KESWICK

Low Manesty Caravan Club Site, Manesty, Keswick, Cumbria, CA12 5UG
Tel: 01768 777275
www.caravanclub.co.uk
Pitches For ⊞ ⊟ **Total** 60
Acreage 12 **Open** March **to** Nov

Access Good **Site** Level
Set in National Trust woodland, close to Derwentwater. Numerous walks from the site. Many visitor attractions within easy reach. Own sanitation required. Non members welcome. Booking essential.
Facilities
Nearby Facilities
Nearest Town Keswick
Directions Leave the M6 at junction 40 and take the A66, on the outskirts of Keswick keep right onto bypass. At roundabout within 1½ miles turn left signposted A5271 Keswick, follow signs onto the B5289. After 4¼ miles turn right over the bridge (care required), s
≠ Keswick

KESWICK

Scotgate Holiday Park, Braithwaite, Keswick, Cumbria, CA12 5TF
Tel: 017687 78343
Email: info@scotgateholidaypark.co.uk
www.scotgateholidaypark.co.uk
Pitches For ▲ ⊞ ⊟ **Total** 165
Open All Year
Access Good **Site** Level
Nearest Bus Stop (Miles) Entrance
Central for good walks. River nearby. Near to pubs and restaurants. NEW luxury toilet block with under-floor heating.
Facilities
Nearby Facilities
Nearest Town Keswick
Directions From Keswick head west on the A66 towards Workington, turn left sp Whinlatter Forest Park to Braithwaite Village.
≠ Penrith

KESWICK

Thirlspot Farm Caravan Park, Thirlspot Farm, Thirlmere, Keswick, Cumbria, CA12 4TN
Tel: 01768 772551
Pitches For ▲ ⊟ **Total** 25
Open March **to** Oct
Site Level
Nearest Bus Stop (Miles) Outside
At the foot of Helvelyn. 250 metres from a lake.
Facilities
Nearby Facilities
Nearest Town Keswick
Directions Situated on the A591, 6 miles from Keswick and 6 miles from Grasmere.
≠ Windermere

KIRKBY LONSDALE

New House Caravan Park, Kirkby Lonsdale, Cumbria, LA6 2HR
Tel: 015242 71590
Email: colinpreece9@aol.com
Pitches For ⊞ ⊟ **Total** 50
Acreage 3½ **Open** March **to** End Oct
Access Good **Site** Lev/Slope
Situated near to the historic town of Kirkby Lonsdale and Devils Bridge. An ideal location to visit lakes and Yorkshire Dales.
Facilities
Nearby Facilities
Nearest Town Kirkby Lonsdale/Kendal
Directions From Kirkby Lonsdale take the A65 towards Settle, after approx. 1½ miles site is on the right 300 yards past Whoop Hall Inn.
≠ Carnforth

KIRKBY LONSDALE

Woodclose Caravan Park, High Casterton, Kirkby Lonsdale, Cumbria, LA6 2SE
Tel: 015242 71597
Email: info@woodclosepark.com
www.woodclosepark.com
Pitches For ▲ ⊞ ⊟ **Total** 17
Acreage 9 **Open** March **to** 14-Nov
Access Good **Site** Lev/Slope
An award winning Park set within the beautiful valley of the River Lune between the Yorkshire Dales and the Lake District National Park. Nine acrea providing a unique holiday base in an area of outstanding natural beauty. New to the site are our Wigwams, a great alternative to the tent! Contact us about our holiday home open day offers.
Facilities
Nearby Facilities
Nearest Town Kirkby Lonsdale
Directions Leave the M6 at junction 36 and take the A65 for approx. 6 miles. Woodclose entrance is past Devils Bridge on the left hand side.

KIRKBY STEPHEN

Pennine View Caravan & Camping Park, Station Road, Kirkby Stephen, Cumbria, CA17 4SZ
Tel: 01768 371717
Pitches For ▲ ⊞ ⊟ **Total** 58
Acreage 2½ **Open** Early March **to** End Oct
Access Good **Site** Level
Nearest Bus Stop (Miles) ½
On the edge of the River Eden and on the outskirts of the small market town of Kirkby Stephen. Ideal for walking and touring the Yorkshire Dales and the Lake District, Teesdale and Durham.
Facilities
Nearby Facilities
Nearest Town Kirkby Stephen
Directions Just off the A685 approx 1 mile from Kirkby Stephen town centre. 11 miles from the M6 junction 38, and 5 miles from the A66 at Brough.
≠ Kirkby Stephen

KIRKBY THORE

Low Moor, Kirkby Thore, Penrith, Cumbria, CA10 1XG
Tel: 017683 61231
www.lowmoorpark.co.uk
Pitches For ▲ ⊞ ⊟ **Total** 12
Acreage 1½ **Open** April **to** October
Access Good **Site** Level
Nearest Bus Stop (Miles) Outside
Open country.
Facilities
Nearby Facilities
Nearest Town Appleby
Directions On the A66 7 miles south east of Penrith, at the end of Temple Sowerby bypass, 1 mile west of Kirkby Thore.
≠ Penrith

LAMPLUGH

Dockray Meadow Caravan Club Site, Lamplugh, Cumbria, CA14 4SH
Tel: 01946 861357
www.caravanclub.co.uk
Pitches For ⊞ ⊟ **Total** 53
Acreage 4½ **Open** March **to** Nov
Access Good **Site** Lev/Slope
Nearest Bus Stop (Miles) ½
Sheltered site alongside a stream with fell scenery. Ideal for walkers. Own sanitation required. Non members welcome. Booking essential.

Facilities ⨍ 🖂 🚿 ⛽ ⊕ 🅿 ⟶ 🔌
Nearby Facilities ✈
Nearest Town Lamplugh
Directions From the A66 Cockermouth bypass turn onto the A5086 sp Egremont. After 6½ miles (300yds past Lamplugh Tip Pub) turn left at signpost for Loweswater. Within ¾ miles turn right signposted Croasdale, site is 50 yards on the left.

LONGTOWN

Camelot Caravan Park, Sandysike, Longtown, Carlisle, Cumbria, CA6 5SZ
Tel: 01228 791248
Pitches For ⛺ ⛟ ⛺ **Total** 20
Acreage 1¼ **Open** March **to** October
Access Good **Site** Level
Nearest Bus Stop (Miles) ¼
Ideal base for the Solway coast, Carlisle Settle Railway, Carlisle Castle, romantic Gretna Green, Hadrians Wall and Border towns. AA 2 Pennants. Waiting List for Secure Storage.
Facilities ⨍ 🖂 ⊕ ⟶ 🚽 🔌 ⛽ ⟲
Nearby Facilities ✈ ✓ ∪
Nearest Town Longtown
Directions On the A7, 1¼ miles south of Longtown on the left. Leave the M6 northbound at junction 44 and take the A7 (Longtown), Park is on the right in 4 miles.
🚆 Carlisle

LONGTOWN

High Gaitle Caravan Park, Gaitle Bridge, Longtown, Carlisle, Cumbria, CA6 5LU
Tel: 01228 791819
Pitches For ⛺ ⛟ ⛺ **Total** 30
Acreage 6 **Open** All Year
Access Good **Site** Level
Nearest Bus Stop (Miles) Entrance
Ideal touring location for the Lake District, South Scotland, Borders, Gretna Green and Hadrians Wall. Great for fishing on the world famous River Esk.
Facilities ⨍ 🖂 ⊕ ⟶ 🚽 🔌 ⛽ ⟲
Nearby Facilities ✈ ✓ ∪ ₽
Nearest Town Longtown
Directions Leave the M6 at junction 44 and take the A7 for 6 miles through Longtown, then take the A6071 towards Gretna, Site is 1¼ miles on the left.
🚆 Carlisle

MARYPORT

Spring Lea Caravan Park, Allonby, Maryport, Cumbria, CA15 6QF
Tel: 01900 881331
Email: mail@springlea.co.uk
www.springlea.co.uk
Pitches For ⛺ ⛟ ⛺ **Total** 35
Acreage 5 **Open** March **to** October
Access Good **Site** Level
Nearest Bus Stop (Miles) ¼
300 yards from the beach with views of Lakeland and Scottish hills. Leisure centre or sauna etc.. Bar/restaurant on site.
Facilities ⨍ 🖂 ⊕ ⟶ 🚽 🔌 ⛽ ⟲
Nearby Facilities ✈ ✓ ≍ ∪
Nearest Town Maryport
Directions 5 miles north of Maryport on the B5300 coast road.
🚆 Maryport

MEALSGATE

The Larches Caravan Park, Mealsgate, Wigton, Cumbria, CA7 1LQ
Tel: 016973 71379 / 71803
Email: thelarches@hotmail.co.uk
www.thelarchescaravanpark.co.uk
Pitches For ⛺ ⛟ ⛺ **Total** 73
Acreage 19 **Open** March **to** October
Access Good **Site** Lev/slope

ADULTS ONLY SITE. Ideal for couples, peace and quiet in the countryside with beautiful views. Excellent toilets.
Facilities ♿ ⨍ 🖂 🖂 ⊕ ⟶ 🚽 🔌 ⛽ ⟲
🏪 ⊕ 🅿 ⟶ 🔌 🏤 ⛽
Nearby Facilities ✈ ✓ ≍ ∪
Nearest Town Wigton
Directions From the north take the A57/A74/A7/A69 to Carlisle, follow the A595 to Mealsgate. From the south leave the M6 at junction 41, take the B5305 Wigton road as far as the A595. Turn left and follow the A595 to Mealsgate.
🚆 Wigton

PENRITH

Flusco Wood Caravan Park, Flusco, Penrith, Cumbria, CA11 0JB
Tel: 01768 480020
Email: info@fluscowood.co.uk
www.fluscowood.co.uk
Pitches For ⛟ ⛺ **Total** 60
Acreage 24 **Open** Easter **to** November
Access Good **Site** Sloping
Hard standing serviced pitches, some set in woodland clearings. 1 mile from the Lake District. ETB 5 Star Graded and Bellamy Gold Award for Conservation.
Facilities ♿ ⨍ 🖂 🖂 ⊕ ⟶ 🚽 🔌 ⛽ ⟲
🏪 ⊕ 🅿 🏤 ⟶ 🔌 ⟲
Nearby Facilities ✈ ✓ ≍ ∪ ₽ ⚘
Nearest Town Penrith
Directions Leave the M6 at junction 40 and travel west on the A66 for 4 miles.
🚆 Penrith

PENRITH

Gillside Caravan & Camping Site, Glenridding, Penrith, Cumbria, CA11 0QQ
Tel: 017684 82346
Email: gillside@btconnect.com
www.gillsidecaravanandcampingsite.co.uk
Pitches For ⛺ ⛟ ⛺ **Total** 65
Acreage 8 **Open** March **to** Mid Nov
Access Good **Site** Level
Nearest Bus Stop (Miles) ½
Foot of Helvellyn, 5 minutes walk from Lake Ullswater.
Facilities ⨍ 🖂 🖂 ⊕ ⟶ 🚽 🔌 ⛽
🏪 ⊕ 🅿 ⟶
Nearby Facilities ✈ ✓ ≍ ∪ ₽ ⚘
Nearest Town Penrith
Directions A592 signposted Ullswater, 14 miles from Penrith. In Glenridding turn right, follow sign for Gillside.
🚆 Penrith

PENRITH

Hillcroft Park, Roe Head Lane, Ullswater, Penrith, Cumbria, CA10 2LT
Tel: 01768 486363
Email: hillcroft@northdales.co.uk
www.northdales.co.uk
Pitches For ⛺ **Total** 22
Open 06-Mar **to** 31-Oct
Site Gentle Slope
Nearest Bus Stop (Miles) ¼
Within the Lake District with views of Lake Ullswater. Ullswater Steamer nearby. 13 electric hook-up pitches available. 90 pitches during August.
Facilities ⨍ 🖂 🖂 ⊕ ⟶ 🚽 🔌 ⛽
🏪 🔌 ⊕ 🅿 ⟶ 🔌 ⟲
Nearby Facilities ✈ ✓ ≍ ∪
Nearest Town Penrith
Directions 7 miles from Penrith. From the A66 take the A592, then take the B5320. Turn right onto the High Street, Roe Head Lane is approx 1 mile.
🚆 Penrith

PENRITH

Lowther Holiday Park, Eamont Bridge, Penrith, Cumbria, CA10 2JB
Tel: 01768 863631
Email: alan@lowther-holidaypark.co.uk
www.lowther-holidaypark.co.uk
Pitches For ⛺ ⛟ ⛺ **Total** 150
Acreage 10 **Open** 01-Mar **to** 14-Nov
Access Good **Site** Level
Nearest Bus Stop (Miles) Outside
Set in 50 acres of wooded parkland on the banks of the River Lowther. Home of the rare and fascinating Red Squirrel.
Facilities ♿ ⨍ 🖂 🖂 ⊕ ⟶ 🚽 🔌 ⛽ ⟲
🏪 ⊕ ⛽ ✗ ⟶ 🅿 🏤 ⊕ 🅿 ⟶ 🔌 ✓ ⟲
Nearby Facilities ✈ ✓ ≍ ∪ ₽ ⚘
Nearest Town Penrith
Directions On the A6 just south of Penrith in the village of Eamont Bridge.
🚆 Penrith

PENRITH

Park Foot Caravan & Camping Park, Howtown Road, Pooley Bridge, Penrith, Cumbria, CA10 2NA
Tel: 017684 86309
Email: holidays@parkfootullswater.co.uk
www.parkfootullswater.co.uk
Pitches For ⛺ ⛟ ⛺ ⛟ **Total** 332
Acreage 40 **Open** March **to** October
Access Good **Site** Lev/Slope
Nearest Bus Stop (Miles) ½
Family run park beside Lake Ullswater with boat launching access. Licensed bar, restaurant and takeaway. Childrens Club during the summer school holidays and two play areas. Pony trekking, mountain bike hire, tennis and table tennis on site. Own access to the lake where customers can fish using their own equipment.
Facilities ♿ ⨍ 🖂 🖂 ⊕ ⟶ 🚽 🔌 ⛽ ⟲
🏪 ⊕ ⛽ ✗ ⟶ 🅿 🏤 ⊕ 🅿 ⟶ 🔌 ✓ 📶
Nearby Facilities ✈ ✓ ≍ ∪ ₽ ⚘
Nearest Town Pooley Bridge
Directions 5 miles SW of Penrith. Leave M6 at junc 40, then take A66 for Ullswater, next roundabout take A592 then road for Pooley Bridge and 1 mile on Howtown Road to site.
🚆 Penrith

PENRITH

Thacka Lea Caravan Site, Thacka Lea, Penrith, Cumbria, CA11 9HX
Tel: 01768 863319
Pitches For ⛟ ⛺ **Total** 25
Acreage 1 **Open** March **to** October
Access Good **Site** Lev/Slope
Nearest Bus Stop (Miles) ¼
Just a 10 minute walk from the town centre. Good touring.
Facilities ⨍ 🖂 🖂 ⊕ ⟶ 🚽 🔌 ⛽ ⊕ 🅿 ⟶ 🔌
Nearby Facilities ✈
Nearest Town Penrith
Directions From south, turn left off the A6, go past the Esso Station at the north end of town. From north, turn right at the Esso Station.
🚆 Penrith

PENRITH

Troutbeck Head Caravan Club Site, Troutbeck, Penrith, Cumbria, CA11 0SS
Tel: 01768 483521
www.caravanclub.co.uk
Pitches For ⛟ ⛺ **Total** 151
Acreage 25 **Open** March **to** Nov
Access Good **Site** Level
Set in countryside, alongside a brook with fabulous views. Only 4 miles from Ullswater. Ideal for walkers and nature lovers. Rookin House Farm Centre adjacent offering go-karting, quad bikes, archery, horse riding and much more. Non members welcome.

CUMBRIA

Booking essential.
Facilities ♿ ✦ 🚿 🔌 🅿️ 🛒 ▢ ☎
⚡ ⛽ ♨ ♨ 🔥 🅿️ ▢
Nearby Facilities ✦ ✦ ⚓ ✦ ∿ ∪
Nearest Town Penrith
Directions Leave M6 at junc 40 and take
A66 sp Keswick. Go straight on at the
roundabout and after approx. 7 miles turn
left onto A5091. Site is 1¼ miles on the right.
NB: No arrivals before 12 noon.
🚆 Penrith

PENRITH

Waterside House Campsite, Waterside
Farm, Howtown Road, Pooley Bridge,
Penrith, Cumbria, CA10 2NA
Tel: 01768 486332
Email: enquire@watersidefarm-
campsite.co.uk
www.watersidefarm-campsite.co.uk
Pitches For ⛺ ⛟ **Total** 120
Acreage 10 **Open** March **to** October
Site Lev/Slope
Nearest Bus Stop (Miles) 1
Alongside the lake shore of Ullswater with
beautiful views of the lake and fells. Footpath
from the site to the local village. Boat and
bike hire available.
Facilities ♿ ✦ 🚿 🔌 🅿️ ✦ 🛒 ⊿ ▢ ☎
⚡ ⛽ ♨ ✕ 🅿️ ▢ ✦ ⊿
Nearby Facilities ✦ ✦ ⚓ ∿ ∪ ♪
Nearest Town Pooley Bridge/Penrith
Directions Leave the M6 at junction 40 and
take the A66 sp Keswick. After 1 mile turn
left onto the A592 for Ullswater. Turn left by
the lake and go over the bridge, turn first right
along Howtown Road. Waterside House is
the second campsite on the right (approx. 1
🚆 Penrith

RAVENGLASS

**Ravenglass Camping & Caravanning
Club Site,** Ravenglass, Cumbria, CA18
1SR
Tel: 01229 717250
www.campingandcaravanningclub.co.uk/
ravenglass
Pitches For ⛺ ⛟ ⛟ **Total** 66
Acreage 5 **Open** 01-Feb **to** 30-Nov
Access Good **Site** Lev/Slope
Nearest Bus Stop (Miles) Outside
Set in 5 acres of mature woodland, this is a
walkers paradise on Cumbrias Western
Coast, where the Lake District National Park
meets the sea. Non members welcome. You
can also call us on 0845 130 7633.
Facilities ✦ 🔌 🅿️ ✦ 🛒 ⊙ ⊿ 🛒 ▢ ☎
⚡ ⛽ ♨ 🅿️ ▢ 🛒 📶
Nearby Facilities ✦ ✦ ✕
Nearest Town Broughton
Directions From the A595 turn west for
Ravenglass, before village turn left to site.
🚆 Ravenglass

SEDBERGH

Cross Hall Farm Caravan Park, Cross
Hall Farm, Cautley, Sedbergh, Cumbria,
LA10 5LY
Tel: 015396 20668
Email: crosshall@btopenworld.com
www.cautleycaravans.co.uk
Pitches For ⛺ ⛟ ⛟ **Total** 15
Acreage 1½ **Open** April **to** Oct
Access Good **Site** Level
10 pitches available for camping in the
adjoining field. Ideal for touring the Lake
District and the Yorkshire Dales, also for
climbing the Howgill Fells and Cautley Spout.
Facilities ✦ 🔌 🅿️ ✦ ⊙ ♨ 🔥 🅿️ 🅿️
Nearby Facilities ✦ ✦ ∪ ✕
Nearest Town Kendal

Directions Leave the M6 at junction 37 and
travel to Sedbergh. Then take the A683
towards Kirkby Stephen for 2½ miles.
🚆 Oxenholme

SEDBERGH

Yore House Farm Caravan Park, Yore
House Farm, Lunds, Sedbergh, Cumbria,
LA10 5PX
Tel: 01969 667358
Email: j.pedley@btinternet.com
Pitches For ⛺ ⛟ ⛟ **Total** 7
Open Easter **to** End Sept
Access Good **Site** Level
Quiet, farm site beside the River Ure. In sight
of the famous Settle to Carlisle railway.
Facilities 🚿 🛒 ☎
Nearby Facilities ✦
Nearest Town Hawes
Directions On the A684 10 miles from
Sedbergh and 6 miles from Hawes, near the
Moorcock Pub. On the North Yorkshire and
Cumbria border.
🚆 Garsdale

SILLOTH

Hylton Caravan Park, Eden Street, Silloth,
Cumbria, CA7 4AY
Tel: 016973 31707
Email: enquiries@stanwix.com
www.stanwix.com
Pitches For ⛺ ⛟ ⛟ **Total** 90
Acreage 18 **Open** 01-Mar **to** 15-Nov
Access Good **Site** Level
Nearest Bus Stop (Miles) ¼
Convenient for the town centre. 213 holiday
home pitches and 90 camping/touring
pitches with mains service hook-ups. New
luxury amenity block with toilets, bathrooms,
launderette and disabled facilities. Sister park
to Stanwix Park Holiday Centre with lots of
super facilities which are free to Hylton
residents.
Facilities ♿ ✦ 🚿 🔌 🅿️ ✦ ⊙ ⊿ 🛒 ▢ ☎
⚡ ⚡ ⛽ ♨ ✕ ♨ 🍴 🔥 🅿️ 🅿️ ▢
Nearby Facilities ✦ ✦ ⚓ ✕ ♪ ♪
Nearest Town Silloth
Directions This park is off Eden Street.
Entering Silloth on the B5302 follow signs
for ½ a mile.
🚆 Carlisle

SILLOTH

Moordale Park, Blitterlees, Silloth,
Cumbria, CA7 4JZ
Tel: 016973 31375
Email: moordalepark@talktalk.net
Pitches For ⛺ ⛟ ⛟ **Total** 12
Acreage 7 **Open** March **to** October
Access Good **Site** Level
Nearest Bus Stop (Miles) Outside
A quiet, simple and spacious site adjacent
to the beach and a golf course. Convenient
for the Lake District and Scotland.
Facilities ✦ 🚿 🔌 🅿️ ✦ ⊙ ♨ 🛒 ▢ ☎
♨ 🔥 🅿️ ♨ 🛒
Nearby Facilities ✦ ✦ ⚓ ∪ ♪ ✕
Nearest Town Silloth
Directions 1 miles from Silloth on the B5300
coast road to Maryport.
🚆 Wigton

SILLOTH

Seacote Caravan Park, Skinburness
Road, Silloth, Wigton, Cumbria, CA7 4QJ
Tel: 016973 31121/31031
Email: seacote@bfcltd.co.uk
www.seacotecaravanpark.co.uk
Pitches For ⛺ ⛟ ⛟ **Total** 20
Acreage 5½ **Open** 01-Mar **to** 15-Nov
Access Good **Site** Level
Nearest Bus Stop (Miles) Outside

Peace and tranquility, adjacent to Solway.
Central to the Lake District and Scottish
Borders.
Facilities ✦ 🚿 🔌 ✦ ⊙ ⊿ 🛒 ▢ ☎
⚡ ♨ ♨ 🔥 🅿️ ♨ ✕
Nearby Facilities ✦ ✦ ∪ ♪
Nearest Town Carlisle
Directions From Carlisle take the A595, then
the A596 and finally the B5302 to Silloth.
🚆 Carlisle

SILLOTH

Solway Holiday Village, Skinburness
Drive, Silloth, Wigton, Cumbria, CA7 4QQ
Tel: 016973 31236
Email: enquiries@hagansleisure.co.uk
www.hagansleisure.co.uk
Pitches For ⛺ ⛟ ⛟
Open March **to** October
Access Good **Site** Level
Nearest Bus Stop (Miles) ¼
Pet Farm, family clubroom, indoor swimming
pool and golf course on site. Near the beach.
Facilities ✦ 🚿 🔌 🅿️ ✦ ⊙ ⊿ 🛒 ▢ ☎
⚡ ⚡ ⛽ ♨ ✕ ♨ 🍴 ♨ ✕ ✕ 🔥 🅿️ 🅿️ ▢ ♨
Nearby Facilities ✦ ✦ ✕ ∪ ♪ ✕
Nearest Town Silloth
Directions Drive into Silloth, turn right at the
Raffa Club and follow road for ½ mile. Turn
right at signpost for holiday village.
🚆 Wigton

SILLOTH

Stanwix Park Holiday Centre, Silloth
(West), Cumbria, CA7 4HH
Tel: 016973 32666
Email: enquiries@stanwix.com
www.www.stanwix.com
Pitches For ⛺ ⛟ ⛟ **Total** 121
Acreage 18 **Open** All Year
Access Good **Site** Level
Nearest Bus Stop (Miles) Outside
Large holiday centre with full range of
facilities for all the family, indoor and outdoor.
Pool with water chute and sunbeds. Indoor
leisure complex. Open all year except Xmas
Day. See our display advertisment.
Facilities ♿ ✦ 🚿 🔌 🅿️ ✦ ⊙ ⊿ 🛒 ▢ ☎
⚡ ♨ ⚡ ⛽ ♨ ✕ ♨ 🍴 ♨ ✕ ✕ 🔥 🅿️ 🅿️ ▢ ♨
Nearby Facilities ✦ ✦ ⚓ ✕ ♪ ✕
Nearest Town Silloth
Directions Enter Silloth on the B5302, turn
left at sea front, 1 mile to West Silloth on the
B5300. Site is on the right.
🚆 Carlisle

SILLOTH

Tanglewood Caravan Park,
Causewayhead, Silloth, Wigton, Cumbria,
CA7 4PE
Tel: 01697 331253
Email:
tanglewoodcaravanpark@hotmail.com
www.tanglewoodcaravanpark.co.uk
Pitches For ⛺ ⛟ ⛟ **Total** 31
Acreage 7½ **Open** 01-Mar **to** 31-Jan
Access Good **Site** Level
Nearest Bus Stop (Miles) Outside
Enjoy the promenade at Silloth, the sandy
west beach and beautiful sunsets over the
Solway Firth. Excellent golf courses.
Facilities ✦ 🚿 🔌 🅿️ ✦ ⊙ ⊿ 🛒 ▢ ☎
⚡ ♨ 🍴 ♨ ♨ 🔥 🅿️ 🅿️ ✕
Nearby Facilities ✦ ✦ ⚓ ∪ ♪ ♪
Nearest Town Silloth
Directions Take the B5302 from Silloth
towards Wigton for 1¼ miles.
🚆 Aspatria/Wigton

ST. BEES

Seacote Park, St Bees, Cumbria, CA27 0ET
Tel: 01946 822777
Email: reception@seacote.com
www.seacote.com
Pitches For ▲ ⊞ ⊟ ⊟ **Total** 32
Acreage 4 **Open** March to October
Access Good **Site** Level
Nearest Bus Stop (Miles) Entrance
Beside a lovely beach in a historic village. Golf links and walks locally. Hotel adjacent which is owned by the Park.
Facilities ⚷ ⨍ 🌐 🔲 🔁 🐧 ⊙ ⌇ ⌁ 🔲 ☎
℠ ⚹ ✕ ▽ 🔲 🛠 🔁 🔲 ⛅
Nearby Facilities ✝ ✔ ⚐ ✕ ∪ ♪ ♫ ✈
Nearest Town Whitehaven
Directions Leave the A595 near Whitehaven or Egremont and take the B5345 following signs to St Bees, then to the beach.
⇥ St. Bees

TROUTBECK

Troutbeck Camping & Caravanning Club Site, Hutton Moor End, Troutbeck, Penrith, Cumbria, CA11 0SX
Tel: 01768 779615
www.campingandcaravanningclub.co.uk/troutbeck
Pitches For ▲ ⊞ ⊟ **Total** 54
Open 09-Mar to 11-Nov
Access Good **Site** Level
Nearest Bus Stop (Miles) ¼
Superb location in unbeatable walking country with fantastic views. Close to both Keswick and Penrith. 70 main tourist attractions in the district. Non members welcome. You can also call us on 0845 130 7633.
Facilities ⚷ ⨍ 🔲 🐧 ⊙ ⌇ 🔲 ☎
℠ ⊙ 🔁 🛠 🔁 🔲 ☎
Nearby Facilities ✝ ∪

Nearest Town Keswick
Directions Leave the M6 at junction 40 and take the A66 towards Keswick. After 8 miles take a sharp left at signpost Wallthwaite, site is on the left.
⇥ Penrith

ULLSWATER

Cove Caravan & Camping Park, Watermillock, Ullswater, Penrith, Cumbria, CA11 0LS
Tel: 01768 486549
Email: info@cove-park.co.uk
www.cove-park.co.uk
Pitches For ▲ ⊞ ⊟ **Total** 50
Acreage 3 **Open** 15-Mar to 31-Oct
Access Good **Site** Lev/Slope
Small, quiet and peaceful Park, 400 ft above Ullswater. Ideal for touring Ullswater & Helvellyn Range, Keswick and Windermere.
Facilities ⚷ ⨍ 🔲 🐧 ⊙ ⌇ ⌁ 🔲 ☎
🐧 🛠 🔲
Nearby Facilities ✝ ✔ ⚐ ✕ ∪ ✈
Nearest Town Penrith
Directions Leave M6 at junction 40 and take A66 west to Rheged roundabout, take A592 to Ullswater. After approx. 4 miles at the T-Junction by the lake turn right onto the A592. After 2 miles turn right at Brackenrigg Inn, Park is 1½ miles on the left.
⇥ Penrith

ULLSWATER

Sykeside Camping Park, Hartsop, Brotherswater, Patterdale, Cumbria, CA11 0NZ
Tel: 01768 482239
Email: info@sykeside.co.uk
www.sykeside.co.uk
Pitches For ▲ ⊞ ⊟ ⊟ **Total** 80

Acreage 15 **Open** All Year
Access Good **Site** Level/Sloping
Nearest Bus Stop (Miles) Entrance
At the foot of Kirkstone Pass with many walks. ¼ of a mile from Brotherswater for fishing.
Facilities ⨍ 🔲 🔁 🐧 ⊙ ⌇ 🔲 ☎
℠ ⊙ 🔁 ✕ 🔁 🔲 🔲
Nearby Facilities ✝ ✔ ⚐ ✕ ∪ ✈
Nearest Town Ambleside
Directions On the A592 between Windermere and Glennridding (Ullswater).
⇥ Windermere

ULLSWATER

The Quiet Site, Ullswater, Penrith, Cumbria, CA11 0LS
Tel: 07768 727016
Email: info@thequietsite.co.uk
www.thequietsite.co.uk
Pitches For ▲ ⊞ ⊟ **Total** 90
Acreage 10 **Open** All Year
Access Fair **Site** Lev/Slope
Nearest Bus Stop (Miles) 1½
Family site set in the idyllic Ullswater Valley. Ideal for walking. The best campsite bar in Britain!. Excellent showers and family bathrooms. Large play field. Carbon neutral.
Facilities ⚷ ⨍ 🔲 🔁 🐧 ⊙ ⌇ ⌁ 🔲 ☎
℠ ⊙ 🔁 ▽ 🔲 🛠 🔁 🔲 🔲 ☇ ⛅ ✈
Nearby Facilities ✝ ✔ ⚐ ✕ ∪ ♪ ✈
Nearest Town Ullswater
Directions Take A592 from Penrith, turn right at lake and right again at Brackenrigg Hotel follow road for 1½ miles, site on right hand side of road.
⇥ Penrith

CUMBRIA

ULLSWATER

Ullswater Caravan Camping & Marine Park, Watermillock, Penrith, Cumbria, CA11 0LR
Tel: 00176 84 86666
Email: info@uccmp.co.uk
www.ullswatercaravanpark.co.uk
Pitches For ▲ ⊞ ⊞ **Total 155**
Acreage 7 Open March **to** 14-Nov
Access Good **Site** Lev/Slope
Nearest Bus Stop (Miles) ½
Lake District National Park. Scenic views. Boat launching and moorings 1 mile.
Facilities & ♪ 🖪 🗓 ⌕ ↑ ⊙ ⌡ 🔲 🔟 🛒
🈯 💧 ♨ 🛉 ⚓ 🖳 🖪 🖾
Nearby Facilities ⌕ ✓ ⚥ ⚄ ∪ ⚲
Nearest Town Penrith
Directions A592 from Penrith, turn right at lake and right again at telephone kiosk, signposted Watermillock Church.
🚃 Penrith

ULLSWATER

Waterfoot Caravan Park, Pooley Bridge, Penrith, Cumbria, CA11 0JF
Tel: 017684 86302
Email: enquiries@waterfootpark.co.uk
www.waterfootpark.co.uk
Pitches For ⊞ ⊞ **Total 34**
Acreage 22 Open 01-Mar **to** 14-Nov
Access Good **Site** Lev/Slope
Waterfoot Park is located in one of the most beautiful locations within the Lake District National Park. Nestled in the grounds of a Georgian mansion, overlooking Ullswater, the Park is an idyllic location for touring vans, motor homes and privately owned holiday homes. (NB: All holiday homes are privately owned and are not available for hire).
Facilities & ♪ 🖪 🗓 ⌕ ↑ ⊙ ⌡ 🔲 🔟 🛒
🈯 💧 ♨ 🛉 ⚓ 🖳 🖪 🖾 🌫 ♒
Nearby Facilities ⌕ ✓ ⚥ ⚄ ∪ ♒ ⚲
Nearest Town Penrith
Directions Leave the M6 at junction 40 and take the A66 for approx. 1 mile. Then take the A592 and Waterfoot can be found on the right hand side. Do not leave the A592 until the Park entrance. NB: SatNav is not compatible in this area.
🚃 Penrith

ULVERSTON

Bardsea Leisure, Priory Road, Ulverston, Cumbria, LA12 9QE
Tel: 01229 584712
Email: reception@bardsealeisure.co.uk
www.bardsealeisure.co.uk
Pitches For ⊞ ⊞ ⊞ **Total 84**
Acreage 10 Open All Year
Access Good **Site** Lev/Slope
Nearest Bus Stop (Miles) ¼
Ideal for touring.

Facilities & ♪ 🖪 🗓 ⌕ ↑ ⊙ ⌡ 🔲 🔟 🛒
🈯 💧 ♨ 🛉 ✕ 🖍 ♨ 🖪 🖾 ✓ 🌬
Nearby Facilities ⌕ ✓ ⚥ ∪ ♒
Nearest Town Ulverston
Directions Leave the M6 at junction 36 and take the A590 then the A5087.
🚃 Ulverston

ULVERSTON

Crake Valley Holiday Park, Water Yeat, Blawith, Nr Ulverston, Cumbria, LA12 8DL
Tel: 01229 885203
Email: crakevalley@coniston1.fslife.co.uk
www.crakevalley.co.uk
Pitches For ▲ **Total 6**
Acreage ¼ **Open** May to Sept **Site** Level
Nearest Bus Stop (Miles) ½
Opposite Coniston Water. Ideal base for touring the Lakes.
Facilities 🗓 ⌕ ↑ ⌡ 🔲 🔟 🛒 🛉
Nearby Facilities ⌕ ✓ ⚥ ⚄ ∪ ♒
Nearest Town Ulverston
Directions Take the A590 Barrow road, turn right at Greenodd onto the A5092. Within 2 miles fork right for Coniston onto the A5084, the Park is 3 miles along on the left hand side.
🚃 Ulverston

WASDALE

Church Stile Farm Holiday Park, Church Stile Farm, Wasdale, Seascale, Cumbria, CA20 1ET
Tel: 01946 726252
Email: church-.knight@btconnect.com
www.churchstile.com
Pitches For ▲ ⊞ **Total 50**
Open 01-Apr **to** 31-Oct
Site Level
River, lake and beach. Great for fell walking and climbing. Ideal for West Water Lake, Great Gable, Muncaster Castle, La Ratty Railway, Whitehaven Harbour and many other visitor attractions.
Facilities & ♪ 🗓 ⌕ ↑ ⊙ ⌡ 🔲 🔟 🛒
🖪 ✕ 🖾
Nearby Facilities ⌕ ✓ ⚥ ∪ ⚲
Nearest Town Egremont
Directions From Gosforth take the A595 and follow signs for Wasdale (approx. 4 miles). Turn left, up the hill, go past the hotel on the left into the village, turn first left past the church.
🚃 Seascale

WASDALE

Wasdale National Trust Campsite, Seascale, Cumbria, CA20 1EX
Tel: 015394 63862
Email: campsite.bookings@nationaltrust.org.uk
www.ntlakescampsites.org.uk

Pitches For ▲ ⊞ **Total 120**
Open All Year
Site Lev/Slope
Spectacular mountain location, remote and peaceful. Just a short distance from Wastwater. Perfect base for walking the high fells.
Facilities & ♪ 🗓 ⌕ ↑ ⊙ ⌡ 🔲 🔟 🛒
🈯 💧 ♨ 🛉
Nearby Facilities ✓ ⚲
Nearest Town Gosforth
Directions From the North on the A595, turn left at Gosforth, site is approx 8 miles.
🚃 Drigg

WATERMILLOCK

Knotts Hill Caravan Park, Watermillock, Penrith, Cumbria, CA11 0JR
Tel: 017684 86309
Email: holidays@parkfootullswater.co.uk
www.knottshill.co.uk
Pitches For ⊞ ⊞ **Total 6**
Acreage 2 Open 01-Mar **to** 15-Nov
Access Good **Site** Sloping
Nearest Bus Stop (Miles) ½
Peaceful location with lovely views of Lake Ullswater. Use of facilities at nearby Park Foot Caravan Park.
Facilities & ♪ 🗓 ⌕ ↑ ⊙ 🔲 🛒 🖪 🖾
Nearby Facilities ⌕ ✓ ⚥ ⚄ ∪ ♒
Nearest Town Penrith
Directions Leave the M6 at junction 40 and take the A66 towards Keswick. At the roundabout take the A592 for Ullswater, at the T-Junction turn right for Glenridding. After 3 miles turn right for Watermillock and the Park is ½ a mile on the right.
🚃 Penrith

WINDERMERE

Braithwaite Fold Caravan Club Site, Glebe Road, Bowness-on-Windermere, Windermere, Cumbria, LA23 3HB
Tel: 01539 442177
www.caravanclub.co.uk
Pitches For ⊞ ⊞ **Total 66**
Acreage 4 Open March **to** Nov
Access Good **Site** Level
Close to the shores of Lake Windermere (with sailing centre) and within walking distance of the town. Not suitable for very large awnings. Non members welcome. Booking essential.
Facilities & ♪ 🗓 ⌕ ↑ ⊙ 🔲 🛒 🖪 🖾
Nearby Facilities ⌕ ✓ ⚥ ⚄
Nearest Town Windermere
Directions Leave M6 at jct 36 and the A590. After 3¼ miles continue onto A591 to Windermere. In Windermere DO NOT turn first or second left into town, continue to the roundabout and turn left onto A592. Follow signs for Bowness Bay, immediately past the pier turn right into Glebe Road, site is on right.
🚃 Windermere

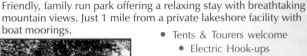

WINDERMERE
Camping & Caravanning Club Site,
Ashes Lane, Staveley, Kendal, Cumbria,
LA8 9JS
Tel: 01539 821119
www.campingandcaravanningclub.co.uk/
windermere
Pitches For Å ⚏ ⚏ **Total** 250
Acreage 24 **Open** 14-Mar **to** 14-Jan
Access Good **Site** Level
Nearest Bus Stop (Miles) 1
Ideal for touring the Lake District. ETB 5 Star
Graded, AA 4 Pennants and David Bellamy
Gold Award for Conservation. Non members
welcome. You can also call us on 0845 130
7633.
Facilities ⚅ ✦ 🏠 ⚌ ⚌ ⌐ ⊙ ⚘ ⚌ ◫ ☎
⚌ ⊘ ✗ ⚑ ⚏ ⚌ ⊡ ⚘ ⚞
Nearby Facilities ⌐ ⚌ ∪
Nearest Town Staveley
Directions From Kendal take the A591
towards Windermere for 1½ miles, follow
signposts.
⚏ Kendal

WINDERMERE
Fallbarrow Park, Rayrigg Road,
Windermere, Cumbria, LA23 3DL
Tel: 01539 569835
Email:
enquiries@southlakelandparks.co.uk
www.fallbarrow.co.uk
Pitches For ⚏ ⚏ **Total** 38
Acreage 32 **Open** March **to** 14-Nov
Access Good **Site** Level
Nearest Bus Stop (Miles) Outside
Set amidst wooded parkland on the shore of
Lake Windermere. Extensive shore with boat
launching facilities. 5 minutes walk from
Bowness. Luxury holiday caravans for hire.
Facilities ⚅ ✦ 🏠 ⚌ ⚌ ⌐ ⊙ ⚌ ⚌ ◫ ☎
⚌ ⊘ ✗ ⚑ ⚌ ⚌ ⚌ ⊡ ⚌
Nearby Facilities ⌐ ⚌ ↥ ⚘ ∪ ⚘ ⚘
Nearest Town Windermere
Directions Leave the M6 at junction 36 and
follow the A591 to Winderemere until you
reach the town centre. Turn left following
signs for Bowness. At Bowness turn right at
the mini roundabout signposted Keswick &
Steamboat Museum, Park is 300 yards on
the left.
⚏ Windermere

WINDERMERE
Hill of Oaks Caravan Estate,
Windermere, Cumbria, LA12 8NR
Tel: 015395 31578
Email: enquiries@hillofoaks.co.uk
www.hillofoaks.co.uk
Pitches For ⚏ ⚏ **Total** 43
Acreage 31 **Open** 01-Mar **to** 14-Nov
Access Good **Site** Lev/Slope

Nearest Bus Stop (Miles) Outside
Nestling on the slopes of ancient woodland,
Hill of Oaks offers exclusive lake frontage
for more than one kilometre along the shore
of Lake Windermere. The Park is family
orientated, with well laid out nature walks
where intrepid explorers can seek out the
wildlife. There is also a natural secure play
area for our younger visitors. The park
welcomes touring caravans and
motorhomes, as well as offering exclusive
sites for holiday homes and lodges.
Facilities ⚅ ✦ 🏠 ⚌ ⌐ ⊙ ⚌ ⚌ ◫ ⚌
⚌ ⊘ ⚌ ⚑ ⚌ ⚌ ◫ ⚌ ⚌ ⚞
Nearby Facilities ⌐ ⚌ ↥ ⚌ ∪ ⚘ ⚘
Nearest Town Windermere
Directions Leave the M6 at junction 36 and
take the A590 to Newby Bridge. Turn right
onto the A592 and the site is 3 miles on the
left hand side.
⚏ Windermere

WINDERMERE
Park Cliffe Camping & Caravan Estate,
Birks Road, Tower Wood, Windermere,
Cumbria, LA23 3PG
Tel: 015395 31344
Email: info@parkcliffe.co.uk
www.parkcliffe.co.uk
Pitches For Å ⚏ ⚏ **Total** 170
Acreage 25 **Open** 01-Mar **to** Mid Nov
Access Good **Site** Lev/Slope
Nearest Bus Stop (Miles) ¼
Near to Lake Windermere with outstanding
views of lakes and mountains, ideal touring.
AA 5 Pennants, Cumbria Tourism Winner
2011, AA Northwest Campsite of the Year
2009 and England for Excellence Silver
Winner 2009.
Facilities ⚅ ✦ 🏠 ⚌ ⚌ ⌐ ⊙ ⚌ ⚌ ◫ ⚌
⚌ ⊘ ⚌ ✗ ⚑ ⚑ ⚌ ◫ ⚌
Nearby Facilities ⌐ ⚌ ↥ ⚌ ∪ ⚘ ⚘ ⚘
Nearest Town Windermere
Directions M6 junction 36, A590 to Newby
Bridge. Turn right onto A592, in 3½ miles turn
right into Birks Road. Park is roughly ½ mile
on the right.
⚏ Windermere

DERBYSHIRE
ASHBOURNE
**Ashbourne Camping & Caravanning
Club Site,** Belper Road (A517), Bradley,
Near Ashbourne, Derbyshire, DE6 3EN
Tel: 01335 370855
www.campingandcaravanning.co.uk/
ashbourne
Pitches For Å ⚏ ⚏ **Total** 50
Open 19-Mar **to** 11-Nov
Access Good **Site** Level
Nearest Bus Stop (Miles) Outside
Ideal for exploring the Derbyshire Peaks and
Dales. Also Open 9th-26th February 2012.
Non members welcome. You can also call
us on 0845 130 7633.
Facilities ⚅ ✦ 🏠 ⚌ ⚌ ⌐ ⊙ ⚌ ⚌ ☎
⚌ ⚌ ⚌ ⊡ ⚌
Nearby Facilities ⚌
Nearest Town Ashbourne
Directions From Ashbourne take the A517
Belper road, pass Bradley and site is
signposted ½ a mile on the right.
⚏ Belper

ASHBOURNE
Bank Top Caravan & Camping, Bank Top
Farm, Fenny Bentley, Ashbourne,
Derbyshire, DE6 1LF
Tel: 01335 350250
Pitches For Å ⚏ ⚏ **Total** 51
Acreage 3 **Open** April **to** 01-Oct
Access Good **Site** Lev/Slope
Nearest Bus Stop (Miles) ¼
Working farm with scenic views from the site.
Ideal for touring Dovedale and other Dales,
also pretty little villages.
Facilities ✦ ◫ ⌐ ⊙ ⚌ ⚌ ⚌ ⚌ ◫ ⚌ ⚞
Nearby Facilities ⌐ ⚌ ↥ ⚌ ∪ ⚘ ⚘ ⚘
Nearest Town Ashbourne
Directions From Ashbourne take the A515
north, then take the B5056 and the site is
200 yards on the right.
⚏ Derby

ASHBOURNE
Blackwall Plantation Caravan Club Site,
Kirk Ireton, Ashbourne, Derbyshire, DE6 3JL
Tel: 01335 370903
www.caravanclub.co.uk
Pitches For ⚏ ⚏ **Total** 130
Acreage 25 **Open** March **to** Nov
Access Good **Site** Level
Set in a beautifully landscaped pine
plantation. Adjacent to Carsington Reservoir
for fishing and sailing. BBQs allowed with
wardens permission. Non members
welcome. Booking essential.
Facilities ⚅ ✦ 🏠 ⚌ ⌐ ⊙ ☎
⚌ ⊘ ⚌ ⊡ ⚌

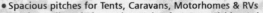

Nearest Town Ashbourne
Directions Take the A517 from Ashbourne, turn left after 4½ miles at signpost Carsington Water, after ¾ miles at crossroads turn right, site is 1 mile on the right.
⇌ Ashbourne

ASHBOURNE
Callow Top Holiday Park, Buxton Road, Ashbourne, Derbyshire, DE6 2AQ
Tel: 01335 344020
Email: enquiries@callowtop.co.uk
www.callowtop.co.uk
Pitches For Å ⊞ ⊟
Acreage 15 **Open** Easter to November
Access Good **Site** Level
Nearest Bus Stop (Miles) ½
Alton Towers only 20 minutes away, Tissington Trail cycle path is adjacent, Carsington Reservoir 5 miles. Many footpaths. Secure Storage for Winter.
Facilities ⚹ ⌀ ⊞ ⊞ ⌐ ⌐ ⊙ ⊿ ⊡ ⊠ ⊟
⊞ ⊙ ⊗ ✕ ⊻ ♠ ⊼ ⊻ ⊗ ⊭ ⊡ ⊡ ⊿ ⊁ ⊶
Nearby Facilities ⌐ ⊿ ⊥ ⊾ ∪ ⊿ ₽
Nearest Town Ashbourne
Directions The access to Callow Top is only ¼ mile from Ashbourne on the A515 Buxton road. The entrance is directly opposite Sandybrook Garage, follow the private road for ½ mile to the end.
⇌ Derby

ASHBOURNE
Newton Grange Caravan Site, Newton Grange, Ashbourne, Derbyshire, DE6 1NJ
Tel: 01335 310214
Pitches For Å ⊞ ⊟ **Total** 15
Acreage 1 **Open** Mid March **to** End Oct
Access Good **Site** Level
Nearest Bus Stop (Miles) ½
Close to Buxton, Matlock and Alton Towers. Tissington Trail adjacent for cycling and walking. Ideal touring.
Facilities ⚹ ⌐ ⊙ ⊭ ⊡
Nearby Facilities ⊿ ⊥ ∪
Nearest Town Ashbourne
Directions On the A515 4½ miles north of Ashbourne.
⇌ Derby

ASHBOURNE
Peak Gateway Ltd., Moor Lane, Osmaston, Ashbourne, Derbyshire, DE6 1NA
Tel: 01335 344643
Email: info@peakgateway.com
www.peakgateway.com
Pitches For Å ⊞ ⊟ **Total** 150
Open 22-Jan **to** 14-Dec
Access Good **Site** Level
Nearest Bus Stop (Miles) Outside

On the door step of the market town of Ashbourne. Ideal for walking in the Peak District. Only a 20 minute drive to Alton Towers.
Facilities ⚹ ⌐ ⊞ ⊞ ⌐ ⊙ ⊿ ⊡
⊞ ⊙ ✕ ⊿ ♠ ⊼ ⊻ ⊭ ⊡ ⊡ ⊿ ⊶ ⊾
Nearby Facilities ⌐ ⊿ ⊥ ⊾ ∪ ⊁
Nearest Town Ashbourne
Directions From Derby take the A52 to Ashbourne, turn left at second sign for Osmaston, site entrance is 100 yards on the right.
⇌ Derby

ASHBOURNE
Rivendale Caravan & Leisure Park, Buxton Road, Alsop-en-le-Dale, Ashbourne, Derbyshire, DE6 1QU
Tel: 01335 310311
Email: cades@rivendalecaravanpark.co.uk
www.rivendalecaravanpark.co.uk
Pitches For Å ⊞ ⊟ **Total** 80
Acreage 35 **Open** Feb **to** Jan
Access Good **Site** Level
Nearest Bus Stop (Miles) ¼
Surrounded by scenic countryside, ideal for walking, cycling and outdoor hobbies. Convenient for Chatsworth, Alton Towers and many other attractions. Yurts and Camping Pods for glamping! Holiday caravans/lodges for hire and luxurious B&B rooms.
Facilities ⚹ ⌐ ⊟ ⊞ ⊞ ⌐ ⊙ ⊿ ⊡ ⊠ ⊟
⊞ ⌐ ⊙ ⊗ ✕ ⊻ ⊞ ♠ ⊼ ⊻ ⊭ ⊡ ⊡ ⊿ ⊶
Nearby Facilities ⌐ ⊿ ⊥ ⊾ ∪ ⊁
Nearest Town Hartington
Directions 6½ miles north of Ashbourne, directly accessed from the A515.
⇌ Buxton

BAKEWELL
Camping & Caravanning Club Site, c/o Hopping Farm, Youlgreave, Bakewell, Derbyshire, DE45 1NA
Tel: 01629 636555
www.campingandcaravanningclub.co.uk/bakewell
Pitches For Å ⊞ ⊟ **Total** 100
Acreage 14 **Open** 29-Mar **to** 05-Nov
Site Sloping
Nearest Bus Stop (Miles) 1
Ideally situated for the Peak District. Near to Haddon Hall and Chatsworth House. BTB 3 Star Graded and AA 1 Pennant. Non members welcome. You can also call us on 0845 130 7633.
Facilities ⚹ ⌐ ⊞ ⊟ ⌀⊠ ⊙ ⊠ ⊙ ⊼ ⊭ ⊶
⊾ ⊚
Nearby Facilities ⌐ ⊿ ∪ ₽
Directions Take the A6 Bakewell to Matlock road, turn onto the B5056 Ashbourne road. After ½ mile take the right hand branch to Youlgreave, turn sharp left after the church into Bradford Lane opposite The George

Hotel. Continue ½ mile to club sign then turn right
⇌ Matlock

BAKEWELL
Chatsworth Park Caravan Club Site, Chatsworth, Bakewell, Derbyshire, DE45 1PN
Tel: 01246 582226
www.caravanclub.co.uk
Pitches For ⊞ ⊟ **Total** 120
Acreage 6½ **Open** All Year
Access Good **Site** Level
Nearest Bus Stop (Miles) ½
Situated in the old walled garden on the Chatsworth Estate with beautiful countryside views. Visit Chatsworth House, 1000 acre park and farm. Non members welcome. Booking essential.
Facilities ⚹ ⌐ ⊞ ⊞ ⌐ ⊙ ⊠ ⊟
⌀⊠ ⊙ ⊠ ⊙ ⊭
Nearby Facilities ⌐ ⊿
Nearest Town Bakewell
Directions From Bakewell take the A619 after 3¾ miles (on the outskirts of Baslow at the mini roundabout turn right signposted Sheffield. Site is 150 yards on the right.
⇌ Bakewell

BAKEWELL
Greenhills Holiday Park, Crowhill Lane, Bakewell, Derbyshire, DE45 1PX
Tel: 01629 813052/813467
Email: info@greenhillsholidaypark.co.uk
www.greenhillsholidaypark.co.uk
Pitches For Å ⊞ ⊟ **Total** 233
Acreage 8 **Open** March **to** Oct
Access Good **Site** Lev/Slope
Nearest Bus Stop (Miles) ¼
In the heart of the Peak District. Close to Chatsworth House and Haddon Hall.
Facilities ⚹ ⌐ ⊞ ⊞ ⌐ ⊙ ⊿ ⊡ ⊠ ⊟
⌀⊠ ⌐ ⊙ ⊗ ✕ ⊻ ⊞ ♠ ⊼ ⊻ ⊭ ⊡ ⊡ ⊿ ⊶ ⊚
Nearby Facilities ⌐ ⊿ ∪ ⊁
Nearest Town Bakewell
Directions 1 mile north west of Bakewell turn left into Crow Hill Lane, turn first right over the cattle grid.
⇌ Matlock

BAKEWELL
Haddon Grove Farm, Bakewell, Derbyshire, DE45 1JF
Tel: 01629 812343
Pitches For Å ⊞ ⊟
Acreage 3 **Open** March **to** Oct
Access Good **Site** Level
Nearest Bus Stop (Miles) ½
Close to Lathkil Dale.
Facilities ⚹ ⌐ ⊞ ⌐ ⊙ ⊿ ⊡ ⊟ ⊙ ⊭ ⊡
Nearby Facilities ⊿ ∪

Nearest Town Bakewell
Directions From Bakewell take the B5055 towards Monyash. Travel for 3 miles then turn left into lane sp Haddon Grove.
⇌ Buxton

BAKEWELL

Stocking Farm Caravan & Camp Site, Stocking Farm, Calver Bridge, Calver, Hope Valley, Derbyshire, S32 3XA
Hope Valley 630516
Pitches For ▲ ⊞ ⊟ **Total** 10
Acreage 1½ **Open** April **to** October
Access Good **Site** Level
Scenic views, idea touring. Married couples and families only. Dogs must be kept on a lead. Booking is essential.
Facilities ⚹ 🏴 🕈 ⊟ 🕈 ⌕ 🖳
Nearby Facilities ∪ ⚹
Nearest Town Bakewell
Directions Out of Bakewell on the A619 fork left onto the B6001 to traffic lights. Turn right then first left, after Derbyshire Craft Centre first left again.
⇌ Grindleford

BAMFORD

Swallowholme Camping & Caravan Park, Station Road, Bamford, Hope Valley, Derbyshire, S33 0BN
Tel: 01433 650981
Email:
swallowholmecamping@btconnect.com
www.swallowholmecampingandcaravanpark.co.uk
Pitches For ▲ ⊞ ⊟ **Total** 65
Acreage 3½ **Open** March **to** Oct
Access Good **Site** Level
Nearest Bus Stop (Miles) Outside
Alongside the River Derwent and close to Derwent Dam. 5 minutes from Hathersage. Outdoor swimming pool nearby. Ideal for walking.
Facilities 🕈 ⊞🖳🕈 ⌕ ⊡ 🛒 🖳 🝙 🖍 ⚹
Nearby Facilities 🏴 🖍 ∪ ⚹
Nearest Town Buxton/Bakewell
Directions On the A6013 on the edge of Bamford Village. 12 miles west of Sheffield off the A525.
⇌ Bamford

BRADWELL

Eden Tree Caravan Park, Eccles Lane, Bradwell, Hope Valley, Derbyshire, S33 9JT
Tel: 01433 623444
Email: edentreecaravanpark@fsmail.net
www.edentreecaravanpark.co.uk
Pitches For ▲ ⊞ ⊟ **Total** 20
Open March **to** October
Access Good **Site** Sloping
Nearest Bus Stop (Miles) ¼
In the heart of the Peak District National Park. Close to Chatsworth House, Castleton, Buxton and many other attractions.
Facilities 🕈 ⊞🖳🕈 ⌕ ⊡ 🝙 🖳 ⊞ 🛒 ⚹
Nearby Facilities 🏴 🖍 ⚲ ∪ ⚹
Nearest Town Bakewell
Directions On the outskirts of the village of Bradwell, 10 miles from Bakewell.
⇌ Hope

BUXTON

Beech Croft Farm, Blackwell in the Peak, Nr Buxton, Derbyshire, SK17 9TQ
Tel: 01298 85330
Email: mail@beechcroftfarm.net
www.beechcroftfarm.net
Pitches For ▲ ⊞ ⊟ **Total** 30
Acreage 3 **Open** All Year
Access Good **Site** Level
Nearest Bus Stop (Miles) ¼

In the centre of a National Park, ideal for walking and touring. Hardstandings have 16 amp hook-up, water tap and TV aerial socket. Hotel and restaurant in 1 mile.
Facilities ⚹⚹🕈 ⊞🖳🕈 ⌕ ⊡ 🛒 ⊡ 🖳
🝙 ⊡ 🛒 ⊞ ⊡ 🛜
Nearby Facilities 🏴 🖍 ∪ ⚲ ⚹
Nearest Town Buxton
Directions Turn off the A6 midway between Buxton and Bakewell, signposted.
⇌ Buxton

BUXTON

Endon Cottage, Hulme End, Buxton, Derbyshire, SK17 0HG
Tel: 01298 84617
Pitches For ▲ ⊞ ⊟ **Total** 30
Acreage 2 **Open** All Year
Access Good **Site** Sloping
Ideal for walking and touring.
Facilities ⊞🖳 🛒 🖳 🝙 🖍
Nearby Facilities
Nearest Town Leek/Buxton
Directions From the main A roads take the B5054 into Hulme End and follow Beresford Lane signs. 10 miles from Leek, Buxton and Ashbourne.
⇌ Buxton

BUXTON

Grin Low Caravan Club Site, Grin Low Road, Ladmanlow, Buxton, Derbyshire, SK17 6UJ
Tel: 01298 77735
www.caravanclub.co.uk
Pitches For ▲ ⊞ ⊟ **Total** 117
Acreage 16 **Open** March **to** Nov
Access Good **Site** Level
Situated in the Peak District National Park. Ideal for walking and cycling. Near to many historic houses. No late night arrivals. Non members welcome. Booking essential.
Facilities ⚹ 🕈 ⊞🖳🕈 ⌕ ⊡ 🖳
🝙 ⊡ 🛒 🛆 🕈⊞ 🛜
Nearby Facilities 🏴
Nearest Town Buxton
Directions From Buxton take the A53 Leek road, after 1½ miles turn left signposted Grin Low. After 300 yards turn left into site road, entrance is ¼ mile.
⇌ Buxton

BUXTON

Newhaven Caravan & Camping Park, Newhaven, Nr Buxton, Derbyshire, SK17 0DT
Tel: 01298 84300
Email:
newhavencaravanpark@btconnect.com
www.newhavencaravanpark.co.uk
Pitches For ▲ ⊞ ⊟ **Total** 125
Acreage 2 **Open** March **to** October
Access Good **Site** Lev/Slope
Ideal centre for touring Peak District, National Park and Derbyshire Dales. Cafe/restaurant opposite site.
Facilities 🕈 ⊞🖳🕈 ⌕ ⊡ 🛒 🖳 🝙
🝙 ⊡ 🛒 🛆 🕈⊞ ⊡ 🖳 🛜
Nearby Facilities 🏴 🖍 🛆 ∪ ⚹
Nearest Town Buxton
Directions Midway between Ashbourne and Buxton on A515. At the junction with A5012.
⇌ Buxton

BUXTON

Pomeroy Caravan & Camping Park, Street House Farm, Pomeroy, Nr Flagg, Buxton, Derbyshire, SK17 9QG
Tel: 01298 83259
Pitches For ▲ ⊞ ⊟ **Total** 30
Acreage 2 **Open** April **to** October
Access Good **Site** Level

Nearest Bus Stop (Miles) 1
Peaceful site adjoining the High Peak Trail. Tarmac road to all pitches. Separate site for campers. 16 miles north of Ashbourne. You can also call us on Mobile: 07980 585545.
Facilities 🕈 ⊞🖳🕈 ⌕ ⊡ 🛒 🖳 🝙
⊡ 🛒⊞ 🖳
Nearby Facilities ∪ ⚹
Nearest Town Buxton
Directions 5 miles south of Buxton on the A515, site is on the right opposite corner sign. Go over the cattle grid and up a 200 yard tarmac drive to the site.
⇌ Buxton

CASTLETON

Losehill Caravan Club Site, Castleton, Hope Valley, Derbyshire, S33 8WB
Tel: 01433 620636
www.caravanclub.co.uk
Pitches For ▲ ⊞ ⊟ **Total** 93
Acreage 6½ **Open** All Year
Access Good **Site** Level
Nearest Bus Stop (Miles) ½
Set in the heart of the Peak National Park with panoramic views. Ideal for outdoor activities such as walking, cycling, potholing, etc.. ½ mile from Peveril Castle. Non members welcome. Booking essential.
Facilities ⚹ 🕈 ⊞🖳🕈 ⌕ ⊡ 🖳
🝙 ⊡ 🛒🕈⊞ ⊡ 🖳
Nearby Facilities 🏴 🖍 ∪ ⚹
Directions From South on the M1, leave at junction 29 and take the A617. In Chesterfield turn onto the A619, after 8¾ miles in Baslow turn right at mini roundabout onto the A623. In Calver turn right onto the B6001, in Grindleford turn left at signpost Hathersage (still on the B6001). After 2½ miles turn left onto the A6187, site is 5 miles on the right.

CASTLETON

Rowter Farm, Castleton, Hope Valley, Derbyshire, S33 8WA
Tel: 01433 620271
www.peakdistrictsnationalpark.com
Pitches For ▲ ⊞ ⊟ **Total** 30
Acreage 4 **Open** End March **to** End Oct
Access Good **Site** Level
One static caravan available for hire.
Facilities ⊞🖳🕈 ⌕ 🛒⊞ ⊡
Nearby Facilities ∪ ⚹
Nearest Town Castleton
Directions From Castleton take the B6061 Winnats Pass road, go to the top and continue for 200 yards, turn left through the gate.
⇌ Hope

DERBY

Beechwood Park, Main Road, Elvaston, Thulston, Derby, Derbyshire, DE72 3EQ
Tel: 01332 751938
Email: colinbeech@btconnect.com
www.beechwoodparkleisure.co.uk
Pitches For ▲ ⊞ ⊟ **Total** 200
Acreage 25 **Open** All Year
Access Good **Site** Level
Nearest Bus Stop (Miles) ½
On the edge of the Peak District with fishing lakes and a childrens go-karting track. Opposite Elvaston Castle & Country Park. Cafe and tackle shop on site. Pub in the village.
Facilities ⚹ 🕈 ⊞🖳🕈 ⌕ ⊡ 🛒 ⊡ 🖳
🝙 ⊡ 🛒⊞ ⊡ 🖳 🛜
Nearby Facilities 🏴 🖍 🛆 ∪ ⚲ ⚹
Nearest Town Derby
Directions From Derby take the A6 towards Loughborough and turn left onto the B5010. Beechwood Park is 1 mile on the right hand side.
⇌ Derby

CAMPING ★ CARAVANNING ★ LOG CABINS ★ FISHING ★ KARTING

Beechwood Park
01332 751938
www.beechwoodparkleisure.co.uk
MAIN ROAD, ELVASTON, THULSTON, DERBYS DE72 3EQ

Come for a weekend break or extended holiday at our peaceful Leisure Complex on the edge of the Peak District. 6 lakes offering fantastic mixed coarse fishing for all ages, plus Children's Go Karting. Full on-site facilities. Opposite Elvaston Castle & Gardens.

DERBY

Shardlow Marina Caravan Park, London Road, Shardlow, Nr Derby, Derbyshire, DE72 2GL
Tel: 01332 792832
Pitches For Å ⊕ ⊕ **Total** 40
Open March **to** Jan
Access Good **Site** Level
Near a river and canal.
Facilities ƒ ⓌⒽⲓ⌂◡⌐⌂☎
☂⛆🗙⊟♨
Nearby Facilities ⌐ ✔
Nearest Town Derby
Directions Junction 1 of A6/A50 Derby southern bypass. 5 miles from Derby.
⛟ Derby

DOVERIDGE

Cavendish Caravan Site, 1 Old Marston Lane, Doveridge, Ashbourne, Derbyshire, DE6 5JS
Tel: 01889 563487
Pitches For Å ⊕ ⊕ **Total** 15
Acreage 3 **Open** All Year
Access Good **Site** Level
Nearest Bus Stop (Miles) Entrance
Ideal for Alton Towers, Dovedale, Sudbury Hall and many pleasant walks.
Facilities ƒ Ⓦ☎☂🗙
Nearby Facilities ⌐
Nearest Town Uttoxeter
Directions 2 miles esst of Uttoxeter on the A50.
⛟ Uttoxeter

EDALE

Cooper's Camp & Caravan Site, Newfold Farm, Edale, Hope Valley, Derbyshire, S33 7ZD
Tel: 01433 670372
Pitches For Å ⊕ ⊕ **Total** 146
Acreage 10 **Open** All Year
Access Good **Site** Sloping
On the start of the Pennine Way. Closed Christmas Day & Boxing Day.
Facilities ƒ Ⓦⲓ⌐◡⌐☂☎🗙⊟✔☂
Nearby Facilities ⌐ ✔ ☂
Nearest Town Buxton
⛟ Edale

EDALE

Fieldhead Campsite, Edale, Hope Valley, Derbyshire, S33 7ZA
Tel: 01433 670386
Email: bookings@fieldhead-campsite.co.uk
www.fieldhead-campsite.co.uk
Pitches For Å
Acreage 3 **Open** All Year
Site Level
Alongside a river, next to Peak District Visitor Centre. 6 fields, 2 of which are by the river. All superb views of Mamtor Ridge and Kinder Scout. At the start of Pennine Way.
Facilities ♿Ⓦⲓ⌐◡⌐⌂🗙
Nearby Facilities ⌐ ✔ ⚓⚲☂⛆♨☂
Nearest Town Castleton
Directions 4½ miles from Castleton.
⛟ Edale

EDALE

Highfield Farm, Upper Booth, Edale, Hope Valley, Derbyshire, S33 7ZJ
Tel: 01433 670245
Pitches For Å ⊕ ⊕
Acreage 10 **Open** Easter **to** October
Access Good **Site** Sloping
Good walking country, near the start of Pennine Way.
Facilities Ⓦⲓ⟊⊟
Nearby Facilities ☂
Nearest Town Buxton
Directions Turn right off the A6187 opposite Hope Church, take minor road to Edale. Follow the road up the valley, pass the turning for Edale Village, at bottom of the hill turn right, go past the viaduct and pass picnic area, round the corner and the house is up ahead.
⛟ Edale

EDALE

Waterside Campsite, Waterside Farm, Barber Booth Road, Edale, Hope Valley, Derbyshire, S33 7ZL
Tel: 01433 670215
Pitches For Å ⊕ ⊕
Open Easter **to** Sept
Access Good **Site** Level
Near to the Pennine Way, Blue John Caverns, Chatsworth House (18 miles) and Bakewell.
Facilities Ⓦⲓ⟊⌐◡⌐☎☂⟊🗙⊟
Nearby Facilities ⛵
Nearest Town Edale
⛟ Edale

ELVASTON

Elvaston Castle Caravan Club Site, Borrowash Road, Elvaston, Derbyshire, DE72 3EP
Tel: 01332 573735
www.caravanclub.co.uk
Pitches For Å ⊕ ⊕ **Total** 44
Acreage 3 **Open** March **to** Nov
Access Good **Site** Level
Set in a 280 acre country park which has a castle with museum and provides play facilities, horse riding and lovely walks. Within easy reach of Nottingham. No arrivals after 8pm as park gates are locked. Non members welcome. Booking essential.
Facilities ƒ Ⓦⲓ⌐◡⌐⌂⟊☎☂🗙⊟
Nearby Facilities ⌐ ✔ ⛵
Nearest Town Derby
Directions From north on the M1 leave at junction 24A onto the A50, at junction 2 leave via slip road signposted Alvaston. At roundabout turn right onto the B5010, continue left on the B5010, after 1 mile turn left into Elvaston Castle Country Park, site is on the left before the car park kiosk.
⛟ Derby

GLOSSOP

Crowden Camping & Caravanning Club Site, Crowden, Glossop, Derbyshire, SK13 1HZ
Tel: 01457 866057
www.campingandcaravanning.co.uk/crowden
Pitches For Å ⊕ ⊕ **Total** 45

Acreage 2½ **Open** 29-Mar **to** 05-Nov
Site Level
Nearest Bus Stop (Miles) 100 metres
In the heart of the Peak District National Park, close to the Pennine Way. BTB 3 Star Graded and AA 2 Pennants. Non members welcome. You can also call us on 0845 130 7633.
Facilities Ⓦⲓ⌐◡⌐☎☂☂🗙⊟
Nearby Facilities ✔ ⚓☂
Directions On the A628 Manchester to Barnsley road, in Crowden follow signs for car park, Youth Hostel and camp site. Camp site is approx. 300 yards from the main road.
⛟ Hadfield/Glossop

HARTINGTON

Barracks Farm Caravan & Camping Site, Beresford Dale, Hartington, Buxton, Derbyshire, SK17 0HQ
Tel: 01298 84261
Pitches For Å ⊕ ⊕ **Total** 40
Acreage 5 **Open** Easter **to** End Oct
Access Good **Site** Level
Alongside river, scenic views and ideal touring.
Facilities Ⓦⲓ⌐◡⌐☎☂🗙⊟
Nearby Facilities
Nearest Town Buxton
Directions Buxton A515 approx 10 miles. After leaving Buxton go on for 7 miles, turn right for Hartington B5054. Go through village for 1½ miles, turn left for Beresford Dale, continue for ¼ mile then turn left again signposted Beresford Dale. The site is 2nd on left.
⛟ Buxton

HAYFIELD

Camping & Caravanning Club Site, Kinder Road, Hayfield, High Peak, Derbyshire, SK22 2LE
Tel: 01663 745394
www.campingandcaravanning.co.uk/hayfield
Pitches For Å ⊕ **Total** 90
Acreage 6 **Open** 29-Mar **to** 05-Nov
Access Difficult **Site** Level
Nearest Bus Stop (Miles) 1
On the banks of the River Sett. Ideal for fell and moorland walkers. 6 miles from a Victorian style swimming pool. 12 miles from Granada Studios. BTB 3 Star Graded and AA 2 Pennants. Non members welcome (no caravans). You can also call us on 0845 130 7633.
Facilities Ⓦⲓ⌐◡⌐⟊☎☂🗙⊟🗗📶
Nearby Facilities ⌐ ∪ ⚲☂
Directions On the A624 Glossop to Chapel en-le-Frith road, the Hayfield by-pass. Wel signed to the village, follow wooden carved signs to the site.
⛟ New Mills

HOPE

Laneside Caravan Park, Laneside Farm, Station Road, Hope, Hope Valley, Derbyshire, S33 6RR
Tel: 01433 620215
Email: laneside@lineone.net
www.lanesidecaravanpark.co.uk
Pitches For Å ⊕ ⊕ **Total** 85

Golden Valley Caravan & Camping Park

COACH ROAD • GOLDEN VALLEY • DERBYS • DE55 4ES

26 acres of woodland with two ponds for Carp fishing. Three childrens play areas with swings, slides and play house. Games Room, Gymnasium and Jacuzzi. Cafe and Bar. Two shower blocks and toilets are of a very high standard. Disabled toilet & shower facilities.

'Great For Families with Children'

AA

GOLD

www.goldenvalleycaravanpark.co.uk
E-mail: enquiries@goldenvalleycaravanpark.co.uk

01773
513881

Acreage 5 **Open** March **to** November
Access Good **Site** Level
Nearest Bus Stop (Miles) Outside
Sheltered riverside setting adjacent to to Hope Village. Wonderful central location for walking and touring the Peak District.
Facilities ⚹ ⚹ 🏠 ⚹ ⚹ ⊙ ⚹ ⚹ ▣ ☎
⚹ ⚹ ⚹ ⚹ ⚹ ⚹ ⚹ ⚹ ⚹ ≋ ⚹
Nearby Facilities ⌐ ⚹ ∪ ⚹ ⚹
Nearest Town Bakewell
≛ Hope

MATLOCK
Birchwood Farm Caravan Park,
Wirksworth Road, Whatstandwell, Nr Matlock, Derbyshire, DE4 5HS
Tel: 01629 822280
www.birchwoodfcp.co.uk
Pitches For ⚹ ⚹ ⚹ ⚹ **Total** 66
Acreage 4 **Open** 25-Mar **to** 31-Oct
Access Good **Site** Sloping
Nearest Bus Stop (Miles) ½
Situated off Midshires Way which leads to High Peak Trail or the Cromford Canal.
Facilities ⚹ ⚹ ⚹ ⚹ ⚹ ⊙ ⚹ ⚹
▣ ☎ ⚹ ⚹ ⚹ ⚹ ⚹ ⚹
Nearby Facilities ⚹ ⚹ ∪ ⚹ ⚹
Nearest Town Wirksworth
Directions Leave the A6 at Whatstandwell Bridge (look for our sign near the telephone box) and take the B5035 towards Wirksworth, after 1 mile turn right down our drive.
≛ Whatstandwell

MATLOCK
Holly Bush Caravan & Camping Site,
The Old Toll Bar, Grange Mill, Matlock, Derbyshire, DE4 4HU
Tel: 01629 650809
Pitches For ⚹ ⚹ ⚹ **Total** 50
Open All Year
Access Good **Site** Level
Ideal for walking.
Facilities ⚹ ⚹ ⚹ ⚹ ⚹ ⚹ ⚹ ⚹ ⚹
Nearby Facilities ⚹ ⚹ ⚹ ∪ ⚹ ⚹ ⚹
Nearest Town Matlock
≛ Matlock

MATLOCK
Lickpenny Caravan Park, Lickpenny Lane, Tansley, Nr Matlock, Derbyshire, DE4 5GF
Tel: 01629 583040
Email: lickpenny@btinternet.com
www.lickpennycaravanpark.co.uk
Pitches For ⚹ ⚹ **Total** 100
Acreage 16 **Open** All Year
Nearest Bus Stop (Miles) ¼
Located in the heart of the Peak District. Garden centre and cafe nearby.

Facilities ⚹ ⚹ ⚹ ⚹ ⚹ ⚹ ⚹ ⚹ ⊙ ⚹ ⚹ ▣ ☎
⚹ ⚹ ⚹ ⚹ ⚹ ⚹ ⚹ ⚹ ⚹ ⚹ ⚹ ⚹
Nearby Facilities ⚹ ⚹ ∪ ⚹ ⚹
Nearest Town Matlock
Directions From Matlock take the A615 towards the M1 for 3 miles, site is signposted on the left. 8 miles from the M1.
≛ Matlock

MATLOCK
Packhorse Farm Bungalow, Packhorse Farm, Tansley, Matlock, Derbyshire, DE4 5LF
Tel: 01629 582781
Pitches For ⚹ ⚹ ⚹ **Total** 20
Acreage 3 **Open** All Year
ADULTS ONLY. Ideal for touring the countryside.
Facilities ⚹ ⚹ ⚹ ⊙ ⚹ ⚹ ⚹ ⚹ ⚹ ⚹ ⚹
Nearby Facilities ⌐ ⚹ ∪ ⚹
Nearest Town Matlock
Directions Take the A615 to Tansley Village, 1½ miles to the site. 4½ miles from Matlock.
≛ Matlock

MATLOCK
Pinegroves Caravan Park, High Lane, Tansley, Matlock, Derbyshire, DE4 5BG
Tel: 01629 534815
Pitches For ⚹ ⚹ **Total** 20
Acreage 7 **Open** April **to** October
Access Good **Site** Level
Nearest Bus Stop (Miles) ½
Peaceful countryside site. Near to many attractions including Tramway Museum, Chatsworth House, Matlock Bath Cable Cars and Lea Rhododendron Gardens.
Facilities ⚹ ⚹ ⚹ ⚹ ⚹ ⌐ ⊙ ⚹ ▣ ☎
⚹ ▣ ⚹ ⚹
Nearby Facilities ⌐ ⚹ ⚹ ∪ ⚹ ⚹
Nearest Town Matlock
Directions Leave the M1 at junction 28, take the A38 to Alfreton then take the A615 towards Matlock. 2 miles after Wessington turn left at the crossroads into High Lane, site is on the left.
≛ Matlock

RIPLEY
Golden Valley Caravan & Camping Park,
Coach Road, Golden Valley, Derbyshire, DE55 4ES
Tel: 01773 513881
Email:
enquiries@goldenvalleycaravanpark.co.uk
www.goldenvalleycaravanpark.co.uk
Pitches For ⚹ ⚹ ⚹ **Total** 120
Acreage 30 **Open** All Year
Access Good **Site** Level
Nearest Bus Stop (Miles) ¼

Near to the Peak District, a canal, the Midland Railway, Matlock and Crich Tramway.
Facilities ⚹ ⚹ ⚹ ⚹ ⚹ ⚹ ⊙ ⚹ ⚹ ▣ ☎
⚹ ⚹ ⚹ ⚹ ⚹ ⚹ ⚹ ⚹ ⚹ ⚹ ⚹ ⚹ ⚹ ⚹
Nearby Facilities ⌐ ⚹ ∪ ⚹
Nearest Town Ripley
Directions Leave the M1 at junction 26 and take the A610 towards Matlock. When in Codnor turn right at the traffic lights then right again onto Alfreton road, site is 2 miles on the left.
≛ Alfreton

SWADLINCOTE
Conkers Camping & Caravanning Club Site, Bath Lane, Moira, Swadlincote, Derbyshire, DE12 6BD
Tel: 01283 224925
www.campingandcaravanningclub.co.uk/conkers
Pitches For ⚹ ⚹ ⚹ **Total** 90
Acreage 4 **Open** All Year
Access Good **Site** Level
Nearest Bus Stop (Miles) ¼
Close to Corrs Visitor Centre, Donnington Park, Grangewood Zoo, Calke Abbey and Twycross Zoo. Non members welcome. You can also call us on 0845 130 7633.
Facilities ⚹ ⚹ ⚹ ⚹ ⚹ ⚹ ⚹ ⚹ ▣ ⚹ ⚹ ⚹
Nearby Facilities
Nearest Town Swadlincote
Directions From Burton-on-Trent take the A444 towards Overseal. Turn into Moira road and take the fourth exit on the left, site is immediately on the right.
≛ Burton-on-Trent

Please check directly with the Park, that any facility you particularly require will be available at the time of your visit.

DEVON

DEVON

ASHBURTON

Parkers Farm Holiday Park, Higher Mead Farm, Ashburton, Devon, TQ13 7LJ
Tel: 01364 654869
Email: parkersfarm@btconnect.com
www.parkersfarmholidays.co.uk
Pitches For ▲ ⬛ ⬛ **Total** 100
Acreage 25 **Open** Easter **to** October
Access Good **Site** Level Terrace
Nearest Bus Stop (Miles) ¼
Friendly, family run, working farm site with spectacular views. Children and pets paradise. Static caravans also for hire.
Facilities ⬛ ⬛ ⬛ ⬛ ⬛ ⬛ ⬛ ⬛ ⬛ ⬛
⬛ ⬛ ⬛ ⬛ ⬛ ⬛ ⬛ ⬛ ⬛ ⬛ ⬛ ⬛
Nearby Facilities ⬛ ⬛ ⬛ ⬛ ⬛ ⬛ ⬛ ⬛
Nearest Town Ashburton
Directions Take the A38 to Plymouth, when you see the sign 26 miles Plymouth take second left marked Woodland - Denbury.
⬛ Newton Abbot

ASHBURTON

River Dart Country Park, Holne Park, Ashburton, Newton Abbot, Devon, TQ13 7NP
Tel: 01364 652511
Email: info@riverdart.co.uk
www.riverdart.co.uk
Pitches For ▲ ⬛ ⬛ **Total** 185
Acreage 90 **Open** 04-Apr **to** 26-Sep
Access Good **Site** Level
Magnificent site with adventure playgrounds, alongside the River Dart. Ideal for Dartmoor.
Facilities ⬛ ⬛ ⬛ ⬛ ⬛ ⬛ ⬛ ⬛ ⬛ ⬛
⬛ ⬛ ⬛ ⬛ ⬛ ⬛ ⬛ ⬛ ⬛ ⬛ ⬛
Nearby Facilities ⬛ ⬛ ⬛ ⬛ ⬛ ⬛ ⬛
Nearest Town Ashburton
Directions From the M5 at Exeter take the A38 towards Plymouth. Exit at Peartree Junction in Ashburton and follow brown tourism signs.
⬛ Newton Abbot

AXMINSTER

Andrewshayes Caravan Park, Dalwood, Axminster, Devon, EX13 7DY
Tel: 01404 831225
Email: info@andrewshayes.co.uk
www.andrewshayes.co.uk
Pitches For ▲ ⬛ ⬛
Acreage 12 **Open** Easter **to** Oct
Access Good **Site** Level
Nearest Bus Stop (Miles) ¼
Close to the Jurassic coast. Outdoor heated pool, bar and take-away food.
Facilities ⬛ ⬛ ⬛ ⬛ ⬛ ⬛ ⬛ ⬛ ⬛ ⬛
⬛ ⬛ ⬛ ⬛ ⬛ ⬛ ⬛ ⬛ ⬛ ⬛ ⬛ ⬛
⬛ ⬛ ⬛
Nearby Facilities ⬛ ⬛ ⬛ ⬛ ⬛ ⬛ ⬛

Nearest Town Axminster
Directions From Axminster take the A35, site is 3 miles on the right.
⬛ Axminster

AXMINSTER

Hawkchurch Country Park, Hawkchurch, Axminster, Devon, EX13 5UL
Tel: 0844 272 9502
Email: enquiries@hawkchurchpark.co.uk
www.hawkchurchpark.co.uk
Pitches For ▲ ⬛ ⬛ **Total** 351
Acreage 17 **Open** 15-Feb **to** 04-Jan
Access Good **Site** Sloping
Nearest Bus Stop (Miles) ¼
Tranquil Park occupying a privileged location, protected by mature woodlands yet with commanding views over the Axe Valley. Only a few minutes drive from beaches and the spectacular Jurassic coastline of Lyme Regis.
Facilities ⬛ ⬛ ⬛ ⬛ ⬛ ⬛ ⬛ ⬛ ⬛ ⬛
⬛ ⬛ ⬛ ⬛ ⬛ ⬛ ⬛ ⬛ ⬛ ⬛
Nearby Facilities ⬛ ⬛
Nearest Town Lyme Regis
Directions From Axminster take A35 towards Dorchester for 3½ miles. At main crossroads turn left onto the B3165 towards Crewkerne. Follow for 2 miles and the Park is on the left.
⬛ Axminster

BARNSTAPLE

Brightlycott Caravan & Camping Site, Brightlycott Barton, Barnstaple, Devon, EX31 4JJ
Tel: 01271 850330
Email: friend.brightlycott@virgin.net
www.brightlycottbarton.co.uk
Pitches For ▲ ⬛ ⬛ **Total** 20
Acreage 4 **Open** 15-Mar **to** 15-Nov
Access Good **Site** Lev/Slope
Extremely peaceful, small, friendly, family run site situated on a former dairy farm with panoramic views. Fridge/freezer facility. New ablutions block with laundry and wash up .
Facilities ⬛ ⬛ ⬛ ⬛ ⬛ ⬛ ⬛ ⬛
⬛ ⬛ ⬛ ⬛ ⬛ ⬛ ⬛ ⬛
Nearby Facilities ⬛ ⬛ ⬛ ⬛
Nearest Town Barnstaple
Directions Leave Barnstaple on the A39 towards Lynton, turn right 1½ miles after the hospital signposted Brightlycott and Roborough.
⬛ Barnstaple

BARNSTAPLE

Greenacres Farm Touring Caravan Park, Bratton Fleming, Barnstaple, North Devon, EX31 4SG
Tel: 01598 763334
Pitches For ⬛ ⬛ **Total** 30
Acreage 4 **Open** April **to** October

Access Good **Site** Level
Nearest Bus Stop (Miles) ¼
Peaceful, secluded park with scenic views. 5 miles from moors and coast, 10 miles from towns. Ideal for touring, walking and cycling.
Facilities ⬛ ⬛ ⬛ ⬛ ⬛ ⬛ ⬛ ⬛ ⬛
⬛ ⬛ ⬛ ⬛ ⬛ ⬛ ⬛ ⬛
Nearby Facilities ⬛ ⬛
Nearest Town Barnstaple
Directions From North Devon link road (A361). Take the A399 to Blackmoor Gate, approx 10 miles. Park signed (300yds from the A399).
⬛ Barnstaple

BIDEFORD

Ashcroft Farm (Camping & Caravanning Club CL) Ashcroft, Woolsery, Bideford, Devon, EX39 5QU
Tel: 01237 431351
Email: vickimeeson@msn.com
Pitches For ▲ ⬛ ⬛ ⬛ **Total** 5
Acreage 2 **Open** April **to** October
Access Good **Site** Lev/Slope
Spacious pitches and 60 acres of farmland available to explore. Children and dogs welcome. Just a short drive to the beautiful coastal footpath and diverse (and dog friendly) beaches.
Facilities ⬛ ⬛ ⬛ ⬛ ⬛ ⬛ ⬛
Nearby Facilities ⬛ ⬛ ⬛ ⬛ ⬛ ⬛
Nearest Town Bideford
Directions From Bideford take the A39 towards Bude. Go past the Milky Way Adventure Park (on the left) and turn next left towards Woolsery. Turn next right, then next left, turn left again and Ashcroft is the next farm.
⬛ Barnstaple

BIDEFORD

Steart Farm Touring Park, Horns Cross, Bideford, Devon, EX39 5DW
Tel: 01237 431836
Email: steartenquiries@btconnect.com
www.steartfarmtouringpark.co.uk
Pitches For ▲ ⬛ ⬛ **Total** 70
Acreage 10¼ **Open** Easter **to** Sept
Access Good **Site** Lev/Slope
Nearest Bus Stop (Miles) ½
Set in 17 acres overlooking Bideford Bay, 1 mile from the sea. 2¼ acre dog exercise area. 2 acre childrens play area.
Facilities ⬛ ⬛ ⬛ ⬛ ⬛ ⬛ ⬛ ⬛ ⬛
⬛ ⬛ ⬛ ⬛ ⬛ ⬛ ⬛ ⬛
Nearby Facilities ⬛ ⬛ ⬛ ⬛
Nearest Town Bideford
Directions From Bideford follow the A39 west (signed Bude). Pass through Fairy Cross and Horns Cross, 2 miles after Horns Cross site will be on the right. 8 miles from Bideford.
⬛ Barnstaple

BRAUNTON

Lobb Fields Caravan & Camping Park, Saunton Road, Braunton, Devon, EX33 1HG
Tel: 01271 812090
Email: info@lobbfields.com
www.lobbfields.com
Pitches For ⅄ ⊕ 🚐 **Total** 180
Acreage 14 **Open** 23-Mar **to** 28-Oct
Access Good **Site** Gentle Slope
Nearest Bus Stop (Miles) Outside
1½ miles from the beach. 1 mile from the Tarka Trail. Disabled toilet and shower.
Facilities ...
Nearby Facilities ...
Directions Take the A361 to Braunton, then take the B3231. The park entrance is 1 mile from Braunton centre on the right.
🚆 Barnstaple

BRIXHAM

Galmpton Touring Park, Greenway Road, Galmpton, Nr Brixham, Devon, TQ5 0EP
Tel: 01803 842066
Email: enquiries@galmptontouringpark.co.uk
www.galmptontouringpark.co.uk
Pitches For ⅄ ⊕ 🚐 **Total** 120
Acreage 9 **Open** Easter **to** Sept
Access Good **Site** Sloping
Nearest Bus Stop (Miles) 1
Superb views of the River Dart. A quiet base for couples and families to explore South Devon. 1½ miles from the beach, boat trips, steam railway, NT gardens and a zoo. Beautiful walks nearby.
Facilities ...
Nearby Facilities ...
Nearest Town Brixham
Directions Follow the A380/A3022 Torbay ring road, on joining the A379 coast road sp Brixham, turn second right sp Galmpton Park. Continue through the village passing the school, park entrance is on the right after approx. 200 yards.
🚆 Paignton

BRIXHAM

Hillhead Caravan Club Site, Hillhead, Brixham, Devon, TQ5 0HH
Tel: 01803 853204
www.caravanclub.co.uk
Pitches For ⅄ ⊕ 🚐 **Total** 239
Acreage 20 **Open** March **to** Jan
Access Good **Site** Lev/Slope
In a great location with many pitches affording stunning views of the sea, South Devon and parts of Dorset. Ideal site for families. Kingswear-Paignton Steam Railway and Paignton Zoo nearby. Non members welcome. Booking essential.

Facilities ...
Nearby Facilities ...
Nearest Town Brixham
Directions From A380 3 miles south of Newton Abbot turn right onto the ring road sp Brixham. After 7 miles at traffic lights turn right onto A3022, just past Churston Golf Course turn right onto A379. At mini roundabout turn right and immediately fork left onto B320
🚆 Paignton

BUCKFAST

Churchill Farm, Buckfastleigh, Devon, TQ11 0EZ
Tel: 01364 642844
Email: apedrick@btinternet.com
www.churchillfarmcampsite.com
Pitches For ⅄ ⊕ 🚐 **Total** 25
Acreage 2 **Open** April **to** October
Access Good **Site** Lev/Slope
Nearest Bus Stop (Miles) ½
Stunning views of Dartmoor and Buckfast Abbey, the latter being within easy walking distance as are the Steam Railway, Butterfly Farm, Otter Sanctuary and local inns. Seaside resort 10 miles.
Facilities ...
Nearby Facilities ...
Nearest Town Buckfastleigh/Buckfast
Directions Exit A38 at Dartbridge, follow signs for Buckfast Abbey, proceed up hill to crossroads. Turn left into no-through road towards church. Farm entrance is opposite the church 1½ miles from the A38.
🚆 Totnes

BUCKFASTLEIGH

Beara Farm Camping Site, Colston Road, Buckfastleigh, Devon, TQ11 0LW
Tel: 01364 642234
Pitches For ⅄ ⊕ 🚐 **Total** 30
Acreage 3¼ **Open** All Year
Access Good **Site** Level
Quiet, select, sheltered site adjoining River Dart. Within easy reach of sea and moors and 1½ miles southeast of Buckfastleigh.
Facilities ...
Nearby Facilities ...
Nearest Town Buckfastleigh
Directions Coming from Exeter take first left after passing South Devon Steam Railway and Butterfly Centre at Buckfastleigh, signpost marked Beara, fork right at next turning then 1 mile to site, signposted on roadside and junctions.
🚆 Totnes

BUDLEIGH SALTERTON

Ladram Bay Holiday Park, Otterton, Budleigh Salterton, Devon, EX9 7BX
Tel: 01395 568398
Email: welcome@ladrambay.co.uk
www.ladrambay.co.uk
Pitches For ⅄ ⊕ 🚐 **Total** 150
Open Easter **to** End Oct
Access Good **Site** Level
Nearest Bus Stop (Miles) ½
Private beach and full entertainment.
Facilities ...
Nearby Facilities ...
Nearest Town Budleigh Salterton
Directions Leave the M5 at junction 30 and take the A3052, then take the B3178, site is one mile through Otterton.
🚆 Exmouth

CHAGFORD

Woodland Springs Adult Touring Park, Venton, Drewsteignton, Devon, EX6 6PG
Tel: 01647 231695
Email: enquiries@woodlandsprings.co.uk
www.woodlandsprings.co.uk
Pitches For ⅄ ⊕ 🚐 **Total** 81
Acreage 4 **Open** All Year
Access Good **Site** Level
ADULTS ONLY. Quiet, secluded site within the Dartmoor National Park, surrounded by wood and farmland. Good access for the larger units and large all-weather pitches. Off season breaks.
Facilities ...
Nearby Facilities ...
Nearest Town Okehampton
Directions From Exeter take the A30, after 17 miles turn left at Whiddon Down Junction onto the A382 towards Moretonhampstead, after ½ a mile turn left at the roundabout, site is 1 mile on the left signpost Venton.
🚆 Exeter

CHUDLEIGH

Holmans Wood Holiday Park, Harcombe, Cross, Chudleigh, Devon, TQ13 0DZ
Tel: 01626 853785
Email: enquiries@holmanswood.co.uk
www.holmanswood.co.uk
Pitches For ⅄ ⊕ 🚐 **Total** 100
Acreage 11 **Open** March **to** End October
Access Good **Site** Level
Nearest Bus Stop (Miles) Outside
Picturesque setting. Ideal touring for Dartmoor, Haldon Forest, Exeter and Torbay. Holiday homes for sale.
Facilities ...
Nearby Facilities ...

Nearest Town Chudleigh
Directions From Exeter take the A38 Towards Plymouth. Go past the racecourse and after 1 mile take the B3344 for Chudleigh. We are on the left at the end of the sliproad.
⚑ Newton Abbot

CLOVELLY
Dyke Green Farm, Camp Site, Dyke Green Farm, Clovelly, Bideford, Devon, EX39 5RU
Tel: 01237 431279
Email: royston.johns@hotmail.co.uk
Pitches For Å ⛺ ⛟ **Total** 25
Acreage 3 **Open** Easter **to** October
Access Good **Site** Level
Nearest Bus Stop (Miles) Entrance
Ideal stop off for touring the coastal path and visiting Clovelly.
Facilities ⌖ ⓕ ⓌⒼ ⌒ ⊙ ☻ ℟ ⊟ ⊙⊁⊟ 🛈 🛜
Nearby Facilities ℾ ✓ ⚓ ⚲ ∪ ₽ ⚐
Nearest Town Clovelly
Directions On the A39 Clovelly Cross roundabout.
⚑ Barnstaple

COMBE MARTIN
Newberry Valley Park, Woodlands, Combe Martin, Devon, EX34 0AT
Tel: 01271 882334
Email: relax@newberryvalleypark.co.uk
www.newberryvalleypark.co.uk
Pitches For Å ⛺ ⛟ **Total** 110
Acreage 20 **Open** Easter **to** October
Access Good **Site** Level
Nearest Bus Stop (Miles) ¼
Beautiful countryside valley site. Combe Martin beach and village within 5 minutes walk. Course fishing lake. Woodland walks. Exmoor National Park nearby. 4 Star Graded.
Facilities ⌖ ⓕ ⓌⒼ ⌒ ⊙ ☻ ℟ ⊟ ⊙
🅿 🅛 ⊟ ⌲ ⊟ ⊟ ✓ ☼ ⚘
Nearby Facilities ℾ ✓ ⚘ ∪ ₽
Nearest Town Combe Martin/Ilfracombe
Directions Leave the M5 at junction 27 and take the A361 to Aller Cross Roundabout. A399 to Combe Martin.
⚑ Barnstaple

COMBE MARTIN
Stowford Farm Meadows, Combe Martin, Devon, EX34 0PW
Tel: 01271 882476
Email: enquiries@stowford.co.uk
www.stowford.co.uk
Pitches For Å ⛺ ⛟ **Total** 700
Acreage 140 **Open** All Year
Access Good **Site** Lev/Slope
Set in 450 acres of beautiful countryside. Ideal touring site at the heart of North Devon. Renowned for our extensive range of facilities at excellent value. Horse riding on site. Caravan repair workshop, caravan accessories shop and caravan sales.
Facilities ⌖ ⓕ ⓌⒼ ⌒ ⊙ ☻ ℟ ⊟ ⊙
🅿 🅛 ⊟ ⓧ ⚲ 🛈 ℟ ↥ ⊙⊁⊟ 🛈 ☼ ⚘ ⚘
Nearby Facilities ℾ ✓ ⚓
Nearest Town Combe Martin
Directions Situated on the A3123 Combe Martin/Woolacombe road at Berry Down.
⚑ Barnstaple

CREDITON
Yeatheridge Farm Caravan & Camping Park, East Worlington, Crediton, Devon, EX17 4TN
Tel: 01884 860330
Email: yeatheridge@talk21.com
www.yeatheridge.co.uk
Pitches For Å ⛺ ⛟ **Total** 85
Open 01-Apr to 01-Oct
Access Good **Site** Lev/Slope
2½ mile woodland walk. Fishing and horse riding on site.
Facilities ⌖ ⓕ ⓌⒼ ⌒ ⊙ ☻ ℟ ⊟ ⊙
🅿 🅛 ⊟ ⓧ ⚲ 🛈 ℟ 🛈 ❄ ⊙⊁⊟ 🛈 ✓ 🛜
Nearby Facilities ℾ
Directions From Tiverton take the B3137 to Witheridge, turn left onto the B3042 and Yeatheridge is 3½ miles on the left.
⚑ Eggesford

CROYDE BAY
Bay View Farm Holidays, Croyde, Devon, EX33 1PN
Tel: 01271 890501
www.bayviewfarm.co.uk
Pitches For Å ⛺ ⛟
Acreage 10 **Open** Easter **to** September
Site Level

Nearest Bus Stop (Miles) Outside
Scenic views. Just a five minute walk to the beach. Ideal touring. Booking is advisable during peak season. Limited statics available. Please send SAE for further information.
Facilities ⌖ ⓕ ⓌⒼ ⌒ ⊙ ☻ ℟ ⊟ ⊙
🅿 🅛 ⊟ ⓧ ⊟ ⊟ ☼
Nearby Facilities ℾ ✓ ⚓ ⚘ ∪ ⚐ ₽ ⚐
Nearest Town Croyde
Directions At Braunton on A361 turn west on main road B3231 towards Croyde Village
⚑ Barnstaple

CROYDE BAY
Ruda Holiday Park, Croyde Bay, Devon, EX33 1NY
Tel: 0844 335 3732
Email: touringandcamping@parkdeanholidays.com
www.parkdeantouring.co.uk
Pitches For Å ⛺ ⛟ **Total** 306
Acreage 220 **Open** March **to** Oct
Access Good **Site** Level
Nearest Bus Stop (Miles) Outside
Our own beach, Croyde Bay is immediately adjacent to camping and touring pitches. Excellent surfing and walking. Indoor Tropical Adventure Pool. FREE kids clubs and live family entertainment.
Facilities ⌖ ⓕ ⓌⒼ ⌒ ⊙ ☻ ℟ ⊟ ⊙
🅿 🅛 ⊟ ⓧ ⚲ 🛈 ℟ 🛈 ❄ ⊙⊁⊟ 🛈 ✓ 🛜
Nearby Facilities ℾ ✓ ⚓ ⚘ ∪ ₽ ⚐
Nearest Town Barnstaple
Directions From Barnstaple take the A361 to Braunton. In the centre of Braunton at the traffic lights turn left onto the B3231 and follow signs to Croyde.
⚑ Barnstaple

CULLOMPTON
Forest Glade Holiday Park, Cullompton, Devon, EX15 2DT
Tel: 01404 841381
Email: enquiries@forest-glade.co.uk
www.forest-glade.co.uk
Pitches For Å ⛺ ⛟ **Total** 80
Acreage 10 **Open** Mid March **to** End Oct
Access See Directions **Site** Level

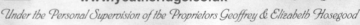

escape to the
stowford
life

Stowford Farm Meadows is a family owned, award winning touring **caravan and camping site** close to Combe Martin, North Devon

Stowford Farm Meadows

COMBE MARTIN · NORTH DEVON · EX34 0PW

FACILITIES INCLUDE

Indoor Heated Swimming Pool · Horse Riding Centre · Mini Indoor Zoo · Woodland Walks · 18 Hole Fun Golf · Restaurants & Bars · Fun Packed Activities · Fantastic Family Entertainment

SPECIAL OFFERS
£49.50 low season
£69.50 mid season
for a weeks holiday including electric check our website for vouchers

Stowford also includes a **Caravan Sales Centre and Accessory Shop** as well as the opportunity to purchase your very own **luxury holiday lodge.**

To save your place or request a brochure call our Booking Hotline

01271 882476

Combe Martin North Devon EX34 0PW

Book online at - www.**stowford**.co.uk

Central for southwest twixt coast and moors. Large flat sheltered camping pitches. Caravans for hire. Free heated indoor swimming pool and Paddling pool. Riding and gliding nearby. Tennis on site.
Facilities ♿ ⚡ ...
Nearby Facilities ...
Nearest Town Cullompton
Directions A373 Cullompton/Honiton, turn for Sheldon at Keepers Cottage Inn, 2½ miles east of Cullompton. Touring caravans via Dunkeswell Road only.
⚆ Honiton/Tiverton Parkway

DARTMOUTH
Dartmouth Camping & Caravanning Club Site, Stoke Fleming, Dartmouth, Devon, TQ6 0RF
Tel: 01803 770253
www.campingandcaravanningclub.co.uk/dartmouth
Pitches For ▲ ⛺ ⛺ **Total** 83
Acreage 6 **Open** 29-Mar **to** 05-Nov
Access Good **Site** Lev/Slope
Nearest Bus Stop (Miles) Outside
A pretty site in an area of outstanding natural beauty. Just a few minutes from the award winning beach of Blackpool Sands and the south west coastal path. 1½ miles from Dartmouth with its historic and royal connections, cobbled streets, bistros and excellent restaurants and pubs. You can also call us on 0845 130 7633.
Facilities ...
Nearby Facilities ...
Nearest Town Dartmouth
Directions From the dual carriageway take the turning sp Totnes. When you reach Totnes take the A381 up the western bypass. In Halwell take the A3122 sp Dartmouth, turn right at mini roundabout onto the A379. Follow road towards Stoke Fleming and the Site is on the
⚆ Totnes

DARTMOUTH
Little Cotton Caravan Park, Dartmouth, Devon, TQ6 0LB
Tel: 01803 832558
Email: enquiries@littlecotton.co.uk
www.littlecotton.co.uk
Pitches For ▲ ⛺ ⛺ **Total** 95
Acreage 7½ **Open** Mid March **to** End Oct
Access Good **Site** Lev/Slope
Nearest Bus Stop (Miles) Outside
Scenic views, ideal touring. Sainsburys opposite entrance. Park and ride service adjacent. Luxurious new toilet and shower facilities.
Facilities ...
Nearby Facilities ...
Nearest Town Dartmouth
Directions Leave A38 at Buckfastleigh and take A384 to Totnes, from Totnes to Halwell on the A381. At Halwell take the A3122 Dartmouth road, Park is on the right at entrance to town.
⚆ Totnes

DARTMOUTH
Woodlands Grove Caravan & Camping Park, Blackawton, Totnes, Devon, TQ9 7DQ
Tel: 01803 712598
Email: holiday@woodlandsgrove.com
www.woodlands-caravanpark.com
Pitches For ▲ ⛺ ⛺ **Total** 210
Acreage 16 **Open** Easter **to** End of Oct
Access Good **Site** Mostly Level
Nearest Bus Stop (Miles) Outside

Combining 5 Star facilities with personal supervision. Spacious pitches in beautiful countryside. 4 miles from Dartmouth coast. Excellent bathrooms, laundry and Free hot showers. Two nights stay gives FREE entrance to our 90 acre Leisure Park. 3 watercoasters, 500m Toboggan Run and Arctic Gliders. All weather fun guaranteed - perfect family holiday! Also 'Adults Only Midweek Special', the perfect rural break for adults.
Facilities ...
Nearby Facilities ...
Nearest Town Dartmouth
Directions 4 miles from Dartmouth on main road A3122 (formally B3207).
⚆ Totnes

DAWLISH
Cofton Country Holidays, Starcross, Nr Dawlish, Devon, EX6 8RP
Tel: 01626 890111
Email: info@coftonholidays.co.uk
www.coftonholidays.co.uk
Pitches For ▲ ⛺ ⛺ ⛺ **Total** 450
Acreage 80 **Open** All Year
Access Good **Site** Level
Nearest Bus Stop (Miles) Outside
In beautiful rural countryside near to sandy Dawlish Warren beach. Clean and tidy family run park. Superb complex with swimming pool. Swan Pub serving meals and a family lounge bar. See our advert on the back cover.
Facilities ...
Nearby Facilities ...
Nearest Town Dawlish
Directions On the A379 Exeter to Dawlish road, ½ mile after the fishing village at Cockwood.
⚆ Starcross

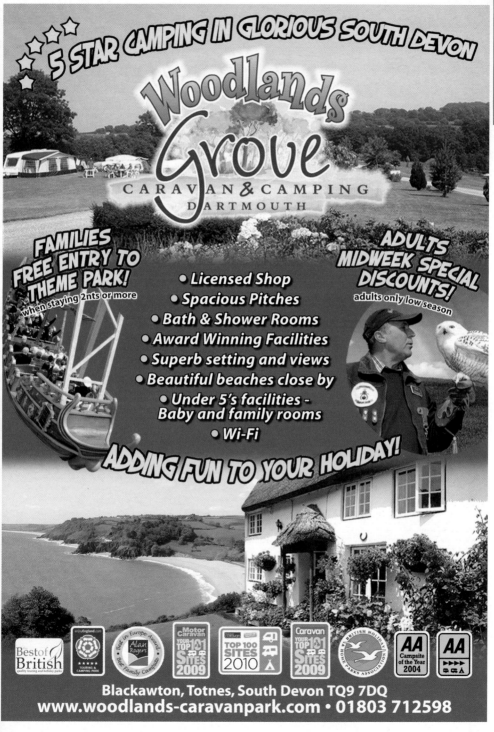

DEVON

a glorious corner of Devon

Four star family-run holiday park just minutes from a Blue Flag beach.
Stunning setting with superb countryside views. WiFi internet access available.

Call 0800 085 8649 www.coftonholidays.co.uk

DAWLISH

Lady's Mile Holiday Park, Exeter Road, Dawlish, Devon, EX7 0LX
Tel: 01626 863411
Email: info@ladysmile.co.uk
www.ladysmile.co.uk
Pitches For ▲ ⛺ 🚐 **Total** 486
Acreage 16 **Open** Mid March **to** End Oct
Access Good **Site** Lev/Slope
Nearest Bus Stop (Miles) Outside
Very close to a Blue Flag beach and near to Dartmoor National Park. Ideal base for exploring Devon.
Facilities ⬧ ⌿ ▥ ⬚ ⌂ ⊙ ⊿ ⬛ ◻ ☎
☲ ⍑ ⊙ ⊜ ✕ ⟟ ♠ ⍀ ⟘ ⚡ ⚓ ⟊ ➤◻ ⬚ ⋇
⚘

Nearby Facilities ⌐ ⟋ ♈
Nearest Town Dawlish
Directions On the A379, 1 mile north of Dawlish and 10 miles south of Exeter.
⚞ Dawlish

DAWLISH

Leadstone Camping, Warren Road, Dawlish, Devon, EX7 0NG
Tel: 01626 864411
Email: post@leadstonecamping.co.uk
www.leadstonecamping.co.uk
Pitches For ▲ ⛺ 🚐 **Total** 137
Acreage 7 **Open** 08-Jun **to** 02-Sep
Access Good **Site** Lev/Slope
Nearest Bus Stop (Miles) Outside
Rolling grassland in a natural secluded bowl within ½ mile of Dawlish Warrens Blue Flag Beach and nature reserve. Ideally situated for discovering Devon.
Facilities ⌿ ▥ ⬚ ⌂ ⊙ ⊿ ⬛ ◻ ☎
☲ ⍑ ⊙ ⍑ ➤◻ ⬚ ⋇ ⚘ ⚲
Nearby Facilities ⌐ ⟋ ⚘ ⚓ ⊍ ♈ ♈
Nearest Town Dawlish
Directions Leave the M5 at junction 30 and take signposted road A379 to Dawlish. As you approach Dawlish, turn left on brow of hill, signposted Dawlish Warren. Our site is ½ mile on the RIGHT.
⚞ Dawlish Warren

DAWLISH WARREN

Peppermint Park, Warren Road, Dawlish Warren, South Devon, EX7 0PQ
Tel: 01626 863436
Email: info@peppermintpark.co.uk
www.parkholidaysuk.com/cades
Pitches For ▲ ⛺ 🚐 **Total** 220
Open March **to** Oct
Access Good **Site** Sloping
Nearest Bus Stop (Miles) ¼
Bars and live entertainment at our sister parks nearby (Dawlish and Golden Sands), also swimming pool at both parks.
Facilities ⬧ ⌿ ▥ ⬚ ⌂ ⊙ ⊿ ⬛ ◻ ☎
☲ ⚲ ➤◻ ⟋ ⋇

Nearest Town Dawlish
Directions Leave M5 at junction 30 and take the A379 to Dawlish. Follow signs to Dawlish Warren and continue down the steep hill and follow the road round to the left, site is 200 yards.
⚞ Dawlish

EXETER

Dartmoor, Barley Meadow Camping & Caravanning Club Site, Crockernwell, Exeter, Devon, EX6 6NR
Tel: 01647 281629
www.campingandcaravanningclub.co.uk/dartmoor
Pitches For ▲ ⛺ 🚐 **Total** 63
Acreage 4 **Open** 08-Mar **to** 05-Nov
Access Good **Site** Level
Nearest Bus Stop (Miles) Outside
Set towards the east of the Dartmoor National Park in the heart of Devon. Non members welcome. You can also call us on 0845 130 7633.
Facilities ⬧ ⌿ ▤ ▥ ⬚ ⌂ ⊙ ⊿ ⬛ ☎
☲ ⍑ ⊙ ⊜ ♠ ⍀ ➤◻ ⬚ ⋇ ⚲ �’
Nearby Facilities ⌐ ⟋
Nearest Town Okehampton
Directions From Okehampton take the A30. Leave at the A382 and turn onto Hask Lane, Site is on the right before Hopperton Lane.
⚞ Exeter

EXETER

Exeter Racecourse Caravan Club Site, Kennford, Exeter, Devon, EX6 7XS
Tel: 01392 832107
www.caravanclub.co.uk
Pitches For ▲ ⛺ 🚐 **Total** 100
Acreage 10 **Open** March **to** Nov
Access Good **Site** Level
Access to racing. Large late night arrivals area. Near to Exeter Cathedral, Dartmoor National Park and Trago Mills Shopping Complex. Non members welcome. Booking essential.
Facilities ⌿ ▤ ▥ ⬚ ⌂ ⊙ ◻ ☎ ☲ ⍑ ⊙ ⊜➤◻
Nearby Facilities ⌐ ⟋
Nearest Town Exeter
Directions From the M5 take the A38, just past Kennford keep to right hand lanes and continue on A38 at A380 junction. After ½ mile move to nearside lane and at the top of steep Haldon Hill turn left sp Exeter Racecourse then immediately right, follow signs to the site.
⚞ Exeter

EXETER

Kennford International Caravan Park, Kennford, Exeter, Devon, EX6 7YN
Tel: 01392 833046
Email: ian@kennfordinternational.com

www.kennfordinternational.co.uk
Pitches For ▲ ⛺ 🚐 **Total** 96
Acreage 15 **Open** All Year
Access Good **Site** Level
Nearest Bus Stop (Miles) Outside
Kennford International is a family run park close to beaches and the city of Exeter. Fishing and the villages of Kenn and Kennford nearby. 10% discount for the over 50s (not available July & August). 7 Night Special available from Sept to Nov.
Facilities ⬧ ⌿ ▥ ⬚ ⌂ ⊙ ⊿ ⬛ ◻ ☎
☲ ⊙ ⊜ ♠ ⍀ ➤◻ ⬚ ⋇
Nearby Facilities ⌐ ⟋ ⊍
Nearest Town Exeter
Directions From the M5 join the A38 towards Plymouth and Torquay. Exit at Kennford Services, pass the garage, go over the bridge and we are on the left. Approx. 10 minutes from Exeter.
⚞ Exeter

EXETER

Springfield Holiday Park, Tedburn St Mary, Exeter, Devon, EX6 6EW
Tel: 01647 24242
Email:
enquiries@springfieldholidaypark.co.uk
www.springfieldholidaypark.co.uk
Pitches For ▲ ⛺ 🚐 **Total** 100
Acreage 9 **Open** 15-Mar **to** 15-Nov
Access Good **Site** Lev/Slope
Nearest Bus Stop (Miles) Outside
Central location for the Moors or the coast, north or south Devon. 20 mins from the seaside.
Facilities ⌿ ▥ ⬚ ⌂ ⊙ ⊿ ⬛ ◻ ☎
⍑ ⊙ ♠ ⍀ ⟘ ➤◻ ⬚ ⟋ ⋇ ⚲
Nearby Facilities ⌐ ⟋ ⊍ ♈
Directions Leave the M5 at junction 31 (Okehampton) and take the A30. Leave at left exit signposted Cheriton Bishop and follow brown tourism signs. For SAT-NAV purposes, please use Postcode EX6 6JN.
⚞ Exeter

EXMOUTH

Devon Cliffs Holiday Park, Sandy Bay, Exmouth, Devon, EX8 5BT
Tel: 01395 226226
Email: devoncliffs@haven.com
www.haventouring.com/todevoncliffs
Pitches For ⛺ 🚐 **Total** 43
Open Mid March **to** End Oct
Access Good **Site** Sloping
Nearest Bus Stop (Miles) Outside
As well as direct beach access, also make the most of kids clubs, family entertainment and water fun. Plus, there are coastal walks and many family attractions right on the doorstep.
Facilities ⬧ ⌿ ▥ ⬚ ⌂ ⊙ ⊿ ⬛ ◻ ☎
☲ ⍑ ⊙ ⊜ ✕ ⟟ ♠ ⍀ ⟘ ⚡ ⚓ ⟊ ➤◻ ⬚ ⋇ ⚘

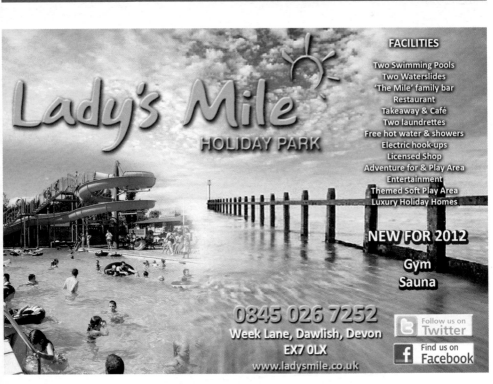

Nearby Facilities ⌐ ✓ ⚓ ⚘ ∪ ⊰ ♫
Nearest Town Exmouth
Directions Leave the M5 at junction 30 and take the A376 for Exmouth. As you come to the outskirts of Exmouth, turn left at the traffic lights and follow signs for Budleigh Salterton and Sandy Bay, this will bring you directly to the Park.
🚂 Exmouth

EXMOUTH

St Johns Caravan & Camping Park, St Johns Road, Exmouth, Devon, EX8 5EG
Tel: 01395 263170
Email: stjohns.farm@virgin.net
www.stjohnsfarm.co.uk
Pitches For Å ⚏ ⊞ **Total** 45
Acreage 6 **Open** March to Mid Jan
Access Good **Site** Sloping
Nearest Bus Stop (Miles) ¼
Quiet location near lovely common land with ponds and a reservoir for fishing. 2 miles to the town and beach.
Facilities ⚿ ⨍ 🄷 🆄🄵 ⌁ ⌐ ⊙ ⚐ ⊟ ⊡ ⬤ 🄷⊞
Nearby Facilities ⌐ ✓ ⚓ ⚘ ∪ ⊰ ♫
Nearest Town Exmouth
Directions Heading towards Exmouth go through Woodbury Village and head for Budleigh Salterton and take the B3180, site is a turning off this road.
🚂 Exmouth

EXMOUTH

Webbers Park, Castle Lane, Woodbury, Exeter, Devon, EX5 1EA
Tel: 01395 232276
Email: reception@webberspark.co.uk
www.webberspark.co.uk
Pitches For Å ⚏ ⊞ **Total** 150
Acreage 15 **Open** Mid March to End Oct
Access Good **Site** Lev/Slope
Nearest Bus Stop (Miles) ¼

Crealy Adventure Park and Exmouths sandy beach nearby.
Facilities ⚿ ⨍ 🄷 🆄🄵 ⌁ ⌐ ⊙ ⌣ ⬤ 🄵 ⬤
🝢 🝙 🅵 ⊙ ⚏ ⌺ ✿ 🌂 🄵 ⊟ ⊡ ⚘ ⚘
Nearby Facilities ⌐ ✓ ⚓ ⚘ ∪ ♫
Nearest Town Exmouth
Directions Leave the M5 at junction 30 and take the A376 to Exmouth. Then take the B3179 to Woodbury and follow brown tourism signs.
🚂 Exeter

GREAT TORRINGTON

Smytham Manor, Little Torrington, Devon, EX38 8PU
Tel: 01805 622110
Email: info@smytham.co.uk
www.smytham.co.uk
Pitches For Å ⚏ ⊞ **Total** 45
Acreage 25 **Open** March to Oct
Access Good **Site** Lev/Slope
Nearest Bus Stop (Miles) Outside
Direct access to the Tarka Trail.
Facilities ⚿ ⨍ 🄷 🆄🄵 ⌁ ⌐ ⊙ ⌣ ⬤ ⊡ ⬤
🝢 🝙 ▽ 🄼 ♨ ⚘ 🌂 🄵 ⊟ ⬤ 🔊 ⊟
Nearby Facilities ⌐ ✓ ⚓ ⚘ ∪ ⊰ ♫ ⚡
Nearest Town Great Torrington
Directions 2 miles south of Great Torrington on the A386.
🚂 Barnstaple

HARTLAND

Hartland Caravan & Camping Park, South Lane, Hartland, Bideford, North Devon, EX39 6DG
Tel: 01237 441876/441242
Email: info@hartlandcamping.co.uk
www.hartlandcamping.co.uk
Pitches For Å ⚏ ⊞ **Total** 60
Acreage 6 **Open** All Year
Access Good **Site** Lev/Slope
Nearest Bus Stop (Miles) Outside

Overlooking Hartland Village, woodlands and the Atlantic coast. Well kept, family run site boasting a new toilet/shower block with baby changing, disabled and family room. Small fishing lake and BBQ. 2 miles from beaches. Some hardstandings. Dishwashing facilities. Just a 3 minute walk to shops and public houses. Close to Hartland Abbey, Hartland Point and many other tourist attractions. Open all year depending on weather.
Facilities ⚿ ⨍ 🄷 🆄🄵 ⌁ ⌐ ⊙ ⌣ ⬤ 🄵 ⬤
🝢 🄼 🄵 ⊟ ⬤ ✓ ⚘
Nearby Facilities ⌐ ✓ ⚓ ⚘ ∪ ⊰ ♫ ⚡
Nearest Town Bideford/Bude
Directions From the A39 take the B3248 to Hartland. On entering the village site is on the left.
🚂 Barnstaple

HOLSWORTHY

Hedley Wood Caravan & Camping Park, Bridgerule, Holsworthy, Devon, EX22 7ED
Tel: 01288 381404
Email: alan@hedleywood.co.uk
www.hedleywood.co.uk
Pitches For Å ⚏ ⊞ **Total** 120
Acreage 16½ **Open** All Year
Access Good **Site** Lev/Slope
Nearest Bus Stop (Miles) ¼
Open and sheltered camping areas with a laid back atmosphere. Dog kennelling facility and a dog walk/nature trail.
Facilities ⚿ ⨍ 🄷 🆄🄵 ⌁ ⌐ ⊙ ⌣ ⬤ 🄵 ⬤
🝢 🅾 ⚏ ✕ ▽ 🄼 ♨ 🄼 ⊟ ⊟ ⚘
Nearby Facilities ⌐ ✓ ⚓ ∪ ♫
Nearest Town Bude/Holsworthy
Directions From Holsworthy take the A3072 towards Bude, at Red Post crossroads turn south onto the B3254 to Launceston. After 2¼ miles turn right to Titson, site entrance is 500 yards on the right.
🚂 Exeter

Hidden Valley
Touring & camping

This 5 star, family run park is set in a beautiful wooded valley, among rolling hills of stunning Devon countryside. Some of the country's most prestigious beaches are just 4 miles away, including Woolacombe and Putsborough Sands. Overlooking the gardens & stream is the licensed shop and a delightful coffee-shop - perfect after a forest walk!

- Luxury 5* facilities • Children's play parks • Coffee shop • Licensed shop
- Wi-Fi • Tourist information area • Dishwashing areas & launderettes
- Bus stop at entrance to site • Dog exercise field • Woodland walks

Ilfracombe's only **5 star** campsite!

Open all year!

Hidden Valley Park, West Down, Nr. Ilfracombe, North Devon EX34 8NU

01271 813 837 • info@hiddenvalleypark.com

www.hiddenvalleypark.com

DEVON

HOLSWORTHY

Noteworthy Caravan & Campsite, Bude Road, Holsworthy, Devon, EX22 7JB
Tel: 01409 253731
Email: enquiries@noteworthy-devon.co.uk
www.noteworthy-devon.co.uk
Pitches For ▲ ⬡ ⬡ **Total** 30
Acreage 5 **Open** All Year
Access Good **Site** Slight Slope
Set on a working Angora goat farm on the Devon/Cornwall border.
Facilities ⬡ ⬡ ⬡ ⬡ ⬡ ⬡ ⬡ ⬡ ⬡ ⬡
Nearby Facilities ⬡ ⬡ ⬡ ⬡ ⬡ ⬡ ⬡ ⬡
Nearest Town Holsworthy/Bude
Directions From Holsworthy take the A3072 towards Bude. The site is 2.7 miles on the right hand side.
⬡ Barnstaple

ILFRACOMBE

Brook Lea Caravan Club Site, West Down, Ilfracombe, Devon, EX34 8NE
Tel: 01271 862848
www.caravanclub.co.uk
Pitches For ⬡ ⬡ **Total** 103
Acreage 9 **Open** March to Oct
Access Good **Site** Lev/Slope
Nearest Bus Stop (Miles) ½
Elevated position with superb views and a woodland walkway. 5 miles from a sandy beach and near to Exmoor National Park and Tarka Trail Cycle Track. Own sanitation required. Non members welcome. Booking essential.
Facilities ⬡ ⬡ ⬡ ⬡ ⬡ ⬡ ⬡ ⬡ ⬡
Nearby Facilities ⬡ ⬡ ⬡ ⬡
Nearest Town Ilfracombe
Directions From Barnstaple take the A361, at Mullacott Cross roundabout turn right onto the A3123. Turn right at caravan sign signposted West Down, site is 1 mile on the left.
⬡ Ilfracombe

ILFRACOMBE

Hele Valley Holiday Park, Hele Bay, Ilfracombe, North Devon, EX34 9RD
Tel: 01271 862460
Email: holidays@helevalley.co.uk
www.helevalley.co.uk
Pitches For ▲ ⬡ ⬡ **Total** 50
Acreage 7 **Open** Easter to Oct
Access Good **Site** Level
Nearest Bus Stop (Miles) ¼
Set within a tranquil secluded valley. Just a few minutes walk to the beach, pubs, shop and coastal path. The only campsite in Ilfracombe.
Facilities ⬡ ⬡ ⬡ ⬡ ⬡ ⬡ ⬡ ⬡ ⬡ ⬡
⬡ ⬡ ⬡ ⬡ ⬡ ⬡ ⬡
Nearby Facilities ⬡ ⬡ ⬡ ⬡ ⬡ ⬡
Nearest Town Ilfracombe
Directions From the A399 in Hele Bay follow signs to turn off main road to a T-Junction. Take a right turn to Hele Valley.
⬡ Barnstaple

ILFRACOMBE

Hidden Valley Touring & Camping Park, West Down, Nr Ilfracombe, North Devon, EX34 8NU
Tel: 01271 813837
Email: relax@hiddenvalleypark.com
www.hiddenvalleypark.com
Pitches For ▲ ⬡ ⬡ ⬡ **Total** 115
Acreage 27 **Open** All Year
Access Good **Site** Level
Nearest Bus Stop (Miles) Outside
This beautiful owner-run touring park offers first class amenities - sheltered, level pitches, glorious tranquil surroundings, an excellent site shop, coffee shop and therapy room.

Ideally located for exploring the North Devon coast and countryside. National Caravan Park of the Year 2009.
Facilities ⬡ ⬡ ⬡ ⬡ ⬡ ⬡ ⬡ ⬡ ⬡ ⬡
⬡ ⬡ ⬡ ⬡ ⬡ ⬡ ⬡ ⬡ ⬡
Nearby Facilities ⬡ ⬡ ⬡ ⬡ ⬡ ⬡ ⬡ ⬡
Nearest Town Ilfracombe
Directions From Barnstaple take the A361 towards Ilfracombe, Park is 8 miles on the left.
⬡ Barnstaple

ILFRACOMBE

Napps Touring Holidays, Napps, Old Coast Road, Berrynarbor, Ilfracombe, Devon, EX34 9SW
Tel: 01271 882557
Email: enquiries@napps.fsnet.co.uk
www.napps.co.uk
Pitches For ▲ ⬡ ⬡ **Total** 250
Acreage 11 **Open** March to November
Access Good **Site** Level
Nearest Bus Stop (Miles) Outside
Probably the most beautiful coastal setting you will see. 200 yards from the beach. Popular family site with woodland and coastal walks. Heated swimming pool, tennis, coffee shop, breakfasts, Devon cream teas and your own local pub on site.
Facilities ⬡ ⬡ ⬡ ⬡ ⬡ ⬡ ⬡ ⬡ ⬡ ⬡
⬡ ⬡ ⬡ ⬡ ⬡ ⬡ ⬡ ⬡ ⬡ ⬡ ⬡
Nearby Facilities ⬡ ⬡ ⬡ ⬡ ⬡
Nearest Town Ilfracombe
Directions On A399, 1¼ miles west of Combe Martin, turn right onto Old Coast Road (signposted). Site 400yds along Old Coast Road.
⬡ Barnstaple

ILFRACOMBE

Watermouth Cove Holiday Park, Berrynarbor, Nr Ilfracombe, North Devon, EX34 9SJ
Tel: 01271 862504
Email: info@watermouthcoveholidays.co.uk
www.watermouthcoveholidays.co.uk
Pitches For ▲ ⬡ ⬡
Acreage 27 **Open** April to October
Access Good **Site** Lev/Slope
Nearest Bus Stop (Miles) Entrance
On the headlands with stunning views across the Channel. Own cove with rock pools and caves. Adjacent to Watermouth Harbour.
Facilities ⬡ ⬡ ⬡ ⬡ ⬡ ⬡ ⬡ ⬡ ⬡
⬡ ⬡ ⬡ ⬡ ⬡ ⬡ ⬡ ⬡ ⬡ ⬡ ⬡
Nearby Facilities ⬡ ⬡ ⬡ ⬡ ⬡
Nearest Town Ilfracombe
Directions From Barnstaple tale the A361 through to Ilfracombe and on to Watermouth Cove.
⬡ Barnstaple

ILFRACOMBE

Watermouth Valley Camping Park, Watermouth, Ilfracombe, North Devon, EX34 9SJ
Tel: 01271 862282
Email: watermouthvalley@hotmail.co.uk
www.watermouthpark.co.uk
Pitches For ▲ ⬡ ⬡ **Total** 155
Acreage 30 **Open** Easter to Mid Sept
Access Good **Site** Level
Nearest Bus Stop (Miles) Outside
Just a 5 minute walk to Watermouth Castle and harbour. Near beaches, Ilfracombe, Combe Martin and Woolacombe.
Facilities ⬡ ⬡ ⬡ ⬡ ⬡ ⬡ ⬡ ⬡ ⬡
⬡ ⬡ ⬡ ⬡ ⬡ ⬡ ⬡ ⬡ ⬡
Nearby Facilities ⬡ ⬡ ⬡ ⬡ ⬡ ⬡ ⬡ ⬡
Nearest Town Ilfracombe

Directions Situated on the A399 Ilfracombe to Combe Martin road, near to Watermouth Harbour.
⬡ Barnstaple

IVYBRIDGE

Cheston Caravan & Camping Park, Folly Cross, Wrangaton Road, South Brent, Devon, TQ10 9HF
Tel: 01364 72586
Email: enquiries@chestoncaravanpark.co.uk
www.chestoncaravanpark.co.uk
Pitches For ▲ ⬡ ⬡ **Total** 24
Acreage 1¾ **Open** 15-Mar to 31-Oct
Access Good **Site** Level
Nearest Bus Stop (Miles) ¼
Set in Dartmoor National Park. Great for a family holiday. Torquay and Paignton nearby. Perfect for walking and sightseeing.
Facilities ⬡ ⬡ ⬡ ⬡ ⬡ ⬡ ⬡ ⬡ ⬡ ⬡
Nearby Facilities ⬡ ⬡ ⬡ ⬡ ⬡ ⬡ ⬡
Nearest Town Ivybridge
Directions From Exeter, after by-passing South Brent, turn left at Wrangaton Cross slip road then right A38. From Plymouth take South Brent (Woodpecker) turn, at end of slip road turn right, go under A38 and rejoin A38 and follow directions from Exeter.

KINGSBRIDGE

Karrageen Caravan & Camping Site, Bolberry, Malborough, Kingsbridge, Devon, TQ7 3EN
Tel: 01548 561230
Email: phil@karrageen.co.uk
www.karrageen.co.uk
Pitches For ▲ ⬡ ⬡ **Total** 70
Acreage 7½ **Open** Easter to Sept
Access Good **Site** Lev/slope
Nearest and best park to Hope Cove, beaches 1 mile away. Situated in beautiful, scenic countryside and surrounded by superb National Trust coastline. Terraced, level, tree lined pitches. Family shower room. Hot take-away food. Superb cliff top walking. A site with a view. Caravans for hire. See our advertisement under Salcombe.
Facilities ⬡ ⬡ ⬡ ⬡ ⬡ ⬡ ⬡ ⬡ ⬡ ⬡
⬡ ⬡ ⬡ ⬡ ⬡ ⬡
Nearby Facilities ⬡ ⬡ ⬡ ⬡ ⬡ ⬡ ⬡
Nearest Town Salcombe
Directions Take the A381 Kingsbridge to Salcombe road, turn sharp right into Malborough Village. In 0.6 miles turn right (sp Bolberry), after 0.9 miles the site is on the right and reception is at the house on the left.
⬡ Totnes/Plymouth

KINGSBRIDGE

Mounts Farm Touring Park, The Mounts, East Allington, Kingsbridge, Devon, TQ9 7QJ
Tel: 01548 521591
Email: mounts.farm@lineone.net
www.mountsfarm.co.uk
Pitches For ▲ ⬡ ⬡ ⬡ **Total** 50
Acreage 8 **Open** April to Oct
Access Good **Site** Level
Nearest Bus Stop (Miles) Outside
Central location in South Devon within easy travelling distance of many beaches and attractions.
Facilities ⬡ ⬡ ⬡ ⬡ ⬡ ⬡ ⬡
⬡ ⬡ ⬡ ⬡ ⬡ ⬡ ⬡
Nearby Facilities ⬡ ⬡ ⬡ ⬡ ⬡ ⬡ ⬡ ⬡
Nearest Town Kingsbridge
Directions From Totnes take the A381 towards Kingsbridge. After 10 miles enter The Mounts and the site entrance is 500 metres on the left.
⬡ Totnes

KINGSBRIDGE
Parkland, Sorley Green Cross,
Kingsbridge, Devon, TQ7 4AF
Tel: 01548 852723
Email: enquiries@parklandsite.co.uk
www.parklandsite.co.uk
Pitches For 🏕 🚐 🚌 🚐
Acreage 3 **Open** All Year
Access Good **Site** Level
Nearest Bus Stop (Miles) ¼
PARKLAND is a high quality traditional site
set in 3 acres of level grounds, located 1 mile
north of Kingsbridge. Just a short distance
from Bantham Beach with panoramic views
of Salcombe and Dartmoor. FREE electric
hook-ups. Full modern heated facilities,
family and disabled suites. Large children's
playground. Free Wi-Fi. Course fishing ½
mile and leisure centre 1 mile. Special breaks
available. All enquiries welcome.
Facilities ♿ ✦ 🖻 🚿 🔥 ☕ 🛒 💈 ☎
🏧 ⛽ 🏪 🍴 ⚡ ⛺ ✿ ❧
Nearby Facilities ▶ ✓ ⚓ ⛵ ∪ ⟿ ♣ ❀
Nearest Town Kingsbridge/Salcombe
Directions From Totnes follow the A381,
main Kingsbridge road, to Sorley Green
Cross. Go straight ahead and the site is 100
yards on the left.

KINGSBRIDGE
**Slapton Sands Camping & Caravanning
Club Site,** Middle Grounds, Slapton,
Kingsbridge, Devon, TQ7 2QW
Tel: 01548 580538
www.campingandcaravanningclub.co.uk/
slaptonsands
Pitches For 🏕 🚐 **Total** 115
Acreage 5½ **Open** 29-Mar **to** 05-Nov
Access Good **Site** Lev/Slope
Nearest Bus Stop (Miles) ¼
Overlooking Start Bay, just a few minutes
from the beach. BTB 4 Star Graded and AA
3 Pennants. Club Member Caravans Only.
Non members welcome. You can also call
us on 0845 130 7633.
Facilities ♿ ✦ 🖻 🚿 🔥 ☕ 💈 ☎
🏧 ⛽ 🏪 🍴 🎔 ❧
Nearby Facilities ▶ ✓ ∪ ♣
Nearest Town Dartmouth
Directions From Kingsbridge take the A379,
site entrance is ¼ mile from the A379, beyond
the brow of the hill approaching Slapton Village.
🚍 Totnes

LYDFORD
Lydford Caravan & Camping Park,
Lydford, Nr Okehampton, Devon, EX20 4BE
Tel: 01822 820497
Email: info@lydfordsite.co.uk
www.lydfordsite.co.uk
Pitches For 🏕 🚐 🚌 **Total** 80
Acreage 7 **Open** 23-Mar **to** 29-Oct

Access Good **Site** Level
Nearest Bus Stop (Miles) ¼
ADULTS ONLY PARK in Dartmoor National
Park with beautiful views. Lydford has the
deepest gorge in the South West. Ideal for
visiting National Trust properties.
Facilities ♿ ✦ 🖻 🚿 🔥 ☕ 💈 ☎ 🍴 ☎
🏧 🎔 ⛽ 🏪 🍴 🎔 ❧
Nearby Facilities ▶ ✓ ⚓ ⛵ ∪ ⟿
Nearest Town Okehampton
Directions From the A30 (DO NOT follow
SatNav) take the A386 sp Tavistock and
Plymouth. After 5 miles turn right to Lydford.
At the war memorial turn right, right fork, site
is on the left.
🚍 Gunnislake

LYNTON
Camping & Caravanning Club Site,
Caffyns Cross, Lynton, Devon, EX35 6JS
Tel: 01598 752379
www.campingandcaravanningclub.co.uk/
lynton
Pitches For 🏕 🚐 🚌 **Total** 105
Acreage 5½ **Open** 29-Mar **to** 05-Nov
Access Good **Site** Lev/Slope
Nearest Bus Stop (Miles) ½
Overlooking the Bristol Channel. 2 miles from
Lynton and Lynmouth. ETB 4 Star Graded
and AA 3 Pennants. Non members welcome.
You can also call us on 0845 130 7633.
Facilities ♿ ✦ 🖻 🚿 🔥 ☕ 💈 ☎
🏧 🎔 🏪 🍴 🎔 ⛽
Nearby Facilities ▶ ✓ ∪ ♣
Nearest Town Lynton
Directions Leave the M5 and take the A361
to Barnstaple. At South Molton turn right to
Blackmoor Gate sp Lynmouth and Lynton.
After 5 miles turn left at the bus shelter, turn
first left then first right to camp site.
🚍 Barnstaple

LYNTON
Channel View Caravan & Camping Park,
Manor Farm, Barbrook, Lynton, Devon,
EX35 6LD
Tel: 01598 753349
Email: relax@channel-view.co.uk
www.channel-view.co.uk
Pitches For 🏕 🚐 🚌 **Total** 70
Acreage 6 **Open** 15-Mar **to** 15-Nov
Access Good **Site** Lev/Slope
Nearest Bus Stop (Miles) ½
On the edge of Exmoor overlooking Lynton
and Lynmouth for panoramic views.
Facilities ♿ ✦ 🖻 🚿 🔥 ☕ 💈 ☎ 🍴 ☎
🏧 🎔 🏪 🍴 🎔 ❧
Nearby Facilities ▶ ✓ ⚓ ⛵ ∪ ♣
Nearest Town Lynton/Lynmouth
Directions On the A39 ½ a mile from
Barbrook.
🚍 Barnstaple

MODBURY
Broad Park Caravan Club Site, Higher
East Leigh, Modbury, Ivybridge, Devon,
PL21 0SH
Tel: 01548 830714
www.caravanclub.co.uk
Pitches For 🚐 🚌 **Total** 113
Open March **to** Nov
Access Poor **Site** Level
Nearest Bus Stop (Miles) ½
Situated between moors and sea, this makes
a splendid base from which to explore South
Devon. Local attractions include Dart Valley
Steamer Trips, Dartmoor Wildlife Park and
Miniature Pony Centre. Non members
welcome. Booking essential.
Facilities ♿ ✦ 🖻 🚿 🔥 ☕ 💈 ☎ 🍴 ☎
🏧 🎔 🏪 🍴 🎔 ❧
Nearby Facilities
Nearest Town Ivybridge
Directions From Exeter heading SW on A38,
after 30 miles pass the Woodpecker Inn and
after ½ a mile take the slip road onto A3121.
At the top of the slip road turn left following
Broad Park sign, at crossroads go straight
across, after 2½ miles continue right just past
California Cross on to B3207. Site is on the
left after 1 mile.
🚍 Ivybridge

MODBURY
Camping & Caravanning Club Site,
California Cross, Modbury, Ivybridge,
Devon, PL21 0SG
Tel: 01548 821297
www.campingandcaravanningclub.co.uk/
californiacross
Pitches For 🏕 🚐 🚌 **Total** 80
Acreage 3¾ **Open** 29-Mar **to** 24-Sep
Access Good **Site** Lev/Slope
Nearest Bus Stop (Miles) ½
Rural setting centrally situated in the South
Hams. Close to the beaches of Salcombe
and Torbay. Take-away food available two
nights a week. 5 miles from Sorley Tunnel
Childrens Adventure Park. Chocks needed
on some pitches. BTB 4 Star Graded and AA
3 Pennants. Non members welcome. You
can also call us on 0845 130 7633.
Facilities ♿ ✦ 🖻 🚿 🔥 ☕ 💈 ☎ 🍴 ☎
🏧 🎔 🏪 🍴 🎔 ❧
Nearby Facilities ▶ ✓ ∪ ♣
Nearest Town Ivybridge
Directions On the A38 travelling south west
take the A3121 to the crossroads, straight
across to the B3196 to California Cross
Hamlet. Turn left after California Cross
Hamlet sign but before the petrol station, site
is on the right.
🚍 Ivybridge

Proprietor: R A Blackler

There's a lot more at...
Pennymoor
Caravan & Camping Park
Modbury · South Devon
**Touring, Camping
& Self Catering Holiday Caravans**
Modbury · South Devon · PL21 0SB
Tel: 01548 830542 / 830020 Fax: 01548 830542
E-mail: enquiries@pennymoor-camping.co.uk
www.pennymoor-camping.co.uk

Owned and run by the same family since 1935
Relaxed spacious rural site, spectacular panoramic
views over the Dartmoor and Devonshire countryside.
Close to the many beautiful attractions of the South Hams.
● Children's play area ● Shop ● Calor gas and camping gas
● Super toilet/shower facilities, free hot water ● Chemical disposal
points ● Laundry room including iron ● Covered dishwashing area
● Good disabled facilities ● Public telephone ● Dog walk area

MODBURY
Pennymoor Caravan Park, Modbury, Nr Ivybridge, Devon, PL21 0SB
Tel: 01548 830542/830020
Email: enquiries@pennymoor-camping.co.uk
www.pennymoor-camping.co.uk
Pitches For Å ⊕ ⊟ **Total** 124
Acreage 11 **Open** 15-Mar **to** 15-Nov
Access Good **Site** Level
Peaceful rural site. Only 5 miles from Bigbury-on-Sea (Burgh Island).
Facilities ⚿ ≬ ▥▣🖵⌐⊙☂▱◲❦
♨◉♨⚑🚿🔲
Nearby Facilities ⌐✓⚓≽∪☞
Nearest Town Modbury/Ivybridge
Directions Approx 30 miles West of Exeter, leave A38 at Wrangaton Cross. Turn left, then straight across at next crossroads and continue for approx 4 miles. Pass petrol garage on left, then take second left, site is 1 mile on the right.
⇥ Ivybridge

MORTEHOE
Easewell Farm Holiday Village & Golf Club Mortehoe Station Road, Mortehoe, Devon, EX34 7EH
Tel: 01271 870343
Email: goodtimes@woolacombe.com
www.woolacombe.com/cades
Pitches For Å ⊕ ⊟ **Total** 302
Open 27-Mar **to** 01-Nov
Access Good **Site** Level
Nearest Bus Stop (Miles) Outside
Close to the Blue Flag beach of Woolacombe and spectacular coastal walks. Choice of 4 Parks and their facilities and entertainment. Fishing nearby. Golf on Park.
Facilities ⚿ ≬ ▥▣🖵⌐⊙☂▱◲❦
♨♫▯◉☎✕♈🔲🔥🗼⚑🚿🔲❦
Nearby Facilities ⌐✓⚓≽∪☞☞☞
Nearest Town Woolacombe
Directions From Barnstaple take the A361 Ilfracombe road to the junction with the B3343 at Mullacott Cross. Turn first left signposted Woolacombe, after 1¾ miles turn right to Mortehoe. Park is 1¼ miles on the right.
⇥ Barnstaple

MORTEHOE
North Morte Farm Caravan & Camping Park, North Morte Road, Mortehoe, Woolacombe, Devon, EX34 7EG
Tel: 01271 870381
Email: info@northmortefarm.co.uk
www.northmortefarm.co.uk
Pitches For Å ⊕ ⊟ **Total** 175
Open April **to** End Oct
Access Narrow **Site** Lev/Slope
Nearest Bus Stop (Miles) ¼
500 yards from Rockham Beach. Adjoining National Trust land. Ideal walking country.
Facilities ⚿ ≬ ▣🖵⌐⊙☂▱◲❦
♨♫▯◉☎✕❦
Nearby Facilities ⌐✓≽∪
Nearest Town Woolacombe
Directions 14 miles from Barnstaple on the A361 take the B3343 and follow signs to Mortehoe. In the village turn right at the Post Office, park is 500 yards on the left.
⇥ Barnstaple

MORTEHOE
Twitchen House Holiday Village, Mortehoe, Woolacombe, North Devon, EX34 7ES
Tel: 01271 870343
Email: goodtimes@woolacombe.com
www.woolacombe.com/cades
Pitches For Å ⊕ ⊟ ⊟ **Total** 339
Acreage 20 **Open** 27-Mar **to** 01-Nov
Access Good **Site** Sloping
Nearest Bus Stop (Miles) Outside
Rural, scenic setting, close to Woolacombes glorious sandy beach and spectacular coastal walks.
Facilities ⚿ ≬ ▣🖵⌐⊙☂▱◲❦
♨♫▯◉☎✕♈🔲🔥🗼⚑🚿🔲❦≋
🛜
Nearby Facilities ⌐✓⚓≽∪☞☞☞
Nearest Town Woolacombe
Directions From Barnstaple/Ilfracombe road (A361) to junction with B3343 at Mullacott Cross, first left signposted Woolacombe for 1¾ miles, then right signposted Mortehoe. Park is 1¼ miles on left.
⇥ Barnstaple

MORTEHOE
Warcombe Farm Camping Park, Mortehoe, Nr Woolacombe, North Devon, EX34 7EJ
Tel: 01271 870690
Email: info@warcombefarm.co.uk
www.warcombefarm.co.uk
Pitches For Å ⊕ ⊟ **Total** 200
Acreage 19 **Open** 15-Mar **to** 31-Oct
Access Good **Site** Mostly Level
Nearest Bus Stop (Miles) Outside
Family run, landscaped site with a beautiful lake and panoramic sea views. Excellent facilities. 1¼ miles to Woolacombe beach.
Facilities ⚿ ≬ ▣🖵⌐⊙☂▱◲❦
♨◉☎✕♈🔲🔥⚑🚿🔲❦≋🛜
Nearby Facilities ⌐✓⚓≽∪
Nearest Town Woolacombe
Directions Turn left off the A361, Barnstaple to Ilfracombe road at Mullacott Cross roundabout signposted Woolacombe. After 2 miles turn right towards Mortehoe. Site is first on the right in less than a mile.
⇥ Barnstaple

NEWTON ABBOT
Dornafield Touring Park, Two Mile Oak, Newton Abbot, Devon, TQ12 6DD
Tel: 01803 812732
Email: enquiries@dornafield.com
www.dornafield.com
Pitches For Å ⊕ ⊟ **Total** 135
Acreage 30 **Open** 15-Mar **to** 02-Jan
Access Good **Site** Level
Nearest Bus Stop (Miles) Outside
Beautiful 14th Century farmhouse location with superb facilities to suit discerning caravanners and campers. Tennis court on site. Booking essential.
Facilities ⚿ ≬ ▣🖵⌐⊙☂▱◲❦
♨▯◉☎🔲🔥⚑🚿🔲❦≋🛜
Nearby Facilities ⌐✓⚓≽∪☞☞☞
Nearest Town Newton Abbot
Directions Take the A381 (Newton Abbot to Totnes), in 2 miles at Two Mile Oak Inn turn right. In ½ mile turn first left, site is 200 yards on the right.
⇥ Newton Abbot

NEWTON ABBOT
Lemonford Caravan Park, Bickington, Newton Abbot, Devon, TQ12 6JR
Tel: 01626 821242
Email: info@lemonford.co.uk
www.lemonford.co.uk
Pitches For Å ⊕ ⊟ **Total** 85
Acreage 7 **Open** All Year
Access Good **Site** Level
Nearest Bus Stop (Miles) ½
In a beautiful setting and scrupulously clean. Close to Torbay and the Dartmoor National Park.
Facilities ⚿ ≬ ▣🖵⌐⊙☂▱◲❦
♨◉♨⚑🚿🔲
Nearby Facilities ⌐✓⚓≽∪☞☞†
Nearest Town Ashburton
Directions From Exeter along A38 take A382 turnoff, on roundabout take 3rd exit and follow site signs to Bickington. From Plymouth take A383 turnoff, follow road for ¼ mile and turn left into site.
⇥ Newton Abbot

NEWTON ABBOT
Ross Park Caravan Park, Park Hill Farm, Moor Road, Ipplepen, Newton Abbot, Devon, TQ12 5TT
Tel: 01803 812983
Email: enquiries@rossparkcaravanpark.co.uk
www.rossparkcaravanpark.co.uk
Pitches For Å ⊕ ⊟ **Total** 110
Acreage 32 **Open** 01-Mar **to** 01-Jan
Access Good **Site** Level
Nearest Bus Stop (Miles) 150 yards
Tranquil and friendly atmosphere in beautiful surroundings. Excellent range of facilities including a bar and restaurant, Tropical Conservatory, play and conservation areas, centrally heated amenities block and a snooker room. Ideal for touring the South Hams area. 6 miles from Torbay and Dartmoor National Park within a 15 minute drive.
Facilities ⚿ ≬ ▣🖵⌐⊙☂▱◲❦
♨♫▯◉☎✕♈🔲🔥🗼⚑🚿🔲❦≋🛜
Nearby Facilities ⌐✓⚓≽∪☞☞†
Nearest Town Newton Abbot
Directions 3 miles from Newton Abbot and 6 miles from Totnes on the A381. At Park Hill crossroads and Texaco Filling Station take the road signposted Woodland and brown tourism sign to Ross Park.
⇥ Newton Abbot

NEWTON ABBOT
The Dartmoor Halfway Inn Caravan Park, Bickington, Newton Abbot, Devon, TQ12 6JW
Tel: 01626 821270
Email: info@dartmoor-halfway-inn.co.uk
www.dartmoor-halfway-inn.co.uk
Pitches For ⊕ ⊟ ⊟ **Total** 25
Acreage 1½ **Open** All Year
Access Good **Site** Level
Nearest Bus Stop (Miles) 1
Esituated in the grounds of The Dartmoor Halfway Inn, beside the River Lemon. Perfect for visits to nearby Dartmoor or the coast.
Facilities ⚿ ≬ ▣🖵⌐⊙☂▱◲❦
◉✕♨⚑🚿🔲

Nearby Facilities ⌐ ✔ U ♃
Nearest Town Newton Abbot
Directions Leave the A38 at the Drumbridges exit and take the third exit sp Liverton. Pass through Bickington and turn left for Newton Abbot, Site is 1 mile on the left.
⚑ Newton Abbot

OKEHAMPTON
Bridestowe Caravan Park, Bridestowe, Nr Okehampton, Devon, EX20 4ER
Tel: 01837 861261
Pitches For Å ⊞ ⊟ **Total** 53
Open March **to** December
Access Good **Site** Level
Nearest Bus Stop (Miles) ½
Dartmoor National Park 2 miles, ideal for walking, cycling, horse riding, fishing and touring Devon and Cornwall. Within easy reach of coastal resorts.
Facilities ∮ ⏥ ⊞⊟♔ ⌐ ⊙ ⊐ ◢ ⌧ ☎
⅊ ⅋ ⊙ ♣ ⏡ ⊟ ☖ ⋇
Nearby Facilities ⌐ ✔ U
Nearest Town Bude
Directions Leave M5 for A30 to Okehampton 3 miles west of Okehampton turn off A30 to Bridestowe village, follow camping signs to site.

OKEHAMPTON
Bundu Camping & Caravan Park,
Sourton Down, Okehampton, Devon, EX20 4HT
Tel: 01837 861611
Email: frances@bundu.plus.com
www.bundu.co.uk
Pitches For Å ⊞ ⊟ **Total** 38
Acreage 4½ **Open** All Year
Access Good **Site** Level
Nearest Bus Stop (Miles) ¼
Situated with access to Dartmoor and adjacent to National Cycleway Route 27. Ideal for touring Devon and Cornwall.
Facilities ∮ ⏥ ⊞⊟♔ ⌐ ⊙ ⊐ ◢ ⌧ ☎
⅊ ⅋ ⊙ ✗ ⊣ ⊟ ☖ ◨ ⅋
Nearby Facilities ⌐ ✔ ⊥ U ♃
Nearest Town Okehampton
Directions On the A30 west, turn off at first slip road taking the A386 to Tavistock. Take first turn left to Sourton Down, site is at the end of the lane.
⚑ Okehampton

PAIGNTON
Beverley Park Holiday Centre,
Goodrington Road, Paignton, Devon, TQ4 7JE
Tel: 01803 661973
Email: info@beverley-holidays.co.uk
www.beverley-holidays.co.uk

Pitches For Å ⊞ ⊟ ⊟ **Total** 180
Acreage 9½ **Open** February **to** December
Access Good **Site** Level
Nearest Bus Stop (Miles) ¼
Views across Torbay. Indoor heated swimming pool, tennis court and sauna on site.
Facilities ♿ ∮ ⊟ ⏥⊞♔ ⌐ ⊙ ◢ ⌧ ☎
⅊ ⅋ ⊙ ⊠ ✗ �室 ⏥ ♣ ⏡ ⋋ ⅋ ⊙ ⊟ ⋇
☏
Nearby Facilities ⌐ ✔ ⊥ ⋋ U ♃ ♃
Nearest Town Paignton
Directions 2 miles south of Paignton (ring road) A3022. Turn left into Goodrington Road.
⚑ Paignton

PAIGNTON
Higher Well Farm Holiday Park, Stoke Gabriel, Totnes, Devon, TQ9 6RN
Tel: 01803 782289
www.higherwellfarmholidaypark.co.uk
Pitches For Å ⊞ ⊟ **Total** 80
Acreage 8 **Open** Easter **to** October
Access Good **Site** Lev/Slope
Nearest Bus Stop (Miles) ¼
Within 4 miles of Torbays beaches, 1 mile from the village of Stoke Gabriel and the River Dart.
Facilities ♿ ⚲ ∮ ⊟ ⏥⊞♔ ⌐ ⊙ ⊐ ◢ ⌧ ☎
⅊ ⅋ ⊙ ☖ ⊣ ⊟ ⊟
Nearby Facilities ⌐ ✔ ⊥ ⋋ ♃ ♃

Hoburne
Torbay

★★★★
4 Star Holiday & Touring Park

Panoramic views across the English Riviera, with Dartmoor and all the attractions of South Devon on your doorstep. Our striking clubhouse includes all the leisure and entertainment you could wish for!

Call: **0844 288 1935**
or visit **hoburne.com/cadest**
Celebrating 100 years of happy holidays

Hoburne
HOLIDAY PARKS

Nearest Town Paignton
Directions From Paignton take A385 towards Totnes, turn off left at Parkers Arms. Go 1½ miles then turn left again, site is 200 yards down road.
🚉 Paignton

PAIGNTON
Hoburne Torbay, Grange Road, Goodrington, Paignton, Devon, TQ4 7JP
Tel: 01803 558010
Email: enquiries@hoburne.com
www.hoburne.com
Pitches For 🚐 🚙 **Total** 139
Acreage 65 **Open** 26-Feb **to** 30-Jan
Access Good **Site** Lev/Slope
Nearest Bus Stop (Miles) ¼
Park with many facilities. Panoramic views over Torbay and within walking distance of Goodrington beach. Just a short drive to Dartmoor.
Facilities ⚑ 🏕 🖾 ♿ ❢ ⊙ ⚒ ☕ 🖻 🎱 ♨ 🎰 🖥 🎭 🏵 🖳 🍴 ※ 🎢 ⚓
Nearby Facilities ⌇ ✈ ⚓ ❄ ∪ ♒ ♞ ✗
Nearest Town Paignton
Directions From junc 31 of M5, travel south for approx 20 miles on A380 to junction with A385. Continue south on A380 (Paignton Ring Road) for 1 mile, turn left into Goodrington Road by Esso Filling Station. After ¾ miles turn left into Grange Road and follow signs
🚉 Paignton

PAIGNTON
Whitehill Country Park, Stoke Road, Paignton, South Devon, TQ4 7PF
Tel: 01803 782338
Email: info@whitehill-park.co.uk
www.whitehill-park.co.uk

Pitches For 🏕 🚐 🚙 🚙 **Total** 330
Acreage 30 **Open** 10-May **to** End Sept
Access Good **Site** Lev/Slope
Nearest Bus Stop (Miles) Outside
Beautifully situated in rolling Devon countryside yet within easy reach of the sea, Torquay and the Dartmoor National Park.
Facilities ♿ ❢ 🖾 ♨ ❢ ⊙ ⚒ ☕ 🖻 🎱 ♨ 🎰 🖥 ☕ ✗ 🖳 🎭 🏵 ⚓ 🍴 🖳 🎢 ※
🛜
Nearby Facilities ⌇ ✈ ⚓ ❄ ∪ ♒ ♞
Nearest Town Paignton
Directions Turn off the A385 at Parkers Arms Pub, ½ mile from Paignton Zoo, signposted Stoke Gabriel. Park is 1 mile along this road.
🚉 Paignton

PAIGNTON
Widend Touring Park, Berry Pomeroy Road, Marldon, Paignton, Devon, TQ3 1RT
Tel: 01803 550116
Pitches For 🏕 🚐 🚙 🚙 **Total** 207
Acreage 22 **Open** Easter **to** October
Site Level
Nearest Bus Stop (Miles) Outside
Quiet, family run park with beautiful Dartmoor and countryside views. Take-away food available.
Facilities ♿ ❢ 🏕 🖾 🖾 ♨ ❢ ⊙ ⚒ ☕ 🖻 🎱 ♨ 🎰 🖥 ✗ ☕ 🚿 🎢 🎭 🏵 🖳 ※
Nearby Facilities ⌇ ✈ ⚓ ❄ ∪ ♒ ♞ ✗
Nearest Town Paignton
Directions Turn into Five Lanes Road towards Berry Pomeroy off the main Torquay ring road (A380) new duel carriageway at Marldon.
🚉 Paignton

PLYMOUTH
Plymouth Sound Caravan Club Site, Bovisand Lane, Down Thomas, Plymouth, Devon, PL9 0AE
Tel: 01752 862325
www.caravanclub.co.uk
Pitches For 🚐 🚙 **Total** 58
Acreage 6 **Open** March **to** Oct
Access Good **Site** Lev/Slope
Nearest Bus Stop (Miles) ½
¾ miles from a sandy beach. Plenty to see and do in the local area. Near a dry ski slope centre, Tamar Valley Railway, Lydford Gorge, Dartington Crystal and National Marine Aquarium. Own sanitation required. Non members welcome. Booking essential.
Facilities ❢ 🏕 🖾 🖾 ♨ ✗ 🚿 🍴 🖻 🎱
Nearby Facilities ⌇ ⚓ ✗
Directions From east on A38 turn off at Marsh Mills flyover via slip road, at roundabout turn left onto A374 sp Plymouth City Centre. After 1¾ miles move to offside lane and follow signs for A379 Kingsbridge. At 4th roundabout turn right into Springfield Rd, at lights turn left into Reservoir Rd, by garage turn right into Staddiscombe Rd, after ½ mile turn left sp HMS Cambridge, after 1 mile turn right sp Down Thomas. At village sign turn right into Bovisand Lane (narrow entrance), site is 150 yards on the right.

PLYMOUTH
Riverside Caravan Park, Leigham Manor Drive, Marsh Mills, Plymouth, Devon, PL6 8LL
Tel: 01752 344122
Email: office@riversidecaravanpark.com
www.riversidecaravanpark.com
Pitches For 🏕 🚐 🚙 🚙 **Total** 259
Acreage 11 **Open** All Year
Access Good **Site** Level
Nearest Bus Stop (Miles) ¼

the great outdoors
touring, camping,
caravans, lodges,
and camping pods

South Devon

so much to do!

- 10 acres of woodland
- walking & cycling
- conservation awards
- outdoor heated pool
- hayloft bar
- children's play areas
- children's craft room
- shop, café & takeaway

01803 782338   *countryside holidays by the sea*   **www.whitehill-park.co.uk**

Adjacent to the River Plym. Perfect base for exploring the South Hams coastline, Dartmoor and South East Cornwall.
Facilities
Nearby Facilities
Nearest Town Plymouth
Directions From Plymouth city centre follow signs for A38 Exeter. After approx. 3 miles you will reach Marsh Mills roundabout, take the exit for Plympton and follow brown tourism signs.
⇌ Plymouth

PUTSBOROUGH

Putsborough Sands Caravan Park,
Manor Farm, Putsborough, Braunton, North Devon, EX33 1LB
Tel: 01271 890230
Email: rob@putsborough.com
www.putsborough.com
Pitches For 🚐 **Total** 25
Acreage 2 **Open** 01-Apr **to** 10-Oct
Access Poor **Site** Level
Nearest Bus Stop (Miles) 1
Adjacent to the multi award winning Putsborough Sands. Unrivalled views over the Atlantic. Booking is essential.
Facilities
Nearby Facilities

Nearest Town Croyde
Directions From Braunton take the B3231 Croyde road and follow signs.
⇌ Barnstaple

SALCOMBE

Alston Farm Camping & Caravan Site,
Nr Salcombe, Kingsbridge, Devon, TQ7 3BJ
Tel: 01548 561260
Email: info@alstoncampsite.co.uk
www.alstoncampsite.co.uk
Pitches For 🏕 🚐 🚐 **Total** 200
Acreage 15 **Open** Easter **to** October
Access Good **Site** Level
Nearest Bus Stop (Miles) 1
Secluded, sheltered site. Dish washing facilities. You can also contact us on Mobile: 07808 030921.
Facilities
Nearby Facilities
Nearest Town Salcombe
Directions Signposted on left of A381 between Kingsbridge and Salcombe towards Salcombe.
⇌ Totnes

SALCOMBE

Bolberry House Farm Caravan & Camping Park, Bolberry, Malborough, Nr Kingsbridge, South Devon, TQ7 3DY
Tel: 01548 561251
Email: enquiries@bolberryparks.co.uk
www.bolberryparks.co.uk
Pitches For 🏕 🚐 🚐 **Total** 70
Acreage 6 **Open** Easter **to** October
Access Good **Site** Level
Nearest Bus Stop (Miles) 1
A friendly and peaceful, family run park on a coastal farm. Wonderful sea views and good access to stunning cliff top walks. Safe sandy beaches 1 mile at the quaint old fishing village of Hope Cove. Salcombes scenic and pretty estuary, a boating paradise - 3 miles. Static Caravans for hire on a smal
Facilities
Nearby Facilities
Nearest Town Salcombe
Directions Take the A381 from Kingsbridge to Malborough. Turn right through the village, follow signs to Bolberry for 1 mile.
⇌ Totnes

VISIT **www.cades.co.uk** TO SEE OUR MONTHLY COMPETITION

SALCOMBE

Higher Rew Touring Caravan & Camping Park, Rew, Malborough, Kingsbridge, South Devon, TQ7 3BW
Tel: 01548 842681
Email: enquiries@higherrew.co.uk
www.higherrew.co.uk
Pitches For ▲ ⬛ 🚐 **Total** 90
Acreage 6 **Open** Easter **to** 31-Oct
Access Fair **Site** Lev/Slope
Sloping Park with level pitches. Only 1 mile from the coastal path and Salcombe Estuary.
Facilities ⨍ 📶 🚻 🏪 ☺ 🍴 🔥 ⬛ 🎱 🍸
🏧 ⬛ 🍴 🅿️🔌
Nearby Facilities ⌨ ✔ ⊥ ≿ ⅃ ℛ
Nearest Town Salcombe
Directions From Kingsbridge take the A381 towards Salcombe. Im Malborough turn sharp right through the village towards Soar, after 1 mile turn left.
🚉 Totnes

SEATON

Berry Barton Caravan & Camping Park, Berry Barton, Branscombe, Seaton, Devon, EX12 3BD
Tel: 01297 680208
Email: tmandaewhite@btconnect.com
www.berrybarton.co.uk
Pitches For ▲ ⬛ 🚐
Acreage 16 **Open** 15-Mar **to** 15-Nov
Access Good **Site** Level
Nearest Bus Stop (Miles) ¼
Situated on a farm in an area of outstanding natural beauty, with our land finishing at the top of the pebble beach at Littlecombe Shute. 1 mile of coastline and the Jurassic Coast for good walks.
Facilities ⨍ 📶 🚻 ☺ 🍴 🔥 ⬛ 🎱 🍸🔌
Nearby Facilities ⌨ ✔ ≿ ∪ ⅃ ℛ
Nearest Town Seaton/Sidmouth

Directions From the M5 at Exeter take the A3052 to Branscombe turning and turn off right following brown tourism signs. At the T-Junction turn left, after 10 metres turn right, at the next T-Junction turn left and the site is on the right after ½ a mile. Berry Bart
🚉 Honiton

SEATON

Leacroft Touring Park, Colyton Hill, Colyton, Devon, EX24 6HY
Tel: 01297 552823
Pitches For ▲ ⬛ 🚐 **Total** 138
Acreage 10 **Open** April **to** September
Access Good **Site** Sloping
Nearest Bus Stop (Miles) 2
Quiet, peaceful site in open countryside. Picturesque villages to explore and woodland walks nearby.
Facilities ⨍ 📶 🚻 🏪 ☺ 🍴 🔥 ⬛ 🎱 🍸
🏧 ⬛ 🏪 🍴 ⬛ 🍴 ❄ ✎
Nearby Facilities ⌨ ✔ ⊥ ∪ ℛ
Nearest Town Colyton
Directions A3052 Sidmouth to Lyme Regis road, 2 miles west of Seaton. Turn left at Stafford Cross international caravan sign, site is 1 mile on the right.
🚉 Axminster

SIDMOUTH

Kings Down Tail Caravan & Camping Park, Salcombe Regis, Sidmouth, Devon, EX10 0PD
Tel: 01297 680313
Email: info@kingsdowntail.co.uk
www.kingsdowntail.co.uk
Pitches For ▲ ⬛ 🚐 **Total** 100
Acreage 5 **Open** 15-Mar **to** 15-Nov
Access Good **Site** Level
Nearest Bus Stop (Miles) Outside

Heated shower block. Local fishermen are happy to take people out on boat trips. Ideal centre for East Devon and West Dorset. Pets are welcome if kept on a lead.
Facilities ⭐ ⨍ 📶 🚻 🏪 ☺ 🍴 🔥 ⬛ 🎱 🍸
🏧 ⬛ 🏪 🍴 ⬛ 🍴 ⬛
Nearby Facilities ⌨ ✔ ∪ ℛ
Nearest Town Sidmouth
Directions On the A3052 3 miles east of Sidmouth, opposite Branscombe Water Tower. Please note that we are NOT in Salcombe Regis Village.
🚉 Honiton

SIDMOUTH

Oakdown Country Holiday Park, Weston, Sidmouth, Devon, EX10 0PT
Tel: 01297 680387
Email: enquiries@oakdown.co.uk
www.oakdown.co.uk
Pitches For ▲ ⬛ 🚐 🚐 **Total** 150
Acreage 16 **Open** April **to** October
Access Good **Site** Level
Nearest Bus Stop (Miles) ¼
Welcome to Oakdown, a Caravan Holiday Park of the Year Winner - SIDMOUTHS MULTI AWARD WINNING PARK near the Jurassic Coast World Heritage Site and beautiful Weston Valley - lovely cliff walks. Oakmead Par 3 Golf Course. Field trail to nearby world famous Donkey Sanctuary. Luxurious Holiday Caravans to let. Awards for 2009/10: ETB 5 Star Grading, AA 5 Pennant De-Luxe Park, David Bellamy Gold and Loo of the Park.
Facilities ⭐ ⨍ 📶 🚻 🏪 ☺ 🍴 🔥 ⬛ 🎱 🍸
🏧 ⬛ 🏪 ✖ 🚗 🏪 ⬛ 🍴 🍴 ⬛ ❄ ✎ 🍸 ⬛
Nearby Facilities ⌨ ✔ ⊥ ≿ ∪ ⅃ ℛ
Directions 1½ miles east of Sidford on A3052, take the second Weston turning at the Oakdown sign. Site 50 yards on left. Also sp with international Caravan/Camping signs.
🚉 Honiton

AA
►►►
⬛⬛▲

KARRAGEEN
Caravan and Camping Park

A friendly, family-run Park on the South Devon coast

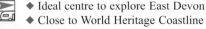

SIDMOUTH

Popplefords, Camp Site, Hill Side House, Exeter Road, Newton Poppleford, Devon, EX10 0DE
Tel: 07815 789137
Email: bo8ster@hotmail.com
Pitches For ▲ ⛺ 🚐 **Total** 7
Open March **to** October
Access Good **Site** Level
Nearest Bus Stop (Miles) Entrance
Alongside RSPB common land. 2 miles from Crealey Fun Park. 15 minutes drive from Sidmouth, Exmouth and beaches.
Facilities ⚪◻⚪⚪⚪◻⚪⚪
⚪✕➤◻⚪
Nearby Facilities ⚪✓⚓✕∪♪
Nearest Town Sidmouth
Directions Leave the M5 at junction 30 and head towards Sidmouth on the A3052. Pass Half Way House on the left, the Site is on the left after a further mile.
🚂 Exeter

SIDMOUTH

Putts Corner Caravan Club Site, Sidbury, Sidmouth, Devon, EX10 0QQ
Tel: 01404 42875
www.caravanclub.co.uk
Pitches For ⛺ 🚐 **Total** 118
Acreage 7 **Open** March **to** Nov
Access Good **Site** Lev/Slope
Nearest Bus Stop (Miles) ¼
Quiet site in pretty surroundings where wildlife and flowers abound. Plenty of walks from the site. Boules pitch, water softening plant and water supply from borehole. 200 yards from a pub. Near the Donkey Sanctuary. Non members welcome. Booking essential.
Facilities ♿⚪◻◻⚪⚪◻⚪⚪
⚪⚪◻➤◻◻⚪
Nearby Facilities ⚪
Nearest Town Sidmouth
Directions From east on A30 Honiton bypass, turn off via slip road at sp Sidmouth A375, at end of slip road turn left then 100 yards and turn left again, after 350 yards turn right onto A375. At Hare & Hounds Inn turn right onto B3174, site is ¼ mile on the right.
🚂 Sidmouth

SIDMOUTH

Salcombe Regis Camping & Caravan Park, Salcombe Regis, Sidmouth, Devon, EX10 0JH
Tel: 01395 514303
Email: contact@salcombe-regis.co.uk
www.salcombe-regis.co.uk
Pitches For ▲ ⛺ 🚐 **Total** 100
Acreage 16 **Open** 10-Mar **to** 27-Oct
Access Good **Site** Level
A park with peace and quiet. Just a 5 minute walk from the Jurassic Coastal Path, and a 5-10 minute drive from Select Sidmouth. Ideally based for touring East Devon.
Facilities ⚪◻◻⚪⚪◻⚪⚪⚪◻⚪⚪
⚪⚪⚪◻➤◻◻⚪✕⚪⚪
Nearby Facilities ⚪✓⚓∪♪
Nearest Town Sidmouth
Directions From Exeter M5 take the A3052 through Sidford towards Lyme Regis. Take second turning to Salcombe Regis, on the left after Golf Range.
🚂 Honiton or Exeter

SLAPTON

Sea View Campsite, Newlands Farm, Slapton, Nr Dartmouth, Devon, TQ7 2RB
Tel: 01548 580366
Email: cades@devon-camping.co.uk
www.camping-devon.co.uk
Pitches For ▲ ⛺ 🚐 **Total** 45
Acreage 10 **Open** 23-May **to** September
Access Good **Site** Level
Nearest Bus Stop (Miles) ½
We have a friendly, uncommercialised, quiet site overlooking beautiful countryside and sea. Within 1 mile of glorious beaches, cliff walks and a nature reserve. Woodlands Leisure Centre is close by with fun for all the family.
Facilities ⚪◻⚪⚪◻⚪⚪⚪➤
Nearby Facilities ⚪✓⚓✕∪♪♪
Nearest Town Dartmouth
Directions From Totnes take the A381 towards Kingsbridge, after Halwell Village take the fourth left signposted Slapton. Go 4 miles to Buckland Cross, proceed for ¼ mile, site is on the left hand side.

SOUTH MOLTON

Riverside Caravan & Camping Park, Marsh Lane, North Molton Road, South Molton, Devon, EX36 3HQ
Tel: 01769 579269
Email: relax@exmoorriverside.co.uk
www.exmoorriverside.co.uk
Pitches For ▲ ⛺ 🚐 🚐 **Total** 42
Acreage 42 **Open** All Year
Access Good **Site** Level
Nearest Bus Stop (Miles) Outside
Beautiful wooded valley with a river for trout fishing and NEW coarse fishing lakes. Tea Room serving food and drink. 15 minute drive to the beach and 10 minute drive to Exmoor. Ideal for walking and touring.
Facilities ♿⚪⚪◻◻◻⚪⚪◻⚪⚪
⚪⚪⚪✕⚪◻◻➤◻◻⚪✕✕
Nearby Facilities ⚪✓∪♪✕
Nearest Town South Molton
Directions 1 mile from South Molton.
🚂 Barnstaple

SOUTH MOLTON

Yeo Valley Holiday Park, The Blackcock Inn, Molland, South Molton, North Devon, EX36 3NW
Tel: 01769 550297
Email: info@yeovalleyholidays.co.uk
www.yeovalleyholidays.co.uk
Pitches For ▲ ⛺ 🚐 **Total** 65
Open 15-Mar **to** 15-Nov
Access Good **Site** Level
Nearest Bus Stop (Miles) 1
Close to Exmoor. Heated indoor swimming pool and The Blackcock Inn on site.
Facilities ⚪◻◻⚪⚪◻⚪⚪
⚪⚪⚪✕⚪⚪◻◻⚪✕
Nearby Facilities ✓∪✕
Nearest Town South Molton
Directions Leave the M5 at junction 27 and take the A361 to South Molton, follow brown tourism signs to Blackcock Inn.
🚂 Tiverton

STOKENHAM

Old Cotmore Farm, Stokenham, Kingsbridge, Devon, TQ7 2LR
Tel: 01548 580240
Email: info@holiday-in-devon.com
www.holiday-in-devon.com
Pitches For ▲ ⛺ 🚐 🚐 **Total** 30

Harford Bridge Park
Dartmoor Holidays by the River Tavy
★★★★

Peter Tavy • Tavistock • Devon • PL19 9LS
www.harfordbridge.co.uk
stay@harfordbridge.co.uk

AA
▶▶▶
⊕ ☒ ♿

01822 810349

ROSE AWARD

Beautiful sheltered park set in Dartmoor. Beside the River Tavy offering riverside and other level spacious pitches. Ideally situated for exploring Dartmoor, West Devon and the Tamar Valley, or simply relaxing on the park. Also luxury self catering Holiday Homes and Lodges. Adjacent to a bus service and Cycle Route 27.

Acreage 22 **Open** 15-Mar **to** Oct
Access Good **Site** Level
Nearest Bus Stop (Miles) ½
Small, family run, picturesque, peaceful site with views over farms and fields. Cliff walks, beaches, fishing and bird watching. Excellent pubs.
Facilities & ∱ ⌂ ⊞ ♿ ⌕ ⊙ 🍴 ▣ ◲ ☕
🔒 ⊙ ⊛ ♠ ⅍ ⊞ ▣ ◲ ☀ ☎
Nearby Facilities ↑ ✓ ⊥ ↿ ∪
Nearest Town Kingsbridge
Directions From Kingsbridge take the A379 towards Dartmouth, go through Frogmore and at the mini roundabout at Stokenham turn right signposted Beesands. The farm is 1 mile on the right.
⇌ Totnes

TAVISTOCK
Harford Bridge Holiday Park, Peter Tavy, Tavistock, Devon, PL19 9LS
Tel: 01822 810349
Email: enquiry@harfordbridge.co.uk
www.harfordbridge.co.uk
Pitches For ⋏ ⊞ ⋒ **Total** 120
Acreage 16½ **Open** All Year
Access Good **Site** Level
Nearest Bus Stop (Miles) Outside
Select family run park set in Dartmoor beside the River Tavy. Camping and Self Catering holidays open All Year. Ideal for exploring Devon and Cornwall.
Facilities & ∱ ⌂ ⊞ ♿ ⌕ ⊙ 🍴 ▣ ◲ ☕
⊙ ⊛ ⅍ ♠ ⅍ ⊞ ▣ ◲ ✓ ☎
Nearby Facilities ↑ ✓ ∪ ᚛ ∦
Nearest Town Tavistock
Directions A386 Okehampton road 2 miles north of Tavistock.
⇌ Plymouth

TAVISTOCK
Langstone Manor Caravan & Camping Park, Langstone Manor, Moortown, Tavistock, Devon, PL19 9JZ
Tel: 01822 613371
Email: web@langstone-manor.co.uk
www.langstone-manor.co.uk
Pitches For ⋏ ⊞ ⋒ **Total** 40
Acreage 5½ **Open** 15-Mar **to** 31-Oct
Access Good **Site** Level
Nearest Bus Stop (Miles) 1½

Direct access onto Dartmoor. Quiet, friendly park with views over moor and farmland. Bar and evening meals. Dogs welcome. ETB 4 Star Graded and AA 4 Pennants.
Facilities ∱ ⌂ ⊞ ♿ ⌕ ⊙ 🍴 ▣ ◲ ☕
🔒 ⊙ ⊛ ⅍ ♠ ⅍ ⊞ ▣ ◲ ✓ ☀
Nearby Facilities ↑ ✓ ⊥ ∪ ᚛ ∦
Directions Take the B3357 from Tavistock towards Princetown, after approx. 2 miles turn right at crossroads, pass over the cattle grid, continue up the hill then turn left following signs for Langstone Manor. We are ½ mile on the right.
⇌ Plymouth

TAVISTOCK
Tavistock Camping & Caravanning Club Site, Higher Longford, Moorshop, Tavistock, Devon, PL19 9LQ
Tel: 01822 618672
www.campingandcaravanningclub.co.uk/tavistock
Pitches For ⋏ ⊞ ⋒ **Total** 90
Acreage 6 **Open** All Year
Access Good **Site** Level
Nearest Bus Stop (Miles) Outside
Lying on the west side of the Dartmoor National Park, ideal for walkers and cyclists. Non members welcome. You can also call us on 0845 130 7633.
Facilities & ∱ ⌂ ⊞ ♿ ⌕ ⊙ 🍴 ▣ ◲ ☕
🔒 ⊙ ⊛ ⅍ ☀ ☎
Nearby Facilities ✓
Nearest Town Tavistock
Directions From Tavistock take the B3357 towards the National Park, site is approx. 2 miles on the right, signposted.
⇌ Plymouth

TAVISTOCK
Woodovis Park, Gulworthy, Tavistock, Devon, PL19 8NY
Tel: 01822 832968
Email: info@woodovis.com
www.woodovis.com
Pitches For ⋏ ⊞ ⋒ **Total** 50
Acreage 14 **Open** April **to** October
Access Good **Site** Level
Nearest Bus Stop (Miles) ½
5 Star BTB Graded Park. Quiet, rural site with outstanding views. Near to Dartmoor, coasts

and Cornwall. Excellent facilities, free showers, laundry/washing-up room. Shop, off-license, farm produce, bread/croissants baked on site. Heated indoor pool, Infrared therapy, sauna and jacuzzi. Petanque court.
Facilities & ∱ ⌂ ⊞ ♿ ⌕ ⊙ 🍴 ▣ ◲ ☕
🔒 ⊙ ⊛ ♠ ⅍ ☀⅍ ⊞ ▣ ◲ ☀ ☎ ☀
Nearby Facilities ↑ ✓ ∪ ᚛ ∦
Nearest Town Tavistock
Directions Take A390 Liskeard road from Tavistock, after 3 miles turn right at the roundabout.
⇌ Plymouth/Gunnislake

TEIGNMOUTH
Coast View Holiday Park, Torquay Road, Shaldon, Teignmouth, South Devon, TQ14 0BG
Tel: 01626 872392
Email: info@coastview.co.uk
www.coastview.co.uk
Pitches For ⋏ ⊞ ⋒ **Total** 250
Acreage 18 **Open** 18-Mar
Access Good **Site** Lev/Slope
Nearest Bus Stop (Miles) Outside
Near the beach with fantastic views.
Facilities ∱ ⌂ ⊞ ♿ ⌕ ⊙ 🍴 ▣ ◲ ☕
🔒 ⊙ ⊛ ⅍ ☀ ⊞ ♠ ⅍ ⅏ ⊞ ▣ ◲
Nearby Facilities ↑ ∪
Nearest Town Teignmouth
Directions On the A379 between Teignmouth and Torquay.
⇌ Teignmouth

TIVERTON
Minnows Touring Park, Sampford Peverell, Tiverton, Devon, EX16 7EN
Tel: 01884 821770
www.ukparks.co.uk/minnows
Pitches For ⋏ ⊞ ⋒ **Total** 60
Acreage 5½ **Open** 05-Mar **to** 29-Oct
Access Good **Site** Level
Nearest Bus Stop (Miles) ¼
Alongside the Grand Western Canal and National Cycle Way, ideal for walking, cycling, fishing, canoeing and bird watching. Centrally placed for coasts, Exmoor and Dartmoor.
Facilities & ∱ ⌂ ⊞ ♿ ⌕ ⊙ 🍴 ⊟
▣ ☎ 🔒 ⅍ ▣ ⊙ ⊛ ⅍ ▣ ◲ ☀
Nearby Facilities ↑ ✓
Nearest Town Tiverton

Directions Leave the M5 at junction 27 and take the A361 signposted Tiverton and Barnstaple. After 500 yards take the slip road signposted Sampford Peverell, turn right at the mini roundabout, site is ¼ of a mile ahead.
≠ Tiverton Parkway

TIVERTON

West Middlewick Farm Caravans & Camping, West Middlewick Farm, Nomansland, Tiverton, Devon, EX16 8NP
Tel: 01884 861235
Email: stay@westmiddlewick.co.uk
www.westmiddlewick.co.uk
Pitches For ▲ ⊕ ⊖ **Total** 25
Acreage 3½ **Open** All Year
Access Good **Site** Level
Nearest Bus Stop (Miles) Outside
Working family farm with lovely walks. Fishing ½ mile. Ideal touring. Log cabins B&B.
Facilities ⬚ ⫪ 🚻 🀫 🀫 ⌐ ⊙ 🖵 ☎
🛈 ⊹ 🖵 🖾 🀫
Nearby Facilities ✓ ∪ ᴫ
Nearest Town Tiverton
Directions Leave the A361 at junction 27 for Tiverton, then take the B3137 to Witheridge. 9 miles from Tiverton.
≠ Tiverton Parkway

TIVERTON

Zeacombe House Caravan Park, East Anstey, Nr Tiverton, Devon, EX16 9JU
Tel: 01398 341279
Email: enquiries@zeacombeadultretreat.co.uk
www.zeacombeadultretreat.co.uk
Pitches For ▲ ⊕ ⊖ **Total** 50
Acreage 4½ **Open** 31-Mar **to** 31-Oct
Access Good **Site** Level
ADULTS ONLY site near to Exmoor, Tarr

Steps, National Trust properties, Tarka Trail and Rosemoor Gardens. Ideal for walking. Evening meal service. TV is now digital, FreeView Box required for standard TV. AA 4 Pennants.
Facilities ⫪ 🚻 🀫 🀫 ⌐ ⊙ 🀫 🖵 ☎
🛈 ⊙ 🀫 🖵 🖾 🀫
Nearby Facilities ⌐ ✓ ∪
Nearest Town Tiverton
Directions Leave the M5 at junc 27 and take A361 to Tiverton. At the roundabout turn right sp A396 to Minehead and Dulverton. After 5 miles turn left at the Exeter Inn, after 1¾ miles turn left at the Black Cat onto the B3227, 5 miles to Knowstone and the site is on left.
≠ Tiverton

TORQUAY

Widdicombe Farm Touring Park, Widdicombe Lane, Marldon, Paignton, Torquay, Devon, TQ3 1ST
Tel: 01803 558325
Email: info@widdicombefarm.co.uk
www.widdicombefarm.co.uk
Pitches For ▲ ⊕ ⊖ ⊖ **Total** 198
Acreage 8 **Open** Mid March **to** Mid Oct
Access Good **Site** Level
Nearest Bus Stop (Miles) ½
ADULTS ONLY PARK ideal for Torquay, Paignton and Dartmouth. Easy access with no narrow country lanes. Bus service from the Park (according to demand). Bargain Breaks available.
Facilities ⬚ ⫪ 🗑 🚻 🀫 ⌐ ⊙ 🀫 🀫 🖵 ☎
🛈 🀫 🖾 ✕ ∇ 🀫 🖾 🀫 ⚡ 🀫 📶
Nearby Facilities ⌐ ✓ 🀫 ᴢ ᴫ
Nearest Town Torquay/Paignton

Directions From the A380 Torquay to Paignton ring road, from Newton Abbot turn right at the roundabout at Kerswell Gardens, go to the top of the hill to the roundabout and go straight on, see Widdicombe Farm on the right, double back at the next roundabout.
≠ Paignton

TOTNES

Steamer Quay Caravan Club Site, Steamer Quay Road, Totnes, Devon, TQ9 5AL
Tel: 01803 862738
www.caravanclub.co.uk
Pitches For ⊕ ⊖ **Total** 40
Acreage 3 **Open** March **to** Oct
Access Good **Site** Level
Nearest Bus Stop (Miles) Outside
Quiet site with lovely views, just a short walk from Totnes centre. Close to Paignton Zoo, Dart River Cruises and South Devon Railway. Non members welcome. Booking essential.
Facilities 🀫 🀫 ⌐ ⊙ 🀫 🖵 ☎ 🛈 ⊙ 🀫 🖵 🖾
Nearby Facilities ⌐ ✓
Nearest Town Totnes
Directions From A38 take either A384 at Buckfastleigh or A385 at South Brent, both roads become A385 at Dartington. In Totnes cross the railway bridge and turn right at the roundabout, after 300 yards turn left over the bridge, turn right into Seymour Road, turn right in to Steamer Quay Road. Site on left.
≠ Totnes

UFFCULME

Waterloo Cross Caravan Park, Uffculme, Devon, EX15 3ES
Tel: 01884 841342
Pitches For ▲ ⊕ ⊖ **Total** 50
Acreage 50 **Open** March **to** Feb
Access Good **Site** Level
Nearest Bus Stop (Miles) Outside
Ideal for touring.

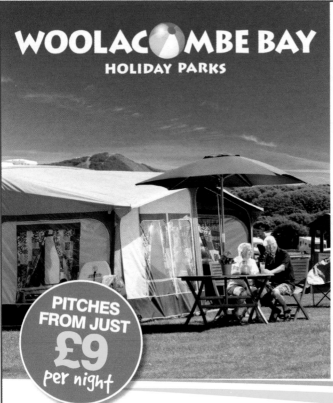

Facilities ⨍ 🏠 📶 ⌂ ☉ ⛽ ☎
🚿 ✕ 🍽 ♿ 🔥 ❄ ⚡
Nearby Facilities ┌ ⟋ ⟋ ∪ ♪
Nearest Town Tiverton
Directions 6 miles from Tiverton and Cullompton.
🚮 Tiverton Parkway

UMBERLEIGH
Camping & Caravanning Club Site, Over Weir, Umberleigh, Devon, EX37 9DU
Tel: 01769 560009
www.campingandcaravanningclub.co.uk/umberleigh
Pitches For ▲ ⛟ ⛺ **Total** 60
Acreage 3 **Open** 29-Mar to 05-Nov
Access Good **Site** Lev/Slope
Nearest Bus Stop (Miles) Entrance
The site enjoys a peaceful and relaxing atmosphere, situated between Exmoor and Dartmoor National Park. Superb golden beaches nearby. BTB 4 Star Graded and AA 3 Pennants. Non members welcome. You can also call us on 0845 130 7633.
Facilities ♿ ⨍ 🏠 📶 ⌂ ☉ ⛽ ⚡ 🏪 ☎
⚡ ⏚ 🔥 🏐 ✕ 🔥 🔥 🔥 ⚡ 📶
Nearby Facilities ┌ ⟋ ⟋ ♪
Nearest Town Barnstaple
Directions From Barnstaple take the A377 and turn right at Umberleigh nameplate.
🚮 Umberleigh

WESTWARD HO!
Braddicks Holiday Centre, Merley Road, Westward Ho!, Devon, EX39 1JU
Tel: 01237 473263
Email: holidays@braddicks.co.uk
www.braddicksholidaycentre.co.uk
Pitches For ▲ **Total** 40
Open May to Oct **Access** Good **Site** Sloping
Nearest Bus Stop (Miles) ½
Beside the Blue Flag beach and on the South West Coastal Path. Nightly entertainment during high season. Just a 5 minute walk from the centre of Westward Ho!. Self catering holidays available.
Facilities ⌂ ⛽ ✕ 🔥 ⚡
Nearby Facilities ┌
Nearest Town Bideford
Directions Leave M5 at jct 27 and take A361 to Barnstaple. Then take A39 to Bideford, continue across the Torridge Bridge and stay on A39, go straight across the roundabout, take the next turning marked Westward Ho! (on the right about ½ a mile from the rbt). Stay on this road for approx 1½ miles which will take you down a steep hill called Stanwell Hill, at the bottom take an immediate left into Merley Road, Braddicks is located at the end of the road on the right.
🚮 Barnstaple

WOOLACOMBE
Damage Barton, Mortehoe, Woolacombe, Devon, EX34 7EJ
Tel: 01271 870502
Email: info@damagebarton.co.uk
www.damagebarton.co.uk
Pitches For ▲ ⛟ ⛺ **Total** 155
Acreage 16 **Open** 15-Mar to 05-Nov
Access Good **Site** Lev/Slope
Nearest Bus Stop (Miles) Outside
Peaceful site with good views, wild flowers and birds. Access to a network of footpaths including the coastal path.
Facilities ⨍ ⌂ 🏠 📶 ⌂ ☉ ⛽ ⚡ 📶 ☎
🏪 📶 ⏚ ☉ 🏪 🔥 📶 ⚡
Nearby Facilities ┌ ⟋ ⤢ ∪ ♪
Nearest Town Woolacombe
Directions Take the A361 from Barnstaple and turn left at the Mullacott Cross roundabout onto the B3343 signposted Woolacombe and Mortehoe. After 1¾ miles

---

turn right signposted Mortehoe, site is on the right after approx. 1 mile.
🚮 Barnstaple

WOOLACOMBE
Europa Park, Beach Road, Woolacombe, Devon, EX34 7AN
Tel: 01271 871425
Email: holidays@europapark.co.uk
www.europapark.co.uk
Pitches For ▲ ⛟ ⛺ **Total** 200
Acreage 10 **Open** All Year
Access Good **Site** Level
Nearest Bus Stop (Miles) Outside
Near the beach.
Facilities ⨍ ⌂ 🏠 📶 ⌂ ⛽ ⌂ ☎
🏪 ⏚ ☉ 🏪 ✕ ☉ 🔥 🏪 🔥 ⚡
Nearby Facilities ┌ ⟋ ♪ ♪
Nearest Town Barnstaple
Directions Follow the A361 to Mullacott Cross, take the first exit onto Bradwell Road, follow road for 1 mile and the Park is on the right.
🚮 Barnstaple

WOOLACOMBE
Golden Coast Holiday Village, Woolacombe, Devon, EX34 7HW
Tel: 01271 870343
Email: goodtimes@woolacombe.com
www.woolacombe.com/cades
Pitches For ▲ ⛟ ⛺ **Total** 125
Open Feb to Jan
Access Good **Site** Lev/Slope
Nearest Bus Stop (Miles) Outside
Close to the Blue Flag beach of Woolacombe, bus service to the beach. Choice of four parks and their facilities, entertainment and accommodation.
Facilities ♿ ⨍ ⌂ 🏠 📶 ⌂ ☉ ⛽ ⌂ ☎ 📶
🏪 📶 ⏚ ☉ 🏪 ✕ ⏚ 🏪 🔥 ⚡ 🔥 🔥 📶
Nearby Facilities ┌ ⟋ ⤢ ∪ ♪ ♪ ✕
Directions Take the A361 to Barnstaple and follow signs for Ilfracombe, take the Woolacombe junction from Mullacott Cross.
🚮 Barnstaple

WOOLACOMBE
Little Roadway Farm, Woolacombe, Devon, EX34 7HL
Tel: 01271 870313
www.littleroadway.co.uk
Pitches For ▲ ⛟ ⛺ **Total** 200
Acreage 20 **Open** March to Nov
Access Good **Site** Lev/Slope
Nearest Bus Stop (Miles) ½
Within 1 mile of Woolacombe beach. Easy access to Putsborough, Croyde, Saunton and Exmoor.
Facilities ⨍ 📶 ⌂ ☉ ⌂ ☎
🏪 📶 ⏚ ☉ 🏪 ✕ 🏪 🔥 ⚡
Nearby Facilities ┌ ⟋ ⤢ ∪ ♪ ♪ ✕
Directions Take the A361 to Mullacott Cross roundabout and turn left towards Woolacombe, follow tourism signs and turn left onto the B3231, Little Roadway Farm is on this road.
🚮 Barnstaple

WOOLACOMBE
Woolacombe Bay Holiday Village, Sandy Lane, Woolacombe, Devon, EX34 7AH
Tel: 01271 870343
Email: goodtimes@woolacombe.com
www.woolacombe.com/cades
Pitches For ▲ **Total** 150
Open 27-Mar to 01-Nov
Nearest Bus Stop (Miles) Outside
Close to the Blue Flag beach of Woolacombe and spectacular coastal walks. Choice of 4 Parks and their facilities and entertainment. Fishing nearby. Golf and tennis on Park.
Facilities ⨍ 📶 ⌂ ☉ ⛽ ⌂ ☎
🏪 📶 ⏚ ☉ 🏪 ✕ 🍽 📶 🏪 🔥 🔥 🔥 ⚡ 🔥 📶 ⚡ ⟋

Nearby Facilities ┌ ⟋ ⤢ ∪ ♪ ♪ ✕
Nearest Town Woolacombe
Directions From Barnstaple take the A361 Ilfracombe road to the junction of the B3343 at Mullacott Cross. Turn first left signposted Woolacombe, after 1¾ miles turn right to Mortehoe, Park is 1 mile on the left.
🚮 Barnstaple

DORSET
BERE REGIS
Rowlands Wait Touring Park, Rye Hill, Bere Regis, Dorset, BH20 7LP
Tel: 01929 472727
Email: enquiries@rowlandswait.co.uk
www.rowlandswait.co.uk
Pitches For ▲ ⛟ ⛺ **Total** 71
Acreage 8 **Open** 15-Mar to 31-Oct
Access Good **Site** Lev/Slope
Nearest Bus Stop (Miles) ½
The Tank Museum and Monkey World nearby.
Facilities ♿ ⨍ ⌂ 🏠 📶 ⌂ ☉ ⛽ ⌂ ☎
🏪 📶 ⏚ ☉ 🏪 🔥 🏪 🔥 📶 🔥 ❄ ⚡
Nearby Facilities ┌ ⟋ ⤢ ∪ ♪ ♪
Nearest Town Wareham
Directions From Bere Regis follow signs for the Tank Museum, Park is ¾ miles from the village on the right hand side at the top of the hill.
🚮 Wool

BLANDFORD
The Inside Park, Blandford, Dorset, DT11 0HG
Tel: 01258 453719
Email: mail@theinsidepark.co.uk
www.theinsidepark.co.uk
Pitches For ▲ ⛟ ⛺ **Total** 100
Acreage 13 **Open** Easter to October
Access Good **Site** Lev/Slope
Rural environment with extensive wildlife. Ideal for touring.
Facilities ♿ ⨍ 📶 ⌂ ☉ ⌂ ☎
🏪 ⏚ ☉ 🏪 🔥 🔥 📶 🔥 ⚡
Nearby Facilities ┌ ⟋ ∪ ♪
Nearest Town Blandford Forum
Directions 1¼ miles south west of Blandford on the road to Winterborne Stickland. Signposted from junction of A350 and A354 on Blandford bypass.

BOURNEMOUTH
Charris Camping & Caravan Park, Candys lane, Corfe Mullen, Wimborne, Dorset, BH21 3EF
Tel: 01202 885970
Email: bookings@charris.co.uk
www.charris.co.uk
Pitches For ▲ ⛟ ⛺ **Total** 45
Acreage 3 **Open** All Year
Access Good **Site** Lev/Slope
Nearest Bus Stop (Miles) ¼
AA 3 Pennants and Caravan & Camping Club listed. Good central site convienient for the coast and New Forest. Poole 7½ miles and Bournemouth 8¼ miles. Cafe/restaurant close by.
Facilities ⨍ ⌂ 🏠 📶 ⌂ ☉ ⌂ ☎
🏪 ⏚ ☉ 🏪 🔥 ⚡
Nearby Facilities ┌ ⟋ ⤢ ∪ ♪
Nearest Town Wimborne
Directions A31 Wimborne bypass 1 mile west of Wimborne. Signs for entrance.
🚮 Poole

BOURNEMOUTH
St Leonards Farm, Ringwood Road, West Moors, Ferndown, Dorset, BH22 0AQ
Tel: 01202 872637
Email: enquiries_stleonards@yahoo.com
www.stleonardsfarm.biz

Pitches For 👤 🚐 🚙
Acreage 12 **Open** April **to** October
Access Good **Site** Level
Nearest Bus Stop (Miles) Outside
AA 3 Pennants.
Facilities 🔧 ⚡ 🛢️ 🚽 🚿 🏪 🔥 ⛱️ 📮 📺 📶
🏓 🛝 🎣 🔥 👟 ☕
Nearby Facilities 🏇 🚴 🛶 🎯 U 🏊 🎏
Nearest Town Bournemouth
Directions On the A31 4 miles west of
Ringwood, opposite the Murco Garage.
🚆 Bournemouth Central

BRIDPORT
Bingham Grange Touring Camping Park,
Binghams Farm, Melplash, Bridport,
Dorset, DT6 3TT
Tel: 01308 488234
Email: enquiries@binghamgrange.co.uk
www.binghamgrange.co.uk
Pitches For 👤 🚐 🚙 🚙 **Total** 111
Acreage 5 **Open** March **to** November
Access Good **Site** Lev/Slope
Nearest Bus Stop (Miles) Outside
EXCLUSIVELY FOR ADULTS. An Award
Winning Park set in an area of outstanding
natural beauty yet only 4½ miles from the
coast. An ideal base to explore Dorset. All
modern heated facilities.
Facilities 🔧 ⚡ 🛢️ 🚽 🚿 🏪 🔥 ⛱️ 📮 📺 📶
🏓 🛝 🎣 🔥 👟 ☕
Nearby Facilities 🏇 🚴 🛶 🎯 U 🏊 🎏 🎯
Nearest Town West Bay/Bridport
Directions Turn off A35 in Bridport at the
roundabout onto A3066, signposted
Beaminster. In 1¼ miles turn left into Farm
Road.
🚆 Dorchester/Crewkerne

BRIDPORT
Eype House Caravan Park, Eype,
Bridport, Dorset, DT6 6AL
Tel: 01308 424903
Email: enquiries@eypehouse.co.uk
www.eypehouse.co.uk
Pitches For 👤 🚙 **Total** 20
Acreage 4 **Open** Easter **to** 30-Sep
On the Dorset coastal path and only 200
yards from the beach. Pitches are levelled
into hill. NO electric hook-ups. Sorry, NO
touring caravans.
Facilities 🚽 🛢️ 🚿 🚽 🏪 📮 📺 📶
🔥 🛝 👟 ☕
Nearby Facilities 🏇 🚴 🛶 🎯 U
Directions Signposted Eype off the A35,
follow signs to the sea.
🚆 Dorchester/Crewkerne

BRIDPORT
Freshwater Beach Holiday Park, Burton
Bradstock, Bridport, Dorset, DT6 4PT
Tel: 01308 897317
Email: office@freshwaterbeach.co.uk
www.freshwaterbeach.co.uk
Pitches For 👤 🚐 🚙 🚙 **Total** 500
Acreage 40 **Open** Mid March **to** Mid Nov
Access Good **Site** Level
Nearest Bus Stop (Miles) Outside
Own private beach. Free family
entertainment (SBH to Mid Sept). Good cliff
walks. NEW leisure complex with 10 pin
bowling, indoor water play, sauna, steam

room and hot tub. Golf course adjoining park.
Pitch price includes 6 people and free club
membership.
Facilities 🔧 ⚡ 🛢️ 🚽 🚿 🏪 🔥 ⛱️ 📮 📺 📶
🏓 🛝 🎣 🔥 👟 ☕
Nearby Facilities 🏇 🚴 🛶 🎯 U
Nearest Town Bridport
Directions From Bridport take B3157
towards Weymouth, Park is 2 miles on the
right.
🚆 Dorchester

BRIDPORT
Graston Copse Holiday Park, Annings
Lane, Burton Bradstock, Bridport, Dorset,
DT6 4QP
Tel: 01308 426947
Email: enquiries@wdlh.co.uk
www.wdlh.co.uk
Pitches For 👤 🚐 🚙 **Total** 48
Open 27-Apr **to** 09-Sep
Access Average **Site** Level
Nearest Bus Stop (Miles) ½
Peaceful location in the Dorset countryside.
25 minutes walk to the beach. Online booking
available or call our Bookings Hotline: 01308
426947.
Facilities 🔧 🛢️ 🚽 🚿 🏪 📮 📺 📶
🏓 🛝 🎣 ☕
Nearby Facilities 🏇 🚴 🛶 🎯 U 🏊 🎏
Nearest Town Bridport
Directions From Bridport take the B3157
coastal road towards Weymouth, then in
Burton Bradstock turn left at the Anchor Pub,
then turn second right into Annings Lane.
🚆 Dorchester

BRIDPORT
Highlands End Holiday Park, Eype,
Bridport, Dorset, DT6 6AR
Tel: 01308 422139
Email: holidays@wdlh.co.uk
www.wdlh.co.uk
Pitches For 👤 🚐 🚙 **Total** 195
Acreage 8 **Open** 16-Mar **to** 04-Nov
Access Good **Site** Level
Nearest Bus Stop (Miles) ½
Exceptional views across Lyme Bay, 500
metres from the beach. Heated swimming
pool, steam room and sauna. Tennis and
Pitch & Putt on site. All weather awning areas.
Online booking available or call our Bookings
Hotline: 01308 426947.
Facilities 🔧 🛢️ 🚽 🚿 🏪 🔥 ⛱️ 📮 📺 📶
🏓 🛝 🎣 🔥 👟 ☕
Nearby Facilities 🏇 🚴 🎯 U 🏊
Nearest Town Bridport
Directions On approach to Bridport from
east (Dorchester) on A35 turn left at
roundabout, follow Bridport By-pass. Second
roundabout take third exit signposted A35
West 1 mile turn left to Eype and follow
signposts.
🚆 Axminster

BRIDPORT
Home Farm Caravan & Campsite,
Rectory Lane, Puncknowle, Nr Dorchester,
Dorset, DT2 9BW
Tel: 01308 897258
Pitches For 👤 🚐 🚙 **Total** 42
Acreage 5 **Open** 01-Apr **to** 05-Oct

Access Good **Site** Lev/Slope
Nearest Bus Stop (Miles) ¼
In a beautiful area, 1½ miles from the
Heritage Coast. Ideal touring.
Facilities 🛢️ 🚿 🚽 🏪 🔥 ⛱️ 📮 📺 📶
Nearby Facilities 🏇 🚴 🎯 U 🏊 🎏
Nearest Town Weymouth
Directions From Dorchester take the A35
towards Bridport, then take the B3157 to
Burton Bradstock. Turn off at Swyre and
follow the road to Puncknowle. Continue past
Rectory Lane and take next left turn into
Hazel Lane, at the T-Junction turn left, turn
left again at the red phone box in to Rectory
Lane. 12 miles from Dorchester.
🚆 Weymouth/Dorchester

BRIDPORT
West Bay Holiday Park, West Bay,
Bridport, Dorset, DT6 4HB
Tel: 0844 335 3732
Email:
touringandcamping@parkdeanholidays.com
www.parkdeantouring.com
Pitches For 👤 🚐 🚙 **Total** 131
Acreage 30 **Open** March **to** Oct
Access Good **Site** Level
Nearest Bus Stop (Miles) Outside
Situated in the heart of West Bay, beside the
beach, harbour and picturesque village.
Indoor pool. FREE kids clubs and live family
entertainment.
Facilities 🔧 🛢️ 🚽 🚿 🏪 🔥 ⛱️ 📮 📺 📶
🏓 🛝 🎣 🔥 👟 ☕
Nearby Facilities 🏇 🎯
Nearest Town Bridport
Directions Take the M3 towards Winchester,
then follow the M27 then the A31. Join the
A35 to Dorchester and head west to Bridport,
then head into West Bay.
🚆 Dorchester

CHARMOUTH
Camping & Caravanning Club Site,
Monkton Wylde Farm, Nr. Charmouth,
Dorset, DT6 6DB
Tel: 01297 32965
www.campingandcaravanningclub.co.uk/
charmouth
Pitches For 👤 🚐 🚙 **Total** 150
Acreage 12 **Open** 09-Mar **to** 29-Oct
Access Good **Site** Level
Nearest Bus Stop (Miles) 1
5 miles from Forde Abbey and Charmouths
fossil beach. 7 miles from Cricket St. Thomas
Wildlife Park. Motorhome service point. ETB
5 Star Graded, AA 4 Pennants and David
Bellamy Gold Award. Non members
welcome. You can also call us on 0845 130
7633.
Facilities 🔧 🛢️ 🚽 🚿 🏪 🔥 ⛱️ 📮 📺 📶
🏓 🛝 🎣 🔥 👟 ☕
Nearby Facilities 🏇 🚴 🎯 U 🏊 🎏
Nearest Town Charmouth
Directions From Dorchester take the A35,
turn right onto the B3165 signposted
Hawkchurch, site is on the left within ¼ of a
mile.
🚆 Axminster

CHARMOUTH

Manor Farm Holiday Centre, Manor Farm, Charmouth, Bridport, Dorset, DT6 6QL
Tel: 01297 560226
Email:
enquiries@manorfarmholidaycentre.co.uk
www.manorfarmholidaycentre.co.uk
Pitches For ▲ ⊕ ⊟ ⊟ **Total** 345
Acreage 30 **Open** All Year
Access Good **Site** Lev/Slope
Nearest Bus Stop (Miles) Outside
Ten minutes level walk to beach, alongside river. In area of outstanding natural beauty. Ideal touring.
Facilities ⚒ ♿ ⋔ 🖳 ⊞ ⬭ ⏚ ⊙ 🍴 ▱ ⊡ 🛒
♨ ⊙ 🛒 ✕ ⛏ ♠ ♪ ⌁ 🐕 🖳 ⊟ ✒ ✗
Nearby Facilities ⌐ ✔ ⏚ ⌐ ⋃ ⋬ ♪
Nearest Town Charmouth
Directions Come off the Charmouth bypass at east end Manor Farm is ¾ miles on the right, in Charmouth.
⇌ Axminster

CHARMOUTH

Monkton Wyld Farm, Charmouth, Dorset, DT6 6DB
Tel: 01297 631131
Email: holidays@monktonwyld.co.uk
www.www.monktonwyld.co.uk
Pitches For ▲ ⊕ ⊟ **Total** 130
Acreage 20 **Open** Mid March **to** End Oct
Access Good **Site** Level
Nearest Bus Stop (Miles) 1
Beautifully landscaped pitches with room to relax, and space for children to play. Friendly, helpful wardens offer every assistance. Spotless shower block. One bedroom self contained flat for rent.
Facilities ⚒ ♿ 🖳 ⊞ ⬭ ⏚ ⊙ 🍴 ▱ ⊡ 🛒
♨ 🏧 ⊙ 🛒 ⛏ ♠ 🖳 ⊟ ✒ ✗ ✗
Nearby Facilities ⌐ ✔ ⏚ ⌐ ⋃ ♪

Directions Take the A35 from Axminster towards Charmouth, cross the county boundary into Dorset and almost immediately turn left down an unmarked lane. Brown tourist sign only.
⇌ Axminster

CHARMOUTH

Newlands Holiday Park, Charmouth, Nr. Bridport, Dorset, DT6 6RB
Tel: 01297 560259
Email: enq@newlandsholidays.co.uk
www.www.newlandsholidays.co.uk
Pitches For ▲ ⊕ ⊟ **Total** 200
Acreage 23
Access Good **Site** Terraced
Nearest Bus Stop (Miles) Outside
Situated in the Heritage Coast village of Charmouth, near Lyme Regis. Wonderful views and walks through National Trust land. A short stroll to the village centre and safe beach.
Facilities ⚒ ♿ 🖳 ⊞ ⬭ ⏚ ⊙ 🍴 ▱ ⊡ 🛒
♨ ⊙ 🛒 ✕ ⛏ ♠ ♪ ⌁ 🐕 🖳 ⊟ 🛒
Nearby Facilities ⌐ ✔ ⏚ ⌐ ⋃ ⋬ ♪
Nearest Town Lyme Regis
Directions Turn off the A35 at the eastern exit for Charmouth, Newlands is situated a short distance on the left hand side.
⇌ Axminster

CHARMOUTH

Wood Farm Caravan & Camping Park, Axminster Road, Charmouth, Bridport, Dorset, DT6 6BT
Tel: 01297 560697
Email: holidays@woodfarm.co.uk
www.woodfarm.co.uk
Pitches For ▲ ⊕ ⊟ **Total** 216
Acreage 12 **Open** March **to** Oct
Access Good **Site** Terraced

Nearest Bus Stop (Miles) ¼
Beach ¾ mile. Country setting. New Offshore Cafe on site. Indoor heated swimming pool. Tennis and coarse fishing ponds on site. Booking essential.
Facilities ⚒ ♿ 🖳 ⊞ ⬭ ⏚ ⊙ 🍴 ▱ ⊡ 🛒
♨ 🏧 ⊙ 🛒 ✕ ♠ ♪ ⌁ 🐕 🖳 ⊟ ✒ ✗ 🛒
Nearby Facilities ⌐ ✔ ⏚ ⋃ ⋬ ♪
Nearest Town Charmouth
Directions On the A35, ½ a mile west of Charmouth.
⇌ Axminster

CHIDEOCK

Golden Cap Holiday Park, Seatown, Chideock, Nr Bridport, Dorset, DT6 6JX
Tel: 01308 426947
Email: enquiries@wdlh.co.uk
www.wdlh.co.uk
Pitches For ▲ ⊕ ⊟ **Total** 260
Acreage 12 **Open** 16-Mar **to** 04-Nov
Site Level/Sloping
Nearest Bus Stop (Miles) ¼
100 metres from beach, overlooked by the famous Golden Cap cliff top. All weather awning areas. Unique location on the Jurassic Coast, ideal for Lyme Regis and Weymouth. Online booking available or call our Bookings Hotline: 01308 426947.
Facilities ♿ 🖳 ⊞ ⬭ ⏚ ⊙ 🍴 ▱ ⊡ 🛒
♨ ⊙ 🛒 ⛏ ♪ ⌁ ⊟ ✒ ✗ ✗ 🛒
Nearby Facilities ⌐ ✔ ⋬ ⋃ ♪
Nearest Town Bridport
Directions Follow the A35 to Chideock, once in the village turn opposite the church into Duck Street signposted Seatown. Follow the lane to the beach and turn left.
⇌ Axminster/Dorchester

CHRISTCHURCH

Mount Pleasant Touring Park, 91 Matchams Lane, Hurn, Christchurch, Dorset, BH23 6AW
Tel: 01202 475474
Email: enq@mount-pleasant-cc.co.uk
www.mount-pleasant-cc.co.uk
Pitches For ▲ ⊞ ➡ **Total** 170
Acreage 7 **Open** All Year
Access Good **Site** Level
Nearest Bus Stop (Miles) 2
Close to the beach, a river for fishing, a dry ski slope and the Wonderland Complex.
Facilities ⨍ 🏠 🗑 📵 ➡ 🚽 🔥 🛒 🍴
🏧 🟢 🛆 🖾 🖻 🔌 🏸 ⚡
Nearby Facilities ✦ 🏊 ⚲ ✈ ∪ ♂ ♠
Nearest Town Christchurch/Bournemouth
Directions From Christchurch go straight through for 4 miles to Hurn. From Bournemouth take the A338.
➝ Bournemouth

CORFE CASTLE

Burnbake Campsite, Rempstone, Corfe Castle, Wareham, Dorset, BH20 5JH
Tel: 01929 480570
Email: info@burnbake.com
www.burnbake.com
Pitches For ▲ ➡ **Total** 130
Acreage 12 **Open** April to October
Site Level
A quiet, secluded site in woodlands with a stream. 4 miles from Studland with its three miles of sandy beach and excellent safe bathing. 4 miles from Swanage.
Facilities ⨍ 🏠 🗑 🚻 ➡ 🚽 ⊙ 🛒 🍴
🏧 🟢 🛆 🖾 🖻 🔌
Nearby Facilities ✦ 🏊 ⚲ ✈ ∪ ♂ ♠ ✗
Nearest Town Swanage
Directions From Wareham take the A351 to Corfe Castle, turn left under the castle onto the B3351 Studland road, through the old railway arches, and take the third turning left signposted Rempstone and follow signs.
➝ Wareham

CORFE CASTLE

Corfe Castle Camping & Caravanning Club Site, Bucknowle, Wareham, Dorset, BH20 5PQ
Tel: 01929 480280
www.campingandcaravanningclub.co.uk/orfecastle
Pitches For ▲ ⊞ ➡ **Total** 80
Open 01-Mar to 31-Oct
Access Good **Site** Lev/Slope
Nearest Bus Stop (Miles) ½
Very close to the historic thousand year old Corfe Castle, which survived the English Civil War, rising above the Isle of Purbeck. Chocks may be required on some pitches. You can also call us on 0845 130 7633.

Facilities ⨍ 🏠 🗑 📵 ➡ 🚽 ⊙ 🛒 🍴
🏧 🟢 🛆 🖾 🖻 🔌
Nearby Facilities ✦ ✦
Nearest Town Wareham
Directions From Wareham head south on the B3075 (South Street) toward Pound Lane. Continue to the roundabout and take second exit onto Furzebrook Road and turn left.
➝ Wareham

DORCHESTER

Crossways Caravan Club Site, Crossways, Dorchester, Dorset, DT2 8BE
Tel: 01305 852032
www.caravanclub.co.uk
Pitches For ⊞ ➡ **Total** 113
Acreage 35 **Open** April to Oct
Access Good **Site** Level
Nearest Bus Stop (Miles) ½
Landscaped site set in 35 acres of woodland. So much to see and do in the local area. 8½ miles from Weymouth beach and attractions. Non members welcome. Booking essential.
Facilities ⨍ 🏠 🗑 📵 ➡ 🚽 🛒 🍴
🏧 🟢 🛆 🖾 🖻 🔌 ⚡
Nearest Town Dorchester
Directions From NE on A31, at the roundabout on the outskirts of Bere Regis turn right onto A35. At Tolpuddle Ball junction turn left onto slip road sp Warmwell, at T-junction turn left, at next T-junction turn right, site is 4 miles on the left (entrance through garage forecourt).
➝ Dorchester

DORCHESTER

Giants Head Caravan & Camping Park, Old Sherborne Road, Dorchester, Dorset, DT2 7TR
Tel: 01300 341242
Email: holidays@giantshead.co.uk
www.giantshead.co.uk
Pitches For ▲ ⊞ ➡ **Total** 50
Acreage 3 **Open** March to October
Access Good **Site** Lev/Slope
Ideal touring, wonderful views, good walking. Car is essential. Chalets available for hire.
Facilities ⨍ 🗑 📵 ➡ 🚽 ⊙ 🛒 🍴
🏧 🟢 🖾 🖻 🔌 ⚡
Nearby Facilities ✦ ✈ ⚲ ∪ ♂
Nearest Town Dorchester
Directions From Dorchester avoiding bypass, at top of town roundabout take Sherborne Road approx 500 yards fork right at Loaders Garage signposted. From Cerne Abbas take the Buckland Newton road.
➝ Dorchester

DORCHESTER

Lyons Gate Caravan Park, Lyons Gate, Dorchester, Dorset, DT2 7AZ
Tel: 01300 345260
Email: info@lyons-gate.co.uk
www.lyons-gate.co.uk
Pitches For ▲ ⊞ ➡ **Total** 90
Acreage 10 **Open** All Year
Access Good **Site** Level
Nearest Bus Stop (Miles) Entrance
Four coarse fishing lakes on site.
Facilities ⨍ 🏠 🗑 📵 ➡ 🚽 ⊙ 🛒 🍴
🏧 🟢 🛆 🖾 🖻 🔌 🏸 ⚡ ✦
Nearby Facilities ✦ ∪
Nearest Town Dorchester
Directions On the A352 between Dorchester and Sherborne.
➝ Dorchester

DORCHESTER

Moreton Camping & Caravanning Club Site, Station Road, Moreton, Nr Dorchester, Dorset, DT2 8BB
Tel: 01305 853801
www.campingandcaravanningclub.co.uk/moreton
Pitches For ▲ ⊞ ➡ **Total** 120
Acreage 7 **Open** 29-Mar to 07-Jan
Access Good **Site** Sloping
Nearest Bus Stop (Miles) ½
A lovely, leafy site on the outskirts of Dorchester. One holiday bungalow to let. BTB 5 Star Graded, AA 3 Pennants and Loo of the Year Award. Non members welcome. You can also call us on 0845 130 7633.
Facilities ⨍ 🏠 🗑 📵 ➡ 🚽 ⊙ 🛒 🍴
🏧 🟢 🛆 🖾 🖻 🔌 🏸 ⚡ ✦
Nearby Facilities ✦ ∪
Nearest Town Dorchester
Directions Take the A35 from Poole, continue past Bere Regis then turn left onto the B3390 signposted Alfpuddle. After approx. 2 miles the site is on the left before Moreton Station, adjacent to the Frampton Arms public house.
➝ Moreton

LULWORTH COVE

Durdle Door Holiday Park, Lulworth Cove, Wareham, Dorset, BH20 5PU
Tel: 01929 400200
Email: durdle.door@lulworth.com
www.lulworth.com
Pitches For ▲ ⊞ ➡ **Total** 175
Acreage 45 **Open** March to October
Access Good **Site** Lev/Slope
Unique cliff top position overlooking the famous landmark of Durdle Door. Sea view hook-ups for motor homes and touring caravans only, and pitches for tents with electric hook-ups.

DORSET

Facilities ⚡ 🚿 📶 ♿ 🚾 ⭐ ☺ 🍳 🔥 🛒 ♻
🛁 🛈 🏪 🅿 ✖ 🍴 🛗 🏮 🔌 🔲
Nearby Facilities 🎣 🚴 ⛰ 🎯 ∪
Nearest Town Wareham
Directions Take the B3077 Wool to West Lulworth road, fork right in West Lulworth Village, entrance is at the top of the hill.
⇒ Wool

LYME REGIS

Hook Farm Camping & Caravan Park, Gore Lane, Uplyme, Lyme Regis, Dorset, DT7 3UU
Tel: 01297 442801
Email: information@hookfarm-uplyme.co.uk
www.hookfarm-uplyme.co.uk
Pitches For ▲ 🚐 🚍 **Total** 100
Acreage 5¾ **Open** 01-Mar **to** 15-Nov
Access Good **Site** Level/Terraced
Nearest Bus Stop (Miles) ¼
The closest campsite to Lyme Regis (1 mile). Peaceful, tranquil site in an area of outstanding natural beauty. Many national footpaths are accessible from the park.
Facilities ♿ ⚡ 🚿 📶 ♿ 🚾 ⭐ ☺ 🍳 🔥 🛒
🛁 🛈 🏪 🅿 🏮 🔲
Nearby Facilities 🎣 🚴 ⛰ 🎯 ∪ ⊿ ♪
Nearest Town Lyme Regis
Directions From the centre of Lyme Regis take the B3165 to Uplyme (1 mile). In Uplyme turn left opposite the Talbot Arms Pub into Gore Lane. The Park is 400 yards on the right hand side.
⇒ Axminster

LYME REGIS

Shrubbery Touring Park, Rousdon, Lyme Regis, Dorset, DT7 3XW
Tel: 01297 442227
Email: info@shrubberypark.co.uk
www.shrubberypark.co.uk
Pitches For ▲ 🚐 🚍 **Total** 120
Acreage 10 **Open** April **to** Nov
Access Good **Site** Level
Nearest Bus Stop (Miles) Outside
Sheltered site. Ideal base for fossil hunters.
Facilities ⚡ 🚿 📶 ♿ 🚾 ⭐ ☺ 🍳 🔥 🛒 ♻
🛁 ☺ 🏪 🅿 🏮 🔲
Nearby Facilities 🎣 🚴 ⛰ 🎯 ∪ ⊿ ♪
Nearest Town Lyme Regis
Directions 3 miles west of Lyme Regis on the A3052 coast road.
⇒ Axminster

OWERMOIGNE

Sandyholme Holiday Park, Moreton Road, Owermoigne, Dorchester, Dorset, DT2 8HZ
Tel: 01308 426947
Email: holidays@wdlh.co.uk
www.wdlh.co.uk
Pitches For ▲ 🚐 🚍 **Total** 143
Acreage 6 **Open** 16-Mar **to** 04-Nov
Access Good **Site** Level
Nearest Bus Stop (Miles) ½
Near to Lulworth Cove, Durdle Door and Ringstead Bay. The nearby towns of Dorchester and Weymouth provide plenty of attractions and sights. Online booking available or call our Bookings Hotline: 01308 426947.

Facilities ♿ ⚡ 🚿 📶 ♿ 🚾 ⭐ ☺ 🍳 🔥 🛒 ♻
🛁 🛈 ☺ 🏪 🅿 🔌 🔲 ☀
Nearby Facilities 🎣 🚴 ⛰ 🎯 ∪
Nearest Town Dorchester/Weymouth
Directions Take the A35 to Dorchester then take the A352 to Broadmayne. Continue for 4 miles, at the roundabout take second exit, take left hand turning onto Moreton Road, Park can be found on the left hand side.
⇒ Moreton

POOLE

Beacon Hill Touring Park, Blandford Road North, Poole, Dorset, BH16 6AB
Tel: 01202 631631
Email: bookings@beaconhilltouringpark.co.uk
www.beaconhilltouringpark.co.uk
Pitches For ▲ 🚐 🚍 **Total** 170
Acreage 30 **Open** Easter **to** 31-Oct
Access Good **Site** level
Nearest Bus Stop (Miles) Outside
Partly wooded, lovely peaceful setting with scenic views, yet only 3 miles from Poole town centre. Close to Sandbanks Beach, Tower Park and the Jurassic Coast. Ideal touring base for Bournemouth, New Forest and Dorset. Coarse fishing and tennis.
Facilities ♿ ⚡ 🚿 📶 ♿ 🚾 ⭐ ☺ 🍳 🔥 🛒 ♻
🛁 🛈 ☺ ✖ 🍴 🛗 🏮 🏪 🔀 🔌 🔲 ✖ ☀ 📶
Nearby Facilities 🎣 🚴 ⛰ 🎯 ∪ ⊿ ♪
Directions Situated on the A350 ½ mile north of the junction with the A35, between Poole and Blandford.
⇒ Poole

POOLE

Huntick Farm Caravan Park, Huntick Road, Lytchett Matravers, Poole, Dorset, BH16 6BB
Tel: 01202 622222
Email: huntickcaravans@btconnect.com
www.huntickfarmcaravanpark.co.uk
Pitches For ▲ 🚐 🚍 **Total** 30
Acreage 4 **Open** April **to** October
Access Good **Site** Level
Nearest Bus Stop (Miles) ½
Very spacious site which is quiet and friendly.
Facilities ⚡ 🚿 📶 ♿ 🚾 ⭐ ☺ 🍳 🔥 🛒
🛈 ☺ 🏪 🔀 🔌 🔲 🔀
Nearby Facilities 🎣 🚴 ⛰ 🎯 ∪ ⊿ ♪
Nearest Town Poole
Directions Turn right off the A350 or left off the A35 and follow signs to Lytchett Matravers. At the Rose & Crown turn into Huntick Road.
⇒ Poole

POOLE

Merley Court Touring Park, Merley, Wimborne, Dorset, BH21 3AA
Tel: 01590 648331
Email: holidays@shorefield.co.uk
www.shorefield.co.uk
Pitches For ▲ 🚐 🚍 **Total** 178
Acreage 15 **Open** 05-Feb **to** 02-Jan
Access Good **Site** Level
Nearest Bus Stop (Miles) ¼
Beautiful 5 Star Park in a rural location with very spacious pitches. Ideal for walking and cycling. Near to the New Forest and Bournemouth.

Facilities ♿ ⚡ 🏪 🛗 📶 ♿ 🚾 ⭐ ☺ 🍳 🔥 🛒 ♻
🛁 🛈 ☺ ✖ 🍴 🛗 🏮 ♻ 🔀 ✖ 🔀 🔌 🔲 ☀ 📶
Nearby Facilities 🎣 🚴 ⛰ 🎯 ∪ ⊿ ♪
Directions 1 mile from Wimborne at the junction of the A31 and the A3349.
⇒ Poole

POOLE

Pear Tree Holiday Park, Organford Road, Holton Heath, Poole, Dorset, BH16 6LA
Tel: 0844 272 9504
Email: enquiries@peartreepark.co.uk
www.peartreepark.co.uk
Pitches For ▲ 🚐 🚍 **Total** 155
Acreage 9 **Open** March **to** October
Access Good **Site** Level
Nearest Bus Stop (Miles) Entrance
A quiet, sheltered park, set out in level, landscaped terraces. Beautiful countryside views. Ideal for Poole Harbour and the New Forest.
Facilities ♿ ⚡ 🛗 🏪 🛒 🍳 🔥 🛒 ♻
🛁 🛈 ☺ 🏪 🅿 🔲
Nearby Facilities 🎣 🚴 ⛰ 🎯 ∪ ⊿ ♪
Nearest Town Bournemouth/Poole
Directions Take the A35 from Poole towards Dorchester, then take the A351 towards Wareham. After approx 2 miles turn right at the traffic lights and the Park is ½ a mile on the left.
⇒ Holton Heath

POOLE

Rockley Park, Hamworthy, Poole, Dorset, BH15 4LZ
Tel: 01202 679393
Email: rockleypark@haven.com
www.haventouring.com/torockleypark
Pitches For ▲ 🚐 🚍 **Total** 60
Open Mid March **to** End Oct
Access Good **Site** Flat/Level area
Nearest Bus Stop (Miles) ½
Impressive 5 Star Holiday Park with direct access to a sandy/pebble beach. Kids clubs, full family entertainment programme, Spa complex, water sports, bowling, multi-sports court and much more.
Facilities ♿ ⚡ 🏪 🛗 📶 ♿ 🚾 ⭐ ☺ 🍳 🔥 🛒 ♻
🛁 🛈 ☺ ✖ 🍴 🛗 ♻ 🔀 ✖ 🔀 🔌 🔲 ☀ 📶
Nearby Facilities 🎣 🚴 ⛰ 🎯 ∪ ⊿ ♪
Nearest Town Poole
Directions From the M27 join the A31 and follow signs to Poole Town Centre. Once in the centre follow signs for Rockley Park. Alternatively, take the Dorchester By-Pass to Poole and follow signs.
⇒ Poole

POOLE

Sandford Holiday Park, Holton Heath, Poole, Dorset, BH16 6JZ
Tel: 0844 335 3732
Email: touringandcamping@parkdeanholidays.com
www.parkdeantouring.com
Pitches For ▲ 🚐 🚍 **Total** 354
Acreage 22 **Open** 02-Mar **to** 02-Nov
Access Good **Site** Level
Nearest Bus Stop (Miles) Outside
Tucked away in a beautiful countryside setting. Spacious, level, private, serviced or Star pitches. Standard pitches also available.

SHRUBBERY

CARAVAN & CAMPING PARK

ROUSDON • LYME REGIS • DORSET DT7 3XW

TEL: (01297) 442227 FAX: (01297) 446086

www.shrubberypark.co.uk

email: info@shrubberypark.co.uk

- 10 acre level site
- Ideal countryside location on the Devon & Dorset border
- Close to Lyme Regis and the Jurassic Coast
- Pitches for tents, caravans & motorhomes
- Electric hook up points
- Spacious modern shower block with disabled facilities
- Free hot water to all showers & basins
- Large children's play area
- Crazy Golf

- Dog walking area
- Fresh milk and other goods available on site
- Ideal base for fossil hunters
- Laundrette
- Dish washing sinks
- Rallies welcome
- Off-peak Special Offers
- Call us for a colour brochure

PITCHES FROM £10 Quoting CADES10*

*Terms and conditions apply

A peaceful camping and touring holiday park perfect for exploring the stunning Dorset coastline

pear tree holiday park

- Minutes from Poole and beaches.
- Convenience shop.
- Local pub just a short walk away.
- Childrens play area.
- Seasonal pitches.
- Mains electricity and waste disposal points.

Pet Friendly

To book call 0844 272 9504 or visit www.peartreepark.co.uk

We've two award winning family parks in Dorset

Visit beautiful Sandford near Poole or West Bay in Bridport.

Enjoy great touring & camping facilities including standard, serviced & star pitches with electrical hook-up points, hot showers, toilets, shop & launderette.

- **FREE** heated indoor & outdoor pools • **FREE** kids' clubs • **FREE** live family entertainment
- Sports courts & adventure play areas
- Cafés, bars & restaurants

we welcome

 tents 🚐 campervans 🚐 motorhomes 🚐 trailor tents 🚐 touring caravans

Parkdean
24 Award Winning UK Holiday Parks

BOOK OR ORDER YOUR FREE BROCHURE NOW parkdeantouring.com 0844 335 3732

Free modern showers and toilets. Heated indoor and outdoor pools. FREE kids clubs and live family entertainment.
Facilities ♿ ✦ 🏢 📶 🅿 🏧 ⊙ ✉ 🛒 🍽 📺 ☀ 📡 📶
Nearby Facilities ► ✦ ⚓ ⛵ ∪ ♪ ♫ ✗
Nearest Town Poole
Directions Located on the A351 (signposted Wareham) which branches off the A35 approx. 5 miles west of Poole. Turn right at Holton Heath traffic lights, park is on the left.
⚐ Wareham

POOLE

South Lytchett Manor Caravan & Camping Park, Dorchester Road, Lytchett Minster, Poole, Dorset, BH16 6JB
Tel: 01202 622577
Email: info@southlytchettmanor.co.uk
www.southlytchettmanor.co.uk
Pitches For ▲ ⊞ 🚐 🚍 **Total** 150
Acreage 20 **Open** 01-Mar **to** 02-Jan
Access Good **Site** Level
Nearest Bus Stop (Miles) Outside
Set in 20 acres of prestigious parkland, immaculately maintained, brand new heated amenity blocks to an exceptional standard. 3 miles from Poole and close to Bournemouth and the Purbecks. Two pubs in the village. A short distance from beautiful beaches. Excellent bus service from the gates. Dog walking around our woods. ETB 5 Stars, Dorset Regional Winner 2008/2009/2010, AA 5 Pennants, Green Tourism Business Scheme Silver and National Accessibility Award Scheme Mobility 1 & Hearing 4.
Facilities ♿ ✦ 🏢 📶 🅿 🏧 ⊙ ✉ 🛒 🍽 📺 📡
Nearby Facilities ► ✦ ⚓ ⛵ ∪ ♪ ♫
Nearest Town Poole

Directions From Poole take A35 dual carriageway. At Bakers Arms Island take the third exit to Lytchett Minster, go through Lytchett Minster and the site is situated on the left 600 yards out of the village.
⚐ Poole

SHAFTESBURY

Blackmore Vale Caravan & Camping Park, Sherborne Causeway, Shaftesbury, Dorset, SP7 9PX
Tel: 01747 851523
Email: info@dche.co.uk
www.blackmorevalecaravanpark.co.uk
Pitches For ▲ ⊞ 🚐 **Acreage** 5 **Open** All Year
Access Good **Site** Level
Friendly, family run Park in the heart of Hardy country. Gym and a lake for fishing. Touring caravan hire, sales and accessories. Self catering also available.
Facilities ✦ 🏢 📶 🅿 🏧 ⊙ ✉ 🛒 🍽 📺
Nearby Facilities ∪
Directions 2 miles west of Shaftesbury on the A30.
⚐ Gillingham

ST. LEONARDS

Back-of-Beyond Touring Park, 234 Ringwood Road, St Leonards, Dorset, BH24 2SB
Tel: 01202 876968
Email: melandsuepike@aol.com
www.backofbeyondtouringpark.co.uk
Pitches For ▲ ⊞ 🚐 **Total** 80
Acreage 28 **Open** 01-Mar **to** 31-Oct
Access Good **Site** Level
Nearest Bus Stop (Miles) ½
Quiet 4 Star ADULTS ONLY country and woodland site with new facilities. Golf and fishing on site. Central for the New Forest, Bournemouth and the World Heritage coast.

Facilities ♿ ✦ 🏢 📶 🅿 🏧 ⊙ ✉ 🛒 🍽 📺
Nearby Facilities ► ✦ ⚓ ⛵ ∪ ♪ ♫
Nearest Town Ringwood
Directions Off the A31 at Boundary Lane roundabout in St. Leonards.
⚐ Bournemouth

ST. LEONARDS

Shamba Holidays, 230 Ringwood Road, St Leonards, Ringwood, Hampshire, BH24 2SB
Tel: 01202 873302
Email: enquiries@shambaholidays.co.uk
www.shambaholidays.co.uk
Pitches For ▲ ⊞ 🚐 🚍 **Total** 150
Acreage 7 **Open** March **to** October
Access Good **Site** Level
Nearest Bus Stop (Miles) ½
Close to Bournemouth and the New Forest. AA 4 Pennants, 4 Star Rose Award, David Bellamy Gold Award for Conservation and 5 Star Loo of the Year Award.
Facilities ♿ ✦ 🏢 📶 🅿 🏧 ⊙ ✉ 🛒 🍽 📺
Nearby Facilities ► ✦ ⚓ ⛵ ∪
Nearest Town Ringwood
Directions Just off the A31 midway between Ringwood and Wimborne.
⚐ Bournemouth

SWANAGE

Downshay Farm, Haycrafts Lane, Swanage, Dorset, BH19 3EB
Tel: 01929 480316
Email: downshayfarm@tiscali.co.uk
www.downshayfarm.co.uk
Pitches For ▲ ⊞ 🚐 **Total** 12
Open Easter **to** 01-Nov
Access Good **Site** Level
Nearest Bus Stop (Miles) ½

Close to Corfe Castle and the Jurassic Coast, Steam rail service.
Facilities ⚌ ⚌ ⚌ ⚌ ⚌ ⚌ ⚌ ⚌ ⚌ ⚌
Nearby Facilities ⚌ ⚌ ⚌ ⚌ ⚌ ⚌ ⚌ ⚌
Nearest Town Swanage
Directions From Wareham take the A351 to Swanage, at Harmans Cross crossroads turn right, site is ½ a mile up the hill on the right.
⚌ Wareham

SWANAGE
Haycraft Caravan Club Site, Haycrafts Lane, Swanage, Dorset, BH19 3EB
Tel: 01929 480572
www.caravanclub.co.uk
Pitches For ⚌ ⚌ **Total** 53
Acreage 6 **Open** March **to** Nov
Access Good **Site** Level
Nearest Bus Stop (Miles) ½
Tranquil site set in the heart of Purbeck countryside, 5 miles from the beach. Ideal for walkers. Just a few minutes walk from the Swanage Light Railway. Non members welcome. Booking essential.
Facilities ⚌ ⚌ ⚌ ⚌ ⚌ ⚌ ⚌ ⚌ ⚌ ⚌ ⚌ ⚌ ⚌ ⚌
Nearby Facilities ⚌ ⚌ ⚌ ⚌
Nearest Town Swanage
Directions From A352, at the mini roundabout on the outskirts of Wareham turn onto A351 sp Swanage. After 6¾ miles at Harmans Cross, just before the petrol station, turn right into Haycrafts Lane, site is ½ mile on the left.
⚌ Swanage

SWANAGE
Tom's Field Camping & Shop, Tom's Field Road, Langton Matravers, Swanage, Dorset, BH19 3HN
Tel: 01929 427110
Email: tomsfield@hotmail.com
www.tomsfieldcamping.co.uk
Pitches For ⚌ ⚌ **Total** 100

Acreage 4½ **Open** Mid March **to** End Oct
Site Lev/Slope
Nearest Bus Stop (Miles) ¼
Set in beautiful countryside, an area of outstanding natural beauty. Coastal walk can be reached in 15 minutes. Only 20 minutes from the Jurassic Coast, Englands only natural world heritage site. Pets are welcome if kept on leads. Walkers Barn available all year by prior arrangement only.
Facilities ⚌ ⚌ ⚌ ⚌ ⚌ ⚌ ⚌ ⚌ ⚌ ⚌ ⚌ ⚌ ⚌
Nearby Facilities ⚌ ⚌ ⚌ ⚌ ⚌ ⚌ ⚌
Nearest Town Swanage
⚌ Wareham

SWANAGE
Ulwell Cottage Caravan Park, Ulwell, Swanage, Dorset, BH19 3DG
Tel: 01929 422823
Email: enq@ulwellcottagepark.co.uk
www.ulwellcottagepark.co.uk

Pitches For ⚐ ⚐ ⚐ **Total** 77
Acreage 13 **Open** 01-Mar **to** 07-Jan
Access Good **Site** Lev/Slope
Nearest Bus Stop (Miles) Outside
Adjoining the Purbeck Hills for scenic walks.
Near sandy beaches.
Facilities ♿ ✦ 🖫 🚿 ♨ ♪ ⌂ ☺ 🍴 🔥 🔲 🍺
♨ 🛒 ✗ 🗜 🚿 ⚑ 🔲 🔲 🛜
Nearby Facilities ⚑ ✔ ⚓ 🎣 ∪ ♬ ♪ ✗
Nearest Town Swanage
Directions 1½ miles from Swanage on
Studland Road. Turn left by telephone box
(left hand side) on side of road.
🚆 Wareham

THREE LEGGED CROSS
Woolsbridge Manor Farm Caravan Park,
Three Legged Cross, Wimborne, Dorset,
BH21 6RA
Tel: 01202 826369
Email: woolsbridge@btconnect.com
www.woolsbridgemanorcaravanpark.co.uk
Pitches For ⚐ ⚐ ⚐ **Total** 100
Acreage 6¾ **Open** March **to** Oct
Access Good **Site** Level
Nearest Bus Stop (Miles) ½
Just a short walk to Moors Valley Country
Park, and a 10 minute drive to Bournemouth.
Facilities ♿ ✦ 🖫 ♨ ♪ ⌂ ☺ 🍴 🔥 🔲 🍺
♨ 🛒 🗜 ♨ 🚿 ⚑ 🔲 🔲 ✔ ♨
Nearby Facilities ⚑ ✔ ⚓ 🎣 ∪ ♬ ♪
Nearest Town Ringwood
Directions Take the A31 west, Ringwood on
the left, stay in left hand lane and
automatically go into slip road. At the
roundabout turn right (third exit) signposted
Three Legged Cross, site is 2 miles along
this road on the right hand side.
🚆 Bournemouth

WAREHAM
East Creech Caravan & Camping Site,
East Creech Farm, East Creech,
Wareham, Dorset, BH20 5AP
Tel: 01929 480519/481312
Email: east.creech@virgin.net
www.eastcreechfarm.co.uk
Pitches For ⚐ ⚐ ⚐ **Total** 80
Acreage 5 **Open** April **to** October
Access Good **Site** Lev/Slope
Nearest Bus Stop (Miles) 2
Free fishing at the Farm.
Facilities ✦ 🚿 ♪ ⌂ ☺ 🔥 🔲 ♨ 🔲 ✔
Nearby Facilities 🎣
Nearest Town Wareham
Directions From Wareham bypass A351,
turn right at the roundabout signposted Blue
Pool. Site is on the right ½ a miles past Blue
Pool.
🚆 Wareham

WAREHAM
Lookout Holiday Park, Stoborough,
Wareham, Dorset, BH20 5AZ
Tel: 01929 552546
Email: enquiries@caravan-sites.co.uk
www.caravan-sites.co.uk
Pitches For ⚐ ⚐ ⚐ **Total** 150
Acreage 15 **Open** All Year
Access Good **Site** Level
Nearest Bus Stop (Miles) Outside
Ideal for touring the Purbecks and Studland
Bay.
Facilities ♿ ✦ 🚿 ♪ ⌂ ☺ 🔥 🔲 🍺
♨ 🛒 🏪 ♨ 🗜 🔲 🔲 ✔ ♨ 🛜
Nearby Facilities ⚑ ✔ ⚓ 🎣 ∪ ♬ ♪
Nearest Town Wareham
Directions 1 mile south of Wareham on the
Swanage road.
🚆 Wareham

WAREHAM
Manor Farm Caravan & Camping Park,
Church Lane, East Stoke, Wareham,
Dorset, BH20 6AW
Tel: 01929 462870
Email: info@manorfarmcp.co.uk
www.manorfarmcp.co.uk
Pitches For ⚐ ⚐ ⚐ **Total** 60
Acreage 2½ **Open** All Year
Access Good **Site** Level
Nearest Bus Stop (Miles) ½
Flat, grass touring park in a rural area of
outstanding natural beauty, central for most
of Dorset. Family run park with clear
facilities. Good walking area near beaches.
Close to Monkey World, Bovington Tank
Museum and the World Heritage Coast or
Pierbeck Cycle Way. RAC Appointed. Winter
storage available. No rallies, No groups and
No commercial vans.
Facilities ♿ ✦ ✦ 🚿 🖫 ♨ ♪ ⌂ ☺ 🍴
🔲 ♨ 🏪 🔥 🔲 🔲 ✔ ♨ 🛜
Nearby Facilities ⚑ ✔ ⚓ 🎣 ∪ ♬ ♪ ✗
Nearest Town Wareham/Lulworth Cove
Directions From Wareham take A352 then
B3070. Turn into Holme Lane, at the
crossroads turn right sp Manor Farm CP. Or
from Wool sp down Bindon Lane, at the
crossroads turn left sp Manor Farm CP, site
is 300 yards on the left.
🚆 Wool/Wareham

WAREHAM
Ridge Farm Camping & Caravan Park,
Barnhill Road, Ridge, Wareham, Dorset,
BH20 5BG
Tel: 01929 556444
Email: info@ridgefarm.co.uk
www.ridgefarm.co.uk
Pitches For ⚐ ⚐ ⚐ **Total** 60
Acreage 3½ **Open** Easter **to** Sept

Access Good **Site** Level
Peaceful, family run site in a rural setting close to the Arne RSPB Reserve. In an area of outstanding natural beauty and ideally situated for the Purbeck Hills, Poole Harbour and the coast. Boat launching nearby.
Facilities ⚏ 🏠 ⬜ ⚿ ☉ ⬛ 🔲 ⬜ ☂
🛢 ⬜ ⬜ ⬜ ⬜ ⬜
Nearby Facilities ▶ ✔ ⚓ ⬆ ∪ ⚲ ♫ ✈
Nearest Town Wareham
Directions Approx. 1½ miles south of Wareham turn left in the village of Stoborough towards Ridge. Follow signs down Barnhill Road to Ridge Farm at the end of the lane.
⇌ Wareham

WAREHAM
Wareham Forest Tourist Park, North Trigon, Wareham, Dorset, BH20 7NZ
Tel: 01929 551393
Email: holiday@warehamforest.co.uk
www.warehamforest.co.uk
Pitches For ⚏ 🚐 🚗 🚙 **Total** 200
Acreage 40 **Open** All Year
Access Good **Site** Level
Tranquil, family owned park set in the forest. Ideal for relaxing and walking. Central location for exploring East Dorset and the Purbeck coastline.
Facilities ⚏ ⬜ 🏠 ⬜ ⬜ ⬜ ☂
🛢 ⬜ ⬜ ⬜ ⬜ ⬜ ⬜
Nearby Facilities ▶ ✔ ⚓ ⬆ ∪ ⚲
Nearest Town Wareham
Directions Located midway between Wareham and Bere Regis in Wareham Forest.
⇌ Wareham

WEYMOUTH
Bagwell Farm Touring Park, Knights in the Bottom, Chickerell, Weymouth, Dorset, DT3 4EA
Tel: 01305 782575
Email: cab@bagwellfarm.co.uk
www.bagwellfarm.co.uk
Pitches For ⚏ 🚐 🚗 🚙 **Total** 320
Acreage 14 **Open** All Year
Access Good **Site** Lev/Slope
Nearest Bus Stop (Miles) ½
A friendly welcome awaits you. 5 miles from Weymouths sandy beach. Close to The Fleet Lagoon and the World Heritage Coast. Access to the coastal path. Seasonal bar, restaurant and take-away on the Park. Ideal location for discovering Dorset and exploring Dorsets Jurassic Coastline. Wheelchair friend
Facilities ⚏ ⬜ ⬜ 🏠 ⬜ ⬜ ☂
🛢 ⬜ ⬜ ⬜ ⬜ ⬜ ⬜
Nearby Facilities ▶ ✔ ⚓ ⬆ ∪ ⚲ ♫ ✈
Nearest Town Weymouth
Directions On the B3157 Weymouth to Bridport road, 500 yards past the Victoria Inn on the left. 1 mile west of Chickerell and 3 miles east of Portesham.
⇌ Weymouth

WEYMOUTH
East Fleet Farm Touring Park, East Fleet Farm, Chickerell, Weymouth, Dorset, DT3 4DW
Tel: 01305 785768
Email: enquiries@eastfleet.co.uk
www.eastfleet.co.uk
Pitches For ⚏ 🚐 🚙 **Total** 400
Acreage 21 **Open** 16-Mar **to** 31-Oct
Access Good **Site** Lev/Slope
Nearest Bus Stop (Miles) Outside
Peaceful countryside location, on the edge of Fleet Water, in the midst of organic farmland, yet only 3 miles from Weymouth with its golden beach and attractions. Large camping and caravan accessories and spares shop.

Facilities ⚏ ⚿ ⬜ ⬜ 🏠 ⬜ ⬜ ⬜ ☂
🛢 ⬜ ⬜ ⬜ ⬜ ⬜ ⬜ ⬜
Nearby Facilities ▶ ✔ ⚓ ⬆ ∪ ⚲ ♫ ✈
Nearest Town Weymouth
Directions 3 miles west of Weymouth on the B3157, go straight over the lights into Fleet Lane.
⇌ Weymouth

WEYMOUTH
Littlesea Holiday Park, Lynch Lane, Weymouth, Dorset, DT4 9DT
Tel: 01305 774414
Email: littlesea@haven.com
www.haventouring.com/tolittlesea
Pitches For ⚏ 🚐 🚙 **Total** 120
Open Mid March **to** End Oct
Access Good **Site** Lev/Slope
Nearest Bus Stop (Miles) Outside
5 Star Holiday Park with a well maintained touring and camping area overlooking the Fleet Lagoon and Chesil Beach. Wide choice of family facilities including kids clubs, entertainment and much more.
Facilities ⚏ ⚿ ⬜ ⬜ ⬜ ⬜ ☂
🛢 ⬜ ⬜ ⬜ ⬜ ⬜ ⬜ ⬜ ⬜
Nearby Facilities ▶ ✔ ⚓ ⬆ ∪ ⚲ ♫
Nearest Town Weymouth
Directions Leave the M5 and follow signs for Weymouth, very well signposted.
⇌ Weymouth

WEYMOUTH
Pebble Bank Caravan Park, 90 Camp Road, Wyke Regis, Weymouth, Dorset, DT4 9HF
Tel: 01305 774844
Email: info@pebblebank.co.uk
www.pebblebank.co.uk
Pitches For ⚏ 🚐 🚙 **Total** 30
Acreage 8 **Open** 1 April/Easter **to** 1st Weekend Nov
Access Good **Site** Level/Sloping
Nearest Bus Stop (Miles) ¼
Quiet family park in a picturesque setting overlooking the Jurassic Coast. 2½ miles from Weymouth beach.
Facilities ⚏ ⬜ ⬜ ⬜ ⬜ ☂
⬜ ⬜ ⬜ ⬜ ⬜ ⬜
Nearby Facilities ▶ ✔ ⚓ ⬆ ∪ ⚲
Nearest Town Weymouth
Directions 2½ miles from Weymouth at the Harbour Crossroads, turn left onto the A354. At the roundabout take the third exit onto the B3156 Portland road, then turn left into Camp Road.
⇌ Weymouth

WEYMOUTH
Portesham Dairy Farm Camp Site, Bramdon Lane, Portesham, Weymouth, Dorset, DT3 4HG
Tel: 01305 871297
Email: info@porteshamdairyfarm.co.uk
www.porteshamdairyfarm.co.uk
Pitches For ⚏ 🚐 🚙 **Total** 80
Acreage 7 **Open** 16-Mar **to** 31-Oct
Access Good **Site** Level
Nearest Bus Stop (Miles) Outside
Ideal touring for Chesil area. Local pub 230 yards. AA 4 Pennant graded.
Facilities ⚿ ⬜ ⬜ ⬜ ⬜ ⬜ ☂
⬜ ⬜ ⬜ ⬜ ⬜ ⬜
Nearby Facilities ▶ ✔ ⬆
Nearest Town Weymouth
Directions 7 miles from Weymouth on B3157 Coast road.
⇌ Weymouth

WEYMOUTH
Sea Barn Farm Camping Park, Fleet, Weymouth, Dorset, DT3 4ED
Tel: 01305 782218
Email: ca@seabarnfarm.co.uk
www.seabarnfarm.co.uk
Pitches For ⚏ 🚙 **Total** 250
Acreage 12 **Open** 15-Mar **to** 31-Oct
Site Level
Fabulous views of the coast and Dorset countrtyside. Access to a coastal footpath. Ideal location for discovering Dorset. New facilities for 2008.
Facilities ⚏ ⚿ ⬜ ⬜ ⬜ ⬜ ☂
🛢 ⬜ ⬜ ⬜ ⬜
Nearby Facilities ▶ ✔ ⚓ ⬆ ∪ ⚲ ♫ ✈
Nearest Town Weymouth
Directions From Weymouth take the B3157 towards Abbotsbury. After 2½ miles at the mini roundabout turn left to Fleet, site is 1 mile on the left.
⇌ Weymouth

WEYMOUTH
Seaview Holiday Park, Preston, Weymouth, Dorset, DT3 6DZ
Tel: 01305 832271
Email: seaview@haven.com
www.haventouring.com/toseaview
Pitches For ⚏ 🚙 **Total** 87
Open Mid March **to** End Oct
Access Good **Site** Sloping
Nearest Bus Stop (Miles) Outside
Just a 15 minute walk from the charming Bowleaze Cove. Enjoy a relaxed Park with the option of entertainment, kids clubs, water fun and fun activities.
Facilities ⚏ ⚿ ⬜ ⬜ ⬜ ⬜ ☂
🛢 ⬜ ⬜ ⬜ ⬜ ⬜ ⬜ ⬜
Nearby Facilities ▶ ✔ ⚓ ⬆ ∪ ⚲ ♫
Nearest Town Weymouth
Directions On the A35 to Dorchester turn off onto the A354 signposted Weymouth. From the centre of Weymouth take the A353 to Preston. The Park is located on the right (after Weymouth Bay Holiday Park).
⇌ Weymouth

WEYMOUTH
Waterside Holiday Park & Spa, Bowleaze Cove, Weymouth, Dorset, DT3 6PP
Tel: 01305 833103
Email: info@watersideholidays.co.uk
www.watersideholidays.co.uk
Pitches For **Total** 70
Acreage 4
Access Good **Site** Level
Nearest Bus Stop (Miles) Outside
Seasonal Touring Pitches ONLY (NO holiday pitches available). Located right on the beach at Bowleaze Cove, Waterside is Weymouths original 5 Star Park as graded by Visit Britain.
Facilities ⚏ ⚿ ⬜ ⬜ ⬜ ⬜ ☂
🛢 ⬜ ⚿ ⬜ ⬜ ⬜ ⬜ ⬜
Nearby Facilities ▶ ✔ ⚓ ⬆ ∪ ⚲
Nearest Town Weymouth
Directions From Dorchester take the A354 to Weymouth, then take the A353 east to Wareham. At the end of the sea wall turn right to Bowleaze Cove.
⇌ Weymouth

WEYMOUTH
West Fleet Holiday Farm, Fleet, Weymouth, Dorset, DT3 4EF
Tel: 01305 782218
Email: ca@westfleetholidays.co.uk
www.westfleetholidays.co.uk
Pitches For ⚏ 🚙 **Total** 250
Acreage 12 **Open** Easter **to** Sept
Site Level
Nearest Bus Stop (Miles) Outside

DORSET, DURHAM

Kids love camping at West Fleet. Outdoor pool, family clubhouse and lots of space to play. New facilities in 2007. Bus service during main season only.
Facilities ⚓ ⚲ 🏠 ☎ ſ ☉ ⊕ ⚑ 🚿 ▣ ❄ ♨
🕎 🛒 🚻 ⟲ 🎣 🚲 ♨ 🔥 ▣ ⚏
Nearby Facilities ſ ✎ ⚓ ⚓ ∪ ⋒ ♣ ☀
Nearest Town Weymouth
Directions From Weymouth take the B3157 towards Abbotsbury. After 2½ miles at the mini roundabout turn left to Fleet, site is 1 mile on the right.
⚞ Weymouth

WIMBORNE
Gundrys Farm Caravan & Camping Park, School Lane, Three Legged Cross, Wimborne, Dorset, BH21 6RU
Tel: 01202 826322
Email: gundrysfarm@gmail.com
Pitches For ⚑ ⚏ ⚏ **Total** 50
Acreage 8 **Open** March **to** October
Access Good **Site** Level
Nearest Bus Stop (Miles) ¼
Friendly, family run park in a beautiful secluded location. All pitches are flat and level. 5 mins from a country park for fishing, golf and walking. 15 mins from Bournemouth and Poole with their sandy beaches, and the New Forest. 15 minute off-road walk to Moors Valley Country Park.
Facilities ſ 🏠 ☎ ſ ☉ 🔥 ▣ 🕎 ☉ ⚏ ♨ ♨
Nearby Facilities ſ ✎ ⚓ ⚓ ∪ ♣ ♣
Nearest Town Ringwood
Directions Take the A31 west 1 mile past Ringwood, follow the slip road and turn right at the roundabout signposted Three Legged Cross and Moors Valley Country Park, site is 1½ miles past Moors Valley on the left (brown tourism sign).
⚞ Bournemouth

WIMBORNE
Springfield Touring Park, Candys Lane, Corfe Mullen, Wimborne, Dorset, BH21 3EF
Tel: 01202 881719
Email: john.clark18@btconnect.com
www.springfieldtouringpark.co.uk
Pitches For ⚑ ⚏ ⚏ **Total** 45
Acreage 3½ **Open** April **to** October
Access Good **Site** Lev/Slope
Nearest Bus Stop (Miles) ¼
Family run park, overlooking the Stour Valley. Free showers and awnings. Convenient for the coast, New Forest, also ferry. Low Season Offers - £80, any 7 days for 2 adults including electric. Practical Caravan Top 100 Parks 2008/09/10/11.
Facilities ⚓ ſ 🏠 ☎ ſ ☉ ⊕ ⚑ ▣ 🔥
🕎 ☉ 🔥 ▣ 🚿
Nearby Facilities ſ ✎ ⚓ ⚓ ∪ ♣ ♣
Nearest Town Wimborne
Directions 1¼ miles west of Wimborne just off main A31.
⚞ Poole

WIMBORNE
Verwood Camping & Caravanning Club Site, Sutton Hill, Woodlands, Wimborne, Dorset, BH21 8NQ
Tel: 01202 822763
www.campingandcaravanningclub.co.uk/verwood
Pitches For ⚑ ⚏ ⚏ **Total** 150
Acreage 12 **Open** 29-Mar **to** 05-Nov
Access Good **Site** Gentle Slope
Beautifully situated next to Ringwood Forest. Miles of safe, sandy beaches at Poole and Bournemouth are a reasonable distance. BTB 4 Star Graded and AA 3 Pennants. Non members welcome. You can also call us on 0845 130 7633.

Facilities ⚓ ſ 🏠 ☎ ſ ☉ ⊕ ⚑ ▣ 🔲 ♨
🕎 ☉ 🛒 🚻 ⟲ 🔥 🔥 ▣ 🚿 ♨ ☀
Nearby Facilities ſ ∪
Nearest Town Ringwood
Directions From Salisbury take the A354, after 13 miles turn left onto the B3081, site is 1½ miles west of Verwood.
⚞ Bournemouth

WIMBORNE
Wilksworth Farm Caravan Park, Cranborne Road, Wimborne, Dorset, BH21 4HW
Tel: 01202 885467
Email: royandwendy@wilksworthfarmcaravanpark.co.uk
www.wilksworthfarmcaravanpark.co.uk
Pitches For ⚑ ⚏ ⚏ **Total** 85
Acreage 11 **Open** April **to** Oct
Access Good **Site** Level
Nearest Bus Stop (Miles) 1
8 miles from Sandbanks Beach and 10 miles from the New Forest. Pets are welcome by prior arrangement.
Facilities ⚓ ſ 🏠 🔥 🏠 ☎ ſ ☉ ⊕ ⚑ ▣ 🔲 ♨
🕎 🕎 ☉ 🛒 ❌ 🔥 ⟲ ♨ 🔥 ▣ ⚏
Nearby Facilities ſ ✎ ⚓ ⚓ ∪ ♣ ♣ ♣
Nearest Town Wimborne
Directions 1 mile north of Wimborne on the B3078.
⚞ Poole

WOOL
Whitemead Caravan Park, East Burton Road, Wool, Dorset, BH20 6HG
Tel: 01929 462241
Email: whitemeadcp@aol.com
www.whitemeadcaravanpark.co.uk
Pitches For ⚑ ⚏ ⚏ **Total** 95
Acreage 5 **Open** Mid March **to** End Oct
Access Good **Site** Level
Nearest Bus Stop (Miles) ¼
Woodland site with several secluded pitches. Off licence on site.
Facilities ſ 🏠 ☎ ſ ☉ ⊕ ⚑ ▣ 🔲 ♨
🕎 🕎 ☉ 🔥 🔥 🔥 ▣ 🚿
Nearby Facilities ſ ✎ ⚓ ⚓ ∪ ♣ ♣ ☀
Nearest Town Wareham
Directions Off the A352 Wareham to Weymouth road. 5 miles west of Wareham and 5 miles north of Lulworth Cove.
⚞ Wool

DURHAM
BARNARD CASTLE
Camping & Caravanning Club Site, Dockenflatts Lane, Lartington, Barnard Castle, Durham, DL12 9DG
Tel: 01833 630228
www.campingandcaravanningclub.co.uk/barnardcastle
Pitches For ⚑ ⚏ ⚏ **Total** 90
Acreage 10 **Open** 29-Mar **to** 05-Nov
Site Level
Nearest Bus Stop (Miles) ½
Well placed for exploring the Pennines and the city of Durham. BTB 5 Star Graded, AA 4 Pennants and Loo of the Year Award. Non members welcome. You can also call us on 0845 130 7633.
Facilities ſ 🏠 ☎ ſ ☉ ⊕ ⚑ ▣ 🔲 ♨
🕎 ☉ 🛒 🔥 🔥 ▣ 🚿 ☀
Nearby Facilities ſ ✎ ∪ ♣
Directions On approach from Scotch Corner take the second turn right for Middleton in Teesdale and Barnard Castle. On approach from Penrith take the B6277 to Middleton in Teesdale. In approx 1 mile take turn off left signposted Raygill Riding Stables. The site is 500 mtrs on left.
⚞ Darlington

BARNARD CASTLE
Cote House Caravan Park, Middleton-in-Teesdale, Barnard Castle, Durham, DL12 0PN
Tel: 07855 888396
Pitches For ⚏ ⚏ **Total** 12
Acreage 16 **Open** March **to** October
Access Good **Site** Level
Set in woodlands by the River Lune. Pets welcome if kept on leads. Winter storage available.
Facilities ⚓ ſ 🏠 ☎ ſ ☉ ⊕ 🔥 🚿
Nearby Facilities ſ ✎ ⚓ ∪ ♣
Nearest Town Barnard Castle
Directions 1½ miles west of Mickleton, by Grassholme Reservoir.
⚞ Darlington

BARNARD CASTLE
Hetherick Caravan Park, Marwood, Barnard Castle, Durham, DL12 8QX
Tel: 01388 488384
Email: info@hetherickcaravanpark.co.uk
www.hetherickcaravanpark.co.uk
Pitches For ⚑ ⚏ ⚏ **Total** 41
Acreage 15 **Open** March **to** October
Access Good **Site** Level
Nearest Bus Stop (Miles) ½
Pleasant park situated on a working farm in open countryside, in the heart of beautiful Teesdale. 3 miles from the pretty market town of Barnard Castle.
Facilities ⚓ ſ 🏠 ☎ ſ ☉ ⊕ ▣ 🔲 ♨
🕎 🕎 ☉ 🔥 🔥 ▣
Nearby Facilities ſ ✎ ⚓ ∪ ♣ ♣
Nearest Town Barnard Castle
Directions Take the B6278 from Barnard Castle towards Eggleston, once past the golf course take the second right turn towards Kinninvie and Woodland.
⚞ Darlington

BARNARD CASTLE
Pecknell Farm Caravan Site, Pecknell Farm, Lartington, Barnard Castle, Co. Durham, DL12 9DF
Tel: 01833 638357
Pitches For ⚏ ⚏ **Total** 20
Acreage 1½ **Open** April **to** October
Access Good **Site** Level
Nearest Bus Stop (Miles) ¼
Ideal walking area, very attractive walk into historic Barnard Castle. Within easy reach of many attractions.
Facilities ſ 🏠 ☎ ſ ☉ ⊕ ⚑ 🔥 🔲 ♨ ♨
Nearby Facilities ſ ✎ ∪ ♣
Nearest Town Barnard Castle
Directions 1½ miles from Barnard Castle on the B6277 to Lartington, we are the first farm on the right.
⚞ Darlington

BARNARD CASTLE
Winston Caravan Park, The Old Forge, Winston, Darlington, Durham, DL2 3RH
Tel: 01325 730228
Email: m.willetts@ic24.net
www.touristnetuk.com/ne/winston
Pitches For ⚑ ⚏ ⚏ **Total** 21
Open March **to** October
Access Good **Site** Level
Nearest Bus Stop (Miles) Outside
Ideally situated for exploring the many attractions in County Durham. Caravan for the disabled available for hire.
Facilities ſ 🏠 ☎ ſ ☉ ⊕ ⚑ ▣ 🔲 ♨
⊕ 🔥 ▣ 🚿
Nearby Facilities ſ ✎ ⚓ ∪ ♣
Nearest Town Darlington
Directions From Darlington take the A67 west for 10 miles, turn left onto the B6274 into Winston Village, site is 400 yards on the right hand side.
⚞ Darlington

CONSETT

Manor Park Caravan & Camping Park,
Manor Park Limited, Broadmeadows, Near
Castleside, Consett, Durham, DH8 9HD
Tel: 01207 501000
Pitches For 🚐 🚍
Open May **to** October
Access Good **Site** Lev/Slope
Ideal base for visiting Durham with its
cathedral and castle, Northumberland,
Beamish Museum and the Angel of the North.
Facilities ⬧ ✦ 🔟 🏧 ┌ ⊙ ┛ ☎
🅿 ◗ 🎵 ⊞ ❄ ⚲
Nearby Facilities ┍ ✔
Nearest Town Consett
Directions Just east off the A68, 3 miles
south of Castleside, sp Broadmeadows.
🚆 Durham

DARLINGTON

Doe Park Caravan Site, Cotherstone,
Barnard Castle, Durham, DL12 9UQ
Tel: 01833 650302
Email: info@doepark.co.uk
www.doepark.co.uk
Pitches For 🚐 🚍 **Total** 70
Open March **to** October
Access Good **Site** Level
Nearest Bus Stop (Miles) Outside
Rural setting with excellent local walks.
Facilities ⬧ ✦ 🔟 🏧 ┌ ⊙ ┛ ⬛ 🔲 ☎
🅿 ◗ ◗ ⊞ ☒ ✔
Nearby Facilities ┍ ✔ ⚓ U ♫
Nearest Town Barnard Castle
Directions Take the B6277 from Barnard
Castle towards Middleton-in-Teesdale for 5
miles to Cotherstone. Site is ¼ mile after
Cotherstone Village.
🚆 Darlington

DURHAM

Finchale Abbey Caravan Park, Finchale
Abbey Farm, Durham, DH1 5SH
Tel: 0191 386 6528
Email: godricawatson@hotmail.com
www.finchaleabbey.co.uk
Pitches For 🚐 🚍 **Total** 40
Acreage 6 **Open** All Year
Access Good **Site** Level
Nearest Bus Stop (Miles) 1
ADULTS ONLY PARK set in the meander of
the River Wear. Ideally situated to visit most
of the North Easts highlights.
Facilities ⬧ ✦ 🔲 🔟 🏧 ┌ ⊙ ☎
🅿 ◗ ◗ ✕ ⊞ 🔲 ◗ 🅰 ❄ ⚲
Nearby Facilities ┍ ✔ ⚓
Nearest Town Durham City
Directions Leave the A1M at junction 63 and
head south on the A167. At Arnson
roundabout follow signs for Finchale Priory,
site is at the same place.
🚆 Durham City

DURHAM

Grange Caravan Club Site, Meadow
Lane, Durham, Co. Durham, DH1 1TL
Tel: 0191 384 4778
www.caravanclub.co.uk
Pitches For 🏕 🚐 🚍 **Total** 76
Acreage 12 **Open** All Year
Access Good **Site** Level
Nearest Bus Stop (Miles) ½

Only 3 miles from the city of Durham with its
castle and cathedral. Beamish Open Air
Museum nearby. Non members welcome.
Booking essential.
Facilities
✦ 🔟 🔲 ┌ ┌ ⊙ 🅿 🔲 ◗ ⬛ ❄ ⊞ ⚲ ⟁
Nearby Facilities ┍ ✔
Nearest Town Durham
Directions Leave the A1(M) via slip road
onto the A690 signposted Durham.
Immediately move to the outside lane to turn
right in 50 yards at brown caravan sign into
Meadow Lane, site entrance is ahead.
🚆 Durham

DURHAM

**Strawberry Hill Farm Caravan &
Camping Park,** Old Cassop, Durham,
Durham, DH6 4QA
Tel: 0191 372 3457
Email: info@strawberryhf.co.uk
www.strawberry-hill-farm.co.uk
Pitches For 🏕 🚐 🚍 **Total** 45
Acreage 6 **Open** March **to** Dec
Access Good **Site** Terraced
Nearest Bus Stop (Miles) ¼
Approx. 4 miles from Durham City, World
Heritage Site, Castle and Cathedral. Caravan
holiday homes for hire.
Facilities ⬧ ✦ 🔟 🔲 ┌ ┌ ⊙ ┛ ⬛ 🔲 ☎
🅿 ◗ ⊞ 🔲 ◗
Nearby Facilities ┍ ✔ U
Nearest Town Durham City
Directions From junction 61 of the A1M take
exit sp Bowburn A177. Travel to the second
set of traffic lights (2.6 miles) and turn right
sp A19 Peterlee and Hartlepool. The Park is
3½ miles on the left.
🚆 Durham City

HARTLEPOOL

Crimdon Dene Holiday Park, Coast
Road, Blackhall Colliery, Nr Hartlepool,
Durham, TS27 4BN
Tel: 0843 309 2559
Email: holidaysales.crimdondene@park-
resorts.com
www.park-resorts.com
Pitches For 🚐 🚍
Open Apr **to** Oct **Access** Good **Site** Level
Right near the Dene with stunning views
along the coast.
Facilities
✦ 🔟 ┌ ┌ ⊙ 🅿 ◗ 🔲 ✕ 🕎 🅰 ⚲ ◗ 🔲 ❄
Nearby Facilities
Nearest Town Hartlepool
Directions From the A19 just south of
Peterlee, take the B1281 and turn sp
Blackhall. Drive through Castle Eden and turn
left, after 3 miles turn right onto the A1086
and follow signs.
🚆 Hartlepool

MIDDLETON-IN-TEESDALE

Mickleton Mill Caravan Park, The Mill,
Mickleton, Barnard Castle, Durham, DL12
0LS
Tel: 01833 640317
Email: mickletonmill@aol.com
www.mickletonmill.co.uk
Pitches For 🚐 🚍 **Total** 4
Acreage 7½ **Open** March **to** October

Access Fair **Site** Level
Nearest Bus Stop (Miles) ½
Set on the banks of the River Lune.
Facilities ✦ 🔟 🔲 ┌ ┌ ⊙ ┛ ⬛ 🔲 ☎
🅿 ⊞ 🔲 ◗ ❄
Nearby Facilities ┍ ✔ ⚓ U ♫
Nearest Town Barnard Castle
Directions From Barnard Castle take the
B6277. In Mickleton take the first turn right
past Blacksmiths Arms, go down the bank
and bear left at the bottom of the hill.
🚆 Darlington

WOLSINGHAM

Bradley Burn Caravan Park,
Wolsingham, Bishop Auckland, Co.
Durham, DL13 3JH
Tel: 01388 527285
Email: stay@bradleyburn.co.uk
www.bradleyburn.co.uk
Pitches For 🚐 🚍 **Total** 5
Open March **to** October
Access Good **Site** Lev/Slope
Nearest Bus Stop (Miles) Outside
Peaceful Park set in beautiful scenery in the
heart of the Durham Dales and on the edge
of the Pennines. Farm shop and cafe.
Facilities ✦ ┌ ┌ 🔲 ◗ ☎ ⬛ ✕ 🅰 ⊞ 🔲 🔲
Nearby Facilities ┍ ✔ U ♫
Nearest Town Wolsingham
Directions 2 miles east of Wolsingham on
the A689 and 2 miles west of the A68/A689
junction.
🚆 Bishop Auckland

ESSEX
BRENTWOOD

**Kelvedon Hatch Camping & Caravanning
Club Site,** Warren Lane, Doddinghurst,
Brentwood, Essex, CM15 0JG
Tel: 01277 372773
www.campingandcaravanningclub.co.uk/
kelvedonhatch
Pitches For 🏕 🚐 🚍 **Total** 90
Acreage 12 **Open** 29-Mar **to** 05-Nov
Access Fair **Site** Level
Nearest Bus Stop (Miles) ½
Peaceful site, good for country walks. 20
miles from the centre of London. Plenty of
sporting activities within easy reach. BTB 3
Star Graded and AA 3 Pennants. Non
members welcome. You can also call us on
0845 130 7633.
Facilities ⬧ ✦ 🔟 🔲 ┌ ┌ ⊙ ┛ ⬛ 🔲 ☎
🅿 ◗ ⬛ 🅰 ❄ ⊞ 🔲 ❄ ⚲ ⚲ 📶
Nearby Facilities ┍ ✔ U ♫
Directions Leave the M25 at junction 28 and
take the A1023 towards Brentwood. Turn left
onto the A128 to Ongar, the site is 3 miles
on the right, signposted.
🚆 Brentwood

CLACTON-ON-SEA

Highfield Grange Holiday Park, London
Road, Clacton-on-Sea, Essex, CO16 9QY
Tel: 0843 309 2562
Email: holidaysales.highfield@park-
resorts.com
www.park-resorts.com
Pitches For 🚐 🚍
Open April **to** October

FEN FARM
CARAVAN SITE
www.fenfarm.co.uk
01206 383275
Quiet family retreat in a rural setting with a tranquil atmosphere.
By the sea and close to Cudmore Grove Country Park,
Fingringhoe Wick Nature Reserve and Abberton Reservoir.
Moore Lane, East Mersea, Colchester, Essex CO5 8FE

Waldegraves & Cosways
Family Holiday Parks
01206 382898
www.waldegraves.co.uk
Mersea Island, Colchester, Essex CO5 8SE

Access Good **Site** Sloping
Close to the town centre and the beach. Near
Clacton-on-Sea.
Facilities
Nearest Town Clacton-on-Sea
Directions Follow the A12 to Colchester,
then take the A120 leading to the A133 to
Clacton. Highfield is situated on the B1441
and clearly signposted.
Clacton-on-Sea

CLACTON-ON-SEA
Martello Beach Holiday Park, Belsize
Avenue, Jaywick, Clacton-on-Sea, Essex,
CO15 2LF
Tel: 0843 309 2566
Email: holidaysales.martellobeach@park-
resorts.com
www.park-resorts.com
Pitches For ▲ ⬛ ⬛ **Total** 100
Open April **to** Oct
Access Good **Site** Level
Next to the beach and only 3 miles from
Clacton town. Ideal base for touring Essex.
Facilities
Nearby Facilities
Nearest Town Clacton-on-Sea
Directions From the A12 take the A120 then
the A133 to Clacton seafront. Turn right and
follow signs through Jaywick.
Clacton-on-Sea

CLACTON-ON-SEA
Orchards Holiday Village, St Osyth,
Clacton-on-Sea, Essex, CO16 8LJ
Tel: 01255 820651
Email: theorchards@haven.com
www.haventouring.com/totheorchards

Pitches For ▲ ⬛ ⬛ **Total** 69
Acreage 140 **Open** Mid March **to** End Oct
Access Good **Site** Level
Nearest Bus Stop (Miles) Outside
A green and tranquil Holiday Park with direct
beach access. Set on the wildlife rich Point
Clear. Offering a wide range of holiday
facilities and family entertainment.
Facilities
Nearby Facilities
Nearest Town St Osyth
Directions From Clacton-on-Sea take the
B1027 towards Colchester. Turn left after the
petrol station and go over the crossroads in
St Osyth. Follow signs to Point Clear and the
Park is 3 miles further on.
Clacton-on-Sea

CLACTON-ON-SEA
Silver Dawn Touring Park, Jaywick Lane,
Clacton-on-Sea, Essex, CO16 8BB
Tel: 01255 421856
www.silverdawntouringpark.co.uk
Pitches For ⬛ ⬛ **Total** 38
Acreage 3 **Open** April **to** October
Access Good **Site** Level
Nearest Bus Stop (Miles) ¼
Sky TV. David Bellamy Silver Award for
Conservation. You can also contact us on
Mobile: 07906 222353.
Facilities
Nearby Facilities
Nearest Town Clacton-on-Sea
Directions Take the A12 then the A120 to
Clacton.
Clacton-on-Sea

COLCHESTER
Colchester Holiday Park Ltd., Cymbeline
Way, Colchester, Essex, CO3 4AG
Tel: 01206 545551
Email: enquiries@colchestercamping.co.uk
www.colchestercamping.co.uk
Pitches For ▲ ⬛ ⬛ **Total** 150
Open All Year **Access** Good **Site** Level
Nearest Bus Stop (Miles) ¼
Situated in a conservation area, yet only 30
minutes walk to the town centre. Zoo,
Rollerworld, leisure complex, golf and the
coast all within 20 minute drive.
Facilities
Nearby Facilities
Directions From London take the A12 to
junction 27 and follow brown tourism signs.
Colchester

HALSTEAD
Gosfield Lake Resort, Church Road,
Gosfield, Essex, CO9 1UD
Tel: 01787 475043
Email: turps@gosfieldlake.co.uk
www.gosfieldlake.co.uk
Pitches For ▲ ⬛ ⬛ ⬛ **Total** 30
Acreage 5 **Open** April **to** October
Access Good **Site** Level
Nearest Bus Stop (Miles) ¼
Lakeside pitches. Fishing and waterskiing
available.
Facilities
Nearby Facilities
Nearest Town Halstead
Directions From Braintree take the A131
towards Halstead. Turn left at High Garrett
traffic lights to Gosfield. Follow brown tourism
signs from the A120.
Braintree

Steeple Bay Holiday Park
Southminster, Essex

TENTS FROM £5 PER NIGHT

FACILITIES INCLUDE:
- Heated leisure pool with poolside patio
- Family entertainment venue
- Private slipway
- Adventure playground

PARK HOLIDAYS
Caravan and Camping

Call now to book 0845 815 9718 Local call rate
www.ParkHolidaysUK.com/cades

Homestead Lake Park

Thorpe Road (B1033)
Weeley, Clacton-on-Sea
Essex CO16 9JN
Tel: 01255 833492
Fax: 01255 831406
e-mail:
lakepark@homesteadcaravans.co.uk

www.homesteadlake.co.uk

TOURING PARK ★★★★

HARWICH

Dovercourt Caravan Park, Low Road, Harwich, Essex, CO12 3TZ
Tel: 01255 243433
Email: enquiries@dovercourtcp.com
www.dovercourtcp.com
Pitches For 🚐 🚓 **Total** 60
Acreage 6 **Open** April **to** October
Access Good **Site** Level
Nearest Bus Stop (Miles) Entrance
Near the beach, Harwich ferries and Constable Country.
Facilities ...
Nearby Facilities ...
Nearest Town Dovercourt
Directions From Colchester take the A120 towards Harwich and follow brown tourism signs from Ramsey roundabout.
🚉 Dovercourt/Harwich

MANNINGTREE

The Strangers Home Inn Caravan & Camping Park, The Street, Bradfield, Manningtree, Essex, CO11 2US
Tel: 01255 870304
Email: enquiries@strangershome.co.uk
www.stargladeleisure.co.uk
Pitches For 🏕 🚐 🚓 🚗 **Total** 53
Acreage 4 **Open** March **to** Oct
Access Good **Site** Level
Nearest Bus Stop (Miles) Outside
The nearest campsite to Harwich Port and in an area of outstanding natural beauty, this family run Park has full facilities and more! Pub, Bed & Breakfast, entertainment and kids play area on site.
Facilities ...
Nearby Facilities ...
Nearest Town Colchester
Directions Leave the A12 at junction 29 then merge onto the A120. Continue on the A120 and at the roundabout take the first exit onto the B1035 Clacton road. Turn right into Heath Road and continue onto The Street.
🚉 Histley

MERSEA ISLAND

Fen Farm Caravan & Camping Site, Moore Lane, East Mersea, Colchester, Essex, CO5 8FE
Tel: 01206 383275
Email: fenfarm@talk21.com
www.fenfarm.co.uk
Pitches For 🏕 🚐 🚓 🚗 **Total** 90
Acreage 5 **Open** Mid March **to** End Oct
Access Good **Site** Level
Quiet, rural, family run site just a 2 minute walk to the beach and on an estuary. Close to a country park.

Facilities ...
Nearby Facilities ...
Nearest Town Colchester
Directions Take the B1025 from Colchester to Mersea, take the left fork to East Mersea. Moore Lane is the first left turn after the Dog & Pheasant Public House.
🚉 Colchester

MERSEA ISLAND

Seaview Holiday Park, Seaview Avenue, West Mersea, Colchester, Essex, CO5 8DA
Tel: 01206 382534
Email: info@westmersea.com
www.westmersea.com
Pitches For 🚐 🚓 **Total** 66
Acreage 18 **Open** April **to** October
Access Good **Site** Level
Nearest Bus Stop (Miles) ¼
Situated alongside out own private sandy beach. Coastal walks and a country park.
Facilities ...
Nearby Facilities ...
Nearest Town Colchester
Directions Take the A12 to Colchester then join the B1025 to Mersea Island. Cross the Strood Channel via 'The Causeway', take the left fork and follow brown tourism signs.
🚉 Colchester

MERSEA ISLAND

Waldegraves Holiday & Leisure Park, Mersea Island, Colchester, Essex, CO5 8SE
Tel: 01206 382898
Email: holidays@waldegraves.co.uk
www.waldegraves.co.uk
Pitches For 🏕 🚐 🚓 **Total** 60
Acreage 45 **Open** March **to** November
Access Good **Site** Level
Nearest Bus Stop (Miles) ½
Ideal family park, surrounded by trees and lakes. Safe private beach. Licensed bar and restaurant, swimming pool, undercover golf driving range, pitch & putt, Family entertainment, play areas and games room, fishing and boating lake. Luxury holiday homes for hire and sale.
Facilities ...
Nearby Facilities ...
Nearest Town Colchester
Directions From Colchester take B1025, 10 miles to West Mersea. Take left fork to East Mersea, second road to right.
🚉 Colchester

SOUTHEND-ON-SEA

Riverside Village Holiday Park, Creeksea Ferry Road, Wallasea Island, Rochford, Essex, SS4 2EY
Tel: 01702 258297
Email: riversidevillage@tiscali.co.uk
Pitches For 🏕 🚐 🚓 **Total** 60
Acreage 25 **Open** March **to** October
Access Good **Site** Level
Nearest Bus Stop (Miles) ½
Alongside the River Crouch and surrounded by SSSI and nature reserves. Part of the Crouch Valley Way, a ramblers delight. Marinas, country pubs and restaurants nearby.
Facilities ...
Nearby Facilities ...
Nearest Town Southend-on-Sea
Directions From A127 through Rochford, follow caravan signs for Ashingdon then Wallasea Island. From Chelmsford left at Battlesbridge, past Hullbridge for Ashingdon then Wallasea.
🚉 Rochford

SOUTHMINSTER

Steeple Bay Holiday Park, Canney Road, Steeple, Southminster, Essex, CM0 7RS
Tel: 01621 773991
Email: steeplebay@parkholidaysuk.com
www.parkholidaysuk.com/cades
Pitches For 🏕 🚐 🚓 **Total** 21
Open March **to** Oct
Access Good **Site** Level
Nearest Bus Stop (Miles) ½
Outdoor swimming pool and village store. Loopy Club for kids. Close to Maldon for bars, restaurants and shopping.
Facilities ...
Nearby Facilities ...
Directions Turn off the A12 onto the A414, then take the B1010/B1012 to Latchington. Follow signs through Mayland then Steeple Village, turn left after the Steeple sign and the Site is 1 mile down the lane.
🚉 Southminster

SOUTHMINSTER

Waterside Holiday Park, Main Road, St Lawrence Bay, Southminster, Essex, CM0 7LY
Tel: 0843 309 2580
Email: holidaysales.waterside@park-resorts.com
www.park-resorts.com
Pitches For 🏕 🚐 🚓
Open April **to** October
Access Good **Site** Level
Near the coast and not far from the town centre.

ESSEX, GLOUCESTERSHIRE

Facilities ⌁ ⌂ ⌒ ♨ ⌶ ☐ ☎
☐ ⊙ ⊗ ✕ ☐ ☐ ⌁ ☀ ☐
Nearby Facilities
Nearest Town Maldon/Colchester
Directions Follow the A12 towards Chelmsford and take the A414 sp Maldon. Take the B1010 and follow signs for St Lawrence, turn left off the main road and the Park is on the right.
⇥ Maldon/Colchester

WALTON-ON-THE-NAZE
Naze Marine Holiday Park, Hall Lane, Walton-on-the-Naze, Essex, CO14 8HL
Tel: 0843 309 2567
Email: holidaysales.nazemarine@park-resorts.com
www.park-resorts.com
Pitches For ♐ ♐
Open April **to** October
Access Good **Site** Level
Nearest Bus Stop (Miles) Outside
Near the beach. 6 miles from Clacton.
Facilities ⌁ ⌂ ⌒ ♨ ☐ ☎
☐ ⊗ ✕ ♐ ☐ ☀ ☐
Nearby Facilities
Nearest Town Clacton-on-Sea
Directions Follow the A12 to Colchester, then take the A120 Harwich road to the A133. Take the A133 and as far as Weeley, then take the B1033 to Walton sea front, the Park is on the left.
⇥ Clacton-on-Sea

WEELEY
Homestead Lake Park, Thorpe Road (B1033), Weeley, Clacton-on-Sea, Essex, CO16 9JN
Tel: 01255 833492
Email: lakepark@homesteadcaravans.co.uk
www.homesteadlake.co.uk

Pitches For ⛺ ♐ ♐ ♐ **Total** 50
Open March **to** October
Access Good **Site** Sloping
Nearest Bus Stop (Miles) ¼
Quiet and relaxing site with a fishing lake. 10 miles from historic Colchester. Beaches and piers of Clacton and Walton within 8 miles. Constable country and Ipswich within 25 miles.
Facilities ⅋ ⌁ ☐ ☐ ⌂ ⌒ ☐ ☎
☐ ⊙ ✕ ♐ ☐ ☐ ⌁
Nearby Facilities ⌒ ⌁ ⏚ ⟓ ∪ ⌁ ♐
Nearest Town Clacton-on-Sea
Directions From the A12 take the A120 towards Harwich then the A133 towards Weeley and Clacton. Then take the B1033 towards Walton, go past the second roundabout and the site entrance is ¼ mile on the left hand side. Entrance through Homestead Caravans.
⇥ Weeley

GLOUCESTERSHIRE
CHELTENHAM
Briarfields Motel & Touring Park, Gloucester Road, Cheltenham, Gloucestershire, GL51 0SX
Tel: 01242 235324
Email: briarfields@hotmail.co.uk
www.briarfields.net
Pitches For ⛺ ♐ ♐ **Total** 92
Acreage 6 **Open** All Year
Access Good **Site** Level
Nearest Bus Stop (Miles) Outside
2 miles from Regency Cheltenham and 6 miles from Gloucester (cathedral and historic docks), with regular buses to both going past the site. Ideal base for touring the Cotswolds and the Forest of Dean.
Facilities ⅋ ⌁ ☐ ⌂ ⌒ ⊙ ⌐ ☐ ☎
☐ ✕ ☐ ☐ ☐

Nearby Facilities ⌒ ⌁ ♐
Nearest Town Cheltenham
Directions Leave the M5 at junction 11 and take the A40 for Cheltenham. At the first roundabout take the first exit onto the B4063 and Briarfields is 200 metres on the left.
⇥ Cheltenham

CHELTENHAM
Cheltenham Racecourse Caravan Club Site, Prestbury Park, Cheltenham, Gloucestershire, GL50 4SH
Tel: 01242 523102
www.caravanclub.co.uk
Pitches For ♐ ♐ **Total** 75
Acreage 7 **Open** April **to** Oct
Access Good **Site** Lev/Slope
Nearest Bus Stop (Miles) ¼
Set on the edge of elegant Cheltenham with panoramic views of the Cleeve Hills. Free racing, putting course adjacent (small charge). Non members welcome. Booking essential.
Facilities ⅋ ⌂ ⌐ ☐ ☎ ☐ ⊙ ⊗ ⌁
Nearby Facilities ⌒
Nearest Town Cheltenham
Directions From west on the A40, 1½ miles past M5 junction at Benhall roundabout turn left into Princess Elizabeth Way. At the roundabout continue straight into Kingsditch Industrial Estate, after ½ mile turn right, at roundabout turn left into racecourse and foll
⇥ Cheltenham

CIRENCESTER
Hoburne Cotswold, Broadway Lane, South Cerney, Cirencester, Gloucestershire, GL7 5UQ
Tel: 01285 860216
Email: enquiries@hoburne.com
www.hoburne.com
Pitches For ⛺ ♐ ♐ **Total** 189

The Red Lion
Riverside Inn & Caravan & Camping Park
Wainlode Hill, Norton,
Gloucester GL2 9LW
01452 730251/01299 400787

Idyllic country location on the banks of the River Severn, ideal for fishing and walking. Close to The Cotswolds, Forest of Dean and Cheltenham. Our 26 acre site welcomes touring caravans, tents and motor caravans, and is OPEN ALL YEAR. Electric hook-ups, full toilet and shower facilities and launderette. Seasonal pitches are available. All year round lodges for sale. Our own country inn serves a wide range of hot and cold food & beverages. Site shop offers fresh milk, groceries and ice cream.

www.redlioninn-caravancampingpark.co.uk

Acreage 70 **Open** March to October
Access Good **Site** Level
Nearest Bus Stop (Miles) ¼
In the centre of the Cotswold Water Park and built around five lakes, this Park is the perfect base for watersports and sightseeing.
Facilities
Nearby Facilities
Nearest Town South Cerney
Directions 4 miles south of Cirencester on the A419, follow signs to Cotswold Hoburne, in the Cotswold Water Park.

CIRENCESTER
Mayfield Touring Park, Cheltenham Road, Perrotts Brook, Cirencester, Gloucestershire, GL7 7BH
Tel: 01285 831301
Email: mayfield-park@cirencester.fsbusiness.co.uk
www.mayfieldpark.co.uk
Pitches For ▲ ⬛ ⬛ **Total** 76
Acreage 10 **Open** All Year
Access Good **Site** Lev/Slope
Nearest Bus Stop (Miles) Outside
In a position central to the Cotswolds with pleasant views and a warm welcome. This site benefits from having a variety of pitch types with something to suit every need. Disabled toilet/shower and baby changing facilities.
Facilities
Nearby Facilities
Directions On A435, 13 miles from Cheltenham and 2 miles from Cirencester. From Cirencester by-pass A419/A417 take the Burford Road exit then follow camping and caravan signs.
⬛ Kemble

CIRENCESTER
Second Chance Caravan Park, Nr Marston Meysey, Wiltshire, SN6 6SZ
Tel: 01285 810675/810939
www.secondchancetouring.co.uk
Pitches For ▲ ⬛ ⬛ **Total** 26
Acreage 2 **Open** March to November
Access Good **Site** Level
Nearest Bus Stop (Miles) ¼
Riverside location with private fishing and access for your own canoe. The first camping/caravan park on the Thames Path, great for exploring the upper reaches of the Thames. Excellent opportunity to visit the old Roman capital of Cirencester and the many attractions of the Cotswolds. AA 2 Pennants.
Facilities
Nearby Facilities
Nearest Town Castle Eaton/Fairford
Directions Between Swindon and Cirencester on the A419. Turn off at the Fairford/Marston Meysey exit and follow the caravan park signs. Proceed approx. 3 miles then turn right at the brown caravan/camping signpost. We are on the right.
⬛ Swindon

COLEFORD
Greenacres Campsite, Scowles Road, Coleford, Gloucestershire, GL16 8QS
Tel: 01594 837753
Email: greenacres2@btinternet.com
www.greenacrescampsite.co.uk
Pitches For ▲ ⬛ ⬛ **Total** 12
Acreage 1½ **Open** April to October
Access Good **Site** Level
Nearest Bus Stop (Miles) ½
Situated in the Forest of Dean near Symonds Yat, in an Area of Outstanding Natural Beauty near a river.
Facilities
Nearby Facilities
Nearest Town Coleford
Directions From Coleford take the main road for Staunton, just out of Coleford turn left towards The Scowles, site is ½ a mile.
⬛ Lydney

COLEFORD
Woodlands View Caravan Park, Chepstow Road, Sling, Coleford, Gloucestershire, GL16 8JA
Tel: 01594 835127
Email: woodland.caravanpark@tiscali.co.uk
www.woodlandsviewcaravanpark.co.uk
Pitches For ▲ ⬛ ⬛ **Total** 21
Acreage 2 **Open** All Year
Access Good **Site** Level
Nearest Bus Stop (Miles) ¼
Small, family run park situated in the Royal Forest of Dean. Near to many attractions including Clearwell Caves, Puzzlewood, Dean Heritage Centre and Dean Forest Railway.
Facilities
Nearby Facilities
Nearest Town Coleford
Directions From Coleford take the B4228 towards Chepstow, after ½ a mile you will pass PuzzleWood on the right, we are signposted ¼ of a mile on the left.
⬛ Lydney

DURSLEY
Hogsdown Farm Caravan & Camping, Hogsdown Farm, Lower Wick, Dursley, Gloucestershire, GL11 6DD
Tel: 01453 810224
www.hogsdownfarm.co.uk
Pitches For ▲ ⬛ ⬛
Acreage 5 **Open** All Year
Access Good **Site** Level
Nearest Bus Stop (Miles) 1
Great for visiting Berkeley Castle, Jenner Museum, Wild Fowl Trust, Weston Birt Arboretum, and the hills and valleys of the Cotswolds.
Facilities
Nearby Facilities
Nearest Town Berkeley
Directions Between junctions 13 and 14 of the M5, off the A38.
⬛ Cam

GLOUCESTER
The Red Lion Inn Caravan & Camping Park, Wainlode Hill, Norton, Gloucestershire, GL2 9LW
Tel: 01452 730251
www.redlioninncaravancampingpark.co.uk
Pitches For ▲ ⬛ ⬛ **Total** 109
Acreage 10 **Open** All Year
Access Good **Site** Level
Nearest Bus Stop (Miles) ½
On the banks of the River Severn with a riverside pub.
Facilities
Nearby Facilities
Nearest Town Gloucester/Tewkesbury
Directions From Tewkesbury take the A38 south for 3 miles, turn right onto the B4213. After 3 miles turn left to Wainlode Hill, 350 yards alongside the River Severn, park is on the left.
⬛ Gloucester

LECHLADE
Bridge House Campsite, Bridge House, Thames Street, Lechlade, Gloucestershire, GL7 3AG
Tel: 01367 252348
Pitches For ▲ ⬛ ⬛ **Total** 80
Acreage 3½ **Open** Apr to Oct **Site** Level
Nearest Bus Stop (Miles) ¼
Ideal for touring Cotswolds and Upper Thames. You can also contact us on Mobile: 07733 015491.
Facilities
Nearby Facilities
Nearest Town Lechlade
Directions ¼ of a mile south of Lechlade on the A361 Swindon road. Opposite Riverside car park.
⬛ Swindon

LYDNEY
Whitemead Forest Park, Parkend, Lydney, Gloucestershire, GL15 4LA
Tel: 0845 345 3425
Email: enquiries@csmaclubretreats.com
www.whitemead.co.uk
Pitches For ▲ ⬛ ⬛ **Total** 110
Acreage 33
Access Good **Site** Lev/Slope
Nearest Bus Stop (Miles) ¼
Climbing, abseiling, zip wire, trapeze, walking, cycling, canoeing, archery, rifle shooting and more.
Facilities
Nearby Facilities
Nearest Town Lydney
Directions Take the B4234 to Parkend, turn left at the crossroads, turn first left and Whitemead is on the left hand side.
⬛ Lydney

MORETON VALENCE
Gables Farm Caravan & Camping Site, Moreton Valence, Gloucestershire, GL2 7ND
Tel: 01452 720331
Pitches For ▲ ⬛ ⬛ **Total** 30
Acreage 3 **Open** March to Nov
Access Good **Site** Level

GLOUCESTERSHIRE

Nearest Bus Stop (Miles) Outside
Facilities ∫ ⬚⬚🆗🏳️📡⊙🍴🍽️🏧🔌
Nearby Facilities ┌ ✈
Nearest Town Gloucester
Directions Leave the M5 at junction 13 and take the A38 north for 2 miles. Or leave the M5 at junction 12 and take the A38 south for 1½ miles.
🚆 Gloucester

MORETON-IN-MARSH

Moreton-In-Marsh Caravan Club Site, Bourton Road, Moreton-in-Marsh, Gloucestershire, GL56 0BT
Tel: 01608 650519
www.caravanclub.co.uk
Pitches For ⬚ 🚐 **Total** 183
Acreage 21 **Open** All Year
Access Good **Site** Level
Nearest Bus Stop (Miles) ¼
Attractive, wooded site offering crazy golf, 5-a-side football, volleyball and a boules pitch. Near Batsford Arboretum & Falconry Centre and Sleepy Hollow Farm Park. Non members welcome. Booking essential.
Facilities ⬚ ∫ ⬚⬚🆗🏳️ ⊙🍴 📡 🏧 📡
⬚⬚🍴🏧⛟🔌🍽️📡
Nearby Facilities ✈
Nearest Town Moreton-in-Marsh
Directions Leave Evesham on the A44, site entrance is on the left approx. 1¼ miles past Bourton-on-the-Hill and 150 yards before Moreton-in-Marsh sign. NB: No arrivals before 1pm at weekends and in peak periods.

SLIMBRIDGE

Tudor Caravanning & Camping Park, Shepherds Patch, Slimbridge, Gloucestershire, GL2 7BP
Tel: 01453 890483
Email: cades@tudorcaravanpark.co.uk
www.tudorcaravanpark.com

Pitches For ⛺ ⬚ 🚐 🚐 **Total** 75
Acreage 7¼ **Open** All Year
Access Good **Site** Level
Sharpness Canal alongside, Slimbridge Wetlands Centre 800 metres, Cotswold Way 5 miles. Pub on our doorstep. NEW toilet and shower block. AA 4 Pennants.
Facilities ⬚ ∫ 🆗⬚🏳️ ⊙🍴 🏧 📡 🍽️
⬚⊙🍴🏧🔌 🍽️ ⛟ 📡 📡
Nearby Facilities ┌ ✈ ⚓ ∪
Nearest Town Dursley/Gloucester
Directions Leave the M5 at junction 13 and follow signs for WWT Wetlands Centre, Slimbridge. 1½ miles off the A38 at the rear of the Tudor Arms Pub.
🚆 Dursley

TEWKESBURY

Croft Farm Leisure & Water Park, Bredons Hardwick, Tewkesbury, Gloucestershire, GL20 7EE
Tel: 01684 772321
Email: alan@croftfarmleisure.co.uk
www.croftfarmleisure.co.uk
Pitches For ⛺ ⬚ 🚐 🚐 **Total** 60
Acreage 10 **Open** March to Oct
Access Good **Site** Level
Nearest Bus Stop (Miles) ¼
Lakeside location with own watersports centre and lake for sailing, windsurfing and canoeing. River Avon close by. Gym and Clubhouse on site.
Facilities ⬚ ∫ ⬚⬚🆗🏳️ ⊙🍴 🏧 📡 🍽️
⬚⊙🍴🏧 🍽️ ⛟🔌🍽️ 📡 📡
Nearby Facilities ┌ ✈ ⚓ 🏌 ∪ 🎣
Nearest Town Tewkesbury
Directions 1½ miles north-east of Tewkesbury on the B4080.
🚆 Ashchurch

TEWKESBURY

Dawleys Caravan Park, Owls Lane, Shuthonger, Tewkesbury, Gloucestershire, GL20 6EQ
Tel: 01684 292622
Email: enquiries@dawleyscaravanpark.co.uk
www.ukparks.co.uk/dawleys
Pitches For ⛺ ⬚ 🚐 **Total** 20
Acreage 3 **Open** April to Sept
Access Fair **Site** Sloping
Nearest Bus Stop (Miles) ½
Secluded rural site, near a river. Close to the M5 and M50.
Facilities ∫ 🆗⬚🏳️ ⊙ 📡 🍴🏧🔌🍽️ ⛟
Nearby Facilities ┌ ✈ ⚓ ∪
Nearest Town Cheltenham/Gloucester
Directions A38 north from Tewkesbury, approimately 2 miles on the left hand side. Or 1¼ miles south on A38 from M50 junction 1.
🚆 Tewkesbury

TEWKESBURY

Mill Avon Holiday Park, Gloucester Road, Tewkesbury, Gloucestershire, GL20 5SW
Tel: 01684 296876
Email: millavon@quinweb.net
www.millavonholidaypark.com
Pitches For ⬚ 🚐 **Total** 24
Open March to December
Access Good **Site** Level
Nearest Bus Stop (Miles) ¼
On the banks of the River Avon with views of the Malvern Hills. Just a short walk to the town centre.
Facilities ∫ 🆗⬚🏳️ ⊙🍴 🏧 📡 🍽️
⬚⊙🍴🏧🔌 🍽️ ✈ ∪
Nearby Facilities ┌ ✈ ⚓ 🏌 ∪
Nearest Town Tewkesbury
Directions On the A38, ¼ of a mile from the town centre.
🚆 Ashchurch

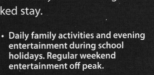

TEWKESBURY

Tewkesbury Abbey Caravan Club Site, Gander Lane, Tewkesbury, Gloucestershire, GL20 5PG
Tel: 01684 294035
www.caravanclub.co.uk
Pitches For Å 🚐 🚌 **Total** 158
Acreage 9 **Open** April to Nov
Access Good **Site** Lev/Slope
Nearest Bus Stop (Miles) ½
Situated adjacent to the ancient Abbey. Many interesting walks, historic buildings and museums locally. Near the Battle Trail and Royal Worcester Factory. Non members welcome. Booking essential.
Facilities
Nearby Facilities
Nearest Town Tewkesbury
Directions Leave the M5 at junc 9 and take the A438 sp Tewkesbury. At the traffic lights by Morrisons go straight on, at the town centre crossroads keep left and after 200 yards turn left into Gander Lane, site is on the left.
⇌ Tewkesbury

TEWKESBURY

Winchcombe Camping & Caravanning Club Site, Brooklands Farm, Alderton, Nr Tewkesbury, Gloucestershire, GL20 8NX
Tel: 01242 620259
www.campingandcaravanningclub.co.uk/winchcombe
Pitches For Å 🚐 🚌 **Total** 80
Acreage 20 **Open** 11-Mar to 15-Jan
Access Good **Site** Level
Nearest Bus Stop (Miles) 1
Set amidst the lovely Cotswold countryside, with its own fishing lake. Lodges available for hire. BTB 4 Star Graded and AA 3 Pennants. Non members welcome. You can also call us on 0845 130 7633.

Facilities
Nearby Facilities
Nearest Town Tewkesbury
Directions From Tewkesbury take the A46, at the roundabout go straight over then take the B4077 to Stow-on-the-Wold, site is on the right in 3 miles.
⇌ Tewkesbury

HAMPSHIRE

ANDOVER

Wyke Down Touring Caravan & Camping Park, Picket Piece, Andover, Hampshire, SP11 6LX
Tel: 01264 352048
Email: p.read@wykedown.co.uk
www.wykedown.co.uk
Pitches For Å 🚐 🚌 **Total** 69
Acreage 3 **Open** All Year
Access Good **Site** Level
Nearest Bus Stop (Miles) ½
Ideal touring centre. Country pub and restaurant with golf driving range.
Facilities
Nearby Facilities
Nearest Town Andover
Directions Follow camping/caravan park signs from the A303, go through the village of Picket Piece and site is on the left in approx. 1 mile.
⇌ Andover

BRANSGORE

Harrow Wood Farm Caravan Park, Poplar Lane, Bransgore, Nr Christchurch, Hampshire, BH23 8JE
Tel: 01425 672487
Email: harrowwood@caravan-sites.co.uk
www.caravan-sites.co.uk

Pitches For 🚐 🚌 **Total** 60
Open 01-Mar to 06-Jan
Access Good **Site** Level
Nearest Bus Stop (Miles) ½
Set in 80 acres of farmland. Within easy reach of the New Forest and the sea.
Facilities
Nearby Facilities
Nearest Town Christchurch
Directions 4 miles from Christchurch on the A35, in Bransgore turn first right after the school into Poplar Lane.
⇌ Hinton Admiral

FAREHAM

Dibles Park, Dibles Road, Warsash, Southampton, Hampshire, SO31 9SA
Tel: 01489 575232
Email: dibles.park@btconnect.com
www.diblespark.co.uk
Pitches For Å 🚐 🚌 **Total** 14
Open All Year
Access Good **Site** Level
Nearest Bus Stop (Miles) ½
Ideal for touring, walking and cycling. Excellent location for cross Channel ferries. Near Hamble Estuary and nature reserves.
Facilities
Nearby Facilities
Nearest Town Fareham/Southampton
Directions Leave the M27 at junc 9 and take the A27 for Fareham. At the next roundabout exit sp Park Gate A27. At the third roundabout take the exit onto Brook Lane. Continue along this road going across 3 roundabouts, at 4th roundabout (mini) take second exit into Dibles Road. Park entrance is 500yds on left hand side.
⇌ Swanwick

HAMPSHIRE

FORDINGBRIDGE

Hill Cottage Farm Camping & Caravan Park, Sandleheath Road, Alderholt, Fordingbridge, Hampshire, SP6 3EG
Tel: 01425 650513
Email: hillcottagefarmcaravansite@supanet.com
www.hillcottagefarmcampingandcaravanpark.co.uk
Pitches For Å ⊞ 🚐 🚃 **Total** 90
Acreage 12 **Open** March **to** November
Access Good **Site** Level
Nearest Bus Stop (Miles) ½
Situated on the edge of the New Forest. Listed in Practical Caravans Top 100 Parks.
Facilities ✦ ⨍ 🖸 🖩 ⬚🗙 ⌂ ⊙↺ 🛁 🖳 🗑
🕰 🏧 🛇 🔆 🟎 ⌖ 🕭 🗐 ✦ 🌺 ⚡ 📶
Nearby Facilities ⌐ 🏊 ⚓ 🛶 ∪ ♬ 🏇 ♞
Nearest Town Fordingbridge
Directions 2 miles from Fordingbridge on the B3078.
🚆 Salisbury

HAMBLE

Riverside Holidays, Satchell Lane, Hamble, Hampshire, SO31 4HR
Tel: 023 8045 3220
Email: enquiries@riversideholidays.co.uk
www.riversideholidays.co.uk
Pitches For Å ⊞ 🚐 🚃 **Total** 77
Acreage 2 **Open** March **to** October
Access Good **Site** Lev/Slight Slope
Nearest Bus Stop (Miles) ½
Overlooking the River Hamble with a marina below the park. In the very pretty village of Hamble. AA 4 Pennants, 3 Star Rose Award and David Bellamy Bronze Award for Conservation.
Facilities ✦ ⨍ 🖸 🖩 ⌂ ⌐ ⊙↺ 🛁 🖳 🗑
🕰 🛇 🟎 🗐 🖳 🔆 ⚡
Nearby Facilities ⌐ 🏊 ⚓ 🛶 ∪
Nearest Town Southampton

Directions Leave the M27 at junction 8, follow signs for Hamble Village on the B3397 for approx. 2 miles, then turn left into Satchell Lane. Riverside is on the left hand side of Satchell Lane above Mercury Marina.
🚆 Hamble

HAYLING ISLAND

Fleet Park, Yew Tree Road, Hayling Island, Hampshire, PO11 0QE
Tel: 023 9246 3684
Email: fleetcampsite@aol.co.uk
www.haylingcampsites.co.uk
Pitches For Å ⊞ 🚐 🚃 **Total** 100
Acreage 2 **Open** March **to** Oct
Access Good **Site** Level
Nearest Bus Stop (Miles) ¼
Level pitches surrounded by oak trees and by a tidal creek.
Facilities ⨍ 🖩 ⌂ ⊙↺ 🖳 🗑 🖲 ⧫ 🗐 🖳 ✦
Nearby Facilities ⌐ 🏊 ⚓ 🛶 ∪
Directions Take the main road into Hayling Island and turn left at the Yew Tree Pub, turn right into the static caravan park, turn second left, then turn second left into the Park.
🚆 Havant

HAYLING ISLAND

Oven Camping Site, Manor Road, Hayling Island, Hampshire, PO11 0QX
Tel: 02392 464695
Email: theovencampsite@talktalk.net
www.haylingcampsites.co.uk
Pitches For Å ⊞ 🚐 🚃 **Total** 330
Acreage 10 **Open** March **to** Dec Incl.
Access Good **Site** Level
Nearest Bus Stop (Miles) Outside
Heated swimming pool. Excellent touring area for Portsmouth, Chichester, New Forest etc. Safe, clean, Blue Flag beaches, excellent for water sports. Excellent Rally site at discount prices.

Facilities ✦ ⨍ 🖩 ⬚🗙 ⌂ ⌐ ⊙↺ 🛁 🖳 🗑
🕰 🛇 🏧 🗙 🖩 ⚓ 🛇 🔆 🟎 🗐 🔆
Nearby Facilities ⌐ 🏊 ⚓ 🛶 ∪ ♬ ♞
Nearest Town Havant
Directions Exit M27 or the A37 at Havant. Take the A3023 from Havant, approx 3 miles after crossing bridge onto Hayling Island bear right at the roundabout. Site is on the left in 450yds.
🚆 Havant

MILFORD-ON-SEA

Lytton Lawn Touring Park, Lymore Lane, Milford-on-Sea, Hampshire, SO41 0TX
Tel: 01590 648331
Email: holidays@shorefield.co.uk
www.shorefield.co.uk
Pitches For Å ⊞ 🚐 🚃 **Total** 135
Acreage 7 **Open** 10-Feb **to** 02-Jan
Access Good **Site** Lev/Slope
Nearest Bus Stop (Miles) Outside
Peaceful, picturesque, rural Park with a small river. 10 minutes walk to the beach. One pitch for a US RV.
Facilities ✦ ⨍ 🖸 🖩 ⬚🗙 ⌂ ⊙↺ 🛁 🖳 🗑
🕰 🛇 🏧 🟎 🗐 🗑
Nearby Facilities ⌐ 🏊 ⚓ 🛶 ∪ ♞
Nearest Town Lymington
Directions On the A337, 3 miles from Lymington and 4 miles from New Milton.
🚆 New Milton

NEW MILTON

Hoburne Bashley, Sway Road, New Milton, Hampshire, BH25 5QR
Tel: 01425 612340
Email: hoburnebashley@hoburne.com
www.hoburne.com
Pitches For ⊞ 🚐 🚃 **Total** 289
Open 05-Feb **to** 30-Oct
Access Good **Site** Lev/Slope
Nearest Bus Stop (Miles) ¾

LINWOOD, NEAR RINGWOOD
HAMPSHIRE BH24 3QT
01425 473789
FAX: (01425) 471558

red shoot camping park

redshoot-campingpark.com
enquiries@redshoot-campingpark.com

This popular little site has been owned and managed by the same family for over 40 years. Beautifully situated in the NEW FOREST, with lovely walks from the camp site gate. Ideal centre for walking, touring and for nature lovers, yet only ½ hour drive from Bournemouth and the sea.

RED SHOOT INN lies adjacent to the camp site, and is an attractive old pub serving real ales, good food and welcoming families.

English Tourist Board

FACILITIES

- ❏ Excellent Toilet/Shower Facilities
- ❏ Electric Hook-ups ❏ Well Stocked Shop & Off Licence
- ❏ Play Area ❏ Laundry Room ❏ Facilities for the Disabled
- ❏ Special Off Peak Tariff
- ❏ Owner supervised to high standard

APPROVED SITE FOR TENTS, CARAVANS & MOTOR HOMES

SHOREFIELD
Camping & Touring
Short breaks & Holidays

Discover   Relax   Explore   Unwind   Enjoy

For full details, ask for our brochure or browse online

Telephone
01590 648331
holidays@shorefield.co.uk

Our touring parks are set in peaceful, unspoilt parkland in the beautiful South Coast area.

There are pitches available for touring caravans, motorhomes or tents. There are great leisure facilities and lots of fun entertainment for everyone. Pamper yourself in our 'Reflections' Elemis Day Spa at Shorefield Country Park, explore the New Forest, or relax on Bournemouth's sandy beaches.

HAMPSHIRE
Oakdene Forest Park
St. Leonards, BH24 2RZ
Forest Edge Holiday Park
St. Leonards, BH24 2SD
Lytton Lawn Touring Park
Milford-on-Sea, SO41 0TX

DORSET
Swanage Coastal Park
Swanage, BH19 2RS
Merley Court Touring Park
Wimborne, BH21 3AA

www.shorefield.co.uk   Ref: CADT

HAMPSHIRE, HEREFORDSHIRE

Within the boundaries of the New Forest, and within 2 miles of the beach. Perfect location for touring, 10 miles from Bournemouth. Own golf course and tennis. Many facilities.
Facilities
Nearby Facilities
Nearest Town New Milton
Directions From the A35 Lyndhurst/Bournemouth road, take the B3055 signposted Sway. Over crossroads at 2¼ miles. Park is ½ a mile on the left.
⇌ New Milton

OWER

Green Pastures Farm, Ower, Romsey, Hampshire, SO51 6AJ
Tel: 023 8081 4444
Email: enquiries@greenpasturesfarm.com
www.greenpasturesfarm.com
Pitches For ▲ ⬤ ⬤ **Total** 45
Acreage 5 **Open** 15-Mar **to** 31-Oct
Access Good **Site** Level
A grassy site on family run farm, within easy reach of the New Forest. Pub with good food only a 20 minute walk. Paultons Park 1 mile. Convenient for ferries. Ample space for children to play in full view of units. Separate toilet/shower room for the disabled. Day kennelling available. Emergency telephone only.
Facilities
Nearby Facilities
Nearest Town Romsey
Directions Leave the M27 at junction 2 and follow signposts for Salisbury for ½ a mile. Then start to follow our own signs. Also signposted from the A36 and the A3090 at Ower.
⇌ Romsey

RINGWOOD

Forest Edge Holiday Park, Boundary Lane, St Leonards, Ringwood, Hampshire, BH24 2SD
Tel: 01590 648331
Email: holidays@shorefield.co.uk
www.shorefield.co.uk
Pitches For ▲ ⬤ ⬤ **Total** 140
Acreage 7 **Open** 01-Feb **to** 02-Jan
Access Good **Site** Level
Nearest Bus Stop (Miles) Outside
Family atmosphere. Near a river and the New Forest. 9 miles from the beach. Use of leisure facilities at Oakdene Park (10 minute walk).
Facilities
Nearby Facilities
Nearest Town Ringwood
Directions 3 miles west of Ringwood on the A31.
⇌ Bournemouth

RINGWOOD

The Red Shoot Camping Park, Linwood, Nr Ringwood, Hampshire, BH24 3QT
Tel: 01425 473789
Email: enquiries@redshoot-campingpark.com
www.redshoot-campingpark.com
Pitches For ▲ ⬤ ⬤ **Total** 130
Acreage 4 **Open** March **to** October
Access Good **Site** Lev/Slope
Situated in a beautiful part of the New Forest. Half hour drive to Bournemouth coast, Salisbury and Southampton. Excellent modern shower facilities. Good pub adjacent. Off peak tariff early and late season.
Facilities
Nearby Facilities

Nearest Town Ringwood
Directions Fron Ringwood take A338, 2 miles north of Ringwood take right turn signed Moyles Court and Linwood. Follow signs to Linwood.
⇌ Brockenhurst

ROMSEY

Hill Farm Caravan Park, Branches Lane, Sherfield English, Romsey, Hampshire, SO51 6FH
Tel: 01794 340402
Email: gjb@hillfarmpark.com
www.hillfarmpark.com
Pitches For ▲ ⬤ ⬤ **Total** 150
Acreage 11 **Open** March **to** October
Access Good **Site** Lev/Slope
Set in beautiful Hampshire countryside we offer a quiet, rural location. Just 3 miles north of the New Forest and only 20 minutes from Salisbury, Winchester and Southampton.
Facilities
Nearby Facilities
Directions From Romsey take the A3090 west, turn right onto the A27 towards Salisbury. In Sherfield English at the first crossroads turn right into Branches Lane, site is approx. 1 mile.
⇌ Romsey

WINCHESTER

Morn Hill Caravan Club Site, Morn Hill, Winchester, Hampshire, SO21 1HL
Tel: 01962 869877
www.caravanclub.co.uk
Pitches For ▲ ⬤ ⬤ **Total** 139
Acreage 9 **Open** March **to** Nov
Access Good **Site** Level
Nearest Bus Stop (Miles) ¼
Large site. Near Paultons Leisure Park, Marwell Zoo, Beaulieu, New Forest, Broadlands and Watercress Railway Line. Non members welcome. Booking essential.
Facilities
Nearby Facilities
Directions Leave the M3 at junction 9, at roundabout keep left onto the A33 signposted Southampton. At Spitfire roundabout turn left onto the A31 signposted Alton, at next roundabout follow signs for Easton, turn immediately right in front of Percy Hobbs Public House. Site is 100yds.
⇌ Winchester

HEREFORDSHIRE

BROMYARD

Boyce Caravan Park, Boyce Farm, Stanford Bishop, Bringsty, Worcestershire, WR6 5UB
Tel: 01886 884248
Email: enquiries@boyceholidaypark.co.uk
www.boyceholidaypark.co.uk
Pitches For ▲ ⬤ ⬤ **Total** 14
Open March **to** Oct
Access Good **Site** Level
Excellent area for walking and sight seeing. Close to the cities of Hereford and Worcester.
Facilities
Nearby Facilities
Nearest Town Bromyard
Directions From the A44 take the B4220 sp Malvern. On entering the village of Stanford Bishop turn sharp left then first right down a private drive.
⇌ Malvern

BROMYARD

Bromyard Downs Caravan Club Site, Brockhampton, Bringsty, Worcestershire, WR6 5TE
Tel: 01885 482607
www.caravanclub.co.uk
Pitches For ⬤ ⬤ **Total** 40
Acreage 4 **Open** March **to** Oct
Access Good **Site** Lev/Slope
Rural, woodland site situated in beautiful countryside. Ideal for walkers. Many historic houses, museums and steam railways nearby. Own sanitation required. Non members welcome. Booking essential.
Facilities
Nearby Facilities
Nearest Town Bromyard
Directions From Leominster on the A44, on the outskirts of Bromyard follow signs for Worcester round Bromyard Bypass, DO NOT go into Bromyard. Site entrance is on the right approx. 1½ miles past Bromyard (¼ mile past the B4220 junction and immediately past road signposted Bromyards Downs).

HAY-ON-WYE

Penlan Caravan & Campsite, Penlan, Brilley, Hay-on-Wye, Herefordshire, HR3 6JW
Tel: 01497 831485
Email: peter@penlan.org.uk
www.penlancampsite.co.uk
Pitches For ▲ ⬤ ⬤ **Total** 20
Acreage 2½ **Open** Easter **to** Oct
Site Level
Peaceful and relaxing site. Ideal for exploring Mid Wales and the black and white villages of Herefordshire. National Trust small holding. Advance booking essential.
Facilities
Nearby Facilities
Nearest Town Hay-on-Wye
Directions From Kington Church follow the Brilley to Whitney-on-Wye road for 4 miles. Look for National Trust signs on the left, turn sharp left into Apostles Lane, Penlan is first on the right.
⇌ Hereford

HEREFORD

Cuckoos Corner, Moreton-on-Lugg, Herefordshire, HR4 8AH
Tel: 01432 760234
Email: cuckooscorner@gmail.com
www.cuckooscorner.com
Pitches For ▲ ⬤ ⬤ **Total** 20
Acreage 1½ **Open** All Year
Access Good **Site** Level
Nearest Bus Stop (Miles) Outside
ADULTS ONLY. Friendly site with pleasant views. 15 hard standings: 5' x 45' feet long. Free broadband. Good touring area. Shop and chip shop nearby. 3 miles north of Hereford. Very reasonable rates.
Facilities
Nearby Facilities
Nearest Town Hereford
Directions 4 miles north of Hereford on the A49, 100 yards beyond signpost Village Centre and Marden. Or 10 miles south of Leominster opposite advance sign Village Centre and Marden.
⇌ Hereford

HEREFORD

Hereford Camping & Caravanning Club Site, The Millpond, Little Tarrington, Hereford, Herefordshire, HR1 4JA
Tel: 01432 890243
www.campingandcaravanningclub.co.uk/hereford

Pitches For 🏕 🚐 🚍 **Total** 55
Acreage 24 **Open** 01-Mar **to** 05-Nov
Access Good **Site** Level
Nearest Bus Stop (Miles) ½
Idyllic rural location next to The Millpond. A perfect spot for fishing, walking, exploring the Malvern Hills and the Wye Valley, or for simply relaxing. Four berth caravan available for hire. Non members welcome. You can also call us on 0845 130 7633.
Facilities 🚻 ♿ 🏪 🍴 ⊙ 📞 🛒 🅿
🔌 ⛽ 🏧 🍽 🎣 🏊 💈 ✉
Nearby Facilities 🎯 ✈ ⛵
Nearest Town Hereford
Directions From Hereford take the A438 and turn left at the A438/Ledbury Road. Follow the A438 and go over one roundabout, then turn left.
🚆 Ledbury

HEREFORD

Lucksall Caravan & Camping Park, Mordiford, Hereford, Herefordshire, HR1 4LP
Tel: 01432 870213
Email: karen@lucksallpark.co.uk
www.lucksallpark.co.uk
Pitches For 🏕 🚐 🚍 **Total** 120
Acreage 17 **Open** 01-Mar **to** 30-Nov
Access Good **Site** Level
Nearest Bus Stop (Miles) Outside
On the banks of the River Wye, ideal for canoeing and walking. ETC 5 Star Graded.
Facilities 🚻 ♿ 🏪 🍴 ⊙ 📞 🛒 🅿 🔌
⛽ 🏧 🍴 ✗ 🍽 🎣 💈 ✉ 🏊 💈 ✉
Nearby Facilities 🎯 ✈ ⛵
Nearest Town Hereford
Directions On the B4224 between Hereford (5 miles) and Ross-on-Wye (9 miles).
🚆 Hereford

LEOMINSTER

Arrow Bank Holiday Park, Nun House Farm, Eardisland, Nr Leominster, Herefordshire, HR6 9BG
Tel: 01544 388312
Email: enquiries@arrowbankholidaypark.co.uk
www.arrowbankholidaypark.co.uk
Pitches For 🏕 🚐 🚍 **Total** 36
Acreage 5 **Open** 01-Mar **to** 07-Jan
Access Good **Site** Level
Nearest Bus Stop (Miles) Entrance
ADULTS ONLY. Peaceful, landscaped park with very spacious and level pitches, set in a beautiful Black and White village. Ideal holiday base.
Facilities 🚻 ♿ 🏪 🍴 ⊙ 📞 🛒 🅿
🔌 ⛽ 🍽 🛒 🅿 ✉ 💈 🏊 ☂
Nearby Facilities 🎯 ✈ ⛵ ⛵
Nearest Town Leominster
Directions 6 miles west of Leominster, off the A44 Rhayadr/Brecon road. On the B4529, enter the village of Eardisland and we are signposted on the right hand side.
🚆 Leominster

LEOMINSTER

Home Farm Caravan Site, Home Farm, Bircher, Leominster, Herefordshire, HR6 0AX
Tel: 01568 780525
Email: dawnhomefarmbb@aol.com
www.homefarmaccommodation.co.uk
Pitches For 🏕 🚐 🚍 **Total** 36
Acreage 20 **Open** All Year
Access Good **Site** Level
Nearest Bus Stop (Miles) Outside
Set amongst green pastures and surrounded by stunning scenery. Near to National Trust properties and the historic town of Ludlow. You can also contact us on Mobile: 07905 212605.

Facilities 🚻 ♿ 🏪 🍴 ⊙ 📞 🛒 🅿 ✉ 💈 🏊 ☂
Nearby Facilities 🎯 ✈ ⛵
Directions 5 miles north of Leominster on the B4362, follow signs for Croft Castle (NT).
🚆 Leominster

LEOMINSTER

Nicholson Farm, Docklow, Leominster, Herefordshire, HR6 0SL
Tel: 07740 717564
Email: tjwbrooke@aol.com
www.nicholsonfarm.co.uk
Pitches For 🏕 🚐 🚍 **Total** 20
Open Easter **to** October
Access Good **Site** Level
A working dairy farm between the small towns of Leominster and Bromyard. Ideal for countryside walking. Near to several National Trust properties, Hereford, Hay-on-Wye and the Black & White Village Trail.
Facilities 🍴 🏪 ⊙ 📞 🛒 🅿 ✉ 🏊 ☂ 💈 🎣 ✉ 🛒 ☂
Nearby Facilities 🎯 ✈ ⛵ ⛵
Nearest Town Leominster
Directions Off the A44 between Leominster and Bromyard, 6 miles from each.
🚆 Leominster

LEOMINSTER

Pearl Lake Leisure Park, Shobdon, Leominster, Herefordshire, HR6 9NQ
Tel: 01568 708326
Email: info@pearllake.co.uk
www.pearllake.co.uk
Pitches For 🏕 🚐 🚍 **Total** 15
Acreage 80 **Open** March **to** November
Access Good **Site** Level
Nearest Bus Stop (Miles) Outside
Outstanding park in a beautiful setting with a 15 acre fishing lake, 9 hole golf course, Crown bowls and woodland walks.
Facilities 🚻 ♿ 🏪 🍴 ⊙ 📞 🛒 🅿 🔌
🔌 ⛽ 🏧 ♿ 🍽 🍴 🛒 🅿 ✉ 🎣
Nearby Facilities ⛵ ⛵
Nearest Town Leominster
Directions Situated on the B4362 in the village of Shobdon.
🚆 Leominster

PETERCHURCH

Poston Mill Park, Peterchurch, Golden Valley, Herefordshire, HR2 0SF
Tel: 01981 550225
Email: info@poston-mill.co.uk
www.bestparks.co.uk
Pitches For 🏕 🚐 🚍 **Total** 64
Acreage 35 **Open** All Year
Access Good **Site** Level
Nearest Bus Stop (Miles) Outside
Highly recommended, beautiful, well maintained park with electric, water and TV (cable) connections on fully serviced pitches. Set on the banks of the River Dore. Shop and Mill Restaurant alongside the Park.
Facilities 🚻 ♿ 🏪 🍴 ⊙ 📞 🛒 🅿 🔌
🔌 ⛽ 🏧 ✗ 🍴 🍽 🛒 🅿 ✉ 💈 🏊 ☂
Nearby Facilities 🎯 ✈ ⛵ ⛵ 🏊
Nearest Town Hereford
Directions On the B4348, 11 miles from Hereford and 11 miles from Hay on Wye.
🚆 Hereford

ROSS-ON-WYE

Broadmeadow Caravan Park, Broadmeadows, Ross-on-Wye, Herefordshire, HR9 7BW
Tel: 01989 768076
Email: broadm4811@aol.com
www.broadmeadow.info
Pitches For 🏕 🚐 🚍 **Total** 150
Acreage 16 **Open** Easter/1st Apr **to** Sept
Access Good **Site** Level
Nearest Bus Stop (Miles) ¼

Lake walks. Fishing on site. Only 10 minutes to the centre of Ross-on-Wye. Ideal touring and walking in the Wye Valley. ETB 5 Star Graded.
Facilities 🚻 ♿ 🏪 🍴 🏊 ⊙ 📞 🛒 🅿 🔌
🔌 ⛽ 🏧 ♿ 🍽 🛒 🅿
Nearby Facilities 🎯 🏊 ✈ ⛵ 🏊 🏊
Nearest Town Ross-on-Wye
Directions Adjacent to the A40 Ross relief road. Access from Pancake roundabout off relief road turning into Ross. Take the first turning right into Ashburton Estate Road, then turn right by Morrisons Supermarket.
🚆 Gloucester

ROSS-ON-WYE

Lower Ruxton Farm, Kings Caple, Herefordshire, HR1 4TX
Tel: 01432 840223
Pitches For 🏕 🚐 🚍 **Total** 20
Acreage 8 **Open** Mid July **to** End Aug only
Site Level
Nearest Bus Stop (Miles) ½
Alongside a river.
Facilities ✗ 🍴 🍽 🅿
Nearby Facilities 🎯 ✈
Nearest Town Ross-on-Wye
Directions A49 from Ross-on-Wye, 1 mile turn right follow signs for Hoarwithy (Kings Caple 4 miles) across river bridge ½ mile sign to Ruxton second farm on right.
🚆 Hereford

SYMONDS YAT WEST

Doward Park Camp Site, Great Doward, Symonds Yat West, Nr Ross-on-Wye, Herefordshire, HR9 6BP
Tel: 01600 890438
Email: enquiries@dowardpark.co.uk
www.dowardpark.co.uk
Pitches For 🏕 🚍 **Total** 27
Acreage 4 **Open** March **to** Oct
Access Good **Site** Level
Very scenic and peaceful site with excellent, clean facilities. Close to the River Wye with woodland and river walks. Ideal base for touring the Wye Valley and the Forest of Dean.
Facilities 🍴 🏪 ⊙ 📞 🛒 🅿 🍽 💈
Nearby Facilities 🎯 ✈ ⛵ 🏊 🏊
Nearest Town Monmouth
Directions On the A40 between Ross-on-Wye and Monmouth. Turn off at Symonds Yat West and follow signs for The Doward.
🚆 Hereford

SYMONDS YAT WEST

Sterretts Caravan Park, Symonds Yat (West), Nr Ross-on-Wye, Herefordshire, HR9 6BY
Tel: 01594 832888
www.ukparks.co.uk/sterretts
Pitches For 🏕 🚐 🚍 **Total** 92
Acreage 9 **Open** Feb **to** Nov
Access Good **Site** Level
Nearest Bus Stop (Miles) ½
Near a river. Ideal for walking, fishing, canoeing, rock climbing and touring the Forest of Dean. Pets welcome with tourers.
Facilities 🍴 🏪 ⊙ 📞 🛒 🅿 🔌 🛒 🅿
🔌 🍽 🅿
Nearby Facilities 🎯 ✈ ⛵ 🏊 🏊
Nearest Town Ross-on-Wye
Directions Take the A40 from Ross-on-Wye or Monmouth to Whitchurch, turn off and go over a small roundabout past the school, after 200 yards you will come to a large car park, drive through.
🚆 Hereford

ENGLAND

HERTFORDSHIRE

BALDOCK

Radwell Mill Lake, Radwell Mill, Baldock, Hertfordshire, SG7 5ET
Tel: 01462 730242
Email: camping@radwellmill.com
www.radwellmill.com
Pitches For ▲ ⬛ **Total** 20
Acreage 3 **Open** April **to** November
Access Good **Site** Level
Nearest Bus Stop (Miles) ½
Quiet site with a lake and orchard. Good for bird watching. New Motorway Services (½ mile away) with cafe/restaurant, shops and take-away food.
Facilities ⬛⬛🚿♿
Nearby Facilities
Nearest Town Baldock
Directions Junction 10 A1(M) then the A507, ½ mile towards Baldock take a lane signed Radwell Only to the lake and site.
🚉 Baldock

CHORLEYWOOD

North Hill Farm, North Hill, Chorleywood, Hertfordshire, WD3 6HA
Tel: 01923 287040
Email: clarks@northhillfarm.co.uk
www.northhillcamping.co.uk
Pitches For ⬛ ⬛
Open All Year
Access Good **Site** Level
Nearest Bus Stop (Miles) ¼
Convenient location for London, within walking distance of Chorleywood Tube Station. Local shops and bars. Ideal for walking with pathways in the Chess Valley.
Facilities ♿ 🚿⬛🚻♿⬛
Nearby Facilities ✚ ✕ ⚓ ∪ ♪
Nearest Town Chorleywood
Directions Leave the M25 at junction 18 and head towards Chorleywood and Amersham on the A404. After 1 mile take a right turn sp Sarratt Village.
🚉 Chorleywood

HERTFORD

Camping & Caravanning Club Site, Mangrove Road (Not Ball Park), Hertford, Hertfordshire, SG13 8AJ
Tel: 01992 586696
www.campingandcaravanningclub.co.uk/hertford
Pitches For ▲ ⬛ ⬛ **Total** 250
Open All Year
Site Level
Set in acres of meadowland. 5 miles from Hatfield House and 20 miles from London. BTB 4 Star Graded, AA 4 Pennants and David Bellamy Gold Award. Non members welcome. You can also call us on 0845 130 7633.
Facilities ♿ ⬛🚿♿⬛
⬛⬛⬛⬛🚻♿⬛⬛🚿♿⬛
Nearby Facilities ✚ ✕ ∪ ♪
Directions From the A10 follow the A414 Hertford signs to the next roundabout (Foxholes) and go straight across, after 200 yards turn left signposted Balls Park and Hertford University. Turn left at the T-Junction into Mangrove Road, go past Simon Balle School, University & Cricket ground. Site is 400yds past cricket club on left.
🚉 North & East Hertford

WALTHAM CROSS

Theobalds Park Camping & Caravanning Club Site, Bulls Cross Ride, Waltham Cross, Hertfordshire, EN7 5HS
Tel: 01992 620604
www.campingandcaravanningclub.co.uk/theobaldspark
Pitches For ▲ ⬛ ⬛ **Total** 90

Acreage 14 **Open** 29-Mar **to** 05-Nov
Access Good **Site** Level
Leafy site just 13 miles from London. Plenty of wildlife to see on the site including birds, foxes, deer and rabbits. Lee Valley nearby which is ideal for boating, sailing and swimming. BTB 3 Star Graded and AA 2 Pennants. Non members welcome. You can also call us on 0845 130 7633.
Facilities ♿ ⬛🚿♿⬛⬛⬛⬛
⬛⬛⬛⬛🚻♿⬛⬛🚿
Nearby Facilities ✚ ✕ ∪ ♪
Nearest Town Waltham Cross
Directions Leave the M25 at junction 25, take the A10 towards London keeping to the right hand lane, turn right at the first set of traffic lights signposted Crews Hill. Turn right at the T-Junction (opposite Pied Bull), turn right behind the dog kennels, site is towards the top of the lane on the right.
🚉 Waltham Cross

ISLE OF MAN

UNION MILLS

Glenlough Campsite, Union Mills, Isle Of Man, IM4 4AT
Tel: 01624 822372/852057
Email: glenloughcampsite@manx.net
www.glenloughcampsite.com
Pitches For ▲ ⬛ **Total** 350
Acreage 15 **Open** April **to** Sept
Site Level
Nearest Bus Stop (Miles) At Entrance
Family run, sheltered site on the TT Course. Located in the scenic central valley. 3 Camping Pods available for the outdoor camping experience with a cosy and peaceful nights sleep! Everyone welcome.
Facilities ♿ ⬛🚿♿⬛⬛ ⬛⬛🐕
Nearby Facilities ✚ ✕ ∪
Nearest Town Douglas
Directions 3 miles from Douglas on the A1 Douglas to Peel road.
🚉 Douglas

ISLE OF WIGHT

ATHERFIELD

Chine Farm Camping Site, Military Road, Atherfield Bay, Nr Chale, Ventnor, Isle Of Wight, PO38 2JH
Tel: 01983 740901
Email: jill@chine-farm.co.uk
www.chine-farm.co.uk
Pitches For ▲ ⬛ ⬛ ⬛ **Total** 80
Acreage 10 **Open** Easter **to** End Sept
Access Good **Site** Level
Nearest Bus Stop (Miles) Outside
Footpath from the Site to the beach. Spacious pitches with wonderful views of the sea, coast and countryside.
Facilities ♿ ⬛🚿♿⬛⬛⬛
⬛⬛⬛🚿♿⬛🚿
Nearby Facilities ✚ ✕ ⚓ ∪ ♪ ♪
Nearest Town Freshwater
Directions Situated on the A3055 coast road, halfway between Freshwater Bay and Ventnor.
🚉 Sandown

COWES

Thorness Bay Holiday Park, Thorness Lane, Thorness, Nr Cowes, Isle Of Wight, PO31 8NJ
Tel: 0843 309 2576
Email: holidaysales.thornessbay@park-resorts.com
www.park-resorts.com
Pitches For ▲ ⬛ ⬛ **Total** 124
Open April **to** Oct
Access Good **Site** Lev/Slope
Nearest Bus Stop (Miles) Outside

In a rural setting amidst woodland running down to the sea.
Facilities ♿ ⬛🚿♿⬛⬛⬛⬛
⬛⬛⬛⬛✕⬛⬛🚿♿⬛⬛🚿
Nearby Facilities
Nearest Town Cowes
Directions From Newport take the A3054 towards Yarmouth. After 1 mile take the first turning right and follow signs to Thorness.
🚉 Ryde

COWES

Waverley Park Holiday Centre, 51 Old Road, East Cowes, Isle Of Wight, PO32 6AW
Tel: 01983 293452
Email: sue@waverley-park.co.uk
www.waverley-park.co.uk
Pitches For ▲ ⬛ ⬛ **Total** 45
Acreage 10½ **Open** All Year
Access Good **Site** Level
Nearest Bus Stop (Miles) ¼
Level all-weather pitches with panoramic views over the Solent. Caf/Restaurant, Licensed Club and Swimming Pool during high season only (Whitsun to Sept).
Facilities ♿ ⬛🚿♿⬛⬛⬛
⬛⬛⬛⬛✕⬛⬛🚿♿⬛⬛
Nearby Facilities ✚ ✕ ⚓ ∪ ♪ ♪
Nearest Town Cowes
Directions Signposted from Red Funnel Ferries, only 500 yards from the East Cowes Terminal.
🚉 Ryde

FRESHWATER

Heathfield Farm Camping, Heathfield Road, Freshwater, Isle Of Wight, PO40 9SH
Tel: 01983 407822
Email: web@heathfieldcamping.co.uk
www.heathfieldcamping.co.uk
Pitches For ▲ ⬛ ⬛ **Total** 60
Acreage 10 **Open** May **to** Sept
Access Good **Site** Level
Nearest Bus Stop (Miles) Outside
Rural park close to beaches. Ideal walking and cycling area.
Facilities ♿ ⬛🚿♿⬛⬛⬛
⬛⬛⬛🚿♿⬛⬛🚿
Nearby Facilities ✚ ⚓ ♪
Nearest Town Freshwater
Directions From Yarmouth (ferry terminal) take the A3054 to Freshwater. After Golden Hill Fort turn left into Heathfield Road, 200 yards to site entrance.
🚉 Shanklin

RYDE

Beaper Farm Camping & Caravan Park, Nr Ryde, Isle Of Wight, PO33 1QJ
Tel: 01983 615210/875184
Email: beaper@btinternet.com
www.beaperfarm.com
Pitches For ▲ ⬛ ⬛ **Total** 150
Acreage 13 **Open** May **to** September
Access Good **Site** Level
Nearest Bus Stop (Miles) ¼
Near to beaches, golf, water sports, fishing trips, horse riding, ice skating, ten pin bowling and nightclubs, plus Isle of Wight Steam Railway.
Facilities ♿ ⬛🚿♿⬛⬛⬛
⬛⬛🚿♿⬛
Nearby Facilities ✚ ✕ ⚓ ∪ ♪
Nearest Town Ryde
Directions On the main A3055 Ryde to Sandown road, go past Tesco roundabout for ½ mile, Beaper Farm is second on the left.
🚉 Ryde

RYDE

Whitefield Forest Touring Park, Brading Road, Ryde, Isle Of Wight, PO33 1QL
Tel: 01983 617069
Email: pat&louise@whitefieldforest.co.uk
www.whitefieldforest.co.uk
Pitches For 🏕 🚐 🚚 **Total** 75
Acreage 23 **Open** Easter **to** October
Access Good **Site** Level
Nearest Bus Stop (Miles) Outside
Set in the ancient woodland of Whitefield Forest. We provide ideal holidays for families, couples and individuals.
Facilities 🛁 ♿ 🚿 🔱 ⛽ 🕇 ⊙ ⌙ ⚌ 🗖 🐕 🖂 🗲 🖳 ⊡
Nearby Facilities ⌐ ↑ ᐟᐟ
Directions From Ryde take the A3055 to Brading, at Tescos roundabout go straight over and the Park is ½ a mile on the left.
⇌ Smallbrook

SANDOWN

Adgestone Camping & Caravanning Club Site, Lower Adgestone Road, Adgestone, Isle Of Wight, PO36 0HL
Tel: 01983 403432
www.campingandcaravanningclub.co.uk/adgestone
Pitches For 🏕 🚐 🚚 **Total** 270
Acreage 22 **Open** 23-Apr **to** 29-Oct
Access Difficult **Site** Level
Nearest Bus Stop (Miles) 1
One of the best locations on the Isle of Wight, 1 mile from Sandown. Adjacent to the River Yar and nestled in the valley beneath Brading Downs, an area of natural beauty. BTB 4 Star Graded and AA 4 Pennants. Non members welcome. You can call us on 0845 130 7633.
Facilities 🛁 ♿ 🚿 🔱 ⚒ ✸ 🔥 🕇 ⊙ ⌙ ⚌ 🗖 ⊡ 🖳 ✿ 📶
Nearby Facilities ⌐ 🏊 ↑ ᐟᐟ ℛ
Nearest Town Sandown
Directions Turn off the A3055 Sandown to Shanklin road at Manor House Pub in Lake. Go past the school and golf course on the left and turn right at the T-Junction, park is 200 yards on the right.
⇌ Sandown

SANDOWN

Old Barn Touring Park, Cheverton Farm, Newport Road, Sandown, Isle Of Wight, PO36 9PJ
Tel: 01983 866414
Email: oldbarn@weltinet.com
www.oldbarntouring.co.uk
Pitches For 🏕 🚐 🚚 **Total** 60
Acreage 5 **Open** 01-May **to** 25-Sep
Access Good **Site** Level
Nearest Bus Stop (Miles) ¼
1½ miles from the seaside towns of Sandown and Shanklin. Grade II Listed Barn used as a TV and games room.

Facilities 🛁 ♿ 🚿 🕇 ⊡ ⌙ ⊙ ⌙ ⚌ 🗖 🖳 📶 🛈 ⊙ 🔥 ⊡ 🖳
Nearby Facilities ⌐ 🏊 ↑ ᐟᐟ U ℛ
Nearest Town Sandown
Directions From Newport take the A3056, Park is on the right ½ mile after Apse Heath mini roundabout.
⇌ Lake

SANDOWN

Queen Bower Dairy Caravan Park, Alverstone Road, Queen Bower, Sandown, Isle Of Wight, PO36 0NZ
Tel: 01983 403840
Email: queenbowerdairy@aol.com
www.queenbowerdairy.co.uk
Pitches For 🏕 🚐 🚚 **Total** 20
Acreage 2¼ **Open** May **to** October
Access Good **Site** Level
Nearest Bus Stop (Miles) ¼
Scenic views, ideal touring. Sell our own produced Dairy products (milk and cream). Public telephone ¼ mile.
Facilities ✸ ♿ 🕇 ⚒ 🔥 ⊡
Nearby Facilities ⌐ 🏊 ↑ ᐟᐟ U ᵎ ℛ
Nearest Town Sandown
Directions On the A3056 Newport to Sandown road, turn into Alverstone Road at Apse Heath crossroads. Park is 1 mile on the left.
⇌ Sandown

SANDOWN

Village Way Caravan & Camping Park, Newport Road, Apse Heath, Sandown, Isle Of Wight, PO36 9PJ
Tel: 01983 863279
Email: norma.smith@btconnect.com
www.villagewaypark.co.uk
Pitches For 🏕 🚐 🚚 **Total** 14
Open All Year **Access** Good **Site** Level
Nearest Bus Stop (Miles) ¼
Near the beach. Free carp fishing on site. Beautiful country walks to the woods and within walking distance of a garden centre and Morrisons. The Heights Leisure Centre is only a mile away.
Facilities ♿ 🕇 ⚒ 🔥 🕇 ⊙ ⌙ ⚌ 🛈 🔥 ⊙ ⌙ ⊡ 🖳 ✿
Nearby Facilities ⌐ ↑ ᐟᐟ U ᵎ ℛ ⚲
Nearest Town Sandown
Directions From Newport take the A22 to Blackwater then the A3056 to Apse Heath. We are on the main A3056.

SHANKLIN

Landguard Holiday Park, Landguard Manor Road, Shanklin, Isle Of Wight, PO37 7PJ
Tel: 0843 309 2564
Email: holidaysales.landguard@park-resorts.com
www.park-resorts.com

Pitches For 🏕 🚐 🚚
Open April **to** October
Access Good **Site** Sloping
Nearest Bus Stop (Miles) ½
Near the beach and ½ a mile from Shanklin.
Facilities ♿ 🕇 ⚒ 🔥 🕇 ⊙ ⌙ ⊡ 🖳
🛈 ⊙ ♿ ✸ 🔥 ⚒ 🔥 ↑ 🔥 ⊡ 🖳 ✿
Nearby Facilities
Nearest Town Shanklin
Directions From Fishbourne turn right onto the B3381, at the traffic lights turn left onto the A3054. From Ryde take the A3055 towards Shanklin, turn first right onto the A3056 and then fourth left and continue to the Park.
⇌ Shanklin

SHANKLIN

Lower Hyde Holiday Park, Landguard Road, Shanklin, Isle Of Wight, PO37 7LL
Tel: 0843 309 2565
Email: holidaysales.lowerhyde@park-resorts.com
www.park-resorts.com
Pitches For 🏕 🚐 🚚
Open April **to** October **Site** Sloping
Nearest Bus Stop (Miles) ¼
Near the beach and town centre.
Facilities 🕇 ♿ 🕇 ⊙ ⌙ ⊡ 🖳
🛈 ⊙ ♿ ✸ 🔥 ⚒ ↑ 🔥 ⊡ 🖳 ✿
Nearby Facilities
Nearest Town Shanklin
Directions From Fishbourne turn right onto the B3331, at the traffic lights turn left onto the A3054 sp Ryde. From Ryde take the A3055 towards Shanklin, turn right onto the A3056 and the Park is quite a way up on the right.
⇌ Shanklin

SHANKLIN

Ninham Country Holidays, Shanklin, Isle Of Wight, PO37 7PL
Tel: 01983 864243
Email: office@ninham-holidays.co.uk
www.ninham-holidays.co.uk
Pitches For 🏕 🚐 🚚 **Total** 98
Acreage 10 **Open** 01-May **to** 30-Sep
Access Very Good **Site** Level
Nearest Bus Stop (Miles) ¼
Country park setting close to Islands premier seaside resort. Outdoor heated swimming pool, on-site carp fishing and bike hire. Great walking and cycling. Ferry tickets issued. On-line booking available.
Facilities ♿ 🕇 ⚒ 🔥 🕇 ⊙ ⌙ ⚌ 🗖 🖳
🛈 ⊙ ♿ ✸ 🔥 ⚒ ↑ 🔥 ⊡ 🖳 ✿
Nearby Facilities ⌐ 🏊 ↑ ᐟᐟ U ᵎ ℛ
Nearest Town Shanklin
Directions Signposted off Newport/Sandown road (A3056). Site entrance is ¼ mile west of Morrisons on the left.
⇌ Shanklin

ST. HELENS

Carpenters Farm Campsite, Carpenters Road, St Helens, Ryde, Isle Of Wight, PO33 1YL
Tel: 01983 874557
Email: info@carpentersfarm.co.uk
www.carpentersfarm.co.uk
Pitches For   Total 70
Acreage 20 **Open** All Year
Access Good **Site** Lev/Slope
Nearest Bus Stop (Miles) Outside
Near to beaches and overlooking SSSI.
Facilities ⚬ ⌿ ⊞ ⊡ ☂ ┌ ⊙ ⌿ ⛴ ⌑ ⎙ 🐾
Nearby Facilities ┌ ↗ ⏛ ∪ ♪
Nearest Town Ryde
Directions On the B3330, 3 miles from Ryde.
⚏ Brading

ST. HELENS

Nodes Point Holiday Park, Nodes Road, St Helens, Ryde, Isle Of Wight, PO33 1YA
Tel: 0843 309 2568
Email: holidaysales.nodespoint@park-resorts.com
www.park-resorts.com
Pitches For ⅄ 🏕 🚐
Open April **to** October
Access Good **Site** Sloping
Good beach access. 5 miles from Ryde.
Facilities ⌿ ⊞ ⊡ ☂ ┌ ⌑ ⎙ 🐾
⛴ ⊙ ⊟ ✕ ⌁ ⚑ ❄
Nearby Facilities ∪
Nearest Town Ryde
Directions Approach Ryde on the A3054 to join the A3055 in town. At the school go straight onto the B3330. After 2 miles as the road bends to the right, the Park is on the left.
⚏ Ryde

YARMOUTH

The Orchards Holiday Caravan & Camping Park, Newbridge, Yarmouth, Isle Of Wight, PO41 0TS
Tel: 01983 531331
Email: info@orchards-holiday-park.co.uk
www.orchards-holiday-park.co.uk
Pitches For ⅄ 🏕 🚐 **Total** 175
Acreage 8 **Open** 20-Feb **to** 02-Jan
Access Good **Site** Lev/Slope
Nearest Bus Stop (Miles) Outside
Excellent multi award winning family park in a peaceful village setting amid downs and meadowland with glorious views. Luxury Facilities Centre has excellent touring facilities. Also take-away food, shop, pool table, table tennis, play areas and dog walk. Excellent walking and cycling. WiFi available. Booking essential.
Facilities ⚬ ⌿ ⊞ ⊡ ☂ ┌ ⊙ ⌿ ⛴ ⌑ ⎙ 🐾
⛴ ⌁ ⊙ ⊟ ⚑ ⌁ ⋏ ⅄ ⚑ ⛴ ❄ ⌑ ⎙ ❄
Nearby Facilities ┌ ↗ ⏛ ∪ ♪
Nearest Town Yarmouth
Directions 4 miles east of Yarmouth and 6 miles west of Newport on B3401. Entrance opposite Newbridge Post Office.
⚏ Lymington

KENT
ASHFORD

Broadhembury Caravan & Camping Park, Steeds Lane, Kingsnorth, Ashford, Kent, TN26 1NQ
Tel: 01233 620859
Email: holidaypark@broadhembury.co.uk
www.broadhembury.co.uk
Pitches For ⅄ 🏕 🚐 🚐 **Total** 80
Acreage 8 **Open** All Year
Access Good **Site** Level

Nearest Bus Stop (Miles) ½
Open all year with centrally heated toilets and showers, en-suite facilities, wheelchair access, playgrounds, games room and every amenity for families. Also adults meadows, the ideal place for those who like things a little quieter! Picturesque villages, sandy beaches, Channel crossings, Canterbury, castles and gardens all within easy reach.
Facilities ⚬ ⌿ ⊞ ⊡ ☂ ┌ ⊙ ⌿ ⛴ ⌑ ⎙ 🐾
⛴ ⌁ ⊙ ⊟ ⚑ ⌁ ⋏ ⅄ ⚑ ⛴ ❄
Nearby Facilities ┌ ↗ ∪ ♪
Nearest Town Ashford
Directions Leave the M20 at junction 10, take the A2070 following signs for Kingsnorth. Turn left at the second crossroads in the village.
⚏ Ashford

BIRCHINGTON

Quex Caravan Park, Park Road, Birchington, Kent, CT7 0BL
Tel: 01843 841273
Email: quex@keatfarm.co.uk
www.keatfarm.co.uk
Pitches For 🏕 🚐 🚐 **Total** 50
Acreage 3 **Open** 07-Mar **to** 07-Nov
Access Good **Site** Level
Ideal base for touring the areas around Thanet and Canterbury.
Facilities ⌿ ⊞ ⊡ ☂ ┌ ⊙ ⌿ ⛴ ⌑ ⎙ 🐾
⛴ ⌁ ⊙ ⊟ ⚑ ⊟ ⎙ ☂
Nearby Facilities ┌ ↗ ⏛ ∪ ♪
Nearest Town Margate/Ramsgate
Directions Follow road signs to Margate. When in Birchington turn right at mini roundabout (sp Margate). Approximately 100yds after roundabout take the first turning on the right and then right again as directed by Tourist Board signs.
⚏ Birchington

BIRCHINGTON
St. Nicholas Camping Site, Court Road, St Nicholas-at-Wade, Birchington, Kent, CT7 0NH
Tel: 01843 847245
Pitches For ⚠ ☺ ☺ **Total** 75
Acreage 3 **Open** March **to** Oct
Access Good **Site** Level
Nearest Bus Stop (Miles) ¼
On the edge of the village with two Pubs serving food and a Post Office.
Facilities ⚙ ∮ ▥▧ ⌇ ∩ ☺ ⌐ ☎ ☒ ⎕ ⌂ ⚑⚑
Nearby Facilities ↑ ↗ ⚓ ∪
Nearest Town Birchington
Directions Turn off the A28 9½ miles north east of Canterbury to St. Nicholas. Or take the A299 from Herne Bay and turn left signposted St. Nicholas-at-Wade, go over the bridge and into Court Road.
🚉 Birchington

BIRCHINGTON
Two Chimneys Holiday Park, Shottendane Road, Birchington, Kent, CT7 0HD
Tel: 01843 841068/843157
Email: info@twochimneys.co.uk
www.twochimneys.co.uk
Pitches For ⚠ ☺ ☺ **Total** 200
Acreage 30 **Open** March **to** October
Access Good **Site** Level
Nearest Bus Stop (Miles) ¼
Country site near lovely beaches. Swimming pool with retractable roof, adventure play area and tennis court on site. Sorry, No dogs. Holiday Caravans available for hire. Storage.
Facilities ⚙ ∮ ▤ ▥▧ ⌇ ∩ ☺ ⌐ ☒ ⎕ ☒ ⌂ ⚑⚑ ☺ ☎ ⌂
Nearby Facilities ↑ ↗ ⚓ ∪ ⚘ ℛ
Nearest Town Margate
Directions 1½ miles from Birchington, turn right into park lane at Birchington Church, left fork "RAF Manston". First left onto B2048 site is ½ a mile on right.
🚉 Birchington

CANTERBURY
Camping & Caravanning Club Site, Bekesbourne La, Canterbury, Kent, CT3 4AB
Tel: 01227 463216
www.campingandcaravanningclub.co.uk/canterbury

Pitches For ⚠ ☺ ☺ **Total** 200
Acreage 20 **Open** All Year
Site Lev/Slope
Nearest Bus Stop (Miles) ¼
Close to Canterbury and within easy reach of the Channel ports. 2 miles from Canterbury Cathedral and Howletts Wildlife Park. Local produce sold in the site shop. BTB 4 Star Graded, AA 3 Pennants and David Bellamy Gold Award. Non members welcome. You can also call us on 0845 130 7633.
Facilities ⚙ ∮ ▥▧ ⌇ ∩ ☺ ⌐ ⌐ ☒ ⎕ ☎ ⌂ ☒ ⌂ ⎕ ▣ ⚑⚑ ☖ ☺
Nearby Facilities ↑ ∪
Directions From Canterbury follow the A257 towards Sandwich, turn right opposite the golf course.
🚉 Canterbury

CANTERBURY
Yew Tree Park, Stone Street, Petham, Canterbury, Kent, CT4 5PL
Tel: 01227 700306
Email: info@yewtreepark.com
www.yewtreepark.com
Pitches For ⚠ ☺ ☺ **Total** 45
Acreage 2 **Open** March **to** Oct
Access Good **Site** Lev/Slope
Nearest Bus Stop (Miles) Outside
30 minutes drive from the coast. Ideal touring area.
Facilities ⚙ ∮ ▥▧ ⌇ ∩ ☺ ⌐ ☒ ⎕ ☎ ⌂ ☒ ▣
Nearby Facilities ↑ ↗ ∪ ℛ
Nearest Town Canterbury
Directions 4 miles south of Canterbury on the B2068, turn right by the Chequers Public House, park entrance is on the left hand side.
🚉 Canterbury

DEAL
Clifford Park Caravans, Clifford Park, Thompson Close, Walmer, Deal, Kent, CT14 7PB
Tel: 01304 373373
Pitches For ⚠ ☺ ☺ **Total** 15
Open March **to** Oct
Access Good **Site** Level
Nearest Bus Stop (Miles) ¼
Just 2 minutes from the village. Ideal for touring and close to ferry ports for the continent.

Facilities ∮ ▥▧ ⌇ ∩ ☺ ⌐ ☒ ⚑ ⎕ ▣ ☒
Nearby Facilities ↑ ↗ ⚓ ∪ ℛ
Nearest Town Deal
Directions On the A258, 1 mile from Deal and 5 miles from Dover.
🚉 Walmer

DOVER
Hawthorn Farm, Martin Mill, Dover, Kent, CT15 5LA
Tel: 01304 852658
Email: hawthorn@keatfarm.co.uk
www.keatfarm.co.uk
Pitches For ⚠ ☺ ☺ **Total** 250
Acreage 27 **Open** March **to** Oct
Access Good **Site** Level
Beautiful Award Winning park in a quiet and peaceful location. Superb toilets and showers.
Facilities ∮ ▥▧ ⌇ ∩ ☺ ⌐ ☒ ⎕ ☎ ⌂ ☒ ☺ ⚑ ⎕ ▣ ⚑⚑ ☖ ☺
Nearby Facilities ↑ ↗ ⚓ ∪
Nearest Town Dover
Directions Martin Mill is approx. 3 miles from Dover, signposted along the main A258 towards Deal.
🚉 Martin Mill

DOVER
Sutton Vale Caravan Park, Vale Road, Sutton-By-Dover, Kent, CT15 5DH
Tel: 01304 374155
Email: bookings@sutton-vale.co.uk
www.sutton-vale.co.uk
Pitches For ⚠ ☺ ☺ **Total** 30
Acreage 6 **Open** March **to** January
Access Good **Site** Level
Nearest Bus Stop (Miles) ¼
In a conservation area in the centre of Dickens country with beautiful country walks. Own local village 17th Century pub, swimming pool and sports field. Next door to horse riding stables. Static holiday homes available for hire.
Facilities ⚙ ∮ ▤ ▥▧ ⌇ ∩ ☺ ⌐ ☒ ⎕ ☎ ⌂ ☒ ✗ ☗ ▣ ⚑ ☺ ☖ ☒ ⎕ ▣ ☒ ⚑ ⚑⚑ ☖ ☺
Nearby Facilities ↑ ↗ ⚓ ∪ ℛ
Directions From the A2 Canterbury to Dover road, 5 miles from Dover at the Whitfield roundabout (McDonalds) take first exit, after 20 yards turn right into Archers Court Road, site is exactly 4 miles on the left (check your milometer!)
🚉 Deal

DYMCHURCH

New Beach Holiday Park, Hythe Road, Dymchurch, Kent, TN29 0JX
Tel: 01303 872234
Email: newbeach@parkholidaysuk.com
www.parkholidaysuk.com/cades
Pitches For A ⚏ ⚏ **Total** 250
Open March **to** Oct
Access Good **Site** Level
Large indoor heated leisure pool. Family entertainment complex. Large touring field.
Facilities
Nearby Facilities
Nearest Town Dymchurch
Directions On the A259 coastal road between Hythe and Dymchurch.
⚎ Folkestone Central

EASTCHURCH

Warden Springs Holiday Park, Thorn Hill Road, Warden Point, Eastchurch, Isle of Sheppey, Kent, ME12 4HF
Tel: 0843 309 2579
Email: holidaysales.wardensprings@park-resorts.com
www.park-resorts.com
Pitches For A ⚏ ⚏
Open April **to** October
Access Good **Site** Sloping
Nearest Bus Stop (Miles) ½
Only 4 miles from Eastchurch and 10 miles from Sheerness.
Facilities
Nearby Facilities
Nearest Town Margate
Directions From the M25 take the A2 and follow until it becomes the M2. At junction 5 take the A249, after 8 miles turn right onto the B2231. In Eastchurch turn left and the Park is signposted from there.
⚎ Margate

FOLKESTONE

Black Horse Farm Caravan Club Site, 385 Canterbury Road, Densole, Folkestone, Kent, CT18 7BG
Tel: 01303 892665
www.caravanclub.co.uk
Pitches For A ⚏ ⚏ **Total** 140
Acreage 11 **Open** All Year
Access Good **Site** Level
Nearest Bus Stop (Miles) ¼
Situated in the heart of farming country. Limited hard standings available March to October only. Close to Canterbury, Dover Castle and the Channel Tunnel. Non members welcome. Booking essential.
Facilities
Nearby Facilities
Nearest Town Folkestone
Directions Leave the M20 at junc 13 (at end) and continue onto the A20. Past the end of the tunnel turn off via slip road and roundabout onto the A260 sp Canterbury, go through Hawkinge into Densole. Site is on the left 200 yards past the Black Horse Inn.
⚎ Folkestone

FOLKESTONE

Camping & Caravanning Club Site, The Warren, Folkestone, Kent, CT19 6NQ
Tel: 01303 255093
www.campingandcaravanningclub.co.uk/folkestone
Pitches For A ⚏ **Total** 80
Open 29-Mar **to** 05-Nov
Access Difficult **Site** Lev/Slope
Nearest Bus Stop (Miles) ½

Just a short walk to the beach. On a clear day you can see France. Fishing off the site on the sea front, 50 yards. BTB 5 Star Graded, AA 3 Pennants and Loo of the Year Award. Non members welcome. You can also call us on 0845 130 7633.
Facilities
Nearby Facilities
Directions From the M2 and Canterbury on the A260 take a left turn at the roundabout into Hill Road, Folkestone. Go straight over the crossroads into Wear Bay Road, turn second left past Martello Tower, site is ½ mile on the right.
⚎ Folkestone

FOLKESTONE

Little Satmar Holiday Park, Winehouse Lane, Capel-le-Ferne, Nr Folkestone, Kent, CT18 7JF
Tel: 01303 251188
Email: satmar@keatfarm.co.uk
www.keatfarm.co.uk
Pitches For A ⚏ ⚏ **Total** 60
Acreage 6 **Open** March **to** October
Access Good
Quiet, secluded park. Convenient for Channel ports and Tunnel.
Facilities
Nearby Facilities
Nearest Town Folkestone
Directions Travelling towards Folkestone on the A20 from Dover, exit left signposted Capel-le-Ferne onto the B2011. After 1 mile turn right into Winehouse Lane.
⚎ Folkestone

FOLKESTONE

Little Switzerland Caravan & Camping Park, Little Switzerland, Wear Bay Road, Folkestone, Kent, CT19 6PS
Tel: 01303 252168
Email: btony328@aol.com
www.caravancampingsites.co.uk
Pitches For A ⚏ ⚏
Open March **to** October
Access Good **Site** Level
Nearest Bus Stop (Miles) Outside
Facilities
Nearby Facilities
Nearest Town Folkestone
Directions From Dover follow Folkestone signs then Country Park signs.
⚎ Folkestone

HERNE BAY

Southview Camping, Southview, Maypole Lane, Hoath, Canterbury, Kent, CT3 4LL
Tel: 01227 860280
Email: southviewcamping@aol.com
www.southviewcamping.co.uk
Pitches For A ⚏ ⚏ **Total** 45
Acreage 3 **Open** April **to** September
Access Good **Site** Level
Nearest Bus Stop (Miles) ¼
Peaceful country setting. Excellent local pub and restaurant. Central location for Canterbury and the beautiful beaches of Thanet.
Facilities
Nearby Facilities
Nearest Town Canterbury
Directions Well signed from the A299 at Herne Bay or the A28 near Canterbury.
⚎ Herne Bay

LEYSDOWN-ON-SEA

Priory Hill Holiday Park, Wing Road, Leysdown-on-Sea, Isle of Sheppey, Kent, ME12 4QT
Tel: 01795 510267
Email: pat.lawrence@prioryhill.co.uk
www.prioryhill.co.uk
Pitches For A ⚏ ⚏ **Total** 36
Acreage 1½ **Open** March **to** October
Access Good **Site** Level
Nearest Bus Stop (Miles) ¼
Seaside park with a clubhouse, indoor heated swimming pool and entertainment on site. Please see our Web Site for details.
Facilities
Nearby Facilities
Nearest Town Leysdown-on-Sea
Directions From the M2 and M20 onto the A249 then the B2231 to Leysdown, follow tourism signs to Priory Hill.
⚎ Sheerness

MAIDSTONE

Bearsted Caravan Club Site, Ashford Road, Hollingbourne, Maidstone, Kent, ME17 1XH
Tel: 01622 730018
www.caravanclub.co.uk
Pitches For ⚏ ⚏ **Total** 69
Acreage 6 **Open** March **to** Jan
Access Good **Site** Lev/Slope
Peaceful stop-off point (for ferries). Near to Leeds Castle. Non members welcome. Booking essential.
Facilities
Nearest Town Maidstone
Directions Leave the M20 at junction 8, at the roundabout turn into road sp Bearsted and Maidstone, site is ½ mile on the left.
⚎ Maidstone

MAIDSTONE

Coldblow Camping, Coldblow Farm, Coldblow Lane, Thurnham, Kent, ME14 3LR
Tel: 01622 730439
Email: coldblow@btconnect.com
www.coldblow-camping.co.uk
Pitches For A ⚏ ⚏ **Total** 5
Acreage 2 **Open** All Year
Access Poor **Site** Level
Stunning countryside location on top of Kent Downs in an area of outstanding natural beauty. Horse riding on site. Ideal for visiting Maidstone, Canterbury and Central London. 40 minutes to ferries. Open all year subject to ground conditions.
Facilities
Nearby Facilities
Nearest Town Maidstone
Directions Leave M20 at junc 8 (do not use J7 if touring), take A20 towards Maidstone. After 1 mile turn first right, after ½ a mile turn right into Water Lane and go to end of road. Go straight across into Coldblow Lane, go up steep narrow hill for and the farm is 1st on right. N.B Do not rely on Sat Nav or Route Finder directions as they are often completely wrong!
⚎ Bearsted

MARDEN

Tanner Farm Touring Caravan & Camping Park, Tanner Farm, Goudhurst Road, Marden, Kent, TN12 9ND
Tel: 01622 832399
Email: enquiries@tannerfarmpark.co.uk
www.tannerfarmpark.co.uk
Pitches For A ⚏ ⚏ **Total** 100
Acreage 15 **Open** All Year
Access Good **Site** Level
Nearest Bus Stop (Miles) Outside

Peaceful, secluded park in the centre of a 150 acre farm, shire horses kept. QIT 5 Star Graded Park and David Bellamy Gold Award. Booking essential.
Facilities ☖ ⌯ 🄴 ☒☖ ⌒ ⊙ ⊣ ⬛ ◻ ☎ 𝕊𝕃 ☖ ☖ 🄃 🄍 🎣 ✥🄿 ☒ ◸ ✈ ⚲
Nearby Facilities ⌒ ⫞ ⚓ U
Nearest Town Maidstone/Tunbridge Wells
Directions From the A262 or A229 onto the B2079. Midway between the village of Marden and Goudhurst.
⚋ Marden

NEW ROMNEY

Marlie Holiday Park, Dymchurch Road, New Romney, Kent, TN28 8UE
Tel: 01797 363060
Email: marliefarm@parkholidaysuk.com
www.parkholidaysuk.com/cades
Pitches For ⋏ ⌑ ⌑ **Total** 250
Open April **to** Oct
Access Good **Site** Level
Nearest Bus Stop (Miles) Outside
Just a 10 minute drive from the beach. Near to Romney, Hythe and Dymchurch.
Facilities ☖ ⌯ ☒☖ ⌒ ⊣ ◻ ☎ 𝕊𝕃 ☖ ✕ ☖ 🄃 ☖ 🄍 🎣 ✥🄿 ✈ ⚲
Nearby Facilities ⌒ ⫞ ⚓ U
Nearest Town New Romney
Directions On the A259 coast road.
⚋ Folkestone Central

RAMSGATE

Manston Caravan & Camping Park, Manston Court Road, Manston, Ramsgate, Kent, CT12 5AU
Tel: 01843 823442
Email: enquiries@manston-park.co.uk
www.manston-park.co.uk
Pitches For ⋏ ⌑ ⌑ **Total** 100
Acreage 7 **Open** April **to** October
Access Good **Site** Level

Nearest Bus Stop (Miles) ¼
Quiet, family park.
Facilities ⌯ ☒☖ ⌒ ⊙ ⊣ ⬛ ◻ ☎ 𝕊𝕃 ☖ ☖ ◸ ⏃🄿 ◻ ☖ ✕
Nearby Facilities ⌒ ⫞ ⚓ U ◸ ⚲
Nearest Town Ramsgate
Directions From the M2 follow the A299 and join the A253 towards Ramsgate. Turn left onto the B2048 then first right onto the B2190 towards KIA. Turn right onto the B2050 across the airfield passing the entrance to KIA. Take the first turning left into Manston Court
⚋ Ramsgate

RAMSGATE

Nethercourt Touring Park, Nethercourt Hill, Ramsgate, Kent, CT11 0RX
Tel: 01843 595485
Email: nethercourtcamp@aol.com
www.campsite-in-kent.co.uk
Pitches For ⋏ ⌑ ⌑ **Total** 50
Acreage 2 **Open** All Year
Access Good **Site** Level
Nearest Bus Stop (Miles) Outside
1¼ miles from the beach and harbour. Sea fishing 1 mile. Indoor swimming pool nearby.
Facilities ☖ ⌯ ☒☖ ⌒ ⊙ ⊣ ⬛ ◻ ☎ 𝕊𝕃 ☖ ☖ 🄃 🄍 🎣 ✥🄿 ◻
Nearby Facilities ⌒ ⫞ ⚓ U ◸ ✈
Directions Off the main London road on the outskirts of the town.
⚋ Ramsgate

ROCHESTER

Woolmans Wood Tourist Caravan Park, Rochester Road (B2097), Chatham, Kent, ME5 9SB
Tel: 01634 867685
Email: johnbedrock@aol.com
Pitches For ⌑ ⌑ **Total** 60
Acreage 5 **Open** All Year

Access Good **Site** Level
Nearest Bus Stop (Miles) ¼
ADULTS ONLY SITE. Rochester Castle and Cathedral, and Chatham Naval Base.
Facilities ⌯ ☒☖ ⌒ ⊙ ⊣ ⬛ ◻ ☎ 𝕊𝕃 ⌾ ☖ ☖🄍◻🄀🔍
Nearby Facilities ⌒ ⫞ ⚓ U ◸ ✈
Nearest Town Rochester
Directions Take the A229 from the M2 junction 3 or the M20 junction 6. Follow caravan signs to the B2097. Park is ¼ mile on the right hand side.
⚋ Chatham

SEVENOAKS

East Hill Farm Park, East Hill Road, Nr Kemsing, Sevenoaks, Kent, TN15 6YD
Tel: 01959 522347
Pitches For ⋏ **Total** 30
Acreage 6 **Open** Apr **to** Oct **Site** Level
Facilities ☒☖ ⌒ ☎
Nearby Facilities ⌒ U
Directions Off the A225. Please telephone for directions.
⚋ Otford

SEVENOAKS

Oldbury Hill Camping & Caravanning Club Site, Styants Bottom, Seal, Sevenoaks, Kent, TN15 0ET
Tel: 01732 762728
www.campingandcaravanningclub.co.uk/oldburyhill
Pitches For ⋏ ⌑ ⌑ **Total** 60
Acreage 6 **Open** 29-Mar **to** 05-Nov
Access Difficult **Site** Sloping
Nearest Bus Stop (Miles) ½
Set in a quiet countryside location, close to a number of National Trust properties. BTB 4 Star Graded and AA 3 Pennants. Non members welcome. You can also call us on 0845 130 7633.

The Hop Farm Camping and Touring Park

In the heart of the Kent countryside

A family run touring park in a beautiful setting within open fields and woodlands, with 500 acres of natural landscape to explore.
Over 300 pitches · Electric hook ups · Hard standings · Newly refurbished toilet/shower block · Close to a major attraction · Dogs welcome
The Hop Farm, Beltring, Paddock Wood, Kent TN12 6PY. 01622 870838, touring@thehopfarm.co.uk. Visit us online at www.thehopfarm.co.uk

Facilities 🅿 ♿ ⛽ 🚿 ♨ 🛁 🍴 📶
🛒 🏪 🎱 ⛱ 🔌 🎮 📺 📶
Nearby Facilities 🏇 ⛵
Nearest Town Sevenoaks
Directions From Sevenoaks take the A25 towards Borough Green, turn left just after the Crown Point Inn, go down the lane to Styants Bottom, site is on the left.
🚉 Borough Green

SEVENOAKS

Thriftwood Holiday Park, Plaxdale Green Road, Stansted, Sevenoaks, Kent, TN15 7PB
Tel: 01732 822261
Email: info@thriftwoodholidaypark.com
www.thriftwoodholidaypark.com
Pitches For ⛺ 🚐 🚍 **Total** 180
Acreage 20 **Open** All Year
Access Good **Site** Lev/Slope
Nearest Bus Stop (Miles) ¼
Award winning family park in a picturesque rural location. Ideal for visiting London and sightseeing in Kent.
Facilities 🅿 ♿ ⛽ 🚿 ♨ 🛁 🍴 📶
🎱 ⛱ 🔌 🛒 🍽 ♫ 🎿
Nearest Town Sevenoaks
Directions Leave the M25 at junction 3 and take the A20 (Brands Hatch).
🚉 Borough Green

SHEERNESS

Sheerness Holiday Park, Halfway Road, Minster-on-Sea, Sheerness, Kent, ME12 3AA
Tel: 01795 662638
Email: sheerness@parkholidaysuk.com
www.parkholidaysuk.com/cades
Pitches For ⛺ 🚐 🚍 **Total** 54
Open March to Oct
Access Good **Site** Level
Nearest Bus Stop (Miles) ¼
Indoor pool and a family entertainment venue. Watersports and sailing nearby.
Facilities ♿ ⛽ 🚿 ♨ 🛁 📶
🎱 ✗ 🍴 🛒 🍽 ♫ 🎿 📶
Nearby Facilities ⚓ ♨
Nearest Town Sheerness
Directions From the M2 and A2 follow signs to Sheerness. Site is ½ a mile from the town on the right.
🚉 Sheerness

TENTERDEN

Spill Land Farm Holiday Park, Benenden Road, Biddenden, Nr Ashford, Kent, TN27 8BX
Tel: 01580 291379
Email: dnem@supanet.com
www.spilllandfarm.co.uk
Pitches For ⛺ 🚐 **Total** 65
Acreage 3 **Open** May to Sept
Access Good **Site** Lev/Slope
Nearest Bus Stop (Miles) 1
ADULTS ONLY. Quiet countryside park, close to Biddenden Vineyards, Pitch n Putt and Chart Hills Golf Club. Central to many gardens and castles. NB: No Under 18s, No Motor Caravans and No Commercial Vehicles.
Facilities ⛽ 🚿 ♨ 🍴 🎱 🔌 🍽 ⛱
Nearby Facilities 🏇 ⛵
Nearest Town Tenterden
Directions From Biddenden Village head towards Tenterden for 1 mile, turn right at left hand bend signposted Vineyard and Hospital. Site is ¼ of a mile on the right behind a white farmhouse.
🚉 Headcorn

TONBRIDGE

The Hop Farm Touring & Camping Park, Maidstone Road, Beltring, Nr Tonbridge, Paddock Wood, Kent, TN12 6PY
Tel: 01622 870838
Email: touring@thehopfarm.co.uk
www.thehopfarm.co.uk/touring
Pitches For ⛺ 🚐 🚍 **Total** 300
Acreage 400 **Open** March to October
Access Good **Site** Level
Nearest Bus Stop (Miles) Outside
Next door to the Hop Farm World of Activities Family Park. Ideal touring base for the heart of Kent.
Facilities
🅿 ♿ ⛽ 🚿 ♨ 🔌 🎱 🍽 🎮 📺 📶
Nearby Facilities 🏇
Nearest Town Paddock Wood
Directions On the A228 near Paddock Wood. Leave the M20 at junction 4 or the M25 at junction 5 and follow brown tourism signs onto the A21 south.
🚉 Paddock Wood

WHITSTABLE

Primrose Cottage Caravan Park, Golden Hill, Whitstable, Kent, CT5 3AR
Tel: 01227 273694
Email: campbell_brian@btconnect.com
Pitches For ⛺ 🚐 🚍
Acreage 1 **Open** March to October
Access Good **Site** Level
Nearest Bus Stop (Miles) ¼
Views of the sea and nearby Whitstable. Superstore nearby. 1 mile to the town centre, 15 minutes to Canterbury and within easy reach by road or rail of Herne Bay, Margate and Dover.
Facilities 🅿 ♿ ⛽ 🚿 ♨ 🍴 🎱 🔌 🍽 🎮
Nearby Facilities 🏇 ⛵ ⚓ ♨ 🏌 ♨ 🎿
Nearest Town Whitstable
🚉 Whitstable

Thank you for choosing a Cade's Guide

WHITSTABLE

Seaview Holiday Park, St Johns Road, Swalecliffe, Whitstable, Kent, CT5 2RY
Tel: 01227 792246
Email: seaview@parkholidaysuk.com
www.parkholidaysuk.com/cades
Pitches For ⛺ 🚐 🚍 **Total** 57
Open March to Oct
Access Good **Site** Level
Nearest Bus Stop (Miles) ¼
Just a 5 minute stroll from Swalecliffe beach. Ideal spot for camping and touring.
Facilities
🅿 ⛽ 🚿 ♨ 🔌 🎱 ✗ 🍴 🎮 ♫ 🎿 📶
Nearby Facilities 🏇
Nearest Town Whitstable
Directions Off the A299, at the double roundabout turn left and go under the railway bridge, at the mini roundabout turn right, after 600 yards turn left down lane to the park (signposted).
🚉 Whitstable

LANCASHIRE

BENTHAM

Lowther Hill Caravan Park, Bentham, Nr Lancaster, Lancashire, LA2 7AN
Tel: 01524 261657
www.caravancampingsites.co.uk/
northyorkshire/lowtherhi
Pitches For ▲ ⚏ ⚍ **Total** 9
Acreage 1¼ **Open** March **to** Nov
Access Good **Site** Sloping
A quiet site (once a farm) with lovely panoramic views. Caravan rallies welcome (up to 25 caravans, function barn available). You wont want to leave!
Facilities ⚒ ☖ ⊞ ⚗ ⌐ ⊡ ☂ ⊁⚏ ⚝
Nearby Facilities ⌐ ✔
Nearest Town High Bentham
Directions Leave the M6 at junction 34 and take the A683 signposted Kirkby Lonsdale. After 6 miles turn right onto the B6480 signposted Bentham. Site is on the left hand side 2 miles east of High Bentham.
⚏ Bentham

BENTHAM

Riverside Caravan Park, High Bentham, Lancaster, Lancashire, LA2 7FJ
Tel: 015242 61272
Email: info@riversidecaravanpark.co.uk
www.riversidecaravanpark.co.uk
Pitches For ⚏ ⚍ ⚎ **Total** 61
Open 01-Mar **to** 02-Jan
Access Good **Site** Level
Alongside a river, just a short walk to the town for shops and pubs. Close to the famous Yorkshire Three Peaks for walking.
Facilities ⚒ ⚒ ⊞ ☖ ⚗ ⌐ ⊡ ☂ ⚐
⚑ ⓘ ⚲ ☖ ⚑ ⚓ ⊁⚏ ⚏ ✔ ⚝ ⚐ ⚑
Nearby Facilities ⌐ ✔ ⚒ ⚓ ⚲ ⚑ ☇
Nearest Town High Bentham
Directions Follow signs from the B6480 in the middle of High Bentham, turn south at the Black Bull Pub.
⚏ High Bentham

BLACKPOOL

Clifton Fields Caravan Park, Peel Road, Nr Blackpool, Lancashire, FY4 5JU
Tel: 01253 761676
www.clifton-fields.co.uk
Pitches For ⚏ **Total** 46
Acreage 12 **Open** March **to** October
Access Good **Site** Slightly Sloping
Nearest Bus Stop (Miles) ¼
Within easy reach of Blackpool, Lytham St Annes and Fleetwood.
Facilities ☖ ⊞ ☖ ⚗ ⌐ ⊡ ☂ ⚐ ⊞ ⊡ ⚝
Nearby Facilities ⌐ ✔ ⚓ ⚲ ⚑ ☇
Nearest Town Blackpool
Directions Blackpool junction 4 on M55 turn left to Kirkham 400yds, straight on at the roundabout to traffic lights. Turn right and immediate left into Peel Road. 350yds second site on the right.
⚏ Blackpool

BLACKPOOL

Marton Mere Holiday Village, Mythop Road, Blackpool, Lancashire, FY4 4XN
Tel: 01253 767544
Email: martonmere@haven.com

www.haventouring.com/tomartonmere
Pitches For ⚏ ⚍ **Total** 197
Acreage 93 **Open** March **to** October
Access Good **Site** Level
Nearest Bus Stop (Miles) Outside
Four Star Holiday Park set on the doorstep of the vibrant seaside resort of Blackpool, yet still offering the peace and tranquility of the Mere Nature Reserve. Come and enjoy the exciting Space Bowl Flume and much more.
Facilities ⚒ ⚒ ⊞ ☖ ⚗ ⌐ ⊡ ☂ ⚐ ⊡ ☂
⚑ ⓘ ⚲ ☖ ⚑ ⚓ ⚑ ⚓ ⊁⚏ ⊡ ⚝ ⚐
Nearby Facilities ⌐ ✔ ⚲ ☇
Nearest Town Blackpool
Directions Take the A583 towards Blackpool, turn right at Clifton Arms traffic lights into Mythop Road, park is 150 yards on the left.

BLACKPOOL

Primrose Bank Caravan Park, High Moor Farm, Singleton Road, Weeton, Preston, Lancashire, PR4 3JJ
Tel: 01253 836273
Email: info@pbcp.co.uk
www.primrosecaravanpark.co.uk
Pitches For ⚏ ⚍ **Total** 30
Acreage 3 **Open** 01-Mar **to** 12-Jan
Access Good **Site** Level
Nearest Bus Stop (Miles) Outside
Ideal for Blackpools Pleasure Beach. Golf and fishing nearby.
Facilities ⚒ ⚒ ⊞ ☖ ⚗ ⌐ ⊡ ☂ ⚐ ⊡ ☂
⚐ ⊁⚏ ⊡ ⚝ ⚑
Nearby Facilities ⌐ ✔ ⚲ ⚑ ⚓ ☇ ⚑
Nearest Town Blackpool
Directions Leave the M55 at Junc 3 and take the A585 to Fleetwood. Take the third turning on the left sp Singleton, at the T-Junction turn left and the Park is 1 mile on the left.
⚏ Poulton-le-Fylde

BLACKPOOL

Redleigh Orchard Touring Caravan Park, Cropper Road, Blackpool, Lancashire, FY4 5LB
Tel: 01253 691459
Email: mdwilky@btinternet.com
www.redleighorchard.co.uk
Pitches For ⚏ ⚍ **Total** 29
Acreage 2 **Open** March **to** Oct
Access Good **Site** Level
Nearest Bus Stop (Miles) ½
2 miles from Blackpools promenade and pleasure beach. Lytham St Annes within easy reach. Garden centre opposite.
Facilities ☖ ⊞ ☖ ⚗ ⌐ ⊡ ☂ ⚐ ⊞ ⊡ ⚝
Nearby Facilities ⌐ ✔ ⚓ ⚲ ⚑ ☇
Nearest Town Blackpool
Directions Leave the M55 at junction 4, at the roundabout turn left, at the next roundabout turn right, go straight across the mini roundabout, at next roundabout turn right, Park is 100 yards.
⚏ Blackpool South

BLACKPOOL

Windy Harbour Holiday Park, Little Singleton, Nr Blackpool, Lancashire, FY6 8NB
Tel: 01253 883064
www.windyharbour.net
Pitches For ⚏ ⚍

Open 01-Mar **to** 15-Nov
Access Good **Site** Level
Alongside the River Wyre. 7 miles from Blackpool.
Facilities ⚒ ⚒ ⊞ ☖ ⚗ ⌐ ⊡ ☂ ⚐ ⊡ ☂
⚑ ⓘ ⚲ ☖ ⚑ ⚓ ⚑ ⚓ ⊁⚏ ⊡ ⚝
⚐
Nearby Facilities ⌐ ✔ ⚒ ⚓ ⚲ ⚑ ☇
Nearest Town Blackpool
Directions Leave the M55 at junction 3, use left hand lane and take the 3rd exit onto the A585 to Fleetwood. After approx. 3 miles, go straight on at the traffic lights and the Park entrance is 300mtrs.
⚏ Poulton-le-Fylde

CARNFORTH

Bay View Holiday Park, A6 Main Road, Bolton-le-Sands, Carnforth, Lancashire, LA5 8ES
Tel: 01524 701508
Email: reception@holgates.co.uk
www.holgates.co.uk
Pitches For ▲ ⚏ ⚍ **Total** 200
Open Mar **to** Oct **Access** Good **Site** Sloping
Nearest Bus Stop (Miles) ¼
Stunning views over Morecambe Bay. Ideal base for exploring the Lake District, North Yorkshire and the Forest of Bowland.
Facilities ⚒ ⊞ ☖ ⚗ ⌐ ⊡ ☂ ⚐ ⊡ ☂
⚑ ⓘ ⚲ ☖ ⚑ ⚓ ⊞ ⚑ ⚓ ⊁⚏ ⊡ ⚝ ⚐ ⚑
Nearby Facilities ⌐ ✔ ⚓ ☇
Nearest Town Carnforth
Directions Leave the M6 at junction 35 and take the A601 for Carnforth. After 1 mile at the traffic lights go straight over, after mini roundabout site is 500 metres on the right.
⚏ Carnforth

CARNFORTH

Hollins Farm, Far Arnside, Off Cove Road, Silverdale, Carnforth, Lancashire, LA5 0SL
Tel: 01524 701508
Email: reception@holgates.co.uk
www.holgates.co.uk
Pitches For ▲ ⚏ ⚍
Acreage 2 **Open** March **to** Oct
Access Good **Site** Lev/Slope
Nearest Bus Stop (Miles) ¼
Situated in an area of outstanding natural beauty, near the shore and a bird reserve.
Facilities ⚒ ⊞ ☖ ⚗ ⌐ ⊡ ☂
⚑ ⓘ ⊁⚏ ⚝ ⚑
Nearby Facilities ⌐ ✔ ⚓ ☇
Nearest Town Arnside
Directions Leave the M6 at junction 35 into Carnforth, follow signs for Silverdale. Go over the level crossing and bear right, after ¾ miles bear left and after ¼ of a mile fork right into Cove Road.
⚏ Arnside/Silverdale

CARNFORTH

Old Hall Caravan Park, Capernwray, Carnforth, Lancashire, LA6 1AD
Tel: 01524 733276
Email: info@oldhallcaravanpark.co.uk
www.oldhallcaravanpark.co.uk
Pitches For ⚏ ⚍ **Total** 38
Open 01-Mar **to** 10-Jan
Access Good **Site** Level
Quiet, peaceful, woodland retreat.

LANCASHIRE

Facilities ⚤ ∮ ⊞ 🆖 ➳ 🏠 ⊙ ➳ ▬ 🔲 🍴 🍽 🛇 🗑 🔤 🌮 🔲 🗑 ⚡ 🌿 🎣 🔈
Nearby Facilities ⌐ ✒ ∪ ⚳
Nearest Town Carnforth
Directions Leave the M6 at junction 35, go to Over Kellet. Turn left in the village of Over Kellet and the park is 1½ miles on the right.
⇌ Carnforth

CARNFORTH

Red Bank Farm, The Shore, Bolton-le-Sands, Carnforth, Lancashire, LA5 8JR
Tel: 01524 823196
Email: mark@redbankfarm.co.uk
www.redbankfarm.co.uk
Pitches For ▲ 🚐 **Total** 50
Acreage 3 **Open** Easter **to** October
Site Lev/Slope
Nearest Bus Stop (Miles) ½
On the shore side of Morecambe Bay. Camp on our organic field and see our organically fed animals, (ie milking cows and sheep).
Facilities 🆖 ➳ 🏠 ⊙ ➳ 🍴 ✕ 🍽 🔲 🗑
Nearby Facilities ⌐ ✒
Nearest Town Morecambe
Directions From the A6 at Bolton-le-Sands, take the A5105 to Morecambe. After 500yds sharp right and right again at the railway bridge, turn left along the shore into the farm.
⇌ Lancaster/Morecambe

CARNFORTH

The Villa Fishery & Caravan Park, Borwick Lane, Borwick, Nr Carnforth, Lancashire, LA6 1JZ
Tel: 01524 781453
Email: enquiries@pureleisure-holidays.co.uk
www.thevillafishery.co.uk
Pitches For 🚐 🚐
Open Mar **to** Oct **Access** Good **Site** Level
Nearest Bus Stop (Miles) ½
Rural location, excellent for fishing as the site consists of four inter-connected lakes that hold a superb mix of coarse fish.
Facilities ∮ 🆖 ➳ ⊙ ➳ 🍴 ⊙ 🍽 🔲 ✒ 🌮 🔈
Nearby Facilities ⌐ ✒ ⟂ ⚲ ∪ ⚳ ⚳ ✗
Nearest Town Carnforth
Directions Leave the M6 at junction 35 and take the A6 north. At the second roundabout take third exit signposted Borwick, site entrance is 150 yeards on the left.
⇌ Carnforth

CLITHEROE

Camping & Caravanning Club Site, Edisford Road, Clitheroe, Lancashire, BB7 3LA
Tel: 01200 425294
www.campingandcaravanningclub.co.uk/clitheroe
Pitches For ▲ 🚐 🚐 **Total** 80
Acreage 6 **Open** 29-Mar **to** 05-Nov
Site Lev/Slope
Nearest Bus Stop (Miles) ½
In the Ribble Valley, on the banks of a river. Local ghost walks on a weekly basis. Near Clitheroe Castle. Near a swimming pool and a dog walk. BTB 4 Star Graded and AA 3 Pennants. Non members welcome. You can also call us on 0845 130 7633.
Facilities ∮ 🆖 ⊞ 🆖 ➳ 🏠 ⊙ ➳ 🍴 🔈 🔲 ⊙ 🍴 🍽 🔲 🗑
Nearby Facilities ⌐ ✒ ∪ ⚳
Directions Nearest main road is the A59. From the west follow the A671 into Clitheroe. Look for the signpost indicating a left turn to Longridge/Sports Centre, turn into Greenacre Road approx 25 metres beyond the pelican crossing. Continue until the T-Junction at Edisford Road, turn left and continue past the church on the right, look for the Sports Centre on the right and car park opposite.
⇌ Clitheroe

CROSTON

Royal Umpire Caravan Park, Southport Road, Croston, Preston, Lancashire, PR26 9JB
Tel: 01772 600257
Email: info@royalumpire.co.uk
www.royalumpire.co.uk
Pitches For ▲ 🚐 🚐 **Total** 200
Acreage 60 **Open** All Year
Access Good **Site** Level
Nearest Bus Stop (Miles) ¼
Near to pubs and restaurants.
Facilities ⚤ ∮ 🆖 ⊞ 🆖 ➳ 🏠 ⊙ ➳ 🍴 🔲 🗑 🔲 ⊙ 🍴 🍽 🔲 🗑 🌮
Nearby Facilities ⌐ ✒ ∪
Nearest Town Preston
Directions Leave the M6 at junction 27 and take the A5209 left towards Parbold. Turn right onto the B5250, turn left onto the A581 for Croston and Southport. At the end of the road turn left and the site is ¼ mile on the right.
⇌ Croston

GARSTANG

Claylands Caravan Park, Weavers Lane, Cabus, Garstang, Nr Preston, Lancashire, PR3 1AJ
Tel: 01524 791242
Email: alan@claylands.com
www.claylands.com
Pitches For ▲ 🚐 🚐 **Total** 36
Acreage 10 **Open** March **to** 31-Jan
Access Good **Site** Level
Nearest Bus Stop (Miles) Outside
On the doorstep to the Trough of Bowland. 20 miles from Blackpool and 40 minutes drive to the Lake District.
Facilities ⚤ ∮ 🆖 ⊞ 🆖 ➳ 🏠 ⊙ ➳ 🍴 🔲 🗑 🔲 ⊙ 🍴 ✕ 🍽 🔲 🍴 🍽 🔲 🗑 🌮
Nearby Facilities ⌐ ✒ ∪ ⚳
Nearest Town Blackpool
Directions Leave the M6 at junction 33, 6 miles to Garstang. Drive past Quattro's and two garages on the left, then turn left into Weavers Lane.
⇌ Lancaster

GARSTANG

Part Raikes Caravan Site, Part Raikes Farm, Garstang Road, Great Eccleston, Lancashire, PR3 0XA
Tel: 01995 672838
Pitches For ▲ 🚐 🚐 **Total** 10
Acreage ½ **Open** March **to** Jan
Access Good **Site** Level
Nearest Bus Stop (Miles) Outside
River bank behind the Park. 20 minutes from Blackpool and an hour to the Lakes.
Facilities ∮ 🆖 ⊞ 🆖 ➳ 🍴 ➳ 🍽 🔲 🍴 🍽 🔲 🗑
Nearby Facilities ✒
Nearest Town Blackpool
Directions Leave the M6 at junction 32 and take the A6 north. 3 miles west at Guys Thatch turn into St Michaels Road, after 3 miles at mini roundabout turn left onto the A586, site is 2 miles on the right.
⇌ Poulton-le-Fylde

GARSTANG

Wyreside Farm Park, Allotment Lane, St Michaels-on-Wyre, Garstang, Lancashire, PR3 0TZ
Tel: 01995 679797
Email: penny.wyresidefarm@talktalk.net
www.riverparks.co.uk
Pitches For ▲ 🚐 🚐 **Total** 16
Acreage 7 **Open** March **to** October
Access Good **Site** Level
Nearest Bus Stop (Miles) Outside
On the banks of the River Wyre. Mowed field to play in. Central for Blackpool, the Lakes and the Trough of Bowland.

Facilities ∮ 🆖 ➳ ⌐ 🍴 🍽 🌮 🔲 🗑
Nearby Facilities ⌐ ✒ ⟂ ⚳ ∪ ⚲ ✗
Nearest Town Garstang/Blackpool
Directions From South, leave M6 at junc 32 and take the A6 north to Garstang. In the village of Billsborrow turn immediately left, after 4 miles at mini roundabout turn right, go past the church, over the bridge, past The Grapes Pub, right hand bend, just before the bus stop. Allotment lane is on the right.
⇌ Preston

HEYWOOD

Gelderwood Country Park, Ashworth Road, Rochdale, Lancashire, OL11 5UP
Tel: 01706 364858
Email: gelderwood@aol.com
www.gelderwoodcaravanpark.co.uk
Pitches For 🚐 🚐 **Total** 34
Acreage 2 **Open** All Year
Access Good **Site** Level
Nearest Bus Stop (Miles) ½
ADULTS ONLY PARK.
Facilities ∮ 🆖 ⊞ 🆖 ➳ 🍴 🍽 🌮 🔲 🗑 A
Nearby Facilities ⌐ ✒ ∪
Nearest Town Heywood
Directions Go into Heywood on the A58, turn left into Bamford Road, at the T-Junction turn left, turn right after 100 yards.
⇌ Bury

LANCASTER

Laundsfield Caravan Park, Stoney Lane, Galgate, Nr Lancaster, Lancashire, LA2 0JZ
Tel: 01524 751763
Pitches For ▲ 🚐 🚐 **Total** 20
Acreage 1 **Open** March **to** Oct
Access Good **Site** Level
Nearest Bus Stop (Miles) 100 yards
Near to a canal marina and Lancaster University.
Facilities 🆖 ➳ 🏠 ⊙ ➳ ⌐ 🔲 🍽 🔲 🗑
Nearby Facilities ⌐ ✒ ⟂ ⚳ ∪
Nearest Town Lancaster
Directions ¼ of a mile from the M6 junction 33. 2 miles from Lancaster.
⇌ Lancaster

LANCASTER

New Parkside Farm Caravan Park, Denny Beck, Caton Road, Lancaster, Lancashire, LA2 9HH
Tel: 01524 770723
www.ukparks.co.uk/newparkside
Pitches For ▲ 🚐 🚐 **Total** 40
Acreage 4 **Open** March **to** October
Access Good **Site** Lev/Slope
Nearest Bus Stop (Miles) ¼
A working farm with beautiful views of Lune Valley. On the edge of Forest of Bowland and close to historic Lancaster and Morecambe Bay. Central for lakes and dales.
Facilities ∮ 🆖 ⊞ 🆖 ➳ 🍴 ➳ 🍽 🌮 🔲 🗑 🔤
Nearby Facilities ⌐ ✒
Nearest Town Lancaster
Directions Leave the M6 at junction 34 and take the A683 towards Kirkby Lonsdale. Park is situated 1 mile on the right.
⇌ Lancaster

LANCASTER

Wyreside Lakes Fishery, Sunnyside Farmhouse, Bay Horse, Lancaster, Lancashire, LA2 9DG
Tel: 01524 792093
Email: wyresidelakes@btconnect.com
www.wyresidelakes.co.uk
Pitches For ▲ 🚐 🚐 **Total** 100
Acreage 120 **Open** All Year
Access Good **Site** Lev/Slope
Set in the beautiful Wyreside Valley with views of the Bowland Fells. 7 lakes to walk around and the beautiful Foxes Wood.

Facilities ⚹ ♿ ⊞ ⊡ ☕ ☏ ⊙ ⏚ ▱ ⊙ ☎ ⊠ ♟ ⊕ ✗ ♉ ⑪ 🛆 ☎ ⊞ ✧ ⚘
Nearby Facilities ↾ U
Nearest Town Garstang
Directions Leave the M6 at junction 33, turn left towards Garstang and follow brown tourism signs.
⇌ Lancaster

LONGRIDGE

Beacon Fell View Caravan Park, Higher Road, Longridge, Nr Preston, Lancashire, PR3 2TF
Tel: 01772 783233
Email: enquiries@hagansleisure.co.uk
www.hagansleisure.co.uk
Pitches For ▲ ⊞ ⊜
Acreage 30 **Open** March to Oct
Access Good **Site** Sloping
Nearest Bus Stop (Miles) Outside
Overlooking the Ribble Valley. 30 minutes from the bright lights of Blackpool. Ideal touring destination for the Lake District and the Yorkshire Dales.
Facilities ♿ ⊞ ⊡ ☕ ☏ ⊙ ⏚ ▱ ⊙ ☎ ⊠ ♟ ⊕ ✗ ♉ ⑪ 🛆 ☎ ⊞ ✧ ⚘
Nearby Facilities ↾ ✓ U ⚲ ⚹
Nearest Town Longridge
Directions In Longridge go straight across the roundabout and keep left at the White Bull Pub, park is 1 mile on the right.
⇌ Preston

MORECAMBE

Glen Caravan Park, Westgate, Morecambe, Lancashire, LA3 3EL
Tel: 01524 423896
Pitches For ⊞ ⊜ **Total** 10
Acreage ½ **Open** March to October
Access Good **Site** Level
Nearest Bus Stop (Miles) ¼
15 minutes walk Morecambe Promenade.
Facilities ♿ ⊡ ☕ ☏ ⊙ ⏚ ▱ ⊙ ☎ ☆ ☎ ⊞ ✧ ⚘
Nearby Facilities ↾ ✓ ⊥ U ⚲
Nearest Town Morecambe
Directions In Morecambe itself close to promenade, Regent Road and Westgate.

MORECAMBE

Greendales Farm & Bowland View Holiday Park, Greendales Farm, Carr Lane, Middleton, Morecambe, Lancashire, LA3 3LH
Tel: 01524 852616
Email: greendalesfarm@tiscali.co.uk
www.greendalesfarmcaravanpark.co.uk
Pitches For ⊞ ⊜ **Total** 24
Acreage 2 **Open** 01-Mar to 14-Jan
Access Good **Site** Level
Nearest Bus Stop (Miles) ¼
Close to the beach. Ideal for the Lake District, Blackpool and Morecambe.
Facilities ♿ ⊞ ⊡ ☕ ☏ ⊙ ⏚ ▱ ⊙ ⊠ 🛆 ☎ ⊞ ✧ ⚘ ⚲

Nearby Facilities ↾ ✓ ⊥ ✤ U ⚲
Nearest Town Morecambe
Directions Leave the M6 at junction 34 and follow signs to Middleton and Overton, turn left into Carr Lane, then turn left at the Greendales Farm sign.
⇌ Morecambe

MORECAMBE

Melbreak Caravan Park, Carr Lane, Middleton, Morecambe, Lancs., LA3 3LH
Tel: 01524 852430
Pitches For ▲ ⊞ ⊜ **Total** 40
Acreage 1½ **Open** March to October
Access Good **Site** Lev/Slope
Nearest Bus Stop (Miles) ½
Near the beach and some of the oldest churches in England. Lovely walking area.
Facilities ♿ ⊞ ⊡ ☕ ☏ ⊙ ⏚
⊠ ⊙ ☎ ⊞ ✧ ⚘
Nearby Facilities ↾ ✓ ⊥ ✤ U ⚲ ⚹
Nearest Town Morecambe
Directions Take the B5274 from Morecambe to the roundabout, go straight across until you get to Middleton, signposted from the junction.
⇌ Morecambe

MORECAMBE

Morecambe Lodge Caravan Park, Shore Lane, Bolton-le-Sands, Carnforth, Lancashire, LA5 8JP
Tel: 01524 824361
Email: andrew@morecambe-lodge.co.uk
www.morecambe-lodge.co.uk
Pitches For ⊞ ⊜ **Total** 25
Acreage 2 **Open** March to Oct
Access Good **Site** Level
Nearest Bus Stop (Miles) ½
Direct access to the beach. Excellent views over the bay across to the Lake Hills. Good for walking, fishing and cycling. US RVs welcome with 16 or 32 amp supply.
Facilities ⚹ ♿ ⊞ ⊡ ☕ ☏ ⊙ ⏚
⊠ ⊙ ☆ ☎ ⊞ ✧ ⚘ ✎ ⟪ 🛜
Nearby Facilities ↾ ✓ ⊥ ✤ U ⚲ ⚹
Nearest Town Morecambe
Directions Take the A6 north from Lancaster to Bolton-le-Sands, turn left at the traffic lights onto the A5105. After 200yds turn right by the first house, travel down towards the beach and over the bridge, Park is on the left hand side.
⇌ Carnforth

MORECAMBE

Venture Caravan Park, Langridge Way, Westgate, Morecambe, Lancashire, LA4 4TQ
Tel: 01524 412986
Email: mark@venturecaravanpark.co.uk
www.venturecaravanpark.co.uk
Pitches For ▲ ⊞ ⊜
Acreage 17 **Open** All Year
Access Good **Site** Level

Beautifully landscaped Park offering a relaxing family holiday experience. Ideal for the Lake District and the Yorkshire Dales.
Facilities ⚹ ♿ ⊞ ⊡ ☕ ☏ ⊙ ⏚ ▱ ⊙ ☎ ⊠ ♟ ⊕ ✗ ⑪ 🛆 ♉ ☆ ☎ ⊞ ⊡ ✧ ⚘
Nearby Facilities ↾ ✓ ⊥ ✤ ⚲ ⚹
Nearest Town Morecambe
Directions Leave the M6 at junction 34 and take the A683 to Morecambe. At the roundabout go straight across onto the A589, at 3rd roundabout take 1st left onto Westgate (sp West Promenade, West End and Sandylands). Go over the bridge and straight across the traffic lights. After ¾ mile turn right after the fire station in to Langridge Way,.
⇌ Morecambe

SOUTHPORT

Riverside Holiday Park, Southport New Road, Banks, Southport, Lancashire, PR9 8DF
Tel: 01704 228886
Email: reception@harrisonleisureuk.com
www.riversideleisurecentre.co.uk
Pitches For ▲ ⊞ ⊜ **Total** 300
Acreage 80 **Open** 14-Feb to 31-Jan
Access Good **Site** Level
Nearest Bus Stop (Miles) Outside
10 minutes from the beach.
Facilities ♿ ⊞ ⊡ ☕ ☏ ⊙ ⏚ ▱ ⊙ ☎ ⊠ ♟ ⊕ ✗ ⑪ 🛆 ♉ ☆ ☎ ⊞ ⊡ ✧ ⚘
Nearby Facilities ↾ ✓ ⊥ U
Directions Leave the M6 at junc 27 and take the A5209 towards Parbold and Burscough. At the junction turn right onto the A59 and continue to the traffic lights in Tarleton, turn left onto the A5105, site is approx. 2 miles on the left.
⇌ Southport

SOUTHPORT

Willowbank Holiday Home & Touring Park, Coastal Road, Ainsdale, Southport, Merseyside, PR8 3ST
Tel: 01704 571566
Email: info@willowbankcp.co.uk
www.willowbankcp.co.uk
Pitches For ⊞ ⊜ **Total** 87
Acreage 10 **Open** 01-Mar to 31-Jan
Access Good **Site** Level
Nearest Bus Stop (Miles) ¼
Ideal for woodland walks and all of Southports attractions. Close to the Trans-Penine Cycle Way. Motorhome service bay and dog walk area. Ideal touring.
Facilities ⚹ ♿ ⊞ ⊡ ☕ ☏ ⊙ ⏚ ▱ ⊙ ☎ ⊠ ♟ ⊕ 🛆 ♉ ☎ ⊞ ⊡
Nearby Facilities ↾ ✓ ⊥ ✤ U ⚲ ⚹
Nearest Town Southport
Directions From South M6-M57/M58 onto the A5036, then take the A5207 onto the A565 for Southport. After RAF Woodvale at traffic lights turn left, park is 150 metres on the left.
⇌ Ainsdale

LANCASHIRE, LEICESTERSHIRE, LINCOLNSHIRE

THORNTON

Kneps Farm Holiday Park, River Road, Stanah, Thornton-Cleveleys, Blackpool, Lancashire, FY5 5LR
Tel: 01253 823632
Email: enquiries@knepsfarm.co.uk
www.www.knepsfarm.co.uk
Pitches For 🚐 🚎 **Total** 60
Acreage 3½ **Open** March **to** Mid Nov
Access Good **Site** Level
Nearest Bus Stop (Miles) Outside
Situated adjacent to the Stanah Amenity and Picnic Area, forming part of the River Wyre Estuary Country Park. A rural retreat close to Blackpool. Camping Pods for hire. We are proud to have been voted Regional Winner for North-West England and Overall Winner in the Practical Caravan Top 100 Sites 2011 Awards.
Facilities 🔥 ⚓ ⼁ 🖤 🔯 🅿 ⊙ ⊣ ⛟
◨ ⛨ 🕽 🖰 🛒 🖳 📶
Nearby Facilities ⼁ ✓ ⚓ ⤢
Nearest Town Blackpool
Directions 5 miles NNE of Blackpool. From the M55 junc 3 take the A585 Fleetwood road to the River Wyre Hotel on the lt, turn rt at the rbt onto the B5412 sp Little Thornton. Turn rt at mini-roundabout after the school onto Stanah Rd, go straight over the next roundabout leading to River Rd.
🚆 Poulton-le-Fylde

THORNTON

Stanah House Caravan Park, River Road, Thornton, Cleveleys, Lancashire, FY5 5LR
Tel: 01253 824000
Email: stanahhouse@talk21.com
Pitches For ⛺ 🚐 🚎 **Total** 60
Acreage 6 **Open** March **to** Oct
Access Good **Site** Sloping
Nearest Bus Stop (Miles) ¼
Alongside the River Wyre and set in the Stanah Ecology Centre.
Facilities ⼁ 🖤 🖰 🅿 ⊙ ⊣ ⛟ ◨ 🖳
⛨ 🕽 🖰 🛒 🖳 📶
Nearby Facilities ⼁ ✓ ⚓ ⤢ ✗ ∪ ⤢
Nearest Town Blackpool
Directions From South: Leave M6 at jct 32 join M55, exit at jct 3 and take A585 following signs to Fleetwood. At the traffic lights by Shell bear right, go straight through next lights, at roundabout by the River Wyre Hotel turn right for Little Thornton and Stanah Picnic Area. After 1 mile turn right into Stanah Road, continue into River Road. You will reach the Wyre Estuary Country Park and the site entrance is third on the right.
🚆 Poulton-le-Fylde

LEICESTERSHIRE

LEICESTER

Hill Top Caravan Park, Hill Top, 67 Old Gate Road, Thrussington, Leicestershire, LE7 4TL
Tel: 01664 424357
Email: mjandstarry@googlemail.com
www.caravancampingsites.co.uk/leicestershire
Pitches For 🚐 🚎 **Total** 10
Acreage 1 **Open** All Year
Access Good **Site** Level
Nearest Bus Stop (Miles) ½
ADULTS ONLY SITE. Within walking distance of two country pubs. 5 minutes drive to two golf courses. Close to Belvoir Castle, Rutland Water, Ragdale Hall Health Spa, National Space Centre and much more. Site Fees from £9 per night.
Facilities ⚓ ⼁ 🖤 🕽 🖰 ⊙ ⊣ ◨ 🖳
Nearby Facilities ⼁ ✓ ⚓ ✗ ∪ ⤢ ⤢ ⤢

Nearest Town Leicester
Directions 9 miles north of Leicester on the A46 Newark road. At Thrussington Rearsby sign turn right, on entering Thrussington turn sharp left at 30mph sign into Old Gate Road, site is 500 yards on the right.
🚆 Syston

LUTTERWORTH

Stanford Hall Caravan Park, Stanford Road, Swinford, Leicestershire, LE17 6DH
Tel: 01788 860387
Email: stanfordpark@yahoo.co.uk
www.stanfordhall.co.uk
Pitches For 🚐 🚎 **Total** 120
Acreage 10½ **Open** All Year
Access Good **Site** Level
Nearest Bus Stop (Miles) ½
Ideal for Stanford Hall, the Grand Union Canal, Silverstone and the NEC.
Facilities ⼁ 🖤 🕽 ⛨ 🖰 ⊣ 🖳 🍴
Nearby Facilities ⼁ ✓ ∪ ⤢
Nearest Town Lutterworth
Directions Only 5 miles from Lutterworth. 10 minutes from Rugby by car.
🚆 Rugby

LINCOLNSHIRE

ALFORD

Woodthorpe Hall Leisure Park, Woodthorpe Hall, Woodthorpe, Alford, Lincolnshire, LN13 0DD
Tel: 01507 450294
Email: enquiries@woodthorpehallleisure.co.uk
www.woodthorpehallleisure.co.uk
Pitches For ⛺ 🚐 🚎 **Total** 60
Open 01-Mar **to** 03-Jan
Access Good **Site** Level
Golf course, golf driving range and fishing lakes on site. 6 miles from the beach and 10 miles from the Georgian market town of Louth.
Facilities ⚓ ⼁ 🖤 🕽 🅿 ⊙ ⊣ 🖳 ◨
⛨ 🖰 ⊘ 🛒 ✗ 🍴 ⚓ 🖤 ⊣ 🖰 🖳 🍴 📶
Nearby Facilities ⼁ ✓ ∪
Nearest Town Alford
Directions Just off the B1373, 1½ miles from Withern Village and 3½ miles from the market town of Alford.
🚆 Skegness

BOSTON

Long Acres (Adult Only) Caravan Park, Station Road, Old Leake, Boston, Lincolnshire, PE22 9RF
Tel: 01205 871555
Email: enquiries@longacres-caravanpark.co.uk
www.longacres-caravanpark.co.uk
Pitches For ⛺ 🚐 🚎 **Total** 40
Acreage 2 **Open** March **to** October
Access Good **Site** Level
ADULTS ONLY PARK with peace and tranquillity. Ideal starting point for exploring Lincolnshires many attractions.
Facilities ⼁ 🖤 🕽 🅿 ⊙ ⊣ ◨ ⛟ ◨ 🖳 🅐 📶
Nearby Facilities ⼁ ✓
Nearest Town Boston
Directions From the A16 take the B1184 (Station Road) at Sibsey. After approx 1 mile at the T-Junction turn left, then after approx 1½ miles turn right into Station Road.
🚆 Boston

BOSTON

Orchard Park, Frampton Lane, Hubberts Bridge, Boston, Lincolnshire, PE20 3QU
Tel: 01205 290328
Email: info@orchardpark.co.uk
www.orchardpark.co.uk

Pitches For ⛺ 🚐 🚎 **Total** 87
Acreage 61 **Open** All Year
Access Good **Site** Level
Nearest Bus Stop (Miles) Outside
ADULTS ONLY. ETB 3 Star Graded, AA 4 Pennants and David Bellamy Gold Award.
Facilities ⚓ ⼁ 🖤 🕽 🅿 ⊙ ⊣ ⛟ ◨ 🖳
⛨ ◨ ⼁ 🛒 ✗ ⼁ ◨ 🖳 ✗ ⤢ 📶 🖳
Nearby Facilities ⼁ ✓ ∪
Nearest Town Boston
Directions Take the A52 from Boston towards Grantham. After approx. 3½ miles turn right at Four Cross Roads Pub onto the B1192, Park is ¼ of a mile.
🚆 Hubberts Bridge

BOSTON

Pilgrims Way Caravan & Camping Park, Church Green Road, Fishtoft, Boston, Lincolnshire, PE21 0QY
Tel: 01205 366646
Email:
pilgrimsway@caravanandcampingpark.com
www.pilgrimsway-caravanandcamping.com
Pitches For ⛺ 🚐 🚎 **Total**
Acreage 3 **Open** All Year
Access Good **Site** Level
Nearest Bus Stop (Miles) Outside
Friendly, family run Park in the heart of the beautiful South Lincolnshire countryside. Within easy reach of the market town of Boston. Ideal for walking, cycling, fishing or simply relaxing. Visit Britain 4 Stars and AA 4 Pennants.
Facilities ⚓ ⼁ 🖤 🕽 🅿 ⊙ ⊣ ⛟ ◨ 🖳
⼁ 🖰 ⚓ ⛨ ⊣ 🖰 🖳 ✗ 📶
Nearby Facilities ⼁ ✓ ∪ ⤢ ⤢ ⤢
Nearest Town Boston/Skegness
Directions Take the A52 east from Boston, in 1 mile, after the junction with the A16 at The Ball Public House, turn right and follow international signs to the Park.
🚆 Boston

BOSTON

The Moorings, Station Road, Swineshead Bridge, Boston, Lincolnshire, PE20 3PS
Tel: 01205 820184
Email: di.mccormack@yahoo.co.uk
www.themoorings.org
Pitches For ⛺ 🚐 🚎 **Total** 5
Acreage 10 **Open** April **to** September
Access Good **Site** Level
Nearest Bus Stop (Miles) ½
Alongside a river for fishing.
Facilities ⼁ 🖤 🛒 ⊣ ◨ 🛒 ✗ ⼁ ⤢ 📶
Nearby Facilities ⼁ ✓ ⚓ ✗ ∪ ⤢
Nearest Town Boston
Directions From the A1121 signed Sleaford, turn left onto the A17 and immediately left over the railway.
🚆 Swineshead Bridge

BOSTON

Walnut Lake Lodges & Camping, Main Road, Algarkirk, Boston, Lincolnshire, PE20 2LQ
Tel: 01205 460482
Email: mariawalnutlakes@yahoo.co.uk
www.walnutlakes.co.uk
Pitches For ⛺ 🚐 🚎 **Total** 8
Acreage 10 **Open** Easter **to** End Sept
Site Level
ADULTS ONLY PARK with fishing on site. Close to Spalding and Boston, many local attractions. 26 miles from Skegness.
Facilities ⼁ 🖤 🕽 🛒 ⊣ ◨ ⼁ 🅐
Nearby Facilities ⼁ ✓ ⚓ ✗ ∪
Nearest Town Boston/Spalding
Directions From the A17/A16 roundabout heading towards Kings Lynn, site is 300 metres on the left.
🚆 Boston/Spalding

CLEETHORPES

Thorpe Park Holiday Centre, Thorpe Park, Cleethorpes, Lincolnshire, DN35 0PW
Tel: 01472 813395
Email: thorpepark@haven.com
www.haventouring.com/tothorpepark
Pitches For 🅰 🚐 🚙 **Total** 141
Open Mid March **to** End Oct
Access Good **Site** Level
Nearest Bus Stop (Miles) Outside
Next to Pleasure Island and the beach. Enjoy kids clubs, a full family entertainment programme, water fun, fishing lake, crazy golf, tennis and so much more.
Facilities
Nearby Facilities U ⚡
Nearest Town Cleethorpes
Directions From the M180 take the A180 and follow signs for Grimsby and Cleethorpes. In Cleethorpes town centre follow signs for Pleasure Island & Holiday Parks.
🚉 Cleethorpes

CROWLAND

The Bridge Caravan Park, Common Drove, Crowland, Peterborough, Cambridgeshire, PE6 0HJ
Tel: 07719 979118
www.thebridgecaravanpark.co.uk

Pitches For 🅰 🚐 🚙 🏕 **Total** 30
Acreage 2 **Open** All Year
Access Good **Site** Level
Nearest Bus Stop (Miles) Outside
Public house and Fishing on site.
Facilities
Nearby Facilities 🎣 ⚡ 🏊 U ⚡ ⛵
Nearest Town Crowland
Directions On the Market Deeping road.

GRANTHAM

Woodland Waters Ltd., Willoughby Road, Ancaster, Grantham, Lincolnshire, NG32 3RT
Tel: 01400 230888
Email: info@woodlandwaters.co.uk
www.woodlandwaters.co.uk
Pitches For 🅰 🚐 🚙 **Total** 80
Acreage 72 **Open** All Year
Access Good **Site** Level
Nearest Bus Stop (Miles) Entrance
Bar and restaurant, five fishing lakes and lovely woodland walks on site. Self catering lodges available for hire.
Facilities
Nearby Facilities 🎣 U
Nearest Town Grantham/Sleaford
Directions On the A153 between Grantham and Sleaford.
🚉 Ancaster

HORNCASTLE

Ashby Park, West Ashby, Nr Horncastle, Lincolnshire, LN9 5PP
Tel: 01507 527966
Email: ashbypark@btconnect.com
www.ukparks.co.uk/ashby
Pitches For 🅰 🚐 🚙 **Total** 120
Acreage 70 **Open** 01-Mar **to** 06-Jan
Access Good **Site** Level
Seven fishing lakes, pub and restaurant ½ mile, swimming pool 1¾ miles. 23 miles to the coast. Static caravans for sale. ETB 4 Star Graded and David Bellamy Gold Award for Conservation.
Facilities
Nearby Facilities 🎣 ⚡ 🏊 U ⚡
Nearest Town Horncastle
Directions 1¾ miles north of Horncastle between the A153 and the A158.
🚉 Lincoln

HUTTOFT

Jolly Common Adult Only Caravan Park, Jolly Common, Sea Lane, Huttoft, Alford, Lincolnshire, LN13 9RW
Tel: 01507 490236
www.jollycommoncaravanpark.co.uk
Pitches For 🚐 🚙
Acreage 9 **Open** 15-Mar **to** 15-Oct
Access Good **Site** Level

Nearest Bus Stop (Miles) ½
ADULTS ONLY SITE set in peaceful countryside. 1 mile from a sandy beach.
Facilities
Nearby Facilities
Nearest Town Sutton-on-Sea
Directions From Sutton-on-Sea head south on the A52 for 4 miles. In the village of Huttoft turn first left, after ¾ miles turn first right and the site is 200 yards on the left.
⚡ Skegness

INGOLDMELLS

Hardy's Touring Site, Sea Lane, Ingoldmells, Skegness, Lincolnshire, PE25 1PG
Tel: 01754 874071
Pitches For 🏕 🚐 **Total** 112
Acreage 5 **Open** Easter **to** October
Access Good **Site** Level
Nearest Bus Stop (Miles) ¼
5 minutes walk from the beach. Next to Fantasy Island and 10 minutes from an animal farm.
Facilities
Nearby Facilities
Nearest Town Skegness/Ingoldmells
Directions Take the A52 north from Skegness to Ingoldmells. At the Ship Inn in Ingoldmells turn right down Sea Lane, towards the sea. Site is ½ mile on the right.
⚡ Skegness

INGOLDMELLS

Valetta Farm Caravan Site, Mill Lane, Addlethorpe, Skegness, Lincolnshire, PE24 4TB
Tel: 01754 763758
Email: leeman22@btinternet.com
Pitches For 🏕 🚐 **Total** 55
Acreage 2 **Open** 25-Mar **to** 20-Oct
Access Good **Site** Level
Nearest Bus Stop (Miles) 1
Quite a pretty site in the country, 1 mile from the beach.
Facilities
Nearby Facilities
Nearest Town Skegness
Directions Turn left off the A158 (Horncastle to Skegness road) on Burgh-le-Marsh bypass at the signpost Ingoldmells and Addlethorpe. Follow signposts for Ingoldmells for 3 miles, turn right by disused mill into Mill Lane. Site is on the left in 150yds.
⚡ Skegness

LINCOLN

Hartsholme Country Park, Skellingthorpe Road, Lincoln, Lincolnshire, LN6 0EY
Tel: 01522 873578
Email: hartsholmecp@lincoln.gov.uk
www.lincoln.gov.uk

Pitches For 🏕 🚐 🚐 **Total** 39
Acreage 2½ **Open** March **to** October
Access Good **Site** Level
Nearest Bus Stop (Miles) Outside
Set amongst mature woodland with a large picturesque lake, as well as open grassland. Adjacent to Swanholme Lakes local nature reserve. Also open weekends only in November, and for Lincolns Christmas Market.
Facilities
Nearby Facilities
Nearest Town Lincoln
Directions 2½ miles south west of Lincoln city centre. Signposted from the A46, on the B1378.
⚡ Lincoln

LINCOLN

Oakhill Leisure, Swinderby Road, Norton Disney, Lincoln, Lincolnshire, LN6 9QG
Tel: 01522 868771
Email: ron@oakhill-leisure.co.uk
www.oakhill-leisure.co.uk
Pitches For 🏕 🚐 🚐 🚐 **Total** 60
Acreage 10 **Open** All Year
Access Good **Site** Level
Peaceful woodland site with open fields and a fishing lake.
Facilities
Nearby Facilities
Nearest Town Lincoln
Directions From the A46 follow brown tourism signs and signs for Thurlby.
⚡ Lincoln

LINCOLN

Shortferry Caravan Park, Ferry Road, Fiskerton, Lincoln, Lincolnshire, LN3 4HU
Tel: 01526 398021
Email: kay@shortferry.co.uk
www.shortferry.co.uk
Pitches For 🚐 🚐 **Total** 75
Acreage 80 **Open** All Year
Access Good **Site** Level
Nearest Bus Stop (Miles) Outside
Situated by a river with 2 fishing ponds. Fishing tackle and bait shop. Entertainment most weekends. Bar meals and take-away in our public house. Seasonal outdoor heated swimming pool.
Facilities
Nearby Facilities
Nearest Town Lincoln
Directions From the A46 Lincoln ring road take the A158 towards Skegness. After approx. 5 miles turn right at Shortferry sign, continue to follow signs for approx. 5 miles.
⚡ Lincoln

MABLETHORPE

Camping & Caravanning Club Site, Highfield, 120 Church Lane, Mablethorpe, Lincolnshire, LN12 2NU
Tel: 01507 472374
www.campingandcaravanningclub.co.uk/mablethorpe
Pitches For 🏕 🚐 🚐 **Total** 105
Acreage 6 **Open** 29-Mar **to** 05-Nov
Access Difficult **Site** Level
Nearest Bus Stop (Miles) 1
Just 1 mile from the sea and award winning beaches. Ideal for cyclists. Near the Lincolnshire Wolds. Swimming pool, play area, bicycle hire, horse racing and dog walk nearby. BTB 4 Star Graded and AA 3 Pennants. Non members welcome. You can also call us on 0845 130 7633.
Facilities
Nearby Facilities
Nearest Town Mablethorpe
Directions On the outskirts of Mablethorpe, on the A1104. Turn into Church Lane after the petrol station on the right, site is 800 yards along the lane on the right hand side.
⚡ Cleethorpes

MABLETHORPE

Denehurst Camp Site, Alford Road, Mablethorpe, Lincolnshire, LN12 1PX
Tel: 01507 472951
Pitches For 🏕 🚐 🚐 🚐
Open March **to** October
Access Good **Site** Level
Nearest Bus Stop (Miles) Outside
Quiet location, just mile from the beach and shops.
Facilities
Nearby Facilities
Nearest Town Mablethorpe
Directions On the A1104 Alford road, ½ mile west of Mablethorpe.
⚡ Skegness

MABLETHORPE

Dunes Holivan Estate, Quebec Road, Mablethorpe, Lincolnshire, LN12 1QH
Tel: 01507 473327
Email: holivans@enterprise.net
www.holivans.co.uk
Pitches For 🚐 🚐 **Total** 25
Acreage 10 **Open** Easter **to** October
Access Good **Site** Level
Nearest Bus Stop (Miles) Outside
Adjacent to sand dunes and the beach. Quiet family run park with a bar.
Facilities
Nearby Facilities
Nearest Town Mablethorpe

Ronam Cottage

01507 490750

Sea Road, Anderby, Nr Skegness PE24 5YA

Quiet park with beautiful views of open countryside.
Good facilities and a high standard of cleanliness.
This highly regarded Camping & Caravanning Club
Site welcomes members and non-members alike.

OPEN ALL YEAR

We Look Forward to Seeing You!

Directions Go into Mablethorpe on the A1104, up to the pullover and turn left into Quebec Road. After ¾ miles turn into the caravan park.
≉ Skegness/Grimsby

MABLETHORPE

Golden Sands Holiday Park, Quebec Road, Mablethorpe, Lincolnshire, LN12 1QJ
Tel: 01507 477871
Email: goldensands@haven.com
www.haventouring.com/togoldensands
Pitches For Å ♣ ♠ **Total** 234
Acreage 10 **Open** Mid March **to** End Oct
Access Good **Site** Level
A lively, beachside Holiday Park with an excellent range of facilities for the whole family, providing a fun-packed enjoyable holiday.
Facilities 🚿 ♦ 🛏 💷 🕿 🗜 ⊙ ⛟ 🔌 ◻ ♥ 🛊 🏪 🎲 🛒 ✗ ☕ 🍴 🏕 🎡 ⛺ ⟱ ☀ ⛽ ⛱ 🍴 ⛵ 🌊
☂
Nearby Facilities ↑ ∪
Nearest Town Mablethorpe
Directions From Mablethorpe town centre, follow the sea front road to the north end for Golden Sands.
≉ Skegness

MARKET DEEPING

The Deepings Caravan Park, Outgang Road, Towngate East, Market Deeping, Lincolnshire, PE6 8LQ
Tel: 01778 344335
Email: info@thedeepings.com
www.thedeepings.com
Pitches For Å ♣ ♠ **Total** 60
Acreage 9 **Open** All Year
Access Good **Site** Level
Family run and owned park with a clubhouse and childrens play area. Fishing on site.
Facilities 🚿 ♦ 🛏 💷 🕿 🗜 ♥
🛊 ⊙ ♀ 🏕 🔌 ◻ 🎲 ⛟ ✎ 🌊 ⛽ ☂ ☀
Nearby Facilities ↑ ⚓ ⛵ ⟱ ∪ ⟲ ♪
Nearest Town Market Deeping
Directions From Peterborough take the A15 to Market Deeping. At the roundabout take second exit, turn right at the Towngate Inn, Park is 2 miles on the left.
≉ Peterborough

MARKET DEEPING/STAMFORD

Tallington Lakes Leisure Park Ltd., Barholm Road, Tallington, Stamford, Lincolnshire, PE9 4RJ
Tel: 01778 347000
Email: info@tallington.com
www.tallington.com
Pitches For Å ♣ ♠ **Total** 63
Open March **to** January
Access Good **Site** Level
Nearest Bus Stop (Miles) ½
Tallington Lakes is a watersports centre offering some of the best water-skiing, jetskiing, sailing, canoeing and wind-surfing in the country. Also there is an outdoor heated swimming pool, dry ski slope, snowboarding, tabogganing, 15 metre climbing wall and Krazy Karts.

Facilities 🚿 ♦ 🛏 💷 🕿 🗜 ⊙ ⛟ 🔌 ◻ ♥
⊙ ♀ 🏕 🔌 ◻ 🎲 ♥ ✎
Nearby Facilities ↑ ∪ ⚓ ⟱ ♪ ♪ ✗
Nearest Town Stamford
Directions 10 mins from Stamford on the A16.
≉ Stamford

MARKET RASEN

Lincolnshire Lanes Caravan & Camping Site, Manor Farm, East Firsby, Market Rasen, Lincolnshire, LN8 2DB
Tel: 01673 878258
Email: robert@lincolnshire-lanes.com
www.lincolnshire-lanes.com
Pitches For Å ♣ ♠ **Total** 21
Acreage 3 **Open** All Year
Access Good **Site** Level
Nearest Bus Stop (Miles) Outside
Small site shop. Disabled toilet. ETB 3 Star Graded and Welcome Host.
Facilities ♦ 🛏 🕿 🗜 ⊙ ⛟ 🔌 ◻ ♥
🛊 ⊙ 🏕 🔌 ◻ 🎲
Nearby Facilities ↑ ✎ ∪
Nearest Town Market Rasen/Lincoln
Directions Take the A15 north from Lincoln, 2½ miles past RAF Scampton turn right and follow brown tourism signs to the site entrance.
≉ Market Rasen/Lincoln

NORTH SOMERCOTES

Lakeside Park, North Somercotes, Nr Louth, Lincolnshire, LN11 7RB
Tel: 01507 358428
Email: enquiries@donamottparks.com
www.donamottparks.com
Pitches For ♣ ♠ **Total** 140
Acreage 15 **Open** 15-Mar **to** 30-Oct
Access Good **Site** Level
Nearest Bus Stop (Miles) Outside
Near the coast. Arrabellas Gymnasium and a multi-use games area with an astroturf soccer pitch.
Facilities 🚿 ♦ 🛏 🕿 🗜 ⊙ ⛟ 🔌 ◻ ♥
🛊 ⊙ ♀ 🏕 ✗ ☕ 🏕 🏕 🎡 🔌 ◻ ⟱ 🌊
Nearby Facilities ↑ ✎ ⚓ ⟱ ∪ ♪
Nearest Town Louth
Directions From Louth take the B1200 through Saltfleet to join the A1031, turn left and the Park is 2 miles on the right.
≉ Grimsby

SALTFLEET

Sunnydale Holiday Park, Sea Lane, Saltfleet, Lincolnshire, LN11 7RP
Tel: 0843 309 2575
Email: holidaysales.sunnydale@park-resorts.com
www.park-resorts.com
Pitches For ♣ ♠
Open Ap **to** Oct **Access** Good **Site** Level
Nearest Bus Stop (Miles) ½
Facilities
♦ 💷 🕿 🗜 ⊙ ⛟ 🔌 🏕 🎲 🍴 🏕 🌊
Nearby Facilities
Nearest Town Mablethorpe
Directions Head towards Louth on the A16, take the B1200 through the villages, at the junction turn left to Saltfleet. Drive through Saltfleet and turn right into Sea Lane, the Park is 400 metres on the left.
≉ Mablethorpe

SCUNTHORPE

Brookside Caravan & Camping Park, Stather Road, Burton-Upon-Stather, Scunthorpe, Lincolnshire, DN15 9DH
Tel: 01724 721369
Email: brooksidecp@aol.com
www.brooksidecaravanpark.co.uk
Pitches For Å ♣ ♠ **Total** 35
Acreage 6 **Open** All Year
Access Good **Site** Level
Nearest Bus Stop (Miles) Outside
Our family run, superbly equipped park, set in an area of outstanding beauty, is the ideal location for visiting North Lincolnshire. 4½ miles from Scunthorpe town centre. Bank Holidays - Adults only. ETB 5 Star Graded.
Facilities 🚿 ♦ 🛏 💷 🕿 🗜 ⊙ ⛟ ◻ ♥
🛊 🔌 ◻ ☂
Nearby Facilities ↑ ✎ ∪ ♪
Nearest Town Scunthorpe
Directions B1430 from Scunthorpe town centre to Burton-Upon-Stather (4 miles) turn left in front of Sheffield Arms public house. From the bottom of the hill travel 250 yards, entrance to Brookside is on the right.
≉ Scunthorpe

SKEGNESS

Butlins, Butlins Skyline Limited, Skegness, Lincolnshire, PE25 1NJ
Tel: 01754 762311
Pitches For ♣ ♠ **Total** 50
Open May **to** October
Access Good **Site** Level
Nearest Bus Stop (Miles) Outside
Holiday resort with a beach!
Facilities 🚿 ♦ 💷 🕿 🗜 ⊙ ◻ ♥
🛊 🔌 ⊙ 🏕 ✗ ☕ 🍴 🏕 🎡 🔌 ◻
Nearby Facilities ↑ ✎ ∪ ⟱ ♪
Nearest Town Skegness
Directions From Skegness take the A52 sp Mablethorpe, site is at the edge of Skegness town.
≉ Skegness

SKEGNESS

Country Meadows Holiday Park, Anchor Lane, Ingoldmells, Skegness, Lincolnshire, PE25 1LZ
Tel: 01754 874455
Email: info@countrymeadows.co.uk
www.countrymeadows.co.uk
Pitches For Å ♣ ♠ **Total** 200
Acreage 10 **Open** March **to** October
Access Good **Site** Level
Nearest Bus Stop (Miles) Outside
5 minutes walk from the beach and a 10 minute walk to Fantasy Island. Adjacent to an animal farm.
Facilities ♦ 🛏 💷 🕿 🗜 ⊙ ⛟ 🔌 ◻ ♥
🛊 ⊙ 🏕 🔌 ◻ ✎
Nearby Facilities ↑ ✎ ⟱ ∪ ♪ ♪
Nearest Town Skegness
Directions On the A52 4 miles north of Skegness. ¾ miles out of Ingoldmells Village turn right into Anchor Lane, go 1 mile down toward the sea and the site is on the left hand side.
≉ Skegness

LINCOLNSHIRE

SKEGNESS

Homelands Caravan Park, Sea Road, Anderby, Skegness, Lincolnshire, PE24 5YB
Tel: 01507 490511
Email: homelandspark@gmail.com
www.ukcampsite.co.uk
Pitches For A ⛺ 🚐 **Total** 10
Acreage 1 **Open** March **to** November
Access Good **Site** Level
Quiet, friendly site in the countryside. Within walking distance of a sandy beach. 4 Berth Static Van also available for hire.
Facilities 🌀 ♿ 🛁 ⊙ 🍴 🍼 🅿 🔌 ⛽
Nearby Facilities ↾ ✈
Nearest Town Skegness/Mablethorpe
Directions Take the A52 Skegness to Mablethorpe road, approx. ¾ miles past Mumby (½ a mile past the B1449 junction) turn right on a sharp bend signposted Anderby, site is on the left in 1¼ miles.
🚾 Skegness/Mablethorpe

SKEGNESS

North Shore Holiday Centre, Elmhirst Avenue, Roman Bank, Skegness, Lincolnshire, PE25 1SL
Tel: 01754 763815
Email: reception@northshore-skegness.co.uk
www.northshore-skegness.co.uk
Pitches For ⛺ 🚐 **Total** 133
Open 01-Mar **to** 30-Nov
Access Good **Site** Level
Nearest Bus Stop (Miles) Outside
Just a short walk to both the beach and Skegness centre. Set well back from the main road, ideal family holiday base. Pitch & Putt and Miniature Golf on site. Camping Pods and all weather touring pitches now available. SORRY NO TENTS.
Facilities 🌀 ♿ 🛁 ⊙ 🍴 ⊙ 🍼 🅿
⛽ 🔌 ♿ ✖ 🍴 ⛽ 🅿
Nearby Facilities ↾ ✈ ⚓ ✈ U ⧖ ♪
Nearest Town Skegness
Directions A52 towards Mablethorpe, 500yds from the A158 junction.
🚾 Skegness

SKEGNESS

Pine Trees Leisure Park, Croft Bank, Skegness, Lincolnshire, PE24 4RE
Tel: 01754 762949
Email: enquiries@pinetreesholidays.co.uk
www.pinetreesholidays.co.uk
Pitches For A ⛺ 🚐 🚎 **Total** 150
Acreage 8 **Open** March **to** Nov
Access Good **Site** Level
Nearest Bus Stop (Miles) Outside
Landscaped fishing lakes and a 180 acre wetland conservation project with bird hides.
Facilities 🌀 ♿ 🛁 ⊙ 🍴 ⊙ 🍼 🅿
⛽ 🅿 ♿ ✖ 🍴 ⛽ 🅿 ✈ ↾ ♪
Nearby Facilities ↾ ✈ ⚓ ✈ U ♪
Nearest Town Skegness
Directions Take the A52 from Skegness (signposted Boston) for 1½ miles, turn right at right hand turning lane.
🚾 Skegness

SKEGNESS

Richmond Holiday Centre, Richmond Drive, Skegness, Lincolnshire, PE25 3TQ
Tel: 01754 762097
Email: sales@richmondholidays.com
www.richmondholidays.com
Pitches For ⛺ 🚐 **Total** 70
Open March **to** Nov
Access Good **Site** Level
Nearest Bus Stop (Miles) Outside
A short walk to the bustling resort of Skegness with funfairs, sandy beaches and donkey rides. Just a short drive from the

Wolds or the wild open scenery of Gibraltar Point Nature Reserve.
Facilities 🌀 ♿ 🛁 ⊙ 🍴 ⊙ 🍼 🅿 ⊙
⛽ 🅿 ⊙ ✖ 🍴 ⛽ 🅿 ✈ ❄ 🅿 ⛽ 🔌 ✈
Nearby Facilities ↾ ✈
Nearest Town Skegness
Directions Follow signs to the coach park on Richmond Drive, we are located approx. ½ a mile past the coach park on the right hand side.
🚾 Skegness

SKEGNESS

Riverside Caravan Park, Wainfleet Bank, Wainfleet, Skegness, Lincolnshire, PE24 4ND
Tel: 01754 880205
Pitches For A ⛺ 🚐 **Total** 30
Acreage 1¼ **Open** 15-Mar **to** 31-Oct
Access Good **Site** Level
Nearest Bus Stop (Miles) Entrance
Alongside a river. Golf 1 mile.
Facilities ♿ 🛁 ⊙ 🍴 ⊙ 🍼 🅿 ⊙ ❄
Nearby Facilities ↾ ✈ ⚒
Nearest Town Skegness
Directions From the A52 Boston to Skegness road, take the B1195 to Wainfleet All Saints by-pass, Site is 1 mile from the by-pass turn off.
🚾 Wainfleet

SKEGNESS

Ronam Cottage, Sea Road, Anderby, Skegness, Lincolnshire, PE24 5YA
Tel: 01507 490750
Pitches For A ⛺ 🚐
Acreage 1½ **Open** All Year
Access Good **Site** Level
Near to Anderby Creek and beach. Countryside walks. 2 hard standings available. Rally Field available. Trailer tents welcome. Camping & Caravanning Club site, non members welcome.
Facilities ♿ 🛁 ⊙ 🍴 🍼 ✈ 🔌
Nearby Facilities ↾ ✈ U
Nearest Town Skegness/Mablethorpe
Directions From Alford take the A1104 and turn onto the A1111 to Bilsby. Turn right onto the B1449 then left onto the A52, turn first right to Anderby. After 1½ miles turn left on the bend, site entrance is 50 yards on the right.
🚾 Skegness

SKEGNESS

Skegness Water Leisure Park, Walls Lane, Ingoldmells, Skegness, Lincolnshire, PE25 1JF
Tel: 01754 899400
Email: enquiries@skegnesswaterleisurepark.co.uk
www.skegnesswaterleisurepark.co.uk
Pitches For A ⛺ 🚐
Acreage 133 **Open** March **to** October
Access Good **Site** Level
Nearest Bus Stop (Miles) ¼
A rural setting with on site fishing and a water ski centre. Close to Butlins (day visitors allowed) and Fantasy Island. Near to beaches.
Facilities 🌀 ♿ 🛁 ⊙ 🍴 ⊙ 🍼 🅿 ⊙
⛽ 🅿 ⊙ ✖ 🍴 ⛽ 🅿 ✈ 🅿 ♪ ❄ ❄
Nearby Facilities ↾ U
Nearest Town Skegness
Directions From Skegness follow the A52 north (sp Mablethorpe) for 3 miles, turn left into Walls Lane at Cheers Pub, Park is ½ a mile on the left.
🚾 Skegness

SKEGNESS

Southview Holiday Park, Burgh Road, Skegness, Lincolnshire, PE25 2LA
Tel: 0843 309 2585
Email: southview@park-resorts.com
www.www.park-resorts.com
Pitches For ⛺ 🚐 **Total** 96
Open April **to** Oct
Nearest Bus Stop (Miles) Entrance
Near the beach.
Facilities 🌀 ♿ 🛁 ⊞ 🛁 ⊙ 🍴 ⊙ 🍼 🅿 ⊙
⛽ 🅿 ⊙ ✖ 🍴 ⛽ 🅿 ✈ ↾ ⊋ ❄ 🅿 ⊞ 🅿 ✈ ❄
❄
Nearby Facilities ↾ ✈ U ⧖ ♪
Nearest Town Skegness
🚾 Skegness

SKEGNESS

Topyard Farm Caravan Site, Croft Bank, Croft, Skegness, Lincolnshire, PE24 4RL
Tel: 01754 880189
Email: topyardfarm@gmail.com
Pitches For A ⛺ 🚐 **Total** 40
Acreage 1½ **Open** March **to** Nov
Access Good **Site** Level
Nearest Bus Stop (Miles) ¼
-
Facilities 🌀 ♿ 🛁 ⊙ 🍴 ⊙ 🍼 🅿
🅿 ⊙ 🍼 ⛽ ✈ 🅿 ❄ ⚒
Nearby Facilities ↾ ✈ U ♪
Nearest Town Skegness
Directions On the A52 Boston to Skegness road, 1 mile from Skegness.
🚾 Skegness

SLEAFORD

Low Farm Touring & Camping Park, Spring Lane, Folkingham, Sleaford, Lincolnshire, NG34 0SJ
Tel: 01529 497322
Email: lowfarmpark@sky.com
www.lowfarmpark.com
Pitches For A ⛺ 🚐 **Total** 36
Acreage 2¼ **Open** Easter **to** End Sept
Access Good **Site** Lev/Slope
Nearest Bus Stop (Miles) ¼
Facilities ♿ 🛁 ⊙ 🍴 ⊙ 🍼
🅿 ⊙ 🍼 ✈ 🅿 ❄ ⚒
Nearby Facilities ↾ ✈ U ♪
Nearest Town Sleaford
Directions 9 miles south of Sleaford on the A15. Go through village, turn right by the Village Hall.
🚾 Sleaford

SPALDING

Ashleigh Caravan Park, Ashleigh House, 45 Broadgate, Whaplode Drove, Spalding, Lincolnshire, PE12 0TN
Tel: 01406 330666
Email: ashleighcaravans@aol.com
Pitches For A ⛺ 🚐 **Total** 12
Acreage ¾ **Open** March **to** Nov
Access Good **Site** Level
Nearest Bus Stop (Miles) Outside
Quiet Camping & Caravan Club Site with two fishing lakes stocked with nine species. Convenient for Fenland attractions including the Spalding Flower Parade.
Facilities ♿ 🛁 ⊙ 🍴 ⊙ 🍼 ✈ 🅿 ⊞ 🅿 ✈
Nearby Facilities ↾ ✈ U
Nearest Town Spalding
Directions From Spalding take the A1073 towards Peterborough. After approx 8 miles turn left onto the B1166, after approx 3½ miles turn left into Broadgate, Whaplode Drove. Site is ¾ miles on the right.
🚾 Spalding

SPALDING

Delph Bank Touring Caravan Park, Old Main Road, Fleet Hargate, Holbeach, Nr Spalding, Lincolnshire, PE12 8LL
Tel: 01406 422910
Email: enquiries@delphbank.co.uk
www.delphbank.co.uk
Pitches For 🚐 🚙 **Total** 45
Acreage 3 **Open** All Year
Access Good **Site** Level
Nearest Bus Stop (Miles) ¼
ADULTS ONLY PARK. An attractive, quiet, tree lined site, convenient for touring the Fens and Lincolnshire/Norfolk coastal resorts. Pubs and eating places within walking distance. BH&HPA Member. ETB 4 Stars and David Bellamy Gold Award.
Facilities ⨍ 🛁 🆖 ⌖ ⌁ ⊙ ⬚ 🚿 🗑 📞 ⬚
▮ 🖂 🛒 🄳 🅿 🛆 ⚡
Nearby Facilities ⌖ 🚴
Nearest Town Holbeach
Directions From Kings Lynn take the A17, Turn left in the village of Fleet Hargate then right, site is on the left. From Spalding take the A151 to Holbeach, continue a further 3 miles to Fleet Hargate, turn right into the village and look for our sign on the right.
⚞ Spalding

SPALDING

Foremans Bridge Caravan Park, Sutton Road, Sutton St James, Spalding, Lincolnshire, PE12 0HU
Tel: 01945 440346
Email: formansbridge@btconnect.com
www.foremans-bridge.co.uk
Pitches For ▲ 🚐 🚙 🚍 **Total** 40
Acreage 2¾ **Open** 01-Mar **to** 15-Jan
Access Good **Site** Level
Nearest Bus Stop (Miles) Entrance
Alongside a river and a cycle route. Near to market towns.
Facilities ⨍ 🛁 🆖 ⌖ ⌁ ⊙ ⬚ 🚿 🗑 📞 ⬚
▮ 🖂 🛒 🄳 🅿 🛆 🚴 ⚡ ⚡
Nearby Facilities ⌖ 🚴 ⚓ 🛆 ⋔ ♞
Nearest Town Long Sutton
Directions From the A17 Holbeach to Kings Lynn road, take the B1390 at the roundabout to Sutton St James. Continue straight and the Site is on the left after approx 2 miles, immediately after the river bridge.
⚞ Spalding

SPALDING

Orchard View Caravan & Camping Park, 102 Broadgate, Sutton St Edmund, Nr Spalding, Lincolnshire, PE12 0LT
Tel: 01945 700482
Email: orchardview@hotmail.co.uk
www.orchardviewholidays.com
Pitches For ▲ 🚐 🚙 🚍 **Total** 38
Acreage 6 **Open** 10-Mar **to** 31-Oct

Access Good **Site** Level
Tranquil Fenland retreat in a unique landscape. Friendly family run park with all facilities and spacious plots. Ideal for touring or just relaxing. Numerous activities and places of interest nearby. You can also contact us on Mobile: 07891 223851.
Facilities ⨍ 🛁 🆖 ⌖ ⌁ ⊙ ⬚ 🚿 🗑 📞 ⬚
▮ ⊙ ⚒ ▽ 🄳 🛆 ⚡ 🅿 🄳 🄳 🚴 ⚡
Nearby Facilities ⌖ 🚴 ⚓ 🛆 ⋔ ⊙ ⚓ ♞
Nearest Town Wisbech
Directions From the A47 Peterborough to Wisbech road, turn left at the third roundabout (after McDonalds) sp Gedney Hill. After 2 miles turn right at the T-junction, turn third left into Broadgate and the Park is ½ a mile on the right.
⚞ March/Spalding

SPILSBY

Meadowlands, Monksthorpe, Great Steeping, Spilsby, Lincolnshire, PE23 5PP
Tel: 01754 830794
www.meadowlandslodgepark.co.uk
Pitches For ▲ 🚐 🚙 🚍 **Total** 20
Acreage 5 **Open** All Year
Access Good **Site** Level
Nearest Bus Stop (Miles) ½
Quiet ADULTS ONLY site in a rural setting. Ideal for walking and cycling. Handy for Skegness and the beautiful Wolds. 3 miles from Spilsby.
Facilities ⨍ 🛁 🆖 ⌖ ⌁ ⊙ ⬚ 🗑 📞
⊙ ⚒ 🖂 🛆 🚴 ⚡
Nearby Facilities ⌖ 🚴 ⊙
Nearest Town Skegness
Directions Take the A16 into Spilsby town then take the Wainfleet road, pass The Bell Inn and after approx. 1 mile turn left signposted Gunby and Heavy Horse Centre, Park is on the right after ¾ miles.
⚞ Wainfleet

STAMFORD

Road End Farm Caravan Site, Road End Farm, Toll Bar, Great Casterton, Stamford, Lincolnshire, PE9 4BB
Tel: 01780 763417
Email: sonnetcooper@aol.com
Pitches For ▲ 🚐 🚙 **Total** 30
Acreage 3 **Open** All Year
Access Good **Site** Gentle Slope
Nearest Bus Stop (Miles) ¼
ADULTS ONLY PARK. 5 miles from Rutland Water for fishing, sailing and other water sports. 3 miles from Burghley House for the Horse Trials. 7 miles from Tallington Lakes for water skiing, climbing and a ski slope. Cafe/Restaurant 100 metres away.
Facilities ⨍ 🆖 ⌖ 🗑 📞 🖂 🄳
Nearby Facilities ⌖ 🚴 ⚓ 🛆 ⊙ ⋔ ♞ ⚡
Nearest Town Stamford

Directions 1 mile north of Stamford on the B1081, turn right at sign for Little Casterton, site is 100 yards on the right.
⚞ Stamford

SUTTON-ON-SEA

Cherry Tree Site, Huttoft Road, Sutton-on-Sea, Lincolnshire, LN12 2RU
Tel: 01507 441626
Email: info@cherrytreesite.co.uk
www.cherrytreesite.co.uk
Pitches For 🚐 🚙 **Total** 60
Acreage 3 **Open** March **to** October
Access Good **Site** Level
Nearest Bus Stop (Miles) Outside
ADULTS ONLY SITE. Beach, golf course and Lincolnshire Wolds. ETB 5 Star Graded.
Facilities ⨍ 🛁 🆖 ⌖ ⌁ ⊙ ⬚ 🚿 🗑 📞 ⬚
▮ ⊙ ⚒ 🖂 🛆 🚴
Nearby Facilities ⌖ 🚴 ⊙ ♞
Nearest Town Sutton-on-Sea
Directions Take the A52 south from Sutton-on-Sea, 1½ miles on the left hand side. Entrance via a lay-by. Tourist Board signs on road.
⚞ Skegness

SUTTON-ON-SEA

Kirkstead Holiday Park, North Road, Trusthorpe, Sutton-on-Sea, Lincolnshire, LN12 2QD
Tel: 01507 441483
Email: mark@kirkstead.co.uk
www.kirkstead.co.uk
Pitches For ▲ 🚐 🚙 **Total** 60
Acreage 6 **Open** March **to** 01-Dec
Access Good **Site** Level
Nearest Bus Stop (Miles) ¼
10 minute walk to the beach. Clubhouse, new shower block. Familys welcome.
Facilities ⨍ 🛁 🆖 ⌖ ⌁ ⊙ ⬚ 🚿 🗑 📞 ⬚
▮ ⊙ ⚒ ✗ ▽ 🄳 ⚒ 🄳 🅿 🄳 🚴 ⚡
Nearby Facilities ⌖ 🚴 ⊙ ♞
Nearest Town Sutton-on-Sea
Directions Take the A52 coast road from Sutton to Mablethorpe, turn off left at Trusthorpe. Signposted from the A52.
⚞ Skegness

SUTTON-ON-SEA

Lakeside Caravan Park, Alford Road, Sutton-on-Sea, Lincolnshire, LN12 2RW
Tel: 01524 781453
Email: enquiries@pureleisure-holidays.co.uk
www.lakeside-caravanpark.co.uk
Pitches For 🚐 🚙 **Total** 12
Acreage 7 **Open** March **to** October
Access Good **Site** Level
Nearest Bus Stop (Miles) Entrance
Idyllic location around a private 4 acre fishing lake, lying just 1 mile north of the beautiful beaches of Sutton-on-Sea.

LINCOLNSHIRE, LONDON

Facilities ⚡ 🔌♨🅿️⊙🍴🚿🚮🛁🍴
🕎🚽🛒🍴🔲🏊‍♂️✏️❄️
Nearby Facilities ⛪🚴⛵⚓🏊‍♂️⛳🎿
Nearest Town Sutton-on-Sea
Directions From the A16 take the junction off the roundabout signposted Alford. Take the A111 towards Sutton-on-Sea and Lakeside is on the left after 5 miles.
🚃 Sutton-on-Sea

TATTERSHALL

Orchard Caravan Park, Chapel Hill, Witham Bank, Tattershall, Lincolnshire, LN4 4PZ
Tel: 01524 781453
Email: enquiries@pureleisure-holidays.co.uk
www.orchard-caravanpark.co.uk
Pitches For 🚐 🚙 **Total** 40
Acreage 5 **Open** Feb **to** Jan
Access Good **Site** Level
Nearest Bus Stop (Miles) Entrance
On the banks of the peaceful River Witham. Ideal spot from which to tour the Lincolnshire countryside. ½ hours drive from the seaside.
Facilities ⚡♨🍴⊙🍴🛁🍴
🕎🚽🛒🍴✖🍷🚽🍴♨🕎🍴❄️
Nearby Facilities ⛪🚴⛵⚓🏊‍♂️⛳🎿
Nearest Town Tattershall
Directions Travel through Tattershall on the A153, turn left after Tattershall Bridge and follow the riverbank to the Park.
🚃 Lincoln

TATTERSHALL

Willow Holt Caravan & Camping Park, Lodge Road, Tattershall, Lincolnshire, LN4 4JS
Tel: 01526 343111
Email: enquiries@willowholt.co.uk
www.willowholt.co.uk
Pitches For ⛺ 🚐 🚙 **Total** 100
Acreage 25 **Open** 15-Mar **to** 31-Oct
Access Good **Site** Level
Nearest Bus Stop (Miles) Outside
Peaceful site, all level pitches, abundant wildlife. Ten acres of fishing lakes on site, free to site occupants. New lakeside statics for sale or rent (occupancy 1 March to 5 Jan).
Facilities ⚡♨🔌♨🍴⊙🍴🛁🍴
🕎🚽🛒🍴✏️❄️🍴
Nearby Facilities ⛪🚴⛵⚓🏊‍♂️⛳🎿
Nearest Town Lincoln/Boston
Directions Take the A153 Sleaford/Skegness road, in Tattershall turn at the market place onto country road signposted Woodhall Spa. In 1½ miles site is on the left. Good wide entrance.

WAINFLEET

Holly Tree Pub & Caravan Park, Little Steeping Road, Thorpe Culvert, Wainfleet, Skegness, Lincolnshire, PE24 4QT
Tel: 01754 880490
Pitches For ⛺ 🚐 🚙 **Total** 70
Acreage 6 **Open** March **to** Nov
Access Good **Site** Level
Set in the heart of rural Lincolnshire alongside the River Steeping. Excellent fishing on and off site. Ideal for touring, 15 minutes from the coast. Family Pub on site.
Facilities ⚡♨🍴🔌♨🍴⊙🍴🍴
🕎🚽🛒🍷♨🍴🚽🍴✏️❄️🍴
Nearby Facilities ⛪🚴⛵⚓
Nearest Town Skegness
Directions Go from Wainfleet All Saints to Thorpe St. Peter, then to Thorpe Culvert Railway station, Little Steeping Road go over the river and onto Holly Tree.
🚃 Wainfleet

WOODHALL SPA

Camping & Caravanning Club Site, Wellsyke Lane, Kirkby-on-Bain, Woodhall Spa, Lincolnshire, LN10 6YU
Tel: 01526 352911
www.campingandcaravanningclub.co.uk/woodhallspa
Pitches For ⛺ 🚐 🚙 **Total** 90
Acreage 6½ **Open** 29-Mar **to** 05-Nov
Access Good **Site** Level
Nearest Bus Stop (Miles) 1
A nature lovers dream with many varieties of birds seen on site. Dish washing facilities. BTB 5 Star Graded, David Bellamy Gold Award and AA 3 Pennants. Non members welcome.
Facilities ♿⚡🔌♨🍴⊙🍴🛁🍴
🕎🚽🛒🍴🔲📶
Nearby Facilities ⛪
Nearest Town Horncastle
Directions From Sleaford or Horncastle take the A153 to Haltham. At the garage turn left towards Kirkby-on-Bain. At the Ebrington Arms turn right, site is 1 mile.
🚃 Metheringham

WOODHALL SPA

Glen Lodge Touring Park, Glen Lodge, Edlington Moor, Woodhall Spa, Lincolnshire, LN10 6UL
Tel: 01526 353523
Pitches For 🚐 🚙 **Total** 35
Acreage 3 **Open** March **to** November
Access Good **Site** Level
Nearest Bus Stop (Miles) 1
Ideal for the woods, the Battle of Britain Memorial Flight, Tattershall Castle and Horncastle (with its antiques).
Facilities ♿⚡🔌♨🍴⊙🍴🔲🍴
⊙🍴🚽🛒♨
Nearby Facilities ⛪🚴⛳⚓🎿
Nearest Town Woodhall Spa
Directions From the mini roundabout in the village turn northeast towards Bardney, after 1 mile turn left, turn right after the bend and the site is 300 yards on the left.
🚃 Metheringham

LONDON (Greater)

ABBEY WOOD

Abbey Wood Caravan Club Site, Federation Rd, Abbey Wood, London, SE2 0LS
Tel: 020 8311 7708
www.caravanclub.co.uk
Pitches For ⛺ 🚐 🚙 **Total** 220
Acreage 9 **Open** All Year
Access Good **Site** Lev/Slope
Nearest Bus Stop (Miles) ½
Spacious site screened by mature trees. Within walking distance of railway link to central London for its attractions. Near the London Eye, Thames Barrier and Splash World at Woolwich. Non members welcome. Booking essential.
Facilities ⚡🔲🔌♨🍴⊙🍴🔲🍴
🕎🚽🛒🍴🔲♨
Nearby Facilities ⛪🚴⚓🎿
Directions From central London on A2 turn off at A221 jct into Danson Rd, follow signs for Bexleyheath to Crook Log (A207 jct). At lights turn right and immediately left into Brampton Rd. After 1½ miles at lights turn left into Bostal Rd (A206), at lights turn right into Basildon Rd (B213). In 300yds turn right into McLeod Rd, at roundabout turn right into Knee Hill, turn second right into Federation Rd, site is 50yds on the left.
🚃 Abbey Wood

CHINGFORD

Lee Valley Campsite, Sewardstone Road, Chingford, London, E4 7RA
Tel: 020 8529 5689

Email: scs@leevalleypark.org.uk
www.leevalleypark.org.uk/wheretostay
Pitches For ⛺ 🚐 🚙 **Total** 200
Acreage 14 **Open** 01-Mar **to** 31-Jan
Access Good **Site** Lev/Slope
Nearest Bus Stop (Miles) Outside
Very close to London and historical Waltham Abbey.
Facilities ♿⚡🔌♨🍴⊙🍴🔲🍴
🕎🚽🛒🍴🔲
Nearby Facilities ⛪🚴⚓
Nearest Town Chingford
Directions From Chingford take the A379.
🚃 Chingford

CRYSTAL PALACE

Crystal Palace Caravan Club Site, Crystal Palace Parade, London, SE19 1UF
Tel: 020 8778 7155
www.caravanclub.co.uk
Pitches For ⛺ 🚐 🚙 **Total** 126
Acreage 6 **Open** March **to** Jan
Access Good **Site** Level
Nearest Bus Stop (Miles) ¼
On the edge of a pleasant park. Ideal for the sights of central London which is easily accessible by public transport (Travelcards sold on site April to November). Non members welcome. Booking essential.
Facilities ♿⚡🔲🔌♨🍴⊙🍴🔲🍴
🕎🚽🛒🍴🔲📶
Nearby Facilities
Directions Site entrance is off the A212 at the junction of Crystal Palace Parade and Westwood Hill.
🚃 Crystal Palace

EDMONTON

Lee Valley Camping & Caravan Park, Meridian Way, Edmonton, London, N9 0AS
Tel: 020 8803 6900
Email: leisurecomplex@leevalleypark.org.uk
www.leevalleypark.org.uk/wheretostay
Pitches For ⛺ 🚐 🚙 🍴
Nearest Bus Stop (Miles) Outside
Direct buses, trains and tubes to London and the West End. Golf course and athletics centre on site, plus a cinema.
Facilities ⚡🔌♨🍴⊙🍴🔲🍴
🕎🚽🛒✖🔲🔲🍴
Nearby Facilities ⛪🚴⚓
Nearest Town London
Directions Exit the M25 at junction 25 and follow signs to the city on the A10. Follow signs to Freezywater A1055. Continue for 6 miles and follow signs to Lee Valley Leisure Complex.
🚃 Edmonton Green

LOUGHTON

The Elms Caravan & Camping Park, Lippitts Hill, High Beach, Loughton, Essex, IG10 4AW
Tel: 020 8502 5652
Email: info@theelmscampsite.co.uk
www.theelmscampsite.co.uk
Pitches For ⛺ 🚐 🚙 **Total** 50
Acreage 3 **Open** March **to** Oct
Access Good **Site** Level
Nearest Bus Stop (Miles) ½
A forest location with small wildlife and many varieties of birds, deer, etc.. Motorcycles welcome.
Facilities ♿⚡🔲🔌♨🍴⊙🍴🔲🍴
🕎🍴🔲🚽🛒✖🍴🔲❄️📶♨🍴
Nearby Facilities ⛪🚴⚓🏊‍♂️⛳🎿
Nearest Town Loughton
Directions There is an Elms link from the station. If travelling by road The Elms is in between the A104 Epping New Road and the A112 Seawardstone Road.
🚃 Loughton

MANCHESTER (Greater)

LITTLEBOROUGH

LITTLEBOROUGH
Hollingworth Lake Caravan Park, Round House Farm, Rakewood, Littleborough, Manchester, OL15 0AS
Tel: 01706 378661
Pitches For 🏕 🚐 🚙 **Total** 45
Acreage 3 **Open** All Year
Access Good **Site** Level
Nearest Bus Stop (Miles) 1
Near a large lake that covers 120 acres. Cafe/Restaurant nearby.
Facilities 🚿 ✆ 🖩 🍴 ⊙ ⌂ 🚮 ▣ ☎
⚍ 🖲 🛒 🖵
Nearby Facilities ⌐ ✠ ⚓ ✦ ∪
Nearest Town Rochdale
Directions Leave the M62 at junction 21, Milnrow B6255. Follow Hollingworth Lake Country Park signs to The Fishermans Inn/ The Wine Press. Take Rakewood Road, then the second on the right.
🚉 Littleborough

MERSEYSIDE

KIRBY
Wirral Country Park Caravan Club Site, Station Road, Thurstaston, Wirral, Merseyside, CH61 0HN
Tel: 01516 485228
www.caravanclub.co.uk
Pitches For 🚐 🚙 **Total** 93
Acreage 8 **Open** March to Nov
Access Good **Site** Level
Set in an area of great natural beauty with sea views. Easy access to the Dee Estuary. Several sports and water sports enthusiasts. Several swimming pools and sports centres nearby. Non members welcome. Booking essential.
Facilities ✆ 🖩 🍴 ⌂ ▣ ☎
🖲 ⊙ 🛒 🖵 🛜
Nearby Facilities ⌐ ✠
Nearest Town Thurstaston
Directions Exit M6 onto M56 westbound, at the end turn left sp Queensferry. At the roundabout turn right onto A540 and stay on this road ignoring signs for Wirral Country Park. Just past Heswall at crossroads in Thurstaston turn left into Station Rd, after 150yds turn right and keep left. After ¾ mile (immediately after bridge) turn right in to site road. Site on left.
🚉 Thurstaston

NORFOLK

ACLE
Broad Farm Trailer Park, Fleggburgh, Burgh St Margaret, Great Yarmouth, Norfolk, NR29 3AF
Tel: 01493 369273
Pitches For 🏕 🚐 🚙 **Total** 350
Acreage 30 **Open** Easter to 30-Sep
Access Good **Site** Level
Situated in the countryside. Ideal for visiting Norfolks many attractions.
Facilities ✆ 🖩 🍴 ⌂ 🚮 ▣ ☎
🖲 ⊙ 🛒 🖵 ⚓ 🛝 ✦ 🖵 ⚍ 🍴 ☀
Nearby Facilities ⌐ ✠ ⚓
Nearest Town Great Yarmouth
Directions 7 miles from Great Yarmouth taking the A1064 when you reach Caister-on-Sea.
🚉 Acle

BURGH ST. PETER
Waveney River Centre, Staithe Road, Burgh St Peter, Norfolk, NR34 0BT
Tel: 01502 677343
Email: info@waveneyrivercentre.co.uk
www.waveneyrivercentre.co.uk
Pitches For 🏕 🚐 🚙 **Total** 48
Open All Year **Access** Poor **Site** Lev/Slope
Nearest Bus Stop (Miles) ¾
Alongside the River Waveney. New showers for 2010 with underfloor heating.
Facilities 🚿 ✆ 🖩 🍴 ⌂ 🚮 ▣ ☎
🖲 ⊙ 🛒 ✗ 🍴 ⚓ 🛝 ✦ 🖵 ⚍ ✦ 🛜
Nearby Facilities ⌐ ✠ ⚓ ∪
Nearest Town Beccles
Directions From the A143 at Haddiscoe, turn into Wiggs Road following brown tourism signs. After 2 miles turn left into Burgh Road and the site is 2½ miles.
🚉 Haddiscoe

CAISTER-ON-SEA
Caister Holiday Park, Ormesby Road, Caister-on-Sea, Norfolk, NR30 5NH
Tel: 01493 728931
Email: caister@haven.com
www.haventouring.com/tocaister
Pitches For 🚐 🚙 **Total** 46
Open Mid March to End Oct
Access Good **Site** Level
Nearest Bus Stop (Miles) Entrance
A lively and popular Holiday Park, next to the beach and near to the Norfolk Broads. Perfect for kids clubs, family entertainment and fantastic water fun.
Facilities ✆ 🖩 🍴 ⌂ 🚮 ▣ ☎
🖲 ⚍ ✗ ∪ ⚓ 🛝 🍴 ✦
Nearest Town Great Yarmouth
Directions From the A47 Norwich (Eastbound) follow signs towards Great Yarmouth. At Acle take the second exit off the roundabout onto the A1064 sp Caister-on-Sea. At the next roundabout take the second exit onto the A149, next roundabout take the first exit onto the Caister by-pass. At the third roundabout take the third exit which will lead you into Caister-on-Sea. The Park is on your left. NB: If using Sat Nav use the street name rather than the postcode.
🚉 Great Yarmouth

CAISTER-ON-SEA
Grasmere Caravan Park, Bultitudes Loke, Yarmouth Road, Caister-on-Sea, Great Yarmouth, Norfolk, NR30 5DH
Tel: 01493 720382
www.grasmere-wentworth.co.uk
Pitches For 🚐 🚙 **Total** 46
Acreage 2 **Open** April to Mid October
Access Good **Site** Level
Nearest Bus Stop (Miles) ¼
½ a mile from the beach, 3 miles to centre of Great Yarmouth. Advance bookings taken for touring site pitches. Each pitch with its own electric, water tap and foul water drain. Some hard standings.
Facilities 🚿 ✆ 🖩 🍴 ⌂ 🚮 ▣ ☎
🖲 ⊙ 🛒 🖵 ▦
Nearby Facilities ⌐ ✠ ⚓ ✦ ♪
Nearest Town Great Yarmouth
Directions Enter Caister from roundabout near Yarmouth Stadium at Yarmouth end of bypass. After ½ mile turn sharp left just before the bus stop.
🚉 Great Yarmouth

CLIPPESBY
Clippesby Hall, Clippesby, Norfolk, NR29 3BL
Tel: 01493 367800
Email: holidays@clippesby.com
www.clippesby.com
Pitches For 🏕 🚐 🚙 **Total** 100
Acreage 30 **Open** All Year
Access Good **Site** Level
Nearest Bus Stop (Miles) Outside
Set in the heart of the Norfolk Broads National Park. Near to nature reserves and tourist attractions. Bellamy Gold Award for Conservation.

Facilities 🚿 ✆ 🖩 🍴 ⌂ 🚮 ▣ ☎
🚱 🖲 🛒 ✗ ∪ ⚓ 🛝 ✦ 🖵 🍴 🛜
Nearby Facilities ⌐ ✠ ∪ ♪
Nearest Town Great Yarmouth
Directions From the A47 Norwich bypass follow tourism signs to the The Broads. At Acle take the A1064, after 2½ miles turn left onto the B1152, after ½ a mile turn left at the Clippesby Village sign, after 400 yards turn right.
🚉 Acle

CROMER
Manor Farm Caravan & Camping Site, Manor Farm, East Runton, Cromer, Norfolk, NR27 9PR
Tel: 01263 512858
Email: manor-farm@ukf.net
www.manorfarmcaravansite.co.uk
Pitches For 🏕 🚐 🚙 **Total** 230
Acreage 16 **Open** Easter to October
Access Good **Site** Lev/Slope
Panoramic sea and woodland views. Spacious, quiet, family run farm site. Ideal for families. Separate field for dog owners.
Facilities 🚿 ☕ ✆ 🖩 🍴 ⌂ 🚮 ▣ ☎
⊙ 🚱 🖵▣
Nearby Facilities ⌐ ✠ ⚓ ∪ ♪
Nearest Town Cromer
Directions Signposted Manor Farm from the A148 and the A149. The A149 is the preferable route if towing.
🚉 Cromer

CROMER
West Runton Camping & Caravanning Club Site, Holgate Lane, West Runton, Cromer, Norfolk, NR27 9NW
Tel: 01263 837544
www.campingandcaravanningclub.co.uk/westrunton
Pitches For 🏕 🚐 🚙 **Total** 200
Acreage 15 **Open** 29-Mar to 05-Nov
Access Difficult **Site** Lev/Slope
Nearest Bus Stop (Miles) ½
Panoramic view of the countryside. Just 1 mile from the sea. Boules pitch on site. BTB 4 Star Graded and AA 4 Pennants. Non members welcome. You can also call us on 0845 130 7633.
Facilities 🚿 ✆ 🖩 🍴 ⌂ 🚮 ▣ ☎
🖲 ⊙ 🚱 ⚍ ▣ 🖵 ☀
Nearby Facilities ⌐ ✠ ⚓ ∪ ♪
Nearest Town Cromer
Directions Take the A148 from Kings Lynn, on approaching West Runton turn left at the Roman Camp Inn, ½ a mile along the track, on the crest of the hill, is the site entrance.
🚉 West Runton

CROMER
Woodhill Park, Cromer Road, East Runton, Cromer, Norfolk, NR27 9PX
Tel: 01263 512242
Email: info@woodhill-park.com
www.woodhill-park.com
Pitches For 🏕 🚐 🚙 🚙 **Total** 300
Acreage 32 **Open** March to Oct
Access Good **Site** Lev/Slope
Nearest Bus Stop (Miles) Outside
Peace and tranquillity with views of the sea and surrounding countryside. A choice of pitch styles and excellent amenity buildings. Rose Award.
Facilities 🚿 ✆ 🖩 🍴 ⌂ 🚮 ▣ ☎
🚱 🖲 ⊙ 🚱 🛒 ✦ 🖵 ▣ 🖵 ☀
Nearby Facilities ⌐ ✠ ⚓ ∪ ♪
Nearest Town Cromer
Directions Set between East and West Runton on the seaside of the A149 Cromer to Sheringham road.
🚉 West Runton

NORTH NORFOLK... *naturally*

Woodhill Park

Relax and enjoy peace and tranquillity with magnificent views of the sea and surrounding North Norfolk countryside.

Touring & camping pitches with multi-service, electric pitches and amenity buildings – including family bathroom and family shower rooms

Enjoy the North Norfolk coast & countryside at your leisure, Woodhill is well placed to take in the delights this unspoilt region has to offer.

Luxury caravan holiday homes to hire many of which overlook the sea. Each has central heating and TV, linen is supplied.

Bookings or **brochure 01263 512242** or online **www.woodhill-park.com**
Woodhill Park, Cromer Road, East Runton, Cromer, Norfolk NR27 9PX

DISS

The Willows Camping & Caravan Park, Diss Road, Scole, Diss, Norfolk, IP21 4DH
Tel: 01379 740271
Pitches For △ ♨ ♨ **Total** 32
Acreage 8 **Open** Easter **to** Mid Oct
Access Good **Site** Level
Nearest Bus Stop (Miles) ¼
Alongside the River Waveney.
Facilities ♒ ♓ ⅏ ♐ ♑ ⊙ ⌇ ♨ ♥
⚏ ⊙ ⌖ ✵⌗ ⊟ ♫ ╱ ╱╲
Nearby Facilities ⌐
Nearest Town Diss
Directions 1½ miles east of Diss on the A1066.
⇶ Diss

DISS

Waveney Valley Holiday Park, Airstation Farm, Airstation Lane, Rushall, Diss, Norfolk, IP21 4QF
Tel: 01379 741690
Email: waveneyvalleyhp@aol.com
www.caravanparksnorfolk.co.uk
Pitches For △ ♨ ♨ ♨ **Total** 45
Acreage 4 **Open** April **to** October
Access Good **Site** Level
Nearest Bus Stop (Miles) ¼
Family run site in a rural position. Horse riding for all ages and abilities on site. Good fishing locally.
Facilities ♒ ♓ ⅏ ♐ ♑ ⊙ ⌇ ♨ ♥
⚏ ⊙ ⌖ ✵ ⊟ ⋀ ⌗ ✵⊟ ⊟ ⊡
Nearby Facilities ⌐ ╱ ╱ ⚓ ╲ ∪ ∂ ♪ ⌇
Nearest Town Harleston
Directions From Diss take the A140, at Dickleburgh in Rushall turn at telephone box towards Pulham, turn into Airstation Lane and site is on the right.
⇶ Diss

DOCKING

The Garden Caravan Site, Barmer Hall Farm, Syderstone, Kings Lynn, Norfolk, PE31 8SR
Tel: 01485 578220/178
Email: nigel@mason96.fsnet.co.uk
www.gardencaravansite.co.uk
Pitches For △ ♨ ♨ **Total** 30
Open March **to** November
Access Good **Site** Lev/Slope
A lovely secluded and sheltered site in a walled garden. Close to the famous North Norfolk coast.
Facilities ♒ ♓ ⅏ ♐ ♑ ⊙ ⌇ ♨ ♥
⚏ ⊙ ♨⌗ ⊟
Nearby Facilities ⌐ ╱ ╱ ⚓ ╲ ∪ ∂
Nearest Town Fakenham
Directions From Fakenham or Kings Lynn take the A148, then take the B1454 towards Hunstanton, 4 miles on the right hand side.

DOWNHAM MARKET

Grange Farm Touring Park, Whittington Hill, Whittington, Kings Lynn, Norfolk, PE33 9TF
Tel: 01366 500075
Email:
relax@grangefarmtouringpark.co.uk
www.grangefarmtouringpark.co.uk
Pitches For ♨ ♨
Open February **to** Dec

Access Good **Site** Level
Nearest Bus Stop (Miles) Outside
Alongside a river for fishing and boating. Only suitable for adults. Within 1 hours drive of Hunstanton, Sheringham and Cromer.
Facilities ⚓ ♓ ⅏ ♐ ♑ ⌇ ♨ ♥ ⚏✵╱ ⚓
Nearby Facilities ⌐
Nearest Town Downham Market
Directions Just off the A134.
⇶ Downham Market

FAKENHAM

Fakenham Racecourse Caravan Club Site, Pudding Norton, Fakenham, Norfolk, NR21 7NY
Tel: 01328 862388
Email:
caravan@fakenhamracecourse.co.uk
www.fakenhamracecourse.co.uk
Pitches For △ ♨ ♨ **Total** 116
Acreage 11½ **Open** All Year
Access Good **Site** Level
Ideal site for a relaxing or active holiday, in comfortable and picturesque surroundings. Local attractions include Norfolk Broads, Sandringham House, Holkham Hall, Thursford Steam Engine Collection and Pensthorpe Waterfowl Park. Non members welcome. Booking essential.
Facilities ⚓ ♓ ⅏ ♐ ♑ ⊙ ⌇ ♨ ♥
⚏ ⊙ ⌖⌗⊟ ⊟ ╱╲
Nearby Facilities ⌐ ╱ ∪ ∂
Nearest Town Fakenham
Directions On approaching Fakenham from all directions, follow "Campsite" and international caravan/camping signs, they all refer to this site.
⇶ Kings Lynn

FAKENHAM

Greenwoods Campsite, Old Fakenham Road, Tattersett, Kings Lynn, Norfolk, PE31 8RS
Tel: 07917 842371
Email: mike@greenwoodscampsite.co.uk
www.greenwoodscampsite.co.uk
Pitches For △ ♨ ♨
Acreage 1 **Open** Mid March **to** Oct
Access Good **Site** Sloping
Nearest Bus Stop (Miles) ¼
All pitches are very spacious and properly marked. Public footpath adjacent to the site, excellent for walking and biking.
Facilities ⚓ ♓ ⅏ ♐ ♑ ⊙ ⌇ ♨ ⊞ ♥ ⋀⌗⊟ ╱╲
Nearby Facilities ⌐ ╱ ⚓ ╲ ∂
Nearest Town Fakenham
Directions From Fakenham take the A148 west for 4 miles, turn left at the Coxford sign, turn left again onto Old Fakenham Road and the site entrance is on the right.
⇶ Kings Lynn

FAKENHAM

The Old Brick Kilns, Little Barney Lane, Barney, Fakenham, Norfolk, NR21 0NL
Tel: 01328 878305
Email: enquiries@old-brick-kilns.co.uk
www.old-brick-kilns.co.uk
Pitches For △ ♨ ♨ **Total** 65
Acreage 13 **Open** 12-Mar **to** 04-Jan
Access Good **Site** Level
Nearest Bus Stop (Miles) 1

Beaches within 20 minutes drive. Near to Sandringham, Blicking Hall, Pensthorpe Nature Reserve, Thursford, Walsingham and Norwich. Strictly no arrivals til after 1.30pm due to narrow access lane. NB: Money Off Vouchers will NOT be accepted on Bank Holidays.
Facilities ⚓ ♓ ⊟ ⅏ ♐ ♑ ⊙ ⌇ ♨ ⊡ ♥
⚏ ⚉ ⊙ ♨ ⌖ ⟟ ⋀ ⋈⌗⊟ ⊟ ╱ ╱╲ ⚓
Nearby Facilities ⌐ ╱ ⚓ ╲ ∪ ∂
Nearest Town Fakenham
Directions From the A148 Fakenham to Cromer road, take the B1354 to Melton Constable. After 300 yards turn right to Barney, then turn first left down Little Barney Lane, Park is at the end in ¾ miles.
⇶ Kings Lynn

GREAT HOCKHAM

Thetford Forest Camping & Caravanning Club Site, Puddledock Farm, Great Hockham, Thetford, Norfolk, IP24 1PA
Tel: 01953 498455
www.campingandcaravanningclub.co.uk/thetfordforest
Pitches For △ ♨ ♨ **Total** 80
Acreage 12 **Open** All Year
Access Good **Site** Level
Nearest Bus Stop (Miles) ½
Very quiet site backing onto the forest, with a network of paths and picnic areas which provide an abundance of birds and wildlife. Sculpture Trail and Go Ape High Wire Adventure. Camping Pods available for hire. Non members welcome. You can also call us on 0845 130 7633.
Facilities ♒ ♓ ⅏ ♐ ♑ ⊙ ⌇ ♨ ⊡ ♥
⚏ ⊙ ⚉ ⊟ ⋀ ⋈⌗⊟ ⊟ ╱ ╱╲ ⚓ ⌇
Nearby Facilities ⌐ ╱ ∪ ⌇
Nearest Town Watton
Directions Midway between Thetford and Watton on the A1075. Turn left at 83 past Forestry Commission picnic site, no roadside sign.
⇶ Thetford

GREAT YARMOUTH

Breydon Water Holiday Park, Butt Lane, Burgh Castle, Great Yarmouth, Norfolk, NR31 9QB
Tel: 0843 309 2550
Email: holidaysales.breydonwater@park-resorts.com
www.park-resorts.com
Pitches For △ ♨ ♨ **Total** 209
Acreage 20 **Open** April **to** October
Access Good **Site** Level
Nearest Bus Stop (Miles) ½
Set in countryside yet only ten minutes from Great Yarmouth. Two bars with entertainment, amusements, swimming pool with slide, Kids Club and play area.
Facilities ♒ ♓ ⅏ ♐ ♑ ⊙ ⌇ ♨ ⊡ ♥
⚏ ⚏ ⊙ ⚉ ⊟ ⌖ ⟟ ⋀ ⋈ ⟟ ✵ ♨⌗⊟ ⊟ ╱╲
Nearby Facilities ⌐ ╱ ⚓ ╲ ∂
Nearest Town Great Yarmouth
Directions From Great Yarmouth follow signs for Lowestoft, after the third roundabout look for the sign for Burgh Castle. Follow for 2½ miles to the T-junction and follow brown tourism signs.
⇶ Great Yarmouth

GREAT YARMOUTH

Burgh Castle Marina, Butt Lane, Burgh Castle, Norfolk, NR31 9PZ
Tel: 01493 780331
Email: info@burghcastlemarina.co.uk
www.burghcastlemarina.co.uk
Pitches For Δ ⊕ ⊕ **Total** 45
Acreage 19
Open Easter **to** Oct
Access Good **Site** Level
Nearest Bus Stop (Miles) ¼
Riverside location, easy stroll to the magnificent Roman ruins and spectacular marshland views. RSPB Reserves nearby. Exhibition on the area in the parks reception.
Facilities ...
Nearby Facilities ...
Nearest Town Gorleston-on-Sea
Directions Approach on the A143 Beccles to Great Yarmouth road. 2 miles south of the A12 intersection follow brown marina signs

to Belton. After ¾ miles turn right for Burgh Castle.
⇌ Great Yarmouth

GREAT YARMOUTH

Burgh Hall, Burgh Hall Leisure Complex, Lords Lane, Burgh Castle, Great Yarmouth, Norfolk, NR31 9EP
Tel: 01493 780365
www.burgh-hall.co.uk
Pitches For Δ ⊕ ⊕
Open Easter **to** Oct
Access Good **Site** Level
Nearest Bus Stop (Miles) ¼
Near the beach. Swimming pool and clunhouse on site.
Facilities ...
Nearby Facilities ...
Nearest Town Great Yarmouth
⇌ Great Yarmouth

GREAT YARMOUTH

Drewery Caravan Park, California Road, California, Gt. Yarmouth, Norfolk, NR29 3QW
Tel: 01493 730845
Pitches For Δ ⊕ ⊕ **Total** 135
Acreage 4 **Open** Easter **to** October
Access Good **Site** Level
Nearest Bus Stop (Miles) ¼
Near the beach. Ideal for Norfolk Broads and Great Yarmouth.
Facilities ...
Nearby Facilities ...
Nearest Town Great Yarmouth
Directions Take the A149 from Great Yarmouth, at the Greyhound Stadium roundabout turn left, at next roundabout take the second exit onto the B1159. Go to roundabout and take the second exit, after ¼ mile turn right into California Road and follow to the end. Site is opposite California tavern. 6 miles from Great Yarmouth.
⇌ Great Yarmouth

GREAT YARMOUTH

Great Yarmouth Racecourse Caravan Club Site, Jellicoe Road, Great Yarmouth, Norfolk, NR30 4AU
Tel: 01493 855223
www.caravanclub.co.uk
Pitches For 🚐 🚙 **Total** 115
Acreage 5¼ **Open** March **to** Nov
Access Good **Site** Level
Nearest Bus Stop (Miles) Outside
300yds from the lively seafront. Adjacent to a racecourse and golf course. Near the Norfolk Broads and Pleasurewood Hills. Dogs on leads at all times. Non members welcome. Booking essential.
Facilities ♿ ⚡ 🍳 🛁 💷 🏪 🍴 ⓘ 🏧 🛒
Nearby Facilities ⌐ ✓ ⚓ ⚘
Nearest Town Great Yarmouth
Directions From north on the A149, at the traffic lights on the south outskirts of Caister turn left into Jellicoe Road. After ¼ mile turn left into the Racecourse entrance (BEWARE of blind turning), go across the racetrack to the site.
⇌ Great Yarmouth

GREAT YARMOUTH

Pampas Lodge Holiday Park, The Street (A143), Haddiscoe, Norfolk, NR14 6AA
Tel: 01502 677265
Email: colinshirley@btinternet.com

Pitches For ⛺ 🚐 🚙 **Total** 60
Acreage 3 **Open** April **to** October
Access Good **Site** Level
Nearest Bus Stop (Miles) Outside
Good touring site for the Norfolk Broads, River Waveney, Great Yarmouth and Gorleston. Near beaches.
Facilities ♿ ⚡ 🍳 🚿 🍴 ⚡ ⓘ 🏧 💷 ✂
Nearby Facilities ⌐ ✓ ⚓ ⚘
Nearest Town Great Yarmouth
Directions On the A143 between Beccles and Great Yarmouth. Behind Haddiscoe Tavern Pub in the village.
⇌ Haddiscoe

GREAT YARMOUTH

Rose Farm Touring & Camping Park, Stepshort, Belton, Great Yarmouth, Norfolk, NR31 9JS
Tel: 01493 780896
Email: myhra@rosefarmtouringpark.co.uk
www.rosefarmtouringpark.co.uk
Pitches For ⛺ 🚐 🚙 **Total** 120
Acreage 10 **Open** All Year
Access Good **Site** Level
Nearest Bus Stop (Miles) ¼
A clean site in peaceful surroundings. Special offers for over 50s.
Facilities ♿ ⚡ 🍳 🚿 🍴 ⚡ ⓘ 🏧 💷 🚻 🏪 🛒 ✂ 📶
Nearby Facilities ⌐ ✓ ⚓ ⚘ ∪ ⚓ ♟

Nearest Town Gorleston
Directions From Great Yarmouth on the bypass take the A143 to Beccles, through Bradwell up to the small dual carriageway. Turn right into new road signposted Belton and Burgh Castle. Down New Road first right at Stepshort, site is first on right.
⇌ Great Yarmouth

GREAT YARMOUTH

The Grange Touring Park, Yarmouth Road, Ormesby St Margaret, Great Yarmouth, Norfolk, NR29 3QG
Tel: 01493 730306
Email: info@grangetouring.co.uk
www.grangetouring.co.uk
Pitches For ⛺ 🚐 🚙 **Total** 70
Acreage 3½ **Open** Easter **to** End Sept
Access Good **Site** Level
Nearest Bus Stop (Miles) ¼
Rural, sheltered site, very convenient for Great Yarmouth and the Norfolk Broads.
Facilities ♿ ⚡ 🍳 🚿 🍴 ⚡ 🛒 ⓘ 🏧 💷 🏪 🛒 📶
Nearby Facilities ⌐ ✓ ⚓ ⚘ ∪
Nearest Town Great Yarmouth
Directions 2 miles north of Great Yarmouth, by the roundabout on the B1159 at the north end of Caister bypass.
⇌ Great Yarmouth

VISIT **www.cades.co.uk** TO SEE OUR MONTHLY COMPETITION

Relax and enjoy the best of North Norfolk

Award-winning Kelling Heath offers a beautiful, natural environment with pitches set amongst rare open heathland with a backdrop of native woodland and pine. Connect with nature... come to Kelling.

Activities
- Woodland walks & nature trails
- Guided walks & events
- Cycle Routes on & off park
- Trim trail, orienteering, petanque and adventure play

Relax
- Health & Fitness Club with indoor pool
- Free outdoor leisure pool
- The Forge: bars, restaurants, take-away
- Village Store
- The Folly open air jazz, folk

We also offer lodges and luxurious holiday homes.

Bookings or brochure 01263 588181
or online www.kellingheath.co.uk
Kelling Heath, Weybourne, Holt, Norfolk NR25 7HW

KELLING HEATH
THE NATURAL ESCAPE

NORFOLK

GREAT YARMOUTH

Vauxhall Holiday Park, Acle New Road, Great Yarmouth, Norfolk, NR30 1TB
Tel: 01493 857231
Email: info@vauxhallholidays.co.uk
www.vauxhall-holiday-park.co.uk
Pitches For A ⌗ ⌗ **Total** 213
Acreage 48 **Open** Easter then Mid May to Sept
Access Good **Site** Level
Nearest Bus Stop (Miles) Outside
Ideal centre for attractions of Great Yarmouth and for exploring the famous Norfolk Broads. 13 Super Pitches available.
Facilities 🖆 ⨍ 🄵 🖵 🕽 🛁 🕽 ⊙ 🚽 ♨ 🄾 🛒 📶
🕿 🎮 🖾 🖥 🍴 🛝 🌳 🎣
Nearby Facilities 🏇 🚴 ⚓ 🐾 ∪
Nearest Town Great Yarmouth
Directions Situated on the A47.
⚐ Great Yarmouth

GREAT YARMOUTH

Wild Duck Holiday Park, Howards Common, Belton, Great Yarmouth, NR31 9NE
Tel: 01493 780268
Email: wildduck@haven.com
www.haventouring.com/towildduck
Pitches For A ⌗ ⌗ **Total** 117
Open Mid March to End Oct
Access Good **Site** Level
Nearest Bus Stop (Miles) Entrance
A relaxed Holiday Park set in 97 acres of woodland and offering family facilities including kids clubs and family entertainment.
Facilities 🖆 ⨍ 🖵 🕽 🛁 🕽 ⊙
🄾 🕿 🎮 🖾 🛒 🍴 🛝 🌳 🎠 🌊 🖥 🖾 🌳
📶
Nearby Facilities 🏇 🚴 🐾 ♒
Nearest Town Great Yarmouth
Directions Take the A47 to Great Yarmouth, at the Asda roundabout take the third exit,proceed over two roundabouts, turn left off the bypass and pick up the A143 for Beccles. At the traffic lights turn right and follow for 2 miles until you reach the dual carriageway. Turn right SP Belton. Go straight over the mini rbt, turn rt at T jct, turn lt at next T jct, park is 200yds on right.
⚐ Great Yarmouth

GREAT YARMOUTH

Willowcroft Camping & Caravan Park, Staithe Road, Repps-with-Bastwick, Norfolk Broads, Norfolk, NR29 5JU
Tel: 01692 670380
Email: willowcroftsite@btinternet.com
www.willowcroft.net
Pitches For A ⌗ ⌗ **Total** 32
Acreage 2 **Open** March to October
Access Good **Site** Level
Nearest Bus Stop (Miles) ½
Beautiful, tranquil site, just a two minute walk to a river for fishing. Safe footpath along the river which leads to Potter Heigham. Excellent new ladies toilets for 2009.
Facilities ⨍ 🖵 🕽 🛁 ⊙ 🄾 🛒
Nearby Facilities 🚴 ⚓ 🐾
Nearest Town Wroxham
Directions From Great Yarmouth take the A149 to Stalham, in Repps turn left into Church Road, then turn right into Staithe Road. Or from Acle take the B1152 to Caister, then take the A149 and follow as above.
⚐ Acle

HARLESTON

Little Lakeland Caravan Park, Wortwell, Harleston, Norfolk, IP20 0EL
Tel: 01986 788646
Email: info@littlelakeland.co.uk
www.littlelakeland.co.uk
Pitches For ⌗ ⌗ **Total** 40

Acreage 4 **Open** March to October
Access Good **Site** Level
Nearest Bus Stop (Miles) ¼
Half acre fishing lake, site library.
Facilities ⨍ 🖵 🕽 🛁 🕽 ⊙ 🚽 🄾 🛒 🖥
🕿 🎮 🖾 🖥 🍴 🛝 🌳
Nearby Facilities 🏇 🚴 ⚓ 🐾 ∪
Nearest Town Harleston
Directions Turn off A143 (Diss to Lowestoft) at roundabout signposted Wortwell. In village turn right about 300 yards after Bell P.H. at bottom of lane turn right into site.
⚐ Diss

HEMSBY

Long Beach Caravan Park, Hemsby, Great Yarmouth, Norfolk, NR29 4JD
Tel: 01493 730023
Email: info@long-beach.co.uk
www.long-beach.co.uk
Pitches For A ⌗ ⌗ **Total** 100
Acreage 5 **Open** Mid March to End Oct
Access Good **Site** Level
Nearest Bus Stop (Miles) ¼
Park adjoins its own private sandy beach and dunes. Sea fishing on site.
Facilities 🖆 ⨍ 🖵 🕽 🛁 🕽 ⊙ 🚽 🄾 🛒
🕿 🎮 🖾 🕽 🛒 🍴 🖾 🖥 🍴 🛝 🌳 🎣 📶
Nearby Facilities 🏇 ⚓ 🐾 ∪
Nearest Town Great Yarmouth
Directions 5 miles north of Great Yarmouth, turn east from the B1159 at Hemsby.
⚐ Great Yarmouth

HEMSBY

Newport Caravan Park, Newport Road, Hemsby, Great Yarmouth, NR29 4NW
Tel: 01493 730405
Pitches For A ⌗ ⌗ **Total** 90
Acreage 4½ **Open** April to October
Access Good **Site** Level
Nearest Bus Stop (Miles) Outside
Situated in the lively village of Hemsby. 500yds from a sandy beach, 5½ miles from Great Yarmouth and the Norfolk Broads.
Facilities ⨍ 🖵 🕽 🛁 ⊙ 🄾 🛒
🕿 🎮 🖾 🍴 🕽 🖾 🖥 📶
Nearby Facilities 🏇 🚴
Nearest Town Great Yarmouth
Directions Take the A47 from Norwich or the A12 from Ipswich and go to Great Yarmouth. In Hemsby/Newport (5½ miles north of Great Yarmouth) take the A149 then the B1159.
⚐ Great Yarmouth

HOLT

Kelling Heath Holiday Park, Weybourne, Holt, Norfolk, NR25 7HW
Tel: 01263 588181
Email: info@kellingheath.co.uk
www.kellingheath.co.uk
Pitches For A ⌗ ⌗ 🚂 **Total** 300
Acreage 250 **Open** Mid Feb to Dec
Access Good **Site** Level
A 250 acre estate of woodland and heather, with magnificent views of the Weybourne coastline. Rose Award.
Facilities 🖆 ⨍ 🄵 🖵 🕽 🛁 🕽 ⊙ 🚽 ♨ 🄾 🛒 📶
🕿 🎮 🖾 🖥 🛒 🍴 🛝 🌊 🖾 🌳 🖥 🎠 🌳 🎣 📶
Nearby Facilities 🏇 🚴 ⚓ 🐾 ∪ ♒ ♒
Nearest Town Sheringham
Directions Turn north at site sign at Bodham on the A148 or turn south off the A149 at Weybourne Church.
⚐ Sheringham

HORSEY

Waxham Sands Holiday Park, Warren Farm, Horsey, Norfolk, NR29 4EJ
Tel: 01692 598325
www.waxhamsandsholidaypark.co.uk
Pitches For A ⌗ ⌗ **Total** 200
Acreage 22 **Open** 20-May to 30-Sep

Access Good **Site** Level
Adjacent to the beach, ideal for sea fishing.
Facilities ⨍ 🖵 🕽 🛁 🕽 ⊙ 🚽 🄾 🛒
🕿 🎮 🖾 🖾 🍴 🕽 🌳 🎣
Nearby Facilities 🏇 🚴 ⚓
Nearest Town Great Yarmouth
Directions Situated on the B1159 main coast road, 12 miles north of Great Yarmouth.
⚐ Great Yarmouth

HUNSTANTON

Manor Park Holiday Village, Manor Road, Hunstanton, Norfolk, PE36 5AZ
Tel: 0843 309 2584
Email: manor.park@park-resorts.com
www.park-resorts.com
Pitches For ⌗ ⌗ **Total** 64
Acreage 1 **Open** April to Oct
Access Good **Site** Level
Nearest Bus Stop (Miles) ½
Situated within a 50 acre park. Near the beach.
Facilities ⨍ 🖵 🕽 🛁 🕽 ⊙ 🄾 🛒
🎮 🖾 🍴 🕽 🖾 🖥
Nearby Facilities 🚴 ⚓
Nearest Town Hunstanton
Directions 1 mile from Hunstanton. From Kings Lynn take the A149 and go right at the roundabout, on entering Hunstanton turn left at the next roundabout.
⚐ Kings Lynn

HUNSTANTON

Searles Leisure Resort, 3 South Beach Road, Hunstanton, Norfolk, PE36 5BB
Tel: 01485 534211
Email: bookings@searles.co.uk
www.searles.co.uk
Pitches For A ⌗ ⌗ 🚂
Open Mid March to Early Nov
Access Good **Site** Level
Nearest Bus Stop (Miles) Outside
Family park 200 metres from the beach, with excellent camping and touring facilities. Pools, Clubhouse, Entertainment, Hair & Beauty Salon and a Golf Course.
Facilities 🖆 ⨍ 🄵 🖵 🕽 🛁 🕽 ⊙ 🚽 🄾 🛒
🕿 🎮 🖾 🖥 🛒 🍴 🕽 🛝 🌳 🎠 🖾 🖥 🍴 🌳
📶
Nearby Facilities 🏇 🚴 ⚓ ∪ ♒
Nearest Town Hunstanton/Kings Lynn
Directions From Kings Lynn take the A149 to Hunstanton. In Hunstanton at the first roundabout turn signposted South Beach. Go straight over the next roundabout and Searles is on the left.
⚐ Kings Lynn

KINGS LYNN

Kings Lynn Caravan & Camping Park, Parkside House, New Road, North Runcton, Kings Lynn, Norfolk, PE33 0RA
Tel: 01553 840004
Email: klcc@btconnect.com
www.kl-cc.co.uk
Pitches For A ⌗ ⌗ 🚂 **Total** 150
Acreage 9 **Open** All Year
Access Good **Site** Level
Nearest Bus Stop (Miles) Outside
Situated in a beautiful parkland setting with mature trees. Well situated for Kings Lynn, inland market towns, the North Norfolk coast, watersports and good pubs. Tescos nearby. Rallies welcome.
Facilities 🖆 ⨍ 🄵 🖵 🕽 🛁 🕽 ⊙ 🚽 🄾 🛒
🕿 🎮 🖾 🖥 🍴 🌳 🎠 🖾 🖥 🍴 🌳 🖥
Nearby Facilities 🏇 🚴 ⚓ ∪ ♒ ♒
Nearest Town Kings Lynn
Directions 1½ miles from the A17, A47, A10 and A149 main Kings Lynn Hardwick roundabout. Take the A47 towards Swaffham and take the first right at North Runcton.
⚐ Kings Lynn

KINGS LYNN
Pentney Park, Main Road, Pentney, Kings Lynn, Norfolk, PE32 1HU
Tel: 01760 337479
Email: holidays@pentney-park.co.uk
www.pentney-park.co.uk
Pitches For 𝘈 ⚲ 🚐 🚍 **Total** 170
Acreage 16 **Open** All Year
Access Good **Site** Level
Nearest Bus Stop (Miles) 1
Near the River Nar Valley Walk, linking to Peddars Way Walk. Ideal base for visiting beautiful Norfolk. Washing up facilities.
Facilities ♿ ⨍ 🚽 🚿 ↻ ⊙ ⊟ ◉ 🔌
𝔖𝔏 ⊙ ⊠ ✗ ⊓ ⤳ ᛒ ⊞ ⊟ ◧ ⌇ 🛜
Nearby Facilities ┡ 🏊 ∪ ⊉
Nearest Town Kings Lynn
Directions Situated on the A47 9 miles east of Kings Lynn and 7 miles west of Swaffham. Turn onto the B1153 to Gayton, entrance is 200 yards.
🚆 Kings Lynn

METHWOLD
Warren House Caravan Park, Warren House, Brandon Road, Methwold, Thetford, Norfolk, IP26 4RL
Tel: 01366 728238
Email: janescarrott@btinternet.com
Pitches For 𝘈 ⚲ 🚐 **Total** 40
Acreage 4 **Open** March to Oct
Access Good **Site** Level
Situated in Thetford Forest and close to Lakenheath Fen RSPB site and NNT Weeting Heath. Good central location for touring East Anglia. Good cycling area.
Facilities 🚾 🚽 🚿 ↻ ⊟ ◉ ⌇ ⚬
Nearby Facilities ┡ 🏊 ℛ
Nearest Town Thetford
Directions 5 miles from Brandon on the B1112.
🚆 Thetford

MUNDESLEY
Sandy Gulls Cliff Top Touring Park, Cromer Road, Mundesley, Norfolk, NR11 8DF
Tel: 01263 720513
Email: info@sandygulls.co.uk
www.sandygulls.co.uk
Pitches For ⚲ 🚐 **Total** 40
Acreage 2½ **Open** Easter to October
Access Good **Site** Level
Nearest Bus Stop (Miles) Outside
ADULTS ONLY TOURING PARK on a cliff top location, overlooking the beach. Near to the Broads National Park. TV Hook-ups. ETB 3 Star Graded Park.
Facilities ♿ ⨍ 🚽 🚿 ↻ ⊙ 🍴 ⚄ ⊟ ◉
🏋 ⊙ ⊠ ⤳ ⊟ ◧ ✗ A
Nearby Facilities ┡ 🏊 ⊥ ✗ ∪ ℛ
Nearest Town Cromer
Directions South along the coast road for 4 miles.
🚆 Cromer

NORFOLK

NORTH WALSHAM

Two Mills Touring Park, Yarmouth Road, North Walsham, Norfolk, NR28 9NA
Tel: 01692 405829
Email: enquiries@twomills.co.uk
www.twomills.co.uk
Pitches For ▲ ⬛ ⬛ **Total** 81
Acreage 8 **Open** 01-Mar to 03-Jan
Access Good **Site** Level
Nearest Bus Stop (Miles) Outside
ADULTS ONLY. Ideally situated for visiting North Norfolks many attractions.
Facilities ♿ ⌁ ⏢ 🛁 ⬛ 🍴 ⌂ ⊙ ◢ ▦ 🍽
🏋 🏧 ⬛ ⏢ ⬛ 🍴 ▲ ✺ ◀ 🎣
Nearby Facilities ⌐ ✦ ⚓ ✈ ∪
Nearest Town North Walsham
Directions Follow Hospital signs passing the Police Station on route. 1 mile on the left from the town centre.
� North Walsham

NORWICH

Camping & Caravanning Club Site, Martineau Lane, Norwich, Norfolk, NR1 2HX
Tel: 01603 620060
www.campingandcaravanningclub.co.uk/norwich
Pitches For ▲ ⬛ ⬛ **Total** 50
Acreage 2½ **Open** 29-Mar to 05-Nov
Access Good **Site** Level
Nearest Bus Stop (Miles) ¼
A rural location close to the city of Norwich. Near to the Norfolk Broads. BTB 3 Star Graded and AA 3 Pennants. Non members welcome. You can also call us on 0845 130 7633.
Facilities ⌁ ⬛ 🍴 ⌂ ⊙ ◢ 🍽
🏋 🏧 ⬛ 🍴 ⬛ ⬛ ✦ ✈
Nearby Facilities ⌐ ✦ ⚓ ⚡ 🏌 ♪
Nearest Town Norwich
Directions From the A47 join the A146 towards Norwich city centre. At the traffic lights turn left, then left again at the Cock Public House. Site is 150 yards on the right.
🚶 Thorpe

NORWICH

Swans Harbour Caravan & Camping Park, Barford Road, Marlingford, Norwich, Norfolk, NR9 5HU
Tel: 01603 759658
Email: info@swansharbour.co.uk
www.swansharbour.co.uk
Pitches For ▲ ⬛ ⬛ **Total** 30
Acreage 4 **Open** All Year
Access Good **Site** Level
Nearest Bus Stop (Miles) ½
Alongside a river with own fishing rights. Hard standing available.
Facilities ♿ ⌁ ⬛ 🍴 ⌂ ⊙ ◢ ▦ 🍽 🍴 ✦
Nearby Facilities ⌐ ✦
Nearest Town Norwich
Directions Turn off the B1108 (Norwich to Watton road). 3 miles past Southern Bypass turn right signposted Marlingford. Follow brown tourist signs to the site.
🚶 Wymondham

POTTER HEIGHAM

Causeway Cottage Caravan Park, Bridge Road, Potter Heigham, Nr Great Yarmouth, Norfolk, NR29 5JB
Tel: 01692 670238
Email: sue324@btinternet.com
www.causewaycottage.webs.com
Pitches For ▲ ⬛ ⬛
Access Good **Site** Level
Nearest Bus Stop (Miles) ¼
Static caravans for hire. Restaurant nearby.
Facilities ⌁ ⬛ 🍴 ⊙ ◢ 🍽 🏋 🏧 ⬛ ⬛
Nearby Facilities ⌐ ✦ ⚓ ✈

Nearest Town Great Yarmouth
Directions Potter Heigham is between Great Yarmouth and Norwich. Turn off the A149 at Potter Heigham, we are 250yds from the river and old bridge.
🚶 Acle

REEDHAM

Reedham Ferry Complex Ltd., Ferry Road, Reedham, Norwich, Norfolk, NR13 3HA
Tel: 01493 700999
Email: reedhamferry@aol.com
www.reedhamferry.co.uk
Pitches For ▲ ⬛ ⬛ **Total** 30
Acreage 4 **Open** March to Oct
Access Good **Site** Level
Nearest Bus Stop (Miles) ¼
Tranquil site alongside a river. Ideal touring.
Facilities ⌁ ⏢ 🛁 ⌂ ⊙ ◢ 🍽
⬛ ✗ ⬛ 🍴 ⬛ ⬛
Nearby Facilities ✦ ⚓ ✈
Nearest Town Norwich/Great Yarmouth
Directions From Acle follow signs for Reedham Ferry.
🚶 Reedham

SANDRINGHAM

Camping & Caravanning Club Site, The Sandringham Estate, Double Lodges, Sandringham, Norfolk, PE35 6EA
Tel: 01485 542555
www.campingandcaravanningclub.co.uk/beadnellbay
Pitches For ▲ ⬛ ⬛ **Total** 275
Acreage 28 **Open** 09-Feb to 19-Nov
Access Good **Site** Lev/Slope
Nearest Bus Stop (Miles) 1
In the grounds of the Royal Estate. Motorhome stop-off. Ice pack and freezing facilities. BTB 5 Star Graded, David Bellamy Gold Award and AA 4 Pennants. Non members welcome. You can also call us on 0845 130 7633.
Facilities ♿ ⌁ ⬛ 🛁 ⌂ ⊙ ◢ 🍽
🏋 🏧 ⬛ 🍴 ⬛ ⬛
Nearby Facilities ⌐ ∪
Nearest Town Kings Lynn
Directions From the A148 Kings Lynn to Cromer road, turn left onto the B1440 sp West Newton. Follow signs indicating tents and caravans to reach the site.
🚶 Kings Lynn

SANDRINGHAM

Sandringham Estate Caravan Club Site, Glucksburg Woods, Sandringham, Norfolk, PE35 6EZ
Tel: 01553 631614
www.caravanclub.co.uk
Pitches For ⬛ ⬛ **Total** 136
Acreage 13 **Open** All Year
Access Good **Site** Lev/Slope
Nearest Bus Stop (Miles) ¼
Set in the heart of the Royal estate, with Sandringham House, museum and grounds on the doorstep. Then theres the Country Park with nature trails, train ride, Visitor Centre, tea room, gift shop and flower stall. Non members welcome. Booking essential.
Facilities ♿ ⌁ ⬛ 🛁 ⌂ ⊙ ◢ 🍽
🏋 🏧 ⬛ 🍴 ⬛ ⬛ ✈
Nearby Facilities
Nearest Town Sandringham
Directions From north on the A149, at the end of Dersingham bypass turn left onto the B1439 at signpost for West Newton, site is within ½ a mile on the left at rustic signpost SECC.

SCRATBY

Green Farm Caravan Park, 100 Beach Road, Scratby, Great Yarmouth, Norfolk, NR29 3NW
Tel: 01493 730440
Email: contact@greenfarmcaravanpark.com
www.greenfarmcaravanpark.com
Pitches For ⬛ ⬛ **Total** 25
Open 26-Mar to 31-Oct
Access Good **Site** Level
Nearest Bus Stop (Miles) Outside
Near the beach.
Facilities ⌁ ⬛ 🍴 ⌂ ◢ ▦ 🍽
🏋 ⬛ ✗ ⬛ ⬛ 🍴 ⬛ ⬛
Nearby Facilities ⌐ ✦ ⚓ ⚡ ∪ ♪
Nearest Town Great Yarmouth
Directions 5 miles north of Great Yarmouth along the coast road between Caister and Hemsby.
🚶 Great Yarmouth

SCRATBY

Scratby Hall Caravan Park, Thoroughfare Lane, Scratby, Great Yarmouth, Norfolk, NR29 3SR
Tel: 01493 730283
Email: scratbyhall@aol.com
www.scratbyhall.co.uk
Pitches For ▲ ⬛ ⬛ **Total** 85
Acreage 5 **Open** Easter to End Sept
Access Good **Site** Level
Nearest Bus Stop (Miles) ½
Set in countryside and off the main road. Ideal for visiting the Norfolk Broads and only ½ a mile from the coast.
Facilities ♿ ⌁ ⬛ 🍴 ⌂ ⊙ ◢ ▦ 🍽
🏋 🏧 ⬛ 🍴 ⬛ ⬛
Nearby Facilities ⌐ ✦ ⚓ ⚡ ∪
Nearest Town Great Yarmouth
Directions Approx. 5 miles north of Great Yarmouth. Take the A149 then the B1159, signposted.
🚶 Great Yarmouth

SHERINGHAM

Beeston Regis Caravan Park, Cromer Road, West Runton, Nr Sheringham, Norfolk, NR27 9QZ
Tel: 01263 823614
Email: info@beestonregis.co.uk
www.beestonregis.co.uk
Pitches For ▲ ⬛ ⬛ **Total** 45
Acreage 60 **Open** 24-Mar to 31-Oct
Access Good **Site** Level
Nearest Bus Stop (Miles) Outside
Cliff top setting with stunning views and direct access to the beach via steps. Within walking distance of Sheringham and Cromer. Woodland walks in an area of natural beauty.
Facilities ♿ ⌁ ⬛ 🍴 ⌂ ⊙ ◢ 🍽
🏋 🏧 ⬛ 🍴 ⬛ ⬛ ✈ ✺ ◀
Nearby Facilities ⌐ ✦ ⚓ ⚡ ∪ 🏌 ♪ ✗
Nearest Town Sheringham
Directions On the A149 coast road between Sheringham and Cromer, at Beeston Regis opposite the school.
🚶 West Runton

STANHOE

The Rickels Caravan & Camping Park, Bircham Road, Stanhoe, Kings Lynn, Norfolk, PE31 8PU
Tel: 01485 518671
Pitches For ▲ ⬛ ⬛ **Total** 30
Acreage 2¼ **Open** March to October
Access Good **Site** Lev/Slope
ADULTS ONLY PARK. Close to local beaches, stately homes, Sandringham and market towns. Dogs £1 per night, short dog walk. Static caravan available for hire.

in the heart of Thetford Forest . . .

Enquiries to
David or Karin
The Dower House
Touring Park,
Thetford Forest,
East Harling, Norfolk
NR16 2SE (01953) 717314
www.dowerhouse.co.uk

Facilities ⓕ 🔲 🔳 🏠 🔆 ⬛ 🔆 🔆 🔆 🔆A
Nearby Facilities ┡ ⏋ ⏦ ⏌ U ⏌ ♪
Nearest Town Hunstanton
Directions From Kings Lynn take the A148
to Hillington, turn left onto the B1153 to Great
Bircham. Fork left onto the B1155 to the
crossroads, straight over. Park is 100yds on
the left.
⚡ Kings Lynn

SWAFFHAM

Breckland Meadows Touring Park, Lynn
Road, Swaffham, Norfolk, PE37 7PT
Tel: 01760 721246
Email: info@brecklandmeadows.co.uk
www.brecklandmeadows.co.uk
Pitches For ⅄ ⬛ ⬛ ⬛ **Total** 45
Acreage 3 **Open** All Year
Access Good **Site** Level
Nearest Bus Stop (Miles) ½
ADULTS ONLY. Small, friendly and very
clean park. Within walking distance of the
town centre for shops, pubs, restaurants,
etc.. Dog walk adjacent to the park. Central
for touring Norfolk. Ideal for walking and
cycling.
Facilities ⏦ ⓕ 🔲 🔳 🏠 🔆 ⬛ 🔆 🏠
🔆 ⬛ 🔆 🔲 🔆A 🔆 🔆 🔆
Nearby Facilities ┡ ⏌ U ♪
Nearest Town Swaffham/Hunstanton
Directions Take the A47 from Kings Lynn to
Swaffham, approx 15 miles. Take the first exit
off the dual carriageway, site is ¾ miles
before Swaffham town centre.
⚡ Kings Lynn

THETFORD

Lowe Caravan Park, Ashdale, 134 Hills
Road, Saham Hills (Nr Watton), Thetford,
Norfolk, IP25 7EZ
Tel: 01953 881051

www.lowecaravanpark.co.uk
Pitches For ⅄ ⬛ ⬛ **Total** 20
Acreage 2 **Open** All Year
Access Good **Site** Lev/Slope
Quiet, relaxing site in the countryside. Only
closed for Christmas and New Year.
Facilities ⓕ 🔲 🔳 🏠 🔆 ⬛ 🔆 🔲
Nearby Facilities ┡ ⏌
Nearest Town Watton
Directions Take the A11 from Thetford then
take the road to Watton. Go through the high
street and take second turn into Saham Road
(past the golf club). Take the second turning
right, turn right at the T-Junction and the Park
is the first drive on the right.
⚡ Thetford

THETFORD

The Covert Caravan Club Site, High Ash,
Hilborough, Thetford, Norfolk, IP26 5BZ
Tel: 01842 878356
www.caravanclub.co.uk
Pitches For ⬛ ⬛ **Total** 103
Acreage 9½ **Open** April **to** Nov
Access Good **Site** Level
Quiet, secluded site set in Forestry
Commission woodland. Ideal for wildlife
lovers. Within easy driving distance of
Swaffham, Norwich and Kings Lynn. Close
to Banham Zoo. Own sanitation required.
Non members welcome. Booking essential.
Facilities ⓕ 🔲 🔳 🏠 🔆 🔆 🔆 🔆 🔲 🔆 🔆
Nearby Facilities
Nearest Town Thetford
Directions From Thetford take the A134, at
the roundabout in Mundford turn right onto
the A1065 signposted Swaffham. Site
entrance is on the left within 2 miles by the
WWII tank.
⚡ Thetford

THETFORD

The Dower House Touring Park, Thetford
Forest, East Harling, Norwich, Norfolk,
NR16 2SE
Tel: 01953 717314
Email: info@dowerhouse.co.uk
www.dowerhouse.co.uk
Pitches For ⅄ ⬛ ⬛ **Total** 140
Acreage 20 **Open** 18th March **to** 2nd Oct
Access Good **Site** Level
Set in Thetford Forest, the site is spacious and
peaceful. Although we have a bar, we have
no amusement arcade or gaming machines.
Facilities ⏦ ⓕ 🔲 🔳 🏠 🔆 ⬛ 🔆 🔲 🔆
🔆 🔆 🔆 🔲 🔆 🔆 🔆 🔆 🔲 🔆 🔆
Nearby Facilities ⏌ U
Nearest Town Thetford
Directions From Thetford take A1066 East
for 5 miles, fork left at camping sign onto
unclassified road, site on left after 2 miles,
signposted.
⚡ Harling Road

WELLS-NEXT-THE-SEA

Stiffkey Campsite, The Greenway, Vale
Farm, Stiffkey, Wells-Next-the-Sea,
Norfolk, NR23 1QP
Tel: 01328 830235
Pitches For ⅄ ⬛ **Total** 80
Acreage 6 **Open** April **to** October
Site Lev/Slope
Nearest Bus Stop (Miles) ¼
Adjoining marsh saltings and the beach. Near
to steam and miniature railway. Good shop and
pub in the village. Local Coast-Hopper bus.
Facilities 🔲 🔳 🏠 🔆 ⬛ 🔆 🔲 🔆
Nearby Facilities ┡ ⏦ ⏌ U ♪
Directions Take the A149 east towards
Cromer, Stiffkey is the next village 3½ miles
from Wells.
⚡ Kings Lynn/Cromer

NORTHAMPTONSHIRE

CORBY

Top Lodge Caravan Club Site, Fineshade, Corby, Northamptonshire, NN17 3BB
Tel: 01780 444617
www.caravanclub.co.uk
Pitches For 🚐 🚗 **Total** 85
Acreage 5½ **Open** March **to** Nov
Access Good **Site** Level
Tranquil, meadowland site surrounded by woodland. Ideal for walking, cycling and bird watching. Within easy reach of the Fens and Rutland Water. Own sanitation required. Non members welcome. Booking essential.
Facilities ∮ 🏠 🚿 ⊙ 🛁 🖃 🖭 🛒 ຣ
Nearby Facilities ⌐ ✓
Nearest Town Corby
Directions From north on the A43, 2¼ miles past the roundabout at the A47 junction turn left signposted Fineshade. After crossing the railway bridge turn left in front of Forestry Commission Station into site.
🚉 Corby

KETTERING

Kestrel Caravans, Windy Ridge, Warkton Lane, Kettering, Northamptonshire, NN16 9XG
Tel: 01536 514301
Pitches For ▲ 🚐 🚗 **Total** 20
Acreage 2 **Open** All Year
Access Good **Site** Level
Nearest Bus Stop (Miles) ½
Very quiet park.
Facilities ∮ 🏠 🚿 ⌐ ⊙ ⊙ 🛁 🖃 🛒
Nearby Facilities ⌐ ✓ ⊥ ⅍ ∪ ₽
Nearest Town Kettering
Directions Leave the A14 at junction 10 and go into Kettering, go past the petrol station and turn next right into Warkton Lane, Park is ½ a mile on the right.
🚉 Kettering

NORTHAMPTON

Billing Aquadrome, Crow Lane, Great Billing, Northampton, Northamptonshire, NN3 9DA
Tel: 01524 781453
Email: enquiries@pureleisure-holidays.co.uk
www.billingaquadrome.com
Pitches For ▲ 🚐 🚗 **Total** 1000
Acreage 234 **Open** Feb **to** Jan
Access Good **Site** Level
Nearest Bus Stop (Miles) Outside
Set in 235 acres of parkland with 7 fishing lakes and rivers. Full Leisure Club and events programme. Ideal for families.
Facilities ⅙ ∮ 🏠 🚿 ⌐ ⊙ ⊙ 🛁 🖃
Nearby Facilities ⌐ ✓ ⊥ ⅍ ∪ ₽
Nearest Town Northampton
Directions Leave the M1 at junction 15 and take the A45 for 6 miles following signs for Billing Aquadrome.
🚉 Northampton

NORTHUMBERLAND

ALNWICK

Railway Inn Caravan Park, Acklington, Morpeth, Northumberland, NE65 9BP
Tel: 01670 760320
Email: info@railway-inn.co.uk
www.railway-inn.co.uk
Pitches For 🚐 🚗 **Total** 22
Acreage 1½ **Open** All Year
Access Good **Site** Level
Nearest Bus Stop (Miles) ½

Only 3 miles from the beach and near to castles.
Facilities ⅙ ∮ 🏠 🚿 ⌐ ⊙ 🍴 🚿 🛁 🖃 🛒
Nearby Facilities ⌐ ✓ ⊥ ⅍ ∪ ₽
Nearest Town Amble
Directions From the A1 take the B6345 sp Felton and Amble, after approx 3 miles the Railway Inn is over the bridge on the right.
🚉 Acklington

ALNWICK

River Breamish Caravan Club Site, Powburn, Alnwick, Northumberland, NE66 4HY
Tel: 01665 578320
www.caravanclub.co.uk
Pitches For ▲ 🚐 🚗 **Total** 79
Acreage 10 **Open** March **to** Nov
Access Good **Site** Level
Nearest Bus Stop (Miles) ¼
Set amid the Cheviot Hills, ideal for walking and cycling. A footbridge in Branton (1 mile) spans the river into Breamish Valley. Close to Alnwick Castle, Chillingham Castle and Wallington House. Non members welcome. Booking essential.
Facilities ⅙ ∮ 🚿 ⌐ ⌐ ⊙ 🛒 🖭 ⊙ 🛁 🖃 🛒 ຣ
Nearby Facilities
Nearest Town Alnwick
Directions From the A1 take the A697 for Wooler. After going through Powburn, immediately after Hedgeley Service Station, turn left signposted Branton, site is ½ mile on the right.
🚉 Alnwick

ASHINGTON

Sandy Bay Holiday Park, North Seaton, Ashington, Northumberland, NE63 9YD
Tel: 0843 309 2570
Email: holidaysales.sandybay@park-resorts.com
www.park-resorts.com
Pitches For 🚐 🚗
Open April **to** October
Access Good **Site** Sloping
Nearest Bus Stop (Miles) Outside
Located next to a beautiful sandy beach. Close to the town centre.
Facilities ∮ 🏠 🚿 ⌐ ⊙ 🛁 🖃
Nearby Facilities
Nearest Town Ashington
Directions From the A1 take the A19 sp Tyne Tunnel, then take the A189 sp Ashington. After 8 miles at the roundabout turn right onto the B1334, the Park is on the right.
🚉 Morpeth

BAMBURGH

Waren Caravan & Camping Park, Waren Mill, Bamburgh, Northumberland, NE70 7EE
Tel: 01668 214366
Email: waren@meadowhead.co.uk
www.meadowhead.co.uk
Pitches For ▲ 🚐 🚗 **Total** 180
Open 14-Mar **to** 31-Oct
Access Good **Site** Lev/Slope
Nearest Bus Stop (Miles) ½
Close to Bamburgh Castle, Holy Island and Alnwick Castle & Gardens.
Facilities ⅙ ∮ 🏠 🚿 ⌐ ⊙ 🍴 🛁 🖃 🛒
Nearby Facilities ⌐ ✓ ⊥ ⅍
Nearest Town Bamburgh
Directions From the A1 take the B1342 towards Bamburgh to Waren Mill. By Budle Bay turn right and follow signs for Waren Caravan Park.
🚉 Berwick-upon-Tweed

BEADNELL BAY

Camping & Caravanning Club Site, Beadnell, Chathill, Northumberland, NE67 5BX
Tel: 01665 720586
www.campingandcaravanningclub.co.uk/sandringham
Pitches For ▲ 🚗 **Total** 150
Acreage 6 **Open** 29-Mar **to** 24-Sep
Site Lev/Slope
Nearest Bus Stop (Miles) Outside
2 miles of sandy beach just over the road. 6 miles from Bamburgh Castle. Laundry drying room. BTB 2 Star Graded and AA 2 Pennants. Non members welcome. You can also call us on 0845 130 7633.
Facilities 🚿 ⌐ ⊙ 🛁 🖃 ⊙ ⌐ ⊙ 🛒 🖃 🖭 ຣ
Nearby Facilities ⌐ ✓ ⊥ ⅍ ∪ ₽
Directions From south leave the A1 and follow the B1430 signposted Seahouses. At Beadnell ignore signs for Beadnell Village, site is on the left after the village, just beyond the left hand bend. From north leave the A1 and follow the B1342 via Bamburgh and Seahouse

BELLINGHAM

Bellingham Camping & Caravanning Club Site, Tweed House, Brown Rigg, Bellingham, Hexham, Northumberland, NE48 2JY
Tel: 01434 220175
www.campingandcaravanningclub.co.uk
Pitches For ▲ 🚐 🚗 **Total** 64
Acreage 5 **Open** 16-Mar **to** 04-Nov
Access Good **Site** Level
Nearest Bus Stop (Miles) ½
Set in Northumberland National Park. Pennine Way passes the site. Near to Kielder Water, Kielder Castle and Hadrians Wall. Ideal for Newcastle and Gateshead shopping. Non members welcome. You can also call us on 0845 130 7633.
Facilities ∮ 🏠 🚿 ⌐ ⊙ 🛁 🖃 🛒
Nearby Facilities ⌐ ✓ ⊥ ⅍ ∪
Nearest Town Kielder
Directions Take the A69, after Hexham in ½ mile turn right signposted Acomb, Chollerford and Bellingham. At Chollerford turn left onto the B6318, go over the river and turn second left onto the B6320 signposted Wark and Bellingham.
🚉 Hexham

BELLINGHAM

Stonehaugh Campsite, Stonehaugh Shields, Hexham, Northumberland, NE48 3BU
Tel: 01434 230798
Email: carole.townsend@btconnect.com
Pitches For ▲ 🚐 🚗 **Total** 50
Acreage 3½ **Open** April **to** Sept
Access Good **Site** Level
Rural site set within Northumberland National Park. Situated between Kielder Water and Hadrians Wall, and close to the Penine Way and cycle routes.
Facilities 🚿 ⌐ ⊙ 🛁 🖃 🛒
Nearby Facilities ⌐
Nearest Town Hexham
Directions From Hexham take the A6079 to Chollerford, go over the bridge and staright over at the roundabout. Then follow the B6320 for Wark and Bellingham, after 5 miles turn left to Stonehaugh.
🚉 Hexham

So easy to reach, So very hard to leave

Images for illustrative purposes only

HOLIDAY PRICES

Holiday Caravans from
£6.50 per person/night

Camping Pitches from
£15.00 per night

Camping Pods from
£25.00 per night
Sleeps Four

Billing Aquadrome holiday park is set in over **200 acres of beautiful Northamptonshire countryside**, and features a wide range of facilities including **fishing, a funfair and amusements, licensed restaurants, bars,** and much more!

HOLIDAY HOMES
AVAILABLE TO PURCHASE
CALL 01604 784 507

All our **Touring, Motorhome** and **Camping** pitches are on level parkland with over 400 electrical hook up points. Our **Camping Pods** are discreetly located in a private wooded area close to all the main amenities. A brand new **Leisure Complex** boasts an **Indoor Pool, Splash Zone, Water Rides, Aqua Bar** and an alfresco **Dining Terrace.**

For bookings and availability call
01524 781 453
www.pureleisure-holidays.co.uk
www.billingaquadrome.com

BILLING AQUADROME
Crow Lane, Great Billing
Northampton NN3 9DA

pure leisure GROUP

ENGLAND

BERWICK-UPON-TWEED

Haggerston Castle, Beal, Nr Berwick-upon-Tweed, Northumberland, TD15 2PA
Tel: 01289 381333
Email: haggerstoncastle@haven.com
www.haventouring.com/
tohaggerstoncastle
Pitches For ⬜ 🚐 **Total** 132
Open Mid March **to** End Oct
Access Good **Site** Level
Nearest Bus Stop (Miles) Outside
Situated in an area of great heritage interest. Lots to do on the Park including kids clubs, family entertainment, horse riding, golf, tennis and so much more.
Facilities ♿ ✦ ⍾ 🛢 🅿 🍴 ☺ ♨ ▭ 🖥 📶 💺 🐾 🌳 🍳 ✕ 🚼 🔔 🍸 ⚓ ⚡ ➕ ▭ 🌊
Nearby Facilities ⚲ ✦ ≾ ∪ ♪
Nearest Town Berwick-upon-Tweed
Directions On the A1, 7 miles south of Berwick-upon-Tweed.
🚆 Berwick

BERWICK-UPON-TWEED

Ord House Country Park, East Ord, Berwick-upon-Tweed, Northumberland, TD15 2NS
Tel: 01289 305288
Email: enquiries@ordhouse.co.uk
www.ordhouse.co.uk
Pitches For ⬜ 🚐 🚐 **Total** 74
Acreage 42 **Open** All Year
Access Good **Site** Lev/Slope
Nearest Bus Stop (Miles) Outside
Award Winning park with an 18th century mansion house containing a licenced club.
Facilities ♿ ✦ 🛢 🅿 🍴 ☺ ▭ 🖥 ➕ ▭ 📶 💺
🐾 🍳 ✕ ⍾ 🔔 ⚓ ➕ ▭ 📶 💺 📶
Nearby Facilities ⚲ ✦ ≾ ⚓ ∪
Nearest Town Berwick-upon-Tweed
Directions Take East Ord road from bypass, follow caravan signpost.
🚆 Berwick-upon-Tweed

BERWICK-UPON-TWEED

Seaview Caravan Club Site, Billendean Road, Spittal, Berwick-upon-Tweed, Northumberland, TD15 1QU
Tel: 01289 305198
www.caravanclub.co.uk
Pitches For ⬜ 🚐 🚐 **Total** 98
Acreage 6 **Open** March **to** Jan
Access Good **Site** Lev/Slope
Nearest Bus Stop (Miles) Outside
Overlooking a river estuary with views of Holy Island. Just a short walk into Berwick. Near a safe sandy beach. Close to Swan Leisure Pool, Lindisfarne Priory and Paxton House. Non members welcome. Booking essential.
Facilities ♿ ✦ ▭ 🖥 🅿 🍴 ▭ ☺
🔔 🛢 🔔 ➕ ▭ ▭ 📶 💺
Nearby Facilities ⚲ ✦ ≾ ⚓ ≾
Nearest Town Berwick-on-Tweed
Directions From the A1 take the A1167 signposted Spittal, at the roundabout turn right into Billendean Terrace, site is ½ mile on the right.
🚆 Berwick-upon-Tweed

DUNSTAN HILL

Camping & Caravanning Club Site, Dunstan Hill, Dunstan, Alnwick, Northumberland, NE66 3TQ
Tel: 01665 576310
www.campingandcaravanningclub.co.uk/
dunstanhill
Pitches For ⬜ 🚐 🚐 **Total** 150
Acreage 14 **Open** 29-Mar **to** 05-Nov
Access Good **Site** Level
Nearest Bus Stop (Miles) Outside
In north east England just 1 mile from the coast. One of the Parks major attractions is Kielder Water, Europes largest man made lake. Access to Dunstanburgh Castle from the site. BTB 4 Star Graded and AA 3 Pennants. Non members welcome. You can also call us on 0845 130 7633.
Facilities ♿ ✦ ▭ 🖥 🅿 🍴 ☺ ♨ ▭ 🖥 ☺
🔔 🛢 🔔 ➕ ▭ 📶 💺 🐾 📶
Nearby Facilities ⚲ ✦ ∪ ♪
Nearest Town Alnwick
Directions Travelling north on the A1 take the B1340 sp Seahouses, follow to the T-Junction at Christon Bank and turn right, take the next right sp Embleton, turn right at the crossroads then first left sp Craster. Travelling south on the A1 take the B6347 through Christon Bank, take a right turn to Embleton, turn right at crossroads, then first left SP Craster. Site is 1 mile on left.
🚆 Alnmouth

HALTWHISTLE

Camping & Caravanning Club Site, Burnfoot Park Village, Haltwhistle, Northumberland, NE49 0JP
Tel: 01434 320106
www.campingandcaravanningclub.co.uk/
haltwhistle
Pitches For ⬜ 🚐 🚐 **Total** 50
Acreage 3½ **Open** 29-Mar **to** 05-Nov
Site Level
Nearest Bus Stop (Miles) ½
On the banks of the River South Tyne for fishing. Close to the Pennine Way. BTB 4 Star Graded and AA 3 Pennants. Non members welcome.
Facilities ✦ ▭ 🖥 🅿 🍴 ☺ ♨ ▭ 🖥 ☺
🔔 🛢 🔔 ➕ ▭ ☺ 📶 📶
Nearby Facilities ✦ ⚓
Directions Follow signs from the A69 by-pass, DO NOT go into Haltwhistle.
🚆 Haltwhistle

HALTWHISTLE

Seldom Seen Caravan Park, Haltwhistle, Northumberland, NE49 0NE
Tel: 01434 320571
www.seldomseencaravanpark.co.uk
Pitches For ⬜ 🚐 🚐 **Total** 20
Open Mar **to** Jan **Access** Good **Site** Level
Nearest Bus Stop (Miles) ¼
Central touring area, ideal for the Roman wall. David Bellamy Gold Award for Conservation.
Facilities ✦ ▭ 🖥 🅿 🍴 ☺ ☺
🔔 🛢 🍸 ▭ ➕ ▭ ✦ 💺
Nearby Facilities ⚲ ✦ ∪ ♪
Nearest Town Haltwhistle
Directions Off the A69 east of Haltwhistle, signposted.
🚆 Haltwhistle

HAYDON BRIDGE

Poplars Riverside Caravan Park, Eastland Ends, Haydon Bridge, Hexham, Northumberland, NE47 6BY
Tel: 01434 684427
Pitches For ⬜ 🚐 🚐 **Total** 14
Acreage 2½ **Open** March **to** October
Access Good **Site** Level
Nearest Bus Stop (Miles) ¼
Small, peaceful site close to the village. Fishing on site. Near to Hadrians Wall.
Facilities ✦ ▭ 🖥 🅿 🍴 ☺ ♨ ▭ 🖥 ☺
🔔 🛢 🔔 ➕ ▭ ☺ 📶 📶
Nearby Facilities ⚲ ✦ ∪ ♪
Nearest Town Hexham
Directions Take the A69 Newcastle to Carlisle road, follow signs from the bridge in the village.
🚆 Haydon Bridge

HEXHAM

Ashcroft Farm Caravan Site, Ashcroft Farm, Bardon Mill, Nr Hexham, Northumberland, NE47 7JA
Tel: 01434 344409
Pitches For ⬜ 🚐 🚐 **Total** 5
Acreage 2 **Open** Easter **to** Sept
Access Good **Site** Level
Nearest Bus Stop (Miles) Entrance
Alongside the River Tyne. Close to the village and its amenities. 2 miles from Hadrians Wall, Vindolanda.
Facilities ☺ 💺 🚼 📶
Nearby Facilities ⚲ ∪
Nearest Town Hexham
Directions Follow the A69 west from Hexham for 11 miles. Turn left into Bardon Mill Village and after 300 metres turn left then next right to the farm.
🚆 Bardon Mill

HEXHAM

Fallowfield Dene Caravan Park, Acomb, Hexham, Northumberland, NE46 4RP
Tel: 01434 603553
Email: info@fallowfielddene.co.uk
www.fallowfielddene.co.uk
Pitches For ⬜ 🚐 🚐
Nearest Bus Stop (Miles) ¼
One Camping Pod on site for hire.
Facilities ♿ ✦ ▭ 🖥 🅿 🍴 ☺ ♨ ▭ 🖥 ☺
🔔 🛢 🔔 ➕ ▭ ☺ 📶 💺 📶
Nearby Facilities ✦
Nearest Town Hexham
Directions From the A69 follow signs for Acomb, Bellingham and Rothbury (A6079).
🚆 Hexham

HEXHAM

Hexham Racecourse Caravan Site, High Yarridge, Hexham, Northumberland, NE46 2JP
Tel: 01434 606847
Email: hexrace.caravan@btconnect.com
Pitches For ⬜ 🚐 🚐 **Total** 50
Open May **to** September
Access Good **Site** Sloping
Nearest Bus Stop (Miles) 2
Set in beautiful open countryside.
Facilities ✦ 🖥 🅿 🍴 ☺ ♨ ▭ 🖥 ☺
🔔 🛢 🔔 ➕ ▭ 💺
Nearby Facilities ⚲ ✦ ⚓ ∪ ♪

Nearest Town Hexham
Directions From the A69 follow signs for Hexham. Follow the main street to the traffic lights and bear left onto the B6305 signposted Allendale. After 3 miles turn left at the T-Junction, site is 1½ miles.
⇌ Hexham

OTTERBURN

Border Forest Caravan Park,
Cottonshope Burnfoot, Nr Otterburn, Northumberland, NE19 1TF
Tel: 01830 520259
Email: info@borderforest.com
www.borderforest.com
Pitches For ⚑ ⊞ **Total** 36
Acreage 3 **Open** All Year
Access Good **Site** Level
Situated in Kielder Forest Park and surrounded by Cottonshope, Burn and River Rede. Ideal walking and touring base. 6 miles south of the Scottish Border at Carter Bar.
Facilities ∮ 🚿 ⊙ ⊿ ≋
🖸 🖴 🕾 🖵 ⊟ 🖊 ⚡ ≋
Nearby Facilities ┌ ✔ ⚓ ⚲ ∪ ⋗ ⅄
Nearest Town Jedburgh/Hexham
Directions Adjacent to A68 - 17 miles to Jedburgh, 28 miles to Hexham, 38 miles to Newcastle.
⇌ Hexham

OVINGHAM

High Hermitage Caravan Park, The Hermitage, Ovingham, Prudhoe, Northumberland, NE42 6HH
Tel: 01661 832250
Email: hermitagegardens@yahoo.co.uk
www.highhermitagecaravanpark.co.uk
Pitches For ⚑ ⊞ **Total** 34
Acreage 8¼ **Open** 01-Mar **to** 07-Jan
Access Good **Site** Gently Sloping
Nearest Bus Stop (Miles) Outside
Quiet, rural, riverside site with extensive wildlife. Grassy slope sheltered by trees on north, east and west sides. Fishing on the Tyne. Giant chess and draughts. Ideal for touring the Roman Wall and associated sites plus gorgeous Northumberland countryside and beaches.
Facilities ∮ 🖸 🖩 ⊞ 🕾 ┌ ⊙ ⊿ 🖸 ⚡
🖵 🖸 ⊟ 🖵 🖊 ≋
Nearby Facilities ┌ ✔ ⚓ ⚲ ∪ ⅄
Nearest Town Prudhoe
Directions Take the A69 to Hexham and take exit to Wylam. Go straight ahead at first crossroads to Wylam, follow road and turn right at the bottom to Ovingham, site entrance is 1½ miles down this river road opposite water intake area. Look out for white painted stones at the bottom of our entrance.
⇌ Prudhoe

ROTHBURY

Clennell Hall Riverside Holiday Park,
Alwinton, Rothbury, Northumberland, NE65 7BG
Tel: 01669 650341
Email: enquiries@clennellhall.co.uk
www.clennellhall.co.uk
Pitches For ⚑ ⊞ **Total** 50
Open March **to** October
Access Good **Site** Level
Nearest Bus Stop (Miles) ½
Lovely quiet park on the fringe of Northumberland National Park. Perfect for relaxing. A walkers and cyclists paradise. By Alnwick Castle featuring Alnwick Garden & Treehouse and Cragside Hall. Within driving distance of the spectacular Northumbrian coastline, Kielder Water & Forest Park and Hadrians Wall.
Facilities ∮ 🖩 🖩 🕾 ┌ ⊿ 🖮
🖸 🖵 🖵 🖸 ⊟

Nearby Facilities ┌ ✔ ⚓ ⚲ ∪ ⋗ ⅄
Nearest Town Rothbury
Directions From the A1 north of Newcastle take the A697 Coldstream road. After 8 miles take the B6344, after 5 miles take the B6341 Rothbury road. Travel through Rothbury and Thropton and turn off to Sharperton and Harbottle. Site is after the bridge on the right. just before Alwinton Village
⇌ Morpeth

ROTHBURY

Nunnykirk Caravan Club Site, Nunnykirk, Morpeth, Northumberland, NE61 4PZ
Tel: 01669 620762
www.caravanclub.co.uk
Pitches For ⊞ ⊞ **Total** 84
Acreage 14 **Open** April **to** Oct
Access Good **Site** Level
Attractive and peaceful site, a wildlife and bird watchers paradise. Simonside Hills nearby, perfect for hill walkers. Close to Hadrians Wall and Wallington Hall & Gardens. Own sanitation required. Non members welcome. Booking essential.
Facilities ∮ 🖸 🖩 ⊿ 🖊
Nearby Facilities ✔
Nearest Town Morpeth
Directions From A1 take A696 sp Jedburgh, after approx. 19¼ miles turn right at Knowesgate Hotel sp Scots Gap. After 2¼ miles turn left onto B6342, after 6 miles cross the bridge at foot of the hill and turn right into a private road, site is ¼ mile on the right.
⇌ Morpeth

SEAHOUSES

Seafield Caravan Park, Seafield Road, Seahouses, Northumberland, NE68 7SP
Tel: 01665 720628
Email: info@seafieldpark.co.uk
www.seafieldpark.co.uk
Pitches For ⊞ ⊞ **Total** 18
Open 09-Feb **to** 09-Jan
Access Good **Site** Level
Nearest Bus Stop (Miles) ¼
In the centre of Seahouses, near the harbour and just a short walk to the beach.
Facilities ⚓ ∮ 🖩 🖩 🕾 ┌ ⊙ ⊿ 🖸 ⚡
🖵 ✗ 🖸 🕾 🖵 🖸 ⊟ 🖵 ≋
Nearby Facilities ┌ ✔ ⚓ ⚲ ∪ ⋗ ⅄
Nearest Town Alnwick
Directions Travelling south leave the A1 at Alnwick and take the B1340 to Seahouses. Travelling north leave the A1 at Belford and take the B1342 through Bamburgh to Seahouses.
⇌ Alnmouth

WOOLER

Highburn House Caravan & Camping Park, Wooler, Northumberland, NE71 6EE
Tel: 01668 281344
Email: relax@highburn-house.co.uk
www.highburn-house.co.uk
Pitches For ⚑ ⊞ ⊞ **Total** 100
Acreage 12 **Open** April **to** December
Access Good **Site** Level
Nearest Bus Stop (Miles) ¼
Stream runs through middle of site, beautiful view over hills and valley.
Facilities ⚓ ∮ ✗ ∮ 🖩 🖩 🕾 ┌ ⊙ ⊿
🖸 🖵 ⚡ 🖸 ⊟ 🖵 ≋
Nearby Facilities ┌ ✔ ∪ ⅄ ⋗
Nearest Town Wooler
Directions Off A1 take A697 to Wooler town centre, at the top of Main Street take left turn, 400 metres on left is our site.
⇌ Berwick

WOOLER

Riverside Country Park, South Road, Wooler, Northumberland, NE71 6NJ
Tel: 01668 281447
Email: riverside@northdales.co.uk
www.northdales.co.uk
Pitches For ⚑ ⊞ ⊞ **Total** 72
Open All Year
Access Good **Site** Level
Nearest Bus Stop (Miles) ½
Quiet country park alongside a river with spectacular views and great facilities.
Facilities ⚓ ∮ 🖸 🖩 🕾 ┌ ⊙ ⊿ 🖸 🖵 ⚡
🖸 🖮 🕾 🖸 ✗ ∧ ⚓ 🕾 🖵 🖸 🖊 ≋
Nearby Facilities ┌ ✔ ∪ ⅄
Nearest Town Wooler
Directions From Wooler in Church Street, bear right onto Market Place, bear left onto The Peth, turn left again onto South Road, Park is approx ½/¾ miles.
⇌ Berwick-Upon-Tweed

NOTTINGHAMSHIRE

CARLTON-ON-TRENT

Carlton Manor Touring Park, Ossington Road (off A1), Carlton-on-Trent, Nr Newark, Nottinghamshire, NG23 6NU
Tel: 01530 835662
Pitches For ⚑ ⊞ ⊞ **Total** 22
Acreage 2 **Open** April **to** Nov
Access Good **Site** Level
Nearest Bus Stop (Miles) ¼
Clean site with spotless toilets. Warden on site at all times. The Great Northern Pub is opposite the Park gates for good food and beer. Train spotting on site. We allow individual motorcyclists, but no groups. Shops, fishing and doctor in village. 10 miles from Robin Hood country, 12 miles from Lincoln and 50 miles from Skegness. You can also contact Mrs Goodman on 07772 037909.
Facilities ∮ 🖩 ┌ ⊙ 🖮 🖵 🖩 ⊟ 🖵 ≋
Nearby Facilities ┌ ✔
Nearest Town Newark
Directions From Newark take the A1 north towards Doncaster, site is 6 miles, signposted.
⇌ Carlton Village

HOLME PIERREPONT

National Water Sports Caravan & Camping Park, Adbolton Lane, Holme Pierrepont, Nottingham, Notts, NG12 2LU
Tel: 0115 982 4721
Email: nwsccampsite@nottscc.gov.uk
www.nwscnotts.com
Pitches For ⚑ ⊞ ⊞ **Total** 300
Acreage 28 **Open** All Year
Access Good **Site** Level
Nearest Bus Stop (Miles) ¼
Set in 270 acres of county park at the National Water Sports Centre. Close to Nottingham Castle and Galleries of Justice.
Facilities ∮ 🖩 🖩 🕾 ┌ ⚡
🖸 🖸 🖴 🕾 🖸 ⊟ 🖵
Nearby Facilities ┌ ✔ ⚓ ⚲ ∪ ⋗ ⅄
Nearest Town Nottingham
Directions Off the A52, signposted National Water Sports Centre, 3 miles from Nottingham city centre.
⇌ Nottingham

MANSFIELD

Tall Trees Park, Old Mill Lane, Forest Town, Mansfield, Nottinghamshire, NG19 0JP
Tel: 01623 626503
Email: info@talltreestouringpark.co.uk
www.talltreestouringpark.co.uk

Pitches For ⚑ 🚐 🚗 **Total** 15
Acreage 3 **Open** All Year
Access Good **Site** Sloping
Nearest Bus Stop (Miles) Entrance
Peaceful rural Park surrounded by open farmland. Within walking distance of amenities. Close to Clumber Park.
Facilities 🚿 ⚡ 🅿 ♿ 🛁 🍴 ⊙ 🚲 🛒 🔵 📞 ⚒ 🍺 🎣 ⚓ 🛒 🔵 ✎
Nearby Facilities 🎣 🚶 ⚓ 🏊 ∪ ⚐ ⛳ ✈
Nearest Town Mansfield
Directions From the A60 at Worksop turn at Fourways onto Old Mill Lane, the Park is on the left hand side.
🚉 Mansfield

NEWARK

Robin Hood Retreat, Middle Plantation, Belle Eau Park, Bilsthorpe, Nottinghamshire, NG22 8TY
Tel: 01623 871457
Email: robinhoodretreat@live.co.uk
Pitches For ⚑ 🚐 🚗 **Total** 24
Acreage 6¼ **Open** All Year
Access Good **Site** Lev/Slope
Nearest Bus Stop (Miles) ½
Near to Rufford Park, Sherwood Forest, Newark and Nottingham.
Facilities 🚿 ⚡ 🅿 ♿ ⊙ 🚲 🛒 🔵 📞
🍺 🍴 🅿 🔵 ✎
Nearby Facilities 🎣 🚶
Nearest Town Mansfield/Newark
Directions From the A617/A614 follow signs for Belle Eau Park Industrial Estate, go through the industrial estate following signs for Robin Hood Retreat.
🚉 Mansfield/Newark

NOTTINGHAM

Manor Farm Caravan Site, Manor Farm, Church Lane, Thrumpton, Nottinghamshire, NG11 0AX
Tel: 0115 983 0341
Pitches For 🚐 🚗 **Total** 12
Acreage 3 **Open** All Year
Access Good **Site** Level
Nearest Bus Stop (Miles) Outside
Facilities 🚿 ⚡ 🅿 ⊙ 🚲 🍺 🍴 🅿 🔵 ⚒
Nearby Facilities 🚶
Nearest Town Nottingham
Directions From the M1 junction 24, take the A453 Nottingham South, after 3 miles turn left to Thrumpton Village.
🚉 Nottingham

NOTTINGHAM

Thorntons Holt Camping Park, Stragglethorpe, Radcliffe-on-Trent, Nottinghamshire, NG12 2JZ
Tel: 0115 933 2125
Email: camping@thorntons-holt.co.uk
www.thorntons-holt.co.uk
Pitches For ⚑ 🚐 🚗 **Total** 155
Acreage 15 **Open** All Year
Access Good **Site** Level
Nearest Bus Stop (Miles) Outside
Only 3 miles from Nottingham. Ideal base for touring Sherwood Forest and the Vale of Belvoir. Pub and restaurant nearby.
Facilities 🚿 ⚡ 🅿 ♿ ⊙ 🚲 🛒 🔵 📞
🍺 🍴 ⊙ 🚲 🛒 🍺 🔵 ✎ 🍴 🎣 🅿 🔵 ✎ ⚒
Nearby Facilities 🎣 🚶 ⚓ ∪ ⚐ ⛳
Nearest Town Nottingham

Directions 3 miles east of Nottingham turn south of A52 towards Cropwell Bishop. Park is ¼ mile on left.
🚉 Radcliffe-on-Trent

RATCLIFFE ON SOAR

Red Hill Marina, Ratcliffe-on-Soar, Nottinghamshire, NG11 0EB
Tel: 01509 672770
www.redhill-marine.co.uk
Pitches For ⚑ 🚐 🚗 **Total** 15
Open All Year **Access** Good **Site** Level
By a river. Train station adjoins site.
Facilities 🚿 ⚡ 🅿 ✕ 🅿 🔵
Nearby Facilities 🎣
Nearest Town Nottingham
Directions Leave the M1 at junction 24 and take the A453, 1½ miles on the left hand side.
🚉 East Midlands Parkway

SUTTON-IN-ASHFIELD

Teversal Camping & Caravanning Club Site, Shardaroba Caravan Park, Silverhill Lane, Teversal, Nottinghamshire, NG17 3JJ
Tel: 01623 551838
www.campingandcaravanningclub.co.uk/ teversal
Pitches For ⚑ 🚐 🚗 **Total** 126
Acreage 6 **Open** All Year
Access Good **Site** Level
Nearest Bus Stop (Miles) ¼
Within easy reach of the market towns Chesterfield, Sutton-in-Ashfield and Mansfield. Six berth caravan available for hire. Gold Enjoy England Excellence Award 2005 and named Caravan Holiday Park of the Year. Non members welcome. You can also call us on 0845 130 7633.
Facilities 🚿 ⚡ 🅿 ♿ 🛁 🍴 ⊙ 🚲 🛒 🔵 📞
🍺 ⊙ 🚲 🛒 🍴 🅿 🔵 ✎ 📶
Nearby Facilities 🎣 🚶 ∪
Nearest Town Sutton-in-Ashfield
Directions Leave the M1 at junction 28 and take the A38 towards Mansfield. Turn left at the lights onto the B6027, go straight over next lights and turn left at the Peacock Hotel. Turn right onto the B6014, turn left at Caravan Arms and site is on the left.
🚉 Sutton-in-Ashfield

TUXFORD

Greenacres Caravan & Touring Park, Lincoln Road, Tuxford, Newark, Nottinghamshire, NG22 0JN
Tel: 01777 870264
Email: stay@greenacres-tuxford.co.uk
www.greenacres-tuxford.co.uk
Pitches For ⚑ 🚐 🚗 **Total** 67
Acreage 4½ **Open** Mid March **to** End Oct
Access Good **Site** Level
Nearest Bus Stop (Miles) Park Entrance
Ideal for night halt or for touring Robin Hood country. Static caravans for sale and hire. Secure Storage during Winter.
Facilities 🚿 ⚡ 🅿 ♿ ⊙ 🚲 🛒 🔵 📞
🍺 ⊙ 🚲 🛒 🍴 🅿 🔵 ✎
Nearby Facilities 🚶
Nearest Town Retford
Directions From A1 (north or south) follow signs. Park is on the left 250yds after Fountain Public House.
🚉 Retford

TUXFORD

Marnham Meadows Holiday Park, Hollowgate Lane, High Marnham, Newark, Nottinghamshire, NG23 6SG
Tel: 01636 822775
Pitches For ⚑ 🚐 🚗 **Total** 35
Open April **to** October
Access Good **Site** Level
Near the River Trent, the National Cycle Path to Lincoln and Sundown Adventure Park. Brownlow Arms Pub just a few minutes walk. Ralley Field.
Facilities 🚿 🅿 🍺 🍴 🅿 🔵 ⚒ ☀
Nearby Facilities 🎣 🚶 ⚐ ⛳
Nearest Town Newark/Lincoln
Directions From Newark take the A1 north to Tuxford, or from Lincoln take the A57 to Dunham.
🚉 Newark/Lincoln

TUXFORD

Orchard Park Touring Caravan & Camping, Orchard Park, Marnham Road, Tuxford, Newark, Nottinghamshire, NG22 0PY
Tel: 01777 870228
Email: info@orchardcaravanpark.co.uk
www.orchardcaravanpark.co.uk
Pitches For ⚑ 🚐 🚗 **Total** 60
Acreage 7 **Open** March **to** November
Access Good **Site** Level
Nearest Bus Stop (Miles) ½
A quiet, sheltered park, spaciously set in an old fruit orchard. Central for Sherwood Forest, Clumber Park, Lincoln and Nottingham.
Facilities 🚿 🚿 ⚡ 🅿 ♿ ⊙ 🚲 🛒 🔵 📞
🍺 🍴 ⊙ 🚲 🛒 🍴 🅿 🔵 ✎ ☀ 🔵 📶
Nearby Facilities 🎣 🚶
Nearest Town Newark
Directions Turn off the A1 dual carriageway at Tuxford, when you reach the T-Junction in the village turn right signposted Lincoln (A57). In ¼ mile turn right signposted Marnham, site is ½ a mile on the right.
🚉 Retford

WORKSOP

Clumber Park Caravan Club Site, Lime Tree Avenue, Clumber Park, Worksop, Nottinghamshire, S80 3AE
Tel: 01909 484758
www.caravanclub.co.uk
Pitches For 🚐 🚗 **Total** 183
Acreage 20 **Open** All Year
Access Good **Site** Level
Situated in 4000 acres of parkland (once part of Sherwood Forest), ideal for walking and cycling. Visitor Centre 10 minutes away. Close to Creswell Crags Cave Tours. Non members welcome. Booking essential.
Facilities 🚿 ⚡ 🅿 ♿ ⊙ 🚲 🛒 🔵 📞 🍺 ⊙ 🚲 🛒 🍴 🅿 🔵 ✎ 📶
Nearby Facilities 🎣 🚶 ∪
Nearest Town Worksop
Directions From the A1, at the roundabout junction of the A57 and the A614 turn onto the A614 signposted Nottingham. After ½ a mile turn right into Clumber Park through a stone arch, after 1 mile turn right, site is 50 yards on the left.
🚉 Worksop

WORKSOP

Riverside Caravan Park, Central Avenue, Worksop, Nottinghamshire, S80 1ER
Tel: 01909 474118
www.riversideworksop.co.uk
Pitches For A ⊕ ⊖ **Total** 60
Acreage 6 **Open** All Year **Site** Level
Nearest Bus Stop (Miles) ¼
Just a 5 minute walk from the town centre, where Market days are wednesday, friday and saturday. Ideal for canal walks and cycling. Showers take £1 coins.
Facilities ⚡
Nearby Facilities ⌐ ✓
Nearest Town Worksop
Directions From the A57 roundabout turn into Newcastle Avenue, turn first left into Stubbing Lane. Turn next right into Central Avenue, go past the cricket ground and into the Park.
⇌ Worksop

OXFORDSHIRE

BANBURY

Anitas Touring Caravan Park & Holiday Cottages, The Yews, Church Farm, Mollington, Banbury, Oxfordshire, OX17 1AZ
Tel: 01295 750731
Email: anitagail@btopenworld.com
www.anitascaravanandcottages.co.uk
Pitches For A ⊕ ⊖ **Total** 36
Acreage 2 **Open** March **to** Dec
Access Good **Site** Lev/Slope
Nearest Bus Stop (Miles) Outside
NEW for 2010 - Five Camping Pods! Please telephone for details. Ideal central location for the Cotswolds, Oxford, Silverstone, Warwick and Stratford. Good walks, cycling and eating locally. Rallies welcome.
Facilities ⚡
Nearby Facilities ⌐ ✓ U
Nearest Town Banbury
Directions From the M40 junction 11 take the A422 towards Banbury, go over two roundabouts and at the third roundabout turn right onto the A423 and travel for 4 miles. Just past Mollington turn site is 150 ys on the left.
⇌ Banbury

BANBURY

Barnstones Caravan & Camping Site, Barnstones, Main Street, Great Bourton, Nr Banbury, Oxfordshire, OX17 1QU
Tel: 01295 750289
Pitches For A ⊕ ⊖ ⊟ **Total** 49
Acreage 3 **Open** All Year
Access Good **Site** Level
Nearest Bus Stop (Miles) Outside
Very beautiful countryside. Ideal for the Cotswolds, Oxford, Stratford-upon-Avon and Warwick.
Facilities ⚡
Nearby Facilities ⌐ ✓ ⚡ U ♪
Nearest Town Banbury
Directions Leave the M40 at junction 11 and follow signs to Southam and Banbury over two roundabouts, at the third roundabout turn onto the A423. After 2 miles turn right signposted Great Bourton, the Site entrance is 120yds on the right.
⇌ Banbury

BENSON

Benson Waterfront, Benson, Wallingford, Oxfordshire, OX10 6SJ
Tel: 01491 838304
Email: sales@bensonwaterfront.com
www.bensonwaterfront.co.uk
Pitches For A ⊕ ⊖ **Total** 23
Acreage ½ **Open** April **to** October
Access Good **Site** Level
On the banks of the beautiful River Thames. Ideal for Oxford, Windsor and London.
Facilities ⚡
Nearby Facilities ⌐ ✓ ⚲
Nearest Town Wallingford
Directions On the A4074 Oxford to Reading road.
⇌ Cholsey

BLETCHINGDON

Diamond Caravan & Camping Park, Islip Road, Bletchingdon, Oxford, Oxfordshire, OX5 3DR
Tel: 01869 350909
Email: warden@diamondpark.co.uk
www.diamondpark.co.uk
Pitches For A ⊕ ⊖ **Total** 37
Open All Year
Access Good **Site** Level
Nearest Bus Stop (Miles) ½
Small family run site. Ideal for Oxford, the Cotswolds and the Chilterns.
Facilities ⚡
Nearby Facilities ⌐ ✓
Nearest Town Kidlington
Directions From Kidlington take the A34 and leave at the junction sp Bletchingdon, Park is 1 mile on the left hand side.
⇌ Islip

BLETCHINGDON

Greenhill Leisure Park, Greenhill Farm, Station Road, Bletchingdon, Oxfordshire, OX5 3BQ
Tel: 01869 351600
Email: info@greenhill-leisure-park.co.uk
www.greenhill-leisure-park.co.uk
Pitches For A ⊕ ⊖ ⊟ **Total** 92
Acreage 7 **Open** All Year
Access Good **Site** Lev/Slope
Quiet and spacious farm site. Pets Corner, farm animals and riverside walks. Two new fishing lakes have been created. Rally field available. 3 miles from Blenheim Palace. Ideal for touring the Cotswolds.
Facilities ⚡
Nearby Facilities ⌐ ✓
Nearest Town Woodstock
Directions 3 miles east of Woodstock and 8 miles north of Oxford on the B4027. 2½ miles from the A34 and 7 miles south of the M40 junction 9.
⇌ Islip

BURFORD

Burford Caravan Club Site, Bradwell Grove, Burford, Oxfordshire, OX18 4JJ
Tel: 01993 823080
www.caravanclub.co.uk
Pitches For ⊕ ⊖ **Total** 119
Acreage 10 **Open** March **to** Nov
Access Good **Site** Level
Attractive and spacious site. Area for volleyball, netball and football (goal posts). Opposite Cotswold Wildlife Park. Non members welcome. Booking essential.
Facilities ⚡
Nearby Facilities ⌐ ✓
Directions Leave Oxford on A40, after approx. 23 miles at large roundabout in Burford turn left onto A361 and follow signs for Cotswold Wildlife Park. After 2 miles at crossroads turn right, DO NOT turn right into New Bradwell Village, site is 70 yards on the right

CHIPPING NORTON

Camping & Caravanning Club Site, Chipping Norton Road, Chadlington, Chipping Norton, Oxfordshire, OX7 3PE
Tel: 01608 641993
www.campingandcaravanningclub.co.uk/chippingnorton
Pitches For A ⊕ ⊖ **Total** 105
Open 29-Mar **to** 05-Nov
Site Lev/Slope
Nearest Bus Stop (Miles) Outside
Perfect for exploring the Cotswolds. 11 miles from Blenheim Palace. BTB 4 Star Graded and AA 3 Pennants. Non members welcome. You can also call us on 0845 130 7633.
Facilities ⚡
Nearby Facilities ⌐ ✓ U ℛ
Directions Take the A44 or the A361 to Chipping Norton. Pick up the A361 Burford road, turn left at the crossroads and the site is 150 yards. From Burford stay on the A361 and turn right at the sign for Chadlington.

HENLEY-ON-THAMES

Swiss Farm International, Marlow Road, Henley-on-Thames, Oxfordshire, RG9 2HY
Tel: 01491 573419
Email: enquiries@swissfarmcamping.co.uk
www.swissfarmcamping.co.uk
Pitches For A ⊕ ⊖ **Total** 160
Acreage 20 **Open** March **to** December
Access Good **Site** Sloping
Ideal for visiting London, Oxford, Windsor and South East England.
Facilities ⚡
Nearby Facilities ⌐ ✓
Nearest Town Henley-on-Thames
Directions From Henley take the A4155 towards Marlow, site is 500 yards on the left after the rugby club.
⇌ Henley-on-Thames

OXFORD

Camping & Caravanning Club Site, 426 Abingdon Road, Oxford, Oxfordshire, OX1 4XG
Tel: 01865 244088
www.campingandcaravanningclub.co.uk/oxford
Pitches For A ⊕ ⊖ **Total** 85
Acreage 5 **Open** All Year
Access Good **Site** Level
Nearest Bus Stop (Miles) Outside

Lincoln Farm Park Oxfordshire
At the Gateway to the Cotswolds
STANDLAKE | OXFORDSHIRE | OX29 7RH **01865 300239**
www.lincolnfarmpark.co.uk info@lincolnfarmpark.co.uk

Small family park, 9 miles from historic Oxford. Village location with two pubs and only 1 mile from the River Thames. AA Campsite of the Year 2010. 5 Star Indoor Leisure Centre and two pools, spas, saunas and a steam room. ◆ Shop ◆ Childrens Play Area ◆ Tenters Kitchen ◆ Dogs Welcome

In one of Britains most popular tourist destinations, this university city has a lot more to offer with more than 650 listed buildings. AA 3 Pennants. Non members welcome. You can also call us on 0845 130 7633.
Facilities
Nearby Facilities
Nearest Town Oxford
Directions From the M40 take the A34 at the A423, turn left immediately after junction into Abingdon Road, site is on the left behind Touchwood Sports.
⚡ Oxford

WITNEY
Hardwick Parks, Downs Road, Standlake, Nr Witney, Oxfordshire, OX29 7PZ
Tel: 01865 300501
Email: info@hardwickparks.co.uk
www.hardwickparks.co.uk
Pitches For Å ⊞ ⊞ **Total** 214
Acreage 40 **Open** April **to** October
Access Good **Site** Level
Nearest Bus Stop (Miles) Outside
On the edge of the Cotswolds. Two lakes on the park. Holiday homes for hire.
Facilities
Nearby Facilities
Nearest Town Witney
Directions A415 Witney to Abingdon road, signposted 4 miles out of Witney on the main road.
⚡ Oxford

WITNEY
Lincoln Farm Park, High Street, Standlake, Nr Witney, Oxfordshire, OX29 7RH
Tel: 01865 300239
Email: info@lincolnfarmpark.co.uk
www.lincolnfarmpark.co.uk
Pitches For Å ⊞ ⊞ **Total** 90
Acreage 8 **Open** 01-Feb **to** Mid Nov
Access Good **Site** Level
Nearest Bus Stop (Miles) Outside
Leisure centre with two indoor swimming pools, saunas, spa and fitness centre. Two village pubs each serving food nearby.
Facilities
Nearby Facilities
Nearest Town Witney
Directions On the A415 5 miles from Witney and 9 miles from Abingdon.
⚡ Oxford

SHROPSHIRE
BISHOPS CASTLE
Cwnd House Farm, Wentnor, Bishops Castle, Shropshire,
Tel: 01588 650237
Pitches For Å ⊞ ⊞ **Total** 10
Acreage 2 **Open** May **to** October
Access Good **Site** Level
Farm site with scenic views. Ideal touring centre.
Facilities
Nearby Facilities
Nearest Town Church Stretton
Directions Cwnd House Farm is on Longden Pulverbatch road from Shrewsbury (13 miles) Bishops Castle is southwest. From Craven Arms take the A489 to Lydham Heath, turn right, site is about 1 mile past the Inn on the Green, take second turn right by the black and white boards.
⚡ Church Stretton

BISHOPS CASTLE
Daisy Bank Caravan Park, Snead, Montgomery, Powys, SY15 6EB
Tel: 01588 620471
Email: enquiries@daisy-bank.co.uk
www.daisy-bank.co.uk
Pitches For Å ⊞ ⊞ **Total** 55
Acreage 6 **Open** All Year
Access Good **Site** Lev/Slope
Nearest Bus Stop (Miles) ½
Quiet and peaceful ADULT ONLY park, in an area of natural beauty. Situated in the heart of the Camlad Valley with scenic views. Perfect for walkers. Also open for Christmas and New Year.
Facilities
Nearby Facilities
Nearest Town Bishops Castle
Directions Situated off the A489 between Craven Arms and Churchstoke. 2 miles east of Churchstoke.
⚡ Craven Arms

BISHOPS CASTLE
The Green Caravan Park, Wentnor, Bishops Castle, Shropshire, SY9 5EF
Tel: 01588 650605
Email: karen@greencaravanpark.co.uk
www.greencaravanpark.co.uk
Pitches For Å ⊞ ⊞ **Total** 140
Open Easter **to** October
Access Good **Site** Level
Picturesque, riverside site in an area of outstanding natural beauty. Superb walking in the countryside. Excellent birdlife. Central for touring. David Bellamy Gold Award for Conservation.
Facilities

Nearby Facilities
Nearest Town Bishops Castle
Directions Follow brown tourism signs from the A488 and the A489.
⚡ Craven Arms

BRIDGNORTH
The Riverside Caravan Park, Kidderminster Road, Bridgnorth, Shropshire, WV15 6BY
Tel: 01746 762393
www.theriversidecaravanpark.co.uk
Pitches For ⊞ ⊞ **Total** 8
Open March **to** January
Access Good **Site** Level
Nearest Bus Stop (Miles) Outside
On the banks of the River Severn. Just a 10 minute walk to Bridgnorth. Watch the Severn Valley Railway steam by.
Facilities
Nearby Facilities
Nearest Town Bridgnorth
Directions From Bridgnorth on the A442 road to Kidderminster, take the first turning on the right (150 metres).
⚡ Telford

BRIDGNORTH
Woodend Farm, Woodend Lane, Highley, Shropshire, WV16 6HY
Tel: 01746 861571
Email: charlesdavies07@btinternet.com
Pitches For Å ⊞ ⊞
Open All Year
Access Good **Site** Lev/Slope
Nearest Bus Stop (Miles) ½
Access to the River Severn and Severn Valley Railway. Village has a new Leisure Centre, large outdoor pool, gardens and an 18 hole golf course. Ideal base for Ludlow, Much Wenlock, Shrewsbury, Ironbridge, Bewdley and safari park. You can also contact us on Mobile: 07976 247473.
Facilities
Nearby Facilities
Nearest Town Bridgnorth
Directions From Bridgnorth take the B4555 to Highley. In Highley turn left opposite the leisure centre, follow the lane down hill bearing to the left until in the farm yard.
⚡ Highley

CHURCH STRETTON
Small Batch, Little Stretton, Church Stretton, Shropshire, SY6 6PW
Tel: 01694 723358
Pitches For Å ⊞ ⊞ **Total** 40
Acreage 1½ **Open** Easter **to** End Sept
Access Good **Site** Level
Scenic views and ideal touring.
Facilities

Directions A49 south, 2 miles south of Church Stretton turn right onto the B5477. Take the second left, at T-Junction turn right up to site through stream.
🚉 Church Stretton

CRAVEN ARMS
Kevindale, Broome, Craven Arms, Shropshire, SY7 0NT
Tel: 01588 660199
Email: keith@kevindale.co.uk
www.kevindale.co.uk
Pitches For 🏕 🚐 🚙 **Total** 12
Acreage 2 **Open** April **to** October
Access Good **Site** Level
Nearest Bus Stop (Miles) Outside
Scenic views, near village inn with good food. Close to Mid Wales Border, ideal walking. Two acre field, rallys welcome.
Facilities ⨍ 🔞 🚿 ⌒ ⊙ 🅿 💷⭑🍴🗑
Nearby Facilities ⌒ ✔ ∪
Nearest Town Craven Arms
Directions From Craven Arms which is situated on the A49 Hereford to Shrewsbury road, take the B4368 Clun/Bishops Castle road, in 2 miles take the B4367 Knighton road and after 1¼ miles turn right into Broome Village.
🚉 Broome

ELLESMERE
Fernwood Caravan Park, Lyneal, Nr Ellesmere, Shropshire, SY12 0QF
Tel: 01948 710221
Email: enquiries@fernwoodpark.co.uk
www.fernwoodpark.co.uk
Pitches For 🚐 🚙 **Total** 60
Acreage 7 **Open** March **to** November
Access Good **Site** Lev/Slope
Nearest Bus Stop (Miles) 1
40 acres of woodland open to caravanners. Lake with wildfowl and coarse fishing.
Facilities 🚽 ⨍ 🔞 🚿 ⌒ ⊙ 🗑 🅿 🗑
🔖 🔞 🛁 ⚑ 🗑 🅿 🗑 ✔ ✻
Nearby Facilities ⌒ ✔ ⚓ ✻
Directions A495 from Ellesmere signposted Whitchurch. In Welshampton, right turn on B5063 signed Wem. Over canal bridge right sign Lyneal.
🚉 Wem

LUDLOW
Westbrook Park, Lynch Lane, Little Hereford, Ludlow, Shropshire, SY8 4AU
Tel: 01584 711280
Email: info@westbrookpark.co.uk
www.bestparks.co.uk
Pitches For 🏕 🚐 🚙 **Total** 60
Acreage 10 **Open** March **to** November
Access Good **Site** Level
Nearest Bus Stop (Miles) ¼
Half a mile of river fishing. Close to the famous town of Ludlow and within a short distance of Tenbury Wells.
Facilities 🚽 ⨍ 🔞 🔞 🚿 ⌒ ⊙ 🗑 🖿 🗑
🔞 🛁 🗑 🅿 🗑 ✔ ✻
Nearby Facilities ⌒ ∪ ⚓
Nearest Town Tenbury Wells
Directions Off the A456. From the north and Ludlow take the A49 then the A456.

MARKET DRAYTON
Wharf Caravan Park, Goldstone, Market Drayton, Shropshire, TF9 2LP
Tel: 01630 661226
Email: info@wharfcaravanpark.co.uk
www.wharfcaravanpark.co.uk
Pitches For **Total** 50
Acreage 5 **Open** All Year
Access Good **Site** Level
Alongside Shropshire Union Canal with a pub on the doorstep. Picturesque, peaceful countryside. Ideal for fishing, walking and

cycling. Central location for Shrewsbury, The Potteries and Iron Bridge.
Facilities ⨍ 🔞 🔞 ⌒ ⊙ 🗑 🗑
✗ 🛁 🗑 🅿 🗑 ✻
Nearby Facilities ⌒ ✔ ✻ ∪ ⚓
Nearest Town Market Drayton
Directions From the A41 take the A529, go through Hinstock Village for approx 2 miles and turn right for Cheswardine. Follow the lane and signs for approx 1 mile, Park is over the canal bridge on the right.
🚉 Wem

MINSTERLEY
The Old School Caravan Park, Shelve, Minsterley, Shrewsbury, Shropshire, SY5 0JQ
Tel: 01588 650410
www.oldschoolcaravanpark.co.uk
Pitches For 🏕 🚐 🚙 **Total** 22
Acreage 1½ **Open** March **to** January
Site Slight Slope
Nearest Bus Stop (Miles) Entrance
In an area of outstanding natural beauty, good walks and fishing. Close to Stiperstones and Long Mynd.
Facilities ⨍ 🔞 🔞 🚿 ⌒ ⊙ 🗑 🗑
🔞 🛁 🗑 🅿 🗑 ✻ ⚑
Nearby Facilities ⌒ ✔ ∪ ⚓
Nearest Town Shrewsbury
Directions On the A5 in Shrewsbury turn onto the A488 to Bishops Castle. After 16 miles go through the village of Hope and the site is on the left 50 metres after the bus stop and phone box.
🚉 Shrewsbury

MUCH WENLOCK
Presthope Caravan Club Site, Stretton Road, Much Wenlock, Shropshire, TF13 6DQ
Tel: 01746 785234
www.caravanclub.co.uk
Pitches For 🚐 🚙 **Total** 73
Acreage 10 **Open** April **to** Sept
Access Good **Site** Level
Interesting site with abundant wildlife, set on the slopes of Wenlock Edge. A walkers paradise. Close to Ironbridge Gorge, museum and bridge. Near Severn Valley Railway and Blists Hill Open Air Museum. Own sanitation required. Non members welcome. Booking essential.
Facilities ⨍ 🔞 🗎 🔞 ⊙ 🗑 🗑 🅿 🗑
Nearby Facilities ✔
Nearest Town Much Wenlock
Directions Leave M54 at junc 6 and take A5223 sp Ironbridge, watch for change of signs from Ironbridge to Much Wenlock. At Jiggers roundabout turn right onto A4169, after 1¾ miles turn left (still on A4169) sp Much Wenlock. At T-junction opposite Gaskell Arms turn right on to A458, after ¼ mile turn left on to B4371, site is 3mls on left.
🚉 Much Wenlock

OSWESTRY
Oswestry Camping & Caravanning Club Site, Cranberry Moss, Kinnerley, Oswestry, Shropshire, SY10 8DY
Tel: 01743 741118
www.campingandcaravanningclub.co.uk/oswestry
Pitches For 🏕 🚐 🚙 **Total** 65
Open All Year
Access Good **Site** Level
Nearest Bus Stop (Miles) Outside
Close to the old Oswestry Hill Fort, Park Hall, Whittington Castle, Shrewsbury Abbey, Attingham Park, Wroxeter Roman City, Offas Dyke and Pistyll Falls. Local produce sold in the site shop. Non members welcome. You can also call us on 0845 130 7633.

Facilities 🚽 ⨍ 🔞 🔞 🚿 ⌒ ⊙ 🗑 🖿 🗑 🗑
🔞 🔞 🗑 🅿 🗑 🗑 ⚏
Nearby Facilities
Nearest Town Oswestry
Directions Turn off the A5 at the roundabout at the north end of the dual carriageway signed B4396 Knockin.
🚉 Shrewsbury

SHREWSBURY
Beaconsfield Farm Holiday Park, Battlefield, Shrewsbury, Shropshire, SY4 4AA
Tel: 01939 210370
Email: mail@beaconsfield-farm.co.uk
www.beaconsfield-farm.co.uk
Pitches For 🚐 🚙 **Total** 60
Acreage 15 **Open** All Year
Access Good **Site** Level
Exclusively for ADULTS over 21 years. 5 Star, well landscaped, level park with coarse fishing. A La Carte restaurant on the park. 1½ miles to Park & Ride. Ideal base for Shrewsbury and the Welsh border. Holiday homes for sale and hire.
Facilities 🚽 ⨍ 🔞 🔞 🚿 ⌒ ⊙ 🗑 🖿 🗑 🗑
🔖 🔞 ✗ ⚑ 🗑 🅿 ⚑ 🗑 ✻ ⚏ ✻
Nearby Facilities ⌒ ✔ ∪ ⚓ ⚓
Nearest Town Shrewsbury
Directions 1½ miles north of Shrewsbury on the A49.
🚉 Shrewsbury

SHREWSBURY
Cartref Caravan & Camping Site, Cartref, Fords Heath, Nr Shrewsbury, Shropshire, SY5 9GD
Tel: 01743 821688
Email: alanpat@edwardscartref.wanadoo.co.uk
www.cartrefcaravansite.co.uk
Pitches For 🏕 🚐 🚙 **Total** 47
Acreage 1½ **Open** Easter **to** October
Access Good **Site** Level
Peaceful countryside. Ideal for touring or an overnight stop. Adult Only section of 11 pitches.
Facilities 🚽 ⨍ 🔞 ⌒ ⊙ 🗑 🗑
🔞 🛁 🗑 🅿 🗑 ✻
Nearby Facilities ⌒ ✔
Directions From Shrewsbury bypass A5 trunk road take the A458 Welshpool West. 2 miles to Ford Village, turn south at Ford, follow camp signs. Signposted from the A5 bypass on the Montgomery junction B4386.
🚉 Shrewsbury

SHREWSBURY
Ebury Hill Camping & Caravanning Club Site, Ebury Hill, Ring Bank, Haughton, Shrewsbury, Shropshire, SY4 4GB
Tel: 01743 709334
www.campingandcaravanningclub.co.uk/eburyhill
Pitches For 🏕 🚐 🚙 **Total** 100
Acreage 18 **Open** 29-Mar **to** 05-Nov
Access Good **Site** Lev/Slope
Set on an ancient Iron Age hill fort, with panoramic views. Close to Shrewsbury and Ironbridge Gorge. Fishing on site. BTB 4 Star Graded, David Bellamy Gold Award and AA 1 Pennant. Non members welcome. You can also call us on 0845 130 7633.
Facilities ⨍ 🔞 🔞 🔞 ⊙ 🔞 🗑 🅿 🗑 ✔ ✻
Nearby Facilities ⌒ ✔ ✻
Nearest Town Shrewsbury
Directions From the A5/A49 take the B5062 signposted Newport, pass Haughmond Abbey and turn left signposted Hadnall. Site is on the left in approx. 1 mile.
🚉 Shrewsbury

SHREWSBURY

Middle Darnford Farm, Ratlinghope,
Pontesbury, Shrewsbury, Shropshire, SY5
0SR
Tel: 01694 751320
Pitches For Å ⊕ ⊛
Acreage 2 **Open** 15-Mar **to** Dec
Access Good **Site** Level
Excellent views.
Facilities ⬚⬚⬚⬚⬚
Nearby Facilities ∪
Nearest Town Church Stretton
Directions From the A49 turn at Leebotwood
and follow the road through Woolstaston over
Long Myn Hill and the Farm is on the left
hand side.
≠ Church Stretton

SHREWSBURY

Severn House, Montford Bridge,
Shrewsbury, Shropshire, SY4 1ED
Tel: 01743 850229
Email:
booking@severnhousecampsite.co.uk
www.severnhousecampsite.co.uk
Pitches For Å ⊕ ⊛ **Total** 25
Acreage 2½ **Open** April **to** October
Access Good **Site** Level
Nearest Bus Stop (Miles) ¼
Riverside site with 300 metres of river for
fishing. Dog walk, local shop, buses, pub and
meals nearby. Regular bus service.
Facilities ⬚⬚⬚⬚⬚⬚⬚⬚⬚
⬚⬚⬚⬚⬚
Nearby Facilities
Nearest Town Shrewsbury
Directions 4 miles north west of Shrewsbury
on the A5 towards Oswestry and North
Wales. At signposts for the site turn onto the
B4380 and Montford Bridge is ½ mile.
≠ Shrewsbury

WEM

Lower Lacon Caravan Park, Wem,
Shropshire, SY4 5RP
Tel: 01939 232376
Email: info@llcp.co.uk
www.llcp.co.uk
Pitches For Å ⊕ ⊛ **Total** 270
Acreage 48 **Open** All Year
Access Good **Site** Level
Nearest Bus Stop (Miles) Outside
Facilities ⬚⬚⬚⬚⬚⬚⬚⬚⬚⬚
⬚⬚⬚⬚⬚⬚⬚⬚⬚⬚⬚⬚⬚⬚
Nearby Facilities ⬚⬚
Nearest Town Wem
Directions 1 mile from Wem on the B5065.
From the A49 then the B5065, 3 miles.
≠ Wem

WHITCHURCH

Green Lane Farm Caravan & Camp Site,
Green Lane Farm, Prees, Whitchurch,
Shropshire, SY13 2AH
Tel: 01948 840460
Email: greenlanefarm@tiscali.co.uk
www.greenlanecaravanpark.co.uk
Pitches For Å ⊕ ⊛ **Total** 22
Acreage 2½ **Open** March **to** Oct
Access Good **Site** Level
Nearest Bus Stop (Miles) ¼
Central for all local attractions, Hawkstone,
Shrewsbury, Chester, Llangollen, Nantwich,
etc..
Facilities ⬚⬚⬚⬚⬚⬚⬚⬚⬚⬚⬚
⬚
Nearby Facilities ⬚⬚∪
Nearest Town Whitchurch
Directions 350 yards off the the main A41
between Whitchurch and Newport.
≠ Whitchurch

WHITCHURCH

Roden View Caravan & Camping, Roden
View, Dobsons Bridge, Whixall,
Whitchurch, Shropshire, SY13 2QL
Tel: 01948 710320
Email: jean@roden-view.co.uk
www.roden-view.co.uk
Pitches For Å ⊕ ⊛ **Total** 14
Acreage 4½ **Open** All Year
Access Good **Site** Level
Near to the Shropshire Union Canal and
Whixall Moss. 5 miles from Ellesmere,
Shropshires Lake District. Large fishing pool.
Facilities ⬚⬚⬚⬚⬚⬚⬚⬚⬚⬚
Nearby Facilities ⬚⬚⬚⬚
Nearest Town Wem
Directions From Shrewsbury Wem Church
turn left after second garage, then turn right
for Whixall, at the next T-Junction turn left
then immediately right, 2½ miles to the next
T-Junction turn right. ½ mile the house is on
the right before Dobsons Bridge.
≠ Wem

SOMERSET

BATH

Bath Chew Valley Caravan Park, Ham
Lane, Bishop Sutton, Somerset, BS39 5TZ
Tel: 01275 332127
Email: enquiries@bathchewvalley.co.uk
www.bathchewvalley.co.uk
Pitches For ⊕ ⊛ **Total** 45
Acreage 4 **Open** All Year
Access Good **Site** Level
Nearest Bus Stop (Miles) ¼
ADULTS ONLY PARK. A site for peace and
tranquility, set in an area of outstanding
natural beauty. Luxury bathroom and toilets.
ETB 5 Star Graded, the only 5 Star Park in
North East Somerset. Practical Caravan Top
100 Overall Winner 2009.

Holiday Resort Unity

Prices From
£4
Per Person
Per Night

- Swimming Pool
- Kids Club
- 18 Hole Golf
- Family Pitch & Putt
- Pets Welcome
- Entertainment
- Special Discounts
- Theme Park
- Sandy Beaches
- Free Showers

More than just a holiday!

Brean Sands, Somerset   Tel : 0845 230 3350   Web : www.hru.co.uk

---

Facilities ⚬ ...
Nearby Facilities
Nearest Town Bath
Directions Approaching Bath on A37 or A38 Bristol to Wells or Bristol to Taunton roads, take A368 which links both to Bishop Sutton, turn opposite the Red Lion Pub.
Bath

BATH
Bury View Farm, Corston Fields, Nr. Bath, Somerset, BA2 9HD
Tel: 01225 873672
Email: salbowd@btinternet.com
Pitches For A ⊞ ⊞ **Total** 18
Acreage 2 **Open** All Year
Access Good **Site** Level
Quiet site, close to the city of Bath and Bristol. Within easy reach of Cheddar, Wells and Longleat. Open all year subject to weather.
Facilities ⚬
Nearby Facilities
Nearest Town Keynsham/Bath
Directions From Bath take the A4 Bristol road, at Newton-St-Loe roundabout take second left onto the A39 for Wells and Weston-super-Mare, Park is 1 mile.
Keynsham/Bath

BATH
Newton Mill Holiday Park, Newton Road, Newton St Loe, Bath, Somerset, BA2 9JF
Tel: 0844 272 9503
Email: enquiries@newtonmillpark.co.uk
www.newtonmillpark.co.uk
Pitches For A ⊞ ⊞ **Total** 215
Acreage 42 **Open** All Year

Access Good **Site** Lev/Slope
Nearest Bus Stop (Miles) ¼
A beautiful, idyllic setting in a hidden valley with a brook running through the Park. Close to the city centre (good public transport). Near to the traffic free Bath to Bristol cycle path and World Heritage Site.
Facilities
Nearby Facilities
Nearest Town Bath
Directions On the A4 Bath to Bristol road, at the roundabout by the Globe Public House take the exit left signposted Newton St Loe, Park is 1 mile on the left.
Bath Spa

BREAN SANDS
Channel View Touring Park, Warren Road, Brean, Burnham-on-Sea, Somerset, TA8 2RR
Tel: 01278 751055
www.breanfarm.co.uk
Pitches For A ⊞ ⊞ **Total** 50
Acreage 3 **Open** April to End Oct
Access Good **Site** Gentle Slope
Nearest Bus Stop (Miles) ½
Quiet and friendly site, on the beach side overlooking farmland.
Facilities
Nearby Facilities
Nearest Town Brean Sands
Directions Leave the M5 at junction 22 and follow signs to Burnham-on-Sea, Berrow and Brean. Site is ¼ mile past the Brean Down Inn on the left hand side.
Highbridge

BREAN SANDS
Holiday Resort Unity at Unity Farm, Coast Road, Brean Sands, Somerset, TA8 2RB
Tel: 01278 751235
Email: admin@hru.co.uk
www.hru.co.uk
Pitches For A ⊞ ⊞ ⊞ **Total** 800
Acreage 200 **Open** February to Nov
Access Good **Site** Level
Nearest Bus Stop (Miles) Outside
200yds from 7 mile beach, own leisure centre with 50 fun fair attractions, pool complex with 3 giant water slides, 18 hole golf course, lake for fishing, horse riding and 10 Pin Bowling. Family entertainment - Easter to November. Special offers for young families and OAPs in June and Sept.
Facilities
Nearby Facilities
Nearest Town Burnham-on-Sea
Directions Leave M5 at junction 22. Follow signs for Berrow and Brean Leisure Park, site on right 4½ miles from the M5.
Weston-Super-Mare

BREAN SANDS
Northam Farm Holiday Park, Brean, Nr Burnham-on-Sea, Somerset, TA8 2SE
Tel: 01278 751244
Email: enquiries@northamfarm.co.uk
www.northamfarm.co.uk
Pitches For A ⊞ ⊞ **Total** 350
Acreage 30 **Open** March to October
Access Good **Site** Level
Nearest Bus Stop (Miles) Outside
Ideal base for seeing Somerset. 6 miles of sandy beach. Our Seagull Inn with family entertainment is within easy walking distance. Excellent facilities, fishing lake and

FLEET AIR ARM MUSEUM
The thrill is being there
See the Aircraft Carrier Experience and Concorde
01935 840565
fleetairarm.com
RNAS Yeovilton, BA22 8HT
THE NATIONAL MUSEUM | ROYAL NAVY

SOMERSET

a diner with take-away food on park. ETC 4 Star Graded and AA 4 Pennants.
Facilities ♿ ⚡ ♨ 🚽 🅿 ☎ ☀ 🛒 ⛽ 🔌 ♻ 🏪 📮 💷 🍴 ⛺ 🔥
Nearby Facilities ► ✓ ⚓ ⅄ U ⚲ ⚡
Nearest Town Burnham-on-Sea
Directions M5 Junction 22. Follow signs to Brean, ¼ mile past Leisure Park on righthand side.
⛟ Weston-super-Mare

BREAN SANDS

Warren Farm Holiday Centre, Brean Sands, Burnham-on-Sea, Somerset, TA8 2RP
Tel: 01278 751227
Email: enquiries@warren-farm.co.uk
www.warren-farm.co.uk
Pitches For ▲ ⊞ ⊞ **Total** 500
Acreage 100 **Open** April to End Oct
Access Good **Site** Level
Nearest Bus Stop (Miles) ¼
Flat, grassy, family park with excellent facilities, indoor play area and family entertainment at the Beachcomber Inn. 100 metres from 5 miles of sandy beach. Dogs are welcome free in designated areas. AA Holiday Centre.
Facilities ♿ ⚡ ♨ 🚽 🅿 ☎ ☀ 🛒 ⛽ 🔌 ♻ 🏪 📮 💷 🍴 ⛺ 🔥 🏪 📮 💷 🍴 ⛺ 🔥 ♻ 🔌
Nearby Facilities ► ✓ ⚓ ⅄ U ⚲
Nearest Town Burnham-on-Sea
Directions Leave M5 at junction 22, follow signs to Burnham-on-Sea, Berrow and Brean on the B3140. Site is 1¼ miles past the leisure centre.
⛟ Weston-super-Mare

BRIDGWATER

Currypool Mill, Cannington, Bridgwater, Somerset, TA5 2NH
Tel: 01278 671135
Email: info@currypoolmill.co.uk
www.currypoolmill.co.uk
Pitches For ▲ ⊞ ⊞ **Total** 42
Open Easter to Mid Nov
Access Good **Site** Level
Quiet location near the Quantock Hills and Somerset coast. Set amongst streams and waterfalls. Dog walking fields, putting and croquet. Disabled toilet and shower.
Facilities ♿ ⚡ ♨ 🚽 🅿 ☎ ☀ 🛒 ⛽ 🔌 ♻ 🏪 📮 💷 🍴 ⛺ 🔥
Nearby Facilities ► ✓ ⚓ ⅄ U ⚲
Nearest Town Bridgwater
Directions From Bridgwater take the A39 Minehead road, after approx. 5 miles take a left hand turning signposted Spaxton and Aisholt. Currypool is approx. ½ a mile on the left.
⛟ Bridgwater

BRIDGWATER

Fairways International Caravan & Camping Park, Bath Road, Bawdrip, Bridgwater, Somerset, TA7 8PP
Tel: 01278 685569
Email:
holiday@fairwaysinternational.co.uk
www.fairwaysinternational.co.uk
Pitches For ▲ ⊞ ⊞ **Total** 200
Acreage 8¼ **Open** All Year
Access Good **Site** Level
Nearest Bus Stop (Miles) ¼
Within easy reach of Cheddar, Wells, Glastonbury, Mendip Hills and Burnham-on-Sea. ACSI Camping Card Discounts. Special Offers - Pensioner weeks in March, Jan, Feb, March, June, Sept, Oct and Dec.

Facilities ♿ ⚡ ♨ 🚽 🅿 ☎ ☀ 🛒 ⛽ 🔌 ♻ 🏪 📮 💷 🍴 ⛺ 🔥
Nearby Facilities ► ✓ ⚓ ⅄ U ⚲ ⚡ ⚲
Nearest Town Bridgwater
Directions Leave the M5 at junction 23 and take the A39 towards Glastonbury, at the junction of the B3141.
⛟ Bridgwater

BRIDGWATER

Mill Farm Caravan & Camping Park, Fiddington, Bridgwater, Somerset, TA5 1JQ
Tel: 01278 732286
www.millfarm.biz
Pitches For ▲ ⊞ ⊞ **Total** 200
Open All Year
Access Good **Site** Level
Unique, sheltered family park. Situated at the foot of the Quantock Hills offering tropical indoor pool, pony rides, boating lake and club with entertainment during high season. Please see our advertisement for more details.
Facilities ♿ ⚡ ♨ 🚽 🅿 ☎ ☀ 🛒 ⛽ 🔌 ♻ 🏪 📮 💷 🍴 ⛺ 🔥 🔌 ♻ 🔌
Nearby Facilities ► ✓ ⚓ ⅄ U
Nearest Town Bridgwater
Directions Leave the M5 at junction 23 or 24 and go through Bridgwater. Follow the A39 towards Minehead for 6 miles. At Keenthorne turn right for Fiddington, Mill Farm is 1 mile.
⛟ Bridgwater

BRUTON

Batcombe Vale Caravan & Camping Park, Batcombe, Shepton Mallet, Somerset, BA4 6BW
Tel: 01749 831207
Email: gary.butler1@virgin.net
www.batcombevale.co.uk

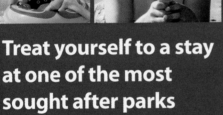

Pitches For Å ⚎ ⛺ **Total** 32
Acreage 7 **Open** April **to** Sept
Access Good **Site** Level
Own secluded valley of lakes and wild gardens. Fishing and boating on site. Near Longleat, Stourhead and Glastonbury. All shops are 2 miles away.
Facilities ⨍ ⌂ ⬚⚏↑ ⌐⊙⌔ ⬚⊡ ⛾
⑫ ⊙⨯⊟⩘
Nearby Facilities ⌐ ⚒ U
Nearest Town Bruton
Directions Access must be via Bruton or Evercreech from where it is well signed.
⚌ Bruton

BURNHAM-ON-SEA
Burnham Association of Sports Clubs, Stoddens Road, Burnham-on-Sea, Somerset, TA8 2DB
Tel: 01278 788355
Email: mail@basc1.plus.com
www.thebasc.org.uk
Pitches For Å ⚎ ⛺ ⛺ **Total** 20
Open April **to** Oct
Access Good **Site** Level
Nearest Bus Stop (Miles) Outside
1½ miles from the beach.
Facilities ⨍ ⬚⚏↑ ⌐⌙⛾⚘⬚
Nearby Facilities ⌐ ⚒ ⚒⚑U ⚐ ⚘ ⚹
⚌ Highbridge

BURNHAM-ON-SEA
Burnham-on-Sea Holiday Village, Marine Drive, Burnham-on-Sea, Somerset, TA8 1LA
Tel: 01278 783391
Email: burnhamonsea@haven.com
www.haventouring.com/toburnhamonsea
Pitches For Å ⚎ ⛺ **Total** 72
Acreage 95 **Open** Mid March **to** End Oct
Access Good **Site** Level
Nearest Bus Stop (Miles) Outside
Enjoy easy access to the beach and promenade, or stroll around the fishing lakes. Plus there's tennis, kids clubs and family entertainment.
Facilities ⨍ ⬚⌂ ⬚⚏↑ ⌐⊙⌔⬚⊡⛾
⚏ ⑫⊙⨯ ⛾⬚⩘⚹ ⚹⊞⊡⚒⩙
⬚
Nearby Facilities ⌐ U
Directions Leave the M5 at junction 22, turn left at the roundabout onto the A38 to Highbridge. Continue over the mini roundabout and railway bridge, turn next left onto the B3139 to Burnham-on-Sea. Turn left at the Total Garage into Marine Drive and the park is 400yds on the left.
⚌ Highbridge

BURNHAM-ON-SEA
Diamond Farm Caravan & Touring Park, Diamond Farm, Weston Road, Brean, Nr Burnham-on-Sea, Somerset, TA8 2RL
Tel: 01278 751263
Email:
trevor@diamondfarm42.freeserve.co.uk
www.diamondfarm.co.uk
Pitches For Å ⚎ ⛺ **Total** 100
Acreage 6 **Open** April **to** 15-Oct
Access Good **Site** Level
Nearest Bus Stop (Miles) Outside
A quiet, family site alongside River Axe and only 800yds from the beach. All modern facilities.
Facilities ⬚⚒ ⨍ ⬚⚏↑ ⌐⊙⌔⬚⊡⛾
⚏ ⑫⊙⨯⬚⛾⚏⬚⩘⚹ ⚒⬚⚹
Nearby Facilities ⌐ ⚑⚒⚑U ⚐ ⚹
Nearest Town Burnham-on-Sea
Directions M5 junction 22, follow signs to Brean, ½ mile past leisure park turn right to Lympsham/Weston-super-Mare. Diamond Farm is 800yds on the left hand side.
⚌ Weston-super-Mare

BURNHAM-ON-SEA
Home Farm Holiday Park, Edithmead, Burnham-on-Sea, Somerset, TA9 4HD
Tel: 01278 788888
Email: info@homefarmholidaypark.co.uk
www.homefarmholidaypark.co.uk
Pitches For ⚎ ⛺ **Total** 650
Acreage 44 **Open** Feb **to** Dec
Access Good **Site** Level
Facilities ⚒ ⨍ ⬚⌂ ⬚⚏↑ ⌐⊙⌔⬚⊡⛾
⚏ ⑫⊙⨯ ⛾⬚⩘⚏⩙⚒ ⚹⊞⊟⚒⩘ ⬚⚹
Nearby Facilities ⌐ ⚒⚑⚒⚑U ⚐ ⚹
Nearest Town Burnham-on-Sea
Directions Just off the M5 Junction 22.
⚌ Burnham-on-Sea

BURNHAM-ON-SEA
Westbrook Farm, Harp Road, Brent Knoll, Somerset, TA9 4HQ
Tel: 01278 760386
www.westbrook-farm.co.uk
Pitches For Å ⚎ ⛺ **Total** 45
Acreage 2 **Open** March **to** End Oct
Access Good **Site** Level
Nearest Bus Stop (Miles) ½
3 miles from Burnham-on-Sea and central for sightseeing in Somerset. Ideal stop-over off the M5.
Facilities ⚒ ⨍ ⬚⚏↑ ⌐⊙⌙⛾
⑫⬚⊟⬚⚏⚹
Nearby Facilities ⌐ ⚒⚑⚒⚑U ⚐ ⚹ ⚹
Nearest Town Burnham-on-Sea
Directions Leave the M5 at junction 22 and take the A38 towards Bristol. After ½ a mile turn right just past the motorhome dealership sp Mark, site is ½ a mile on the left.
⚌ Highbridge

CHARD
Alpine Grove Woodland Park, Forton, Chard, Somerset, TA20 4HD
Tel: 01460 63479
Email: stay@alpinegrovetouringpark.com
www.alpinegrovetouringpark.com
Pitches For Å ⚎ ⛺ **Total** 40
Acreage 8 **Open** 01-Apr **to** 30-Sep
Access Good **Site** Level
Nearest Bus Stop (Miles) ¼
Ideal for woodland walks and fossil hunting. 20 minutes from the World Heritage coastline. New self catering log cabins available for hire all year round. ETC 4 Star Graded, AA 3 Pennants and Gold David Bellamy Award.
Facilities ⚒ ⨍ ⬚⌂ ⬚⚏↑ ⌐⊙⌔⬚⊡⛾
⚏ ⑫⊙⨯⬚⩙⊞⊡⬚⩘ ⬚
Nearby Facilities ⌐ ⚒ U ⚐
Nearest Town Chard
Directions From Chard take the A30 signposted Cricket St Thomas, turn right onto the B3167 and follow brown tourism signs.
⚌ Crewkerne

CHARD
Barleymows Farm Shop & Restaurant, Snowdon Hill Farm, Chard, Somerset, TA20 3PS
Tel: 01460 62130
Email: barleymows@btconnect.com
www.barleymows.com
Pitches For Å ⚎ ⛺ ⛺ **Total** 8
Acreage 5 **Open** All Year
Access Good **Site** Level
Nearest Bus Stop (Miles) ½
Quiet location with beautiful views. Farm shop and restaurant on site. Summer holiday Maize Maze and fun park. Open all year, weather permitting.
Facilities ⨍ ⛾ ⑫ ⨯ ⬚⩘⬚
Nearby Facilities ⌐ ⚒ U ⚐
Nearest Town Chard
Directions Take the A30 west from Chard, Park is ¾ miles on the right hand side.
⚌ Crewkerne

CHARD
Five Acres Caravan Club Site, Beetham, Chard, Somerset, TA20 3QA
Tel: 01460 234519
www.caravanclub.co.uk
Pitches For ⚎ ⛺ **Total** 73
Acreage 5 **Open** March **to** Oct
Access Good **Site** Level
Peaceful and pleasant park set in South Somerset countryside. Near Chard Reservoir & Nature Reserve which hosts 150 species of bird including Osprey. Close to Montacute House and Cricket St. Thomas Wildlife Park. Non members welcome. Booking essential.

Facilities ⚊ 🏠 ⬛ ⬛ ⬛ ⬛ ⬛ ⬛
⬛ ⬛ ⬛ ⬛ ⬛ ⬛ ⬛ ⬛
Nearest Town Chard
Directions From east on the A303, at the crossroads at the end of Ilminster bypass turn left by the thatched cottage into a narrow lane signposted Crickleaze. Site is second entrance on the left (250 yards). NB: DO NOT use first entrance as its difficult to back out
⚏ Chard

CHEDDAR
Broadway House Holiday Park, Axbridge Road, Cheddar, Somerset, BS27 3DB
Tel: 0844 272 9501
Email: enquiries@broadwayhousepark.co.uk
www.broadwayhousepark.co.uk
Pitches For 🏕 🚐 🚗 **Total** 442
Acreage 30 **Open** March **to** Oct
Access Good **Site** Sloping
Nearest Bus Stop (Miles) Outside
Centrally situated in the spectacular setting of the Mendip Hills. 1 mile from Cheddar Gorge and 18 miles from Bristol. Ideal for visiting Wookey Hole Caves, Clarks Village and Longleat. Short drive to seaside resorts.
Facilities ⬛ ⬛ ⬛ ⬛ ⬛ ⬛ ⬛ ⬛
⬛ ⬛ ⬛ ⬛ ⬛ ⬛ ⬛ ⬛ ⬛
Nearby Facilities ⬛ ⬛ ⬛ ⬛
Nearest Town Cheddar
Directions Leave the M5 at junction 22 and follow brown tourist signs for Cheddar Gorge. We are midway between Cheddar and Axbridge on the A371.
⚏ Worle

CHEDDAR
Bucklegrove Holiday Park, Wells Road, Rodney Stoke, Cheddar, Somerset, BS27 3UZ
Tel: 01749 870261
Email: info@bucklegrove.co.uk
www.bucklegrove.co.uk

Pitches For 🏕 🚐 🚗 **Total** 150
Acreage 7½ **Open** 04-Mar **to** 04-Jan
Access Good **Site** Level/Gently Sloping
Nearest Bus Stop (Miles) Entrance
Family friendly Park in the heart of Somerset with stunning views. Near to Cheddar Gorge. Free indoor heated pool. Ideal for walking and touring.
Facilities ⬛ ⬛ ⬛ ⬛ ⬛ ⬛ ⬛ ⬛ ⬛
⬛ ⬛ ⬛ ⬛ ⬛ ⬛ ⬛ ⬛ ⬛ ⬛ ⬛
Nearby Facilities ⬛ ⬛ ⬛ ⬛ ⬛
Nearest Town Cheddar
Directions Midway between Wells and Cheddar on the A371.
⚏ Weston-super-Mare

CHEDDAR
Cheddar Bridge Touring Park, Draycott Road, Cheddar, Somerset, BS27 3RJ
Tel: 01934 743048
Email: enquiries@cheddarbridge.co.uk
www.cheddarbridge.co.uk
Pitches For 🏕 🚐 🚗 **Total** 45
Acreage 3½ **Open** 01-Mar **to** 15-Nov
Access Good **Site** Level
Nearest Bus Stop (Miles) ¼
ADULTS ONLY SITE. Just a short walk to the Gorge and Caves. On the edge of the village for pubs and restaurants. 6 riverside static caravans and 2 apartments available for hire.
Facilities ⬛ ⬛ ⬛ ⬛ ⬛ ⬛ ⬛ ⬛
⬛ ⬛ ⬛ ⬛ ⬛ ⬛ ⬛
Nearby Facilities ⬛ ⬛ ⬛ ⬛ ⬛
Nearest Town Cheddar
Directions On the A371, 100 yards south of Cheddar Village.
⚏ Weston-Super-Mare

CHEDDAR
Netherdale Caravan & Camping Site, Bridgwater Road, Sidcot, Winscombe, Somerset, BS25 1NH
Tel: 01934 843007
Email: camping@netherdale.net
www.netherdale.net
Pitches For 🏕 🚐 🚗 **Total** 25
Acreage 3½ **Open** March **to** October
Access Good **Site** Lev/Slope
Excellent walking area, footpath from site to valley and Mendip Hills. Good views. Cafe/restaurant adjoining site. Many historical places and beaches within easy reach. Pets welcome on a lead. Only individual motorcycles accepted, not groups. 3 miles from a dry ski slope and a well equipped sports centre.
Facilities ⬛ ⬛ ⬛ ⬛ ⬛ ⬛ ⬛
⬛ ⬛ ⬛ ⬛ ⬛ ⬛
Nearby Facilities ⬛ ⬛ ⬛ ⬛ ⬛
Nearest Town Cheddar
Directions Midway between Bristol and Bridgwater on A38. From Weston-super-Mare follow A371 to join A38 at Sidcot Corner, site is ¼ mile south. From Wells and Cheddar follow A371 westwards to join A38, a mile south of site.
⚏ Weston-super-Mare

CHEDDAR
Rodney Stoke Inn, Rodney Stoke, Nr Cheddar, Somerset, BS27 3XB
Tel: 01749 870209
Email: annetteneil@aol.com
www.rodneystokeinn.co.uk
Pitches For 🏕 🚐 🚗 **Total** 31
Acreage 2 **Open** March **to** October
Access Good **Site** Level
Nearest Bus Stop (Miles) ¼
ADULTS ONLY SITE in a central location for the Cheddar Gorge and Caves, the City of Wells and Wookey Hole Caves.

Facilities ⚑ 🏕🖉🏳🍴✕♨🖵🅿Ⓐ
Nearby Facilities 🏳✈⚓Ů☇
Nearest Town Cheddar
Directions Take the A371 from Cheddar towards Wells for 3 miles.
➼ Weston-Super-Mare

CHEDDAR
Splott Farm, Blackford, Nr Wedmore, Somerset, BS28 4PD
Tel: 01278 641522
Pitches For ⚊ ⚌ ⚍ **Total** 32
Acreage 4¼ **Open** March to November
Access Good **Site** Gentle Slope
Nearest Bus Stop (Miles) ½
Very peaceful site with views of the Mendip Hills (and Quantocks), very rural area. Ideal touring, Weston-super-Mare, Wells, Cheddar, Burnham-on-Sea, Wookey.
Facilities ⚑ 🏕🏳🍴☉Ⓟ🐕▥🛁🐾☇⚘
Nearby Facilities 🏳✈⚓☇Ů☇🏹☇
Nearest Town Burnham-on-Sea/Cheddar
Directions Leave M5 at junction 22, 2 miles to Highbridge, take B3139 Highbridge/Wells road, about 5 miles.
➼ Highbridge

CONGRESBURY
Oak Farm Touring Park, Weston Road, Congresbury, Somerset, BS49 5EB
Tel: 01934 833246
Pitches For ⚊ ⚌ ⚍ **Total** 40
Open 31-Mar to October
Access Good **Site** Level
Nearest Bus Stop (Miles) ¼
Pub and restaurant close by. You can also call us on Mobile 07989 319686.
Facilities ⚑ 🏕🏳☉🍴▥🛁☇⚘
Nearby Facilities 🏳✈⚓☇Ů☇🏹☇
Nearest Town Weston-super-Mare
Directions 4 miles from junc. 21 on M5, on the A370 midway between Bristol and Weston Super Mare.
➼ Yatton

CROWCOMBE
Quantock Orchard Caravan Park, Flaxpool, Crowcombe, Taunton, Somerset, TA4 4AW
Tel: 01984 618618
Email: member@flaxpool.freeserve.co.uk
www.quantock-orchard.co.uk
Pitches For ⚊ ⚌ ⚍ **Total** 77
Acreage 7½ **Open** All Year
Access Good **Site** Level
Nearest Bus Stop (Miles) ¼
Award winning campsite surrounded by stunning panoramic views of the Quantock Hills, and situated next to the West Somerset Railway. Luxury holiday homes available for hire.

Facilities 🛁⚑ ⚑🏳🏕🖉🏳🍴☉◻🛁🖵🅿
⚒🐕🗼🖈🚶▥🛁✕🖵🖵💮♨⚘
Nearby Facilities 🏳✈⚓☇Ů🏹☇
Nearest Town Taunton/Minehead
Directions Midway between Taunton and Minehead on the A358. Approx. 1 mile from south of Crowcombe Village.
➼ Taunton

DULVERTON
Exe Valley Caravan Site, Bridgetown, Somerset, TA22 9JR
Tel: 01643 851432
Email: paul@paulmatt.fsnet.co.uk
www.exevalleycamping.co.uk
Pitches For ⚊ ⚌ ⚍ **Total** 50
Acreage 4 **Open** Mid March to Mid Oct
Access Good **Site** Level
Nearest Bus Stop (Miles) Outside
ADULTS ONLY. Most improved site in Exmoor. Within Exmoor National Park. Free fly fishing on site. Just a few minutes walk from the local pub serving good food. Motorhome service point.
Facilities ⚑ 🏳🏕🖉🏳🍴☉◻🛁🖵🅿
⚒🐕🛁🖈🖵🅿Ⓐ☇
Nearby Facilities 🏳✈⚓☇Ů
Nearest Town Dulverton
Directions Leave the M5 at junction 27 and take the A361 towards Tiverton. From the roundabout on the Tiverton by-pass take the A396 signposted Minehead. Take care after 7 miles to stay on the A396 at the Black Cat filling station, and DO NOT go through Dulverton. turn left 100yds beyond Badgers Holt pub in the centre of Bridgetown.

DULVERTON
Exmoor House Caravan Club Site, Dulverton, Somerset, TA22 9HL
Tel: 01398 323268
www.caravanclub.co.uk
Pitches For ⚌ ⚍ **Total** 67
Acreage 4 **Open** March to Jan
Access Good **Site** Level
Nearest Bus Stop (Miles) ¼
Quiet and pretty site with valley views. 200 yards from the village. Ideal base to explore Exmoor National Park. Near the Lorna Doone Trail, Dunster Castle and Knightshayes Court. Non members welcome. Booking essential.
Facilities 🛁⚑ 🏳🏕🖉🏳🍴☉🅿⚘
⚒🐕🛁🖈🖵☇
Nearby Facilities ✈
Nearest Town Dulverton
Directions Leave M5 at junc 27 and take A361 sp Barnstaple, after 6 miles at the roundabout turn right onto A396. At roundabout by Exeter Inn turn left sp Dulverton, at Black Cat junction on sharp left

hand bend bear right to crossroads and continue straight on A396.

DULVERTON
Lakeside Caravan Club Site, Higher Grants, Exebridge, Dulverton, Somerset, TA22 9BE
Tel: 01398 324068
www.caravanclub.co.uk
Pitches For ⚌ ⚍ **Total** 80
Acreage 11 **Open** March to Nov
Access Good **Site** Level
Nearest Bus Stop (Miles) ½
Situated in a quiet village with lovely views towards Exmoor. Ideal for keen anglers. Within easy reach of Exmoor National Park and Lorna Doone country. Near Rosemoor Gardens, Dunkery Beacon and Dunster Castle. Non members welcome. Booking essential.
Facilities 🛁⚑ 🏳🏕🖉🏳🍴🅿⚘
⚒🐕🛁🖈🖵🅿Ⓐ✈☇
Nearby Facilities ✈
Nearest Town Dulverton
Directions Leave M5 at junc 27 and take A361 towards Barnstaple. After 6 miles at the roundabout turn right onto A396, at the roundabout by Exeter Inn turn left sp Dulverton. At Black Cat junction on sharp left hand bend keep right, at crossroads by Exebridge Petrol Station, continue on A396. Site is 2½ miles on left.

EXFORD
Westermill Farm, Exford, Exmoor, Somerset, TA24 7NJ
Tel: 01643 831238
Email: cad@westermill.com
www.westermill.com
Pitches For ⚊ ⚌ ⚍ **Total** 60
Acreage 6 **Open** All Year
Access Poor **Site** Level
Nearest Bus Stop (Miles) 2½
Beautiful, secluded site in a hidden valley beside a river for fishing, bathing and paddling. Fascinating 500 acre farm with Waymarked walks. Centre of Exmoor National Park. Free hot showers. Camp fire areas. Charming cottages nestling by trees for hire. David Bellamy Gold Award for Conservation.
Facilities 🏳🏕🍴☉🖵🅿🖵☇
⚒🐕🛁🖈🖵✈
Nearby Facilities Ů
Nearest Town Minehead
Directions Leave Exford on the Porlock road. After ½ a mile fork left, continue for 2 miles along the valley until Westermill is seen

on a tree and fork left.
🚭 Taunton

FROME

**Seven Acres Touring Caravan &
Camping Park,** West Woodlands, Frome,
Somerset, BA11 5EQ
Tel: 01373 464222
Pitches For 🛆 ⊞ ⊟ **Total** 32
Acreage 7 **Open** March **to** October
Access Good **Site** Level
As seen on national television. Acres of level,
landscaped grounds with a stream
meandering through. On the outskirts of the
Longleat Estate and within easy reach of
Stourhead, Cheddar Caves and Stonehenge.
Facilities ⨍ 🏠 🕼 ⌂ 🟆 🕃 🤚 🖃 🔁
Nearby Facilities ⌁ ✔ ∪ ♪
Nearest Town Frome
Directions From the Frome by-pass take the
B3092 towards Maiden Bradley and Mere.
Seven Acres is situated approx. 1 mile from
the by-pass.
🚭 Frome

GLASTONBURY

Greenacres Camping, Barrow Lane,
North Wootton, Glastonbury, Somerset,
BA4 4HL
Tel: 01749 890497
Email: stay@greenacres-camping.co.uk
www.greenacres-camping.co.uk
Pitches For 🛆 ⊟ **Total** 40
Acreage 4½ **Open** April **to** Sept
Site Level
Nearest Bus Stop (Miles) 2
Quiet site in stunning Somerset countryside,
with views of Glastonbury Tor and the Mendip
Hills. Ideal for families. Huge pitches! Cycle
hire on site.
Facilities ⨍ 🕼 ⌂ 🟆 🕃 🤚 ⬛
🕊 🕭 🕃 ⌂ 🛆 ♿ 🖃 🔁 🗚 🤝
Nearby Facilities ⌁ ✔ ∪ ♪
Nearest Town Glastonbury
Directions Leave the M5 at junction 23 and
take the A39 to Glastonbury. Follow signs
from Brownes Garden Centre. Or follow signs
from the A361 at Steanbow for 2 miles.
🚭 Castle Cary

GLASTONBURY

The Old Oaks Touring Park, Wick Farm,
Wick, Glastonbury, Somerset, BA6 8JS
Tel: 01458 831437
Email: info@theoldoaks.co.uk
www.theoldoaks.co.uk
Pitches For 🛆 ⊞ ⊟ ⊞ **Total** 100
Acreage 10 **Open** 10-Feb **to** 12-Nov
Access Good **Site** Level/Sloping
Nearest Bus Stop (Miles) 1½
ADULT ONLY Park in a stunning location with
beautiful views. Blissfully tranquil. Ideal for
walking, cycling or just relaxing. ¾ miles from
Glastonbury Tor. Camping Cabins/Pods for
Glamping.
Facilities 🕭 ⨍ 🏠 🕼 🕼 ⌂ 🟆 🕃 ⬛ 🖃 🔁
🕊 🕃 ⌂ 🛆 🤚 🖃 🗚 🤝
Nearby Facilities ⌁ ✔ ∪ ♪
Nearest Town Glastonbury
Directions From Glastonbury take the A361
towards Shepton Mallet. In 2 miles turn left
at signpost for Wick, Park is on the left in 1
mile.
🚭 Castle Cary

HIGHBRIDGE

Greenacre Place Touring Caravan Park,
Bristol Road, Edithmead, Highbridge,
Somerset, TA9 4HA
Tel: 01278 785227
Email: info@greenacreplace.com
www.greenacreplace.com
Pitches For ⊞ ⊟ **Total** 10

Acreage 1 **Open** March **to** November
Access Good **Site** Level
Nearest Bus Stop (Miles) ½
ADULTS ONLY. Small, peaceful caravan park
with easy access. Short drive to sandy
beaches. Ideally placed for touring Somerset.
Facilities ⨍ 🕼 ⌂ 🟆 🕃 🕼 🕃 🖃 🤚 🤝
Nearby Facilities ⌁ ✔ ⚘ ∪ ♪ ♪
Nearest Town Burnham-on-Sea
Directions Just off the M5 junction 22.
🚭 Highbridge

ILMINSTER

Thornleigh Caravan Park, Hanning Road,
Horton, Ilminster, Somerset, TA19 9QH
Tel: 01460 53450
Email: thornleighsite@btinternet.com
www.thornleighcaravansite.co.uk
Pitches For 🛆 ⊞ ⊟ **Total** 20
Acreage 1¼ **Open** March **to** October
Access Good **Site** Level
Flat site in a village location, ideal for touring
Somerset and Devon. Heated shower block.
½ hour drive to the south coast. 6 miles to
Cricket St Thomas Gardens. National Trust
properties nearby. Village Inn with restaurant,
Post Office, stores and public telephone nearby.
Ideal rally site with village hall close by.
Facilities 🕭 ⨍ 🏠 🕼 ⌂ 🟆 🕃 ⬛ 🕼 🤚 🖃 🔁 🤝
Nearby Facilities ⌁ ✔ ♪
Nearest Town Ilminster
Directions A303 West Ilminster, take the
A358 signposted Chard. ¼ mile turn right
signposted Horton and Broadway. Site on the
left opposite the church, ¾ mile.
🚭 Taunton/Crewkerne

LANGPORT

**Bowdens Crest Caravan & Camping
Park,** Bowdens, Langport, Somerset, TA10
0DD
Tel: 01458 250553
Email: bowcrest@btconnect.com
www.bowdenscrest.co.uk
Pitches For 🛆 ⊞ ⊟ **Total** 30
Open All Year
Access Good **Site** Level
Nearest Bus Stop (Miles) 2
Panoramic views across Somerset levels.
Facilities 🕭 ⨍ 🏠 🕼 ⌂ 🟆 🕃 ⬛ 🖃 🤝
🕊 🕃 ⌂ 🛆 🕼 ⊞ 🤚 🖃 🔁 🗚 🤝
Nearby Facilities ⌁ ✔ ♪
Nearest Town Langport
Directions Off the A372 Langport to
Bridgwater road.
🚭 Bridgwater

LANGPORT

Thorney Lakes Caravan Site, Thorney
Lakes, Muchelney, Langport, Somerset,
TA10 0DW
Tel: 01458 250811
Email: enquiries@thorneylakes.co.uk
www.thorneylakes.co.uk
Pitches For 🛆 ⊞ ⊟ **Total** 36
Acreage 7 **Open** March **to** November
Access Good **Site** Level
Site is an orchard on Somerset Moors. Ideal
for walking and cycling.
Facilities ⨍ 🕼 ⌂ 🟆 🕃 🤚 🖃 ✔ 🤝
Nearby Facilities ⌁ ✔
Nearest Town Langport
Directions Turn off the A303 dual
carriageway signposted Martock, Ash and
Kingsbury Episcopi. Follow signs to
Kingsbury Episcopi, at the T-Junction in the
village turn right, site is 1 mile on the right.
🚭 Yeovil/Taunton

MARTOCK

Southfork Caravan Park, Parrett Works,
Martock, Somerset, TA12 6AE

Tel: 01935 825661
Email: southforkcaravans@btconnect.com
www.southforkcaravans.co.uk
Pitches For 🛆 ⊞ ⊟ **Total** 27
Acreage 2 **Open** All Year
Access Good **Site** Level
Nearest Bus Stop (Miles) Outside
Set in open countryside near River Parrett.
Numerous places of interest nearby for all age
groups. Ideal base for touring. 3 holiday homes
for hire. Caravan storage available. Visit Britain
5 Star Rose Award Graded for 2011.
Facilities ⨍ 🕼 ⌂ 🟆 🕃 ⬛ 🖃 🤝
🕊 🕃 🛆 🕼 🖃 🔁
Nearby Facilities ⌁ ✔ ♪
Nearest Town Martock/Yeovil
Directions Situated 2 miles north west of
A303 (between Ilchester and Ilminster). From
A303 east of Ilminster, at roundabout take
first exit sp South Petherton and follow
camping signs. From A303 west of Ilchester,
after Cartgate roundabout (junction with
A3088 to Yeovil) take exit SP and follow
camping signs.
🚭 Yeovil

MINEHEAD

Butlins Minehead, Warren Road,
Minehead, Somerset, TA24 5SH
Tel: 01643 700515
Email:
touringcaravans.minehead@bourne-
leisure.co.uk
www.butlins.com
Pitches For ⊞ ⊟ **Total** 44
Open April **to** Nov
Access Good **Site** Level
Nearest Bus Stop (Miles) Outside
Our fabulous Minehead Resort has a Touring
Site for caravan holiday makers. Beautifully
set in Exmoor National Park there's plenty
to do in the local countryside, at the lakes
and on the soft sand beaches. Make
Minehead your caravan destination for your
next trip.
Facilities 🕭 ⨍ 🏠 🕼 🕼 ⌂ 🟆 🕃 ⬛ 🖃 🔁 🤝
🕊 🕃 🕼 🤚 🛆 🕼 🖃 🔁 🤝
Nearby Facilities ⌁ ✔ ⚘ ∪ ♪ ♪ 🗚
Nearest Town Minehead
Directions Heading north take the M5 to
Taunton (Junction 25), then the A358 and
A39 to Minehead. Heading south on the M5,
you can follow the signposts for the A39 from
junction 24. You can't miss us, we're just half
a mile along the seafront road from Minehead.
🚭 Taunton

MINEHEAD

Camping & Caravanning Club Site, Hill
Road, North Hill, Minehead, Somerset,
TA24 5LB
Tel: 01643 704138
www.campingandcaravanningclub.co.uk
Pitches For 🛆 ⊟ **Total** 60
Acreage 3¾ **Open** 23-Apr **to** 24-Sep
Access Poor **Site** Sloping
In Exmoor National Park with fine views of
the town of Minehead. Sloping site, chocks
required. BTB 4 Star Graded and AA 3
Pennants. Non members welcome. You can
also call us on 0845 130 7633.
Facilities ⨍ 🏠 🕼 ⌂ 🟆 🕃 ⬛ 🖃 🔁 🤝
🕼 🕃 🛆 🕼 🖃 🔁 🤝
Nearby Facilities ⌁ ✔ ⚘ ∪ ♪
Nearest Town Minehead
Directions From the A39 head towards the
town centre, in the main street turn opposite
W.H.Smith into Blenheim Road, after 50
yards turn left again. Go up the hill and left
around a hairpin bend, turn right at the
cottages. Go past the church on the right and
continue round two bends, site is on the right.
🚭 Minehead

A touring site with a **difference**

Hayden Cannon, 6 making a splash with dad, Kevin on the Master Blaster.

Have fun at the funfair

Enjoy the thrills of Splash Waterworld

Try something new

See the latest shows

Get more from your break

- Sub tropical water world fun
- Unlimited traditional funfair rides
- A great range of sports and activities
- Entertainment throughout the day
- Spectacular evening shows

Butlin's
Minehead

For more information or to make a booking, please call one of our friendly advisers.

Phone **0845 070 4763**
7 days a week 9am-5pm

Save **an extra 5%**
when quoting Cades on booking, and in addition to existing offers*

VISIT **www.cades.co.uk** TO SEE OUR MONTHLY COMPETITION

MINEHEAD

Hoburne Blue Anchor, Blue Anchor Bay, Nr Minehead, Somerset, TA24 6JT
Tel: 01643 821360
Email: blueanchor@hoburne.com
www.hoburne.com
Pitches For 🚐 🚗 **Total** 103
Acreage 29 **Open** 26-Feb **to** 30-Oct
Access Good **Site** Level
Nearest Bus Stop (Miles) Outside
On the seafront and bordered by Exmoor, this is a peaceful touring and static Park in a prefect location.
Facilities ✦ 🖤🅗🖫🖶🏧🚶⊙🍴🍺💈☎
♨🏊🏦🎱❄🍴➳🛒🔥🐕🏕
Nearby Facilities ┍ ✔ 🛆🛥⋃ ♨ ♪ 🎣
Nearest Town Minehead
Directions Leave the M5 at junction 25 and take the A358 signposted Minehead. After approx 12 miles, at Carhampton, turn left onto the B3191 signposted Blue Anchor. Park is 1½ miles on the right.
⇻ Minehead

MINEHEAD

Minehead & Exmoor Caravan & Camping Park, Porlock Road, Minehead, Somerset, TA24 8SW
Tel: 01643 703074
www.mineheadandexmoorcamping.co.uk
Pitches For 🛆 🚐 🚗 **Total** 50
Acreage 3½ **Access** Good **Site** Level
Nearest Bus Stop (Miles) Outside
Situated on the edge of Exmoor National Park.
Facilities 🛆 ✦ 🖤🅗🖫🖶🏧🚶⊙🍴🍺
🍴⊙🏦🏠🔥🛒❄🐕🎣
Nearby Facilities ┍ ✔ 🛆🛥⋃
Nearest Town Minehead
Directions 1 mile west of Minehead town centre on the A39, Park is on the right hand side.
⇻ Taunton

MINEHEAD

St. Audries Bay Holiday Club, West Quantoxhead, Minehead, Somerset, TA4 4DY
Tel: 01984 632515
Email: info@staudriesbay.co.uk
www.staudriesbay.co.uk
Pitches For 🛆 🚐 🚗 **Total** 20
Acreage 12 **Open** Easter **to** Oct
Access Good **Site** Level
Nearest Bus Stop (Miles) ½
For 78 years we have provided relaxing holidays at our family owned, award winning Park. Situated in a beautiful coastal position with splendid sea views and beach access.
Facilities 🛆 ✦ 🖤🅗🖫🖶🏧🚶⊙🍴🍺💈☎
♨🏊🏦❌🍴🛥🏠♪🔥🛒➳🖶🐕
Nearby Facilities ┍ ✔ 🛆🛥⋃ ♪
Nearest Town Minehead
Directions 15 miles from the M5 junction 23, off the A39. 15 miles from Taunton, follow the A358 to Williton then the A39.
⇻ Taunton

PORLOCK

Burrowhayes Farm Caravan & Camping Site & Riding Stables, West Luccombe, Porlock, Nr Minehead, Somerset, TA24 8HT
Tel: 01643 862463
Email: info@burrowhayes.co.uk
www.burrowhayes.co.uk
Pitches For 🛆 🚐 🚗 **Total** 120
Acreage 8 **Open** 15-Mar **to** 31-Oct
Access Good **Site** Lev/Slope
Nearest Bus Stop (Miles) ¼
Real family site set in glorious National Trust scenery on Exmoor. Ideal for walking. Riding stables on site.
Facilities 🛆 ✦ 🖤🅗🖫🖶🏧🚶⊙🍴🍺💈☎
♨🏊⊙🏦🛒🖶🐕
Nearby Facilities ┍ ✔ 🛆🛥 ♪

Directions 5 miles west of Minehead on A39, left hand turning to West Luccombe, site is ¼ mile on the right.
⇻ Taunton

PORLOCK

Porlock Caravan Park, Highbank, Porlock, Nr Minehead, Somerset, TA24 8ND
Tel: 01643 862269
Email: info@porlockcaravanpark.co.uk
www.porlockcaravanpark.co.uk
Pitches For 🛆 🚐 🚗 **Total** 40
Acreage 3½ **Open** Mid March **to** October
Access Good **Site** Level
Nearest Bus Stop (Miles) ¼
Scenic views, Ideal touring and walking.
Facilities 🛆 ✦ 🖤🅗🖫🖶🏧🚶⊙🍴🍺💈☎
♨🏦🏠🖶🖶❄🐕🎣
Nearby Facilities ┍ ✔ 🛆⋃ ♪
Nearest Town Minehead
Directions A39 from Minehead to Lynton, take the B3225 in Porlock to Porlock Weir. Site signposted.
⇻ Taunton

SPARKFORD

Long Hazel Park, High Street, Sparkford, Nr Yeovil, Somerset, BA22 7JH
Tel: 01963 440002
Email: longhazelpark@hotmail.com
www.longhazelpark.co.uk
Pitches For 🛆 🚐 🚗 🚗 **Total** 50
Acreage 3½ **Open** All Year
Access Good **Site** Level
Nearest Bus Stop (Miles) Outside
ADULTS ONLY. Full disabled shower unit. Near to an inn and restaurant. Ideal for touring or an overnight halt. Haynes International Motor Museum and Fleet Air Arm Museum nearby. Two pine lodges for hire with wheelchair access and 12 pine

An unbeatable location on the Somerset coast near Minehead. Close to Exmoor, the Quantocks and the West Somerset Steam Railway. Simple facilities in which to relax and unwind.

Call: **0844 288 1940**
or visit **hoburne.com/cadesba**
Celebrating 100 years of happy holidays

Hoburne HOLIDAY PARKS

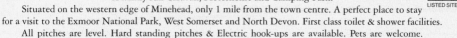

lodges for sale. Please note, dogs are not permitted in the pine lodges.
Facilities ⬥ ✦ ⊞ ☖ ⚲ ⌐ ☉ ⬥ 🍴 ▣ ☎ 🏧 ⊚ ☒ ✕ 🕭 ▣ A ⚥ ❄ 🛜
Nearby Facilities ⌐ ✒ ⚓ U ♪
Directions From Wincanton take the A303 to the end of Sparkford by-pass. At the services turn left into Sparkford Village, site is approx. 400 yards on the left.
🚆 Yeovil/Sherborne/Castle Cary

·STREET

Bramble Hill Caravan & Camping Park, Bramble Hill, Walton, Nr Street, Somerset, BA16 9RQ
Tel: 01458 442548
Pitches For ⚑ ⊞ 🚐 🚑 **Total** 30
Acreage 2 **Open** Easter **to** October
Access Good **Site** Level
ADULTS ONLY. Peaceful and quiet Park. Dogs are welcome if kept on leads. 1½ miles from Sainsburys. Well secured caravan storage available.
Facilities ✦ ⊞ ⚲ ⌐ ☉ ☎ 🕭 ▣ A ⚥ ⚲
Nearby Facilities ⌐ ✒
Nearest Town Street
Directions Take the A39 from Street to Walton for 2 miles, pass the church and the Pike & Musket Pub and turn left, signposted. Park is 500 metres.
🚆 Castle Cary

TAUNTON

Ashe Farm Caravan & Camp Site, Ashe Farm, Thornfalcon, Taunton, Somerset, TA3 5NW
Tel: 01823 443764
Email: info@ashefarm.co.uk
www.ashefarm.co.uk
Pitches For ⚑ ⊞ 🚐 **Total** 30

Acreage 7 **Open** April **to** October
Access Good **Site** Level
Nearest Bus Stop (Miles) ¼
Ideal touring centre, easy reach of Quantock and Blackdown Hills.
Facilities ⬥ ✦ ⊞ ☖ ⚲ ⌐ ☉ ⬥ 🍴 ▣ ☎
🕭 ⊚ ▣ ⚥
Nearby Facilities ⌐ ✒ U ♪
Nearest Town Taunton
Directions 4 miles southeast Taunton on A358, turn right at the Nags Head towards West Hatch, site is ¼ mile on the right.
🚆 Taunton

TAUNTON

Cornish Farm Touring Park, Cornish Farm, Shoreditch, Taunton, Somerset, TA3 7BS
Tel: 01823 327746
Email: info@cornishfarm.com
www.cornishfarm.com
Pitches For ⚑ ⊞ 🚐 **Total** 50
Acreage 3½ **Open** All Year
Access Good **Site** Level
Nearest Bus Stop (Miles) ½
Excellent facilities. Ideal touring park. Good for the racecourse and Somerset County Cricket Ground. AA 4 Pennants.
Facilities ⬥ ✦ ⊞ ☖ ⚲ ⌐ ☉ ⬥ ▣ ☎
🕭 ⊚ ✕ 🕭 ▣ 🛜
Nearby Facilities ⌐ ✒ ♪
Nearest Town Taunton
Directions Leave the M5 at junction 25, at first traffic lights turn left, turn third left into Ilminster Road. At the roundabout turn right, next roundabout turn left, at the T-Junction follow brown tourism signs to the site. Total of 3 miles from the M5.
🚆 Taunton

TAUNTON

Holly Bush Park, Culmhead, Taunton, Somerset, TA3 7EA
Tel: 01823 421515
Email: info@hollybushpark.com
www.hollybushpark.com
Pitches For ⚑ ⊞ 🚐 **Total** 30
Acreage 2 **Open** All Year
Access Good **Site** Level
Nearest Bus Stop (Miles) ¼
In an Area of Outstanding Natural Beauty.
Facilities ✦ ⊞ ☖ ⚲ ⌐ ☉ ⬥ 🍴 ▣ ☎
🕭 ⊚ ✕ 🕭 ❄ ⚲ 🛜
Nearby Facilities ⌐ U
Directions From Taunton follow signs for the Racecourse and Corfe on the B3170, 3 miles from Corfe turn right at crossroads towards Wellington. Turn right at the next T-Junction, site is 200yds on the left.
🚆 Taunton

TAUNTON

Tanpits Farm Caravan & Camping Park, Dyers Lane, Bathpool, Taunton, Somerset, TA2 8BZ
Tel: 01823 270663
Pitches For ⚑ ⊞ 🚐 **Total** 30
Acreage 2 **Open** March **to** November
Access Good **Site** Level
Nearest Bus Stop (Miles) ¼
Cinema, bowling alley, pubs and take-aways close by. Near the Quantock Hills and a canal for walking and cycling.
Facilities ⬥ ✦ ⊞ ☖ ⚲ ⌐ ☉ ⬥ ▣ 🕭 ⊚ ▣ 🛜
Nearby Facilities ✒
Directions Leave the M5 at junction 25 and take the A38 to Bridgwater. In the village of Bathpool turn left to Monkton Heathfield, after 500 yards turn left again.
🚆 Taunton

SOMERSET

TAUNTON

Waterrow Touring Park, Waterrow, Wiveliscombe, Taunton, Somerset, TA4 2AZ
Tel: 01984 623464
Email: waterrowpark@yahoo.co.uk
www.waterrowpark.co.uk
Pitches For ⛺ ⛟ ⛞ **Total** 45
Acreage 8 **Open** All Year
Access Good **Site** Landscaped
Nearest Bus Stop (Miles) Outside
EXCLUSIVELY FOR ADULTS. In a peaceful, attractive location in the Tone Valley with a woodland river walk. Excellent heated facilities. One luxury holiday home and an Elizabethan cottage (sleeps 3) for hire. Good pub nearby. Watercolour painting holidays. Ideal touring base.
Facilities ♿ ⚕ 🅿 🛁 🚿 ⛽ ⏧ ☉ ⏚ ▣ 🛒 🍴
🏊 🍳 🚲 🖃 🛢 ✉ 🛊 ♨ 🛜
Nearby Facilities ↑ ✓ 🛆 ⚘ ∪ ₽
Nearest Town Taunton
Directions Leave the M5 at junc 25 and take the A358 sp Minehead. Then take the B3227 sp Wiveliscombe, 3 miles after Wiveliscombe you will pass the Rock Pub, the park is on the left within 300 yards.
⛟ Taunton/Tiverton

WELLINGTON

Cadeside Caravan Club Site, Nynehead Road, Wellington, Somerset, TA21 9HN
Tel: 01823 663103
www.caravanclub.co.uk
Pitches For ⛟ ⛞ **Total** 16
Acreage 4¾ **Open** All Year
Access Good **Site** Level
Nearest Bus Stop (Miles) Outside
Rural site with countryside views. Surrounded by Quantock Hills, Brendon Hills and Blackdown Hills. Non members welcome. Booking essential.
Facilities ⚕ 🅿 🛁 🚿 ⏚ ▣ 🛒 ✉
Nearby Facilities ↑
Nearest Town Wellington
Directions Leave the M5 at junction 26 and take the A38 signposted Wellington, at roundabout turn onto the B3187 signposted Wellington. After ½ mile turn right signposted Nynehead, site is 80 yards on the right.

WELLINGTON

Gamlins Farm Caravan Park, Gamlins Farmhouse, Greenham, Wellington, Somerset, TA21 0LZ
Tel: 01823 672859
Email: nataliehowe@hotmail.com
Pitches For ⛺ ⛟ ⛞ **Total** 30
Acreage 4 **Open** March to End Oct
Access Good **Site** Level
Nearest Bus Stop (Miles) Outside
Scenic valley setting with a Free coarse fishing lake. 45 minutes from the coast. Ideal for touring, Exmoor, Quantocks and The Blackdowns. Static caravans available for hire. You can also telephone us on mobile: 07967 683738.
Facilities ⚕ 🅿 🛁 🚿 ⛽ ⏧ ☉ ⏚ ▣ 🛒 ✉
🏊 🖃 ✉ ♨
Nearby Facilities ↑ ✓ ∪
Directions Take the M5 to junction 26 Wellington, then take the A38 towards Tiverton and Exeter. On the dual carriageway turn right to Greenham, go over two sets of crossroads, round a bend and the site is on the right. Follow brown tourism signs from J26 for 6 mile
⛟ Taunton/Tiverton

WELLINGTON

Greenacres Touring Park, Haywards Lane, Chelston, Wellington, Somerset, TA21 9PH
Tel: 01823 652844
Email: enquiries@greenacres-wellington.co.uk
www.greenacres-wellington.co.uk
Pitches For ⛟ ⛞ **Total** 40
Acreage 2½ **Open** 01-Apr to 30-Sep
Access Good **Site** Level
Nearest Bus Stop (Miles) ¼
Exclusive ADULTS ONLY NEW PARK with all new facilities. Situated in the countryside with views of Blackdown and the Quantock Hills. Pub and restaurant within walking distance. You can also contact us on Mobile: 07774 205755. AA 4 Pennants and Visit Britain 4 Stars.
Facilities ♿ ⚕ 🅿 🛁 🚿 ⏧ ☉ ⏚ ⛽ ▣ 🛒
Nearby Facilities ✓ ∪ ₽
Nearest Town Wellington
Directions Leave the M5 at junction 26 and take the Wellington road for 1½ miles to the Chelston roundabout, take the first exit onto the A38 West Buckland Road, after 500 yards turn left.
⛟ Taunton

WELLS

Cheddar Camping & Caravanning Club Site, Mendip Heights, Townsend, Priddy, Wells, Somerset, BA5 3BP
Tel: 01749 870241
www.campingandcaravanningclub.co.uk/cheddar
Pitches For ⛺ ⛟ ⛞ **Total** 90
Acreage 4½ **Open** 15-Mar to 05-Nov
Access Good **Site** Lev/Slope
Situated in a designated area of outstanding natural beauty, in the heart of the Mendip Hills. Holiday caravan available for hire. Non members welcome. You can also call us on 0845 130 7633.
Facilities ⚕ 🅿 🛁 🚿 ⏧ ☉ ⏚ ▣ 🛒 ✉
🏊 🖃 🛢 ⛽ ✉ ♨ ⚘ 🛜
Nearby Facilities ✓ ∪
Nearest Town Wells
Directions From Wells take the A39 north east for 3½ miles, then take the B3135 towards Cheddar for 4½ miles. Signposted ¼ mile north west of Priddy.

WELLS

Homestead Park, Wookey Hole, Wells, Somerset, BA5 1BW
Tel: 01749 673022
Email: homesteadpark@onetel.com
www.homesteadpark.co.uk
Pitches For ⛺ **Total** 30
Acreage 2 **Open** Easter to October
Access Good **Site** Level
Nearest Bus Stop (Miles) Outside
ADULTS ONLY - Sorry no children. TENTS ONLY. Sheltered site on the banks of the River Axe. Ideal for Wookey Hole Caves, National Trust sites, Mendip Hills, walking and climbing. Leisure centre nearby.
Facilities 🛁 🚿 ⏧ ☉ ⏚ ⛽ ▣ 🛒 🖃 ✉
Nearby Facilities ↑ ✓ ∪
Directions Leave Wells by A371 towards Cheddar, turn right for Wookey Hole. Site 1¼ miles on the left in the village.
⛟ Bristol/Bath

WESTON-SUPER-MARE

Country View Holiday Park, 29 Sand Road, Sand Bay, Weston-super-Mare, Somerset, BS22 9UJ
Tel: 01934 627595
Email: info@cvhp.co.uk
www.cvhp.co.uk

Pitches For ⛺ ⛟ ⛞ **Total** 185
Acreage 10 **Open** March to Jan
Access Good **Site** Level
Nearest Bus Stop (Miles) ¼
200 yards from Sand Bay beach. Heated swimming pool and bar on site. Excellent toilet/shower facilities.
Facilities ♿ ⚕ 🅿 🛁 🚿 ⏧ ☉ ⏚ ⛽ ▣ 🛒 🍴
🏊 🍳 🚲 🖃 🛢 ✉ 🛊 ♨ ⚘ 🛜
Nearby Facilities ↑ ✓ 🛆 ⚘ ∪ ♫ ₽ 🎣
Nearest Town Weston-super-Mare
Directions Leave the M5 at junction 21, follow signs to Sand Bay along The Queensway into Lower Norton Lane, turn right into Sand Road.
⛟ Weston-super-Mare

WESTON-SUPER-MARE

Dulhorn Farm Holiday Park, Weston Road, Lympsham, Weston-super-Mare, Somerset, BS24 0JQ
Tel: 01934 750298
Email: dfhp@btconnect.com
www.dulhornfarmholidaypark.co.uk
Pitches For ⛺ ⛟ ⛞ **Total** 87
Acreage 3 **Open** March to Oct
Access Good **Site** Level
Nearest Bus Stop (Miles) ¼
Quiet family site situated on a working farm in the countryside. Some facilities for the disabled. Ideal touring. Only 5 miles from Weston-super-Mare.
Facilities ♿ ⚕ 🅿 🛁 🚿 ⏧ ☉ ⏚ ⛽ ▣ 🛒 🍴
🏊 🍳 🚲 🖃 🛢 ✉ 🛊 ♨ ⚘ 🛜
Nearby Facilities ↑ ✓ 🛆 ⚘ ∪ ♫ 🎣
Nearest Town Weston-super-Mare
Directions On the A370, 5 miles from Weston-super-Mare and 4 miles from Burnham-on-Sea.
⛟ Weston-super-Mare

WESTON-SUPER-MARE

Sand Farm, Sand Farm Lane, Sand Bay, Weston-super-Mare, Somerset, BS22 9UF
Tel: 01934 620995
Email: christine.bates@tiscali.co.uk
www.kewstoke.org/stay.htm
Pitches For ⛺ ⛟ ⛞ **Total** 11
Acreage 1¼ **Open** Easter to Oct
Access Good **Site** Level
Quiet, farm site, 100 yards from the beach. Ideal for touring and walking. Regular (open top) bus service to W-S-M, 2½ miles from the town centre. Static caravans available for hire. Ralleys welcome. Bring Your Horse On Holiday, stables available. You can also contact us on Mobile: 07949 969722.
Facilities ⚕ 🅿 🛁 🚿 ⏧ ☉ ⏚ ⛽ ▣ 🛒 🍴
Nearby Facilities ↑ ✓ 🛆 ⚘ ∪ ♫ 🎣 ✕
Nearest Town Weston-super-Mare
Directions Leave M5 at junc 21 and head towards W-S-M, then take the slip road for Sand Bay. Follow all signs to Sand Bay until the beach is in front of you, turn right into Beach Road then next right into Sand Farm Lane.
⛟ Weston-super-Mare

WESTON-SUPER-MARE

West End Farm Caravan Park, Laneys Drove, Locking, Weston-super-Mare, Somerset, BS24 8RH
Tel: 01934 822529
Email: robin@westendfarm.org
www.westendcaravan.com
Pitches For ⛺ ⛟ ⛞ **Total** 75
Acreage 10 **Open** All Year
Access Good **Site** Level
Nearest Bus Stop (Miles) ½
Just 2½ miles from the beach. Ideal for touring and the Mendips.
Facilities ♿ ⚕ 🅿 🛁 🚿 ⏧ ☉ ⏚ ⛽ ▣ 🛒 🍴
🏊 ⛽ 🖃 🛢 ✉ ♨

ENGLAND

Nearby Facilities ┌ ✔ ∪ ♠ ✗
Nearest Town Weston-super-Mare
Directions Leave the M5 at junction 21 and follow signs for the Helicopter Museum. Turn right after the Helicopter Museum into Laney's Drove.
≠ Weston-super-Mare

WILLITON

Home Farm Holiday Centre, St Audries Bay, Williton, Somerset, TA4 4DP
Tel: 01984 632487
Email:
mike@homefarmholidaycentre.co.uk
www.homefarmholidaycentre.co.uk
Pitches For ▲ ⌂ ➍ **Total** 40
Open All Year
Access Good **Site** Terraced
Nearest Bus Stop (Miles) Outside
Private beach, sea fishing. Good base for touring Exmoor. 2 miles from West Somerset Railway. Holiday caravans and chalets for hire.
Facilities ✦ ⌂ ⓦ ♠ ┌ ⊙ ⌿ ➍ ▣ ☎
⚲ ⓠ ♡ ▥ ▥ ⅗ ╬ ▣ ⊟ ⅗
Nearby Facilities ┌ ✔ ⊿ ∪
Nearest Town Williton/Watchet
Directions Leave M5 at Junction 23, follow A39 towards Minehead for 17 miles. At West Quantoxhead take first right turn after St. Audries Garages (sp Doniford) B3191 take first right turning in ½ mile to our drive.
≠ Taunton

WINCANTON

Wincanton Racecourse Caravan Club Site, Wincanton, Somerset, BA9 8BJ
Tel: 01963 34276
www.caravanclub.co.uk
Pitches For ▲ ⌂ ➍ **Total** 57
Acreage 5 **Open** March **to** Oct
Access Good **Site** Level
Nearest Bus Stop (Miles) ½
Attractive site with beautiful views of Bruton Forest and the Downs. Close to Stourhead House, Hadspen Garden and Haynes Motor Museum. 9 hole Pay & Play golf adjacent, discounts available. Non members welcome. Booking essential.
Facilities
╚ ✦ ⓦ ♠ ┌ ▢ ⓠ ⓠ ➍ ▥ ╬ ▣ ⊟ ⅗
Nearby Facilities ┌
Directions From east on the A303 take the B3081 signposted Wincanton Racecourse, follow signs for the racecourse through Charlton Musgrove. At junction turn left signposted racecourse, site is 1½ miles on the right.
≠ Wincanton

WINSFORD

Halse Farm Caravan & Tent Park, Halse Farm, Winsford, Exmoor, Somerset, TA24 7JL
Tel: 01643 851259
Email: cad@halsefarm.co.uk
www.halsefarm.co.uk
Pitches For ▲ ⌂ ➍ **Total** 44
Acreage 3 **Open** 16-Mar **to** 31-Oct
Access Good **Site** Lev/Slope
Nearest Bus Stop (Miles) 1
In Exmoor National Park, on a working farm with beautiful views. Ideal for those who enjoy peaceful countryside. Quality heated toilet block and FREE showers. David Bellamy Gold Award for Conservation and ETC 4 Star Graded.
Facilities ╚ ✦ ⓦ ♠ ┌ ⊙ ⌿ ➍ ▣ ☎
▥ ⓠ ♣ ▥ ╬ ▣ ⊟ ⅗
Nearby Facilities ┌ ✔ ⊿ ⅍ ∪ ♠
Nearest Town Dulverton
Directions Signposted from the A396 Tiverton to Minehead road. In Winsford take small road in front of Royal Oak Inn. 1 mile up hill and over cattle grid, our entrance is immediately on the left.
≠ Taunton

STAFFORDSHIRE

ALTON

Alton, The Star Camping & Caravanning Club Site, Star Road, Cotton, Stoke-on-Trent, Staffordshire, ST10 3DW
Tel: 01538 702219
www.campingandcaravanningclub.co.uk
Pitches For ▲ ⌂ ➍ **Total** 195
Open 01-Mar **to** 12-Nov
Access Good **Site** Sloping
Nearest Bus Stop (Miles) ¼
Situated in the centre of beautiful countryside within 9 miles of Leek, Uttoxeter and Ashbourne. Close to Alton Towers. Within easy reach of the Peak District and Dovedale. Non members welcome. You can also call us on 0845 130 7633.
Facilities ╚ ✦ ⓦ ♠ ┌ ⊙ ⌿ ➍ ▣ ☎
▥ ⓠ ♣ ▥ ╬ ▣ ⊟
Nearby Facilities ┌ ✔ ⊿ ∪ ♠ ✗
Nearest Town Cheadle
Directions From the A52 take the B5417, 1¼ miles from Alton Towers.
≠ Blyth Bridge

BURTON-ON-TRENT

Willowbrook Farm, Burton Road, Alrewas, Burton-on-Trent, Staffordshire, DE13 7BA
Tel: 01283 790217
Pitches For ▲ ⌂ ➍
Acreage 3 **Open** All Year
Access Good **Site** Level

Nearest Bus Stop (Miles) ½
Close to Twycross Zoo, Drayton Manor Park, Lichfield Cathedral, National Memorial Arboretum and Tamworths Snowdome.
Facilities ✦ ⓦ ┌ ♠ ▣ ⓠ ⅗ ▣
Nearest Town Lichfield/B-on-T
Directions On the south bound side of the main A38 Burton-on-Trent and Lichfield road, ½ a mile north of Alrewas.
≠ Lichfield

CANNOCK

Camping & Caravanning Club Site, Old Youth Hostel, Wandon, Rugeley, Staffordshire, WS15 1QW
Tel: 01889 582166
www.campingandcaravanningclub.co.uk/cannockchase
Pitches For ▲ ⌂ ➍ **Total** 60
Acreage 5 **Open** 29-Mar **to** 05-Nov
Site Sloping
On the edge of Cannock Chase. 12 miles from Drayton Manor Park. BTB 4 Star Graded and AA 3 Pennants. Non members welcome. You can also call us on 0845 130 7633.
Facilities ✦ ⓦ ♠ ┌ ⊙ ⌿ ➍ ▣ ☎
▥ ⓠ ♣ ▥ ⊟ ⅗
Nearby Facilities ┌ ✔ ∪ ♠
Directions Take the A460 to Hednesford, turn right at signpost Rawnsley/Hazelslade, then turn first left, site is ½ mile past the golf club.
≠ Rugeley Town

CHEADLE

Hales Hall Caravan & Camping Park, Oakamoor Road, Cheadle, Staffordshire, ST10 4QR
Tel: 01538 753305
Email:
enquiries@haleshallcaravanandcampingpark.com
www.haleshallcaravanandcampingpark.com
Pitches For ▲ ⌂ ➍ **Total** 50
Acreage 6 **Open** March **to** October
Access Good **Site** Sloping
Nearest Bus Stop (Miles) Entrance
Only 5 miles from Alton Towers.
Facilities ✦ ⓦ ♠ ┌ ⊙ ⌿ ➍ ▣ ☎
▥ ⓠ ✗ ♡ ♣ ▥ ╬ ▣ ⊟ ✔ ⅗ ⅗ ⚲
Nearby Facilities ┌ ✔ ∪ ✗
Nearest Town Cheadle
Directions 1 mile from Cheadle on the B5417 en-route to Alton Towers.
≠ Stoke-on-Trent

LEEK

Blackshaw Moor Caravan Club Site, Leek, Staffordshire, ST13 8TW
Tel: 01538 300203
www.caravanclub.co.uk
Pitches For ⌂ ➍ **Total** 89
Acreage 8½ **Open** March **to** Jan

Access Good **Site** Level
Nearest Bus Stop (Miles) ¼
Situated on the edge of the Peak District with lovely views and walks. Just a short walk from Tittesworth Reservoir & Nature Reserve. Only 9 miles from Alton Towers. Non members welcome. Booking essential.
Facilities ⛺ ♿ ⓗ ⓦⓖ ⓐ ⓡ ⓞ ☕
ⓘ ⓞ ⓢ ⓐ ✚ ⓔ ➿ ⚡ 📶
Nearby Facilities ⓡ ⌗ ⚓ ⚒
Nearest Town Leek
Directions From Leek take the A53, site is on the right ¼ mile past the Three Horseshoes Inn.
⚑ Leek

LEEK

Camping & Caravanning Club Site,
Blackshaw Grange, Blackshaw Moor, Leek, Staffordshire, ST8 8TL
Tel: 01538 300285
www.campingandcaravanningclub.co.uk/ leek
Pitches For ⛺ ♨ 🚐 **Total** 70
Acreage 6 **Open** All Year
Site Lev/Slope
Nearest Bus Stop (Miles) ¼
On the edge of the Peak District. Ideal for visiting Alton Towers. BTB 4 Star Graded and AA 3 Pennants. Non members welcome. You can also call us on 0845 130 7633.
Facilities ⛺ ♿ ⓗ ⓦⓖ ⓐ ⓡ ⓞ ➿ ⚡ ⓞ ☕
ⓘ ⓞ ⓢ ⓐ ✚ ⓔ ➿ ⚒ 📶
Nearby Facilities ⓡ ⌗ ⚒
Directions Just 2 miles from Leek on the A53 Leek to Buxton road. The site is located 200 yards past the sign for Blackshaw Moor on the left hand side.
⚑ Buxton

LEEK

Glencote Caravan Park, Station Road, Nr Leek, Staffordshire, ST13 7EE
Tel: 01538 360745
Email: canistay@glencote.co.uk
www.glencote.co.uk
Pitches For ⛺ ♨ 🚐 **Total** 70
Acreage 6 **Open** Feb to Dec
Access Good **Site** Level
Nearest Bus Stop (Miles) Outside
Situated in the heart of the Churnet Valley. Close to the Heritage Railway and canalside pubs. Ideal base for the Peak District and Potteries. ETC 5 Star Graded, David Bellamy Gold Award and Top 100 Sites Regional Winner.
Facilities ⛺ ♿ ⓗ ⓦⓖ ⓐ ⓡ ⓞ ➿ ⚡ ⓞ ☕
⚗ ⓘ ⓞ ⓢ ⓐ ❀ ✚ ⓔ ➿ ⚡ 📶
Nearby Facilities ⓡ ⌗ ⚓ ⚒ ⌗
Nearest Town Leek
Directions 3½ miles south of Leek off the A520 Stone to Leek road.
⚑ Stoke-on-Trent

LICHFIELD

Cathedral Grange Touring Caravan Park, Grange Lane, Lichfield, Staffordshire, WS13 8HX
Tel: 07980 685093
Pitches For ⛺ ♨ 🚐 🚍
Open All Year
Access Good **Site** Level
Nearest Bus Stop (Miles) ¼
Near to Lichfield Cathedral. Just a short drive to Drayton Manor Park, Darwin House, a snowdome and an Odeon. You can also call us on Mobile: 07966 403938.
Facilities ♿ ⓗ ⓦⓖ ⓐ ⓡ ➿ ⚡ ⓐ ✚
Nearby Facilities
Nearest Town Lichfield

Directions From Lichfield take the A51 towards Rugeley, at the traffic lights turn right onto Eastern Avenue, then turn first left into Grange Lane.
⚑ Lichfield

LONGNOR

Longnor Wood Holiday Park, Newtown, Longnor, Near Buxton, Derbyshire, SK17 0NG
Tel: 01298 83648
Email: info@longnorwood.co.uk
www.longnorwood.co.uk
Pitches For ⛺ ♨ 🚐 🚍 **Total** 47
Acreage 10½ **Open** March to 10-Jan
Access Good **Site** Level
Nearest Bus Stop (Miles) 1¼
ADULTS ONLY PARK surrounded by woods and set in rolling countryside.
Facilities ♿ ⓗ ⓦⓖ ⓐ ⓡ ⓞ ➿ ⚡ ⓐ ⓞ ☕
⚗ ⓘ ⓞ ❀ ⓔ ⓐ ➿ 📶
Nearby Facilities ⓡ ⌗ ⚓ ⚒ ∪ ⌗ ⌗
Nearest Town Buxton
Directions From the village of Longnor, follow brown tourism caravan signs along the Leek road.
⚑ Buxton

STOKE-ON-TRENT

Cross Inn Caravan & Campsite, Cross Inn, Hoftens Cross, Cauldon Low, Stoke-on-Trent, Staffordshire, ST10 3EX
Tel: 01538 308338
Email: phillipkemp40@msn.com
www.the-crossinn.co.uk
Pitches For ⛺ ♨ 🚐
Acreage 2
Access Good **Site** Level
Nearest Bus Stop (Miles) Entrance
Close to Alton Towers, the Peak District National Park and Blackbrook Zoo.
Facilities ⛺ ♿ ⓗ ⓦⓖ ⓐ ⓡ ⓞ ➿ ⚡ ⓐ ⓞ ☕
⚗ ⓘ ✕ ⓞ ❀ ✚ ⓔ ➿ 📶
Nearby Facilities ⓡ ⌗ ⚓ ∪ ⌗ ⌗
Nearest Town Leek
Directions On the A52 Leek to Ashbourne road.
⚑ Leek

UTTOXETER

Uttoxeter Racecourse Caravan Club Site, Wood Lane, Uttoxeter, Staffordshire, ST14 8BD
Tel: 01889 564172
www.caravanclub.co.uk
Pitches For ⛺ ♨ 🚐 **Total** 76
Acreage 3 **Open** March to Nov
Access Good **Site** Level
Surrounded by the Weaver Hills. Free admission to racecourse, bar, betting area, picnic area and play area. Golf course adjacent. Close to Alton Towers, Lichfield Cathedral and Sudbury Hall. Non members welcome. Booking essential.
Facilities ⓗ ⓦⓖ ⓐ ⓡ ⓞ ⓐ ⓞ ☕
ⓘ ⓞ ⓢ ⓐ ✚ ⓔ ➿
Nearby Facilities ⓡ
Nearest Town Uttoxeter
Directions From the A50 take the A518 sp Racecourse, site is 1½ miles on the left. Turn into third gate at Caravan Club sign.
⚑ Uttoxeter

SUFFOLK

BUNGAY

Outney Meadow Caravan Park, Bungay, Suffolk, NR35 1HG
Tel: 01986 892338
www.outneymeadow.co.uk
Pitches For ⛺ ♨ 🚐 🚍
Acreage 8 **Open** 01-Mar to 01-Nov
Access Good **Site** Level
Nearest Bus Stop (Miles) ½
Beside the River Waveney for fishing and canoeing.
Facilities ⓗ ⓦⓖ ⓐ ⓡ ⓞ ➿ ⚡ ⓐ ⓞ ☕
⚗ ⓘ ⓞ ✚ ⓔ ⓐ ⚒
Nearby Facilities ⓡ ⌗ ⚒
Nearest Town Bungay
Directions Signposted from the roundabout junction of the A143 and A144 near Bungay.
⚑ Diss

BURY ST EDMUNDS

The Dell Touring Park, Beyton Road, Thurston, Bury St Edmunds, Suffolk, IP31 3RB
Tel: 01359 270121
Email: thedellcaravanpark@btinternet.com
www.thedellcaravanpark.co.uk
Pitches For ⛺ ♨ 🚐 **Total** 60
Open All Year
Access Good **Site** Level
Nearest Bus Stop (Miles) Outside
Ideal for touring East Anglia. 1 hour from Cambridge, Norwich and coast. Free Wi-Fi. New hard standing pitches. Excellent toilet blocks.
Facilities ⛺ ♿ ⓗ ⓦⓖ ⓐ ⓡ ⓞ ➿ ⚡ ⓐ ⓞ ☕
ⓘ ⓞ ✚ ⓔ ⓐ ⚒ 📶
Nearby Facilities ⓡ ⌗ ⌗
Nearest Town Bury St Edmunds
Directions Take A14 eastbound 6 miles from Bury follow Thurston signs.
⚑ Thurston

DARSHAM

Haw Wood Farm Caravan Park, Hinton, Darsham, Saxmundham, Suffolk, IP17 3QT
Tel: 01986 784248
Email: bookings@hawwoodfarm.co.uk
www.hawwoodfarm.co.uk
Pitches For ⛺ ♨ 🚐 🚍 **Total** 60
Acreage 12 **Open** March to 14-Jan
Access Good **Site** Level
Quiet countryside site. Easy access to Southwold and Dunwich. Close to a national nature reserve and RSPB Minsmere.
Facilities ⓗ ⓦⓖ ⓐ ⓡ ☕ ⚗ ⓞ ⓐ ➿ ⚒
Nearby Facilities ⓡ ⌗ ⚓ ⌗ ∪ ⌗
Nearest Town Southwold
Directions Turn off the A12 100 yards north of the junction with the A144 at the Little Chef, travel along the single track road for ¾ miles and Haw Wood is on the right.
⚑ Darsham

DUNWICH

Cliff House Holiday Park, Minsmere Road, Dunwich, Suffolk, IP17 3DQ
Tel: 01728 648282
Email: info@cliffhouseholidays.co.uk
www.cliffhouseholidays.co.uk
Pitches For ⛺ ♨ 🚐 🚍 **Total** 120
Acreage 30 **Open** March to Oct
Access Good **Site** Level
Cliff top woodland setting with sea views and direct access to the beach. In an area of outstanding natural beauty near to Minsmere Bird Reserve, Southwold and Aldeburgh, and only 30 miles from Norwich and Ipswich.
Facilities ⛺ ♿ ⓗ ⓦⓖ ⓐ ⓡ ⓞ ➿ ⚡ ⓐ ⓞ ☕
⚗ ⓘ ⓞ ⓢ ✕ ⓨ ⓜ ❀ ⓐ ✚ ⓔ ➿ ⚡ 📶
Nearby Facilities ⓡ ⌗ ⚓ ⌗ ∪ ⌗ ⌗ ⌗

Nearest Town Dunwich
Directions From the A12 north at Yoxford, turn right to Westleton, at the end turn left, then turn right to Dunwich. Follow brown tourism signs to Cliff House.
⇌ Darsham

EYE

Honeypot Caravan & Camping Park, Wortham, Eye, Suffolk, IP22 1PW
Tel: 01379 783312
Email: honeypotcamping@talk21.com
www.honeypotcamping.co.uk
Pitches For ⋀ ⛺ ⛟ **Total** 35
Acreage 7 **Open** Mid April **to** Mid Sept
Access Good **Site** Level
Nearest Bus Stop (Miles) Outside
Highly recommended site with plenty of peace and quiet. Fishing on site. Discounts available, please enquire (excludes Bank Holidays).
Facilities ⨍ 🚻⇌⌂⊙⌐ ⬛ 🔲 ☎
🏵 🅿 🔥 🗙 🛆 🚽🔲 🔲 ✍ 🔧
Nearby Facilities
Nearest Town Eye
Directions Four miles south west of Diss, on the south side of the A143.
⇌ Diss

FELIXSTOWE

Peewit Caravan Park, Walton Avenue, Felixstowe, Suffolk, IP11 2HB
Tel: 01394 284511
Email: peewitpark@aol.com
www.peewitcaravanpark.co.uk
Pitches For ⋀ ⛺ ⛟ **Total** 40
Acreage 3 **Open** Easter/1 April **to** 31-Oct
Access Good **Site** Level
Nearest Bus Stop (Miles) ½
Quiet and secluded setting, 900 metres from the seafront. Central for North Essex and coastal Suffolk.
Facilities ♿ ⨍ 🚻⇌⌂⊙⌐ ⬛ 🔲 ☎
🏵 🅿 🔥 🛆🚽🔲
Nearby Facilities ⌐ ✓ 🛆 🐟 ♪
Directions Take the A14 to Felixstowe Docks, at Gate No.1 turn towards the town centre, site is 100 metres on the left.
⇌ Felixstowe

HADLEIGH

Polstead Camping & Caravanning Club Site, Holt Road, Bower House Tye, Polstead, Suffolk, CO6 5BZ
Tel: 01787 211969
www.campingandcaravanningclub.co.uk/polstead
Pitches For ⋀ ⛺ ⛟ **Total** 50
Acreage 3½ **Open** 14-Feb **to** 14-Jan
Access Good **Site** Level
Nearest Bus Stop (Miles) Outside
On the edge of a beautiful conservation area. Near to Long Melford, Sudbury and the Stour Valley where Willy Lots (Constable) is located. Non members welcome. You can also call us on 0845 130 7633.
Facilities ⨍ 🔲 🅷 🚻⇌⌂⊙⌐ ⬛ ☎
🏵 🅿 🔥 🚽🔲 🔲 📶
Nearby Facilities
Nearest Town Hadleigh
Directions From the A134, A14 or A12 join the A1071 (Hadleigh road). Site is in Polstead Heath off Holt Road.
⇌ Sudbury

IPSWICH

Low House Touring Caravan Centre, Low House, Bucklesham Road, Foxhall, Ipswich, Suffolk, IP10 0AU
Tel: 01473 659437
Email: low.house@btinternet.com
www.tourbritain.com
Pitches For ⋀ ⛺ ⛟ **Total** 30

Acreage 3½ **Open** All Year
Access Good **Site** Level
Camp in a beautiful garden packed with ornamental trees and plants, arches and bower doves, rabbits, bantams and guinea fowl. Wildlife all around. Ornamental Tree Walk and Pets Corner. New friendly wardens. Heated toilet and shower block.
Facilities ⨍ 🚻⇌⌂⊙⌐ ⬛ ☎
🏵 🅿 🔥 🛆🚽🔲 🔲 ✍ 🔥 ⋃ ♪
Nearby Facilities ⌐ ✓ 🛆 🐟 ⋃ ♪
Nearest Town Ipswich
Directions Turn off A14 Ipswich Ring Road (South) via slip road onto A1156 (sp East Ipswich). In 1 mile turn right (signposted), in ½ mile turn right sp Low House, site is on the left in ¼ mile.
⇌ Ipswich

IPSWICH

Orwell Meadows Leisure Park, Priory Lane, Ipswich, Suffolk, IP10 0JS
Tel: 01473 726666
Email: reception@orwellmeadows.co.uk
www.orwellmeadows.co.uk
Pitches For ⋀ ⛺ ⛟ **Total** 80
Open 01-Mar **to** 14-Jan
Access Good **Site** Level
Nearest Bus Stop (Miles) ½
A quiet, family run park, ideally situated for touring beautiful Suffolk. Adjacent to the Orwell Country Park. Forest and river walks.
Facilities ♿ ⨍ 🚻⇌⌂⊙⌐ ⬛ 🔲 ☎
🏵 🅿 🔥 🗙 🔲 🛆 🔥 🚽🔲 🔲 �ヾ
Nearby Facilities ⌐ ✓ 🛆
Directions From the A14 heading towards Felixstowe take first exit after Orwell Bridge, at the roundabout turn left and first left again, then follow signs.
⇌ Ipswich

KESSINGLAND

Camping & Caravanning Club Site, Whites Lane, Kessingland, Nr Lowestoft, Suffolk, NR33 7TF
Tel: 01502 742040
www.campingandcaravanningclub.co.uk/kessingland
Pitches For ⋀ ⛺ ⛟ **Total** 90
Acreage 5 **Open** 29-Mar **to** 05-Nov
Access Good **Site** Level
Nearest Bus Stop (Miles) ½
Next to Suffolk Wildlife Park. Set in a quiet seaside resort, close to Great Yarmouth. 5 miles from Pleasurewood Hills. BTB 4 Star Graded, AA 4 Pennants and Loo of the Year Award. Non members welcome. You can also call us on 0845 130 7633.
Facilities ♿ ⨍ 🚻⇌⌂⊙⌐ ⬛ ☎
🏵 🅿 🔥 🛆🚽🔲 🔲
Nearby Facilities ⌐ ✓ 🐟 ♪
Nearest Town Lowestoft
Directions From Lowestoft on the A12, leave at roundabout in Kessingland following Wildlife Park signs. Turn right through park entrance.
⇌ Lowestoft

LEISTON

Cliff House Caravan Park, Sizewell Common, Leiston, Suffolk, IP16 4TU
Tel: 01728 830724
Email: enquiries@cliffhousepark.co.uk
www.cliffhousepark.co.uk
Pitches For ⋀ ⛺ ⛟ **Total** 60
Acreage 17 **Open** 15-Mar **to** 30-Nov
Access Good **Site** Level
On the beach. Sea fishing from a private beach. Ideal for bird watching, shore fishing, walking and cycling.
Facilities ⨍ 🚻⇌⌂⊙⌐ ⬛ 🔲 ☎
🏵 🅿 🔥 🗙 🔲 🔥 🚽🔲 🔲 ��ヾ 📶
Nearby Facilities ⌐ ✓ 🛆 🐟 ⋃
Nearest Town Leiston

Directions From Leiston take the turning to Sizewell Beach (2 miles), turn right sp Sizewell Hall, before the entrance gates to the Hall turn left to Cliff House.
⇌ Saxmundham

LOWESTOFT

Chestnut Farm, Gisleham, Lowestoft, Suffolk, NR33 8EE
Tel: 01502 740227
Pitches For ⋀ ⛺ ⛟ **Total** 40
Acreage 3 **Open** April **to** Oct
Access Good **Site** Level
Sheltered country meadow site. 2 miles from Kessingland Beach.
Facilities ⨍ 🚻⇌⌂⊙ ⬛ ☎
Nearby Facilities ⌐ ✓ 🛆 🔥 ⋃ ♪
Nearest Town Lowestoft
Directions Turn off the A12 at Kessingland bypass southern roundabout sp Rushmere, Mutford and Gisleham. The farm drive is second on the left after ¾ mile.
⇌ Oulton Broad

LOWESTOFT

Heathland Beach Caravan Park Ltd., London Road, Kessingland, Lowestoft, Suffolk, NR33 7PJ
Tel: 01502 740337
Email: heathlandbeach@btinternet.com
www.heathlandbeach.co.uk
Pitches For ⋀ ⛺ ⛟ **Total** 63
Acreage 5 **Open** April **to** Oct
Access Good **Site** Level
Nearest Bus Stop (Miles) Outside
Privately owned park surrounded by countryside. Beach access.
Facilities ♿ ⨍ 🚻⇌⌂⊙⌐ ⬛ 🔲 ☎
🏵 🅿 🔥 🔲 🔥 🛆 🔥 🗙 🚽🔲 🔲 ✍ ☀ヾ
Nearby Facilities ⌐ ✓ 🛆 🔥 ⋃ ♪
Nearest Town Lowestoft
Directions 3 miles south of Lowestoft off the old A12, take the B1437.
⇌ Lowestoft

LOWESTOFT

Kessingland Beach Holiday Park, Beach Lane, Nr Lowestoft, Suffolk, NR33 7RN
Tel: 0843 309 2563
Email:
holidaysales.kessinglandbeach@park-resorts.com
www.park-resorts.com
Pitches For ⋀ ⛺ ⛟ **Total** 90
Open April **to** Oct **Site** Level
Nearest Bus Stop (Miles) ½
A lively park close to sandy beaches and attractions.
Facilities ⨍ 🚻⇌⌂⊙⌐ ⬛ 🔲 ☎
🏵 🅿 🗙 🔲 🔥 ☀ 🚽🔲 🔲 ☀ヾ
Nearest Town Lowestoft
Directions From Ipswich take the A12 north, at Kessingland roundabout take the third exit, follow road through the village, at the beach follow the road to the right and take the left fork.
⇌ Lowestoft

NAYLAND

Rushbanks Farm, Bures Road, Wiston/Nayland, Colchester, Essex, CO6 4NA
Tel: 01206 262350
Pitches For ⋀ ⛺ ⛟
Open May **to** October
Access Good **Site** Level
On the north banks of the River Stour. Please book in advance. You can also telephone us on Mobile: 07860 325064.
Facilities 🚻⇌🔥✍
Nearby Facilities ⌐ ✓
Directions 7 miles from Colchester on the A134.
⇌ Bures

SUFFOLK

SAXMUNDHAM

Carlton Meres Country Park, Rendham Rd., Carlton, Saxmundham, Suffolk, IP17 2QP
Tel: 01728 603344
Email: enquiries@carlton-meres.co.uk
www.lifestylelivinguk.com
Pitches For 🚐 🚙 **Total** 100
Open 28-Mar **to** 01-Nov
Access Good **Site** Level
On site facilities include a tennis court, swimming pool, fishing lakes, sauna/steam room, gym and bar. Well behaved children welcome.
Facilities ♿ ⅃ 🅗 🆙 🖙 📮 ⚲ 🔌 ◻ 🍴
🌡 🅿 ✗ 🍷 🎡 ⚓ ➤🍴🗄 🥢 🌦 🛜
Nearby Facilities ⌐ ⅃ ⚓ Ü
Nearest Town Saxmundham
Directions Follow brown tourism signs from the A12.
🚉 Saxmundham

SAXMUNDHAM

Carlton Park Camping & Caravan Site, North Entrance, Saxmundham, Suffolk, IP17 1AT
Tel: 01728 604413
Email: info@carltonpark.info
www.carltonpark.info
Pitches For ⛺ 🚐 🚙 **Total** 75
Acreage 7½ **Open** April **to** October
Access Good **Site** Sloping
Nearest Bus Stop (Miles) ½
Situated in rolling countryside, close to the Suffolk heritage coast.
Facilities ♿ ⅃ 🆙 🖙 📮 ⊙⋅🍴 ◻ 🅿 🍴 ❀🌦🌦
Nearby Facilities ⌐ ⅃ ⚓ Ü 🄿
Nearest Town Aldeburgh
Directions From the A12 Ipswich to Lowestoft road, take the B1121, go through the town and the site is on the left.
🚉 Saxmundham

SAXMUNDHAM

Whitearch Touring Park, Main Road, Benhall, Saxmundham, Suffolk, IP17 1NA
Tel: 01728 604646
www.caravancampingsites.co.uk
Pitches For ⛺ 🚐 🚙 **Total** 50
Acreage 14½ **Open** April **to** October
Access Good **Site** Level
Nearest Bus Stop (Miles) ¼
Fishing and tennis on site. No cycling on site. Near the Suffolk coast, Snape Maltings Concert Hall, Minsmere Bird Reserve, American Theme Park and castles.
Facilities ♿ ⅃ 🅗 🆙 🖙 📮 ⊙⋅🍴 ◻ 🍴
🌡 🅿 ⚓ 🎡 ❀➤🍴 ⅃ 🌦
Nearby Facilities ⌐ ⅃ 🎣 Ü 🄿
Nearest Town Saxmundham
Directions Just off the main A12 junction with the B1121 at the Ipswich end of Saxmundham by-pass.
🚉 Saxmundham

SHOTLEY

Shotley Caravan Park, Gate Farm Road, Shotley, Suffolk, IP9 1QH
Tel: 01473 787421
www.shotleycaravanpark.com
Pitches For 🚐 🚙
Acreage 7 **Open** March **to** October
Access Good **Site** Lev/Slope
Nearest Bus Stop (Miles) Outside
ADULTS ONLY SITE. Enjoy peace and tranquillity in this area of outstanding natural beauty, with panoramic views over the River Orwell. Large pond with ducks. Free eggs from our chickens for all caravanners. Ideal site for the over 50s. Tourers/rallies welcome. Close to a marina, restaurants, pubs, fish & chips, church, doctors and garage. Easy access from the A12/A14.

Facilities ⅃ 🅗 🆙 🔌 🖙➤🍴📮A🌦 ⚲
Nearby Facilities ⌐ ⅃ ⚓ Ü 🄿
Nearest Town Ipswich/Felixstowe
Directions From Orwell Bridge take exit A137 and follow the B1456 once in Shotley (10 miles from Ipswich). Go past the Rose Pub on the right and after 1 mile turn left into Gate Farm Road and go through the green gates.
🚉 Ipswich

STOWMARKET

Stonham Barns Caravan & Camping Park, Pettaugh Road, Stonham Aspal, Stowmarket, Suffolk, IP14 6AT
Tel: 01449 711901
Email:
enquiries@stonhambarnsleisure.co.uk
www.stargladeleisure.co.uk
Pitches For ⛺ 🚐 🚙 **Total** 60
Acreage 3 **Open** All Year
Access Good **Site** Level
Nearest Bus Stop (Miles) ¼
Excellent facilities for all the family. Ideal for exploring the beautiful Suffolk countryside. Golf course, shops, restaurant, showground and owl sanctuary all on site. Quiet areas available. Large groups welcome.
Facilities ♿ ⅃ 🅗 🆙 🖙 📮 ⊙⋅🍴 ◻ 🍴
🌡 🅿 🍷 ✗ 🎡 ⚓➤🍴🗄 ⅃ 🌦
Nearby Facilities ⌐ ⅃ 🎣 Ü 🄿 🄿
Nearest Town Bury St Edmunds
Directions From the A14 between Ipswich and Stowmarket, leave at Junction 51, at the roundabout take the third exit onto the A140, then turn right onto the A1120 to Stonham Aspal.
🚉 Stowmarket

SUDBURY

Willowmere Caravan Park, Bures Road, Little Cornard, Sudbury, Suffolk, CO10 0NN
Tel: 01787 375559/310422
Email: awillowmere@aol.com
Pitches For ⛺ 🚐 🚙 **Total** 40
Acreage 2 **Open** Easter **to** 01-Oct
Access Good **Site** Level
Nearest Bus Stop (Miles) Outside Site
Quiet country park near a river.
Facilities ♿ ⅃ 🆙 🖙 📮 ⊙⋅🍴 ◻ 🍴➤🍴
Nearby Facilities ⌐ ⅃ 🎣 Ü 🄿
Nearest Town Sudbury
Directions Leave Sudbury on the B1508 to Bures and Colchester, 1 mile from Sudbury.
🚉 Sudbury

THEBERTON

Cakes & Ale, Abbey Lane, Theberton, Suffolk, IP16 4TE
Tel: 01728 831655
Email: cakesandalepark@gmail.com
www.cakesandale.net
Pitches For ⛺ 🚐 🚙 **Total** 50
Open April **to** October
Access Good **Site** Level
Nearest Bus Stop (Miles) 1.5
ADULTS ONLY Park. 1 mile from Leiston Abbey ruins and 3 miles from Minsmere Bird Sanctuary. Central for the Heritage Coast.
Facilities ♿ ⅃ 🅗 🆙 🖙 📮 ⊙⋅🍴 ◻ 🍴
🌡 🅿 ✗ 🎡 ⚓ ❀➤🍴🗄 ⅃ 🌦
Nearby Facilities ⌐ ⅃ ⚓ Ü 🄿
Nearest Town Leiston
Directions Take the B1122 north, turn left opposite Sizewell turning on the edge of Leiston and follow brown tourism signs.
🚉 Saxmundham

WOODBRIDGE

Moat Barn Touring Caravan Park, Dallinghoo Road, Bredfield, Woodbridge, Suffolk, IP13 6BD
Tel: 01473 737520
www.moatbarn.co.uk
Pitches For ⛺ 🚐 🚙 **Total** 34
Acreage 2 **Open** March **to** January
Access Good **Site** Level
Nearest Bus Stop (Miles) Outside
Quiet, family run park in a rural location. No facilities for children. No large campers vans accepted. Ideal for touring and exploring the Heritage Coast.
Facilities ⅃ 🆙 🖙 📮 ⊙⋅🍴 ◻ 🍴 🗄🆙📮
Nearby Facilities ⌐ ⅃ ⚓ Ü 🄿 🄿
Nearest Town Woodbridge
Directions On the A12 midway between Wickham Market and Woodbridge turn to Bredfield. Turn right at Village Pump and go through the village past the pub and church, follow road through the S bend and Park is 150 yards on the left.
🚉 Woodbridge

WOODBRIDGE

Moon and Sixpence, Newbourne Road, Waldringfield, Woodbridge, Suffolk, IP12 4PP
Tel: 01473 736650
Email: enquiries@moonandsixpence.eu
www.moonandsixpence.eu
Pitches For ⛺ 🚐 🚙 **Total** 75
Acreage 5 **Open** April **to** October
Access Good **Site** Level
Nearest Bus Stop (Miles) Outside
Picturesque location. Sheltered, terraced site. Own private lake and sandy beach. Compact 9 hole golf course, 3 hard tennis courts and volley ball/basket ball courts.
Facilities ⅃ 🅗 🆙 🖙 📮 ⊙⋅🍴 ◻ 🍴
🌡 🅿 ✗ 🍷 🎡 ⚓ ❀➤🍴🗄 ⅃ 🛜
Nearby Facilities ⌐ ⅃ ⚓ Ü 🄿 🄿
Nearest Town Woodbridge
Directions Turn off A12, Ipswich Eastern By-Pass, onto unclassified road signposted Waldringfield, Newbourn. Follow caravan direction signs.
🚉 Woodbridge

WOODBRIDGE

Run Cottage Touring Park, Alderton Road, Hollesley, Woodbridge, Suffolk, IP12 3RQ
Tel: 01394 411309
Email: contact@run-cottage.co.uk
www.run-cottage.co.uk
Pitches For ⛺ 🚐 🚙 **Total** 20
Acreage 3½ **Open** All Year
Access Good **Site** Level
Nearest Bus Stop (Miles) ¼
Quiet, peaceful and secluded site set in 3½ acres of parkland. On Suffolks Heritage Coast, ideal for walking, cycling and bird watching.
Facilities ♿ ⅃ 🅗 🆙 🖙 📮 ⊙⋅🍴 ◻ 🍴 🗄🆙📮
Nearby Facilities ⌐ ⅃ ⚓ Ü
Nearest Town Woodbridge
Directions Turn off the A12 at Melton onto the A1152, at next roundabout turn right onto the B1083. Turn next left to Hollesley then turn right into The Street at Hollesley, go through the village and over the small bridge, site is 100 yards on the left.
🚉 Woodbridge

WOODBRIDGE

St Margaret's Caravan & Camp Site, St Margaret's House, Hollesley Road, Shottisham, Woodbridge, Suffolk, IP12 3HD
Tel: 01394 411247
Email: aji@me.com
www.stmargaretscampsite.co.uk
Pitches For ⛺ 🚐 🚙 **Total** 30
Acreage 2½ **Open** April **to** Oct
Access Good **Site** Level

Nearest Bus Stop (Miles) ¼
Facilities ∮ 🎖️🖵⚲⌂🏳️⚲🏕️
Nearby Facilities ⌁✦⚓⛵⛴
Nearest Town Woodbridge
⚍ Melton

SURREY
CHERTSEY
Camping & Caravanning Club Site,
Bridge Road, Chertsey, Surrey, KT16 8JX
Tel: 01932 562405
www.campingandcaravanningclub.co.uk/
chertsey
Pitches For ▲ ⬛ ⬛ **Total** 200
Acreage 8 **Open** All Year
Site Level
Nearest Bus Stop (Miles) 1
On the banks of the River Thames, fishing
on site. Table tennis on site. 4 miles from
Thorpe Park. Close to London. BTB 4 Star
Graded and AA 4 Pennants. Non members
welcome. You can also call us on 0845 130
7633.
Facilities ⚿ ∮ 🖵🖵🖵⚲⌂⊙🍴⚌🔲⚲
🏳️⚽🏧🔔Å🏕️🍴🎽✦🏕️
Nearby Facilities ⌁✦⚓🏊⚓
Directions Leave the M25 at junction 11 and
follow the A317 to Chertsey. At the
roundabout take the first exit to the traffic
lights and go straight across to the next set
of traffic lights, turn right and after 400 yards
turn left into the site.
⚍ Chertsey

HORSLEY
Camping & Caravanning Club Site,
Ockham Road North, East Horsley, Surrey,
KT24 6PE
Tel: 01483 283273
www.campingandcaravanningclub.co.uk/
horsley
Pitches For ▲ ⬛ ⬛ **Total** 130
Acreage 9½ **Open** 29-Mar **to** 05-Nov
Access Good **Site** Level
Nearest Bus Stop (Miles) 1
Peaceful site, only 40 minutes from London
by train. Fishing lake on site. Non members
welcome. You can also call us on 0845 130
7633.
Facilities ⚿ ∮ 🖵🖵🖵⚲⌂⊙🍴⚌🔲⚲
🏳️⚽🏧🔔Å🏕️🍴🎽✦🏕️
Nearby Facilities ⌁✦⛵⚓⚲
Nearest Town Guildford
Directions Leave the M25 at junction 10 and
travel south on the A3. Turn left onto the
B2039, the site is the fourth turning on the
right.
⚍ East Horsley

LALEHAM
Laleham Camping Club, Laleham Park,
Thameside, Laleham, Middlesex, TW18
1SS
Tel: 01932 564149
www.lalehamcampingclub.co.uk
Pitches For ▲ ⬛ ⬛
Open April **to** 01-Oct
Access Good **Site** Level
Nearest Bus Stop (Miles) ½
Alongside the River Thames.
Facilities ∮ 🖵⚲⌂⊙🍴⚌🔲🏳️🏕️🏕️
Nearby Facilities ⌁✦⛵⚓🏊⚲
Nearest Town Staines
⚍ Staines

LINGFIELD
Long Acres Caravan & Camping Park,
Newchapel Road, Lingfield, Surrey, RH7
6LE
Tel: 01342 833205
Email: longacrescamping@yahoo.co.uk
www.longacrescamping.co.uk
Pitches For ▲ ⬛ ⬛ **Total** 60
Acreage 7 **Open** All Year
Access Good **Site** Level
Nearest Bus Stop (Miles) ½
Ideal for visiting London, Surrey, Kent,
Sussex, Hever Chartwell, Ardingly
Showground, Wakehurst Place and many
other attractions.
Facilities ∮ 🖵🖵🖵⚲⌂⊙🍴⚌🔲🏳️🏕️
🏳️⚽🏧🔔🔲🏧⚲
Nearby Facilities ⌁✦
Nearest Town East Grinstead
Directions From the M25 junc 6 take the A22
south towards East Grinstead. At Newchapel
roundabout turn left onto the B2028 to
Lingfield, site is 700 yards on the right.
⚍ Lingfield

REDHILL
Alderstead Heath Caravan Club Site,
Dean Lane, Redhill, Merstham, Surrey,
RH1 3AH
Tel: 01737 644629
www.caravanclub.co.uk
Pitches For ⬛ ⬛ **Total** 150
Acreage 30 **Open** All Year
Access Good **Site** Level
Nearest Bus Stop (Miles) ½
Quiet, level pitched site which drops into
rolling wooded countryside, and has
wonderful views of the North Downs. Close
to Wisley Gardens, NT Chartwell, Thorpe
Park and Chessington World of Adventure.
Non members welcome. Booking essential.
Facilities ⚿ ∮ 🖵🖵🖵⚲⌂⌂ 🔲🏕️
🏳️⚽🏧🔔🔲🏧🔔✦🏕️
Nearby Facilities ⌁✦
Nearest Town Redhill
Directions Leave M25 at junction 8 and take
A217 signposted Reigate, after 300yds fork
left signposted Merstham. At T-junction turn
left onto A23, after ½ mile turn right into
Shepherds Hill signposted Caterham, after
1 mile turn left into Dean Lane (DO NOT turn
in to Dean Lane at Little Chef). Site is 175yds
on right.
⚍ Redhill

SUSSEX (EAST)
BATTLE
Brakes Coppice Park, Forewood Lane,
Crowhurst, East Sussex, TN33 9AB
Tel: 01424 830322
Email: brakesco@btinternet.com
www.brakescoppicepark.co.uk
Pitches For ▲ ⬛ ⬛ **Total** 30
Acreage 3¼ **Open** March **to** October
Access Good **Site** Sloping
Nearest Bus Stop (Miles) 1
Secluded, 11 acre woodland park with level
pitches. TV aerial point to serviced pitches.
Facilities ∮ 🖵🖵🖵⚲⌂⊙🍴⚌🔲🏕️
🏳️⚽🏧🔔🔲🏧✦🏕️
Nearby Facilities ⌁✦⛵🏊⚓⚲
Directions Turn right off the A2100 (Battle
to Hastings road) 2 miles from Battle. Follow
signs to Crowhurst, 1¼ miles turn left into
site.
⚍ Crowhurst

BATTLE
Crazy Lane Tourist Park, Whydown Farm,
Crazy Lane, Sedlescombe, East Sussex,
TN33 0QT
Tel: 01424 870147
www.crazylane.co.uk
Pitches For ▲ ⬛ ⬛ **Total** 36
Acreage 3 **Open** 01-Mar **to** 31-Oct
Access Good **Site** Level
Nearest Bus Stop (Miles) Outside
15 minutes to the beach. Ideal for the
countryside and Hastings. NEW shower and
toilet block.
Facilities ⚿ ∮ 🖵🖵🖵⚲⌂⊙🍴⚌🔲🏕️
🏳️⚽🏧🔔🔲🏧✦🏕️
Nearby Facilities ⌁✦⛵🏊⚓⚲⚲
Nearest Town Battle/Hastings
Directions Travelling south on A21, turn left
into Crazy Lane, 100 yds past junction A21/
B2244, opposite Black Brooks Garden
Centre.
⚍ Battle

BATTLE
Normanhurst Court Caravan Club Site,
Stevens Crouch, Battle, East Sussex,
TN33 9LR
Tel: 01424 773808
www.caravanclub.co.uk
Pitches For ⬛ ⬛ **Total** 149
Acreage 18 **Open** March **to** Oct
Access Good **Site** Lev/Slope
Set in a former garden with splendid trees
and shrubs, and lovely views of the Downs.
Close to Battle Abbey, Hastings, Rye and
Sussex vineyards. Non members welcome.
Booking essential.
Facilities ⚿ ∮ 🖵🖵🖵⚲⌂ 🔲🏕️
🏳️⚽🏧🔔🔲🏧🔔✦🏕️
Nearby Facilities ⌁✦
Nearest Town Battle
Directions From the A269 in Ninfield take
the B2204 signposted Battle. Just past
Catsfield keep left, after 1¼ miles turn left
onto the A271 signposted Eastbourne, site
is ½ mile on the left.
⚍ Battle

BATTLE
Senlac Wood, Catsfield Road, Catsfield,
Nr Battle, East Sussex, TN33 9LN
Tel: 01424 773969
Email: senlacwood@xlinternet.co.uk
www.senlacwood.co.uk
Pitches For ▲ ⬛ ⬛ **Total** 50
Acreage 10 **Open** March **to** Oct
Access Good **Site** Level
Nearest Bus Stop (Miles) Outside
In a woodland setting with walks and fishing
nearby. Ideal for touring this historic 1066
country. Approx. 7 miles from the beach.
Facilities ∮ 🖵🖵🖵⚲⌂⊙ 🏕️
🏳️⚽🏧🔔🔲🏧🔔✦🏕️
Nearby Facilities ⌁✦⛵⚓⚲
Nearest Town Battle
Directions From Battle take the A271 North
Trade Road, after about 2½ miles turn left
onto the B2204. Site is on the left in ½ a
mile.
⚍ Battle

BEXHILL-ON-SEA
**Cobbs Hill Farm Caravan & Camping
Park,** Watermill Lane, Bexhill-on-Sea, East
Sussex, TN39 5JA
Tel: 01424 213460
Email: cobbshillfarmuk@hotmail.com
www.cobbshillfarm.co.uk
Pitches For ▲ ⬛ ⬛ 🚐 **Total** 55
Acreage 17½ **Open** April **to** October
Access Good **Site** Level

SUSSEX (EAST)

ENGLAND

Situated on a small farm in quiet countryside with a network of footpaths leading from the Park. Spacious play area and an animal viewing area. Two static caravans available for hire.
Facilities ⚙ ✦ 🄷 ⛽ ⌂ ☺ 🛆 📮 ▣ 🛒
🏕 ⊕ ⛘ 🛆 🏊✦◫🄳 ▣ ☀ ⚓ 🛜
Nearby Facilities ┌ ✎ ⊥ ⋃ ℛ
Nearest Town Bexhill-on-Sea
Directions Signposted off the A269. Turn into Watermill Lane and the Site is 1 mile on the left.
🚆 Bexhill-on-Sea

BEXHILL-ON-SEA

Kloofs Caravan Park, Sandhurst Lane, Bexhill-on-Sea, East Sussex, TN39 4RG
Tel: 01424 842839
Email: camping@kloofs.com
www.kloofs.com
Pitches For ▲ ⊞ ⊟ **Total** 62
Acreage 22 **Open** All Year
Access Good **Site** Level
Nearest Bus Stop (Miles) ½
Quiet, tranquil, rural park only 2 miles from the beach.
Facilities ⚙ ✦ 🄵 🄷 ⛽ ⌂ ☺ 🛆 📮 ▣ 🛒
🏕 ⊕ ⊕ ⛘ 🛆 🏊✦◫▣ ☀ ⚓
Nearby Facilities ┌ ✎ ⋃ ⋃ ℛ
Nearest Town Bexhill-on-Sea
Directions From the A259 at the Bexhill/Little Common roundabout turn into Peartree Lane, go up the hill to the crossroads and turn left into Whydown Road, Sandhurst Lane is 300 metres on the left.
🚆 Cooden Beach

BRIGHTON

Sheepcote Valley Caravan Club Site, East Brighton Park, Brighton, East Sussex, BN2 5TS
Tel: 01273 626546
www.caravanclub.co.uk
Pitches For ▲ ⊞ ⊟ **Total** 169
Acreage 17 **Open** All Year
Access Good **Site** Level
Nearest Bus Stop (Miles) ½
Situated in the South Downs, adjacent to recreation grounds. Only 2 miles from Brighton with its beach, pier, Royal Pavilion, sea life centre, boutiques and seafront attractions. Non members welcome. Booking essential.
Facilities ⚙ ✦ 🄵 🄷 ⛽ ⌂ 🛒
▣ ⊕ 🛆 🛆 ◫🄳 ▣ 🛜
Nearby Facilities ┌ ⊥ ⋋
Nearest Town Brighton
Directions From A27 take B2123 signposted Falmer, at lights by Downs Hotel turn right into Warren Road. At next lights turn left into Wilson Avenue, cross the racecourse and after 1¼ miles turn left at foot of the hill (last turn before the lights) into East Bright.
🚆 Brighton

CROWBOROUGH

Camping & Caravanning Club Site, Goldsmith Recreation Ground, Crowborough, East Sussex, TN6 2TN
Tel: 01892 664827
www.campingandcaravanningclub.co.uk/crowborough
Pitches For ▲ ⊞ ⊟ **Total** 90

Acreage 13 **Open** 29-Mar **to** 05-Nov
Site Lev/Slope
Nearest Bus Stop (Miles) Outside
On the edge of Ashdown Forest. Adjacent to a sports centre. Kitchen available at extra charge. BTB 4 Star Graded and AA 3 Pennants. Non members welcome. You can also call us on 0845 130 7633.
Facilities ⚙ ✦ 🄷 ⛽ ⌂ ☺ 🛆 📮 ▣ 🛒
▣ ⊕ 🛆 ⛘ ◫🄳 ▣ ☀ 🛜
Nearby Facilities ┌ ✎ ⋃ ⋃
Directions Take the A26 turn off into the entrance to Goldsmiths Ground signposted leisure centre, at the top of the road turn right into site lane.
🚆 Jarvis Brook

EASTBOURNE

Fairfields Farm Caravan & Camping Park, Eastbourne Road, Westham, Pevensey, East Sussex, BN24 5NG
Tel: 01323 763165
Email: enquiries@fairfieldsfarm.com
www.fairfieldsfarm.com
Pitches For ▲ ⊞ ⊟ **Total** 60
Acreage 3 **Open** April to Oct
Access Good **Site** Level
Nearest Bus Stop (Miles) ¼
2 miles from the beach and 3 miles from Eastbourne town centre.
Facilities ⚙ ✦ 🄵 🄷 ⛽ ⌂ ☺ 🛆 📮 ▣ 🛒
🏕 ⊕ ⊕ 🛆 ◫🄳 ▣ ✎ ⚓
Nearby Facilities ┌ ✎ ⊥ ⋋ ⋃ ℛ
Nearest Town Eastbourne
Directions On the B2191 in the village of Westham. 3 miles east of Eastbourne.
🚆 Pevensey & Westham

HASTINGS

Stalkhurst Caravan Park, Stalkhurst Cottage, Ivyhouse Lane, Hastings, East Sussex, TN35 4NN
Tel: 01424 439015
Email: stalkhurstpark@yahoo.co.uk
Pitches For ▲ ⊞ **Total** 11
Open 01-Mar **to** 15-Jan
Access Good **Site** Sloping
2½ miles to the beach. Heated swimming pool.
Facilities ✦ 🄷 ⛽ ⌂ ☺ ⚓ ✎ ⚓
Nearby Facilities ┌ ✎ ⊥ ⋋ ⋃ ℛ
Nearest Town Hastings
Directions From Hastings take A259 towards Rye, turn left onto B2093, in ½ mile turn right into Ivyhouse Lane. Or from the A21 take the B2093 for 2½ miles, turn left into Ivyhouse Lane.
🚆 Hastings

HORAM

Horam Manor Touring Park, Horam, Nr Heathfield, East Sussex, TN21 0YD
Tel: 01435 813662
Email: camping@horam-manor.co.uk
www.horam-manor.co.uk
Pitches For ▲ ⊞ ⊟ **Total** 90
Acreage 7 **Open** March to October
Access Good **Site** Lev/Slope
Nearest Bus Stop (Miles) ¼
A tranquil rural setting, but with plenty to do on the estate, and many places to visit.
Facilities ⚙ ✦ 🄵 🄷 ⛽ ⌂ ☺ 🛆 📮 ▣ 🛒
▣ ⊕ 🛆 🛆 ◫🄳 ▣ 🛜

Nearby Facilities ┌ ✎ ⋃ ℛ
Nearest Town Heathfield/Eastbourne
Directions On A267, 3 miles south of Heathfield, 10 miles north of Eastbourne.
🚆 Eastbourne/Polegate

HORAM

Woodland View Touring Park, Horebeech Lane, Horam, Heathfield, East Sussex, TN21 0HR
Tel: 01435 813597
Pitches For ▲ ⊞ ⊟ **Total** 25
Acreage 2 **Open** March to Nov
Access Good **Site** Sloping
Nearest Bus Stop (Miles) ¼
Next to the Cuckoo Trail.
Facilities ✦ 🄷 ⛽ ⌂ ☺ 🛆 📮 ▣ 🛒 ▣ 🏊
Nearby Facilities ┌ ✎ ⊥ ⋋ ⋃ ℛ ✦
Nearest Town Eastbourne/Polegate
Directions ¼ of a mile off the A267.
🚆 Eastbourne/Polegate

PEVENSEY

Normans Bay Camping & Caravanning Club Site, Normans Bay, Pevensey, East Sussex, BN24 6PR
Tel: 01323 761190
www.campingandcaravanningclub.co.uk/normansbay
Pitches For ▲ ⊞ ⊟ **Total** 200
Acreage 13 **Open** 29-Mar **to** 05-Nov
Access Good **Site** Level
Nearest Bus Stop (Miles) ½
Site has its own beach and is close to where the Normans landed. BTB 4 Star Graded and AA 3 Pennants. Non members welcome. You can also call us on 0845 130 7633.
Facilities ⚙ ✦ 🄷 ⛽ ⌂ ☺ 🛆 📮 ▣ 🛒
🏕 ⊕ ⊕ 🛆 ⛘ ◫🄳 ▣ ☀ 🛜
Nearby Facilities ┌ ✎ ⋋ ⋃ ℛ
Nearest Town Pevensey
Directions From the A259 in Pevensey Bay Village take the first turn left (coast road) signed Beachlands only. After 1¼ miles site is on the left hand side.
🚆 Normans Bay

PEVENSEY BAY

Bay View Park, Old Martello Road, Pevensey Bay, Nr Eastbourne, East Sussex, BN24 6DX
Tel: 01323 768688
Email: holidays@bay-view.co.uk
www.bay-view.co.uk
Pitches For ▲ ⊞ ⊟ **Total** 94
Acreage 34 **Open** March to Oct
Access Good **Site** Level
Nearest Bus Stop (Miles) ¼
AA 3 Pennant Graded Park, next to the beach. 9 hole golf course on site. Near to Eastbournes Sunshine Coast. Gold David Bellamy Conservation Award.
Facilities ⚙ ✦ 🄵 🄷 ⛽ ⌂ ☺ 🛆 📮 ▣ 🛒
🏕 ⊕ 🛆 ⛘ ◫🄳 ▣ 🛜
Nearby Facilities ┌ ✎ ⊥ ⋋ ℛ
Nearest Town Eastbourne
Directions 2 miles from Eastbourne centre off the A259.
🚆 Pevensey Bay

RYE

Camber Sands Holiday Park, New Lydd Road, Camber, Nr Rye, East Sussex, TN31 7RT
Tel: 0843 309 2553
Email: holidaysales.cambersands@park-resorts.com
www.park-resorts.com
Pitches For Å ⌷ ⇔ **Total** 70
Open April **to** October
Access Good **Site** Level
Nearest Bus Stop (Miles) Outside
Opposite a gorgeous sandy beach.
Facilities
Nearby Facilities
Nearest Town Rye
Directions From the M25 take the M20 and exit at junction 10. Take the A2070 and follow signs to Hastings and Rye. 1 mile before Rye turn left sp Camber, the Park is 3 miles on the left.
⇌ Rye

SEAFORD

Buckle Holiday Park, Marine Parade, Seaford, East Sussex, BN25 2QR
Tel: 01323 897801
Email: info@buckleholidaypark.co.uk
www.buckleholidaypark.co.uk
Pitches For Å ⌷ ⇔ **Total** 150
Open All Year
Access Good **Site** Level
Nearest Bus Stop (Miles) ¼
Adjacent to the beach. Between Brighton and Eastbourne and near to Seven Sisters and South Downs.
Facilities
Nearby Facilities
Nearest Town Seaford
Directions 1 mile from Seaford and 8 miles from Brighton.
⇌ Bishopstone

UCKFIELD

Heaven Farm, Furners Green, Uckfield, East Sussex, TN22 3RG
Tel: 01825 790226
Email: heavenfarmleisure@btinternet.com
www.heavenfarm.co.uk
Pitches For Å ⌷ ⇔ ⇔ **Total** 30
Acreage 4 **Open** All Year
Access Good **Site** Lev/Slope
Nearest Bus Stop (Miles) 1
Farm museum, The Stable Reataurant & Tea Rooms, nature trail and organic farm shop. Ideal for National Trust gardens, Bluebell Railway and Brighton. Booking is essential.
Facilities
Nearby Facilities
Nearest Town Uckfield
Directions On the A275 between East Grinstead (A22) and Haywards Heath (A272).
⇌ Haywards Heath

UCKFIELD

Honeys Green Caravan Park, Easons Green, Halland, Uckfield, East Sussex, TN22 5GJ
Tel: 01732 860205
Email: honeysgreenpark@tiscali.co.uk
Pitches For Å ⌷ ⇔ **Total** 22
Acreage 17 **Open** Easter **to** October
Access Good **Site** Level
Nearest Bus Stop (Miles) ¼
Small, peaceful, rural park in a pretty wooded location with our own coarse fishing lake. Lovely walks nearby.
Facilities
Nearby Facilities

Nearest Town Uckfield
Directions On the A22, 3 miles south of Uckfield at the Halland roundabout take the B2192 signposted Blackboys/Heathfield, Park is a few hundred yards on the left.
⇌ Uckfield

WINCHELSEA

Rye Bay Caravan Park, Pett Level Road, Winchelsea Beach, East Sussex, TN36 4NE
Tel: 01797 226340
Pitches For ⌷ ⇔ **Total** 40
Open Whitsun **to** Mid Sept
Access Good **Site** Fairly Level
Nearest Bus Stop (Miles) Outside
Near the beach.
Facilities
Nearby Facilities
Nearest Town Hastings
Directions 3 miles west of Rye and 7 miles east of Hastings.
⇌ Rye

SUSSEX (WEST)

ARUNDEL

Maynards Caravan & Camping Park, Crossbush, Arundel, West Sussex, BN18 9PQ
Tel: 01903 882075
Pitches For Å ⌷ ⇔ **Total** 70
Acreage 3 **Open** All Year
Access Good **Site** Level
Nearest Bus Stop (Miles) Outside
3 miles from a sandy beach. Near Arundel Castle and Wild Fowl Reserve.
Facilities
Nearby Facilities
Nearest Town Arundel
Directions Just off the main A27, turn into the Beefeater Restaurant car park.
⇌ Arundel

ARUNDEL

Ship & Anchor Marina, Heywood & Bryett Ltd, Ford, Arundel, West Sussex, BN18 0BJ
Tel: 01243 551262
Email: enquiries@shipandanchormarina.co.uk
Pitches For Å ⌷ ⇔ **Total** 160
Acreage 12 **Open** March **to** October
Access Good **Site** Level
Beside the River Arun with a public house on site. 3 miles to beaches. Advance booking is advisable for hook-ups and groups.
Facilities
Nearby Facilities
Nearest Town Arundel/Littlehampton
Directions From the A27 at Arundel, follow road signposted to Ford for 2 miles. Site is on the left after level-crossing at Ford.
⇌ Ford

·BILLINGHURST

Limeburners (Camping) Ltd., Lordings Road, Newbridge, Billinghurst, West Sussex, RH14 9JA
Tel: 01403 782311
Email: chippy.sawyer@virgin.net
Pitches For Å ⌷ ⇔ ⇔ **Total** 40
Open April **to** October
Access Good **Site** Level
Nearest Bus Stop (Miles) 1½
Attached to a public house.
Facilities
Nearby Facilities

Nearest Town Billinghurst
Directions 1½ miles west of Billinghurst on the A272, turn left onto the B2133, Park is 500 yards on the right.
⇌ Billinghurst

BOGNOR REGIS

Rowan Park Caravan Club Site, Rowan Way, Bognor Regis, West Sussex, PO22 9RP
Tel: 01243 828515
www.caravanclub.co.uk
Pitches For Å ⌷ ⇔ **Total** 94
Acreage 8 **Open** March **to** Nov
Access Good **Site** Level
Nearest Bus Stop (Miles) ½
2 miles from the beach, South Coast World and a leisure centre. Close to Weald & Downland Open Air Museum, D-Day Museum & Battle of Britain Aviation and Amberley Chalk Pits Museum. Non members welcome. Booking essential.
Facilities
Nearby Facilities
Nearest Town Bognor Regis
Directions From north on the A29, ½ mile past Shripney Village at the roundabout turn right into Rowan Way, site is 100 yards on the right, opposite Halfords.
⇌ Bognor Regis

CHICHESTER

Bell Caravan Park, Bell Lane, Birdham, Nr Chichester, West Sussex, PO20 7HY
Tel: 01243 512264
Pitches For ⌷ ⇔ **Total** 15
Acreage ¼ **Open** March **to** October
Access Good **Site** Level
Nearest Bus Stop (Miles) ¼
Facilities
Nearby Facilities
Nearest Town Chichester
Directions From Chichester take the A286 towards Wittering for approx. 4 miles. At Birdham turn left into Bell Lane, site is 500yds on the left.
⇌ Chichester

CHICHESTER

Camping & Caravanning Club Site, Main Road, Southbourne, Hampshire, PO10 8JH
Tel: 01243 373202
www.campingandcaravanningclub.co.uk/chichester
Pitches For Å ⌷ ⇔ **Total** 58
Acreage 3 **Open** 02-Feb **to** 19-Nov
Access Good **Site** Level
Nearest Bus Stop (Miles) ½
500 yards through a footpath to the beach. Ideal touring, well placed for visiting the Sussex Downs and south coast resorts. Close to the City of Portsmouth. BTB 3 Star Graded and AA 3 Pennants. Non members welcome. You can also call us on 0845 130 7633.
Facilities
Nearby Facilities
Nearest Town Chichester
Directions On the A259 from Chichester, site is on the right past Inlands Road.
⇌ Southbourne

CHICHESTER

Chichester Lakeside Holiday Park, Vinnetrow Road, Chichester, West Sussex, PO20 1QH
Tel: 01243 787715
Email: lakeside@parkholidaysuk.com
www.parkholidaysuk.com/cades
Pitches For Å ⌷ ⇔ **Total** 350

SUSSEX (WEST)

Open March **to** Nov
Access Good **Site** Level
Nearest Bus Stop (Miles) ½
Set in 220 acres of scenic parkland and a
nature reserve with over 150 acres of water
covering 12 lakes. Outdoor heated leisure
pool and fishing on site.
Facilities 👤 ♿ 🚿 📶 ♨ ⚡ 🔌 ⛽ ☎
♿ ✕ ♿ 📺 ♨ ⚡🔌🚽 🏊 ☕ 📶
Nearby Facilities
Nearest Town Chichester
Directions Take the A27 to Chichester until
you reach the Bognor Road roundabout, take
the Pagham exit which leads to Lakeside.
🚆 Chichester

CHICHESTER

Ellscott Park, Sidlesham Lane, Birdham,
Chichester, West Sussex, PO20 7QL
Tel: 01243 512003
Email: camping@ellscottpark.co.uk
www.ellscottpark.co.uk
Pitches For ⛺ 🚐 🚍 **Total** 50
Acreage 3 **Open** 01-Apr **to** Mid Oct
Access Good **Site** Level
Nearest Bus Stop (Miles) ¼
The famous West Wittering beach. 1½ miles
from Chichester Harbour for yachting and
boating. Ideal site for walking, cycling and
sight-seeing.
Facilities 👤 ♿ 🚿 ♨ ⚡🔌🚽 ☎
♿ ⚡🔌📺 🔌 📶 📶
Nearby Facilities 🏇 ✓ ⚓ 🛥 ∪ 🎣 ♪
Nearest Town Chichester
Directions From the A27 Chichester by-pass
turn south onto the A286 towards Witterings.
Travel for approx. 4 miles then turn left
towards Butterfly Farm, site is 500 metres
on the right.
🚆 Chichester

CHICHESTER

Red House Farm, Earnley, Chichester,
West Sussex, PO20 7JG
Tel: 01243 512959
Email: bookings@rhfcamping.co.uk
www.rhfcamping.co.uk
Pitches For ⛺ 🚐 🚍 **Total** 50
Acreage 4½ **Open** Easter **to** October
Access Good **Site** Level
Nearest Bus Stop (Miles) ¼
Flat and open site on a working farm in a
country area. 1 mile from the village and
beach. No all male or female groups
permitted.
Facilities 👤 ♿ 🚿 ♨ ⚡🔌🚽 ☎ 🏊 ☕ 📶 📶
Nearby Facilities ✓ ⚓ 🛥 ∪
Nearest Town Bracklesham Bay
Directions From Chichester take the A286
south to Witterings, after 5 miles turn left onto
the B2198 opposite the garage to
Bracklesham Bay. After 1 mile on sharp right
hand bend turn left to Earnley, site is 200
yards on the left.
🚆 Chichester

CHICHESTER

Stubcroft Farm Campsite, Stubcroft Lane,
East Wittering, Chichester, West Sussex,
PO20 8PJ
Tel: 01243 671469
Email: mail@stubcroft.com
www.stubcroft.com
Pitches For ⛺ 🚐 🚍 🚍 **Total** 50
Acreage 5 **Open** All Year
Access Good **Site** Level
Nearest Bus Stop (Miles) ¼
Secluded site on a working sheep farm.
Within walking distance of the South Coasts
best beaches and Chichester Harbour. Many
attractions within a 15-20 minute drive.

Facilities 👤 ♿ 🚿 📶 ♨ ⚡🔌⛽ ☎
♿ ⚡🔌 🔌📶 ✓ 📶
Nearby Facilities 🏇 ✓ ⚓ 🛥 ∪ 🎣 ♪
Nearest Town Chichester/The Witterings
Directions From the A286 Chichester by-
pass, take the A286 south for The Witterings.
After 3-4 miles at the mini roundabout by the
Total Garage fork left onto the B2198. ½ a
mile past the Bell Pub turn right into Tile Barn
Lane, after the S bend go 200 yards over 2
🚆 Chichester

GRAFFHAM

Camping & Caravanning Club Site,
Great Bury, Graffham, Petworth, West
Sussex, GU28 0QJ
Tel: 01798 867476
www.campingandcaravanningclub.co.uk/
graffham
Pitches For ⛺ 🚐 🚍 **Total** 90
Open 29-Mar **to** 05-Nov
Site Sloping
Set in 20 acres of woodland with many walks.
Gas BBQs only. BTB 4 Star Graded and AA
3 Pennants. Non members welcome. You
can also call us on 0845 130 7633.
Facilities 👤 ♿ 🚿 📶 ♨ ⚡🔌🚽 ⚡ 📺 ☎
♿ ⚡🔌 🔌📶 🔌 📶 📶
Nearby Facilities ∪
Directions From Petworth take the A285,
pass Badgers Pub on the left and the BP
Garage on the right, take the next right turn
signposted Selham Graffham (with brown
camping sign), follow signs to site. From
Chichester take the A285 through Duncton
and turn left signposted Selham, Graffham
(with brown camping sign).
🚆 Chichester

HENFIELD

Farmhouse Caravan & Camping Site,
Tottington Drive, Small Dole, Henfield,
West Sussex, BN5 9XZ
Tel: 01273 493157
Pitches For ▲ ⊞ ⊟ **Total** 70
Acreage 4 **Open** March **to** November
Access Good **Site** Level
Nearest Bus Stop (Miles) ¼
Small farm site within the South Downs
National Park. Beach 5 miles, Brighton and
Worthing 10 miles.
Facilities ⌇ ⊞ ⌐ ⌂ ♿ ⌸ 🛒 ⌗ ⌴ ♦
Nearby Facilities ⌐ ⌇ ⋃
Nearest Town Brighton
Directions Turn first left off A2037 (Henfield/
Upperbeeding). After Small Dole sign into
Tottington Drive, farm at end.
⇆ Shoreham

HORSHAM

Honeybridge Park, Honeybridge Lane,
Dial Post, Nr Horsham, West Sussex,
RH13 8NX
Tel: 01403 710923
Email: enquiries@honeybridgepark.co.uk
www.honeybridgepark.co.uk
Pitches For ▲ ⊞ ⊟ **Total** 200
Acreage 15 **Open** All Year
Access Good **Site** Level
Nearest Bus Stop (Miles) ¼
Delightfully situated within an Area of
Outstanding Natural Beauty. A rural retreat
with a relaxed atmosphere providing
spacious touring and camping pitches,
heated amenity blocks, licensed shop and
play area. Ideal touring base, convenient for
the coast, London and theme parks. Luxury
lodges and static caravans for sale.
Facilities ⌇ ⌁ ⊞ ⊞ ⌐ ⌂ ⊙ ⌴ ⌸ ⌐ 🛒
⌇ ⌂ ⊞ ♦ ⌸ ⊞ ⌐ ⊟ ⋇ ♦
Nearby Facilities ⌐ ⌇ ⋌ ⌿
Nearest Town Worthing
Directions 10 miles south of Horsham on
the A24, turn at Old Barn Nurseries.
⇆ Horsham

HORSHAM

Sumners Ponds Fishery & Campsite,
Chapel Road, Barns Green, Horsham,
West Sussex, RH13 0PR
Tel: 01403 732539
Email: sumnersponds@dsl.pipex.co.uk
www.sumnersponds.co.uk
Pitches For ▲ ⊞ ⊟ **Total** 86
Acreage 40 **Open** All Year
Access Good **Site** Level
Nearest Bus Stop (Miles) ¼
Extensive fishing on four lakes. Woodland
paths and pasture. Lakeside cafe, village pub
and shop within a 5 minute walk.

Facilities ♿ ⌇ ⊞ ⊞ ⌐ ⌂ ⊙ ⌴ 🛒 ⌐ 🛒
⌇ ⌦ ⌧ 🛒 ⌸ ⊞ ⊟ ⌇ ⋇
Nearby Facilities ⌐ ⌇ ⋌
Nearest Town Horsham
Directions Take the A264 from Horsham
towards Billingshurst and Bognor. Pass the
Toyota garage on the right and turn left on
the humpback bridge. Follow road to Barns
Green and pass the pub and shop then look
for signs on the right.
⇆ Horsham

LITTLEHAMPTON

Daisyfields Touring Park, Cornfield
Close, Worthing Road, Littlehampton,
West Sussex, BN17 6LD
Tel: 01903 714240
Email: daisyfields@f2s.com
www.camping-caravaning.co.uk
Pitches For ▲ ⊞ ⊟ **Total** 80
Acreage 6½ **Open** All Year
Nearest Bus Stop (Miles) ¼
1½ miles to a sandy beach. 1 mile to the
River Arun. Open all year dependant on the
weather. Pets welcome with camper vans
and caravans only. No commercial vehicles.
Facilities ⌇ ⊞ ⌐ ⊙ 🛒
⌗ ⌸ ♦ ⌸ ⊟ ⌸
Nearby Facilities ⌐ ⌇ ⌴ ⋇ ⋃ ⌿ ⌿
Nearest Town Littlehampton
Directions The site is situated on the A259
Worthing to Bognor Regis, between two Body
Shop roundabouts. 3 miles from Arundel.
⇆ Littlehampton

LITTLEHAMPTON

Littlehampton Caravan Club Site, Mill
Lane, Wick, Littlehampton, West Sussex,
BN17 7PH
Tel: 01903 716176
www.caravanclub.co.uk
Pitches For ▲ ⊞ ⊟ **Total** 117
Acreage 6 **Open** March **to** Jan
Access Good **Site** Lev/Slope
Within walking distance of the town and
beach. Non members welcome. Booking
essential.
Facilities ⌇ ⊞ ⌐ ⌂ ⊙ ⌴ 🛒 🛒
⌗ ⌸ ⌦ ⊟ ⌇ ⌀
Nearby Facilities
Nearest Town Littlehampton
Directions From the A27 take the A284, Site
entrance is on the left of Mill Lane just past
the village of Lyminster.
⇆ Littlehampton

SELSEY

Warner Farm Touring Park, Warner Lane,
Selsey, West Sussex, PO20 9EL
Tel: 01243 604499
Email: touring@bunnleisure.co.uk

www.warnerfarm.co.uk
Pitches For ▲ ⊞ ⊟ **Total** 200
Acreage 10 **Open** March **to** October
Access Good **Site** Level
Nearest Bus Stop (Miles) Outside
Near the beach.
Facilities ♿ ⌇ ⊞ ⊞ ⌐ ⌂ ⊙ ⌴ 🛒 ⌐ 🛒
⌗ ⌸ ⊞ ♦ ⌿ ⋇ ♦ 🛒 ⌸ ⊟ ♦
Nearby Facilities ⌐ ⌇ ⌴ ⋇ ⋃ ⌿
Nearest Town Chichester
Directions From the A27 Chichester take the
B2145 to Selsey. On entering Selsey turn
right into School Lane. Follow signs for
Warner Farm Touring Park.
⇆ Chichester

SLINDON

Camping & Caravanning Club Site,
Slindon Park, Nr Arundel, West Sussex,
BN18 0RG
Tel: 01243 814387
www.campingandcaravanningclub.co.uk/
slindon
Pitches For ▲ ⊞ ⊟ **Total** 40
Acreage 2 **Open** 29-Mar **to** 24-Sep
Access Good **Site** Lev/Slope
Nearest Bus Stop (Miles) ½
Within the National Trust property of Slindon
Park. 6 miles from Goodwood Racecourse.
BTB 2 Star Graded and AA 1 Pennant. Non
members welcome. You can also call us on
0845 130 7633.
Facilities ⌇ 🛒 ⌸ ⌀ 🛒 ⌐ ⊟ ⌂ ⌇
Nearby Facilities ⌐ ⌇
Nearest Town Chichester
Directions From the A27 Chichester to
Fontwell road, turn left into Brittons Lane
(second turn left after the B2233 on the right),
then take the second turn right to Slindon.
Site is on this road.
⇆ Barnham

WEST WITTERING

Nunnington Farm Camping Site,
Nunnington Farm, West Wittering, West
Sussex, PO20 8LZ
Tel: 01243 514013 No Booking
Email: enquiries@nunningtonfarm.com
www.camping-in-sussex.com
Pitches For ▲ ⊞ ⊟ **Total** 125
Acreage 4½ **Open** Easter **to** Mid October
Access Good **Site** Level
Nearest Bus Stop (Miles) Outside
Near the beach.
Facilities ♿ ⌇ ⊞ ⌐ ⌂ ⊙ ⌴ 🛒 ⌐ 🛒
⌗ ⌸ ⌀ 🛒 ⌸ ⊟
Nearby Facilities ⌐ ⌇ ⌴ ⋇ ⋃ ⌀
Nearest Town Chichester
Directions 7 miles south of Chichester on
the A286 - B2179. 200yds before village on
left, look for signs.
⇆ Chichester

WEST WITTERING

Wicks Farm Camping Park, Redlands Lane, West Wittering, Chichester, West Sussex, PO20 8QE
Tel: 01243 513116
www.wicksfarm.co.uk
Pitches For 🏕 🚐 🚍 **Total** 40
Acreage 2¼ **Open** April **to** October
Access Good **Site** Level
Nearest Bus Stop (Miles) ¼
Facilities
Nearby Facilities
Nearest Town West Wittering/Chichester
Directions From Chichester take the A286 for Birdham, then take the B2179 for West Wittering.
⇌ Chichester

WORTHING

Northbrook Farm Caravan Club Site, Titnore Way, Worthing, West Sussex, BN13 3RT
Tel: 01903 502962
www.caravanclub.co.uk
Pitches For 🚐 🚍 **Total** 70
Acreage 12½ **Open** March **to** Nov
Access Good **Site** Level
Nearest Bus Stop (Miles) ½
Set in open countryside yet only 2 miles from the coast. West Worthing Tennis Club adjacent for tennis, squash, restaurant and bar. Near to Arundel Castle. NB: Own sanitation required. Non members welcome. Booking essential.
Facilities
Nearby Facilities
Nearest Town Worthing
Directions From north on A24, in Findon at roundabout junction with A280 turn right sp Chichester. After 4 miles at roundabout take second exit to roundabout on far side of bridge over A27 and turn left (first exit sp Ferring). After ¾ miles at brown sign turn left in to Titnore Way. Site is 120yds on left.
⇌ Worthing

WARWICKSHIRE

LONG COMPTON

Long Compton Camping, Mill Farm, Barton Road, Long Compton, Shipston-on-Stour, Warwickshire, CV36 5NZ
Tel: 01608 684663
Pitches For 🏕 🚐 🚍 **Total** 11
Acreage 3 **Open** April **to** October
Nearest Bus Stop (Miles) ½
On the fringe of the Cotswolds.
Facilities
Nearby Facilities
Nearest Town Moreton-in-Marsh
Directions Turn off A3400 in Long Compton for Barton-on-the-Heath. Site on right in ½ a mile.
⇌ Moreton-in-Marsh

STRATFORD-UPON-AVON

Dodwell Park, Evesham Road, Stratford-upon-Avon, Warwickshire, CV37 9SR
Tel: 01789 204957
Email: enquiries@dodwellpark.co.uk
www.dodwellpark.co.uk
Pitches For 🏕 🚐 🚍 **Total** 50
Acreage 2 **Open** All Year
Access Good **Site** Lev/Slope
Nearest Bus Stop (Miles) Outside
Over 50 years as a family business. Ideal for the Shakespeare Theatre, the Cotswolds and Warwick Castle.
Facilities
Nearby Facilities

Nearest Town Stratford-upon-Avon
Directions 2 miles southwest of Stratford on B439 (formerly the A439)- Not the racecourse site.
⇌ Stratford-upon-Avon

STRATFORD-UPON-AVON

Island Meadow Caravan Park, Aston Cantlow, Warwickshire, B95 6JP
Tel: 01789 488273
Email: holiday@islandmeadowcaravanpark.co.uk
www.islandmeadowcaravanpark.co.uk
Pitches For 🏕 🚐 🚍 **Total** 34
Acreage 3 **Open** March **to** October
Access Good **Site** Level
Nearest Bus Stop (Miles) ¼
Small, quiet island, adjacent to a picturesque village. Cafe/Restaurant and childrens play area nearby. Ideal centre for Shakespeare Country.
Facilities
Nearby Facilities
Nearest Town Stratford-upon-Avon
Directions From the A46 or the A3400 follow signs for Aston Cantlow Village. Park is ½ mile west of the village in Mill Lane.
⇌ Wilmcote

STRATFORD-UPON-AVON

Riverside Caravan Park, Tiddington Road, Stratford-upon-Avon, Warwickshire, CV37 7AB
Tel: 01789 292312
Email: riverside@stratfordcaravans.co.uk
www.stratfordcaravans.co.uk
Pitches For 🚐 🚍 **Total** 90
Acreage 8 **Open** April **to** October
Access Good **Site** Lev/Slope
Nearest Bus Stop (Miles) ¼
River Taxi to and from the town centre. Childrens play area nearby.
Facilities
Nearby Facilities
Nearest Town Stratford-upon-Avon
Directions On the B4086 1¼ miles from the town centre, just before entering Tiddington Village.
⇌ Stratford-upon-Avon

STUDLEY

Outhill Caravan Park, Outhill, Studley, Warwickshire, B80 7DY
Tel: 01527 852160
Pitches For 🚐 🚍 **Total** 15
Acreage 1 **Open** April **to** October
Access Good **Site** Level
Peace and quiet. No electricity and no hot water. Advance booking is essential.
Facilities
Nearby Facilities
Nearest Town Henley-in-Arden
Directions From A435 (Birmingham to Evesham road) turn towards Henley-in-Arden on A4189. Take third turning to the right (approx 1¼ miles), check in at Outhill Farm (first on left).

WARWICK

Warwick Racecourse Caravan Club Site, Hampton Street, Warwick, Warwickshire, CV34 6HN
Tel: 01926 495448
www.caravanclub.co.uk
Pitches For 🚐 🚍 **Total** 55
Acreage 3¼ **Open** March **to** Jan
Access Good **Site** Level
Nearest Bus Stop (Miles) ¼
Grass and tarmac site in the racecourse enclosure. Very short walk to the centre of Warwick and its castle. Only 8 miles from

Stratford-upon-Avon. Non members welcome. Booking essential.
Facilities
Nearby Facilities
Nearest Town Warwick
Directions Leave the M40 at junction 15 and take the A429 sp Warwick. After 1 mile at brown camping sign turn left into Shakespeares Avenue, at T-junction turn right onto the B4095, site is ½ mile on the left.
⇌ Warwick

WOLVEY

Wolvey Caravan & Camping Park, Villa Farm, Wolvey, Nr Hinckley, Leicestershire, LE10 3HF
Tel: 01455 220493/220630
www.wolveycaravanpark.itgo.com
Pitches For 🏕 🚐 🚍 **Total** 110
Acreage 7 **Open** All Year
Access Good **Site** Level
Nearest Bus Stop (Miles) Outside
A quiet site, ideally situated to explore the many places of interest in the Midlands.
Facilities
Nearby Facilities
Nearest Town Hinckley
Directions Leave the M6 at junction 2 and take the B4065, follow signs for Wolvey and camping signs. Or leave the M69 at junction 1 and take the B4065, follow signs for Wolvey and camping signs.
⇌ Hinckley

WEST MIDLANDS

HALESOWEN

Clent Hills Camping & Caravanning Club Site, Fieldhouse Lane, Romsley, Halesowen, West Midlands, B62 0NH
Tel: 01562 710015
www.campingandcaravanningclub.co.uk/clenthills
Pitches For 🏕 🚐 🚍 **Total** 95
Acreage 7½ **Open** 29-Mar **to** 05-Nov
Access Good **Site** Sloping
Nearest Bus Stop (Miles) ½
In the heart of the West Midlands. Ideal for walkers and cyclists. BTB 4 Star Graded and AA 3 Pennants. Non members welcome. You can also call us on 0845 130 7633.
Facilities
Nearby Facilities
Nearest Town Halesowen
Directions Travelling northwest on the M5, leave at junction 3 onto the A456. Then take the B4551 to Romsley, turn right at Sun Hotel, take the 5th left turn then the next left and the site is 300 yards on the left hand side.
⇌ Old Hill

MERIDEN

Somers Wood Caravan Park, Somers Road, Meriden, North Warwickshire, CV7 7PL
Tel: 01676 522978
Email: enquiries@somerswood.co.uk
www.somerswood.co.uk
Pitches For 🚐 🚍 **Total** 48
Acreage 4 **Open** All Year
Access Good **Site** Level
Nearest Bus Stop (Miles) ½
ADULTS ONLY SITE. Adjacent to a golf course with clubhouse. Approx. 3 miles from the N.E.C. Birmingham. Fishing adjacent.
Facilities
Nearby Facilities

Nearest Town Solihull
Directions Leave the M42 at junction 6, take the A45 to Coventry. Immediately on the left pick up signs for the A452 Leamington. Down to roundabout and turn right onto the A452 signed Leamington/Warwick, at the next roundabout turn left into Hampton Lane. Site is ½ mile on left hand side.
⚆ Hampton-in-Arden

SUTTON COLDFIELD

Camping & Caravanning Club Site,
Kingsbury Water Park, Bodymoor Heath Lane, Sutton Coldfield, West Midlands, B76 0DY
Tel: 01827 874101
www.campingandcaravanningclub.co.uk/ kingsburywaterpark
Pitches For Å ⊞ ⊟ **Total** 150
Open All Year **Site** Level
Nearest Bus Stop (Miles) 1
Surrounding the site are the 600 acres of Kingsbury Water Park. BTB 5 Star Graded, AA 4 Pennants and Loo of the Year Award. Non members welcome. You can also call us on 0845 130 7633.
Facilities ⚅ ✦ ⊡ ⊞ ⊮ ⚟ ⊙ ⊿ ⊴ ⊡ 📞
⚏ ⊚ ⊠ ⊁ ⊞ ⊡ ⊾ 🛜
Nearby Facilities ⌐ ✔ ⊀ ⊿
Directions Leave the M42 at junction 9 and take the B4097 towards Kingsbury. At the roundabout turn left and continue past the main entrance to the water park, go over the motorway and turn next right, follow lane for ½ mile to the site.
⚆ Tamworth

WILTSHIRE

BRADFORD-ON-AVON

Church Farm Touring Caravan & Camping Site, Church Farm, Winsley, Bradford-on-Avon, Wiltshire, BA15 2JH
Tel: 01225 722246
Email: stay@churchfarmcottages.com
www.churchfarmcamping.co.uk
Pitches For Å ⊞ ⊟ **Total** 20
Open Easter **to** Oct **Access** Good **Site** Level
Nearest Bus Stop (Miles) ¼
Countryside site on a working farm in an area of outstanding natural beauty. Ideal for Bath,

Bradford-on-Avon, the Kennet & Avon Canal, Stonehenge, Salisbury and Longleat Safari Park, also close to three National Trust properties and gardens.
Facilities ✦ ⊡ ⚟ ⌐ ⊙ ⊿ ⊴ ⊡ 📞
⚏ ✕ ⊞ ⊡ ⚟
Nearby Facilities ⌐ ✔ ⊀ ⊙ ⊿
Nearest Town Bradford-on-Avon
Directions From Bradford-on-Avon take the B3108 towards Winsley, do not turn into Winsley Village but continue on the B3108 until you see Church Farm on the right.
⚆ Bradford-on-Avon

CALNE

Blackland Lakes, Blackland Leisure Ltd, Stockley Lane, Calne, Wiltshire, SN11 0NQ
Tel: 01249 810943
Email: enquiries@blacklandlakes.co.uk
www.blacklandlakes.co.uk
Pitches For Å ⊞ ⊟ **Total** 180
Acreage 15 **Open** All Year
Access Good **Site** Level
Nearest Bus Stop (Miles) Outside
A natural, interesting, scenic and secure site with three lakes for super coarse fishing. 1 mile perimeter trail for dogs, walking and cycling. Winter bookings must be prepaid.
Facilities ⚅ ✦ ⊡ ⊞ ⊮ ⚟ ⌐ ⊙ ⊿ ⊴ ⊡ 📞
⚏ ⊚ ⊠ ⊞ ⊡ ⊿ ⚞ ⚟
Nearby Facilities ⌐ ⊀ ⊙ ⊿
Nearest Town Calne
Directions Signposted from the A4 east of Calne.
⚆ Chippenham

CHIPPENHAM

Piccadilly Caravan Park, Folly Lane West, Lacock, Chippenham, Wiltshire, SN15 2LP
Tel: 01249 730260
Email: piccadillylacock@aol.com
Pitches For Å ⊞ ⊟ **Total** 43
Acreage 2½ **Open** April **to** October
Access Good **Site** Level
Nearest Bus Stop (Miles) ¼
Close to the National Trust village of Lacock, Piccadilly is a small, family run, beautifully maintained Park.
Facilities ✦ ⊡ ⊞ ⊮ ⚟ ⌐ ⊙ ⊿ ⊴ ⊡ 📞
⚏ ⊚ ⊠ ⊞ ⊡
Nearby Facilities ⌐ ✔ ⊙ ⊿

Nearest Town Chippenham
Directions Turn right off the A350 Chippenham to Melksham road, 5 miles south of Chippenham, close to Lacock. Signposted to Gastard (with caravan symbol).
⚆ Chippenham

CHIPPENHAM

Plough Lane Caravan Site, Kington Langley, Chippenham, Wiltshire, SN15 5PS
Tel: 01249 750146
Email: enquiries@ploughlane.co.uk
www.ploughlane.co.uk
Pitches For ⊞ ⊟ **Total** 50
Acreage 4 **Open** Easter **to** End Oct
Access Good **Site** Level
Nearest Bus Stop (Miles) Outside
ADULTS ONLY SITE.
Facilities ⚅ ✦ ⊡ ⊞ ⊮ ⚟ ⌐ ⊙ ⊿ ⊴ ⊡ 📞
⚏ ⊚ ✕ ⊞ ⊡ ⚟
Nearby Facilities ⌐ ✔ ⊿
Nearest Town Chippenham
Directions Well signposted from the A350 north of Chippenham.
⚆ Chippenham

DEVIZES

Camping & Caravanning Club Site,
Spout Lane, Nr Seend, Melksham, Wiltshire, SN12 6RN
Tel: 01380 828839
www.campingandcaravanningclub.co.uk/ devizes
Pitches For Å ⊞ ⊟ **Total** 90
Open All Year
Site Level
Nearest Bus Stop (Miles) ¼
Bordering the Kennet & Avon Canal. BTB 4 Star Graded, AA 4 Pennants and David Bellamy Silver Award. Non members welcome. You can also call us on 0845 130 7633.
Facilities ⚅ ✦ ⊡ ⊞ ⊮ ⚟ ⌐ ⊙ ⊿ ⊴ ⊡ 📞
⊚ ⊠ ⊞ ⊁ ✕ ⊞ ⊡ 🛜
Nearby Facilities ✔
Directions Take the A365 from Melksham, turn right down the lane beside Three Magpies Public House, site is on the right.
⚆ Melksham

DEVIZES

Lower Foxhangers Campsite, Lower Foxhangers Farm, Rowde, Devizes, Wiltshire, SN10 1SS
Tel: 01380 828254
Email: sales@foxhangers.co.uk
www.foxhangers.com
Pitches For ⚠ 🚐 🚌 **Total** 18
Acreage 2 **Open** Easter **to** Oct
Access Good **Site** Lev/Slope
Nearest Bus Stop (Miles) ½
Located beside Kennet Avon Canal for walking, fishing, boating and cycling.
Facilities
Nearby Facilities
Nearest Town Devizes
Directions 2 miles west of Devizes on the A361. ½ mile east of the A361 and the A365.
🚉 Chippenham

DEVIZES

The Bell Camping, Touring & Motorcaravan Site, Andover Road, Lydeway, Devizes, Wiltshire, SN10 3PS
Tel: 01380 840230
Pitches For ⚠ 🚐 🚌 **Total** 26
Acreage 5 **Open** April **to** October
Access Good **Site** Level
Nearest Bus Stop (Miles) Entrance
Ideal for Stonehenge, Avebury, Bath, Longleat Safari Park, ational Trusts Lacock and Bowood.
Facilities
Nearby Facilities
Nearest Town Devizes
Directions 5 miles east of Devizes on the A342 Andover road.
🚉 Pewsey

MALMESBURY

Burton Hill Caravan Park, Arches Lane, Burton Hill, Malmesbury, Wiltshire, SN16 0EH
Tel: 01666 826880
Email: stay@burtonhill.co.uk
www.burtonhill.co.uk
Pitches For ⚠ 🚐 🚌 **Total** 30
Acreage 2 **Open** April **to** Oct
Access Good **Site** Level
Nearest Bus Stop (Miles) Outside
Surrounded by countryside with open views. Short walk into town. Many local visitor attractions. Excellent touring base. New shower block.
Facilities
Nearby Facilities
Nearest Town Malmesbury
Directions ½ mile south of Malmesbury on the A249, entrance is by the 30/40 mph signs, turn into Arches Lane.
🚉 Chippenham

MARLBOROUGH

Hillview Park, Hillview Park House, Sunnyhill Lane, Oare, Marlborough, Wiltshire, SN8 4JG
Tel: 01672 563151
Pitches For ⚠
Open April **to** Sept
Access Good **Site** Level
Nearest Bus Stop (Miles) Outside
½ a mile from Kennet & Avon Canal. Cycleway nearby. No hard standings, caravans and motor vans over 20 feet cannot be accommodated. Sorry, no children over the age of 5.
Facilities
Nearby Facilities
Nearest Town Marlborough
Directions 5 miles south of Marlborough on the A345 junction.
🚉 Pewsey

NETHERHAMPTON

Coombe Caravan Park, Coombe Nurseries, Race Plain, Netherhampton, Salisbury, Wiltshire, SP2 8PN
Tel: 01722 328451
Email: enquiries@coombecaravanpark.co.uk
www.coombecaravanpark.co.uk
Pitches For ⚠ 🚐 🚌 **Total** 60
Acreage 3 **Open** March **to** Oct
Access Good **Site** Level
Adjacent to racecourse (flat racing), ideal touring, lovely views.
Facilities
Nearby Facilities
Nearest Town Salisbury
Directions Take A36-A30 Salisbury - Wilton road, turn off at traffic lights onto A3094 Netherhampton - Stratford Tony road, cross on bend following Stratford Tony road, 2nd left behind racecourse, site on right, signposted.
🚉 Salisbury

ORCHESTON

Stonehenge Touring Park, Orcheston, Nr Shrewton, Wiltshire, SP3 4SH
Tel: 01980 620304
Email: stay@stonehengetouringpark.com
www.stonehengetouringpark.com
Pitches For ⚠ 🚐 🚌 **Total** 30
Acreage 2 **Open** All Year
Access Good **Site** Level
Nearest Bus Stop (Miles) ¼
5 miles from Stonehenge and Salisbury Plain. Within easy reach Bath and the New Forest. ETB 3 Star Graded and AA 3 Pennants.
Facilities
Nearby Facilities
Nearest Town Salisbury
Directions On the A360, 11 miles from both Salisbury and Devizes.
🚉 Salisbury

SALISBURY

Camping & Caravanning Club Site, Hudsons Field, Castle Road, Salisbury, Wiltshire, SP1 3RR
Tel: 01722 320713
www.campingandcaravanningclub.co.uk/salisbury
Pitches For ⚠ 🚐 🚌 **Total** 150
Acreage 4½ **Open** 29-Mar **to** 05-Nov
Access Good **Site** Lev/Slope
Nearest Bus Stop (Miles) Outside
1½ miles from Salisbury, plenty to do in the area. BTB 4 Star Graded and AA4 Pennants. Non members welcome. You can also call us on 0845 130 7633.
Facilities
Nearby Facilities
Nearest Town Salisbury
Directions 1½ miles from Salisbury and 7 miles from Amesbury on the A345. Hudsons Field is a large open field next to Old Sarum.
🚉 Salisbury

SALISBURY

Green Hill Farm Caravan & Camping Park, Greenhill Farm, New Road, Landford, Salisbury, Wiltshire, SP5 2AZ
Tel: 01794 324117
Email: info@greenhillholidays.co.uk
www.greenhillholidays.co.uk
Pitches For ⚠ 🚐 🚌 🚗 **Total** 160
Acreage 15 **Open** All Year
Access Good **Site** Level
Nearest Bus Stop (Miles) Outside

On the edge of the New Forest, you can walk into the forest directly from the Park.
Facilities
Nearby Facilities
Nearest Town Romsey/Salisbury
Directions Leave the M27 at junction 2 and take the A36 towards Salisbury. In Plaitford look out for the BP garage, turn next left into New Road.
🚉 Romsey

TILSHEAD

Brades Acre, Tilshead, Salisbury, Wiltshire, SP3 4RX
Tel: 01980 620402
Email: bradesacre@hotmail.co.uk
www.bradesacre.co.uk
Pitches For ⚠ 🚐 🚌 **Total** 35
Acreage 1½ **Open** All Year
Access Good **Site** Level
Nearest Bus Stop (Miles) ¼
Touring for Stonehenge, Salisbury Cathedral, Wilton and Longleat Houses. Avebury, Orcheston riding.
Facilities
Nearby Facilities
Nearest Town Salisbury/Devizes
Directions A360, 10 miles to Devizes, 13 miles to Salisbury.
🚉 Salisbury

TROWBRIDGE

Stowford Manor Farm, Stowford, Wingfield, Trowbridge, Wiltshire, BA14 9LH
Tel: 01225 752253
Email: stowford1@supanet.com
www.stowfordmanorfarm.co.uk
Pitches For ⚠ 🚐 🚌 **Total** 20
Acreage 1½ **Open** Easter **to** End Oct
Access Good **Site** Level
Alongside a river for fishing and swimming. Next to a Medieval farm.
Facilities
Nearby Facilities
Nearest Town Trowbridge
Directions From Trowbridge take the A366 west towards Radstock for 3 miles, farm is on the left hand side.
🚉 Trowbridge

WARMINSTER

Longleat Caravan Club Site, Warminster, Wiltshire, BA12 7NL
Tel: 01985 844663
www.caravanclub.co.uk
Pitches For 🚐 🚌 **Total** 165
Acreage 14 **Open** March **to** Nov
Access Good **Site** Level
The Caravan Clubs most beautiful parkland site, set in the heart of the Longleat Estate. Miles of woodland walks. Just a short walk from Longleat House & Safari Park with its maze and childrens adventure castle. Non members welcome. Booking essential.
Facilities
Nearby Facilities
Directions From the A36 Warminster bypass take the A362 sp Frome. At roundabout turn left into Longleat Estate entrance and follow Longleat House route through the toll booths for 2 miles, then Caravan Club pennant signs for 1 mile.

WESTBURY

Brokerswood Country Park, Brokerswood, Nr Westbury, Wilts., BA13 4EH
Tel: 01373 822238
Email: info@brokerswoodcountrypark.co.uk
www.brokerswoodcountrypark.co.uk

Pitches For 🏕 🚐 🚙 🚌 **Total** 65
Acreage 5 **Open** All Year
Access Good **Site** Level
Site adjoins an 80 acre area of forest open to the public. Woodland walks, narrow gauge railway, adventure playground and fishing lake.
Facilities ♿ ∮ 🗓 🎇 🖍 🍴 ⊙ ⅃ 🍽 🔄 🗑 ☎
🏧 ⊘ ✗ ⼝ 🢫 🔄 🗒 ✔
Nearby Facilities ┎ ✔ 🢫 ⚘ U ₽
Nearest Town Westbury/Trowbridge
Directions At Yarnbrook on the A350, turn onto the A363 and follow road. At The Rising Sun Pub turn left, then turn left off the right hand bend before Southwick and continue for 2½ miles.
⋢ Westbury

WORCESTERSHIRE
BEWDLEY

Bank Farm Holiday Parks Ltd., Bank Farm, Arley, Bewdley, Worcestershire, DY12 3ND
Tel: 01299 401277
Email: bankfarm@tinyworld.co.uk
www.bankfarmholidaypark.co.uk
Pitches For 🚐 🚙 **Total** 5
Open All Year
Access Good **Site** Level
Alongside a river in the Wyre Forest with river and valley views. 9 hole pitch n putt on site. Near the River Severn and the Severn Valley Railway Station at Arley. Holiday homes for hire and sale.
Facilities ∮ 🗓 🎇 🖍 🍴 ⊙ ⅃ 🗑 ☎
🏧 🐾 ⼝ ⚒ 🢫 🔄 🗒 ✔
Nearby Facilities ┎ ✔ U ₽
Nearest Town Bewdley
Directions Just off the B4194 3½ miles outside Bewdley, near Kidderminster.
⋢ Kidderminster

EVESHAM

Evesham Vale Caravan Park, Yessell Farm, Boston Lane, Charlton, Nr Evesham, Worcestershire, WR11 2RD
Tel: 01386 860377
Pitches For 🏕 🚐 🚙 **Total** 40
Acreage 20 **Open** April to October
Access Good **Site** Level
Nearest Bus Stop (Miles) Outside
On the Blossom Trail route, near a river for fishing. Central for the Cotswolds, Stratford and Worcester.
Facilities ♿ ∮ 🗓 🎇 🖍 🍴 ⊙ ⅃ 🗑 ☎
🏧 ⊘ ⼝ 🢫 ⚘
Nearby Facilities ┎ ✔ U
Nearest Town Evesham
Directions From Evesham take the A44, after approx 1½ miles turn right for Charlton. Park is on the left hand side after approx. ¾ miles.
⋢ Evesham

EVESHAM

Ranch Caravan Park, Station Road, Honeybourne, Nr Evesham, Worcestershire, WR11 7PR
Tel: 01386 830744
Email: enquiries@ranch.co.uk
www.ranch.co.uk
Pitches For 🚐 🚙 **Total** 120
Acreage 48 **Open** March to November
Access Good **Site** Level
Nearest Bus Stop (Miles) ¼
Situated in meadow land in Vale of Evesham on north edge of Cotswolds. Meals available in licensed club.
Facilities ♿ ∮ 🗓 🎇 🖍 🍴 ⊙ ⅃ 🍽 🔄 🗑 ☎
🏧 ⊘ 🐾 ✗ ⼝ 🠪 🢫 🔄 🗒 ⚘ ✔
Nearby Facilities ┎ ✔ U

Nearest Town Evesham
Directions From Evesham take B4035 to Badsey and Bretforton. Turn left to Honeybourne. At village crossroads take Bidford direction, site on left in 400 yards.
⋢ Evesham

GREAT MALVERN

Camping & Caravanning Club Site, Blackmore Camp Site No.2, Hanley Swan, Worcestershire, WR8 0EE
Tel: 01684 310280
www.campingandcaravanningclub.co.uk/blackmore
Pitches For 🏕 🚐 🚙 **Total** 200
Acreage 17 **Open** All Year
Access Good **Site** Level
Close to the River Severn. Situated in the Malvern Hills, ideal walking country. Close to the market towns of Ledbury, Tewkesbury and Evesham. BTB 5 Star Graded and AA 4 Pennants. Non members welcome. You can also call us on 0845 130 7633.
Facilities ♿ ∮ 🗓 🎇 🖍 🍴 ⊙ ⅃ 🗑 ☎
🏧 🐾 🢫 ⼝ ⚒ 🠪 🔄 🗒 ⚘ 🍴 ☎
Nearby Facilities ✔ U ₽
Nearest Town Great Malvern
Directions Take the A38 to Upton-on-Severn, turn north over the river bridge, turn second left then first left signposted Hanley Swan. Site is on the right after 1 mile.
⋢ Malvern

KIDDERMINSTER

Wolverley Camping & Caravanning Club Site, Brown Westhead Park, Wolverley, Nr Kidderminster, Worcestershire, DY10 3PX
Tel: 01562 850909
www.campingandcaravanningclub.co.uk/wolverley
Pitches For 🏕 🚐 🚙 **Total** 120
Acreage 12 **Open** 29-Mar to 05-Nov
Access Good **Site** Lev/Slope
Nearest Bus Stop (Miles) ¼
A quiet and secluded site with pretty walks along the canal, and some excellent pubs. BTB 3 Star Graded and AA 3 Pennants. Non members welcome. You can also call us on 0845 130 7633.
Facilities ♿ ∮ 🗓 🎇 🖍 🍴 ⊙ ⅃ 🗑 ☎
🏧 🐾 ⊙ ⼝ ⚒ ⼝ 🢫 🔄 🗒 ⚘
Nearby Facilities ┎ ✔ U ₽
Nearest Town Kidderminster
Directions From Kidderminster take the A449 to Wolverhampton, turn left at the traffic lights onto the B4189 signposted Wolverley. Look for brown camping sign and turn right, the site entrance is on the left.
⋢ Kidderminster

MALVERN

Kingsgreen Caravan Park, Berrow, Nr Malvern, Worcestershire, WR13 6AQ
Tel: 01531 650272
Pitches For 🏕 🚐 🚙 **Total** 45
Acreage 3 **Open** 01-Mar to End Oct
Access Good **Site** Level
Beautiful walks on the Malvern Hills and Malvern with its famous Elgar Route. Historic Black and White timbered towns, Tewkesbury and Upton-on-Severn. BH & HPA Member.
Facilities ♿ ∮ 🗓 🖍 🍴 ⊙ ⅃ 🗑 ☎
🏧 ⊙ 🐾 🔄 ✔ ⼝
Nearby Facilities ┎ ✔
Nearest Town Ledbury/Malvern
Directions From Ledbury take the A417 towards Gloucester. Go over the M50 then take the first turning left to Malvern, we are 1 mile on the right. OR M50 Southbound junction 2, turn left onto the A417, in 1 mile turn left to the Malverns.
⋢ Ledbury/Malvern

SHRAWLEY

Brant Farm Caravan Park, Shrawley, Worcestershire, WR6 6TD
Tel: 01905 621008
Pitches For 🏕 🚐 🚙 **Total** 12
Acreage 1 **Open** April to 30-Oct
Access Good **Site** Level
Nearest Bus Stop (Miles) ¼
Quiet location in scenic woodland. Two pubs within a 5 minute walk.
Facilities 🗓 🎇 🖍 ⅃ 🍽 🔄 🗒 ⚘
Nearby Facilities ✔
Nearest Town Stourport-on-Severn
Directions Take the A449 from Worcester to Holt Heath, then take the B4196 signposted Shrawley. Continue to the Rose & Crown Pub and the Park is 100 yards further on on the left hand side.
⋢ Kidderminster/Worcester

STOURPORT-ON-SEVERN

Lickhill Manor Caravan Park, Lickhill Manor, Stourport-on-Severn, Worcestershire, DY13 8RL
Tel: 01299 871041/877820
Email: excellent@lickhillmanor.co.uk
www.lickhillmanor.co.uk
Pitches For 🏕 🚐 🚙 🚌 **Total** 120
Acreage 9 **Open** All Year
Access Good **Site** Level
Nearest Bus Stop (Miles) ¼
Alongside river (fishing rights held). Walks through the unspoilt Wyre Forest. West Midlands Safari Park and Severn Valley Railway nearby.
Facilities ♿ ∮ 🗓 🎇 🖍 🍴 ⊙ ⅃ 🗑 ☎
🏧 ⊙ 🐾 🢫 ⼝ 🠪 🢫 🔄 🗒 ⚘
Nearby Facilities ┎ ✔ 🢫 ⚘ U ₽
Nearest Town Stourport-on-Severn
Directions From Stourport take the B4195 to Bewdley, at traffic lights on the crossroads follow caravan signs, after ½ mile turn right at the sign.
⋢ Kidderminster

STOURPORT-ON-SEVERN

Lincomb Lock Caravan Park, Lincomb Lock, Titton, Stourport-on-Severn, Worcestershire, DY13 9QR
Tel: 01299 823836
Email: lincomb@hillandale.co.uk
www.hillandale.co.uk
Pitches For 🏕 🚐 🚙 🚌 **Total** 14
Acreage 1 **Open** 01-Mar to 06-Jan
Access Good **Site** Level
Nearest Bus Stop (Miles) ½
ADULTS ONLY. Alongside a river. Many local attractions including West Midlands Safari Park, Severn Valley Railway, Riverside Amusements, the ancient Wyre Forest and local museums.
Facilities ∮ 🗓 🎇 🖍 🍴 ⊙ ⅃ 🗑 ☎
🏧 🠪 🢫 🔄 🗒 ✔ A
Nearby Facilities ┎ ✔ 🢫 ⚘ U ₽
Nearest Town Stourport-on-Severn
Directions 1 mile from Stourport on the A4025 turn right at park signs. Or from the A449 join the A4025 at Crossway Green, after 1 mile turn left at park signs.
⋢ Kidderminster

WORCESTER

Ketch Caravan Park, Bath Road, Worcester, Worcestershire, WR5 3HW
Tel: 01905 820430
Pitches For 🏕 🚐 🚙 🚌 **Total** 32
Acreage 6½ **Open** April to End October
Access Good **Site** Level
Nearest Bus Stop (Miles) ¼
On the River Severn.
Facilities ∮ 🗓 🖍 🍴 ⊙ ⅃ 🗑 🏧 ⊙ ✗ 🠪 ✔
Nearby Facilities ┎ ✔
Nearest Town Worcester

Directions Leave the M5 at junction 7 and follow signs for Malvern until you come to the A38. Turn for Worcester and park entrance is approx. 100 yards on the left.
⇌ Worcester

WORCESTER

Mill House Caravan & Camping Site, Mill House, Hawford, Worcester, Worcestershire, WR3 7SE
Tel: 01905 451283
Email: millhousecaravansite@yahoo.co.uk
www.facebook.com/millhousecaravansite
Pitches For ▲ ⚏ ⚌ **Total** 100
Acreage 6 **Open** April **to** October
Access Good **Site** Level
Nearest Bus Stop (Miles) ¼
Small river around the site. Ideal centre for touring. NO commercial vehicles permitted. Unit size restrictions.
Facilities ∮ 🏕 🄿 ⊙ ♿ ⚷ ⚑ 🖃 ✒
Nearby Facilities ┢ ✒
Nearest Town Worcester
Directions On the A449 3 miles north of the centre of Worcester.
⇌ Worcester

WORCESTER

Peachley Leisure, Martley Road, Lower Broadheath, Worcester, Worcestershire, WR2 6QX
Tel: 01905 641309
Email: peachleyleisure@live.co.uk
www.peachleyleisure.com
Pitches For ▲ ⚏ ⚌ **Total** 83
Acreage 7 **Open** 06-Feb **to** 06-Jan
Access Good **Site** Level
Nearest Bus Stop (Miles) ½
Quad trekking on site. Near to Worcester Cathedral, Elgar Museum, Worcester Racecourse, Commandery and the Malvern Hills.
Facilities ⚶ ∮ 🎏 🄷 🏕 🄿 ⊙ ⊿ 🖳 🖃 ☎
♫ ✗ 🖃 🖃 ✒ ⚞ ⚲
Nearby Facilities ┢ ✒ ⚓ ∪ ♫ ⚵
Nearest Town Worcester
Directions 3 miles from Worcester on the A443 Hylton road, turn left onto the B4204 Martley Road.
⇌ Worcester

WORCESTER

Seaborne Leisure, Court Meadow, Kempsey, Worcester, Worcestershire, WR5 3JL
Tel: 01905 820295
Email: enquiries@seaborneleisure.co.uk
www.seaborneleisure.co.uk
Pitches For ⚏ ⚌ **Total** 105
Acreage 40 **Open** March **to** Oct
Access Good **Site** Level
Nearest Bus Stop (Miles) ¼
Adjacent to the River Severn with views towards the Malvern Hills. Ideally situated for places of interest.
Facilities ⚶ ∮ 🄷 🏕 🄿 ⊙ ⊿ 🖃 ☎
♫ ⊙ ✗ ✦ 🖃 🖃 ⚞
Nearby Facilities ┢ ✒ ∪
Nearest Town Worcester
Directions 2 miles south of Worcester. From Worcester take the A38 towards Tewkesbury, when in the village of Kempsey turn right by the village shop (Church Street), site is signposted, approx 50 yards down Court Meadow.
⇌ Worcester

WYTHALL

Chapel Lane Caravan Club Site, Chapel Lane, Wythall, Birmingham, B47 6JX
Tel: 01564 826483
www.caravanclub.co.uk
Pitches For ⚏ ⚌ **Total** 108

Acreage 14 **Open** All Year
Access Good **Site** Level
Nearest Bus Stop (Miles) Outside
Rural and open site set in the shadow of an old chapel. The Transport Museum is adjacent, and a short walk leads you to Becketts Farm Shop which has a restaurant. Only 9 miles from the NEC and close to many museums. Non members welcome. Booking essential.
Facilities ⚶ ∮ 🏕 🄿 ⊙ ⊿ 🖃 ☎
♫ ⊙ ⚙ ⚑ ✦ 🖃 ⚞ ⚲
Nearby Facilities ┢ ✒
Nearest Town Birmingham
Directions From north on M1 leave at junction 23A and take A42/M42, exit at junction 3 and take A435. At roundabout turn left into Middle Lane, after 150 yards turn left into Chapel Lane, after 300 yards turn right by the church then immediately turn right again int
⇌ Birmingham NEC

YORK (County Of)
YORK

Acomb Grange, Grange Lane, York, YO23 3QZ
Tel: 0871 288 4763
Email: info@acombgrange.co.uk
www.acombgrange.co.uk
Pitches For ▲ ⚏ ⚌ **Total** 5
Acreage 2 **Open** All Year
Access Fair **Site** Level
Nearest Bus Stop (Miles) ½
Fishing on site in a restored Mediaeval moat. Near the City of York and the Moors and Dales. Self Catering accommodation also available.
Facilities ∮ 🏕 🄿 ⊙ ⊿ 🖃 ☎ ⚞ ✒
Nearby Facilities ┢ ✒ ⚓
Nearest Town York
Directions Take the A59 to Harrogate and follow signs to Acomb. Turn into Askham Lane then turn into Grange Lane. Do Not follow Sat Nav, there are mapping errors to this Park.
⇌ York

YORK

Beechwood Grange Caravan Club Site, Malton Road, York, YO32 9TH
Tel: 01904 424637
www.caravanclub.co.uk
Pitches For ⚏ ⚌ **Total** 115
Acreage 11 **Open** March **to** Jan
Access Good **Site** Level
Set in open countryside, yet only 3 miles from York. Boules pitch on site. Plenty to do and see in York from river cruises to the Jorvik Viking Centre and the National Railway Museum. Non members welcome. Booking essential.
Facilities ⚶ ∮ 🄷 🏕 🄿 ⊙ 🖃 ☎
♫ ⊙ ⚙ ✦ 🖃 ⚞
Nearby Facilities ┢
Nearest Town York
Directions Turn off the A64 onto the A1237 signposted Thirsk. At roundabout turn right into road signposted local traffic only, site is at the end of the drive.
⇌ York

YORK

Chowdene Camping & Caravan Site, Chowdene, Malton Road, York, YO32 9TD
Tel: 01904 289359
Email: touraco@talktalk.net
www.caravanstv.co.uk
Pitches For ▲ ⚏ ⚌ **Total** 20
Acreage 1½ **Open** March **to** Nov
Access Good **Site** Level
Nearest Bus Stop (Miles) Adjacent

Small, quiet, family run site. VW Camper friendly and we welcome the smaller camper vehicles. Excellent for York and its many attractions. Adjacent to a Park & Ride. Some hardstandings available.
Facilities ∮ 🄷 🄿 ☎ ✦ 🖃
Nearby Facilities ┢ ✒
Nearest Town York
Directions From the A1 take the A64 for approx 17 miles. Ignoring the first turning, take the A1036 at the roundabout for York. After 1 mile (at the third roadabout with a large tile shop), continue and drive slowly for 200 yards and see our site sign on the right,
⇌ York

YORK

Moor End Farm, Acaster Malbis, York, YO23 2UQ
Tel: 01904 706727
Email: roger@acaster99.fsnet.co.uk
www.moor-end-farm.co.uk
Pitches For ▲ ⚏ ⚌ **Total** 20
Acreage 1 **Open** Easter **to** Oct
Access Good **Site** Level
Nearest Bus Stop (Miles) Outside
Ideal for York and the York/Selby cycle track.
Facilities ⚶ ∮ 🄷 🏕 🄿 ⊙ ⊿ 🖃 ☎ 🄼 ✦ 🖃 🖃
Nearby Facilities
Nearest Town York
Directions Off A64 going west turn off at Copmanthorpe and follow symbols and Acaster signs to village.
⇌ York

YORK

Moorside Caravan Park, Lords Moor Lane, Strensall, York, YO32 5XJ
Tel: 01904 491865/491208
www.moorsidecaravanpark.co.uk
Pitches For ▲ ⚏ ⚌ **Total** 50
Open March **to** October
Access Good **Site** Level
NO CHILDREN. Fishing lake on site. Near York Golf Course.
Facilities ⚶ ∮ 🄷 🏕 🄿 ⊙ ⊿ 🖃 ☎
♫ ⚞ ⚙ ✒ ✦ 🄰 ⚲ ⚵
Nearby Facilities ┢ ✒
Nearest Town York
Directions Take the A1237, then take the Strensall turn and head towards Flaxton.
⇌ York

YORK

Naburn Lock Caravan Park, Naburn, York, YO19 4RU
Tel: 01904 728697
Email: petercatherine@naburnlock.co.uk
www.naburnlock.co.uk
Pitches For ⚏ ⚌ **Total** 100
Open 01-Mar **to** 06-Nov
Access Good **Site** Level
Nearest Bus Stop (Miles) Outside
Close to the historic City of York. One hours drive from the Yorkshire Dalesand seaside resorts. Adults only area.
Facilities ⚶ ✦ ∮ 🄷 🏕 🄿 ⊙ ⊿ 🖃 ☎
♫ ⊙ ⚙ ✦ 🖃 🖃
Nearby Facilities ┢ ✒ ∪
Nearest Town York
Directions From the A19/A64 interchange at the McArthur Glen Designer Outlet, take the A19 for York, after 200 yards turn first left onto the B1222.
⇌ York

YORK

Rowntree Park Caravan Club Site, Terry Avenue, York, YO23 1JQ
Tel: 01904 658997
www.caravanclub.co.uk
Pitches For ▲ ⚏ ⚌ **Total** 102
Acreage 4 **Open** All Year

Access Good **Site** Level
Nearest Bus Stop (Miles) ½
On the banks of the River Ouse. Within walking distance of York. Close to York Minster, Jorvik Viking Centre, Castle Howard, York Castle Museum and The Shambles. Non members welcome. Booking essential.
Facilities ⚷ ✤ ⌂ �📶 ⇌ ⌐ 🚻 ⊙ 🍴
🅿 ❤⏦ ▣ ⊡ 📶
Nearby Facilities ⌐ ✈ ⚓ ⚘
Nearest Town York
Directions From A64 south of York take A19 sp York Centre, DO NOT turn onto A1237. After 2 miles join the one-way system sp City Centre, at Mecca Bingo keep left and continue over bridge. Turn left immediately before Swan Pub, after 250 yards turn right into Terry Aavenue. Site on right.
⇌ York

YORK

York Touring Caravan Site, Towthorpe Moor Lane, Towthorpe, York, YO32 9ST
Tel: 01904 499275
Email: info@yorkcaravansite.co.uk
www.yorkcaravansite.co.uk
Pitches For ⚊ ♨ ⛺ **Total** 28
Open All Year
Access Good **Site** Level
Golf range and 9 hole golf course on site. ETB 4 Star Graded and AA 4 Pennants.
Facilities ⚷ ✤ ☐ ⌐ ⇌ ⌐ ⊙ 🍴 ▣ 🚻
❌⏦ ▣ ⊡
Nearby Facilities ⌐ ✈
Nearest Town York
Directions From the A64 take turnoff signposted Strensall and Haxby, site is 1½ miles on the right.
⇌ York

YORKSHIRE (EAST)
BRANDES BURTON

Fosse Hill Caravan Park, Catwick Lane, Brandes Burton, Driffield, East Yorkshire, YO25 8SB
Tel: 01964 542608
Email: janet@fossehill.co.uk
www.fossehill.co.uk
Pitches For ⚊ ♨ ⛺ **Total** 110
Open March to October
Access Good **Site** Level
Nearest Bus Stop (Miles) 1
Family run site set in countryside. Just 1 mile from the village of Brandesburton, and only 3 miles from the seaside town of Hornsea. Excellent base for visiting the North Yorks Moors, York, Beverley, Hull and the famous Deep.
Facilities ⚷ ✤ ☐ ⌐ ⇌ 🅿 ⊡ 🍴
🏵 ⊙ ♨ ❌ ▽ 🚻 ♠ ⏦ ❤⏦ ▣ ▣ 🌣
Nearby Facilities ⌐ ✈ ⚓ ⚘ ⓤ
Nearest Town Hornsea
Directions ½ a mile east of the A165 Hull to Bridlington road.
⇌ Beverley

BRIDLINGTON

Fir Tree Caravan Park, Jewison Lane, Bridlington, East Yorkshire, YO16 6YG
Tel: 01262 676442
Email: info@flowerofmay.com
www.flowerofmay.com
Pitches For ♨ ⛺ **Total** 46
Acreage 25 **Open** March to Oct
Access Good **Site** Level
Pets are welcome by arrangement only.
Facilities ✤ ☐ ⌐ ⇌ ⌐ ⊙ 🍴 🅿 ⊡ 🍴
🏵 ⊙ ☐ ♨ ▽ 🚻 ♠ ⏦ ❤⏦ ▣ ⊡ 🌣 📶
Nearby Facilities ⌐ ✈ ⚓ ⚘ ⓤ ⚓ ⚘
Nearest Town Bridlington

Directions From roundabout on A165 take B1255 to Flamborough for 2 miles. Jewison Lane is on the left and site is on the left after the level crossing.
⇌ Bridlington

BRIDLINGTON

Poplars Touring Park, 45 Jewison Lane, Sewerby, Bridlington, East Yorkshire, YO15 1DX
Tel: 01262 677251
www.the-poplars.co.uk
Pitches For ⚊ ♨ ⛺ **Total** 30
Acreage 1½ **Open** 05-Mar to 31-Oct
Access Good **Site** Level
Nearest Bus Stop (Miles) ½
Small quiet site in a good touring location. ¾ miles to the beach. Pub with food adjacent.
Facilities ✤ ☐ ⌐ ⇌ ⌐ ⊙ 🍴 ❤⏦ ▣
Nearby Facilities ⌐ ✈ ⓤ
Nearest Town Bridlington
Directions From Bridlington take the B1255 towards Flamborough for 1½ miles. Jewison Lane is a left turn off the Z bend after Marton Hall.
⇌ Bridlington

BRIDLINGTON

South Cliff Caravan Park, Wilstthorpe, Bridlington, East Yorkshire, YO15 3QN
Tel: 01262 671051
Email: southcliff@eastriding.gov.uk
www.southcliff.co.uk
Pitches For ⚊ ♨ ⛺ **Total** 184
Open March to Nov
Access Good **Site** Level
Direct access to the beach. Golf course adjacent to the park. Special Offers on touring pitches in low and mid season.
Facilities ⚷ ✤ ☐ ⌐ ⇌ ⌐ ⊙ 🍴 ▣ 🍴
🏵 ⊙ ☐ ❌ ▽ 🚻 ♠ ⏦ ♣ ❤⏦ ▣ ⊡ 🌣
Nearby Facilities ⌐ ✈ ⚓ ⓤ ⚘ ⚓
Nearest Town Bridlington
Directions Take the A165 main route into Bridlington.
⇌ Bridlington

BRIDLINGTON

Thorpe Hall Caravan & Camping Site, Rudston, Driffield, East Yorkshire, YO25 4JE
Tel: 01262 420393
Email: caravansite@thorpehall.co.uk
www.thorpehall.co.uk
Pitches For ⚊ ♨ ⛺ **Total** 92
Acreage 4½ **Open** March to October
Access Good **Site** Level
Nearest Bus Stop (Miles) Outside
Very sheltered site, set within the old Kitchen Garden walls of Thorpe Hall on the Yorkshire Wolds. Buses three times a week on Wednesday, Thursday and Friday.
Facilities ⚷ ✤ ☐ ⌐ ⇌ ⌐ ⊙ 🍴 ▣ 🍴
🏵 ⊙ ☐ 🚻 ♠ ⏦ ❤⏦ ▣ ⊡ ✈ 📶
Nearby Facilities ⌐ ✈ ⓤ ⚘
Nearest Town Bridlington
Directions 4 miles inland from Bridlington on the B1253.
⇌ Bridlington

DRIFFIELD

Seaside Caravan Park, Ulrome, Driffield, East Yorkshire, YO25 8TT
Tel: 01262 468228
www.seaside-caravan-park.co.uk
Pitches For ⚊ ♨ ⛺ **Total** 130
Acreage 12 **Open** Mid March to Oct
Access Good **Site** Level
Nearest Bus Stop (Miles) Outside
Adjacent to the beach with views from Brid Bay to Flamborough Head.

Facilities ⚷ ✤ ☐ ⌐ ⇌ ⌐ ⊙ 🍴 ▣ ⊡ 🍴
🏵 ⊙ ☐ ❤⏦ ▣ 🌣
Nearby Facilities ⌐ ✈ ⚓ ⓤ ⚘
Nearest Town Bridlington
Directions From Bridlington take the A165 south, after 5 miles turn left onto the B1242 signposted Hornsea. After 1½ miles go through Ulrome Village to the Park.
⇌ Bridlington

GOOLE

Dobella Lane Farm, Rawcliffe, Goole, East Yorkshire, DN14 8SQ
Tel: 01405 839261
Pitches For ⚊ ♨ ⛺ **Total** 5
Acreage ½ **Open** All Year
Access Good **Site** Level
Nearest Bus Stop (Miles) ¼
Very private garden site on a working farm. English country garden, ideal for bird watching. Pub and restaurant in the village, and a new area for skateboarding. Near to Goole Docks Waterways Museum, Howden Minster, Selby Abbey and Blacktuft Sands.
Facilities ⚷ ✤ ☐ ⌐ ⇌ ▣ ⊙ 🍴 ▣ 🍴
Nearby Facilities ⌐ ✈ ⚓ ⓤ ⚘ ⚓
Nearest Town Goole
Directions Leave the M62 at junction 36 and head towards Selby into Rawcliffe. In the village turn left and follow road for ½ a mile, at the brick bus shelter turn left, go over the motorway and we are the first farm on the right.
⇌ Rawcliffe

HORNSEA

Four Acres Caravan Park, Hornsea Road, Atwick, Driffield, East Yorkshire, YO25 8DG
Tel: 01964 536940
Email: caravanfouracres@aol.com
www.fouracrescaravanpark.co.uk
Pitches For ♨ ⛺ **Total** 61
Acreage 4 **Open** March to End Oct
Access Good **Site** Level
Nearest Bus Stop (Miles) Outside
Near to the beach, local pub, indoor bowls, swimming baths and a Sunday market.
Facilities ✤ ☐ ⌐ ⇌ ⌐ ⊙ 🍴 ▣ 🍴
🏵 ⊙ ☐ ❤⏦ ▣ 🌣 ♠
Nearby Facilities ⌐ ✈ ⚘
Nearest Town Hornsea
Directions As you approach Hornsea turn left at the roundabout on the B1242 for approx. 2 miles, site is on the right hand side.
⇌ Bridlington

HULL

Sand-le-Mere Caravan Park, Main Street, Tunstall, East Yorkshire, HU12 0JF
Tel: 01964 670403
Email: info@sand-le-mere.co.uk
www.sand-le-mere.co.uk
Pitches For ♨ ⛺ **Total** 20
Acreage 140
Access Good **Site** Level
Nearest Bus Stop (Miles) Outside
Near the beach and all facilities.
Facilities ✤ ☐ ⇌ ⌐ ⊙ 🍴 ▣ ⊡ 🍴
🏵 ⊙ ☐ ❌ ▽ 🚻 ♠ 🥤 ❤⏦ ▣ ▣ ✈ 🌣
Nearby Facilities ⌐ ✈ ⓤ ⚘
Nearest Town Withernsea
Directions From Hull take the A1033 to Hedon, turn left at the roundabout to Preston and follow signs for Burton Pidsea and Roos.
⇌ Hull

POCKLINGTON

South Lea Caravan Park, The Balk, Pocklington, East Yorkshire, YO42 2NX
Tel: 01759 303467
Email: info@south-lea.co.uk
www.south-lea.co.uk

Pitches For ⊼ ⌂ ⌂ **Total** 72
Acreage 15 **Open** March **to** Oct
Access Good **Site** Level
Nearest Bus Stop (Miles) ½
Spacious 4 Star site, ideally situated for York (12 miles) and the coast (25 miles). Gold David Bellamy Award for Conservation. You can also contact us on Mobile: 07989 616095.
Facilities
Nearby Facilities
Nearest Town Pocklington
Directions From the A64 take the A1079 York to Hull road. At the Yorkway Motel turn onto the B1247 signposted Pocklington, the Park is 400 yards on the left.
⇌ York

SKIPSEA
Mill Farm Country Park, Mill Lane, Skipsea, East Yorkshire, YO25 8SS
Tel: 01262 468211
Pitches For ⊼ ⌂ ⌂ **Total** 56
Acreage 6 **Open** 16-Mar **to** 30-Sep
Access Good **Site** Level
Nearest Bus Stop (Miles) Outside
Farm walk, beach nearby. RSPB site at Bempton. Good centre for many places of local interest. Nearby there is a village shop and a Post Office, a pub and a heated swimming pool.
Facilities
Nearby Facilities
Nearest Town Hornsea
Directions The A165 Hull to Bridlington Road, at Beeford take B1249 to Skipsea. At crossroads turn right, then first left up Cross Street which leads on to Mill Lane, site is on the right.
⇌ Bridlington

SKIPSEA
Skipsea Holiday Park, Mill Lane, Skipsea, East Yorkshire, YO25 8TZ
Tel: 0843 309 2573
Email: holidaysales.skipsea@park-resorts.com
www.park-resorts.com
Pitches For ⊼ ⌂ ⌂
Open March **to** October
Access Good **Site** Sloping
Nearest Bus Stop (Miles) ½
In a countryside setting.
Facilities
Nearby Facilities
Nearest Town Skipsea
Directions From Bridlington take the A165 to Kingston-Upon-Hull, the Skipsea turning is signposted 8 miles south of Bridlington.

STAMFORD BRIDGE
Weir Caravan Park, Stamford Bridge, East Yorkshire, YO41 1AN
Tel: 01759 371377
Email: enquiries@yorkshireholidayparks.co.uk
www.yorkshireholidayparks.co.uk
Pitches For ⊼ ⌂ ⌂ **Total** 20
Acreage 7 **Open** March **to** Oct
Access Good **Site** Level
Nearest Bus Stop (Miles) ¼
On the edge of a river. 5 minute walk from the village and shops, pubs, etc..
Facilities
Nearby Facilities
Nearest Town York
Directions From the A166 Bridlington road, turn left before the bridge.
⇌ York

WILBERFOSS
Fangfoss Park, Fangfoss, York, East Yorkshire, YO41 5QB
Tel: 01759 380491
Email: info@fangfosspark.co.uk
www.fangfosspark.co.uk
Pitches For ⊼ ⌂ ⌂ ⌂ **Total** 75
Acreage 5 **Open** 01-Mar **to** 25-Nov
Access Good **Site** Level
Nearest Bus Stop (Miles) ½
Ideal for York, North Yorkshire Moors and Castle Howard. 40 minutes from the coast.
Facilities
Nearby Facilities
Nearest Town York
Directions From the A64 take the A1079 towards Hull. After 5 miles turn left into Wilberfoss Village, turn next left and the site is 2 miles.
⇌ York

WITHERNSEA
Willows Holiday Park, Hollym Road, Withernsea, East Yorkshire, HU19 2PN
Tel: 01964 612233
Email: info@highfield-caravans.co.uk
www.willowsholidaypark.co.uk
Pitches For ⌂ ⌂ **Total** 40
Acreage 9 **Open** 04-Mar **to** 31-Oct
Access Good **Site** Level
Nearest Bus Stop (Miles) Outside
Only a 10 minute walk to the beach and a 15 minute walk to the town. Near a Tesco store.
Facilities
Nearby Facilities
Nearest Town Withernsea
Directions Take the M62 to Hull then take the A1033 to Withernsea. Willows is the first site on the left on entering Withernsea.
⇌ Hull

WITHERNSEA
Withernsea Sands Holiday Park, Waxholme Road, Withernsea, East Yorkshire, HU19 2BS
Tel: 0843 309 2583
Email: holidaysales.withernsea@park-resorts.com
www.park-resorts.com
Pitches For ⊼ ⌂ ⌂
Open April **to** October
Access Good **Site** Level
Nearest Bus Stop (Miles) Outside
Ideally located for exploring the Yorkshire coast.
Facilities
Nearby Facilities
Nearest Town Hornsea
Directions Leave the M62 at junction 38 and take the A63 through Hull. At the end of the dual carriageway turn right onto the A1033 and follow signs for Withernsea, go through the village and at the mini roundabout turn left, turn right at the lighthouse and the Park is on the left.
⇌ Hornsea

YORKSHIRE (NORTH)
AYSGARTH
Little Cote Site, West Burton, Aysgarth, North Yorkshire, DL8 4JY
Tel: 01969 663450
Pitches For ⊼ ⌂ ⌂ **Total** 20
Acreage 2 **Open** March **to** October
Access Good **Site** Lev/Slope
Nearest Bus Stop (Miles) ½
Small, quiet site alongside a river. Own car is essential. Ideal touring.
Facilities
Nearby Facilities
Directions From the A684 Aysgarth/Northallerton road, 2 miles east of Aysgarth take the B6160 to West Burton, fork left Walden for ¾ miles.
⇌ Northallerton

BARDEN
Howgill Lodge, Barden, Skipton, North Yorkshire, BD23 6DJ
Tel: 01756 720655
Email: info@howgill-lodge.co.uk
www.howgill-lodge.co.uk
Pitches For ⊼ ⌂ ⌂ **Total** 50
Open April **to** Oct
Access Good (Narrow) **Site** Terraced Slope
Nearest Bus Stop (Miles) ¼
Beautiful views. Ideal for walking or touring.
Facilities
Nearby Facilities
Nearest Town Skipton
Directions From the A59 take the B6160 signposted Burnsall. Immediately after Barden Tower turn right, go over the river, site lane is 1½ miles on the left by the phone box.
⇌ Skipton

BENTHAM
Riverside Caravan Park, High Bentham, Lancaster, Lancashire, LA2 7FJ
Tel: 015242 61272
Email: info@riversidecaravanpark.co.uk
www.riversidecaravanpark.co.uk
Pitches For ⌂ ⌂ **Total** 61
Acreage 6 **Open** 01-Mar **to** 02-Jan
Access Good **Site** Level
Nearest Bus Stop (Miles) ½
Riverside site, great for families. Flat footpaths for easy walking. We sell milk, eggs, tea and coffee. Local shops and pub just a 5 minute walk.
Facilities
Nearby Facilities
Nearest Town High Bentham
Directions Follow caravan signs off the B6480 at The Black Bull Hotel in High Bentham.
⇌ High Bentham

BOLTON ABBEY
Strid Wood Caravan Club Site, Bolton Abbey, Skipton, North Yorkshire, BD23 6AN
Tel: 01756 710433
www.caravanclub.co.uk
Pitches For ⌂ ⌂ **Total** 57
Acreage 4 **Open** March **to** Jan
Access Good **Site** Level
Nearest Bus Stop (Miles) Outside
Situated in the Bolton Abbey estate, this pretty site is surrounded by woodland and the Yorkshire Dales. Many miles of walks around the site. Close to Bolton Priory and Skipton castle. Non members welcome. Booking essential.
Facilities
Nearby Facilities
Nearest Town Skipton
Directions From the A59 Gisburn to Harrogate road, at Bolton Bridge roundabout take the B6160 sp Bolton Abbey. After 2¾ miles turn right into Strid car park, go through the double gates ahead into the site.
⇌ Skipton

BOROUGHBRIDGE

Blue Bell Caravan Park, Kirby Hill, Boroughbridge, North Yorkshire, YO51 9DS
Tel: 07946 549529
Email: townend450@btinternet.com
Pitches For 🚐 🚏 **Total** 24
Acreage 2 **Open** March **to** December
Nearest Bus Stop (Miles) Outside
Well drained and dry site.
Facilities ⚡ 🛁 🚻 ⊙ 🍴 🏪 🏊 💶 ↗🖃 ⚥
Nearby Facilities ┡ ✔ ⚓ ✝ 🏊 ♣ ✗
Nearest Town Ripon
Directions On the B6265 in Kirby Hill, at the rear of the Blue Bell Pub.
⇌ Harrogate

BOROUGHBRIDGE

Camping & Caravanning Club Site, Bar Lane, Roecliffe, Boroughbridge, North Yorkshire, YO51 9LS
Tel: 01423 322683
www.campingandcaravanningclub.co.uk/boroughbridge
Pitches For ⚑ 🚐 🚏 **Total** 85
Acreage 5 **Open** All Year
Site Level
On the banks of the River Ure for fishing, boat launching facility. Table tennis and pool table on site. Close to the Yorkshire Dales. Lodges available for hire. BTB 5 Star Graded and AA 4 Pennants. Non members welcome. You can also call us on 0845 130 7633.
Facilities ⚡ 🛁 🚻 🚽 ⊙ 🍴 🛒 🏊
🏪 🔋 ⛽ 🔑 ♣ 🏧 🗑 🖃 ↗ 📶
Nearby Facilities ↗ ✔ ⚓ U ℛ
Directions From junction 48 of the A1M north and southbound slip roads, follow signs for Bar Lane Industrial Estate and Roecliffe Village. Site entrance is ¼ mile from the roundabout.
⇌ Harrogate

BOROUGHBRIDGE

Old Hall Holiday Park, Skelton Road, Langthorpe, Boroughbridge, North Yorkshire, YO51 9BZ
Tel: 01423 322130
Email: phil@yhlparks.co.uk
www.yhlparks.co.uk
Pitches For ⚑ 🚐 🚏
Acreage 7½ **Open** Easter/1 April **to** Oct
Access Good **Site** Level
Nearest Bus Stop (Miles) ¼
Near a river. Close to the market town of Boroughbridge (5-10 min. walk). 600 yards from a pub serving food. NB: Cades Vouchers accepted, but NOT Bank Holidays.
Facilities ⚡ 🛁 🚻 ⊙ 🍴 ▣ 🖃 ☎
🔋 ⛽ ♣ 🏧 🗑 ▣ ↗ ⚥
Nearby Facilities ↗ ✔ ⚓ ✗ U ℛ
Nearest Town Boroughbridge
Directions From Boroughbridge follow the main road in the direction of Kirby Hill and Ripon. After approx. ½ a mile turn left to Langthorpe and Newby Hall. Park is the second entrance on the right hand side.
⇌ Harrogate

CLAPHAM

Flying Horseshoe Caravan Site, Clapham, North Yorkshire, LA2 8ES
Tel: 01524 251175
Email: alan@laughing-gravy.co.uk
www.laughing-gravy.co.uk
Pitches For ⚑ 🚐 🚏
Open Good Friday **to** 01-Nov
Access Good **Site** Level
Nearest Bus Stop (Miles) Outside
Close to the coast and lakes. Ideal for countryside walking, near Three Peaks Walks.
Facilities 🍴 🛁 🚻 🚽 🏪 ⊙ 🍴 🏪 ▣ 📮 ⚥
Nearby Facilities
Nearest Town Settle
Directions From the A65 follow signs for Clapham Station, site is behind a hotel opposite the station.
⇌ Clapham (Opposite)

EASINGWOLD

Easingwold Caravan Park, The White House, Thirsk Road, Easingwold, York, North Yorkshire, YO6 3NF
Tel: 01347 821479
Email: kathryn.hood@hotmail.co.uk
Pitches For ⚑ 🚐 🚏 **Total** 30
Acreage 5 **Open** March **to** Oct
Access Good **Site** Level
Nearest Bus Stop (Miles) ½
Ideal for the North Yorkshire Moors and Castle Howard.
Facilities 🍴 🛁 🚻 🚽 ⊙ 🍴 🏪 ☎ ⚥
Nearby Facilities ↗ ✔ U ℛ
Nearest Town Thirsk
Directions From York take the A19 north for 15 miles. At second roundabout take the Easingwold road and the Park is 500 yards on the left.
⇌ Thirsk

FILEY

Centenary Way Camping & Caravan Park, Muston Grange, Filey, North Yorkshire, YO14 0HU
Tel: 01723 516415
Pitches For ⚑ 🚐 🚏 **Total** 75
Acreage 3½ **Open** March **to** October
Access Good **Site** Level
Nearest Bus Stop (Miles) ¼
Just a ten minute walk to the beach and Filey town. Handy for Scarborough and Bridlington. 45 minutes to the North Yorkshire Moors, York and Whitby.
Facilities
🍴 🛁 🚻 ⊙ 🍴 🏊 🔋 ♣ 🏧 🗑 🖃 ☎
Nearby Facilities ↗ ✔ ⚓ ✗ U ℛ
Directions Take the A165 from Bridlington, at the roundabout turn right onto the A1039, after 200 yards turn right into Centenary Way, follow lane to the very end.
⇌ Filey

FILEY

Filey Brigg Caravan Park, Country Park, Church View Drive, Filey, North Yorkshire, YO14 9ET
Tel: 01723 513852
Email: fileybrigg@scarborough.gov.uk
Pitches For 🚏 **Total** 154
Acreage 9 **Open** Easter **to** New Years
Access Good **Site** Level

Nearest Bus Stop (Miles) ¼
Sea views from the Park. Just a short walk to the town and beach.
Facilities ⚡ 🍴 🛁 🚻 🚽 🍴 ⊙ 🍴 🏊 🖃 ☎
🔋 🏧 ✗ 🗑 🖃
Nearby Facilities ↗ ✔ ⚓ ✗ U ℛ
Nearest Town Filey
Directions Follow signs for Country Park.
⇌ Filey

FILEY

Muston Grange Caravan Park, Muston Road, Filey, North Yorkshire, YO14 0HU
Tel: 01723 512167
www.mustongrange.com
Pitches For 🚐 🚏 **Total** 250
Open March **to** Oct
Access Good **Site** Level
Nearest Bus Stop (Miles) ¼
A 10 minute walk to Filey town with its shops and glorious sandy beach. Ideal for walking.
Facilities ⚡ 🍴 🛁 🚻 🚽 🍴 ⊙ 🍴 🏊 🖃 ☎
🔋 ⊙ 🏧 🗑 🖃 ⚥ ♣
Nearby Facilities ↗ ✔ ⚓ U ℛ
Nearest Town Filey
Directions Off the A165 Bridlington to Filey road.
⇌ Filey

FILEY

Orchard Farm Holiday Village, Stonegate, Hunmanby, Filey, North Yorkshire, YO14 0PU
Tel: 01723 891582
Email: info@orchardfarmholidayvillage.co.uk
www.orchardfarmholidayvillage.co.uk
Pitches For ⚑ 🚐 🚏 **Total** 85
Acreage 14 **Open** March **to** Oct
Access Good **Site** Level
Nearest Bus Stop (Miles) ¼
1 mile from the beach. Ideal base for all North Yorkshire attractions.
Facilities 🍴 🛁 🚻 🚽 🍴 ⊙ 🍴 🏊 🖃 ☎
🔋 ⊙ 🏪 ▣ ♣ 🏧 🗑 🖃 ↗
Nearby Facilities ┡
Nearest Town Filey
Directions From Filey take the A165 towards Bridlington, Hunmanby is 2 miles on the right.
⇌ Hunmanby

FILEY

Primrose Valley Holiday Park, Primrose Valley, Filey, North Yorkshire, YO14 9RF
Tel: 01723 513771
Email: primrosevalley@haven.com
www.haventouring.com/toprimrosevalley
Pitches For 🚐 🚏 **Total** 49
Open Mid March **to** End Oct
Access Good **Site** Level
Nearest Bus Stop (Miles) Outside
Large and lively 5 Star Holiday Park with direct access to a sandy beach. Wide choice of facilities including a boating lake, family entertainment, kids clubs and water fun.
Facilities ⚡ 🍴 🛁 🚻 🚽 🍴 ⊙ 🍴 🏊 🖃 ☎
🔋 ▣ ⊙ 🏪 ✗ ▽ ♣ 🏧 🗑 🖃 ↗ 📶
Nearby Facilities ┡ ⚓ ℛ
Nearest Town Filey
Directions From the A64 at Staxton roundabout take the A165 signposted Bridlington, park is between Scarborough and Bridlington.
⇌ Filey

FILEY

Reighton Sands Holiday Park, Reighto Gap, Filey, North Yorkshire, YO14 9SH
Tel: 01723 890476
Email: reightonsands@haven.com
www.haventouring.com/toreightonsands
Pitches For 🏕 🚐 🚍 **Total** 317
Open Mid March to End Oct
Access Good **Site** Lev/Slope
Nearest Bus Stop (Miles) Outside
A quiet and easy going Holiday Park with direct access to miles of glorious sand. Enjoy kids clubs, family entertainment, a golf course and water fun.
Facilities ...
Nearby Facilities ...
Nearest Town Filey/Scarborough
Directions Signposted on the A165 Filey to Bridlington road, 2 miles south of Filey.
🚂 Filey

GRASSINGTON

Hawkswick Cote Park, Arncliffe, Skipton, North Yorkshire, BD23 5PX
Tel: 01756 770226
Email: hawkswickcote@northdales.co.uk
www.northdales.co.uk
Pitches For 🏕 🚐 🚍 **Total** 38
Open Mar to Nov **Access** Good **Site** Level
Nearest Bus Stop (Miles) 2.5
Ideal for those who love the outdoors, with hiking, cycling, fishing & horse riding close by.
Facilities ...
Nearby Facilities ...
Nearest Town Skipton
Directions From Skipton take the B6265, at Threshfield take the B6160. ¼ of a mile past Kilnsey bear left towards Arncliffe, the Park is 1½ miles on the left.
🚂 Skipton

GRASSINGTON

Threaplands Camping & Caravan Park, Threaplands House, Cracoe, Nr Skipton, North Yorkshire, BD23 6LD
Tel: 01756 730248
Pitches For 🏕 🚐 🚍 **Total** 30
Acreage 8 **Open** March to October
Access Good **Site** Level
Nearest Bus Stop (Miles) ¼
Scenic views. Bakery on site selling fresh bread, cakes and milk etc.. Ideal for touring and walking.
Facilities ...
Nearby Facilities ...
Nearest Town Skipton
Directions 6 miles from Skipton on the B6265 to Cracoe. ¼ mile past Cracoe keep going straight on, site is ¼ mile on the left.
🚂 Skipton

HARROGATE

Bilton Park, Village Farm, Bilton Lane, Harrogate, North Yorkshire, HG1 4DH
Tel: 01423 863121
Email: welcome@biltonpark.co.uk
www.biltonpark.co.uk
Pitches For 🏕 🚐 🚍
Acreage 8½ **Open** April to October
Access Good **Site** Level
Nearest Bus Stop (Miles) ½
Facilities ...
Nearby Facilities ...
Nearest Town Harrogate
Directions From the A59 in Harrogate, turn at Skipton Pub into Bilton Lane, Park is 1½ miles down the road.
🚂 Harrogate

HARROGATE

High Moor Farm Caravan Park, Skipton Road, Harrogate, North Yorkshire, HG3 2LT
Tel: 01423 563637
Email: highmoorfarmpark@btconnect.com
www.highmoorfarmpark.co.uk
Pitches For 🏕 🚐 🚍 **Total** 300
Open 1 April/Easter to 31-Oct
Access Good **Site** Level
Nearest Bus Stop (Miles) Outside
Facilities ...
Nearby Facilities ...
Nearest Town Harrogate
Directions On the A59 4 miles from Harrogate on the left hand side.
🚂 Harrogate

HARROGATE

Maustin Park, Kearby with Netherby, Nr Wetherby, North Yorkshire, LS24 4BZ
Tel: 0113 288 6234
Email: info@maustin.co.uk
www.maustin.co.uk
Pitches For 🏕 🚐 🚍 **Total** 25
Open 01-Mar to 28-Jan
Access Good **Site** Level
ADULTS ONLY PARK in the heart of Emmerdale country. Ideal touring base for the Dales, and close to Harewood House and the floral town of Harrogate.
Facilities ...
Nearby Facilities ...
Nearest Town Harrogate/Wetherby
Directions Within easy reach of the A1.
🚂 Pannal

HARROGATE

Ripley Caravan Park, Ripley, Harrogate, North Yorkshire, HG3 3AU
Tel: 01423 770050
Email: ripleycaravanpark@talk21.com
www.ripleycaravanpark.com
Pitches For 🏕 🚐 🚍 **Total** 100
Acreage 25 **Open** Easter to October
Access Good **Site** Level
Nearest Bus Stop (Miles) ¼
Quiet family site, ideal for touring the Dales, Harrogate and York. David Bellamy Gold Award, AA 5 Pennants and ETB 5 Star Graded.
Facilities ...
Nearby Facilities ...
Nearest Town Harrogate
Directions From Harrogate take A61 towards Ripon, after 3 miles at Ripley roundabout take the B6165 Knaresborough road, site is 300 yards on the left.
🚂 Harrogate

HARROGATE

Rudding Holiday Park, Follifoot, Harrogate, North Yorkshire, HG3 1JH
Tel: 01423 870439
Email: holiday-park@ruddingpark.com
www.ruddingpark.co.uk
Pitches For 🏕 🚐 🚍 **Total** 141
Acreage 30 **Open** March to Jan
Access Good **Site** Level
Nearest Bus Stop (Miles) Outside
Ideal location for exploring the Moors, Dales and cities. Only 3 miles from the Spa town of Harrogate. Golf on site.
Facilities ...
Nearby Facilities ...
Nearest Town Harrogate
Directions From the A1 take the A59 to the A658 and turn south signposted Bradford. Continue for 4½ miles then turn right and follow signs.
🚂 Harrogate

HARROGATE

Shaws Trailer Park, Knaresborough Road, Harrogate, North Yorkshire, HG2 7NE
Tel: 01423 884432
www.residentialsite.uk
Pitches For 🏕 🚐 🚍 **Total** 77
Acreage 11 **Open** All Year
Access Good **Site** Level
Nearest Bus Stop (Miles) Entrance
A quiet and peaceful ADULTS ONLY park. Ideal for touring Yorkshire Dales, spa town of Harrogate (1½ miles) and gardens, Knaresborough (4 miles) and historic York. Health centre next door. Caravan and Motorhomes max. 25 ft.

Facilities & ✝ ⌷ ⌷ ⛟ Γ ⊙ ✦ ⛿ ☎ ⌷ ⊙ ✦ Ⅰ 🔒 ♿
Nearby Facilities Γ ✦ ✕ ♞
Nearest Town Harrogate
Directions On the A59 between Harrogate and Starbeck Railway Station. Entrance is adjacent to Johnsons Cleaners, 100 yards south of the Ford garage.
⇥ Starbeck

HARROGATE
The Yorkshire Hussar Inn Holiday Caravan Park, Markington, Harrogate, North Yorkshire, HG3 3NR
Tel: 01765 677327
Email: enquiry@yorkshire-hussar-inn.co.uk
www.yorkshire-hussar-inn.co.uk
Pitches For Å ⊞ ⊟ **Total** 20
Acreage 5 **Open** April **to** October
Access Good **Site** Level
Ideal touring centre for the Dales. LUXURY HOLIDAY CARAVANS FOR HIRE. Situated at the rear of an Inn in a garden setting in the village. Fountains Abbey 1¼ miles.
Facilities ✝ ⌷ ⛟ Γ ⊙ ✦ ⛿ 🔒 ☎ ⌷ ⊙ ✦ Ⅰ ♿
Nearby Facilities Γ ✓ U ♿ ♞
Nearest Town Harrogate/Ripon
Directions 1 mile west of A61 (Harrogate/Ripon road). Ripon 5 miles. Harrogate 7 miles.
⇥ Harrogate

HAWES
Bainbridge Ings Caravan & Camping Site, Hawes, North Yorkshire, DL8 3NU
Tel: 01969 667354
Email: janet@bainbridge-ings.co.uk
www.bainbridge-ings.co.uk
Pitches For Å ⊞ ⊟ **Total** 80
Acreage 5 **Open** April **to** October
Access Good **Site** Level
Nearest Bus Stop (Miles) ½
A quiet, clean, family run site with beautiful views and only ½ mile from Hawes. Motorcycles are accepted but not in groups of more than two.
Facilities ✝ ⌷ ⛟ Γ ⊙ ✦ ⛿ 🔒 ⊙ ✦ Ⅰ ♿
Nearby Facilities ✓
Directions Approaching Hawes from Bainbridge on the A684 turn left at the signpost marked Gayle and we are 300yds on at the top of the hill.
⇥ Garsdale

HAWES
Honeycott Caravan Park, Ingleton Road, Hawes, North Yorkshire, DL8 3LH
Tel: 01969 667310
Email: info@honeycott.co.uk
www.honeycott.co.uk
Pitches For Å ⊞ ⊟ **Total** 13
Acreage 1½ **Open** March **to** October

Access Good **Site** Sloping
Nearest Bus Stop (Miles) ¼
Peaceful Park with great views, just a 10 minute walk from Hawes. Ideal base from which to explore the Yorkshire Dales.
Facilities ✝ ⌷ ⛟ Γ ⊙ ✦ ⛿ ☎ Ⅰ 🔒 ⊙ ✦ Ⅰ ♿
Nearby Facilities ✓ ⚓ ✕ U ♿ ♞ ♞
Nearest Town Hawes
Directions 1½ a mile west of Hawes on the B6255 Ingleton road. 17 miles west of Leyburn and 20 miles east of the M6 junction 37.
⇥ Garsdale

HAWES
Shaw Ghyll, Simonstone, Hawes, North Yorkshire, DL8 3LY
Tel: 01969 667359
Email: rogerstott@aol.com
www.yorkshirenet.co.uk/accgde/ydcotts.htm
Pitches For Å ⊞ **Total** 30
Acreage 2½ **Open** 01-Apr **to** End Oct
Access Good **Site** Level
Quiet sheltered site, ideal for walks and families, pleasant aspect, river and lovely scenic walks.
Facilities ✝ ⛟ Γ ⊙ ✦ ☎ ♿ Ⅰ ♞
Nearby Facilities ✓ ✕ U ♿
Nearest Town Hawes
Directions 2 miles north of Hawes following the Muker road.

HELMSLEY
Foxholme Touring Caravan & Camping Park, Harome, Helmsley, North Yorkshire, YO62 5JG
Tel: 01439 771904
Pitches For Å ⊞ ⊟ **Total** 60
Acreage 6 **Open** Easter **to** October
Access Good **Site** Level
Nearest Bus Stop (Miles) 1
ADULTS ONLY PARK in an ideal touring area. Near National Park, Abbeys and Herriot country.
Facilities & ✝ ⌷ ⛟ Γ ⊙ ✦ ⛿ ☎ Ⅰ 🔒 ⊙ ✦ ⌷ ♿ ♞ ⚓
Nearby Facilities Γ U ♿
Nearest Town Helmsley
Directions A170 towards Scarborough, after ½ mile turn right to Harome, turn left at church, through village, follow caravan signs.
⇥ Malton

HELMSLEY
Golden Square Caravan Park, Oswaldkirk, Helmsley, York, North Yorkshire, YO62 5YQ
Tel: 01439 788269
Email:
reception@goldensquarecaravanpark.com
www.goldensquarecaravanpark.com

Pitches For Å ⊞ ⊟ **Total** 110
Acreage 10 **Open** 01-Mar **to** 31-Oct
Access Good **Site** Level
Nearest Bus Stop (Miles) Outside
Secluded site with magnificent views of North Yorkshire Moors. Ideal for visiting the city of York. Shop. Indoor/Outdoor play areas. Award winning facilities. Family/disabled bathroom. De-Lux all service pitches. Indoor/Outdoor swimming pool nearby. New development for holiday homes.
Facilities & ✝ ⌷ ⛟ Γ ⊙ ✦ ⛿ 🔒 ⊙ ✦ Ⅰ 🔒 ⊙ ✦ ⌷ ♿ ♞
Nearby Facilities Γ ✓ U ♿ ♞
Nearest Town Helmsley
Directions 2 miles south of Helmsley. First right off the B1257 to Ampleforth.
⇥ Thirsk/Malton

HELMSLEY
Wombleton Caravan Park, Moorfield Lane, Wombleton, Kirkbymoorside, North Yorkshire, YO62 7RY
Tel: 01751 431684
Email: info@wombletoncaravanpark.co.uk
www.wombletoncaravanpark.co.uk
Pitches For Å ⊞ ⊟ **Total** 118
Acreage 5 **Open** March **to** October
Access Good **Site** Level
Nearest Bus Stop (Miles) 1
Ideal for North Yorkshire Steam Railway, Duncombe Park, Nunnington Hall, Rievauly Abbey, Helmsley Castle and Flamingo Land.
Facilities ✝ ⌷ ⛟ Γ ⊙ ✦ ⛿ 🔒 ⊙ ✦ ⌷ ♿ Ⅰ
Nearby Facilities Γ ✓ U
Nearest Town Helmsley
Directions Leave Helmsley by A170 for 4 miles, turn right for Wombleton. Go through Wombleton and the Park is ½ a mile on the left.

HELMSLEY
Wrens of Ryedale, Gale Lane, Nawton, North Yorkshire, YO62 7SD
Tel: 01439 771260
Email: maria@wrensofryedale.co.uk
www.wrensofryedale.co.uk
Pitches For Å ⊞ ⊟ **Total** 45
Acreage 3½ **Open** April **to** October
Access Good **Site** Level
Nearest Bus Stop (Miles) ¼
Attractive, quiet, family run site. Situated on edge of Yorkshire Moors National Park. Very good centre for touring.
Facilities ✝ ⛟ Γ ✦ ⌷ ♿ ⛿ ☎ Ⅰ 🔒 ⊙ ✦ ♞
Nearby Facilities Γ ✓ U ♿ ♞
Nearest Town Scarborough/York

YORKSHIRE (NORTH)

Directions Leave Helmsley by the A170. 2½ miles to Beadlam, pass the church on left, in 20 yards turn right. Site is 500 yards down the lane.
⇌ Malton

INGLETON

The Trees Caravan Park, Westhouse, Ingleton, North Yorkshire, LA6 3NZ
Tel: 015242 41511
Email: stocks@greenwoodleghe.co.uk
www.caravancampingsites.co.uk/northyorkshire/thetrees
Pitches For 🚐 🚙 **Total** 29
Acreage 3 **Open** April **to** October
Access Good **Site** Level
Set in beautiful country scenery. Ideal for walking and touring. Mountains, caves and waterfalls nearby.
Facilities ⚹ ✚ ⬚ ⬚ ⬚ ⬚ ⬚ ⬚ ⬚ ⬚ ⬚
Nearby Facilities ⬚ ⬚ ⬚ ⬚ ⬚ ⬚
Nearest Town Ingleton
Directions From Ingleton, travel 1¼ miles along the A65 towards Kirkby Lonsdale (about ¼ mile past the A687 junction - Country Harvest). Turn left at signpost for Lower Westhouse, site is on the left in 50yds.
⇌ Bentham

KNARESBOROUGH

Allerton Park Caravan Park, Allerton Mauleverer, Nr Knaresborough, North Yorkshire, HG5 0SE
Tel: 01423 330569
Email: enquiries@yorkshireholidayparks.co.uk
www.yorkshireholidayparks.co.uk
Pitches For ⚑ 🚐 🚙 **Total** 20
Acreage 17 **Open** 01-Feb **to** 03-Jan
Access Good **Site** Level
Nearest Bus Stop (Miles) ½
Woodland park with plenty of wildlife and walks. David Bellamy Silver Award for Conservation.
Facilities ⬚ ⬚ ⬚ ⬚ ⬚ ⬚ ⬚ ⬚ ⬚ ⬚ ⬚ ⬚
Nearby Facilities ⬚ ⬚ ⬚
Nearest Town Knaresborough
Directions On the A59 York to Harrogate road, ½ mile east of Aim.
⇌ Harrogate

KNARESBOROUGH

Kingfisher Caravan & Camping Park, Low Moor Lane, Farnham, Knaresborough, North Yorkshire, HG5 9JB
Tel: 01423 869411
Pitches For ⚑ 🚐 🚙 **Total** 50
Acreage 10 **Open** March **to** October
Access Good **Site** Level
Nearest Bus Stop (Miles) Outside
Ideal touring base for the Dales, convenient for Harrogate and York. Adjacent to a golf range.
Facilities ⬚ ⬚ ⬚ ⬚ ⬚ ⬚ ⬚ ⬚
Nearby Facilities ⬚ ⬚ ⬚ ⬚ ⬚ ⬚
Nearest Town Knaresborough
Directions From Knaresborough take the A6055. In 1¼ miles turn left to Farnham Village, in Farnham turn left, park is approx. 1 mile on the left.
⇌ Knaresborough

KNARESBOROUGH

Knaresborough Caravan Club Site, New Road, Scotton, Knaresborough, North Yorkshire, HG5 9HH
Tel: 01423 860196
www.caravanclub.co.uk
Pitches For ⚑ 🚐 🚙 **Total** 74
Acreage 8 **Open** March **to** Jan
Access Good **Site** Lev/Slope
Nearest Bus Stop (Miles) ¼
Surrounded by mature trees and hedges. Riverside walks, tennis, pitch 'n' putt and boating in the local area. Close to Ripley Castle, Old Court House Museum and Old Mother Shiptons Cave. Non members welcome. Booking essential.
Facilities ⬚ ⬚ ⬚ ⬚ ⬚ ⬚ ⬚ ⬚ ⬚ ⬚ ⬚ ⬚
Nearby Facilities ⬚ ⬚ ⬚
Nearest Town Knaresborough
Directions Leave A1 at junc 47 and take A59 sp Knaresborough. At roundabout turn right onto the A59 and continue through Knaresborough, at junction with traffic lights turn left and continue on A59. At next lights turn right onto B6165, at petrol station turn right
⇌ Knaresborough

KNARESBOROUGH

Spen House Caravan Site, Spen House, Minskip, York, North Yorkshire, YO51 9JF
Tel: 01423 322542
Email: sam@spenhouse.freeserve.co.uk
www.spenhouse.co.uk
Pitches For ⚑ 🚐 🚙
Acreage 3½ **Open** All Year
Access Good **Site** Level
Nearest Bus Stop (Miles) Outside
Family and dog friendly site with pitches for 5 Vans and unlimited tents. Ideal base for walking, biking, sightseeing or simply relaxing!
Facilities ⬚ ⬚ ⬚ ⬚ ⬚ ⬚ ⬚ ⬚ ⬚ ⬚ ⬚
Nearby Facilities ⬚ ⬚ ⬚ ⬚ ⬚ ⬚ ⬚ ⬚
Nearest Town Boroughbridge
Directions Leave the A1 Motorway at junction 48 and follow signs for Minskip on the A6055 for ½ a mile. Site is on the right hand side of the village 200 meters.
⇌ Knaresborough

LEYBURN

Akebar Park, Leyburn, North Yorkshire, DL8 5LY
Tel: 01677 450201
Email: info@akebarpark.com
www.akebarpark.com
Pitches For ⚑ 🚐 🚙 **Total** 200
Acreage 40 **Open** March **to** Dec
Access Good **Site** Level
Nearest Bus Stop (Miles) Entrance
Situated on a family farm in a sheltered valley in Lower Wensleydale, alongside streams and ponds at the entrance to the Yorkshire Dales National Park. Private 18 hole golf course.
Facilities ⬚ ⬚ ⬚ ⬚ ⬚ ⬚ ⬚ ⬚ ⬚ ⬚
Nearby Facilities ⬚ ⬚ ⬚
Nearest Town Leyburn

Directions From the A1 at Leeming Bar take the A684 to Bedale and Leyburn. Park entrance is 7 miles.
⇌ Northallerton

LEYBURN

Constable Burton Hall Caravan Park, Constable Burton, Leyburn, North Yorkshire, DL8 5LJ
Tel: 01677 450428
Email: caravanpark@constableburton.com
www.cbcaravanpark.co.uk
Pitches For 🚐 🚙 **Total** 120
Acreage 10 **Open** Mid March **to** October
Access Good **Site** Lev/Slope
Nearest Bus Stop (Miles) Entrance
Ideal for walking and touring. Many castles, gardens and historic houses nearby. No childrens play area and strictly no games.
Facilities ⬚ ⬚ ⬚ ⬚ ⬚ ⬚ ⬚ ⬚ ⬚ ⬚
Nearby Facilities ⬚ ⬚
Nearest Town Leyburn
Directions On the A684 midway between Bedale and Leyburn.
⇌ Northallerton

LEYBURN

Lower Wensleydale Caravan Club Site, Harmby, Leyburn, North Yorkshire, DL8 5NU
Tel: 01969 623366
www.caravanclub.co.uk
Pitches For ⚑ 🚐 🚙 **Total** 92
Acreage 10 **Open** March **to** Nov
Access Good **Site** Level
Situated in the hollow of a disused quarry, now overrun with wild flowers and mosses. Ducks and rabbits roam the site freely. Ideal for walking. Close to Constable Burton Gardens, Bolton Castle and Middleham Castle. Non members welcome. Booking essential.
Facilities ⬚ ⬚ ⬚ ⬚ ⬚ ⬚ ⬚ ⬚ ⬚
Nearby Facilities ⬚
Nearest Town Leyburn
Directions From the A684, in Harmby turn off by the Pheasant Inn, cross the railway bridge and immediately turn left at brown caravan sign. Follow signs to the entrance.
⇌ Leyburn

MASHAM

Old Station Caravan & Camping Park, Old Station, Low Burton, Masham, North Yorkshire, HG4 4DF
Tel: 01765 689569
Email: oldstation@tiscali.co.uk
www.oldstation-masham.co.uk
Pitches For ⚑ 🚐 🚙 **Total** 50
Acreage 3 **Open** March **to** Nov
Access Good **Site** Level
Nearest Bus Stop (Miles) Outside
Picturesque and peaceful countryside site just outside the town, with Dales scenery. Bus route to the Dales. Convenient for local events and attractions.
Facilities ⬚ ⬚ ⬚ ⬚ ⬚ ⬚ ⬚ ⬚ ⬚ ⬚ ⬚ ⬚
⬚ ⬚ ⬚ ⬚ ⬚ ⬚ ⬚ ⬚
Nearby Facilities ⬚ ⬚ ⬚ ⬚
Nearest Town Masham

Directions From Ripon take the A6108 north west for 8 miles. Or from Bedale take the B6268 south west for 4 miles. Or from Leyburn take the A6108 south for 8 miles.
⇷ Northallerton

MUKER
Usha Gap Caravan & Camp Site, Usha Gap, Muker, Richmond, North Yorkshire, DL11 6DW
Tel: 01748 886214
Email: ushagap@btinternet.com
www.ushagap.btinternet.co.uk
Pitches For Å ⌗ ⇌ **Total** 24
Acreage 1 **Open** All Year
Access Good **Site** Level
Nearest Bus Stop (Miles) Outside
Alongside a small river. Shops and a pub ¼ mile. Ideal touring and good walking.
Facilities ⌗ ⌾ ⌶ ⌿ ⊙ ⌻ ⌺ ⌹
Nearby Facilities ⌲
Nearest Town Hawes
⇷ Darlington

NORTHALLERTON
Cote Ghyll Caravan & Camping Park, Osmotherley, Northallerton, North Yorkshire, DL6 3AH
Tel: 01609 883425
Email: hills@coteghyll.com
www.coteghyll.com
Pitches For Å ⌗ ⇌ ⇌ **Total** 77
Acreage 7 **Open** 01-Mar **to** 31-Oct
Access Good **Site** Level
Nearest Bus Stop (Miles) ¼
Beautiful site in a peaceful valley location within the North York Moors National Park. 5 Star facilities. Heated shower blocks with bathroom. New play area. Stream. Excellent walking and cycling area. Village pubs and shops just a 10 minute walk. Rose Award holiday caravans for hire and sale.
Facilities ⌶ ⌕ ⌀ ⌾ ⌶ ⌿ ⊙ ⌻ ⌺ ⌹ ⌗
⌇ ⌇ ⊙ ⌺ ⌀ ⌶ ⌱ ⌲ ⌹ ⌣ ⌢
Nearby Facilities ⌳ ⌿ ⌲ ⌲
Nearest Town Northallerton
Directions Exit the A19 dual carriageway at the A684 Northallerton junction. Follow signs into Osmotherley Village. At the T-junction in the centre of the village turn left. On leaving the village the site is ¼ mile on the right.
⇷ Northallerton/Thirsk

PATELEY BRIDGE
Manor House Farm Caravan Site, Manor House Farm, Summerbridge, Harrogate, North Yorkshire, HG3 4JS
Tel: 01423 780322
Pitches For Å ⌗ ⇌
Open March **to** October
Access Good **Site** Terraced
Close to the River Nidd and the Nidderdale Way. Ideal for walking. Sorry, No Dogs.
Facilities ⌶ ⌾ ⌶ ⌿ ⊙ ⌻ ⌺ ⌹ ⌹
⌇ ⌇ ⌱ ⌣ ⌢ ⌣
Nearby Facilities ⌳ ⌿ ⌲ ⊙ ⌲ ⌲
Nearest Town Harrogate/Pateley Bridge
Directions Situated on the B6165 between Harrogate and Pateley Bridge.
⇷ Harrogate

PATELEY BRIDGE
Riverside Caravan Park, Low Wath Road, Pateley Bridge, Harrogate, North Yorkshire, HG3 5HL
Tel: 01423 711383
Email: riversidecp@btinternet.com
Pitches For Å ⌗ ⇌ **Total** 50
Open April **to** October
Access Good **Site** Level
Nearest Bus Stop (Miles) ¼
Situated amidst beautiful scenery by the River Nidd, yet only a 5 minute walk from Pateley Bridge. Fishing permits are available from reception. 5 minute walk from an indoor swimming pool.
Facilities ⌶ ⌾ ⌶ ⌿ ⊙ ⌻ ⌺ ⌹ ⌹
⊙ ⌹ ⌱ ⌿
Nearby Facilities ⌳ ⌿ ⌲ ⊙ ⌲ ⌲
Nearest Town Pateley Bridge
Directions From Harrogate take the B6165 into Pateley Bridge. Go down the main street and over the bridge (River Nidd), turn right at the petrol station into Low Wath Road and the entrance is on the right just past the first bungalow.
⇷ Harrogate

PATELEY BRIDGE
Studfold Farm Caravan & Camping Park, Studfold Farm, Lofthouse, Harrogate, North Yorkshire, HG3 5SG
Tel: 01423 755210
Email: ianwalker@studfold.fsnet.co.uk
www.studfoldfarm.co.uk
Pitches For Å ⌗ ⇌ **Total** 41
Acreage 2 **Open** April **to** Oct
Access Good **Site** Level
Nearest Bus Stop (Miles) ½
Family run Park on a Dales farm at the head of Nidderdale. Area of outstanding natural beauty. Recently opened award winning Explore, Discover & Learn Trail.
Facilities ⌶ ⌶ ⌾ ⌶ ⌿ ⌺ ⌹
⌇ ⌇ ⊙ ⌺ ⌀ ⌶ ⌣
Nearby Facilities ⌳ ⌿ ⊙ ⌲ ⌲
Nearest Town Harrogate
Directions 7 miles north of Pateley Bridge off the B6265 Ripon to Skipton road.
⇷ Harrogate

PICKERING
Black Bull Caravan Park, Malton Road, Pickering, North Yorkshire, YO18 8EA
Tel: 01751 472528
Email:
enquiries@blackbullcaravanpark.com
www.blackbullcaravanpark.com
Pitches For Å ⌗ ⇌ ⇌ **Total** 72
Acreage 4 **Open** March **to** October
Access Good **Site** Level
Nearest Bus Stop (Miles) Entrance
Central location for many attractions and the gateway to the North Yorks Moors and steam railway, Eden Camp, Flamingoland and much more. Holiday Caravans also available for hire.
Facilities ⌶ ⌾ ⌶ ⌿ ⊙ ⌻ ⌺ ⌹ ⌹
⌇ ⌇ ⊙ ⌺ ⌿ ⌀ ⌧ ⌶ ⊙ ⌣ ⌣
Nearby Facilities ⌳ ⌿
Nearest Town Pickering
Directions 1 mile south of Pickering on the A169 Malton road.
⇷ Malton

PICKERING
Overbrook Caravan Park, Maltongate, Thornton-le-Dale, Nr Pickering, North Yorkshire, YO18 7SE
Tel: 01751 474417
Email:
enquiry@overbrookcaravanpark.co.uk
www.overbrookcaravanpark.co.uk
Pitches For ⌗ ⇌ **Total** 50
Acreage 3½ **Open** March **to** 07-Jan
Access Good **Site** Sloping
Nearest Bus Stop (Miles) ½
ADULTS ONLY park in one of North Yorkshires prettiest villages. Peaceful, picturesque location.
Facilities ⌶ ⌾ ⌶ ⌿ ⊙ ⌻ ⌺ ⌹ ⌹ ⌧ ⌣ ⌣ ⌣ ⌣
Nearby Facilities ⌳ ⌿ ⊙
Nearest Town Pickering
Directions From the A1 follow the A64 onto the A169, then the A170 from Pickering.
⇷ Malton

PICKERING
Rosedale Caravan Park, Rosedale Abbey, Pickering, North Yorkshire, YO18 8SA
Tel: 01751 417272
Email: info@flowerofmay.com
www.flowerofmay.com
Pitches For Å ⌗ ⇌
Open Easter **to** End October
Access Good **Site** Level
Nearest Bus Stop (Miles) ¼
Idyllic retreat. Ideal for walking and hiking through the beautiful North Yorkshire Moors.
Facilities ⌶ ⌶ ⌾ ⌶ ⌿ ⊙ ⌻ ⌺ ⌹ ⌹
⌇ ⌇ ⊙ ⌺ ⌀ ⌧ ⌶ ⊙ ⌣
Nearby Facilities ⌳ ⌿ ⊙
Nearest Town Pickering
Directions Turn off the A170 towards Rosedale.
⇷ Malton

PICKERING
Vale of Pickering Caravan Park, Carr House Farm, Allerston, Pickering, North Yorkshire, YO18 7PQ
Tel: 01723 859280
Email: tony@valeofpickering.co.uk
www.valeofpickering.co.uk
Pitches For Å ⌗ ⇌ **Total** 120
Acreage 8 **Open** 05-Mar **to** 03-Jan
Access Good **Site** Level
Nearest Bus Stop (Miles) 1
High standard of service and superb facilities. Peaceful play area and games area. ETB 5 Star Graded.
Facilities ⌶ ⌶ ⌾ ⌶ ⌿ ⊙ ⌻ ⌺ ⌹ ⌹
⌇ ⌇ ⊙ ⌺ ⌀ ⌧ ⌶ ⌶ ⊙ ⌣ ⌣
Nearby Facilities ⌳ ⌿ ⊙
Nearest Town Scarborough
Directions From Pickering take the A170 to Allerston, turn right opposite Cayley Arms Hotel, due south 1¼ miles.
⇷ Malton

PICKERING
Wayside Caravan & Camping Park, Wrelton, Pickering, North Yorkshire, YO18 8PG
Tel: 01751 472608
Email: wrelton@waysideholidaypark.co.uk
www.waysideparks.co.uk
Pitches For ⌗ ⇌ **Total** 45

YORKSHIRE (NORTH)

Acreage 5 **Open** Easter **to** Early Oct
Access Good
Nearest Bus Stop (Miles) ¼
Ideal for touring the North York Moors. Walks nearby and historic steam railway.
Facilities ⚷ ♂ 🅗 🕮 ⌐ 🏳 ⊙ 🔥 🕳 🖰 📶
🖭 🔊🏊🛁🔲🖃 ⚡
Nearby Facilities ⌐ ✈ ∪ ♉
Nearest Town Pickering
Directions 2½ miles west of Pickering off the A170 at Welton, turn right off the by-pass.
⚞ Malton

RICHMOND

Hargill House Caravan Club Site, Gilling West, Richmond, North Yorkshire, DL10 5LJ
Tel: 01748 822734
www.caravanclub.co.uk
Pitches For 🚐 🚙 **Total** 66
Acreage 4½ **Open** March **to** Nov
Access Good **Site** Lev/Slope
Nearest Bus Stop (Miles) Outside
Situated in Herriot country with wonderful views of the Yorkshire Dales National Park. Non members welcome. Booking essential.
Facilities ⚷ ♂ 🅗 🕮 ⌐ 🔥 🛁 ⚡
🖭 🔊🛁🖃 📶
Nearby Facilities ⌐ ✈
Nearest Town Richmond
Directions Leave the A1 at Scotch Corner and take the A66 signposted Penrith. At the crossroads turn left signposted Gilling West, site is 100 yards on the left.
⚞ Richmond

RICHMOND

Orchard Caravan Park, Reeth, Richmond, North Yorkshire, DL11 6TT
Tel: 01748 884475
Email: peter.daly7@btinternet.com
Pitches For 🏕 🚐 🚙 **Total** 56
Acreage 3½ **Open** 01-Apr **to** 31-Oct
Access Good **Site** Level
Nearest Bus Stop (Miles) ½
All grassed area in an apple orchard, beside the River Swale. Sports area adjacent. Ideal for walkers.
Facilities ♂ 🅗 ⌐ 🏳 ⊙ 🔥🛁🖃 🕳
Nearby Facilities ⌐ ✈ ∪ ♉
Nearest Town Richmond
Directions Approx. 11½ miles from Richmond.
⚞ Darlington

RICHMOND

Scotch Corner Caravan Park, Scotch Corner, Richmond, North Yorkshire, DL10 6NS
Tel: 01748 822530
Email: marshallleisure@aol.com
www.scotchcornercaravanpark.co.uk

Pitches For 🏕 🚐 🚙 **Total** 96
Acreage 10 **Open** Easter **to** October
Access Good **Site** Level
Nearest Bus Stop (Miles) Outside
Cafe/Restaurant adjacent. Ideal for touring.
Facilities ⚷ ♂ 🅗 🕮 ⌐ 🏳 ⊙ 🔥 🛁 🖰 📶
🔊🛁 🖃🔲 🕳 ⚒
Nearby Facilities ⌐ ✈ ∪ ♉
Nearest Town Richmond
Directions Leave the A1 at Scotch Corner and take the A6108 signposted Richmond. Continue for approx. 250 yards then cross the central reservation and return for 200 yards, Park entrance is on the left.
⚞ Darlington

RICHMOND

Tavern House Caravan Park, Newsham, Nr Richmond, North Yorkshire, DL11 7RA
Tel: 01833 621223
Email:
kathy@tavernhouse.orangehome.co.uk
Pitches For 🏕 🚐 🚙 **Total** 6
Acreage 1½ **Open** March **to** October
Access Good **Site** Lev/Slope
Nearest Bus Stop (Miles) Outside
ADULTS ONLY PARK, ideal for walking, fishing and visiting historic towns.
Facilities ♂ 🅗 🕮 ⌐ ⊙ 🔥 🛁🏊🛁🖃 🕳
Nearby Facilities ⌐ ✈ ⚒ ∪
Nearest Town Barnard Castle/Richmond
Directions 7 miles west from Scotch Corner on the A66 turn left, 1 mile into the middle of the village, on the right.
⚞ Darlington

RIPON

River Laver Holiday Park, Studley Road, Ripon, North Yorkshire, HG4 2QR
Tel: 01765 690508
Email: riverlaver@lineone.net
www.riverlaver.co.uk
Pitches For 🚐 🚙 **Total** 8
Acreage 5 **Open** 01-Mar **to** End Nov
Access Good **Site** Level
Ideal base for the Yorkshire Moors and Dales. Easy access to Fountains Abbey and road network.
Facilities ⚷ ♂ 🅗 🕮 ⌐ 🏳 ⊙ 🔥 🛁 🖰 📶
🔊🛁🖃 ✈ 📶
Nearby Facilities ⌐ ✈
Nearest Town Ripon
Directions ½ mile from Ripon on the B6265 towards Fountains Abbey.
⚞ Harrogate

RIPON

Riverside Meadows Country Caravan Park, Ure Bank Top (Dept No.1), Ripon, North Yorkshire, HG4 1JD
Tel: 01765 602964
Email: info@flowerofmay.com
www.flowerofmay.com

Pitches For 🏕 🚐 🚙 **Total** 200
Acreage 28 **Open** March **to** October
Access Good **Site** Lev/Slope
Nearest Bus Stop (Miles) ½
Countryside park alongside a river. Ideal for touring the Yorkshire Dales. Bar complex for all the family. Pets are welcome by arrangement.
Facilities ♂ 🅗 🕮 ⌐ ⊙ 🔥 🛁 🖰 📶
🔊 🖭 🔊🛁▽🛁🍴🏊 🕳 📶 ⚒
Nearby Facilities ⌐ ✈ ⚓ ∪
Nearest Town Ripon
Directions Leave the A1 onto the A61 north of Ripon town centre, ½ mile.
⚞ Harrogate

RIPON

Sleningford Watermill, North Stainley, Ripon, North Yorkshire, HG4 3HQ
Tel: 01765 635201
www.sleningfordwatermill.co.uk
Pitches For 🏕 🚐 🚙 **Total** 90
Acreage 14 **Open** April **to** October
Access Good **Site** Level
Nearest Bus Stop (Miles) Outside
Alongside a river for fly fishing. Ideally situated for the Yorkshire Dales and Moors. 2 miles from Lightwater Valley Theme Park.
Facilities ⚷ ♂ 🅗 🕮 ⌐ ⊙ 🔥 🛁 🖰 📶
🔊 🖭 🔊🛁🖃 ✈ 🕳
Nearby Facilities ⌐ ✈ ∪ ♉ ⚒
Nearest Town Ripon
Directions From Ripon take the A6108 north for 5 miles, go through North Stainley and the Park is on the right.
⚞ Thirsk

SCARBOROUGH

Blue Dolphin Holiday Centre, Gristhorpe Bay, Filey, North Yorkshire, YO14 9PU
Tel: 01723 515155
Email: bluedolphin@haven.com
www.haventouring.com/tobluedolphin
Pitches For 🏕 🚐 🚙 **Total** 343
Acreage 5 **Open** 23-Mar **to** 25-Oct
Access Good **Site** Lev/Slope
Nearest Bus Stop (Miles) Outside
A large and lively Five Star Holiday Park with many superb facilities and activities from crazy golf to climbing walls! There's something for the whole family to enjoy.
Facilities ⚷ ♂ 🅗 🕮 ⌐ 🏳 ⊙ 🔥 🛁 🖰 📶
🔊 🖭 🔊🛁✗▽🛁🏊 ⚒ 🎿 🍴 🖃🔲🖃 ✈ 🕳
📶
Nearby Facilities ⌐ ✈ ⚓ ⚒ ∪ ⚓ ♉
Nearest Town Scarborough
Directions 2½ miles north of Filey off the A165 coast road.
⚞ Filey

FLOWER OF MAY

Magical Family Holidays

Discover the Beauty Surrounding Yorkshires Finest Holiday Parks

A choice of Holiday Parks situated at the Coast, on the Moors and in the Countryside of North Yorkshire.

Our well maintained Parks are superbly located within easy reach of North Yorkshires stunning landscapes and well known attractions.

AA ▶▶▶▶▶
01723 584311

AA ▶▶▶▶
01765 602964

AA ▶▶▶▶
01751 417272

AA ▶▶▶▶
01347 810829

Welcome
to Yorkshire
yorkshire.com

Relax, Explore and Enjoy!

www.flowerofmay.com

SCARBOROUGH

Camping & Caravanning Club Site, Field Lane, Burniston Road, Scarborough, North Yorkshire, YO13 0DA
Tel: 01723 366212
www.campingandcaravanningclub.co.uk/scarborough
Pitches For ▲ ⊕ ⊟ **Total** 300
Acreage 20 **Open** 29-Mar **to** 05-Nov
Nearest Bus Stop (Miles) Outside
Near the beach and the North Yorks Moors National Park. Non members welcome. You can also call us on 0845 130 7633.
Facilities ⚸ ♪ 🚻 📷 ⓟ ⌁ ☉ ◢ 🛒 🍴 ⓞ ☂ ✦ ⌨ ⊡ ☂
Nearby Facilities ┣ ✦ ♪ ᛝ
Directions Located 1 mile north of Scarborough on the west side of the A165.
⇥ Scarborough

SCARBOROUGH

Cayton Village Caravan Park, Mill Lane, Cayton Bay, Scarborough, North Yorkshire, YO11 3NN
Tel: 01723 583171
Email: info@caytontouring.co.uk
www.caytontouring.co.uk
Pitches For ▲ ⊕ ⊟ **Total** 310
Acreage 21 **Open** 01-Mar **to** 31-Oct
Access Good **Site** Level
Nearest Bus Stop (Miles) Outside
Luxurious facilities, playground, shop, dog walk and bus service from park entrance. Seasonal pitches, winter storage and caravan sales. Grass, hard standing and super sites. Low season supersaver & OAP discounts. Scarborough 3 miles, Filey 4 miles, Beach ½ mile. Adjoining village with pubs, chip shop and PO.
Facilities ⚸ ♪ 🚻 📷 ⓟ ⌁ ☉ ◢ 🛒 ⓞ ☂
🍴 ⓞ ☂ ⊟ 🔥 ✦ ⌨ ⊡ ☂ ☂
Nearby Facilities ┣ ✦ ♪ ᛝ ⋃ ♪ ♪ ✗
Nearest Town Scarborough
Directions On the A165, 3 miles south of Scarborough turn inland at Cayton Bay roundabout. The park is ½ a mile on the right hand side. From the A64 take the B1261 sp Filey. At Cayton take the second left at the Blacksmiths Arms on to Mill Lane, the park is on the left hand side.
⇥ Seamer

SCARBOROUGH

Flower of May Holiday Park, Lebberston Cliff, Scarborough, North Yorkshire, YO11 3NU
Tel: 01723 584311
Email: info@flowerofmay.com
www.flowerofmay.com
Pitches For ▲ ⊕ ⊟ **Total** 300
Acreage 13 **Open** Easter **to** October
Access Good **Site** Level
Nearest Bus Stop (Miles) Outside
Family run park with superb facilities. Exciting playground, luxury leisure centre with indoor pool and golf. Family bars. Supermarket. Serviced pitches now available with metered electric. Pets are welcome by arrangement.
Facilities ⚸ ⚸ ♪ 🚻 📷 ⓟ ⌁ ☉ ◢ 🛒
ⓞ ☂ ⓢ ⓞ ☂ 🍴 🔥 ᛝ ⌨ ⊡ ☂ ✦
☂
Nearby Facilities ┣ ✦ ♪ ᛝ ⋃ ♪ ♪
Nearest Town Scarborough
Directions 3 miles south of Scarborough off A165 signposted at roundabout.
⇥ Scarborough

SCARBOROUGH

Jasmine Park, Cross Lane, Snainton, Scarborough, North Yorkshire, YO13 9BE
Tel: 01723 859240
Email: enquiries@jasminepark.co.uk
www.jasminepark.co.uk
Pitches For ▲ ⊕ ⊟ **Total** 100
Acreage 5 **Open** March **to** October
Access Good **Site** Level
Nearest Bus Stop (Miles) ½
Picturesque, quiet park in an ideal location for exploring Scarborough, Pickering and the North Yorks Moors.
Facilities ⚸ ⚸ ♪ 🚻 📷 ⓟ ⌁ ☉ ◢ 🛒
ⓞ ☂ ⓢ ⓞ ☂ ⓜ ⌨ ⊡ ☂ ✦ ☂
Nearby Facilities ┣ ✦ ᛝ ⋃ ♪
Nearest Town Scarborough
Directions Turn off the A169 at the traffic lights, signposted.
⇥ Scarborough

SCARBOROUGH

Lebberston Touring Park, Filey Road, Lebberston, Scarborough, North Yorkshire, YO11 3PE
Tel: 01723 585723
Email: info@lebberstontouring.co.uk

www.lebberstontouring.co.uk
Pitches For ⊕ ⊟ **Total** 125
Acreage 7½ **Open** March **to** October
Access Good **Site** Lev/Slope
Quiet, country park. Well spaced pitches with extensive views over Vale of Pickering and the Yorkshire Wolds. All pets on a lead. Dog area. Trailer tents accepted. Visit Britain 5 Stars and AA 4 Pennants.
Facilities ⚸ ♪ 🚻 📷 ⓟ ⌁ ☉ ◢ 🛒 ⓞ ☂
⊠ ⓞ ☂ 🔥 ⌨ ⊡ ☂ ✦ ☂
Nearby Facilities ┣ ✦ ♪ ᛝ ⋃ ♪
Nearest Town Scarborough/Filey
Directions From A64 or A165 take B1261 to Lebberston and follow signs.
⇥ Scarborough/Filey

SCARBOROUGH

Scalby Close Park, Burniston Road, Scarborough, North Yorkshire, YO13 0DA
Tel: 01723 365908
Email: info@scalbyclosepark.co.uk
www.scalbyclosepark.co.uk
Pitches For ▲ ⊕ ⊟ **Total** 42
Acreage 3 **Open** March **to** October
Access Good **Site** Level
Nearest Bus Stop (Miles) ½
Sheltered, tree lined, level pitches. Ideal for touring North Yorkshire Moors and the coast. Near to Scarborough.
Facilities ⚸ ♪ 🚻 📷 ⓟ ⌁ ☉ ◢ 🛒 ☂
ⓞ ⌨ ⊡ ☂ ᛝ
Nearby Facilities ┣ ✦ ᛝ ⋃ ♪ ♪
Nearest Town Scarborough
Directions 2 miles north of Scarboroughs North Bay, signed 400 yards.
⇥ Scarborough

SCARBOROUGH

St Helens Caravan & Camping, Wykeham, Scarborough, North Yorkshire, YO13 9QD
Tel: 01723 862771
Email: caravans@wykeham.co.uk
www.sthelenscaravanpark.co.uk
Pitches For ▲ ⊕ ⊟ **Total** 250
Acreage 36 **Open** 15-Feb **to** 15-Jan
Access Good **Site** Level
Nearest Bus Stop (Miles) Outside
Family park near the North Yorkshire Moors and beaches. Ideal base for touring. AA 5 Pennants.

VISIT **www.cades.co.uk** TO SEE OUR MONTHLY COMPETITION

St Helens in the Park

ST. HELENS TOURING CARAVAN & CAMPING PARK
WYKEHAM • SCARBOROUGH • YO13 9QD
TEL/FAX: (01723) 862771

St. Helens nestles on the edge of the beautiful North Yorkshire Moors National Park, just 6 miles from Scarborough. This 36 acre site is divided into terraces with tree screening to create more intimate areas - a feature which enables different areas to vary in character and outlook. With first class facilities, St. Helens is ideal for young families. For dog owners there is a 3 acre dog run exclusively for pets. For those without children, St. Helens offers an 'Adult Zone' which provides peace and quiet. Fishing and watersports at nearby Wykeham Lakes, Cycle Route through Wykeham Estate and a short pathway leads you to a country pub and restaurant. Seasonal Pitches. Storage Welcomed.

www.sthelens caravanpark.co.uk

OPEN 11 MONTHS OF THE YEAR.

Facilities ♿ ✚ 🗑 🚺 ⛽ ℯ 🔌 ⊙ ⌂ ▰ 🔲 🛒 🕎 🏐 🎱 🎣 ✕ 🛝 ♨ 🐕 🌳
Nearby Facilities ✝ ✓ ⚓ ⚘ ∪
Nearest Town Scarborough
Directions 5 miles west of Scarborough on the A170, 12 miles east of Pickering.
🚂 Scarborough

SELBY

Oakmere Caravan Park, Hill Farm, Skipwith, Selby, North Yorkshire, YO8 5SN
Tel: 01757 288910
Email: oakmerecaravan@aol.com
www.oakmerecaravan.webeden.co.uk
Pitches For 🚐 🚎 **Total** 30
Acreage 5 **Open** March **to** Nov
Access Good **Site** Level
Nearest Bus Stop (Miles) Entrance
On site coarse fishery. Close to historic York, the market town of Selby and a designer outlet. 45 minutes form the East coast.
Facilities ♿ ✚ 🚺 ⛽ ℯ ⊙ 🔌 ▰ 🔲 🛒 🕎 ⊙ ▰ 🔲 🛒
Nearby Facilities ✝ ✓ ⚓ ∪ 🎠 🐎
Nearest Town York
Directions From York take the A19 signposted Selby. At Escrick turn left signposted Skipwith, Oakmere is 3 miles on the left.
🚂 York

SETTLE

Langcliffe Park, Settle, North Yorkshire, BD24 9LX
Tel: 01729 822387
Email: info@langcliffe.com
www.langcliffe.com
Pitches For ⚑ 🚐 🚎 **Total** 75
Acreage 13 **Open** 01-Mar **to** 15-Jan
Access Good **Site** Level
Nearest Bus Stop (Miles) ¼
Peaceful site in a beautiful area, surrounded by the Yorkshire Dales. Located 1 mile from Settle to Carlisle railway.
Facilities ♿ ✚ ✝ 🗑 🚺 ⛽ ℯ ⊙ ▰ 🔲 🛒 🕎 ⊙ ▰ 🍴 ⛺ ♨ 🛜
Nearby Facilities ✝ ✓ ∪ 🎠 🐎
Nearest Town Settle
Directions From the A65 south, take the B6479 into Settle. Go through Market Square, under the viaduct, then turn first right to Horton in Ribblesdale, Park is on the left.
🚂 Settle

SKIPTON

Eshton Road Caravan Site, Eshton Road, Gargrave, Nr Skipton, North Yorkshire, BD23 3PN
Tel: 01756 749229
Pitches For ⚑ 🚐 🚎
Acreage 2 **Open** All Year
Access Good **Site** Level
Nearest Bus Stop (Miles) Outside

Alongside the Leeds Liverpool Canal, on the edge of the Yorkshire Dales National Park.
Facilities ✚ 🗑 🚺 ⛽ ℯ ⊙ 🔌 ⛺ 🕎 🐕 ✓
Nearby Facilities ✝ ✓ ∪
Directions 4 miles from Skipton on the A65.
🚂 Gargrave

SLINGSBY

Camping & Caravanning Club Site, Railway Street, Slingsby, North Yorkshire, YO62 4AN
Tel: 01653 628335
www.campingandcaravanningclub.co.uk/slingsby
Pitches For ⚑ 🚐 🚎 **Total** 60
Acreage 3 **Open** 29-Mar **to** 05-Nov
Access Good **Site** Level
Nearest Bus Stop (Miles) ½
An ideal base to discover the North Yorkshire Moors. York with all its attractions is just a short drive away. BTB 5 Star Graded and AA 3 Pennants. Non members welcome. You can also call us on 0845 130 7633.
Facilities ♿ ✚ 🗑 🚺 ⛽ ℯ ⊙ 🔌 ▰ 🔲 🛒 🕎 ⊙ ▰ 🍴 ⛺ ♨ 🐕
Nearby Facilities ✝ ✓ ∪
Directions From the A64 turn left signposted Castle Howard, drive through Castle Howard Estate until you reach the Malton to Helmsly road. Go straight into Slingsby Village, go round the bend onto Railway Street and continue through the village ¼ mile to the site entrance.
🚂 Malton

SLINGSBY

Robin Hood Caravan Park, Slingsby, York, North Yorkshire, YO62 4AP
Tel: 01653 628391
Email: info@robinhoodcaravanpark.co.uk
www.robinhoodcaravanpark.co.uk
Pitches For ⚑ 🚐 🚎 **Total** 48
Acreage 4 **Open** March **to** October
Access Good **Site** Level
Nearest Bus Stop (Miles) ¼
In the heart of picturesque Ryedale, this privately owned park offers peace and tranquillity. An ideal centre for York, the Moors, Heartbeat country and the seaside resorts of Scarborough, Whitby and Filey.
Facilities ♿ ✚ ✝ 🗑 🚺 ⛽ ℯ ⊙ 🔌 ▰ 🔲 🛒 🕎 🏐 🎱 ⊙ ▰ ♨ 🐕 🔲 🛒 🛜
Nearby Facilities ✝ ✓ ∪ 🐎
Nearest Town Malton
Directions Direct access from the B1257 Malton to Helmsley road.
🚂 Malton

SNEATON

Low Moor Caravan Club Site, Sneaton, Whitby, North Yorkshire, YO22 5JE
Tel: 01947 810505
www.caravanclub.co.uk
Pitches For 🚐 🚎 **Total** 92
Acreage 12 **Open** March **to** Nov
Access Good **Site** Level
Tranquil site in the North Yorks Moors National Park (Heartbeat country). 5 miles from a sandy beach. Ideal for walkers. Boules pitch and mini golf on site. Own sanitation required. Non members welcome. Booking essential.
Facilities ✚ 🗑 🚺 ℯ ⊙ 🏐 🎱 🐕 🔌 🔲 ℯ
Nearby Facilities ✓
Directions From the A171 take the B1416 signposted Ruswarp, after 3¾ miles on a sharp left hand bend continue through red gates signposted Maybeck (care required), site is ½ mile on the right.
🚂 Whitby

TADCASTER

Whitecote Caravan Park, Ryther Road, Ulleskelf, Nr Tadcaster, North Yorks., LS24 9DY
Tel: 01937 835231
www.whitecotecaravanpark.co.uk
Pitches For ⚑ 🚐 🚎
Open 01-Mar **to** 31-Jan
Access Good **Site** Level
Nearest Bus Stop (Miles) ¼
Holiday caravan for hire.
Facilities 🚺 ⛽ ℯ ⊙ 🔲 🏐 🎱 🎣 ✕ 🐕 🔲 🛒
Nearby Facilities ✝ ✓
Nearest Town York
🚂 Ulleskelf

THIRSK

Hillside Caravan Park, Canvas Farm, Knayton, Thirsk, North Yorkshire, YO7 4BR
Tel: 01845 537349
Email: info@hillsidecaravanpark.co.uk
www.hillsidecaravanpark.co.uk
Pitches For 🚐 🚎 **Total** 35
Acreage 5 **Open** 04-Feb **to** 04-Jan
Access Good **Site** Level
Quiet family run site in a beautiful rural location at the foot of the Hambleton Hills. Ideally situated for exploring the Yorkshire Moors and Dales, and Herriot country. Good walking area.
Facilities ♿ ✚ 🗑 🚺 ⛽ ℯ ⊙ 🔌 ▰ 🔲 🛒 🕎 ⊙ ▰ 🍴 🔲 🛒
Nearby Facilities ✝ ✓ ∪
Nearest Town Thirsk
Directions Exit the A19 dual carriageway signposted Knayton, and follow signs into Knayton Village. Pass the Dog & Gun Public House on the left and leave the village, go straight over the crossroads and the site entrance is 1 mile on the left.
🚂 Northallerton

THIRSK

Sowerby Caravan Park, Sowerby, Thirsk,
North Yorkshire, YO7 3AG
Tel: 01845 522753
Email: sowerbycaravans@btconnect.com
www.ukparks.co.uk/sowerby
Pitches For ⚎ ⚏ **Total** 25
Acreage 1½ **Open** March **to** October
Access Good **Site** Level
Nearest Bus Stop (Miles) ½
Alongside a river. Ideal location for touring.
Facilities ♿ ⚲ ♒ ⊞ ⏢ ⌂ ⏚ ☂ ☺ ♨ ⌨ ⬭ 🖻 ⚐
⚲ ☊ ♨ ♿ ⊞ ⛗ ⬭ 🅿 ⬭ ☇
Nearby Facilities ⏚ 🏊 ⛵ U
Nearest Town Thirsk
Directions From Thirsk go through Sowerby
towards Dalton, the park is ½ mile south of
Sowerby on the right.
⚎ Thirsk

THIRSK

Thirsk Racecourse Caravan Club Site,
Thirsk, North Yorkshire, YO7 1QL
Tel: 01845 525266
www.caravanclub.co.uk
Pitches For ⚎ ⚎ ⚏ **Total** 60
Acreage 3 **Open** March **to** Oct
Access Good **Site** Level
Situated in the racecourse, surrounded by the
Dales and Moors. Just a 5 minute walk to
Thirsk town centre. Close to Rievaulx Abbey.
Non members welcome. Booking essential.
Facilities ♿ ♒ ⊞ ⛗ ♒ ⌂ ☺ ♨ ☂ ☂
⚐ 🖻 ⬭ 🅿 🖻
Nearby Facilities ⏚
Directions From north on the A1 turn off onto
the B6267 signposted Thirsk. After 2¼ miles
at the T-junction turn left onto the A61, site
is 4¼ miles on the left, just past racecourse
buildings.
⚎ Thirsk

THORNABY-ON-TEES

White Water Caravan Club Site, Tees
Barrage, Stockton-on-Tees, TS18 2QW
Tel: 01642 634880
www.caravanclub.co.uk
Pitches For ⚎ ⚏ ⚏ **Total** 115
Acreage 15 **Open** All Year
Access Good **Site** Level
Nearest Bus Stop (Miles) ½
Part of the largest white water canoeing and
rafting course in Britain. Teeside Park nearby
provides shopping, cinema and bowling alley.
Just a short drive to the coast. Non members
welcome. Booking essential.
Facilities ♿ ⚲ ⊞ ⛗ ♒ ⌂ ☺
⚐ 🖻 ☊ ⛗ ⎈ ♒ ⬭ 🅿 🖻 ⚲ ☇
Nearby Facilities ⏚ 🏊 ⛵ ⚓
Nearest Town Stockton-on-Tees
Directions From A19 take A66 sp Darlington.
Follow signs for Teeside Retail Park, continue
in nearside lane and after 200yds take first
exit sp Teeside Retail Park. At lights turn right
over A66, cross railway bridge, go straight
over mini roundabout and cross Tees barrage
bridge. Site is on right past Talpore pub.
⚎ Stockton-on-Tees

WHITBY

**Abbot's House Farm Camping & Caravan
Site,** Abbot's House Farm, Goathland,
Whitby, North Yorkshire, YO22 5NH
Tel: 01947 896270
www.abbotshouse.org.uk
Pitches For ⚎ ⚏ ⚏ **Total** 90
Acreage 2½ **Open** March **to** October
Access Good **Site** Level
Nearest Bus Stop (Miles) ½
The North Yorkshire Moors Steam Railway runs
through the farm. Yorkshire Televisions
Heartbeat country. 9 miles from Whitby, 25
miles from Scarborough & 40 miles from York.

Facilities ♿ ⛗ ♒ ⌂ ⚲ ☇ ⎈ ☊ 🅿 🖻 ⬭ ☇
Nearby Facilities ⏚ 🏊 ⛵ U ♒
Nearest Town Whitby
Directions From Whitby take the A171 west
for approx. 3 miles, turn south onto the A169,
after approx. 6 miles turn right signposted
Goathland. Turn left opposite Goathland
Garage.
⚎ Goathland

WHITBY

Burnt House Caravan Park, Ugthorpe,
Whitby, North Yorkshire, YO21 2BG
Tel: 01947 840448
Pitches For ⚏ **Total** 30
Acreage 7 **Open** End March **to** 3rd
Weekend Oct
Access Good **Site** Level
Nearest Bus Stop (Miles) ¼
Ideal base for touring coast or countryside.
4 miles from the beach.
Facilities ♒ ⊞ ⛗ ♒ ⌂ ☺ ☇ ☂ 🅿 ⬭ ☇
Nearby Facilities ⏚ 🏊 ⛵ U ♒
Nearest Town Whitby
Directions 8½ miles north of Whitby on the
A171 towards Guisborough, signposted
Ugthorpe Village.
⚎ Whitby

WHITBY

Grouse Hill Caravan & Camping Park, Nr
Robin Hoods Bay, Fylingdales, Whitby,
North Yorkshire, YO22 4QH
Tel: 01947 880543/880560
Email: info@grousehill.co.uk
www.grousehill.co.uk
Pitches For ⚎ ⚏ ⚏ **Total** 198
Acreage 14 **Open** March **to** Oct
Access Good **Site** Level
Nearest Bus Stop (Miles) ¼
Friendly family run site, set in a tranquil

moorland valley. Excellent base to explore the coast and country. 3 miles to the nearest beach (Boggle Hole), and a 5 minute walk to the local country inn.
Facilities ⚑ ⛭ ▯ ⬡ ☂ ⟟ ⊙ ⟲ ⬛ ▢ ☎
⚋ ⚑ ⬡ ⊗ ✗ ⟟ ⊞ ▢ ☀ ⚲
Nearby Facilities ⟋ ⟍ ⚓ ∿ ∪ ℛ
Nearest Town Whitby
Directions Signed just off the A171 Scarborough to Whitby road, behind the Flask Inn.
⇝ Whitby

WHITBY
Middlewood Farm Holiday Park, Middlewood Lane, Fylingthorpe, Robin Hoods Bay, Whitby, North Yorkshire, YO22 4UF
Tel: 01947 880414
Email: info@middlewoodfarm.com
www.middlewoodfarm.com
Pitches For ⚑ ⬡ ⚋ **Total** 120
Acreage 7 **Open** 01-Mar **to** 04-Jan
Access Good **Site** Level
Nearest Bus Stop (Miles) ¼
Peaceful family park, 10 minutes walk to the beach, pubs, shops and Robin Hoods Bay. Disabled facilities, bath and parent and baby room. Only 5 miles from Whitby. Magnificent views and walks.
Facilities ⚑ ⛭ ▯ ⬡ ☂ ⟟ ⊙ ⟲ ⬛ ▢ ☎
▯ ⬡ ⟟ ⊞ ▢ ☀
Nearby Facilities ⟋ ⟍ ⚓ ∿ ∪ ℛ
Nearest Town Whitby
Directions Signposted. Take the A171 Scarborough to Whitby road, 3 miles south of Whitby take the Fylingthorpe and Robin Hoods Bay road. At Fylingthorpe Post Office turn onto Middlewood Lane, park is 500 yards on the left.
⇝ Whitby

WHITBY
Northcliffe Holiday Park, High Hawsker, Whitby, North Yorkshire, YO22 4LL
Tel: 01947 880477
Email: enquiries@northcliffe-seaview.com
www.northcliffe-seaview.com
Pitches For ⚑ **Total** 62
Open Mid March **to** Early Nov
Access Good
Nearest Bus Stop (Miles) ¼
Exclusive SEASONAL ONLY Touring Park. Luxury Award Winning park with panoramic sea views. All weather, all mains, individual plots. We're a Double Winner - YTB and ETC. Caravan Holiday Park of the Year 1999. Woodland Shop/cafe/take-away. New childrens play park.
Facilities ⚑ ⛭ ▯ ⬡ ☂ ⟟ ⊙ ⟲ ⬛ ▢ ☎
⚋ ⚑ ⬡ ✗ ⟟ ▢ ☀ ☎
Nearby Facilities ⟋ ⟍ ⚓ ∿ ∪ ℛ ⚲
Nearest Town Whitby
Directions South from Whitby 3 miles, turn left B1447 to Robin Hoods Bay.
⇝ Whitby

WHITBY
Runswick Bay Caravan & Camping Park, Hinderwell Lane, Runswick Bay, North Yorkshire, TS13 5HU
Tel: 01947 840997
Pitches For ⚑ ⬡ ⚋ **Total** 60
Acreage 6 **Open** Easter **to** October
Access Good **Site** Level
Nearest Bus Stop (Miles) Outside
Clifftop location with a 5 minute walk to the beach.
Facilities ⚑ ⛭ ▯ ⬡ ☂ ⟟ ⟲ ⬛ ▢ ☎
▯ ⟟ ⊞
Nearby Facilities ⟋ ⟍ ⚓ ∿ ∪ ℛ
Nearest Town Whitby

Directions From Whitby take the A174, after 9 miles turn right signposted Runswick. At the T-Junction turn left and the site is 400 yards on the right.
⇝ Whitby

WHITBY
Serenity Caravan & Camping Park, High Street, Hinderwell, Whitby, North Yorkshire, TS13 5JH
Tel: 01947 841122
Email: patandni@aol.com
www.serenitycaravanpark.co.uk
Pitches For ⚑ ⬡ ⚋ **Total** 40
Acreage 5½ **Open** 01-Mar **to** End Oct
Access Good **Site** Sloping
Nearest Bus Stop (Miles) ¼
A very quiet, sheltered and secure, predominately adult site with lovely country views. Spectacular coastal, country and moorland walks. Close proximity to Cleveland Way, Runswick Bay and Staithes. Village shops and pubs all nearby.
Facilities ⚑ ▯ ⬡ ☂ ⟟ ⊙ ⟲ ⬛ ▢ ☎
▯ ⬡ ⟟ ⊞ ☀
Nearby Facilities ⟋ ⟍ ⚓ ∿ ∪ ℛ
Nearest Town Whitby
Directions From Whitby take the A174 signposted Sandsend. Go through Sandsend and Lythe and continue to Hinderwell.
⇝ Whitby

WHITBY
York House Caravan Park, Back Lane, Hawsker, Whitby, North Yorkshire, YO22 4LW
Tel: 01947 880354
Email: info@yorkhousecaravanpark.co.uk
www.yorkhousecaravanpark.co.uk
Pitches For ⚑ ⬡ ⚋ **Total** 100
Acreage 9 **Open** March **to** October
Access Good **Site** Lev/Slope
Nearest Bus Stop (Miles) ¼
Ideally placed for Whitby and Robin Hoods Bay, with many walks and cycle trails.
Facilities ⛭ ⚑ ▯ ⬡ ☂ ⟟ ⟲ ▢ ☎
⚋ ⬡ ⊗ ✗ ⟟ ▯ ▦ ⟟ ⊞ ▢ ☀ ☎
Nearby Facilities ⟋ ⟍ ⚓ ∿ ∪ ℛ
Nearest Town Whitby
Directions 3 miles south of Whitby on the A171 in the village of Hawsker.
⇝ Whitby

YORK (Near)
Alders Caravan Park, Home Farm, Alne, York, North Yorkshire, YO61 1RY
Tel: 01347 838722
Email: enquiries@homefarmalne.co.uk
www.alderscaravanpark.co.uk
Pitches For ⚑ ⬡ ⚋ **Total** 87
Acreage 12 **Open** March **to** October
Access Good **Site** Level
Nearest Bus Stop (Miles) ¼
Set in parkland on a working farm with woodland walks. On the bus route to York. Ideal touring base for the Dales, Moors, coast and York.
Facilities ⛭ ⚑ ▯ ⬡ ☂ ⟟ ⊙ ⟲ ⬛ ▢ ☎
⚋ ▯ ⬡ ⊞ ▢ ☀
Nearby Facilities ⟋ ⟍ ℛ
Nearest Town York
Directions Take the A19 north of York after Shipton by Beningbrough and follow brown tourism signs to Alne Village. Park is in the centre of the village.
⇝ York

YORK (Near)
Cawood Park, Ryther Road, Cawood, Vale of York, North Yorkshire, YO8 3TT
Tel: 01757 268450
Email: enquiries@cawoodpark.com
www.cawoodpark.com
Pitches For ⚑ ⚋ **Total** 60
Acreage 10 **Open** All Year
Access Good **Site** Level
Nearest Bus Stop (Miles) ½
Here at Cawood Holiday Park, which is a quiet rural park, we have worked hard to create an environment which keeps its natural simplicity to provide a trouble free holiday. Some pitches have views over our fishing lake. Ideal for York.
Facilities ⛭ ⚑ ▯ ⬡ ☂ ⟟ ⟲ ⬛ ☎
⚋ ⬡ ⊗ ☂ ⚲ ▦ ⊞ ▢
Nearby Facilities ⟋ ⚓ ∪
Nearest Town York/Selby
Directions From the A19 take the B1222 signposted Cawood, oppositethe entrance to Escrick Park Estate. Follow road and go over the bridge, at the traffic lights turn right and Cawood Park is ½ a mile on the left.
⇝ York/Selby

YORK (Near)
Goosewood Holiday Park, Sutton-on-the-Forest, York, North Yorkshire, YO61 1ET
Tel: 01347 810829
Email: enquiries@goosewood.co.uk
www.flowerofmay.com
Pitches For ⚑ ⚋ **Total** 100
Acreage 15 **Open** 01-Feb **to** 02-Jan
Access Good **Site** Level
Nearest Bus Stop (Miles) ¼
Wooded walks and a fishing lake. Ideal for sightseeing in York and the Dales.
Facilities ⚋ ⛭ ⚑ ▯ ⬡ ☂ ⟟ ⊙ ⟲ ⬛ ☎
▢ ☎ ⚲ ⬡ ⊗ ▦ ⟟ ⊞ ▢ ⟋ ☀ ⚲ ☎
Nearby Facilities ⟋ ⟍ ∪
Nearest Town York
Directions From the A1237 York ring road, take the B1363 to Helmsley, 4 miles to Goosewood.
⇝ York

YORK (Near)
Home Farm Camping & Caravan Park, Moreby, Stillingfleet, York, North Yorkshire, YO19 6HN
Tel: 01904 728263
Email: home_farm@hotmail.co.uk
Pitches For ⚑ ⬡ ⚋ **Total** 25
Acreage 3 **Open** February **to** December
Access Good **Site** Level
Nearest Bus Stop (Miles) Outside
Alongside the River Ouse. Ideal base to tour York and surrounding Dales and North Yorkshire Moors. 4 miles to the nearest shop or supermarket.
Facilities ▯ ⬡ ☂ ⟟ ⊙ ⬛ ⊗ ▦ ⟟ ⊞ ▢ ⟋
Nearby Facilities ⟋ ∪
Nearest Town York
Directions On the B1222 between the village of Naburn and Stllingfleet. 6 miles south of York City walls.
⇝ York

YORK (Near)
Hutton Le Hole Caravan Park, Westfield Lodge, Hutton le Hole, York, North Yorkshire, YO62 6UG
Tel: 01751 417261
Email: rwstrickland@farmersweekly.net
www.westfieldlodge.com
Pitches For ⚑ ⬡ ⚋ **Total** 42
Acreage 5 **Open** Easter **to** Oct
Access Good **Site** Level
Excellent for the North Yorkshire Moors. Many local scenic walks. Centrally located for the coast and York.

Facilities ⅃ ♿ ⌂ ▯⌖ ⌐ ☏⊙♨ ▯ 🛒
🛢 ⊟ ➶ 🎣 ⌘ ⛆

Nearby Facilities ⌖ ∪ ⚲
Nearest Town Pickering
Directions Approx. 7 miles west of Pickering on the A170 turn right (north) at Keldholme signposted Hutton Le Hole. After approx 2 miles go over the cattle grid, site is on the left before the village.
≠ Malton

YORK (Near)
Sheriff Hutton Camping & Caravanning Club Site, Bracken Hill, Sheriff Hutton, North Yorkshire, YO60 6QG
Tel: 01347 878660
www.campingandcaravanningclub.co.uk/sheriffhutton
Pitches For Å ♛ 🚐 Total 90
Acreage 10 **Open** 29-Mar **to** 05-Nov
Access Good **Site** Level
Nearest Bus Stop (Miles) ¾
Close to the city of York. BTB 4 Star Graded, AA 3 Pennants and Loo of the Year Award. Non members welcome. You can also call us on 0845 130 7633.
Facilities ⅃ ♿ ⌂ ▯⌖ ⌐ ☏⊙♨ 🛒 ▯ 🛒
🛢 ⊟ ⚙ 🅿️⛆ 🎣 ☏
Nearby Facilities ⌖ ✎ ⚲ ∪
Nearest Town York
Directions From York follow signposts for Earswick Strensall, keep left at the filling station and Ship Inn, site is second on the right.
≠ York

YORK (Near)
The Ponderosa Caravan Park, East Moor, Sutton-on-the-Forest, Nr York, North Yorkshire, YO61 1ET
Tel: 01347 811233
Pitches For Å ♛ 🚐 Total 40
Acreage 3 **Open** All Year
Access Good **Site** Level
Nearest Bus Stop (Miles) Outside
Near to the historic city of York, North Yorkshire Moors and many local attractions.
Facilities ⌂ ▯⌖ ⌐ ☏⊙♨ 🛒 ▯ 🛒
🛢 🛒 🎣 ⛆
Nearby Facilities ✎
Nearest Town York
Directions Signposted 800 yards off the B1363 Wigginton to Helmsley road, 6 miles from York.
≠ York

YORK (Near)
Willow House Caravan Park, Wigginton Road, Wigginton, York, North Yorkshire, YO32 2RH
Tel: 01904 750060
Email: info@willowhouseyork.co.uk
www.willowhouseyork.co.uk
Pitches For Å ♛ 🚐 Total 32
Acreage 4 **Open** All Year
Access Good **Site** Level
Nearest Bus Stop (Miles) Outside
ADULTS ONLY SITE. 3 miles from the centre of York. Handy for the Yorkshire Moors, Wolds, Dales and the coast. Shopping centres nearby.
Facilities ⅃ ⌂ ▯⌖ ⌐ ☏⊙♨ 🛒 ▯ 🛒
🛢 ⊙ ✗ 🛒 ✎ ⼁ ⼂ ⛆
Nearby Facilities ✎
Nearest Town York
Directions From York take the A1237 bypass to the B1363 Wigginton Road, site is ½ a mile on the right.
≠ York

YORKSHIRE (SOUTH)
BARNSLEY
Greensprings Touring Park, Rockley Lane, Worsbrough, Barnsley, South Yorkshire, S75 3DS
Tel: 01226 288298
Pitches For Å ♛ 🚐 Total 60
Acreage 4 **Open** April **to** October
Access Good **Site** Lev/Slope
Nearest Bus Stop (Miles) 1
Country site, well wooded with pleasant walks. Convenient for the M1. Ideal location for Sheffield venues.
Facilities ⅃ ▯⌖ ⌐ ☏⊙♨ ▯⼂ ▯ ⼁ ⛆
Nearby Facilities ⌖ ✎ ∪ ⚲
Nearest Town Barnsley
Directions Junction 36 on M1. A61 to Barnsley, take left turn after ¼ mile signed to Pilley. Site is 1 mile along this road.
≠ Barnsley

ROTHERHAM
Thrybergh Country Park, Doncaster Road, Thrybergh, Rotherham, South Yorkshire, S65 4NU
Tel: 01709 850353
www.rotherham.gov.uk
Pitches For ♛ 🚐 Total 24
Acreage 1½ **Open** All Year
Access Good **Site** Level
Nearest Bus Stop (Miles) Entrance
35 acre fly fishery with surfaced footpath on site. NEW toilet and show blocks for 2012.
Facilities ⅃ ⌂ ▯⌖ ⌐ ☏⊙♨ ▯ 🛒
🛢 ⼂ ✗ ⼁ 🛒 ▯ 🛒 ⛆
Nearby Facilities ⌖ ✎ ⼀ ⚌ ⚲ ✗
Nearest Town Rotherham
Directions 4 miles north of Rotherham on the A630 between Thrybergh and Hooton Roberts.
≠ Rotherham

SHEFFIELD
Fox Hagg Farm, Lodge Lane, Rivelin, Sheffield, South Yorkshire, S6 5SN
Tel: 0114 230 5589
Pitches For Å ♛ 🚐 Total 60
Acreage 2 **Open** April **to** October
Access Good **Site** Level
Nearest Bus Stop (Miles) ¼
On the outskirts of the Peak District, scenic views and nature walks. Ideal touring. All new showers.
Facilities ⅃ ▯ ⌂ ▯⌖ ⌐ ☏⊙♨ ▯ 🛒 ⼁ 🛒 ⛆
Nearby Facilities ⌖ ✎ ∪ ✗
Nearest Town Sheffield
Directions Off the A57, near Rivelin Post Office.
≠ Sheffield

THORNE
Elder House Touring Park, Crow Tree Bank, Thorne Levels, Nr Doncaster, South Yorkshire, DN8 5TD
Tel: 01405 813173
Pitches For ♛ 🚐 Total 10
Acreage 2 **Open** All Year
Access Good **Site** Level
Peaceful, landscaped, rural and natural site. Near to Doncaster Racecourse, Transport Museum and Epworth Home of The Wesleys. Disabled toilet and shower. NB: We are CLOSED for Xmas & New Year. ETB 4 Star Graded Site.
Facilities ✗ ⅃ ⌂ ▯⌖ ⌐ ☏⊙♨ 🛒 🛒 ⼁🛒
Nearby Facilities ⌖ ✎
Directions Leave the M180 at junction 1 and take the A18 towards Scunthorpe. 2 miles after the roundabout, at the Black Bull Inn, turn right. After ½ mile turn left into farm drive and follow through to the park.
≠ Thorne South

YORKSHIRE (WEST)
ELLAND
Elland Hall Farm Caravan Site, Exley Lane, Elland, West Yorkshire, HX5 0SL
Tel: 01422 372325
Email: enquiries@ellandhallfarm.co.uk
www.ellandhallfarm.co.uk
Pitches For Å ♛ 🚐 Total 10
Acreage 1 **Open** April **to** Oct
Access Good **Site** Level
Facilities ⅃ ▯⌖ ⌐ ☏⊙ ▯ 🛒 ▯
Nearby Facilities
Nearest Town Elland
Directions From Elland take the Brighouse road, at the railway bridge turn left into Exley Lane.
≠ Halifax

HAWORTH
Upwood Holiday Park, Blackmoor Road, Oxenhope, Haworth, West Yorkshire, BD22 9SS
Tel: 01535 644242
Email: info@upwoodpark.co.uk
www.upwoodpark.co.uk
Pitches For Å ♛ 🚐 Total 100
Acreage 10 **Open** 01-Mar **to** 04-Jan
Access Good **Site** Lev/Slope
Nearest Bus Stop (Miles) Outside
Pleasantly situated close to the Yorkshire Dales National Park. Beautiful, panoramic views over the surrounding countryside. One mile from the Bronte Village of Haworth and Worth Steam Railway. 12 Camping and Mega Pods available.
Facilities ⅃ ▯ ⌂ ▯⌖ ⌐ ☏⊙♨ 🛒 ▯ 🛒
🛢 ⊙ ⼂ ✗ ⼁ ▯ ⼀ 🅿️⛆ ▯ 🛒 ⛆ ☏
Nearby Facilities ⌖ ✎ ⼀ ⚌ ∪ ⚲
Nearest Town Keighley
Directions Situated off the A629 Keighley to Halifax road. Turn by the Flappit Pub onto the B6144 towards Haworth, after 1 mile turn left onto Blackmoor Road, and the site entrance is by the bus stop.
≠ Keighley

HEBDEN BRIDGE
Lower Clough Foot Caravan Club Site, Cragg Vale, Hebden Bridge, West Yorkshire, HX7 5RU
Tel: 01422 882531
www.caravanclub.co.uk
Pitches For ♛ 🚐 Total 45
Acreage 2½ **Open** March **to** Nov
Access Good **Site** Level
Nearest Bus Stop (Miles) Outside
Screened site bordered by a stream. Three walks adjacent to the site. Visit Brontes Haworth Parsonage, walk the Moors and Pennine Way. Horse drawn canal boat rides available at Hebden Bridge (2½ miles). Own sanitation required. Non members welcome. Booking essential.
Facilities ⅃ ⌂ ⼂ ⊙ ☏🅿️▯ 🛒 ⛆
Nearby Facilities ⌖ ✎ ⼀ ⼂
Nearest Town Hebden Bridge
Directions Leave the A646 in Mythomroyd Village and take the B6138 signposted Rochdale (care required, narrow bridge). Site is 1 mile on the right.
≠ Hebden Bridge

HEBDEN BRIDGE
Pennine Camp & Caravan Site, High Greenwood House, Heptonstall, Hebden Bridge, West Yorkshire, HX7 7AZ
Tel: 01422 842287
Pitches For Å ♛ 🚐 Total 20
Open April **to** October
Site Lev/Slope
Nearest Bus Stop (Miles) 1
Booking for dates is advisable.

ENGLAND

Facilities ⛱ 🚿 🚻 ⊙ ☎ ▯
Nearby Facilities ┌ ✔ ∪ ♪
Nearest Town Hebden Bridge
Directions From Hebden Bridge take Heptonstall road then follow tent and caravan signs.
⇌ Hebden Bridge

HOLMFIRTH

Holme Valley Camping & Caravan Park, Thongsbridge, Holmfirth, West Yorkshire, HD9 7TD
Tel: 01484 665819
Email: enquiries@holmevalleycamping.com
www.holmevalleycamping.com
Pitches For ▲ ⬛ ⬛ **Total** 62
Acreage 4½ **Open** All Year
Access Good **Site** Lev/Slope
Nearest Bus Stop (Miles) ¼
Picturesque location surrounded by meadows and woodland in the heart of Last of the Summer Wine country. Angling in the Mill Dam and river.
Facilities ♿ ⛱ 🚿 🚻 ☇ ┌ ⊙ ⌕ 🛒 🔌 ▯ 🛒
⚲ 🏠 🍴 🛒 ✖ ▤ ⬛ ⬛ ✿ ☀ ♥
Nearby Facilities ┌ ✔ ∪ ♪
Nearest Town Holmfirth
Directions 1 mile north of Holmfirth off the A6024. Follow private road down to valley bottom, passing bottle banks at the entrance.
⇌ Brockholes

LEEDS

Glenfield Caravan Park, 120 Blackmoor Lane, Bardsey, Leeds, West Yorkshire, LS17 9DZ
Tel: 01937 574657
Email: glenfieldcp@aol.com
www.ukparks.co.uk/glenfieldcp
Pitches For ▲ ⬛ ⬛ **Total** 30
Acreage 3½ **Open** All Year
Access Good **Site** Level
Beautifully kept park. Lovely walks and places to eat nearby. Close to golf courses and a nature reserve for walking. Easy access and ideal touring base. New 5 Star heated shower block with toilets and laundry.
Facilities ♿ ⛱ 🚿 🚻 ☇ ┌ ☇ 🔌 ▯ 🛒
⚲ 🏠 🛒 ✖ ▤ ♥
Nearby Facilities ┌ ✔ ∪ ♪
Nearest Town Leeds
Directions From Leeds take the A58 towards Wetherby, after approx 8 miles turn left at Shadwell Harewood sign. After 1 mile take right hand fork, continue for 1 mile and site is on the left at the bottom of the hill.
⇌ Leeds

LEEDS

Moor Lodge Caravan Park, Blackmoor Lane, Bardsey, Leeds, West Yorkshire, LS17 9DZ
Tel: 01937 572424
Email: rodatmlcp@aol.com
www.moorlodgecaravanpark.co.uk
Pitches For ▲ ⬛ ⬛ **Total** 12
Acreage 8 **Open** All Year
Access Good **Site** Level
Nearest Bus Stop (Miles) ½
ADULTS ONLY. Immaculate countryside park.
Facilities ✖ ⛱ 🚻 🚿 ┌ ⊙ ⌕ 🛒 ▯
⚲ 🏠 🛒 ▤ ▯
Nearby Facilities ┌ ✔ ∪ ♪ ♪
Nearest Town Leeds
Directions Turn off the A1 at Wetherby and take the A58 towards Leeds for 4 miles, turn right after the New Inn Pub (Ling Lane). At the crossroads turn right and Moor Lodge is at the bottom of the hill on the right.
⇌ Leeds

OTLEY

Clarion Lodge Campsite, West Chevin Road, Menston, Nr Otley, West Yorkshire, LS29 6BL
Tel: 01943 871619
Email: clarionlodgecamp@aol.com
www.clarionlodgecampsite.co.uk
Pitches For ▲ ⬛ ⬛ **Total** 20
Acreage 2 **Open** March **to** November
Access Good **Site** Level
Nearest Bus Stop (Miles) ½
Small, quiet, family run with spectacular countryside views.
Facilities ⛱ 🚿 🚻 ☇ ┌ ⊙ ☎ ▯
Nearby Facilities ┌ ✔ ✖ ∪
Nearest Town Otley
Directions From Otley take the A660 towards Guiseley. Turn left at the crossroads near the Hare & Hounds onto Buckle Lane, keep left at Chevin Inn and the Site is 200 yards on the right.
⇌ Guiseley

SHIPLEY

Dobrudden Caravan Park, Baildon Moor, Baildon, Shipley, West Yorkshire, BD17 5EE
Tel: 01274 581016
Email: peter@dobrudden.co.uk
www.dobrudden.co.uk
Pitches For ▲ ⬛ ⬛ **Total** 20
Acreage 10 **Open** 1st Feb **to** 31-Jan
Access Good **Site** Lev/Slope
Nearest Bus Stop (Miles) 1
In the middle of moorland, handy for the Dales and Moors. Local to Bronte Country. Ideal for touring and visiting Leeds.
Facilities ⛱ 🚿 🚻 🚿 ┌ ⊙ ⌕ 🛒 🛒
⚲ 🏠 🛒 ✖ ▤ ✿ ♥
Nearby Facilities ┌ ✔ ∿ ∪ ♪ ♪
Nearest Town Baildon/Shipley/Bingley
⇌ Baildon

SILSDEN

Brown Bank Caravan Park, Brown Bank Lane, Silsden, West Yorkshire, BD20 0NN
Tel: 01535 653241
Email: timlaycock@btconnect.com
Pitches For ▲ ⬛ ⬛ **Total** 15
Acreage 12 **Open** April **to** October
Access Good **Site** Level
Nearest Bus Stop (Miles) Outside
On the edge of Ilkley Moor with good views and excellent walks. Ideal base for touring. Many attractions within 15 miles.
Facilities ⛱ 🚿 🚻 ☇ ┌ ⊙ ⌕ 🛒
⚲ 🏠 ▥ ✿ ▯ ☀
Nearby Facilities ┌ ✔ ∪ ♪ ♪
Nearest Town Silsden
Directions From Silsden take the A6034, turn right on the bend into Brown Bank Lane, site is 1½ miles on the right. Also signposted from Addingham on the A6034.
⇌ Steeton

SILSDEN

Dales Bank Holiday Park, Low Lane, Silsden, Keighley, West Yorkshire, BD20 9JH
Tel: 01535 653321/656523
Pitches For ▲ ⬛ ⬛ **Total** 52
Acreage 5 **Open** April **to** Oct
Access Good **Site** Level
Nearest Bus Stop (Miles) 1
Central for Ilkley, Craven Dales and Bronte Country. Bed & Breakfast available.
Facilities ♿ ⛱ 🚿 🚻 ☇ ┌ ⊙ ⌕ 🛒
⚲ 🏠 🛒 ✖ ♀ ▥ ▲ ✿ ✖ ▤ ⬛ ⬛ ☀ ♥ ♥
Nearby Facilities ┌ ✔ ∪ ♪ ♪
Nearest Town Silsden

Directions In Silsden turn up one way street Briggate, after 100 yards turn into Bradley Road, after ¾ miles turn right, site entrance is third on the right.
⇌ Steeton

SILSDEN

Lower Heights Farm, Silsden, West Yorkshire, BD20 9HW
Tel: 01535 653035
Email: mmsrowling@aol.com
Pitches For ▲ ⬛ ⬛ **Total** 5
Acreage 2 **Open** Easter **to** Oct
Access Good **Site** Level
Nearest Bus Stop (Miles) ½
Quiet site with good views. Only 5 caravan pitches but any number of tents.
Facilities ⛱ 🚿 🚻 ☇ ┌ ▥ 🔌 ▯ ☀
Nearby Facilities ┌ ✔ ∪ ♪
Nearest Town Skipton
Directions 1 mile from Silsden off A6034.
⇌ Steeton

WETHERBY

Haighfield Caravan Park, 5 Blackmoor Lane, Bardsey, Leeds, West Yorkshire, LS17 9DY
Tel: 01937 574658
Email: haighfieldcp@aol.com
www.haighfieldcaravanpark.co.uk
Pitches For ▲ ⬛ ⬛ **Total** 30
Acreage 3 **Open** All Year
Access Good **Site** Level
Nearest Bus Stop (Miles) Outside
ADULTS ONLY Small family run and owned Park. Close to Leeds, York and Harrogate. Ideal for touring Yorkshire. Holiday homes for hire and sale. Visit Britain 5 Stars.
Facilities ♿ ✖ ⛱ 🚿 🚻 ☇ ┌ ⊙ ⌕
🛒 🏠 🛒 ▥ 🔌 ▯ ▤ ▲ ☀ ♥
Nearby Facilities ┌ ✔ ∿ ∪ ♪
Nearest Town Wetherby
Directions Exit the A1/M1 link at Wetherby and follow the A58 Wetherby and Leeds road. Go through Collingham and turn right onto Church Lane into Bardsey. Go past Bardsey Church and the Bingley Arms, the Park is at the top of the hill on the left.
⇌ Leeds

ANGLESEY

WALES

ANGLESEY

AMLWCH
Point Lynas Caravan Park, Llaneilian, Amlwch, Anglesey, LL68 9LT
Tel: 01407 831130
Email: enquiries@pointlynas.com
www.pointlynas.com
Pitches For ▲ ⊞ **Total** 10
Acreage 1 **Open** April **to** Oct
Access Good **Site** Level
Nearest Bus Stop (Miles) ¼
Set in a quiet away from it all area. 200 metres from Porth Eilian Cove and Anglesey Coastal Path.
Facilities ⚍ ⊞♿🅿⊙⚍🅿🔲☎
🔲⚍🅿🔲⚍
Nearby Facilities ⚓ ⚓
Nearest Town Amlwch
Directions From the A5025 at Cerrig Man follow signs for Llaneilian and then Porth Eilian. Park is on the left 400 metres past Llaneilian Church.
⚐ Bangor/Holyhead

AMLWCH
Tyn Rhos, Penysarn, Amlwch, Anglesey, LL69 9YR
Tel: 01407 830574
Pitches For ▲ ⊞ **Total** 40
Acreage 2 **Open** Easter **to** September
Access Good **Site** Level
Nearest Bus Stop (Miles) Outside
Near the village shops, post office and inn. Sports centre, beaches and swimming all 2 miles. Cafe/restaurant and licensed club within 200yds. 6 berth caravan available for hire, all mod cons.
Facilities ⚍ ⊞♿🅿⊙⚍🔲⚍🅿🔲⚍ ⚍
Nearby Facilities ⚓ ⚓⚓⚓ ⚓ ⚓
Nearest Town Amlwch
Directions A5025 turn off bypass to village of Penysarn. Take the first right after Y Bedol Public House and cross the cattle grid. 100yds up the drive.
⚐ Bangor

BEAUMARIS
Kingsbridge Caravan Park, Llanfaes, Beaumaris, Anglesey, LL58 8LR
Tel: 01248 490636
Email: info@kingsbridgecaravanpark.co.uk
www.kingsbridgecaravanpark.co.uk
Pitches For ▲ ⊞ **Total** 48
Acreage 14 **Open** March **to** October
Access Good **Site** Level
Nearest Bus Stop (Miles) ¼
4 Star Park with 2 underfloor heated shower blocks. 2 miles from historic Beaumaris. Telephone booking.
Facilities ⚍ ⊞♿🅿⊙⚍☎
🔲🔲⚍🅿🔲⚍
Nearby Facilities ⚓ ⚓⚓⚓⚓ ⚓⚓
Nearest Town Beaumaris
Directions 1¼ miles past Beaumaris Castle. At crossroads turn left, 400yds to the site.
⚐ Bangor

BENLLECH
Ad Astra Caravan Park, Brynteg, Nr Benllech, Anglesey, LL78 7JH
Tel: 01248 853283
Email: brian@brynteg3.fsnet.co.uk
www.adastracaravanpark.co.uk
Pitches For ▲ ⊞ ⊞
Acreage 3 **Open** March **to** October
Access Good **Site** Level
Nearest Bus Stop (Miles) Outside
Scenic views, ideal base for touring.

Facilities ♿ ⚍ ⊞⊞♿🅿⊙⚍⚍🔲☎
🔲⊙⚍🅿🔲⚍⚍
Nearby Facilities ⚓ ⚓⚓⚓⚓ ⚓⚓
Nearest Town Benllech
Directions Turn left up the hill from Benllech Village square onto the B5108. Drive 1½ miles to California Inn, turn left onto the B5110. Park is 500 yards on right hand side.
⚐ Bangor

BENLLECH
Bodafon Caravan & Camping Park, Bodafon, Benllech, Anglesey, LL74 8RU
Tel: 01248 852417
Email: robert@bodafonpark.co.uk
www.bodafonpark.co.uk
Pitches For ▲ ⊞ ⊞ **Total** 50
Acreage 5 **Open** March **to** October
Access Good **Site** Level
Nearest Bus Stop (Miles) ¼
Quiet family site with good views, ¾ miles from the beach. Ideal touring.
Facilities ⚍ ⊞ ⊞♿🅿⊙⚍☎
🔲⊙⚍🔲⚍⚍ ⚍
Nearby Facilities ⚓ ⚓⚓⚓⚓ ⚓
Nearest Town Benllech Bay
Directions A5025 through Benllech, ¼ mile on left going through 30mph signs.
⚐ Bangor

BENLLECH
Cae Mawr Caravan Club Site, Llangefni Road, Marianglas, Anglesey, LL73 8NY
Tel: 01248 853737
www.caravanclub.co.uk
Pitches For ⊞ **Total** 76
Acreage 6½ **Open** March **to** Oct
Access Good **Site** Level
A sheltered site with cheerful hydrangers. 1 mile from the beach. Close to Beaumaris Castle, Butterfly Palace, Sea Zoo and NT Plas Newydd. Own sanitation required. Non members welcome. Booking essential.
Facilities ⚍ ⊞ ☎ 🔲⊙⚍🔲⚍
Nearby Facilities ⚓ ⚓⚓
Nearest Town Benllech
Directions From A55 on approaching Bangor continue onto A5 sp Holyhead. Cross Britannia Bridge and leave dual carriageway via second slip road and turn right onto A5025. In Benllech continue on A5025 (DO NOT turn left) then turn left onto B5110. Site is on the right
⚐ Benllech

BENLLECH
Fedw-Uchaf Caravan & Camping Park, Fedw-Uchaf, Brynrefail, Dulas, Anglesey, LL70 9HZ
Tel: 01248 410414
Email: stanleyclark433@btinternet.com
www.fedw-uchaf.co.uk
Pitches For ▲ ⊞ ⊞ **Total** 80
Acreage 6 **Open** March **to** October
Access Good **Site** Level/slight slope
Nearest Bus Stop (Miles) ¼
Lovely views of the sea, Snowdon, woodland and mountains. Just a short walk to the beach and village. We have many pets including donkeys, rheas, llamas, ducks, ponies and more.
Facilities ♿ ⚍ ⊞🅿⊙⚍☎
🔲⊙⚍🅿🔲⚍⚍
Nearby Facilities ⚓ ⚓⚓⚓⚓ ⚓⚓⚓
Nearest Town Benllech
Directions Go across Britannia Bridge then take the A5025 and to Brynrefail. Turn next left and Fedw-Uchaf is ¼ of a mile on the right hand side.
⚐ Bangor

BENLLECH
Garnedd Touring Park, Lon Bryn Mair, Brynteg, Anglesey, LL78 8QA
Tel: 01248 853240
Email: mike@garnedd.com
www.garnedd.com
Pitches For ▲ ⊞ **Total** 20
Acreage 9 **Open** March **to** October
Access Good **Site** Level
Nearest Bus Stop (Miles) ¼
Five beaches within 5 minutes of the site. Wonderful views. Cottage and static caravan available for hire. You can also call us on Mobile: 07973 156371.
Facilities ⚍ ⊞🅿⊙⚍🔲☎
🔲⊙⚍🅿🔲⚍
Nearby Facilities ⚓ ⚓⚓⚓ ⚓
Nearest Town Benllech
Directions From Menai Bridge take the A5025 signposted Amlwch and Benllech. After entering Benllech turn left at Londis Garage, turn into the fourth lane, site is 600 yards on the right.

BENLLECH
Golden Sunset Holidays, Benllech, Anglesey, LL74 8SW
Tel: 01248 852345
www.goldensunsetholidays.com
Pitches For ▲ ⊞ ⊞
Acreage 20 **Open** April **to** Sept
Access Good **Site** Lev/Slope
Nearest Bus Stop (Miles) Outside
Elevated coastal site with superb views.
Facilities ♿ ⚍ ⊞🅿⊙⚍☎🔲⚍⚍ ⚍
📶
Nearby Facilities ⚓ ⚓⚓⚓⚓ ⚓⚓⚓
Nearest Town Llangefni
Directions Take the A55 across the bridge, take second turn onto the A5025 to Benllech.
⚐ Bangor

BENLLECH
Home Farm Caravan Park, Marianglas, Anglesey, LL73 8PH
Tel: 01248 410614
Email: enq@homefarm-anglesey.co.uk
www.homefarm-anglesey.co.uk
Pitches For ▲ ⊞ ⊞
Open April **to** Oct
Access Good **Site** Level
Nearest Bus Stop (Miles) ½
1 to 1½ miles from various beaches.
Facilities ♿ ⚍ ⊞🅿⊙⚍🔲☎
🔲⊙⚍🔲⚍🔲⚍⚍⚍
Nearby Facilities ⚓ ⚓⚓⚓⚓ ⚓⚓
Nearest Town Benllech
Directions Follow the A5025 from bridge for 11 miles, go through Benllech, keep left at the roundabout towards Amlwch. Park is ½ mile on the left, 300 yards after the church.
⚐ Bangor

BENLLECH
Penrhos Caravan Club Site, Brynteg, Benllech, Anglesey, LL78 7JH
Tel: 01248 852617
www.caravanclub.co.uk
Pitches For ⊞ **Total** 90
Acreage 9 **Open** March **to** Oct
Access Good **Site** Lev/Slope
Nearest Bus Stop (Miles) Outside
2 miles from a safe sandy beach. Near a farm trail, bird sanctuary, Beaumaris Castle and Sea Zoo. Take a trip on Snowdons rack and pinion mountain railway for breathtaking views. Non members welcome. Booking essential.
Facilities ⚍ ⊞🅿⊙ 🔲⚍🔲⚍⚍ ⚍
📶
Nearby Facilities ⚓ ⚓⚓

180 VISIT **www.cades.co.uk** TO SEE OUR MONTHLY COMPETITION

Nearest Town Benllech
Directions On A55 approaching Bangor continue on A5 sp Holyhead. Cross Britannia Bridge and leave dual carriageway via second slip road and turn right onto A5025. In Benllech continue on A5025 (DO NOT turn left) and turn left onto B5110. At crossroads with California pub. Go straight on and site is ½ mile on the right.
⛺ Benllech

BENLLECH

Plas Uchaf Caravan Park, Benllech Bay, Benllech, Anglesey, LL74 8NU
Tel: 01407 763012
Pitches For ⛺ ⛐ ⛟ **Total** 100
Acreage 16 **Open** March **to** October
Access Good **Site** Level
Nearest Bus Stop (Miles) ½
Family room, tarmac roads and perimeter parking, 30 plus picnic tables and 3 toilet blocks. Near the beach.
Facilities symbols
Nearby Facilities symbols
Nearest Town Benllech
Directions ½ a mile from Benllech, signposted on the B5108 up the hill after the fire station.
⛺ Bangor

BENLLECH

Ty Newydd Caravan Park, Llanbedrgoch, Anglesey, LL76 8TZ
Tel: 01248 450677
Email: mike@tynewydd.com
www.tynewydd.com
Pitches For ⛺ ⛐ ⛟ **Total** 48
Acreage 2 **Open** March **to** October
Access Good **Site** Level
Nearest Bus Stop (Miles) Outside
1 mile from the beach. Heated indoor swimming pool.
Facilities symbols
Nearby Facilities symbols
Nearest Town Benllech
Directions From Britannia Bridge take the A5025 for Amlwch. After passing through Pentraeth Village bear left at the lay-by and the site is ¾ miles on the right hand side.
⛺ Bangor

BRYNSIENCYN

Fron Caravan & Camping Site, Brynsiencyn, Anglesey, LL61 6TX
Tel: 01248 430310
Email: mail@froncaravanpark.co.uk
www.froncaravanpark.co.uk
Pitches For ⛺ ⛐ ⛟ **Total** 70
Acreage 5¼ **Open** Easter **to** September
Access Good **Site** Level
Nearest Bus Stop (Miles) Outside
Ideal for touring Anglesey and North Wales. Wales Tourist Board 5 Star Grading.
Facilities symbols
Nearby Facilities symbols
Nearest Town Llanfairpwllgwyn
Directions At start of Llanfairpwllgwyn turn left onto A4080 to Brynsiencyn follow road through village site is ¼ mile after village.
⛺ Bangor

LLANFWROG

Penrhyn Bay Caravan Park, Llanfwrog, Holyhead, Anglesey, LL65 4YG
Tel: 01407 730496/730411
Email: penrhyn.bay@btinternet.com
www.penrhynbay.com
Pitches For ⛺ ⛐ ⛟ **Total** 200
Acreage 15 **Open** 15-Mar **to** 31-Oct
Access Good **Site** Level

Nearest Bus Stop (Miles) 2
On the coast overlooking the beach on one side and Holyhead Harbour on the other. Fishing, sailing, cycling and plenty of walks.
Facilities symbols
Nearby Facilities symbols
Nearest Town Valley/Holyhead
Directions Take the A55 to Anglesey, take exit 3 to Valley, turn right at the traffic lights onto the A5025 and go through Llanfachraeth. Take the first turn left signposted Llanfwrog, Sandy Beach and Penrhyn, Site is on this road.
⛺ Valley/Holyhead

LLANGEFNI

Mornest Caravan Park, Pentre Berw, Gaerwen, Anglesey, LL60 6HU
Tel: 01248 421725
Email: heulwen@ygors.plus.com
www.mornestcaravanpark.co.uk
Pitches For ⛺ ⛐ ⛟ **Total** 45
Open March **to** October
Access Good **Site** Lev/Slope
Nearest Bus Stop (Miles) ¼
Facilities symbols
Nearby Facilities symbols
Nearest Town Llangefni
Directions Go over Menai Bridge and take exit 7 off and follow signs through Gaerwen.
⛺ Bangor

MOELFRE

Melin Rhos Caravan Park, Lligwy, Moelfre, Anglesey, LL24 8RU
Tel: 01248 852417
Email: robert@bodafonpark.co.uk
www.bodafonpark.co.uk
Pitches For ⛺ ⛐ ⛟ **Total** 40
Acreage 4 **Open** March **to** Oct
Access Good **Site** Level
Quarter of an hours walk to the lovely beach at Lligwy.
Facilities symbols
Nearby Facilities symbols
Nearest Town Benllech
Directions From Benllech continue along the A5025, at the roundabout turn left, after 2 miles go down a three lane hill and back up, at the top of the hill turn right and the site is approx. ½ a mile on the left.
⛺ Bangor

MOELFRE

Tyddyn Isaf Camping & Caravan Park, Lligwy Bay, Dulas, Anglesey, LL70 9PQ
Tel: 01248 410203
Email: mail@tyddynisaf.co.uk
www.tyddynisaf.co.uk
Pitches For ⛺ ⛐ ⛟ **Total** 80
Acreage 16 **Open** March **to** October
Access Good **Site** Sloping
Family run park with a private footpath to a fine, sandy beach. Loo of the Year Winner, AA 5 Pennant Premier Park, David Bellamy Gold Award, Welcome Host Award, WTB 5 Star Graded and Finalist of Practical Caravan Top 100 Parks in 2011.
Facilities symbols
Nearby Facilities symbols
Nearest Town Benllech
Directions Take the A5025 from Britannia Bridge, go through Benllech approx. 8 miles, continue to Moelfre Island via left staying on the main road to Brynrefail Village. Turn right opposite the telephone box and International camping sign, we are ½ mile on the right down the lane.
⛺ Bangor

MOELFRE

Tyn Rhos Caravan Park, Moelfre, Anglesey, LL72 8NL
Tel: 01248 852417
Email: robert@bodafonpark.co.uk
www.bodafonpark.co.uk
Pitches For ⛺ ⛐ ⛟ **Total** 50
Acreage 10 **Open** March **to** October
Access Good **Site** Level
Near Lligwy Beach. Surrounded by numerous footpaths, including coastal path, fishing and ancient monuments.
Facilities symbols
Nearby Facilities symbols
Nearest Town Benllech
Directions From Benllech proceed along the A5025 to the roundabout, turn right to Moelfre and at MDM Design turn left for 2 miles, site is on the right.
⛺ Bangor

NEWBOROUGH

Awelfryn Caravan Park, Newborough, Llanfairpw, Anglesey, LL61 6SG
Tel: 01248 440230
Pitches For ⛺ ⛐ ⛟
Acreage 1½ **Open** March **to** Oct
Access Good **Site** Level
Nearest Bus Stop (Miles) ¼
1½ miles to the beach.
Facilities symbols
Nearby Facilities symbols
Nearest Town Newborough
Directions From Menai Bridge take the A4080 left to Newborough. In the village at the crossroads before the White Lion Pub, turn left into Church Road, site is on the left after the church.
⛺ Llanfairpw

PENTRAETH

Clai Mawr Caravan Park, Park Lodge, Pentraeth, Anglesey, LL75 8DX
Tel: 01248 450467
Email: claimawr@onetel.net
www.claimawr-holidays-anglesey.co.uk
Pitches For ⛐ ⛟ **Total** 14
Acreage 4 **Open** March **to** October
Access Good **Site** Level
Nearest Bus Stop (Miles) Entrance
Quiet, family run site overlooking Red Wharf Bay and the Snowdon mountains.
Facilities symbols
Nearby Facilities symbols
Nearest Town Benllech
Directions On the A55, cross Britannia Bridge then take the second exit, turn right onto the A5025. Go through Pentraeth until the 40mph sign, entrance is on the right.
⛺ Bangor

PENTRAETH

Rhos Caravan Park, Rhos Farm, Pentraeth, Anglesey, LL75 8DZ
Tel: 01248 450214
Email: rhosfarm@googlemail.com
www.rhoscaravanpark.co.uk
Pitches For ⛺ ⛐ ⛟ **Total** 90
Acreage 15 **Open** March **to** October
Access Good **Site** Level
Nearest Bus Stop (Miles) ¼
Near beach and central location for Anglesey, good views of Snowdonia.
Facilities symbols
Nearby Facilities symbols
Nearest Town Red Wharf Bay
Directions Through Pentraeth on A5025 main road. Site entrance on left 1 mile north of Pentraeth.
⛺ Bangor

RHOSNEIGR

Shoreside Camp & Caravan Park, Station Road, Rhosneigr, Anglesey, LL64 5QX
Tel: 01407 810279
Email: shoresidecamping@gmail.com
www.shoresidecamping.co.uk
Pitches For ▲ ⬛ ⬛ **Total** 100
Acreage 6 **Open** Easter **to** October
Access Good **Site** Lev/Slope
Nearest Bus Stop (Miles) Outside
Bowling and tennis. Near the beach and opposite a golf club. 10 miles from Holyhead, day trips to Dublin.
Facilities ⬛ ⬛ ⬛ ⬛ ⬛ ⬛ ⬛ ⬛ ⬛ ⬛ ⬛ ⬛
Nearby Facilities ⬛ ⬛ ⬛ ⬛ ⬛ ⬛ ⬛ ⬛
Nearest Town Rhosneigr
Directions Take the A55 to junction 5, then take the A4080 to Rhosneigr, opposite the golf club.
⬛ Rhosneigr

RHOSNEIGR

Tyn Llidiart Camping Site, Tyn Llidiart, Tywyn Trewan, Bryngwran, Anglesey, LL65 3SW
Tel: 01407 810678
Email: ruthtynllidiart@aol.com
Pitches For ▲ ⬛ ⬛ **Total** 5
Acreage ¾ **Open** All Year
Access Fair **Site** Level
Pleasant, quiet site near the beach.
Facilities ⬛ ⬛ ⬛ ⬛ ⬛ ⬛ ⬛
Nearby Facilities ⬛ ⬛ ⬛ ⬛ ⬛ ⬛ ⬛
Nearest Town Rhosneigr
Directions Take the A5 to Bryngwran, turn by the Post Office, after approx. 1 mile you will pass a garage on the left and three white cottages on the right, at the third cottage turn right, then fork right, go over the cattle grid and the site is on the left.
⬛ Holyhead

TREARDDUR BAY

Tyn Rhos Camping Site, Ravenspoint Road, Trearddur Bay, Holyhead, Anglesey, LL65 2AX
Tel: 01407 860369
Pitches For ▲ ⬛ ⬛ **Total** 200
Acreage 20 **Open** March **to** October
Access Good **Site** Lev/Slope
Nearest Bus Stop (Miles) ½
Well established family run site, rural location with modern facilities. Views of Snowdonia, coastal walks, sandy beaches (Blue Flag Award) 10 minutes. Holyhead port town to Ireland - 3 miles. Separate rally field also available. Visit Wales 3 Star Graded.
Facilities ⬛ ⬛ ⬛ ⬛ ⬛ ⬛ ⬛ ⬛ ⬛ ⬛
Nearby Facilities ⬛ ⬛ ⬛ ⬛ ⬛ ⬛ ⬛
Nearest Town Holyhead
Directions Follow the A55 across Anglesey, leaving at junction 2. First left off roundabout and follow signs for Trearddur Bay B4545. After approx. 1½ miles turn right onto Ravenspoint Road (after the Spar shop on the left), ¾ miles to the shared entrance, take left hand branch.
⬛ Holyhead

TREARDDUR BAY

Valley of the Rocks, Porthdafarch Road, Trearddur Bay, Holyhead, Anglesey, LL65 2LL
Tel: 01407 765787
Open March **to** Oct
Access Good **Site** Lev/Slope
Nearest Bus Stop (Miles) 1

Near to the beach, boating, fishing, Southstack Lighthouse, Holyhead Mountain and many nice walks.
Facilities ⬛ ⬛ ⬛ ⬛ ⬛ ⬛ ⬛ ⬛ ⬛ ⬛ ⬛ ⬛
Nearby Facilities ⬛ ⬛ ⬛ ⬛ ⬛ ⬛ ⬛ ⬛
Nearest Town Holyhead
⬛ Holyhead

VALLEY

Bodowyr Caravan & Camping Park, Bodowyr, Bodedern, Anglesey, LL65 3SS
Tel: 01407 741171
Email: bodowyr@yahoo.com
www.bodowyrcaravansite.co.uk
Pitches For ▲ ⬛ ⬛ **Total** 30
Acreage 2 **Open** March **to** October
Access Good **Site** Level
Nearest Bus Stop (Miles) ½
Peaceful farm 3 miles from beaches and close to a wide range of sporting facilities. Convenient for touring Anglesey and ferries to Ireland.
Facilities ⬛ ⬛ ⬛ ⬛ ⬛ ⬛ ⬛ ⬛ ⬛ ⬛ ⬛ ⬛ ⬛ ⬛ ⬛
Nearby Facilities ⬛ ⬛ ⬛ ⬛ ⬛ ⬛
Nearest Town Holyhead
Directions From Holyhead take the A55, turn off at the Bodedern exit (junction 4) and turn left for Bodedern. Bodowyr is the first turning on the left. Site has international camping signs from the A5 junction.
⬛ Valley

VALLEY

Pen-Y-Bont Farm Caravan & Camping Site, Four Mile Bridge, Valley, Anglesey, LL65 3EY
Tel: 01407 740481
Email: rowennpr@aol.com
Pitches For ▲ ⬛ ⬛ **Total** 20
Acreage 4 **Open** Easter **to** End Oct
Access Good **Site** Level
Nearest Bus Stop (Miles) ¼
Small, quiet, family site in an idyllic scenic location, near to beautiful beaches and the coastal path for walking. Ideal location for wind surfing, canoeing and cycling.
Facilities ⬛ ⬛ ⬛ ⬛ ⬛ ⬛ ⬛
Nearby Facilities ⬛ ⬛ ⬛ ⬛ ⬛ ⬛ ⬛
Nearest Town Holyhead/Trearddur Bay
Directions Leave the A55 at exit 2 following signs for Valley and Trearddur Bay (approx 2 miles). Site is on the right before approaching Four Mile Bridge.
⬛ Valley/Holyhead

BRIDGEND

PORTHCAWL

Brodawel Camping Park, Brodawel House, Moor Lane, Nottage, Porthcawl, Bridgend, CF36 3EJ
Tel: 01656 783231
Pitches For ▲ ⬛ ⬛ **Total** 100
Acreage 5 **Open** April **to** October
Access Good **Site** Level
Nearest Bus Stop (Miles) ¼
Convenient to all beaches, very central for touring area. Off Licence. Designer Village Wales 3 miles.
Facilities ⬛ ⬛ ⬛ ⬛ ⬛ ⬛ ⬛ ⬛ ⬛
Nearby Facilities ⬛ ⬛ ⬛ ⬛ ⬛ ⬛ ⬛ ⬛
Nearest Town Porthcawl
Directions Leave the M4 at junction 37, turn onto the A4229 for Porthcawl for 2 miles, signposted Moor Lane.
⬛ Pyle

CAERPHILLY

ABERCARN

Cwmcarn Forest Campsite, Cwmcarn Forest Visitor Centre, Nantcarn Road, Cwmcarn, Crosskeys, Caerphilly, NP11 7FA
Tel: 01495 272001
Email: cwmcarn-vc@caerphilly.gov.uk
www.cwmcarnforest.co.uk
Pitches For ▲ ⬛ ⬛ **Total** 26
Open 02-Jan **to** 23-Dec
Access Good
Nearest Bus Stop (Miles) ½
Beautiful valley setting. Good local walks and fishing. 17km mountain bike trail.
Facilities ⬛ ⬛ ⬛ ⬛ ⬛ ⬛ ⬛ ⬛ ⬛ ⬛ ⬛ ⬛
Nearby Facilities ⬛
Nearest Town Crosskeys
Directions Leave the M4 at junction 28 (signposted Risca Brynmawr) and take the A467 north for approx 7 miles. Forest Drive is well signposted with brown tourism signs.
⬛ Crosskeys

BLACKWOOD

Penyfan Caravan & Leisure Park, Manmoel Road, Oakdale, Blackwood, Caerphilly, NP12 0HY
Tel: 01495 226636
Email:
caroline@penyfancaravanpark.co.uk
www.penyfancaravanpark.co.uk
Pitches For ▲ ⬛ ⬛ **Total** 100
Acreage 42 **Open** All Year
Access Good **Site** Level
Quiet site. Ideal for walking and touring. Great for the whole family.
Facilities ⬛ ⬛ ⬛ ⬛ ⬛ ⬛ ⬛ ⬛ ⬛ ⬛ ⬛ ⬛ ⬛ ⬛ ⬛ ⬛
Nearby Facilities ⬛
Nearest Town Blackwood
Directions Leave the M4 at junction 28 and take the A467 to Crumlin. At the traffic lights turn left and follow signs to Penyfan Pond, at traffic lights turn right, at roundabout take third exit to Manmoel.
⬛ Newbridge

CARMARTHENSHIRE

CARMARTHEN

Coedhirion Farm Park, Coedhirion, Llanddarog, Carmarthen, Carmarthenshire, SA32 8BQ
Tel: 01267 275666
Email: welshfarmhouse@hotmail.com
www.welshfarm.co.uk
Pitches For ▲ ⬛ ⬛ **Total** 10
Acreage 1½ **Open** March **to** October
Access Good **Site** Level
Nearest Bus Stop (Miles) Entrance
A small Park on a working farm amidst woodland and countryside. 5 minutes from the National Botanic Garden of Wales and 15 minutes from Ffos Las Racecourse. B&B and sewlf catering cottage also available.
Facilities ⬛ ⬛ ⬛ ⬛ ⬛ ⬛ ⬛
Nearby Facilities ⬛ ⬛ ⬛ ⬛ ⬛ ⬛ ⬛ ⬛
Nearest Town Carmarthen
Directions From Carmarthen take the A48 east for 6 miles, turn right then immediately right again into our driveway.
⬛ Carmarthen

CARMARTHEN

Pant Farm Caravan & Camping Park, Llangunnor Road, Carmarthen, Carmarthenshire, SA31 2HY
Tel: 01267 235665
Pitches For ▲ ⬛ ⬛

Open March **to** November
Access Good **Site** Level
Nearest Bus Stop (Miles) Entrance
ADULTS ONLY SITE. Central and convenient location for touring South Wales.
Facilities ⚿ ⌦ ⌂ ⏚ ▣ ☀
Nearby Facilities ⌦ ✔ ⚓ ☂ ∪ ♪
Nearest Town Carmarthen
Directions On the B4300 east of Carmarthen.
⇥ Carmarthen

CLYNDERWEN

Derwenlas, Clynderwen, Carmarthenshire, SA66 7SU
Tel: 01437 563504
Pitches For ▲ ♿ ⊟ **Total** 4
Open April **to** September
Access Good **Site** Level
Facilities ⚿ ⌦ ⌂ ⊙ ⌨ ▣ ☎
⛽ ▤ ⚑ ⌂ ☀
Nearby Facilities ⌦ ✔ ⚓ ☂ ∪
Nearest Town Narberth
Directions 3 to 3½ miles north of Narberth on the A478.
⇥ Clynderwen

CROSS HANDS

Black Lion Caravan & Camping Park, 78 Black Lion Road, Gorslas, Cross Hands, Llanelli, Carmarthenshire, SA14 6RU
Tel: 01269 845365
Email: baz@caravansite.com
www.caravansite.com
Pitches For ▲ ♿ ⊟ **Total** 45
Acreage 12 **Open** April **to** September
Access Good **Site** Lev/Slope
Nearest Bus Stop (Miles) ¼
Surrounded by trees and natural beauty. Near to the Botanic Garden of Wales, Aberglasney - A Garden Lost in Time, Carreg Cennon Castle, Millenium Coastal Path and Llaneli.
Facilities ♿ ⚿ ⌦ ⌂ ⊙ ⌨ ▤ ▣ ☎
⛽ ▤ ⚑ ⌂ ☀ ⚲ ☏
Nearby Facilities ⌦ ✔
Nearest Town Cross Hands
Directions From the A48 at Cross Hands, follow signs to Gorslas, turn sharp right at the crossroads into Black Lion Road, site is ½ mile on the right.
⇥ Ammanford

KIDWELLY

Tanylan Farm Holidays, Tanylan Farm, Kidwelly, Carmarthenshire, SA17 5HJ
Tel: 01267 267306
Email: tanylanfarm@gmail.com
www.tanylanfarmholidays.co.uk
Pitches For ▲ ♿ ⊟ **Total** 100
Acreage 8 **Open** Easter **to** End Sept
Access Good **Site** Level
Level ground on a former dairy farm. 400 yards from the beach. Membership to Park Resorts.
Facilities ♿ ⚿ ⌦ ⌂ ⊙ ⌨ ▤ ▣ ☎
⛽ ⛽ ⊙ ▤ ⌂ ☀
Nearby Facilities ⌦ ✔ ∪ ♪
Nearest Town Kidwelly
Directions In Kidwelly turn left at the Spar Supermarket, take the coastal road to Ferryside for approx. 1 mile and turn left at the duck pond.
⇥ Kidwelly

LAUGHARNE

Broadway Caravan Park, Broadway, Laugharne, Carmarthenshire, SA33 4NU
Tel: 01994 427272
Pitches For ▲ ♿ ⊟ **Total** 6
Acreage 2
Access Good **Site** Level
Nearest Bus Stop (Miles) Outside

Disabled toilet & shower.
Facilities ⚿ ⌦ ⌂ ☎ ⊙ ⌨ ▣ ☀
Nearby Facilities ⌦ ✔ ⚓ ☂ ∪ ♪ ⚲
Nearest Town Laugharne
Directions Take the A4066 from St. Clears to Laugharne, continue to Pendine and site is ½ mile on the left.
⇥ Carmarthen

LLANDDEUSANT

Black Mountain Caravan Park, Llanddeusant, Llangadog, Carmarthenshire, SA19 9YG
Tel: 01550 740217
Email: davidandsharon@blackmountainholidays.co.uk
www.blackmountainholidays.co.uk
Pitches For ▲ ♿ ⊟ **Total** 25
Acreage 6 **Open** All Year
Access Good **Site** Lev/Slope
Small family run Park set in the Brecon Beacons. Ideal for walking, fishing and caving.
Facilities ⚿ ⚿ ⌦ ⌂ ⊙ ⌨ ▤ ▣ ☎ ☎
Nearby Facilities ✔ ∪
Nearest Town Llangadog
Directions Take the A40 to Llangadog then the A4069 signposted Brynaman. Turn left at a disused pub (Three Horseshoes) and continue for 3 miles to Red Pig Pub.
⇥ Llangadog

LLANDOVERY

Camping & Caravanning Club Site, Rhandirmwyn, Llandovery, Carmarthenshire, SA20 0NT
Tel: 01550 760257
www.campingandcaravanningclub.co.uk/rhandirmwyn
Pitches For ▲ ♿ ⊟ **Total** 90
Acreage 11 **Open** 29-Mar **to** 05-Nov
Access Good **Site** Level
Set in the beautiful Welsh countryside on the banks of the Afon Tywi. Ideal for fishing. Lodges available for hire. WTB 4 Star Graded, AA 3 Pennants, David Bellamy Gold Award and Loo of the Year Award. Non members welcome. You can also call us on 0845 130 7633.
Facilities ♿ ⚿ ⌂ ⌦ ⌂ ⊙ ⌨ ▤ ▣ ☎
⊙ ▤ ⚑ ▣ ⌂ ☀ ⚲ ☏
Nearby Facilities ⌦ ✔ ∪
Nearest Town Llandovery
Directions From Llandovery take the A483, turn left signposted Rhandirmwyn. Turn left at the Post Office in Rhandirmwyn, site is on the left before the river.
⇥ Llandovery

LLANDOVERY

Erwlon Caravan & Camping Park, Brecon Road, Llandovery, Carmarthenshire, SA20 0RD
Tel: 01550 721021
Email: enquiries@erwlon.co.uk
www.erwlon.co.uk
Pitches For ▲ ♿ ⊟ **Total** 80
Acreage 10 **Open** All Year
Access Good **Site** Level
Nearest Bus Stop (Miles) ¼
Ideal touring base for South Wales. Award winning facilities.
Facilities ♿ ⚿ ▤ ⌂ ⌦ ⌂ ⊙ ⌨ ▤ ▣ ☎
⛽ ⊙ ▤ ⚑ ▣ ✔ ☀ ☏
Nearby Facilities ⌦ ✔ ∪ ♪
Nearest Town Llandovery
Directions ½ a mile east of Llandovery off the A40 towards Brecon.
⇥ Llandovery

LLANGADOG

Abermarlais Caravan Park, Llangadog, Carmarthenshire, SA19 9NG
Tel: 01550 777868
Email: aberma@tiscali.co.uk
www.abermarlaiscaravanpark.co.uk
Pitches For ▲ ♿ ⊟ **Total** 88
Acreage 20 **Open** 16-Mar **to** 16-Nov
Access Good **Site** Level
Nearest Bus Stop (Miles) Outside Brecon Beacons National Park.
Facilities ⚿ ⌂ ⌦ ⌂ ⊙ ☀
⛽ ⊙ ▤ ⚑ ⌂ ▣
Nearby Facilities ✔ ∪
Nearest Town Llandovery
Directions On the A40, 6 miles west of Llandovery and 6 miles east of Llandeilo.
⇥ Llangadog

LLANGADOG

Pont Aber, Gwynfe, Llangadog, Carmarthenshire, SA19 9TA
Tel: 01550 740202
Email: info@pontaber.com
www.pontaber.com
Pitches For ▲ ♿ ⊟
Access Good **Site** Level
Alongside the Swadde River in the Brecon Beacons. Luxury 4 Star Bed & Breakfast and a self catering cottage.
Facilities ⌂ ▤ ⚑ ⌂ ✔ ⚲ ☏
Nearby Facilities ✔ ∪
Nearest Town Llandielo/Llandovery
Directions From Llandielo or Llandovery take the A40 to Llangadog, then take the A4069 towards Brynaman for 4 miles.
⇥ Llangadog

LLANWRDA

Maesbach Caravan & Camping Park, Horseshoe Valley, Ffarmers, Llanwrda, Carmarthenshire, SA19 8EX
Tel: 01558 650650
Email: admin@maesbach.plus.com
Pitches For ▲ ♿ ⊟ **Total** 20
Acreage 5 **Open** March **to** Oct
Access Good **Site** Lev/Slope
Nearest Bus Stop (Miles) 1
Tranquil family run peace lovers' retreat with magnificent countryside views, ideal for a relaxing holiday escape. Quiet lanes are perfect for walking, cycling and horse riding, or explore sandy beaches at the coast. Ideally placed for touring West Wales. Visit Llyn Brianne Reservoir, Roman Dolaucothi Gold Mines, Aberglasny or National Botanical Gardens, RSPB Reserve or Red Kite feeding station at Llanddeusant, Abergorlech mountain bike trail at Brechfa Forest or the village of Llandewi Brefi as featured in the TV series 'Little Britain', or why not just stay on the park and enjoy the silence!!
Facilities ⚿ ⌂ ⌦ ⌂ ⌂ ⌨ ☀
⛽ ⊙ ⚑ ▣ ☀ ⚲
Nearby Facilities ✔ ∪
Nearest Town Lampeter
Directions Turn right off A482 (Llanwrda to Lampeter road) 1½ miles past Pumpsaint sp Ffarmers, after approx. 1½ miles at Ffarmers turn right opposite the Drovers Arms Public House, Park is on the left in approx. ¾ miles.
⇥ Llanwrda

NEWCASTLE EMLYN

Afon Teifi Caravan & Camping Park, Pentrecagal, Newcastle Emlyn, Carmarthenshire, SA38 9HT
Tel: 01559 370532
Email: afonteifi@btinternet.com
www.afonteifi.co.uk
Pitches For ▲ ♿ ⊟ **Total** 110
Acreage 6½ **Open** March **to** October

WALES

CARMARTHENSHIRE, CEREDIGION (CARDIGANSHIRE)

Access Good **Site** Level
Nearest Bus Stop (Miles) Outside
Situated by the River Teifi in the beautiful Teifi Valley. Only 20 minutes from numerous Cardigan Bay beaches. Swimming nearby. Ideal touring centre.
Facilities ⬧ ✦ 🅷 🆎 ᴾ ☉ ⬡ ↵ 🔲 🞉 ♨
🅿 ⓘ🄲 🅿 🅰 🄼 ✦ 🔌 ✦ ⚓
Nearby Facilities ⌐ ✦ ♪
Nearest Town Newcastle Emlyn
Directions On the A484 2 miles east of Newcastle Emlyn.
⚉ Carmarthen

NEWCASTLE EMLYN
Moelfryn Caravan & Camp Park, Pant-Y-Bwlch, Newcastle Emlyn, Carmarthenshire, SA38 9JE
Tel: 01559 371231
Email:
moelfryn@moelfryncaravanpark.co.uk
www.moelfryncaravanpark.co.uk
Pitches For ⛺ ♟ ♞ **Total** 25
Acreage 3 **Open** 01-Mar **to** 10-Jan
Access Good **Site** Level
Situated in a tranquil, rural setting with panoramic views for relaxation. Perfect base for exploring the beauty of West Wales.
Facilities ✦ 🅷 🆎 ᴾ ☉ ⬡ 🞉
ॐ 🄲 🅰 🔌 🄼 🔲 🄳 🗻 ♨ 🛜 ✦ ☂
Nearby Facilities ⌐ ✦ ⚓ ↘ ∪ ⚡ ↗
Nearest Town Newcastle Emlyn
Directions From Carmarthen take the A484 to Cynwyl Elfed. Pass the Blue Bell Inn and take the left fork after approx. 200 yards B4333 towards Hermon and stay on this road for 7 miles. There is a brown sign on your left, take that turn and site is ¼ mile on the righ
⚉ Carmarthen

PEMBREY
Pembrey Country Park Caravan Club Site, Pembrey, Llanelli, Carmarthenshire, SA16 0EJ
Tel: 01554 834369
www.caravanclub.co.uk
Pitches For ♞ ♞ **Total** 130
Acreage 12 **Open** March **to** Jan
Access Good **Site** Level
Set on the edge of a 520 acre country park. Vast range of outdoor sporting activities available including horse riding, dry slope skiing and toboggan riding, pitch 'n' putt and sea fishing. Ideal for walkers and bird/butterfly watchers. Only 1 mile from a Blue Flag sandy beach. Non members welcome. Booking essential.
Facilities ⬧ ✦ 🅷 🆎 ᴾ 🔲 🞉
🅿 ⓘ🄲 🅰 🄼 🔌 🄳 🞉 🛜
Nearby Facilities ⌐ ✦ ⚓ 🗻 ∪

Nearest Town Llanelli
Directions Leave M4 at junc 48 and take A4138 sp Llanelli, on the outskirts of Llanelli turn right onto A484. In Pembrey Village turn left at signpost Pembrey Country Park and follow signs to Country Park, site is on the right before park gates.
⚉ Llanelli

ST. CLEARS
Afon Lodge Caravan Park, Parciau Bach, St Clears, Carmarthenshire, SA33 4LG
Tel: 01994 230647
Email: egoodman35@hotmail.com
Pitches For ⛺ ♞ **Total** 70
Open 01-Mar **to** 09-Jan
Access Good **Site** Level
Tranquil site, ideal for touring.
Facilities ✦ 🅷 🆎 ᴾ ⬡ ↵ 🔲 🞉
🄲 🅰 🄼 🔌 🄳 ♨
Nearby Facilities ⌐ ✦ ⚓ 🗻 ∪ ↗ ⚡ ↗
Nearest Town St Clears
Directions From St. Clears traffic lights take Llanboidy Road. In a 100 yards fork right, then first right, first right.
⚉ Carmarthen/Whitland

CEREDIGION (CARDIGANSHIRE)
ABERAERON
Aeron Coast Caravan Park, North Road, Aberaeron, Ceredigion, SA46 0JF
Tel: 01545 570349
Email: enquiries@aeroncoast.co.uk
www.aeroncoast.co.uk
Pitches For ⛺ ♞ ♞ **Total** 100
Acreage 8 **Open** 01-Mar **to** End Oct
Access Good **Site** Level
Nearest Bus Stop (Miles) ¼
Good family facilities. Aberaeron is a recognised beauty spot. Picturesque harbour, coastal and river walks. Only 200yds from shops. 5 Star Graded.
Facilities ⬧ ✦ 🅷 🆎 ᴾ ☉ ↵ 🔲 🞉
ॐ ⓘ🄲 🅰 🔌 ✖ 🄼 🄳 🗻 🞉 🛜
Nearby Facilities ⌐ ✦ ⚓ 🗻 ∪ ⚡ ↗ ↗
Nearest Town Aberaeron
Directions Main coastal road A487 on northern edge of Aberaeron, follow brown tourism signs. Filling station at entrance.
⚉ Aberystwyth

ABERAERON
Cwmsaeson Caravan Park, Oakford, Aberaeron, Ceredigion, SA47 0RY
Tel: 01545 581067
Email: elin@cwmsaeson.co.uk
www.cwmsaeson.co.uk
Pitches For ♞ ♞ **Total** 25
Acreage 3 **Open** March **to** October
Access Good **Site** Level

Quiet family site set in open countryside with wonderful views. Ideal touring location for the coast.
Facilities ⬧ ✦ 🅷 🆎 ᴾ ☉ 🞉 ♨ 🗻
Nearby Facilities ✦ ∪
Directions From the A487 at Llwyncelyn (from the south) turn right towards Oakford. After 1¼ miles at the T-Junction in Oakford Village turn left, site is 800 yards on the left.
⚉ Aberystwyth

ABERPORTH
Caerfelin Caravan Park, Aberporth, Nr Cardigan, Ceredigion, SA43 2BZ
Tel: 01239 810540
Pitches For ♞ ♞ **Total** 5
Open Mid March **to** 31-Oct
Access Good **Site** Level
Nearest Bus Stop (Miles) ¼
Well sheltered park nestled in a woodland valley. Just a 5 minute walk to sandy beaches and the village of Aberporth. Friendly welcome assured.
Facilities ⬧ ✦ 🅷 🆎 ᴾ ☉ ↵ 🔲 🞉
🅿 🄲 🔌 🄳
Nearby Facilities ⌐ ✦ ⚓ 🗻 ∪ ⚡
Directions Turn north off the A487 at Blaenannerch onto the B433 to Aberporth. Enter the village of Aberporth and turn right at St. Cynwyls Church, park is 200 yards on the left.
⚉ Carmarthen

ABERPORTH
Dolgelynen Holiday Park, Aberporth, Nr Cardigan, Ceredigion, SA43 2HS
Tel: 01239 811095
Pitches For ♞ ♞ ♞
Access Good **Site** Lev/Slope
Nearest Bus Stop (Miles) Outside
Quiet site overlooking the sea. 1 mile from the beach. Many eating places close by.
Facilities ✦ 🅷 🆎 ᴾ 🔲 🞉 🞉 🅿 🄲 🔌 🄳
Nearby Facilities ⌐ ✦ ⚓ 🗻 ∪
Nearest Town Cardigan
Directions From Cardigan take the A487, then take the B4333, second turning. From Aberystwyth take the A487 towards Cardigan, before Cardigan take the first turning onto the B4333 sp Aberporth, site is 1 mile on the right.
⚉ Cardigan

ABERYSTWYTH
Bryncarnedd Caravan Park, Clarach Road, Aberystwyth, Ceredigion, SY23 3DG
Tel: 01970 612444
Email: marinehotell@btconnect.com
www.marinehotelaberystwyth.co.uk
Pitches For ⛺ ♞ ♞ ♞ **Total** 50
Open All Year
Access Good **Site** Level

WALES

Nearest Bus Stop (Miles) Outside
Ideal touring.
Facilities 🚻 ♿ ₽ ⌐ ⊙ 🍴 🍺
🏪 ⊙ ⊕ ▣ ⌂ 🏕 ※ 🛈 ♨
Nearby Facilities ⌐ ✓ ⚓ ✕ U ⚲ ♪ ⚞
Nearest Town Aberystwyth
Directions Take the A487 from Aberystwyth
and turn left onto the B4572, Bryncarnedd is
¼ of a mile. ½ a mile from Aberystwyth.
🚆 Aberystwyth

ABERYSTWYTH

Morfa Bychan Holiday Park, Aberystwyth,
Ceredigion, SY23 4QQ
Tel: 01970 617254
Email: morfa@hillandale.co.uk
www.hillandale.co.uk
Pitches For ▲ ⊞ 🚐 🚗 **Total** 75
Acreage 6 **Open** March to October
Access Good **Site** Sloping
100 acre park overlooking Cardigan Bay with
our own private beach. Heated swimming
pool, water hook-ups.
Facilities ♿ ⅃ ▣ 🚻 ♿ ₽ ⌐ ⊙ 🍴 ⊿ 🍺 ⚙ 🍺
🏪 ⊙ ▣ 🏪 ⌂ ☰ 🕱 ⊟ 🍴 ⚙ ※ ♨
Nearby Facilities ⌐ ✓ ⚓ ✕ U ♪
Nearest Town Aberystwyth
Directions Take the A487 south from
Aberystwyth, after ½ mile signposted to the
right, but this is NOT suitable for touring
caravans who should continue for 2½ miles
and turn right at the second sign. Follow signs
for 1½ miles.
🚆 Aberystwyth

ABERYSTWYTH

Ocean View, North Beach, Clarach Bay,
Aberystwyth, Ceredigion, SY23 3DT
Tel: 01970 828425
Email: enquiries@oceanviewholidays.com
www.oceanviewholidays.com
Pitches For 🚐 🚗 **Total** 24
Open March to October
Access Good **Site** Level
Nearest Bus Stop (Miles) Outside
Small select park, short walk to popular
beach. Glorious views, ideal touring area of
magic Mid-Wales.
Facilities ⅃ ▣ 🚻 ♿ ₽ ⌐ ⊙ ⊿ 🔲 🍺
🏪 ⊙ ▣ 🏪 ⌂ 🕱 ▣ 🕱 ※ ✓
Nearby Facilities ⌐ ✓ ⚓ ✕ U ⚲ ⚞
Nearest Town Aberystwyth
Directions Take the A487 Aberystwyth to
Machynlleth road. Turn in Bow Street for
Clarach Bay. Follow road to the beach.
Ocean View is on the right.
🚆 Aberystwyth

BORTH

Brynowen Holiday Park, Brynowen Lane,
Borth, Nr Aberystwyth, Ceredigion, SY24
5LS
Tel: 0843 309 2551
Email: holidaysales.brynowen@park-
resorts.com
www.park-resorts.com
Pitches For 🚐 🚗
Open April to October
Access Good **Site** Sloping
Nearest Bus Stop (Miles) Outside
Near to Cardigan Bay and close to the beach.
Facilities ⅃ 🚻 ♿ ₽ ⌐ ⊙ ⊿ 🔲 🍺
🏪 🕱 ✕ ♨ ⌂ 🕱 ▣ ※
Nearby Facilities
Nearest Town Aberystwyth
Directions Take the A487 through
Aberystwyth and turn left onto the B4353,
the Park is on your left as you approach
Borth.
🚆 Borth

BORTH

Glanlerry Caravan Park, Borth,
Ceredigion, SY24 5LU
Tel: 01970 871413
Email:
enquiries@glanlerrycaravanpark.co.uk
www.glanlerrycaravanpark.co.uk
Pitches For ▲ ⊞ 🚐
Open April to October
Access Good **Site** Level
Nearest Bus Stop (Miles) Outside
Family only camping site. Sheltered touring
area, alongside a river bank with spectacular
scenery. ½ a mile from the beach.
Facilities ♿ ⅃ 🚻 ♿ ₽ ⌐ ⊙ ⊿ 🍺
🔲 ⊙ ▣ 🕱 ▣ ⊟ ☰ ※ 🛈
Nearby Facilities ⌐ ✓ ⚓ U ⚞
Nearest Town Borth
🚆 Borth

CARDIGAN

**Brongwyn Touring Caravan & Camping
Park,** Brongwyn Mawr, Penparc, Cardigan,
Ceredigion, SA43 1SA
Tel: 01239 613644
Email: enquiries@cardiganholidays.co.uk
www.tentsandtourers.co.uk
Pitches For ▲ ⊞ 🚐 **Total** 20
Acreage 3 **Open** May to Sept
Access Good **Site** Level
Nearest Bus Stop (Miles) ½
Peaceful countryside setting with an indoor
pool and spa (discounted multi-day passes
for campers). 3 miles from a beautiful beach.
Facilities ♿ ⅃ 🚻 ♿ ₽ ⌐ ⊙ ⊿ 🍺
🏪 🕱 ✕ ♨ 🕱 ⅃ ⊟ ▣ 🕱 ☰ ※
Nearby Facilities ⌐ ✓ ⚓ U ⚲
Nearest Town Cardigan
Directions 3 miles north of Cardigan on the
A487, turn left at the crossroads in Penparc
signed Mwnt. Go straight across the next small
crossroads and turn right opposite the sign.
🚆 Aberystwyth

CARDIGAN

Penralltllyn Caravan Park, Cilgerran,
Cardigan, Pembrokeshire, SA43 2PR
Tel: 01239 682350
Pitches For ▲ ⊞ 🚐 **Total** 20
Acreage 1 **Open** Easter to Oct
Site Level
Approx. 15 minutes from lots of beaches.
Plenty of woodland walks and lakes in the
valley.
Facilities ⅃ 🚻 ₽ ⌐ ⊙ 🕱 ⊿
Nearby Facilities ⌐ ✓ ⚓ U ⚲
Nearest Town Cardigan
Directions 3 miles south east of Cardigan
on the A484 (Cardigan to Carmarthen road).
Turn over the bridge at Llechryd, go straight
for 1½ miles, after crossroads Site is second
entrance on the right. Wide farm lane which
is kept in good condition.
🚆 Carmarthen

CARDIGAN

Ty-Gwyn Caravan Park, Min-Y-Mor, Mwnt,
Cardigan, Ceredigion, SA43 1QH
Tel: 01239 614518
Pitches For ▲ ⊞ 🚐 **Total** 30
Acreage 6 **Open** April to October
Site Lev/Slope
Farm site by an ancient church. Just a 10
minute walk to Mwnts sandy beach. Dolphins
and seals are often seen in the bay.
Facilities ⅃ 🚻 ♿ ₽ ⌐ ⊙ 🕱 ▣
Nearby Facilities ⌐ ✓ ⚓ ✕ U ⚲
Nearest Town Cardigan
Directions Leave the A487 at Cardigan to
pick up the B4548 Gwbert and Mwnt road,
follow signs to Mwnt. 5 miles north west of
Cardigan.
🚆 Carmarthen

DEVILS BRIDGE

Erwbarfe Farm Caravan Park, Devils
Bridge, Aberystwyth, Ceredigion, SY23
3JR
Tel: 01970 890358
Email: enquiries@erwbarfe.co.uk
www.erwbarfe.co.uk
Pitches For ▲ ⊞ 🚐 **Total** 30
Acreage 7 **Open** March to Oct
Access Good **Site** Level/Sloping
Nearest Bus Stop (Miles) 2
Ideal area for walking, fishing, mountain
biking and bird watching (Red Kite area). 1
mile from Devils Bridge Waterfalls and only
3 miles from Nant-Yr-Arian Mountain Biking
Centre.
Facilities ⅃ 🚻 ♿ ₽ ⌐ ⊙ ⊿ 🔲 🍺
🕱 🏪 ⊙ ⌂ 🕱 ▣ 🕱 ※ 🛈 ✓ U ⚲
Nearby Facilities ⌐ ✓ ⚓ ✕ U ⚲
Nearest Town Aberystwyth
Directions 12 miles inland from Aberystwyth
take the A44, then take the A4120 in
Ponterwyd towards Devils Bridge.
🚆 Aberystwyth

DEVILS BRIDGE

Woodlands Caravan Park, Devils Bridge,
Aberystwyth, Ceredigion, SY23 3JW
Tel: 01970 890233
Email:
enquiries@woodlandsdevilsbridge.co.uk
www.woodlandsdevilsbridge.co.uk
Pitches For ▲ ⊞ 🚐 **Total** 50
Acreage 8 **Open** Easter to October
Access Good **Site** Level
Quiet country site adjoining a farm. Within
walking distance of the famous Devils Bridge
& Waterfalls and steam train. Excellent
mountain bike trail nearby and bike shelter
on site. Ideal for walking, bird watching,
fishing and touring, or just relaxing!
Facilities ⅃ 🚻 ♿ ₽ ⌐ ⊙ ⊿ 🔲 🍺
🕱 🏪 ⊙ ⌂ ✕ 🕱 ⅃ ⊟ ▣ 🕱 ☰ ※
Nearby Facilities ⌐ ✓ ⚓ ✕ U ⚲ ⚞
Nearest Town Aberystwyth
Directions 12 miles East of Aberystwyth on
A4120 in Devils Bridge village and 300yds
from bridge. Or 3 miles south west of
Ponterwyd, turn off A44 at Ponterwyd.
🚆 Aberystwyth

LAMPETER

Hafod Brynog Caravan Park, Ystrad
Aeron, Felinfach, Lampeter, Ceredigion,
SA48 8AE
Tel: 01570 470084
Email: hafod@brynog.wanadoo.co.uk
Pitches For ▲ ⊞ 🚐 **Total** 30
Acreage 8 **Open** Easter to End Sept
Access Good **Site** Lev/Slope
Nearest Bus Stop (Miles) ¼
A quiet site with beautiful views. 6 miles from
Cardigan Bay. Ideal for coastal and inland
touring, or just relaxing.
Facilities ⅃ 🚻 ₽ ⌐ ⊙ ⊿ 🔲 🍺
🏪 ⊙ ⊕ ▣ ⌂
Nearby Facilities ⌐ ✓ ⚓ ✕ U ⚲ ♪
Nearest Town Aberaeron
Directions On the main A482 Lampeter to
Aberaeron road, 6 miles from both. Site
entrance is opposite the church and next to
the pub in the village of Ystrad Aeron.
🚆 Aberystwyth

**Thank you for
choosing Cade's**

WALES

CEREDIGION (CARDIGANSHIRE)

LLANARTH

Llain Activity Centre, Llanarth, Ceredigion, SA47 0PZ
Tel: 01545 580127
Email: enquiries@llain.com
www.llain.com
Pitches For Å ⌂ ☝ **Total** 4
Acreage 2 **Open** April to Oct
Access Good **Site** Sloping
Nearest Bus Stop (Miles) ½
Daily activities on site during school holidays.
Facilities
Nearby Facilities
Nearest Town New Quay
Directions Take the A487 south from Aberaeron towards Cardigan for 3 miles.
⌖ Aberystwyth

LLANARTH

Llanina Caravan Park, Llanarth, Nr New Quay, Ceredigion, SA47 0NP
Tel: 01545 580947
Email: llaninacaravanpark@tiscali.co.uk
www.llaninacaravanpark.co.uk
Pitches For Å ⌂ ☝ **Total** 45
Acreage 5 **Open** 01-Apr to 29-Oct
Access Good **Site** Level
Nearest Bus Stop (Miles) Outside
2 miles from a sandy beach.
Facilities
Nearby Facilities
Nearest Town New Quay
Directions Entrance is on the A487 at the B4342 junction to New Quay. 20 miles south of Aberystwyth and 18 miles north of Cardigan.
⌖ Aberystwyth

LLANARTH

Shawsmead Caravan Club Site, Oakford, Llanarth, Ceredigion, SA47 0RN
Tel: 01545 580423
www.caravanclub.co.uk
Pitches For Å ⌂ ☝ **Total** 50
Acreage 4 **Open** March to Oct
Access Good **Site** Level
Peaceful meadowland site with pleasant views of the coast and Cardigan Bay. 4 miles from the coast. Ideal for bird watching including Red Kite. Close to two cheese factories and local craft centres. Non members welcome. Booking essential.
Facilities
Nearby Facilities
Nearest Town Llanarth
Directions From the A487, in Llwyncelyn turn onto the B4342 signposted Ystrad Aeron. At the crossroads go straight on, site is 1¼ miles on the right.
⌖ Llanarth

LLANGRANNOG

Maes Glas Caravan Park, Penbryn, Sarnau, Llandysul, Ceredigion, SA44 6QE
Tel: 01239 654268
Email: enquiries@maesglascaravanpark.co.uk
www.maesglascaravanpark.co.uk
Pitches For Å ⌂ ☝ **Total** 10
Acreage 4 **Open** March to October
Access Good **Site** Level
Nearest Bus Stop (Miles) Outside
Near Penbryn beach. David Bellamy Gold Award for Conservation. Buses in summer only.
Facilities
Nearby Facilities
Nearest Town Llangrannog

Directions Turn off the A487 between Cardigan and New Quay in the village of Sarnau by the old church, signposted Penbryn. Follow the road down for ¾ miles to the telephone box, at next junction bear left and the park entrance is on the right.
⌖ Aberystwyth

LLANON

Woodlands Holiday Park, Llanon, Ceredigion, SY23 5LX
Tel: 01974 202342
Email:
info@woodlandsholidayparkllanon.co.uk
www.woodlandsholidayparkllanon.co.uk
Pitches For Å ⌂ ☝ **Total** 40
Acreage 4 **Open** March to December
Access Good **Site** Level
Nearest Bus Stop (Miles) ¼
Ideal for a quiet, relaxing break. 200 metres from the beach. 3 miles from the quaint harbourside town of Aberaeron.
Facilities
Nearby Facilities
Nearest Town Aberaeron
Directions 3 miles north of Aberaeron on the A487, in the village of Llanon, turn left at the International sign towards the sea.
⌖ Aberystwyth

LLANRHYSTUD

Pengarreg Caravan Park, Llanrhystud, Ceredigion, SY23 5DJ
Tel: 01974 202247
Email: miller_i@btconnect.com
Pitches For Å ⌂ ☝
Open March to January
Access Good **Site** Level
Nearest Bus Stop (Miles) ¼
On the beach and by a river. Ideal for hillside walks. Two play areas.
Facilities
Nearby Facilities
Nearest Town Aberystwyth
Directions 9 miles south of Aberystwyth on the A487, opposite the Texaco Garage.
⌖ Aberystwyth

NEW QUAY

Cardigan Bay Camping & Caravanning Club Site, Llwynhelyg, Cross Inn, Ceredigion, SA44 6LW
Tel: 01545 560029
www.campingandcaravanningclub.co.uk/cardiganbay
Pitches For Å ⌂ ☝ **Total** 90
Acreage 14 **Open** 29-Mar to 05-Nov
Access Difficult **Site** Lev/Slope
Nearest Bus Stop (Miles) 1
Near to golden beaches, forests and lakes. 3 miles from horse racing and close to many attractions. WTB 4 Star Graded and AA 3 Pennants. Non members welcome. You can also call us on 0845 130 7633.
Facilities
Nearby Facilities
Directions From the A487 Cardigan to Aberystwyth road, at Synod Inn turn left onto the A486 signposted New Quay. After 2 miles in the village of Cross Inn turn left after the Penrhiwgated Arms Pub, site is on the right after approx. ¾ miles.
⌖ Aberystwyth

NEW QUAY

Cei Bach Country Club, Parc-Y-Brwcs, Cei Bach, New Quay, Ceredigion, SA45 9SL
Tel: 01545 580237
Email: paul.wynne4@virgin.net
www.cei-bach.co.uk
Pitches For Å ⌂ ☝ **Total** 60
Acreage 3 **Open** March to October
Access Poor **Site** Sloping
Nearest Bus Stop (Miles) 1
On the beach with great views of the coast line. Coastal walk to Aberaeron.
Facilities
Nearby Facilities
Nearest Town New Quay
Directions From the A487 take the B4342 for New Quay. Follow the road to Quay-West and Cambrian Hotel crossroads, take the road signed for Cei Bach for 1 mile.
⌖ Aberystwyth

NEW QUAY

Pencnwc Holiday Park, Cross Inn, New Quay, Llandysul, Ceredigion, SA44 6NL
Tel: 01545 560479
Email: holidays@pencnwc.co.uk
www.pencnwc.co.uk
Pitches For Å ⌂ ☝ **Total** 100
Acreage 10 **Open** March to October
Access Good **Site** Level
Nearest Bus Stop (Miles) Outside
Open spaces. 2 miles from the beach. Ideal touring.
Facilities
Nearby Facilities
Nearest Town Aberystwyth
Directions Take the A487 south to Synod Inn, then take the A486 towards New Quay, Park is 2 miles on the left.
⌖ Aberystwyth

NEW QUAY

Wern Mill Camping Site, Gilfachreda, New Quay, Ceredigion, SA45 9SP
Tel: 01545 580699
Pitches For Å ⌂ ☝ **Total** 50
Acreage 2½ **Open** Easter to October
Access Good **Site** Level
Very sheltered, family site. ½ mile from two sandy beaches. Idyllic walks. Ideal centre for touring Mid Wales.
Facilities
Nearby Facilities
Nearest Town New Quay
Directions From Aberystwyth take the A487 via Aberaeron to Llanarth. Gilfachrheda is located 1½ miles from Llanarth on the B4342 to New Quay road.
⌖ Aberystwyth

NEWCASTLE EMLYN

Cenarth Falls Holiday Park, Cenarth, Newcastle Emlyn, Ceredigion, SA38 9JS
Tel: 01239 710345
Email: enquiries@cenarth-holipark.co.uk
www.cenarth-holipark.co.uk
Pitches For Å ⌂ ☝ **Total** 30
Acreage 2 **Open** March to Mid Nov
Access Good **Site** Level
Nearest Bus Stop (Miles) ¼
Ideal touring location for the coast and countryside. Near Coastal National Park. Indoor swimming pool with sauna, steam rooms, jacuzzi and leisure suite. Holders of numerous awards including Wales in Bloom, Calor Gas Best Park in Britain Award and David Bellamy Gold Award.

WALES

WALES

Facilities ♿ ⚐ 🚻 📶 🔥 🅿 ☉ 🍴 ♨ ⊠ 🛒 📮
🛈 🛎 🏊 ⚓ 🎿 🛶 🏔 ⚲ 🛵 ∪ 🎣
Nearby Facilities 🛆 🚲 🏔 ∪ 🎣
Nearest Town Newcastle Emlyn
Directions 3 miles west of Newcastle Emlyn on the A484. Cross Cenarth Bridge and travel for ¼ mile, turn right at directional signs for the park.
⭢ Carmarthen

SARNAU
Brynawelon Touring & Camping Park, Sarnau, Llandysul, Ceredigion, SA44 6RE
Tel: 01239 654584
Email: info@brynaweloncp.co.uk
www.brynaweloncp.co.uk
Pitches For ⛺ ⚐ 🚐 **Total** 40
Acreage 4 **Open** March **to** October
Access Good **Site** Level
Nearest Bus Stop (Miles) ¼
Quiet family site with rural surroundings. 2 miles from Penbryn Beach.
Facilities ⚐ ⚑ 🚻 📶 🔥 🅿 ☉ 🍴 ♨ ⊠ 🛒 📮
🛈 🛎 🏊 ⚓ 🛵 🎿 ⚲ 🛶
Nearby Facilities 🛆 🚲 🏔 ∪ 🎣
Nearest Town Cardigan
Directions Travelling north on A487 take a right turn at Sarnau crossroads, site is 600 yards on the left.
⭢ Carmarthen

SARNAU
Treddafydd Farm, Treddafydd, Sarnau, Llandysul, Ceredigion, SA44 6PZ
Tel: 01239 654551
Pitches For ⛺ ⚐ 🚐 **Total** 10
Acreage 1 **Open** May **to** Sept
Access Good **Site** Sloping
Nearest Bus Stop (Miles) ½
1 mile from sandy Penbryn beach.
Facilities ⚐ 🚻 🅿 ☉ 🍴 ♨ ⊠ 🛒 📮
Nearby Facilities 🛆 🚲 🎣 ∪
Nearest Town Cardigan
Directions 1 mile from the A487, in the village of Sarnau turn by the church then first left.
⭢ Carmarthen/Aberystwyth

CONWY
ABERGELE
Henllys Farm Camping & Touring Site, Henllys, Towyn, Abergele, Conwy, LL22 9UF
Tel: 01745 351208
Pitches For ⛺ ⚐ 🚐 **Total** 280
Acreage 14 **Open** March **to** October
Access Good **Site** Level
Nearest Bus Stop (Miles) ¼
Level site adjoining farm land, yet close to attractions.
Facilities ♿ ⚐ 🚻 📶 🔥 🅿 ☉ 🍴 ♨ ⊠ 🛒 📮
🛈 🛎 🏊 ⚓ 🛵
Nearby Facilities 🛆 🚲 🎣 ∪
Nearest Town Rhyl
Directions 3 miles west of Rhyl on the A548 coast road.
⭢ Rhyl

ABERGELE
Hunters Hamlet Touring Caravan Park, Sirior Goch Farm, Betws-Yn-Rhos, Abergele, Conwy, LL22 8PL
Tel: 01745 832237
Email: huntershamlet@aol.com
www.huntershamlet.co.uk
Pitches For ⚐ 🚐 **Total** 23
Acreage 2 **Open** 21-Mar **to** 31-Oct
Access Good **Site** Lev/Slope
Nearest Bus Stop (Miles) ½

Peaceful site proud of its cleanliness. Ideal for coast or country. Visit Bodnant Gardens, castles and a factory outlet. Family bathroom. Ideal touring. AA 4 Pennants.
Facilities ♿ ⚐ 🚻 📶 🔥 🅿 ☉ 🍴 ♨ ⊠ 🛒 📮
🛈 🛎 🏊 ⚓ 📮 ⊟ 🛵 📶
Nearby Facilities 🛆 🚲 🎣
Nearest Town Abergele
Directions Leave the A55 at junc 24 into Abergele. At the second set of traffic lights turn left onto the A548, after 2½ miles at the crossroads turn right, site is ½ a mile on the left.
⭢ Abergele/Pensarn

ABERGELE
Roberts Caravan Park, Waterloo Service Station, Penrefail Cross Roads, Abergele, Conwy, LL22 8PN
Tel: 01745 833265
Email: gailyroberts@btinternet.com
Pitches For ⚐ 🚐 **Total** 60
Open Mid March **to** End Oct
Access Good **Site** Lev/Slope
Nearest Bus Stop (Miles) Outside
A quiet, tidy site with a well stocked shop. Near the beach and within easy reach of the Snowdonia mountain range.
Facilities ⚐ 🚻 🅿 🔥 ☉ 🍴 ♨ 🛒 📮
🛈 🛎 🏊 ⚓ 🛵 📶 🏔 ⊟ ⊡ 🛵
Nearby Facilities 🛆 🚲 🏔 ∪ 🎣 ⚲
Nearest Town Abergele
Directions From Abergele take the A548 Llanrwst road for 2 miles, at the crossroads of the B5381 turn left towards St. Asaph, site is 100 yards on the right of the junction.
⭢ Rhyl

ABERGELE
Ty Mawr Holiday Park, Towyn Road, Towyn, Abergele, Conwy, LL22 9HG
Tel: 0843 309 2577
Email: holidaysale.tymawr@park-resorts.com
www.park-resorts.com
Pitches For ⚐ 🚐 **Total** 406
Open April **to** Oct **Site** Level
Nearest Bus Stop (Miles) Outside
Close to the fun and amusements of seaside Rhyl and scenic Snowdonia.
Facilities ⚐ 🚻 🅿 🔥 ☉ 🍴 ♨ ⊠ 🛒 📮
🛈 🛎 🏊 ⚓ ⚲ 🏊 ✤ ⊟ ⊡ 🛵
Nearby Facilities
Nearest Town Rhyl
Directions Take the A55 to North Wales past Prestatyn and Rhyl. Leave the dual carriageway at Abergele turning and follow the A548 to Towyn. Park is ¼ of a mile on the right.
⭢ Rhyl

BETWS-Y-COED
Camp Snowdonia, Tan Aeldroch Farm, Dolwyddelan, Conwy, LL25 0LZ
Tel: 01690 750225
Email: ruegg.peel@virgin.net
Pitches For ⛺ ⚐ 🚐 **Total** 34
Acreage 3 **Open** End March **to** End Oct
Access Good **Site** Level
Nearest Bus Stop (Miles) ½
Tranquil, unspoilt site on a working hill farm in Snowdonia National Park. In the stunning Lledr Valley with pitches alongside the River Lledr. Campfires allowed. Walks and mountain biking from the site. Pub, restaurant and shop 2 miles.
Facilities 🚻 ✤ 📮
Nearby Facilities 🛆 🚲 🏔 ∪ 🎣 ⚲
Nearest Town Betws-y-Coed
Directions From the A5 before Betws Bridge turn onto the A470. Pass under the railway viaduct and turn left to the site after approx ¾ miles.
⭢ Pont-y-Pant

BETWS-Y-COED
Rynys Farm Camping Site, Rynys Farm, Nr Betws-y-Coed, Llanrwst, Conwy, LL26 0RU
Tel: 01690 710218
Email: carol@rynys-camping.co.uk
www.rynys-camping.co.uk
Pitches For ⛺ ⚐ 🚐 **Total** 6
Acreage 6 **Open** All Year
Access Good **Site** Level
Nearest Bus Stop (Miles) ¼
Very scenic and peaceful site with excellent clean facilities. Central for touring.
Facilities ⚐ 🚻 🅿 ☉ ♨ ⊠ 🛒 ✤ 📮
Nearby Facilities
Nearest Town Betws-y-Coed
Directions 2 miles south of Betws-y-Coed Left by Conway Falls, 200yds from A5.
⭢ Betws-y-Coed

BETWS-Y-COED
Y Giler Arms, Rhydlydan, Pentrefoelas, Conwy, LL24 0LL
Tel: 01690 770612
Email: gilerarms@hotmail.co.uk
www.giler.co.uk
Pitches For ⛺ ⚐ 🚐 🚐 **Total** 20
Acreage 4 **Open** All Year
Access Good **Site** Level
On the edge of Snowdonia National Park.
Facilities ⚐ 🚻 🅿 ☉ 🍴 ♨ ⊠ 🛒 📮
🛈 ✗ 🛎 ⚓ 🏔 ✤ ⊟ ⊡ 🛵 🎿 📶
Nearby Facilities 🛆 🚲 🎣 ∪ ⚲ 🏹
Nearest Town Betws-y-Coed
Directions On the A5 between Glasfryn and Pentrefoelas.
⭢ Betws-y-Coed

COLWYN BAY
Bron-Y-Wendon Touring Caravan Park, Wern Road, Llanddulas, Colwyn Bay, Conwy, LL22 8HG
Tel: 01492 512903
Email: stay@northwales-holidays.co.uk
www.northwales-holidays.co.uk
Pitches For ⚐ 🚐 **Total** 130
Acreage 8 **Open** All Year
Access Good **Site** Lev/Slope
Nearest Bus Stop (Miles) ¼
Pitches have coastal views. Just a short walk to the beach. Site is ideal for seaside and touring. Visit Wales 5 Star Graded, AA 5 Pennants and Top 100 Park.
Facilities ♿ ⚐ 🚻 📶 🔥 🅿 ☉ 🍴 ♨ ⊠ 🛒 📮
🛈 🛎 🏊 ⚓ 🛵 ✤ ⊟ ⊡ 🛵 🎿 📶
Nearby Facilities 🛆 🚲 🏔 ∪ 🎣 ⚲ 🏹
Nearest Town Colwyn Bay
Directions Follow the A55 into North Wales and take the Llanddulas junction (A547), junction 23. Follow tourist information signs to the park.
⭢ Colwyn Bay

COLWYN BAY
Dinarth Hall, Rhos-on-Sea, Colwyn Bay, Conwy, LL28 4PX
Tel: 01492 548203
Pitches For ⛺ ⚐ 🚐 🚐 **Total** 65
Acreage 7 **Open** Easter **to** Oct
Access Good **Site** Level
Nearest Bus Stop (Miles) ¼
1 mile from the seaside resort of Llandudno, and next door to a golf course.
Facilities ⚐ 🚻 🅿 ☉ 🍴 ♨ ⊠ 🛒 📮
🛈 🛎 🏊 ⚓ ✤ 📮
Nearby Facilities 🛆 🚲 🏔 ∪ 🎣 ⚲ 🏹
Nearest Town Llandudno
Directions Take the B5115 from Colwyn Bay towards Llandudno for approx. 2 miles.
⭢ Colwyn Bay

CONWY, DENBIGHSHIRE

CONWY

Conwy Touring Park, Conwy, LL32 8UX
Tel: 01492 592856
Email: sales@conwytouringpark.co.uk
www.conwytouringpark.co.uk
Pitches For ▲ ⊕ ⊟ **Total** 300
Acreage 70 **Open** Easter
Access Good **Site** Level
Nearest Bus Stop (Miles) Outside
Scenic views, ideal for touring Snowdonia. Special Offers. Caravan servicing and storage available.
Facilities ⬚ ⬚ ⬚ ⬚ ⬚ ⬚ ⬚ ⬚ ⬚ ⬚ ⬚ ⬚ ⬚ ⬚ ⬚ ⬚
Nearby Facilities ⬚ ⬚ ⬚ ⬚ ⬚ ⬚ ⬚ ⬚
Nearest Town Conwy
Directions Leave the A55 at junction 18 and follow signs for Conwy. At Conwy Castle turn left onto the B5106 Trefriw Road. After 1½ miles you will see our sign on the left.
⇌ Conwy

CONWY

Tyn Terfyn Touring Caravan Park, Tal Y Bont, Conwy, LL32 8YX
Tel: 01492 660525
www.tynterfyn.co.uk
Pitches For ▲ ⊕ ⊟ **Total** 15
Acreage 2 **Open** 14-Mar to October
Access Good **Site** Level
Nearest Bus Stop (Miles) Outside
Scenic views, good walking, fishing and boating. Ideal touring location.
Facilities ⬚ ⬚ ⬚ ⬚ ⬚ ⬚ ⬚ ⬚ ⬚
Nearby Facilities ⬚ ⬚ ⬚ ⬚ ⬚ ⬚ ⬚ ⬚
Nearest Town Conwy
Directions From Conwy travel approx 5 miles on the B5106 until road sign for Tal-y-Bont. First house on the left after sign.

CONWY

Wern Farm Caravan Park, Wern Farm, Tyn-Y-Groes, Conwy, LL32 8SY
Tel: 01492 650257
Pitches For ⊕ ⊟ **Total** 24
Acreage 2½ **Open** 15-Mar to 31-Oct
Access Good **Site** Sloping
Nearest Bus Stop (Miles) Outside
Facilities ⬚ ⬚ ⬚ ⬚ ⬚ ⬚ ⬚ ⬚ ⬚
Nearby Facilities ⬚ ⬚ ⬚ ⬚ ⬚
Nearest Town Conwy
Directions Take the A55 to Conwy then the B5106 signposted Trefriw. Site is 4 miles (1 mile past the Groes Inn).
⇌ Llandudno Junction

LLANRWST

Bodnant Caravan Park, Nebo Road, Llanrwst, Conwy Valley, LL26 0SD
Tel: 01492 640248
Email: ermin@bodnant-caravan-park.co.uk
www.bodnant-caravan-park.co.uk
Pitches For ▲ ⊕ ⊟ **Total** 54
Acreage 4 **Open** March to October
Access Good **Site** Level
Nearest Bus Stop (Miles) ¼
Small, quiet, pretty farm site. Ideal touring centre. 26 times Winner of Wales in Bloom. Multi serviced pitches. 2 holiday caravans for hire. Rally field available.
Facilities ⬚ ⬚ ⬚ ⬚ ⬚ ⬚ ⬚ ⬚ ⬚ ⬚ ⬚ ⬚
Nearby Facilities ⬚ ⬚ ⬚ ⬚ ⬚ ⬚ ⬚ ⬚
Nearest Town Llanrwst
Directions Turn off the A470 south in Llanrwst onto the B5427 signposted Nebo. Site is 300 yards on the right, opposite the leisure centre.
⇌ Llanrwst

LLANRWST

Bron Derw Touring Caravan Park, Bron Derw, Llanrwst, Conwy, LL26 0YT
Tel: 01492 640494
Email: bronderw@aol.com
www.bronderw-wales.co.uk
Pitches For ⊕ ⊟ **Total** 43
Acreage 4 **Open** March to Oct
Access Good **Site** Level
Nearest Bus Stop (Miles) ½
Ideal for exploring the Snowdonia mountain range and the North Wales coast. Adults Only field separate from the main touring site.
Facilities ⬚ ⬚ ⬚ ⬚ ⬚ ⬚ ⬚ ⬚ ⬚ ⬚ ⬚
Nearby Facilities ⬚ ⬚ ⬚ ⬚ ⬚ ⬚ ⬚ ⬚
Nearest Town Llanrwst
Directions From the A5 or A55 take the A470 into Llanrwst. Tunr into Parry Road (by Llanddoged) and go to T-Junction, turn left and the Park entrance is on the right.
⇌ Llanrwst

PENMAENMAWR

Trwyn Yr Wylfa Farm, Trwyn Yr Wylfa, Penmaenmawr, Conwy, LL34 6SF
Tel: 01492 622357
Pitches For ▲ ⊕ **Total** 100
Acreage 10 **Open** Apr to Sept **Site** Level
Nearest Bus Stop (Miles) Outside
Secluded site in Snowdonia National Park.
Facilities ⬚ ⬚ ⬚ ⬚ ⬚ ⬚ ⬚
Nearby Facilities ⬚ ⬚ ⬚ ⬚ ⬚
Nearest Town Penmaenmawr
Directions Leave the A55 at junction 16 for Penmaenmawr. Turn by Mountain View Hotel, farm is ¼ mile east.
⇌ Penmaenmawr

PENMAENMAWR

Tyddyn Du Touring Park, Conwy Old Road, Penmaenmawr, Conwy, LL34 6RE
Tel: 01492 622300
Email: stay@tyddyndutouringpark.co.uk
www.tyddyndutouringpark.co.uk
Pitches For ▲ ⊕ **Total** 100
Acreage 5 **Open** 22-Mar to 31-Oct
Access Good **Site** Lev/Slope
Nearest Bus Stop (Miles) ¼
ADULTS ONLY site overlooking Conwy Bay to Llanudno and Anglesey. Heated toilet and shower block with disabled facilities and laundry. Close to the A55 so ideal for touring Snowdonia.
Facilities ⬚ ⬚ ⬚ ⬚ ⬚ ⬚ ⬚ ⬚ ⬚ ⬚ ⬚ ⬚ ⬚
Nearby Facilities ⬚ ⬚ ⬚ ⬚ ⬚
Nearest Town Penmaenmawr
Directions 1 mile east of Penmaenmawr. Take the A55 from Conwy and at junction 16 turn left at the roundabout after the Shell Garage and sharp left again. Site access is on the right after The Gladstone.
⇌ Penmaenmawr

TY-NANT

Glan Ceirw Caravan Park, Ty Nant, Corwen, Conwy, LL21 0RF
Tel: 01490 420346
Email: glanceirwcaravanpark@yahoo.co.uk
Pitches For ▲ ⊕ ⊟ **Total** 12
Acreage 5 **Open** March to August
Access Good **Site** Lev/Slope
Nearest Bus Stop (Miles) ½
Ideal for cycling, walking, canoeing, white water rafting and sailing.
Facilities ⬚ ⬚ ⬚ ⬚ ⬚ ⬚ ⬚ ⬚ ⬚ ⬚ ⬚
Nearby Facilities ⬚ ⬚ ⬚ ⬚ ⬚
Nearest Town Corwen
Directions On the A5 between Corwen and Betws-Y-Coed.
⇌ Betws-Y-Coed

DENBIGHSHIRE

CORWEN

Hendwr Caravan Park, Llandrillo, Corwen, Denbighshire, LL21 0SN
Tel: 01490 440210
Email: johnhendwr@btinternet.com
www.hendwrcaravanpark.co.uk
Pitches For ▲ ⊕ ⊟ **Total** 40
Acreage 2¼ **Open** April to October
Access Good **Site** Level
Alongside a river, good walking and fishing (must become a member of the Angling Club). Wonderful views and an excellent touring centre for North Wales.
Facilities ⬚ ⬚ ⬚ ⬚ ⬚ ⬚ ⬚ ⬚ ⬚ ⬚ ⬚ ⬚
Nearby Facilities ⬚ ⬚ ⬚ ⬚ ⬚
Nearest Town Corwen/Bala
Directions From Corwen (A5) take the B4401 for 4 miles, turn right at sign Hendwr. Site is on the right in ¼ mile. From Bala take the A494 for 1½ miles, turn right onto the B4401 via Llandrillo. Site is 1 mile north on the left. Follow brown tourism signs from Corwen.
⇌ Ruabon

LLANGOLLEN

Ddol Hir Caravan Park, Pandy Road, Glyn Ceiriog, Llangollen, Denbighshire, LL20 7PD
Tel: 01691 718681
www.ukparks.com
Pitches For ▲ ⊕ ⊟ **Total** 25
Acreage 6 **Open** March to October
Access Good **Site** Level
Nearest Bus Stop (Miles) ¼
Pretty riverside Park in a scenic valley with mountain walks. Trout fishing and pony trekking. Within walking distance of shops and pubs.
Facilities ⬚ ⬚ ⬚ ⬚ ⬚ ⬚ ⬚ ⬚ ⬚ ⬚
Nearby Facilities ⬚ ⬚ ⬚ ⬚ ⬚
Nearest Town Llangollen
Directions Turn off the A5 at Chirk onto the B4500, park is on the left approx. 6 miles, just through the village of Glyn Ceiriog.
⇌ Chirk

LLANGOLLEN

Ty-Ucha Caravan Park, Maesmawr Road, Llangollen, Denbighshire, LL20 7PP
Tel: 01978 860677
Pitches For ⊕ ⊟ **Total** 40
Acreage 5 **Open** Easter to October
Access Good **Site** Level
Nearest Bus Stop (Miles) 1
Quiet site with outstanding panoramic views. Ideal for walking and touring.
Facilities ⬚ ⬚ ⬚ ⬚ ⬚ ⬚ ⬚ ⬚
Nearby Facilities ⬚ ⬚ ⬚ ⬚ ⬚
Nearest Town Llangollen
Directions 1 mile east of Llangollen on the A5, 200 yards signposted.
⇌ Ruabon

LLANGOLLEN

Wern Isaf Caravan & Camping Park, Wern Isaf Farm, Llangollen, Denbighshire, LL20 8DU
Tel: 01978 860632
Email: wernisaf@btopenworld.com
www.wernisaf.co.uk
Pitches For ▲ ⊕ ⊟
Acreage 4 **Open** Easter to October
Access Good **Site** Lev/Slope
Nearest Bus Stop (Miles) ½
Quiet and very scenic site overlooking Llangollen. Ideal for touring North Wales. Nearby we have horse riding, a steam railway, white water rafting and very scenic walks. You can also contact us on Mobile: 07974 797828.

WALES

Facilities ♦ 🔲 🔳 🄻🔦 ┏ ⊙ 🤚 🗑
🔲 🔘 🔺🔲 ☀
Nearby Facilities ┏ ⁄ ⚓ ⚓ ∪ ♉ ⚔
Nearest Town Llangollen
Directions In Llangollen turn up behind
Bridge End Hotel, go over the canal bridge
and turn right into Wern Road, site is ½ a
mile on the right.
⚏ Ruabon

PRESTATYN

Nant Mill Farm Caravan & Tenting Park,
Nant Mill, Prestatyn, Denbighshire, LL19
9LY
Tel: 01745 852360
Email: nantmilltouring@aol.com
www.nantmilltouring.co.uk
Pitches For ⛺ ⛽ 🚐 **Total** 150
Acreage 5 **Open** Easter **to** October
Access Good **Site** Lev/Slope
Nearest Bus Stop (Miles) Outside
Near town shops. ½ a mile from the beach.
Ideal for touring North Wales. Restaurant and
bar 200 yards away.
Facilities ♿ ♦ 🔳🔦┏ ⊙ 🤚 🗑 ⊙ 🗑
🔲 🔺 ⚙ 🔲
Nearby Facilities ┏ ⁄ ⚓ ⚓ ∪ ♉ ♉
Nearest Town Prestatyn
Directions ½ mile east of Prestatyn on A548
coast road.
⚏ Prestatyn

PRESTATYN

Presthaven Sands Holiday Park, Shore
Road, Gronant, Prestatyn, Denbighshire,
LL19 9TT
Tel: 01745 856471
Email: presthavensands@haven.com
www.haventouring.com/
topresthavensands
Pitches For ⛽ 🚐 **Total** 30
Acreage 12 **Open** Mid March **to** End Oct
Access Good **Site** Level
Nearest Bus Stop (Miles) Outside
Alongside 7 miles of beaches and sand
dunes. Kids clubs and family entertainment
- day and night. Many holiday attractions like
Conwy Castle are within easy reach.
Facilities ♦ 🔲 🔳🔦┏ ⊙ 🤚 🗑 🗑
🔲 🔲 🔘 ✕ 🔲 🔳 🔺 🌳🔲 🔲 🔲 ⎙
Nearby Facilities ┏ ⁄ ⚓ ⚓ ∪ ♉
Nearest Town Prestatyn/Rhyl
Directions Take the A548 out of Prestatyn
towards Gronant, the park is signposted left,
then entrance is ½ mile further on the right.
⚏ Prestatyn/Rhyl

RUTHIN

Dyffryn Ial Caravan Site, Troell Yr Alun,
Llanarmon-Yn-Ial, Near Mold,
Denbighshire, CH7 5TA
Tel: 01824 780286
Pitches For ⛽ 🚐 **Total** 18
Acreage ½ **Open** March **to** Oct
Access Good **Site** Level
Nearest Bus Stop (Miles) Outside
ADULTS ONLY SITE alongside the River
Alyn in an area of outstanding natural beauty.
Near Clwydian Hills, Offas Dyke walk and
Country Park Loggerheads. Over 100 walks
in the area. Ideal for touring North Wales.
Facilities ♦ 🔳🔦┏ ⊙ 🤚 🗑 🗑
Nearby Facilities ┏ ⁄ ⚓ ⚓ ∪ ♉ ⚔
Nearest Town Mold/Ruthin
Directions 6 miles from both Mold and
Ruthin on the A494, take the B5430 towards
Llanarmon-Yn-Ial, site is on the right 1 mile
before Llanarmon Village.
⚏ Wrexham

ST. ASAPH

Penisar Mynydd Caravan Park, Caerwys
Road, Rhuallt, St Asaph, Denbighshire,
LL17 0TY
Tel: 01745 582227
Email: contact@penisarmynydd.co.uk
www.penisarmynydd.co.uk
Pitches For ⛺ ⛽ 🚐 **Total** 75
Acreage 6 **Open** 01-Mar **to** 15-Jan
Access Good **Site** Lev/Slope
Quiet, rural park. Large flat tent area. Close
to Rhyl and Prestatyn. Ideal for touring the
main A55 coastal route to Holyhead. Adults
Only field. Superpitches available.
Facilities ♿ ♦ 🔲 🔳🔦┏ ⊙ 🤚 🗑 ⊙ 🗑
🔲 🔘 🔲 ☀ 🔺
Nearby Facilities ┏ ⁄ ⚓ ∪
Nearest Town Prestatyn
Directions Leave the A55 Chester to Bangor
road at junction 29, park is 500 yards on the
right.
⚏ Prestatyn

FLINTSHIRE
GRONANT

Greenacres Caravan Park, Shore Road,
Gronant, Flintshire, LL19 9SS
Tel: 01745 854061
Email: info@greenacrescaravanpark.co.uk
Pitches For ⛽ 🚐 **Total** 40
Open 01-Mar **to** 31-Oct
Access Good **Site** Level
Nearest Bus Stop (Miles) Outside
500 yards from the beach. Two licensed
premises with live entertainment. Health suite
and swimming pool.
Facilities 🔺 ♦ 🔲 🔳🔦┏ ⊙ 🗑 🗑
🔲 🔲 ✕ 🔲 🔳 🔺 🌳 🔲
Nearby Facilities ┏ ♉
Nearest Town Prestatyn
Directions 2 miles from Prestatyn off the
main A548 coast road.
⚏ Prestatyn

MOLD

Fron Farm Caravan Park, Fron Farm,
Rhes-Y-Cae Road, Hendre, Mold,
Flintshire, CH7 5QW
Tel: 01352 741482
Email: stay@fronfarmcaravanpark.co.uk
www.fronfarmcaravanpark.co.uk
Pitches For ⛺ ⛽ 🚐 **Total** 70
Acreage 5 **Open** April **to** Oct
Access Good **Site** Level
Nearest Bus Stop (Miles) ½
Farm site with animals to see and scenic
views. Pony rides and tractor rides at
weekends.
Facilities ♿ 🔳🔦┏ ⊙ 🗑
🔲 🔘 🔺🔲 ☀
Nearby Facilities ┏ ⁄ ∪ ⚔
Nearest Town Mold
Directions From Mold take the A541 towards
Denbigh, pass through Rhydymwyn and
Hendre, turn right at the next crossroads for
Rhes-Y-Cae.
⚏ Flint

GWYNEDD
ABERDARON

Bryn Ffynnon Caravan Site,
Rhoshirwaun, Pwllheli, Gwynedd, LL53
8LF
Tel: 01758 730643
Pitches For ⛽ 🚐 **Total** 20
Open 01-Mar **to** End Oct
Access Good **Site** Level
Nearest Bus Stop (Miles) 1

Near to the beach and the village.
Facilities 🔺 ♦ 🔲 🔳🔦┏ ⊙ 🤚 🗑 ⊙ 🗑
🔲 🔘 🔺🔲 ☀
Nearby Facilities ┏ ⁄ ⚓ ⚓ ∪ ♉ ♉ ⚔
Nearest Town Pwllheli
Directions From the A499 take the B4413,
go through Sarn and continue to Aberdaron.
⚏ Pwllheli

ABERDARON

Mur Melyn Camping Site, Mur Melyn,
Aberdaron, Pwllheli, Gwynedd, LL53 8LW
Tel: 01758 760522
Email: murmelyn@hotmail.co.uk
www.murmelyncamping.co.uk
Pitches For ⛺ ⛽ 🚐 **Total** 60
Acreage 2½ **Open** Easter **to** October
Access Good **Site** Level
Nearest Bus Stop (Miles) 1
Near the beach and a river with scenic views.
Ideal for touring Wales.
Facilities ♦ 🔳┏ ⊙ 🗑
Nearby Facilities ┏ ⁄ ⚓ ⚓ ∪
Nearest Town Pwllheli
Directions Take A499 west from Pwllheli,
then fork onto to B4413 at Llanbedrog about
3 miles before Aberdaron take Whistling
Sand road. Turn left at Pen-y-Bont House to
site ½ mile.
⚏ Pwllheli

ABERDARON

Tir Glyn Caravan Park, Tir Glyn Farm,
Uwchmynydd, Aberdaron, Pwllheli,
Gwynedd, LL53 8DA
Tel: 01758 760248
Email: tirglyn@btconnect.com
www.tirglyn.com
Pitches For ⛺ ⛽ 🚐 **Total** 30
Acreage 3 **Open** May **to** October
Access Good **Site** Lev/Slope
Nearest Bus Stop (Miles) ½
Surrounded by National Trust land,
overlooking the sea for scenic views. Near
beaches. Local authority licence. Static
caravan for hire.
Facilities ♦ 🔳🔦┏ ⊙ 🤚 🗑 ⊙ 🗑
🔲 🔘 🔺🔲 ☀
Nearby Facilities ┏ ⁄ ⚓ ⚓ ∪
Nearest Town Aberdaron/Abersoch
Directions Pwllheli to Abersoch road, take
the B4413 at Llanbedrog to Aberdaron. In
Aberdaron Village turn right on the bridge
signed Uwchmynydd, keep left then turn first
left, we are first farm on the left.
⚏ Pwllheli

ABERSOCH

Beach View Caravan Park, Bwlchtocyn,
Abersoch, Gwynedd, LL53 7BT
Tel: 01758 712956
Pitches For ⛺ ⛽ 🚐 **Total** 47
Acreage 5 **Open** Mid March **to** Mid Oct
Access Good **Site** Level
Nearest Bus Stop (Miles) ¼
Just a very short walk to the beach. Ideal
touring area.
Facilities ♦ 🔳🔦┏ ⊙ 🤚 🗑 ⊙ 🗑
🔲 🔘 🔺🔲 ☀
Nearby Facilities ┏ ⁄ ⚓ ⚓ ∪ ♉ ⚔
Nearest Town Abersoch
Directions Drive through Abersoch and Sarn
Bach, go over the crossroads and turn next
left signposted Bwlchtocyn and Porthtocyn
Hotel. Go past the chapel and take left turn
following signs for Porthtocyn Hotel, Beach
View Park is on the left.
⚏ Pwllheli

ABERSOCH

Bryn Bach Caravan & Camping Site,
Tyddyn Talgoch Uchaf, Bwlchtocyn,
Abersoch, Gwynedd, LL53 7BT
Tel: 01758 712285
Email: brynbach@abersochcamping.co.uk
www.abersochcamping.co.uk
Pitches For ⚠ ⬛ ⬛ **Total** 50
Acreage 4 **Open** March **to** October
Access Good **Site** Lev/Slope
Nearest Bus Stop (Miles) ¼
Just a short walk to two sandy beaches. Golf, water sports and go karting nearby.
Facilities ⬛ ⬛ ⬛ ⬛ ⬛ ⬛ ⬛ ⬛ ⬛ ⬛ ⬛
⬛ ⬛ ⬛ ⬛ ⬛ ⬛ ⬛
Nearby Facilities ⬛ ⬛ ⬛ ⬛ ⬛ ⬛ ⬛
Nearest Town Abersoch
Directions From Abersoch take the road for Sarn Bach, after approx. 1 mile turn left signposted Bwlchtocyn. Stay on this road and Bryn Bach is approx. 1 mile on the left.
⬛ Pwllheli

ABERSOCH

Bryn Celyn Isaf Camping & Caravan Site, Bryn Celyn Isaf, Cilan, Abersoch, Pwllheli, Gwynedd, LL53 7DB
Tel: 01758 713583
Pitches For ⚠ ⬛ ⬛ **Total** 25
Acreage 1½ **Open** Easter **to** Oct
Access Good **Site** Sloping
Nearest Bus Stop (Miles) Outside
Families only. Footpath runs through the farmyard to Hells Mouth beach.
Facilities ⬛ ⬛ ⬛ ⬛ ⬛ ⬛
Nearby Facilities ⬛ ⬛ ⬛ ⬛ ⬛ ⬛
Nearest Town Abersoch
Directions Travel through the villages of Abersoch and Sarn Bach on the Cilan main road. Pass the turning for Bwlchtocyn and then pass 6 houses on the left and turn sharp right by Tirlon.
⬛ Pwllheli

ABERSOCH

Deucoch Touring & Camping Park, Sarn Bach, Abersoch, Gwynedd, LL53 7LD
Tel: 01758 713293
Email: info@deucoch.com
www.deucoch.com
Pitches For ⚠ ⬛ ⬛ **Total** 70
Acreage 5 **Open** March **to** October
Access Good **Site** Level
Nearest Bus Stop (Miles) Outside
Overlooking Abersoch beach and the Snowdonia mountain range. Within walking distance of Abersoch Village and the beach.
Facilities ⬛ ⬛ ⬛ ⬛ ⬛ ⬛ ⬛ ⬛ ⬛ ⬛
⬛ ⬛ ⬛
Nearby Facilities ⬛ ⬛ ⬛ ⬛ ⬛
Nearest Town Abersoch

ABERSOCH

Directions Take the Bwlchtocyn road out of Abersoch, at the crossroads in Sarn Bach turn right, go past the school on the left and the Site is on the right.
⬛ Pwllheli

ABERSOCH

Nant-Y-Big, Cilan, Abersoch, Pwllheli, Gwynedd, LL53 7DB
Tel: 01758 712686
Email: nantybig@nantybig.co.uk
www.nantybig.co.uk
Pitches For ⚠ ⬛ ⬛ **Total** 80
Acreage 10 **Open** Easter **to** End Oct
200 metres from the beautiful sandy Porth Ceiriad beach.
Facilities ⬛ ⬛ ⬛ ⬛ ⬛ ⬛ ⬛ ⬛ ⬛ ⬛
Nearby Facilities ⬛ ⬛ ⬛ ⬛ ⬛ ⬛ ⬛
Nearest Town Abersoch
Directions 2½ miles south of Abersoch. Go through the next village of Sarn Bach and follow signposts for Cilan. After approx. 500 metres turn left at No Through Road sign.
⬛ Pwllheli

ABERSOCH

Sarn Farm Caravan & Camping Site,
Sarn Farm, Sarn Bach, Abersoch, Pwllheli, Gwynedd, LL53 7BG
Tel: 01758 713583
Email: sarnfarm@hotmail.com
Pitches For ⚠ ⬛ ⬛ **Total** 40
Acreage 2 **Open** Easter **to** Oct
Access Good **Site** Level
Nearest Bus Stop (Miles) Outside
Within walking distance of the beach and 1 mile from Abersoch Village. Lovely views of Snowdon and Cardigan Bay.
Facilities ⬛ ⬛ ⬛ ⬛ ⬛ ⬛ ⬛ ⬛ ⬛ ⬛
Nearby Facilities ⬛ ⬛ ⬛ ⬛ ⬛ ⬛
Nearest Town Abersoch
Directions On the main Abersoch to Cilan road, in the village of Sarn Bach, on the left.
⬛ Pwllheli

ABERSOCH

Tan-y-Bryn Touring & Camping Park,
Tan-y-Bryn Farm, Sarn Bach, Abersoch, Gwynedd, LL53 7DA
Tel: 01758 712093
www.tanybrynfarm.co.uk
Pitches For ⚠ ⬛ ⬛ **Total** 30
Acreage 3 **Open** April **to** October
Access Good **Site** Level
Nearest Bus Stop (Miles) Outside
Tranquil surroundings with breathtaking views. A short walk to beaches and the village of Abersoch.
Facilities ⬛ ⬛ ⬛ ⬛ ⬛ ⬛ ⬛ ⬛ ⬛ ⬛
⬛ ⬛ ⬛ ⬛
Nearby Facilities ⬛ ⬛ ⬛ ⬛ ⬛

ABERSOCH

Nearest Town Abersoch
Directions From Pwllheli take the A499 to Abersoch then on to Sarn Bach, we are the first farm after the junction to Bwlchtocyn.
⬛ Pwllheli

ABERSOCH

The Willows (Yr Helyg), Mynytho, Abersoch, Gwynedd, LL53 7RW
Tel: 01758 740676
Email: annamali2@aol.com
www.the-willows-abersoch.co.uk
Pitches For ⚠ ⬛ ⬛ **Total** 53
Acreage 10 **Open** March **to** Nov
Access Good **Site** Level
Nearest Bus Stop (Miles) ¼
5 Star multi award winning site. Refined, quiet and charming with stunning views. Close to beaches. Suitable for the more discerning customer.
Facilities ⬛ ⬛ ⬛ ⬛ ⬛ ⬛ ⬛ ⬛ ⬛ ⬛
⬛ ⬛ ⬛ ⬛ ⬛ ⬛ ⬛ ⬛ ⬛ ⬛ ⬛
Nearby Facilities ⬛ ⬛ ⬛ ⬛ ⬛ ⬛ ⬛
Nearest Town Abersoch
Directions From Pwllheli take the A499 towards Abersoch. At Llanbedrog turn right onto the B4413. Once reaching Mynytho take the first right.
⬛ Pwllheli

ABERSOCH

Tyn-y-Mur Touring & Camping Park, Lon Garmon, Abersoch, Gwynedd, LL53 7UL
Tel: 01758 713223
Email: info@tyn-y-mur.co.uk
www.tyn-y-mur.co.uk
Pitches For ⚠ ⬛ ⬛ **Total**
Open March **to** October
Access Good **Site** Level
Nearest Bus Stop (Miles) Outside
Near the beach with superb, uninterrupted, panoramic coastal views of Abersoch Bay and Hells Mouth.
Facilities ⬛ ⬛ ⬛ ⬛ ⬛ ⬛ ⬛ ⬛ ⬛
⬛ ⬛ ⬛ ⬛ ⬛ ⬛ ⬛
Nearby Facilities ⬛ ⬛ ⬛ ⬛ ⬛
Nearest Town Abersoch
Directions On the A499 Pwllheli to Abersoch road, on approaching Abersoch turn right at Land & Sea Services Garage, site is then ¾ miles on the left hand side.
⬛ Pwllheli

ARTHOG

Garthyfog Camping Site, Garthyfog Farm, Arthog, Gwynedd, LL39 1AX
Tel: 01341 250338
Email: abcjohnson@btinternet.com
www.garthyfog.co.uk
Pitches For ⚠ ⬛ ⬛ **Total** 20
Acreage 5 **Open** All Year **Site** Lev/Slope

WALES

2 miles from Fairbourne, safe bathing, sandy beach and shops. Beautiful scenery, panoramic views. 300 yards from main road, sheltered from wind. Mains cold water. Plenty of room for children to play around the farm, rope-swing, little stream, etc. Two log cabins available to let.
Facilities ⬚ ⌂ ⊙ ⤳ ▱
Nearby Facilities ⌐ ✓ ⚓ ⚘ ∪ ♐ ♣ ✝
Nearest Town Barmouth/Dolgellau
Directions A493, 6 miles from Dolgellau, left by Village hall, look for signs on right hand side.
⇴ Morfa Mawddach

BALA
Bryn Gwyn Caravan & Camping Park, Godrer Aran, Llanuwchllyn, Bala, Gwynedd, LL23 7UB
Tel: 01678 540687
Pitches For ⚊ ▱ ⇢ **Total** 10
Acreage 2½ **Open** Easter to End Oct
Access Good **Site** Level
Nearest Bus Stop (Miles) ½
Small, peaceful riverside park within easy walking distance of the village inn (excellent reasonable meals available). Country walks and bird watching along the lanes. Ideal touring centre for North and Mid Wales. Good for cycling tours and hill walking. Six seasonal touring pitches with electric and hard standings.
Facilities ⚒ ! ⬚ ⬚ ⌂ ⊙ ⤳ ▱
❑ ▱ ⤳ ⬚ ▱
Nearby Facilities ⌐ ✓ ⚓ ✣ ✝
Nearest Town Bala
Directions From Bala take the A494 and travel alongside Bala Lake for approx. 5 miles. Turn right immediately after 40mph speed limit sign on approaching Llanuwchllyn Village.
⇴ Wrexham

BALA
Camping & Caravanning Club Site, Crynierth Caravan Park, Cefn-Ddwysarn, Bala, Gwynedd, LL23 7LN
Tel: 01678 530324
www.campingandcaravanningclub.co.uk/bala
Pitches For ⚊ ▱ ⇢ **Total** 50
Acreage 4 **Open** 29-Mar to 05-Nov
Access Good **Site** Level
Situated on the edge of Snowdonia National Park. 4 miles from Bala Lake. Good for watersports. Ideal touring site. WTB 4 Star Graded and AA 3 Pennants. Non members welcome. You can also call us on 0845 130 7633.
Facilities ⚙ ! ⬚ ⬚ ⌂ ⊙ ⤳ ▱ ▱
▱ ❑ ▱ ⬚ ▱ ❑ ⬚
Nearby Facilities ⌐ ✓ ∪ ♐

Nearest Town Bala
Directions From the A5 turn onto the A494 to Bala. At signpost Cefn-Ddwysarn turn right before the red phone box, site is 400 yards on the left.
⇴ Ruabon

BALA
Glanllyn-Lakeside Caravan & Camping Park, Bala, Gwynedd, LL23 7SS
Tel: 01678 540227
Email: info@glanllyn.com
www.glanllyn.com
Pitches For ⚊ ▱ ⇢ ⇢ **Total** 100
Acreage 14 **Open** Easter to October
Access Good **Site** Level
Nearest Bus Stop (Miles) Outside
Level parkland with trees. Alongside a lake and river, large launching area for sailing.
Facilities ! ⬚ ⬚ ⌂ ⊙ ⤳ ▱ ⬚ ▱
▱ ⬚ ⬚ ▱ ❑ ▱ ✣ ✦
Nearby Facilities ⌐ ✓ ⚓ ∪ ♐ ✝
Nearest Town Bala
Directions 3 miles south west of Bala on the A494, situated on the left alongside Bala Lake.
⇴ Wrexham

BALA
Pen Y Bont Touring & Camping Park, Llangynog Road, Bala, Gwynedd, LL23 7PH
Tel: 01678 520549
Email: penybont-bala@btconnect.com
www.penybont-bala.co.uk
Pitches For ⚊ ▱ ⇢ **Total** 95
Acreage 6 **Open** March to End of Oct
Access Good
Nearest Bus Stop (Miles) ½
100 yards from Bala Lake and just a 15 minute walk into Bala.
Facilities ⚙ ! ⬚ ⬚ ⬚ ⌂ ⊙ ⤳ ▱ ⬚ ▱
▱ ▱ ⬚ ⬚ ▱ ❑ ▱ ✣ ✦
Nearby Facilities ⌐ ✓ ⚓ ✣ ♐ ✝
Nearest Town Bala
Directions ½ a mile from Bala on the B4391 to Llangynog.
⇴ Wrexham

BALA
Ty-Isaf Camping Site, Llangynog Road, Bala, Gwynedd, LL23 7PP
Tel: 01678 520574
www.tyisafbala.co.uk
Pitches For ⚊ ▱ ⇢ **Total** 30
Acreage 2 **Open** April/Easter to Oct
Access Good **Site** Level
Working farm alongside a stream for fishing. Log fires. Ideal touring.
Facilities ! ⬚ ⬚ ⌂ ⊙ ⤳ ▱
▱ ⬚ ⬚ ▱ ❑ ▱ ✣ ✦
Nearby Facilities ⌐ ✓ ⚓ ✣ ∪ ✝
Nearest Town Bala

Directions 2½ miles southeast of Bala on the B4391, near the telephone kiosk and post box.
⇴ Ruabon

BALA
Tyn Cornel Camping & Caravan Park, Frongoch, Bala, Gwynedd, LL23 7NU
Tel: 01678 520759
Email: tyncornel@mail.com
www.tyncornel.co.uk
Pitches For ⚊ ▱ ⇢ **Total** 67
Acreage 10 **Open** Easter to Oct
Access Good **Site** Level
Nearest Bus Stop (Miles) ¼
Quiet and clean 4 Star site beside the River Tryweryn. Next door to the National White Water Centre, watch the thrills and spills of the white water rafting, or take part! Ideally situated for touring North Wales. Indoor swimming pool nearby.
Facilities ⚙ ! ⬚ ⌂ ⊙ ⬚ ▱
▱ ▱ ⬚ ⬚ ▱ ❑ ▱ ✣ ✦
Nearby Facilities ⌐ ✓ ⚓ ✣ ∪ ✝
Nearest Town Bala
Directions 4 miles from Bala on the A4212 Porthmadog road.
⇴ Ruabon

BANGOR
Dinas Farm Camping & Touring Site, Dinas Farm, Halfway Bridge, Bangor, Gwynedd, LL57 4NB
Tel: 01248 364227
Pitches For ⚊ ▱ ⇢ ⇢ **Total** 35
Acreage 4 **Open** Easter to End Oct
Access Good **Site** Level
Nearest Bus Stop (Miles) 50 yards
Sheltered site on the banks of the River Ogwen. Centrally situated for beaches and mountains. Fishing on site with a permit.
Facilities ! ⬚ ⬚ ⌂ ⊙ ⤳ ▱ ⬚ ▱ ✝
Nearby Facilities ⌐ ✓ ⚓ ∪ ♐ ♣ ✝
Nearest Town Bangor
Directions Leave the A55 at junc 11 and take the A5 towards Bethesda for 1 mile. Turn right at Halfway Bridge towards Tregarth then turn first left.
⇴ Bangor

BARMOUTH
Benar Beach Camping & Touring Site, Talybont, Barmouth, Gwynedd, LL44 2RX
Tel: 01341 247001/247571
Pitches For ⚊ ▱ ⇢
Acreage 9 **Open** March to October
Access Good **Site** Level
Nearest Bus Stop (Miles) 1
Friendly family site 100 yards from miles of golden sand dunes. By Taith Ardudwy Way which is a 24 mile pathway. Ideal base for touring Snowdonia with its gardens, castles,

WALES

GWYNEDD

caverns, railways and much more.
Facilities ♿ ⚲ ⛳ ♪ ⌂ ⊙ 🛁 ☕
🏧 ♨ 🚿 ♨ 👶 🛈 ⛲ ❄
Nearby Facilities ► ✎ ⚓ ⊾ ↳ ∪ ♪ 🏃
Nearest Town Barmouth
Directions 5 miles north of Barmouth on the A496 turn left by Llanddwywe Church ½ mile after Talybont Village, site is 100 yards from the beach on the left.
🚃 Dyffryn Ardudwy

BARMOUTH

Hendre Mynach Touring Caravan & Camping Park, Barmouth, Gwynedd, LL42 1YR
Tel: 01341 280262
Email: mynach@lineone.net
www.hendremynach.co.uk
Pitches For ⛺ ⚲ ⛳ ⚲ **Total** 240
Acreage 10 **Open** 01-Mar to 09-Jan
Access Good **Site** Level
Nearest Bus Stop (Miles) Outside
100yds from a safe, sandy beach, 20 minutes walk down the promenade to Barmouth town centre. An excellent base for estuary and mountain walks. Pubs nearby with childrens room. Near to cycle route 8.
Facilities ♿ ⚲ ♨ ⚲ ♪ ⌂ ⊙ 🛁 ☕
🏧 ♨ 🚿 ♨ ✗ ♨ 👶 🛈 ⛲ ❄
Nearby Facilities ► ✎ ⚓ ⊾ ↳ ∪ ♪ 🏃
Nearest Town Barmouth
Directions ½ a mile north of Barmouth on the A496 Barmouth to Harlech road.
🚃 Barmouth

BARMOUTH

Islawrffordd Caravan Park, E G Evans & Sons Ltd, Tal-y-Bont, Nr Barmouth, Gwynedd, LL43 2AQ
Tel: 01341 247269
Email: info@islawrffordd.co.uk
www.islawrffordd.co.uk
Pitches For ⛺ ⚲ ⛳
Open March to Dec
Access Good **Site** Level
Nearest Bus Stop (Miles) ¼
Next to the beach with no roads or railway lines to cross. Visit Wales 5 Star Grading and AA 5 Pennants.
Facilities ♿ ⚲ ♨ ⚲ ♪ ⌂ ⊙ 🛁 ☕
🏧 ♨ 🚿 ♨ ✗ ♨ 🛈 ⛲ ❄
Nearby Facilities ► ✎ ∪ ♪ 🏃
Nearest Town Barmouth
Directions Just off the A496 approx. 3½ miles north of Barmouth in the village of Tal-y-Bont.
🚃 Tal-y-Bont

BARMOUTH

Moelfre View Caravan Park, Talybont, Nr Barmouth, Gwynedd, LL43 2AQ
Tel: 01341 247100
Email: enquiries@sunnysands.co.uk
www.sunnysands.co.uk
Pitches For ⛺ ⚲ ⛳ ⚲ **Total** 54
Acreage 5 **Open** 01-Mar to 11-Jan
Access Good **Site** Level
Nearest Bus Stop (Miles) ½
Very close to the beach. Use of indoor pool and club facilities on our sister park 5 minutes away. Ideal for touring and exploring.

Facilities ♿ ⚲ ♨ ⚲ ♪ ⌂ ⊙ 🛁 ☕
🏧 ♨ 🛒 ⛲ ♪ ⛲ 👶 🛈 ⛲ ❄ 📶
Nearby Facilities ► ✎ ⚓ ⊾ ↳ ∪ ♪ 🏃
Nearest Town Barmouth
Directions From the A496 Barmouth to Harlech road, turn left just before the old stone bridge at Talybont Village. Go straight down towards the beach and the Park is on the left.
🚃 Talybont

BARMOUTH

Parc Isaf Farm, Dyffryn Ardudwy, Gwynedd, LL44 2RJ
Tel: 01341 247447
Email: post@parcisaf.co.uk
www.parcisaf.co.uk
Pitches For ⛺ ⚲ ⛳ ⚲ **Total** 30
Acreage 3 **Open** March to October
Access Good **Site** Lev/Slope
Nearest Bus Stop (Miles) ½
Overlooking Cardigan Bay. Plenty of mountain and woodland walks. Harlech Castle and Portmeirion (Italian village) close by.
Facilities ⚲ ♨ ⌂ ⊙ 🛁 ☕
Nearby Facilities ✎ ⚓ ∪ 🏃
Nearest Town Barmouth
Directions From Barmouth take the A496 north for 5 miles, go through the small village of Talybont, ¼ mile on, opposite the church on the left there is a right hand turn through pillar gateway. Second farm on the right, signposted.
🚃 Dyffryn Ardudwy/Talybont

BARMOUTH

Sunnysands Caravan Park, Talybont, Nr Barmouth, Gwynedd, LL43 2LQ
Tel: 01341 247301
Email: enquiries@sunnysands.co.uk
www.sunnysands.co.uk
Pitches For ⚲ ⛳ ⚲ **Total** 25
Acreage 2 **Open** 01-Mar to 30-Nov
Access Good **Site** Level
Nearest Bus Stop (Miles) Entrance
Family park situated right on the beach. Ideal spot for relaxing, walking and exploring the area. Indoor heated pool and New Horizons for entertainment.
Facilities ♿ ⚲ ♨ ⚲ ♪ ⌂ ⊙ 🛁 ☕
🏧 ♨ 🚿 ♨ ✗ ♨ 🛒 ⛲ ♪ ⛲ 👶 🛈 ⛲ ❄ 📶
Nearby Facilities ► ✎ ⚓ ⊾ ↳ ∪ ♪ 🏃
Nearest Town Barmouth
Directions From the A496 Barmouth to Harlech road, 3 miles from Barmouth you pass the Wayside Pub on the right, the Park is ½ a mile further on the left.
🚃 Talybont

BARMOUTH

Trawsdir Touring Caravans & Camping Park, Llanaber, Barmouth, Gwynedd, LL42 1RR
Tel: 01341 280999
Email: enquiries@trawsdir.co.uk
www.barmouthholidays.co.uk
Pitches For ⛺ ⚲ ⛳ ⚲ **Total** 100
Access Good **Site** Level
Nearest Bus Stop (Miles) ¼

Near the beach and overlooking Cardigan Bay. Super Pitches for American RVs. State of the art toilets and facilities. Visit Wales 5 Star Grading.
Facilities ♿ ⚲ ♨ ♨ ♨ ♪ ⌂ ⊙ 🛁 ☕ 🏧
🏧 ♨ 🛒 ⛲ ♪ ⛲ ❄
Nearby Facilities ► ✎ ⚓ ↳ ♪ 🏃
Nearest Town Barmouth
Directions 2½ miles north of Barmouth on the A496.
🚃 Barmouth

CAERNARFON

Bryn Gloch Caravan & Camping Park, Betws Garmon, Caernarfon, Gwynedd, LL54 7YY
Tel: 01286 650216
Email: eurig@bryngloch.co.uk
www.campwales.co.uk
Pitches For ⛺ ⚲ ⛳ ⚲ **Total** 150
Acreage 28 **Open** March to Oct
Access Good **Site** Level
Nearest Bus Stop (Miles) Outside
Award winning site with scenic views. Plenty of flat and mountain walks in the area. Ideal touring centre and only 2 miles from Snowdon. AA 4 Pennants and AA Best Campsite in Wales 2005.
Facilities ⚲ ♨ ♨ ♨ ♪ ⌂ ⊙ 🛁 ☕ 🏧
🏧 ♨ 🛒 ⛲ ♪ ♨ ♨ ⛲ ♪ ⛲ 👶 🛈 ⛲ ❄ 📶
Nearby Facilities ► ✎ ⚓ ↳ ∪ ♪ 🏃
Nearest Town Caernarfon
Directions 4½ miles south west of Caernarfon on A4085. Site on right opposite Betws Garmon church.
🚃 Bangor

CAERNARFON

Challoner Caravan Park, Erw Hywel Farm, Llanrug, Caernarfon, Gwynedd, LL55 2AJ
Tel: 01286 672985
Email: susanchalloner@btinternet.com
Pitches For ⛺ ⚲ ⛳ ⚲ **Total** 35
Open 01-Mar to 10-Jan
Access Good **Site** Level
Nearest Bus Stop (Miles) Outside
Wetland and wild life meadow situated on site with Buzzards, Bats and Owls. Ideal for touring Snowdonia. 3 miles from Caernarfon Castle.
Facilities ♿ ⚲ ♨ ⚲ ♪ ⌂ ⊙ 🛁 ☕
🏧 ⛲ ♪ ⛲ 🛈
Nearby Facilities ► ✎ ⚓ ↳ ∪ ♪ 🏃
Nearest Town Caernarfon
Directions On the A4086 from Caernarfon towards Llanberis.
🚃 Bangor

CAERNARFON

Coed Helen Caravan Club Site, Coed Helen Road, Caernarfon, Gwynedd, LL54 5RS
Tel: 01286 676770
www.caravanclub.co.uk
Pitches For ⚲ ⛳ ⚲ **Total** 45
Acreage 2 **Open** March to Oct
Access Good **Site** Lev/Slope
Nearest Bus Stop (Miles) ¼

Just a 10 minute walk to Caernarfon and 5 miles from the beach. Small lounge bar on site. Shop and swimming pool (May to Sept) adjacent. Close to Welsh Highland Railway, Caernarfon Castle and The National Museum of Wales. Non members welcome. Booking essential.
Facilities ⨍ �📷🍴📻◎ 🏋 🎮 🔢📶🔌🔲
Nearby Facilities ⌐ ✈
Nearest Town Caernarfon
Directions In Caernarfon on the A487, by the River Seiont bridge turn into Fford Pant Road, then turn right into Coed Helen Road. At the T-junction turn left, site is 200 yards on the left.
⇌ Caernarfon

CAERNARFON
Cwm Cadnant Valley Camping & Caravan Park, Llanberis Road, Caernarfon, Gwynedd, LL55 2DF
Tel: 01286 673196
Email: cades@cwmcadnant.co.uk
www.cwmcadnant.co.uk
Pitches For ⋀ ⊞ ⊟ **Total** 69
Open March **to** Oct
Access Good **Site** Sloping
Nearest Bus Stop (Miles) Outside
Cafe/restaurant and indoor swimming pool nearby. You can also call us on FreePhone: 0800 043 5941.
Facilities ⛽ ⨍ 📷🍴📻◎ 🍴🔲 ☎
🏋🎮🔢🔌🔲🗑️ 📶
Nearby Facilities ⌐ ✈ ⚓
Nearest Town Caernarfon
Directions On the A4086, 1km from the town centre.
⇌ Bangor

CAERNARFON
Llys Derwen Camping & Caravan Site, Ffordd Bryngwyn, Llanrug, Nr Caernarfon, Gwynedd, LL55 4RD
Tel: 01286 673322
Email: llysderwen@aol.com
www.llysderwen.co.uk
Pitches For ⋀ ⊞ ⊟ **Total** 20
Acreage 4½ **Open** March **to** Oct
Access Good **Site** Level
Nearest Bus Stop (Miles) ¼
Small family run site. 2 miles from Llanberis and the foot of Mount Snowdon. Static caravans also available for hire.
Facilities ⛽ ⨍ 📷🍴📻◎🍴🔲 ☎ 🍴🔌
Nearby Facilities ⌐ ✈ ⚓ ⤬ U ♙ ♀ ⚲
Nearest Town Caernarfon
Directions From Caernarfon take the A4086 towards Llanberis. In the village of Llanrug turn right at the Glyntwrog Public House, site entrance is 100 yards on the right.
⇌ Bangor

CAERNARFON
Plas Gwyn Caravan & Camping Park, Plas Gwyn, Llanrug, Caernarfon, Gwynedd, LL55 2AQ
Tel: 01286 672619
Email: info@plasgwyn.co.uk
www.plasgwyn.co.uk
Pitches For ⋀ ⊞ ⊟ **Total** 40
Acreage 4 **Open** March **to** October
Access Good **Site** Level
Nearest Bus Stop (Miles) End of Drive
Small, peaceful park. 3 miles from Snowdonia Mountains and 5 miles from the beach. Award winning hire caravans. En-suite bed and breakfast available in the house.
Facilities ⨍ 📻📷📻◎🍴🔲 ☎
🏋️ ◎🔌🔲🗑️ 🗑️ 📶 📶
Nearby Facilities ⌐ ✈ ⚓ ⤬ U ♙ ♀ ⚲
Nearest Town Caernarfon

Directions 3 miles from Caernarfon on the A4086, signposted on right.
⇌ Bangor

CAERNARFON
Rhyd-y-Galen Caravan & Camping Park, Bethel, Caernarfon, Gwynedd, LL55 1UL
Tel: 01286 650216
Email: info@copacamping.co.uk
www.wales-camping.co.uk
Pitches For ⋀ ⊞ ⊟ **Total** 56
Acreage 4 **Open** March **to** Oct
Access Good **Site** Level/Sloping
Nearest Bus Stop (Miles) Outside
1½ miles from Plas Menai Watersports Centre. Snowdon Footpath only 15 minutes away.
Facilities ⚓ ⨍ 📻📷📻◎🍴🔲 ☎
🏋️🎮🔢🔌🔲🗑️ 🗑️
Nearby Facilities ⌐ ✈ ⚓ ⤬ U ♙ ♀ ⚲
Nearest Town Caernarfon
Directions 2 miles east of Caernarfon on the B4366.
⇌ Bangor

CAERNARFON
Riverside Camping, Seiont Nurseries, Pontrug, Caernarfon, Gwynedd, LL55 2BB
Tel: 01286 678781
Email: brenda@riversidecamping.co.uk
www.riversidecamping.co.uk
Pitches For ⋀ ⊞ ⊟ **Total** 60
Acreage 4½ **Open** Easter **to** October
Access Good **Site** Level
Nearest Bus Stop (Miles) Entrance
Secluded, landscaped site, bordered by a salmon river and adjacent to a picturesque garden centre. Mill Cafe with a spacious balcony, serving delicious home made meals. Plenty of space for childrens ball games. Wonderful place to relax after exploring Snowdonia. Six hard standings available. Permits available for fishing.
Facilities ⛽ ⨍ 📻📻◎🍴🔲 ☎
🏋️🎮🔢🔌🔲🗑️ ✈
Nearby Facilities ⌐ ✈ ⚓ ⤬ U ♙ ♀
Nearest Town Caernarfon
Directions 2 miles out of Caernarfon on the right hand side of the A4086 (Llanberis road).
⇌ Bangor

CAERNARFON
Talymignedd Campsite, Nantlle, Caernarfon, Gwynedd, LL54 6BT
Tel: 01286 880374
Email: sioned-jones@btinternet.com
Pitches For ⋀ ⊞ ⊟
Open March **to** Oct
Access Good **Site** Level
Nearest Bus Stop (Miles) ½
Very central location, ideal for the nice beaches and touring. Plenty of walking and climbing locally. Very close to the foot of Snowdon.
Facilities ⨍ 📻📷📻◎ 🍴🔲 ✈
Nearby Facilities ⌐ ✈ U ⚲
Nearest Town Caernarfon
Directions From Caernarfon take the Porthmadog road. When you enter the roundabout in Penygroes take the B4418 towards Rhyd-ddu.
⇌ Porthmadog/Bangor

CAERNARFON
Tyn Rhos Farm Caravan Park, Tyn Rhos Farm, Saron, Llanwnda, Caernarfon, Gwynedd, LL54 5UH
Tel: 01286 830362
www.tynrhosfarm.co.uk
Pitches For ⋀ ⊞ ⊟ **Total** 25
Acreage 2 **Open** March **to** Mid Jan
Access Good **Site** Level
Nearest Bus Stop (Miles) Outside

2½ miles from the beach, 1 mile from steam railway and cycle track. All pitches are hard standing.
Facilities ⨍ 📻📷📻◎🍴🔲 ☎ ✈
Nearby Facilities ⌐ ✈ ⚓ ⤬ U ♙ ♀ ⚲
Nearest Town Caernarfon
Directions From Caernarfon take the A487, after passing Tesco go straight on at the roundabout, turn first right to Saron Llanfaglan, entrance is 3 miles on the left.
⇌ Bangor

CAERNARFON
White Tower Caravan Park, Llandwrog, Caernarfon, Gwynedd, LL54 5UH
Tel: 01286 830649
Email: whitetower@supanet.com
www.whitetowerpark.co.uk
Pitches For ⋀ ⊞ ⊟ **Total** 68
Acreage 6 **Open** March **to** November
Access Good **Site** Level
Nearest Bus Stop (Miles) Outside
2½ miles from the beach, 3¼ miles from Caernarfon. Splendid views of Snowdon. Central for touring Llyn Peninsula, Anglesey and Snowdonia.
Facilities ⛽ ⨍ 📻📷📻◎🍴🔲
◎🔲
🏋️🎮🔢♀🏊⤬⤬🐾🔌🔲🔲🗑️
🗑️📶
Nearby Facilities ⌐ ✈ ⚓ ⤬ U ♙ ♀ ⚲
Nearest Town Caernarfon
Directions From Caernarfon follow the A487 Porthmadog road for approx ¼ mile, go past McDonalds, straight ahead at the roundabout and take the first turning on the right. We are 3 miles on the right.
⇌ Bangor

CHWILOG
Tyddyn Heilyn Caravan Park, Chwilog, Pwllheli, Gwynedd, LL53 6SW
Tel: 01766 810441
Email: tyddyn.heilyn@tiscali.co.uk
Pitches For ⋀ ⊞ ⊟ **Total** 5
Access Good **Site** Level
Beautiful tree lined public footpath near the site to the beach. 15 minutes from Pwllheli, Porthmadog and Snowdonia. Wi-Fi available if your stay is for a week or more.
Facilities ⤬ ⨍ 📻📷◎🍴🔌🔲🗑️ 📶
Nearby Facilities ⌐ ✈ ⚓ ⤬ U ♙ ♀ ⚲
Nearest Town Pwllheli
Directions From the A497 take the B4354, in Chwilog Village turn right opposite Madryn Arms, second site on the right, signpost at entrance.
⇌ Criccieth

CLYNNOG FAWR
Aberafon Camping & Caravan Site, Gyrn Goch, Caernarfon, Gwynedd, LL54 5PN
Tel: 01286 660295
Email: hugh@maelor.demon.co.uk
www.aberafon.co.uk
Pitches For ⋀ ⊞ ⊟ **Total** 65
Acreage 10 **Open** April **to** October
Access Poor **Site** Level
Nearest Bus Stop (Miles) Outside
Near the beach. Site shop only open during the summer holidays.
Facilities ⨍ 📻📷📻◎🍴🔲 ✈
🏋️🎮🔢🔌🔲🗑️
Nearby Facilities ⌐ ✈ ⚓ ⤬ U ♙ ♀ ⚲
Nearest Town Caernarfon
Directions From Caernarfon take the A499 towards Pwllheli, site is 1 mile after Clynnog Fawr on the right hand side.
⇌ Bangor

WALES

GWYNEDD

CRICCIETH
Cae-Canol Caravan & Camping,
Criccieth, Gwynedd, LL52 0NB
Tel: 01766 522351
Pitches For ▲ ⊕ ⊟ **Total** 25
Acreage 3 **Open** April **to** October
Access Very Good **Site** Level
Nearest Bus Stop (Miles) Outside
Sheltered, grassy site. Private trout fishing available for caravanners and campers. Delightful riverside walk nearby. Ideal for touring.
Facilities 🏕 ✦ 🚿 🅿 ⊙ 😊 🏆 🔌 ⊟ 🔲
Nearby Facilities ⌐ ✦ ⚓ 🏊 ∪ ♬ ♣ ⚡
Nearest Town Criccieth
Directions Take the B4411 from Criccieth for 2 miles. Also 2½ miles from the A487 towards Criccieth.
⚞ Criccieth

CRICCIETH
Eisteddfa Caravan & Camping Site,
Eisteddfa Lodge, Pentrefelin, Criccieth, Gwynedd, LL52 0PT
Tel: 01766 522696
Email: eisteddfa@criccieth.co.uk
www.eisteddfapark.co.uk
Pitches For ▲ ⊕ ⊟ **Total** 120
Acreage 22 **Open** March **to** October
Access Good **Site** Lev/Slope
Nearest Bus Stop (Miles) Outside
Spectacular views of Cardigan Bay and the mountains. Plenty of footpaths for walking.
Facilities ✦ 🚿 🅿 ⊙ 😊 🔲 🏆
🔲 😊 ✕ 🏔 🔌 ⊟ 🔲 ☀
Nearby Facilities ⌐ ✦ ⚓ 🏊 ∪ ♬ ♣ ⚡
Nearest Town Criccieth
Directions On the A497 Porthmadog to Criccieth road, 1½ miles north east of Criccieth. Entrance is at the west end of Pentrefelin beside the Plas Gwyn Nursing Home.
⚞ Criccieth

CRICCIETH
Llanystumdwy Camping & Caravanning Club Site, Tyddyn Sianel, Llanystumdwy, Criccieth, Gwynedd, LL52 0LS
Tel: 01766 522855
www.campingandcaravanningclub.co.uk/llanystumdwy
Pitches For ▲ ⊕ ⊟ **Total** 70
Acreage 4 **Open** 29-Mar **to** 05-Nov
Access Good **Site** Sloping
Nearest Bus Stop (Miles) Outside
Situated just outside Criccieth with scenic coastal views. Nearby attractions include Ffestiniog Railway and Snowdonia National Park. WTB 4 Star Graded and AA 3 Pennants. Non members welcome. You can also call us on 0845 130 7633.
Facilities 🛁 ✦ 🅿 🚿 🅿 ⊙ 😊 🔌 ⊟ 🔲 🏆
🔲 😊 🏆 ✕ 🔌 ⊟ 🔲 🛜
Nearby Facilities ⌐ ✦ ∪ ♬
Directions From Criccieth take the A497 and turn second right signposted Llanstumdwy, site is on the right.
⚞ Criccieth

CRICCIETH
Llwynbugeilydd Caravan Park,
Llwynbugeilydd Farm, Criccieth, Gwynedd, LL52 0PN
Tel: 01766 522235
Pitches For ▲ ⊕ ⊟ **Total** 30
Acreage 5 **Open** March **to** October
Access Good **Site** Level
Nearest Bus Stop (Miles) Outside
Views of Snowdonia from the site. Situated away from traffic noise. Very clean facility. 1 mile from the beach and charming town of Criccieth. ½ a mile from first class sea trout and salmon fishing on the River Dwyfor.

Senior Citizens price reductions in Low Season. AA 2 Pennants and WTB 4 Star Graded.
Facilities ✦ 🚿 🅿 🅿 ⊙ 😊 🔌 🔲 🏔 ✖
Nearby Facilities ⌐ ✦ ⚓ 🏊 ∪ ♬ ♣ ⚡
Nearest Town Criccieth
Directions From the A55 take the A487, after Bryncir turn right onto the B4411, site is on the left in 3½ miles. From Porthmadog take the A497 to Criccieth town centre, turn right onto the B4411, site is 1 mile on the right.
⚞ Criccieth

CRICCIETH
Muriau Bach, Rhoslan, Criccieth, Gwynedd, LL52 0NP
Tel: 01766 530642
Pitches For ▲ ⊕ ⊟ **Total** 25
Acreage 1¼ **Open** March **to** October
Access Good **Site** Level
Attractive, clean, level site, near to the sea and mountains and central to all places of interest. Ideal for retired couples who enjoy peace and quiet (at reduced terms). Commanding the best views in the area, nice walks nearby. Cycle track nearby that leads to Caernarfon. Rock climbing at Tremadog. Bowling green, highland railway and two leisure centres all within easy reach.
Facilities ✦ 🚿 🅿 🅿 ⊙ 😊 🔌 🔲 🔲
Nearby Facilities ⌐ ✦ ⚓ 🏊 ∪ ♬ ♣ ⚡
Nearest Town Criccieth
Directions Coming from Porthmadog on the A487, turn left onto the B4411. Fourth entrance on the left over a cattle grid, with a drive leading up to the site.
⚞ Criccieth

CRICCIETH
Tyddyn Morthwyl, Criccieth, Gwynedd, LL52 0NF
Tel: 01766 522115
Email: trumper@henstabl147.freeserve.co.uk
Pitches For ▲ ⊕ ⊟ **Total** 40
Acreage 6 **Open** March **to** October
Access Good **Site** Level
Nearest Bus Stop (Miles) Outside
Central for mountains of Snowdonia and beaches of Lleyn Peninsula. Level and sheltered with mountain views. One static caravan available for hire.
Facilities ✦ 🚿 🅿 ⊙ 😊 🔌 🏔 ⊟ 🔲 🔲
Nearby Facilities ⌐ ✦ ⚓ 🏊 ∪ ♬ ♣ ⚡
Nearest Town Criccieth
Directions 1½ miles north of Criccieth on B4411 main road to Caernarfon.
⚞ Criccieth

DINAS MAWDDWY
Tynypwll Caravan & Camping Site, Dinas Mawddwy, Machynlleth, Powys, SY20 9JF
Tel: 01650 531326
Pitches For ▲ ⊕ ⊟
Open April **to** Sept
Access Good **Site** Level
Nearest Bus Stop (Miles) ¼
Riverside site with lovely scenery. Ideal for walking, fishing and touring.
Facilities ✦ 🚿 🅿 🔌
Nearby Facilities ✦ ⚡
Nearest Town Barmouth/Aberystwyth
Directions From the A470 turn right to the village of Dinas Mawddwy, turn right by The Red Lion, site is the first left, entrance over the bridge. 10 miles from Dolgellau and 12 miles from Machynlleth.
⚞ Machynlleth

DOLGELLAU
Dolgamedd Camping & Caravan Site,
Dolgamedd, Bontnewydd, Dolgellau, Gwynedd, LL40 2DG
Tel: 01341 450221/450356
Email: mair@dolgamedd.co.uk
www.midwalesholidays.co.uk
Pitches For ▲ ⊕ ⊟ **Total** 85
Acreage 11 **Open** April **to** October
Access Good **Site** Level
Nearest Bus Stop (Miles) Outside
Situated on an 84 acre sheep farm alongside a river for fishing and swimming. NEW top class facilities building with campers kitchen. Camp fires allowed on the river bank, barbecues and picnic tables. 11 miles from the coast.
Facilities 🛁 ✦ 🎏 🚿 🅿 ⊙ 😊 🔌 🔲 🏆
🔌 🏔 ⊟ 🔲 ✦ ☀ 🛜
Nearby Facilities ⌐ ✦ ⚓ 🏊 ∪ ♬ ♣ ⚡
Nearest Town Dolgellau
Directions 3 miles from Dolgellau on the A494 towards Bala, turn right at Bontnewydd onto the B4416 towards Brithdir. Continue over the bridge and Dolgamedd is on the left.
⚞ Machynlleth

DOLGELLAU
Dolserau Uchaf, Dolgellau, Gwynedd, LL40 2DE
Tel: 01341 422639
Pitches For ⊕ ⊟ **Total** 20
Acreage 1¼ **Open** Easter **to** October
Access Good **Site** Level
Nearest Bus Stop (Miles) Outside
Quiet site with open views of the Cader Idris Range. Ideal for walking and cycling.
Facilities ✦ 🚿 🅿 🅿 ⊙ 😊 🔌 🔲
Nearby Facilities ⌐ ✦ ⚓ ∪
Nearest Town Dolgellau
Directions 2½ miles east of Dolgellau on the A494.
⚞ Barmouth

DOLGELLAU
Llwyn-Yr-Helm Farm, Brithdir, Dolgellau, Gwynedd, LL40 2SA
Tel: 01341 450254
Email: info@llwynyrhelmcaravanpark.co.uk
www.llwynyrhelmcaravanpark.co.uk
Pitches For ▲ ⊕ ⊟ **Total** 25
Acreage 2½ **Open** Easter **to** End Oct
Access Good **Site** Lev/Slope
Nearest Bus Stop (Miles) ¼
Seasides, hills, mountains, rivers, lakes and slate mines. Ideal for walking and mountain biking at Coed Y Brenin.
Facilities ✦ 🚿 🅿 🅿 ⊙ 😊 🔌 🔲 🔲 🏆
🔌 😊 🏔 ⊟ 🔲 ☀
Nearby Facilities ⌐ ✦ ⚓ 🏊 ∪ ♬ ♣ ⚡
Nearest Town Dolgellau
Directions Turn off the A470 or the A494 onto the B4416 to Brithdir. At the phonebox and village hall turn into a minor road, Park is ½ a mile on the left.
⚞ Machynlleth

DOLGELLAU
Pant-y-Cae, Arthog, Dolgellau, Gwynedd, LL39 1LJ
Tel: 01341 250892
Email: pantycaefarm@btconnect.com
www.pantycae.co.uk
Pitches For ▲ ⊕ ⊟ **Total** 56
Acreage 5 **Open** All Year
Access Good **Site** Sloping
Nearest Bus Stop (Miles) 1
3 miles from the beach. Near Cregennan Lakes for fishing and Cadair Idris for mountain walking, bird watching and mountain biking.

WALES

WALES

Facilities ♦ ⅏ ⌐ ☎♨⊡⬚
Nearby Facilities ⌐ ✓ ⚓ ❤ ∪ ⚲ ⚶
Nearest Town Dolgellau/Fairbourne
Directions From Dolgellau take the A493, quarry on the left hand side then turn left for Cregennan Lakes, site is ¾ miles up the single track road.
≠ Fairbourne

DOLGELLAU

Tanyfron Camping & Caravan Park, Arran Road, Dolgellau, Gwynedd, LL40 2AA
Tel: 01341 422638
Email: info@tan-y-fron.co.uk
www.campsitedolgellau.co.uk
Pitches For ▲ ⬠ ⬟ **Total** 43
Acreage 3¼ **Open** 01-Mar **to** 07-Jan
Access Good **Site** Level
Nearest Bus Stop (Miles) ¼
Small 5 Star Holiday Park, just a few minutes walk from Dolgellau and the supermarket. 8 miles to beaches. Ideal base for touring, walking, cycling, fishing and golf. All hard standing pitches with hook ups. 4 Star B&B available. Internet connection.
Facilities ♦ ⊡⅏⌐⊙♨⊿⬚☎ ⅏⌗⊡☼
Nearby Facilities ⌐ ✓ ⚓ ∪ ⚲ ⚶
Nearest Town Dolgellau
Directions From Welshpool take the A470, after the Little Chef turn off for Dolgellau, site is ½ a mile on the le ft, by the 30mph sign.
≠ Barmouth

DOLGELLAU

Tyddyn Farm, Islawrdref, Dolgellau, Gwynedd, LL40 1TL
Tel: 01341 422472
Pitches For ▲ ⬠ ⬟
Open All Year
Access Good **Site** Lev/Slope
Beautiful views of Cader Idris Mountain and alongside a river. Plenty of walks and fishing locally. ¼ of a mile from Lake Hotel.
Facilities ☎♨⊡
Nearby Facilities ⌐ ✓ ∪ ⚶
Nearest Town Dolgellau
Directions 2 miles from Dolgellau on the Cader road. Pass Gwernan Lake Hotel, ¼ of a mile turn right through a wooden gate, go over the cattle grid and turn left.
≠ Machynlleth

DYFFRYN ARDUDWY

Murmur-yr-Afon Touring Caravan & Camping Site, Dyffryn Ardudwy, Gwynedd, LL44 2BE
Tel: 01341 247353
Email: mills@murmuryrafon25.freeserve.co.uk
www.murmuryrafon.co.uk
Pitches For ▲ ⬠ ⬟ **Total** 77
Acreage 4 **Open** March **to** October
Access Good **Site** Level
Nearest Bus Stop (Miles) Outside
1 mile from beach. Set in sheltered and natural surroundings, 100yds from village and shops, petrol stations and licensed premises.
Facilities ♿ ♦ ⊡⅏⌐⊙♨⊿⬚☎
⅏⌗⊡☼
Nearby Facilities ⌐ ✓ ⚓ ∪ ⚲ ⚶ ⚶
Nearest Town Barmouth
Directions Take the A496 coast road from Barmouth towards Harlech. Caravan Site is located 100yds on the right after the Spar shop.
≠ Dyffryn

FFESTINIOG

Llechrwd Riverside Campsite, Maentwrog, Blaenau Ffestiniog, Gwynedd, LL41 4HF
Tel: 01766 Maentwrog 590240
Email: llechrwd@hotmail.com
www.llechrwd.co.uk
Pitches For ▲ ⬠ ⬟
Acreage 5 **Open** Easter **to** October
Access Good **Site** Level
Nearest Bus Stop (Miles) Outside
Riverside camp within Snowdonia National Park, with meadow walk. Near Ffestiniog Railway.
Facilities ♿ ♦ ⊡⅏⌐⊙♨⊿⬚☎⌗⊡☼
Nearby Facilities ⌐ ✓ ⚓ ∪ ⚶
Directions On the A496. Blaenau Ffestiniog 3 miles, Porthmadog 8 miles.
≠ Blaenau Ffestiniog

HARLECH

Woodlands Caravan Park, Harlech, Gwynedd, LL46 2UE
Tel: 01766 780419
Email: grace@woodlandscp.fsnet.co.uk
www.woodlandscp.fsnet.co.uk
Pitches For ⬠ ⬟ **Total** 18
Acreage 2 **Open** March **to** October
Access Good **Site** Level
Nearest Bus Stop (Miles) ¼
Near the beach, shops and a golf course. Adjacent to Harlech Castle. Swimming pool nearby. Centrally heated shower and toilet building. Ideal touring.
Facilities ♦ ⊡⅏⌐⊙♨⊿⬚☎
⅏⊙⌗⊡☼
Nearby Facilities ⌐ ✓ ⚓ ∪ ⚲ ⚶ ⚶
Nearest Town Harlech
Directions Leave A496 at Harlech railway crossing, site signposted at crossing at foot of castle.
≠ Harlech

LLANBEDROG

Bolmynydd Camping Park, Llanbedrog, Pwllheli, Gwynedd, LL53 7UP
Tel: 07882 850820
Email: info@bolmynydd.co.uk
www.bolmynydd.co.uk
Pitches For ▲ **Total** 48
Acreage 2 **Open** April **to** End Oct
Access Poor **Site** Level
Nearest Bus Stop (Miles) ¼
5 minute walk to the beach, shop and pub. Panoramic views of Snowdonia and Lleyn Peninsula. Excellent facilities. WTB 5 Star Graded. Booking is essential at peak times.
Facilities ♦ ⊡⅏⌐⊙♨⊿⬚☎
⅏⊙⌗⊡☼⚲
Nearby Facilities ⌐ ✓ ⚓ ∪ ⚲ ⚶ ⚶
Nearest Town Abersoch
Directions From Pwllheli take the A499 to Llanbedrog for 3½ miles. Continue towards Abersoch for ½ a mile and turn first left after Llanbedrog Riding Centre (by the red post box). Site is ½ a mile on the left.
≠ Pwllheli

LLANBEDROG

Wern Newydd Tourer Park, Llanbedrog, Pwllheli, Gwynedd, LL53 7PG
Tel: 01758 740220
Email: office@wern-newydd.co.uk
www.wern-newydd.co.uk
Pitches For ▲ ⬠ ⬟ ⬟ **Total** 25
Acreage 2½ **Open** March **to** October
Access Good **Site** Level
Nearest Bus Stop (Miles) ¼
Peaceful location on the beautiful Lleyn Peninsula. Near the beach and village with its country pubs and bistro. The area offers many walks, watersports activities and attractions.

Facilities ♦ ⊡⅏⌐⊙♨⊿⬚☎ ⅏⌗⊡☼⚲
Nearby Facilities ⌐ ✓ ⚓ ∪ ⚲ ⚶ ⚶
Nearest Town Abersoch
Directions From Pwllheli take the A499 towards Abersoch, in Llanbedrog turn right onto B4413 sp Aberdaron. Continue through the village, go past the chemists (on the right) then take the first turning right onto an unclassified road, site is 700 yards on the right.
≠ Pwllheli

LLANBERIS

Snowdon View Caravan Park, Brynrefail, Nr Llanberis, Caernarfon, Gwynedd, LL55 3PD
Tel: 01286 870349
Email: enquiries@snowdonviewpark.co.uk
www.snowdonviewpark.co.uk
Pitches For ⬠ ⬟ **Total** 137
Open 01-Mar **to** 03-Jan
Access Good **Site** Level
Nearest Bus Stop (Miles) ¼
Ideal for the Snowdon mountains and railway, and Lake Padarn.
Facilities ♦ ⊡⅏⌐⊙♨⊿⬚☎
⅏⊙⬚✕⏃⎏⅏⚑⚲❤⌗⊡☼⚲⚲
Nearby Facilities ⌐ ✓ ⚓ ∪ ⚲ ⚶
Nearest Town Caernarfon
Directions Leave the A55 at junction 11 and take the B4366/A4244.
≠ Bangor

MORFA NEFYN

Graeanfryn Farm, Morfa Nefyn, Gwynedd, LL53 6YQ
Tel: 01758 720455
Email: jan@campingnorthwales.co.uk
www.campingnorthwales.co.uk
Pitches For ▲ ⬠ ⬟ **Total** 30
Acreage 1½ **Open** All Year
Access Good **Site** Level
Nearest Bus Stop (Miles) ¼
Rural location, 1 mile from the beach. Barbecue area. Cafe/Restaurant nearby. One static caravan for hire. Camping and Caravan Club 3 Star Site and WTB 3 Star Graded.
Facilities ♦ ⅏⌐⊙♨ ⅏❤⊡☼
Nearby Facilities ⌐ ✓ ⚓ ∪ ⚲
Nearest Town Pwllheli
Directions From Pwllheli take the A497 for 5 miles, at the roundabout turn left and then turn next left. Entrance to the site is 50 yards on the right.
≠ Pwllheli/Bangor

PORTHMADOG

Black Rock Sands Camping & Touring Park, Morfa Bychan, Porthmadog, Gwynedd, LL49 9YH
Tel: 01766 513919
www.blackrocksands.webs.com
Pitches For ▲ ⬠ ⬟ **Total** 140
Acreage 9 **Open** March **to** October
Access Good **Site** Level
Nearest Bus Stop (Miles) ½
Adjacent to a 7 mile sandy beach.
Facilities ♿ ♦ ⅏⌐⊙♨⊿⬚☎
⅏⊙⬚❤⊡☼
Nearby Facilities ⌐ ✓ ⚓ ∪ ⚲ ⚶ ⚶
Nearest Town Porthmadog
Directions From Porthmadog take the road to Morfa Bychan, turn right just before the beach.
≠ Porthmadog

PORTHMADOG
Garreg Goch Caravan Park, Black Rock Sands, Morfa Bychan, Porthmadog, Gwynedd, LL49 9YD
Tel: 01766 512210
Email: info@garreggochcaravanpark.co.uk
www.garreggochpark.co.uk
Pitches For 🚐 🚎 **Total** 7
Open 01-Mar to 10-Jan
Access Good **Site** Level
Nearest Bus Stop (Miles) Entrance
Small, quiet, peaceful family park with beautiful views. Just a 10 minute walk to Black Rock Sands with its 2 miles of golden sands.
Facilities 🔣 🔣 🔣 🔣 🔣 🔣 🔣 🔣 🔣
🔣 🔣 🔣 🔣 🔣 🔣 🔣
Nearby Facilities 🔣 🔣 🔣 🔣
Nearest Town Porthmadog
Directions Turn off the A487 in Porthmadog High Street at the Original Factory Shop. Go straight for 2 miles, after the Spar Shop turn third left.
🚃 Porthmadog

PORTHMADOG
Glan-Y-Mor Camping Park, Morfa Bychan, Porthmadog, Gwynedd, LL49 9YH
Tel: 01766 514640
Pitches For 🔺 🚎 **Total** 60
Acreage 5 **Open** May to September
Site Level
Nearest Bus Stop (Miles) ½
Adjacent to a 7 mile sandy beach.
Facilities 🔣 🔣 🔣 🔣 🔣 🔣 🔣
Nearby Facilities 🔣 🔣 🔣 🔣 🔣 🔣 🔣
Nearest Town Porthmadog
Directions From Porthmadog take the road to Morfa Bychan, continue to the beach, entrance is on the left.
🚃 Porthmadog

PORTHMADOG
Greenacres Holiday Park, Black Rock Sands, Morfa Bychan, Porthmadog, Gwynedd, LL49 9YG
Tel: 01766 512781
Email: greenacres@haven.com
www.haventouring.com/togreenacres
Pitches For 🚐 🚎 **Total** 48
Open Mid March to End Oct
Access Good **Site** Level
Nearest Bus Stop (Miles) Outside
Next to the stunning Black Rock Sands. Enjoy sport and leisure facilities including bike hire, 9 hole Pitch n Putt and kart hire. Plus kids clubs and a full family entertainment programme.
Facilities 🔣 🔣 🔣 🔣 🔣 🔣 🔣 🔣 🔣 🔣 🔣
🔣 🔣 🔣 🔣 🔣 🔣 🔣 🔣 🔣 🔣 🔣 🔣
🔣
Nearby Facilities 🔣 🔣 🔣 🔣
Nearest Town Porthmadog
Directions After going over the toll bridge at Porthmadog, go along the high street and turn between the Post Office and Factory Shop. ¼ mile on through the village of Morfa Bychan, take the right fork to Black Rock Sands, Greenacres is about 2 miles.
🚃 Porthmadog

PORTHMADOG
Tyddyn Adi Caravan & Camping Park, Tyddyn Adi, Morfa Bychan, Nr Black Rock Sands, Porthmadog, Gwynedd, LL49 9YW
Tel: 01766 512933
Email: tyddynadi@btconnect.com
www.tyddynadi.co.uk
Pitches For 🔺 🚐 🚎 🚎 **Total** 50
Acreage 28 **Open** March to September
Access Good **Site** Level
Nearest Bus Stop (Miles) Entrance
At the foot of Moel-y-Gest Mountain and near Black Rock Sands. Perfect base from which to explore Snowdonia.
Facilities 🔣 🔣 🔣 🔣 🔣 🔣 🔣
🔣 🔣 🔣 🔣 🔣 🔣
Nearby Facilities 🔣 🔣 🔣 🔣 🔣 🔣 🔣
Nearest Town Porthmadog
Directions Take the A487 from Caernarfon, turn right at The Factory Shop and follow signs for Morfa Bychan. We are opposite Greenacres (Haven).
🚃 Porthmadog

PORTHMADOG
Tyddyn Llwyn Caravan Park, Morfa Bychan Road, Porthmadog, Gwynedd, LL49 9UR
Tel: 01766 512205
Email: info@tyddynllwyn.com
www.tyddynllwyn.com
Pitches For 🔺 🚐 🚎 **Total** 153
Acreage 18 **Open** March to 01-Nov
Access Good **Site** Lev/Slope
Nearest Bus Stop (Miles) Entrance
Only 2 miles from Black Rock Sands. In a sheltered valley beneath Moel Y Gest Mountain with beautiful wooded scenery.
Facilities 🔣 🔣 🔣 🔣 🔣 🔣 🔣 🔣 🔣
🔣 🔣 🔣 🔣 🔣 🔣 🔣 🔣 🔣 🔣 🔣 🔣
Nearby Facilities 🔣 🔣 🔣 🔣 🔣 🔣
Nearest Town Porthmadog
Directions From the high street turn by the Post Office signposted Black Rock Sands. Park is on the right hand side. Less than 1km from the town centre.
🚃 Porthmadog

PWLLHELI
Abererch Sands Holiday Centre, Pwllheli, Gwynedd, LL53 6PJ
Tel: 01758 612327
www.abererch-sands.co.uk
Pitches For 🔺 🚐 🚎
Open March to Oct
Access Good **Site** Level
Nearest Bus Stop (Miles) ¼
Adjacent to the beach. Heated indoor swimming pool.
Facilities 🔣 🔣 🔣 🔣 🔣 🔣 🔣
🔣 🔣 🔣 🔣 🔣 🔣 🔣 🔣 🔣
Nearby Facilities 🔣 🔣 🔣 🔣 🔣 🔣 🔣 🔣
Nearest Town Pwllheli
Directions From Pwllheli take the A497 towards Porthmadog for 1 mile, turn right at first roundabout and follow road to the Site.
🚃 Pwllheli

PWLLHELI
Bodwrog Farm, Bodwrog, Llanbedrog, Pwllheli, Gwynedd, LL53 7RE
Tel: 01758 740341
Email: enq@bodwrog.co.uk
www.bodwrog.co.uk
Pitches For 🔺 🚐 🚎 **Total** 70
Acreage 5 **Open** 01-Mar to 31-Oct
Access Good **Site** Sloping
Nearest Bus Stop (Miles) ½
Superb coastal views. 1 miles from a sandy, sheltered beach. Quiet, scenic walks. Local restaurants and pubs within 1 mile.
Facilities 🔣 🔣 🔣 🔣 🔣 🔣 🔣 🔣 🔣 🔣
🔣 🔣 🔣 🔣 🔣 🔣 🔣
Nearby Facilities 🔣 🔣 🔣 🔣 🔣 🔣
Nearest Town Abersoch
Directions From Pwllheli take the A499 to Llanbedrog, turn right opposite Glyn-Y-Weddw Pub onto the B4413. After 1 mile site is the third opening on the left after the Ship Inn, cattle grid inside entrance.
🚃 Pwllheli

PWLLHELI
Hafan Y Mor, Pwllheli, Gwynedd, LL53 6HJ
Tel: 01758 612112
Email: hafanymor@haven.com
www.haventouring.com/tohafanymor
Pitches For 🚐 🚎 **Total** 72
Open Mid March to End Oct
Access Good **Site** Sloping
Nearest Bus Stop (Miles) Outside
A large, active Holiday Park on the shores of the spectacular Tremadog Bay. Direct beach access. Kids clubs, water fun, family entertainment and so much more.
Facilities 🔣 🔣 🔣 🔣 🔣 🔣 🔣 🔣 🔣 🔣
🔣 🔣 🔣 🔣 🔣 🔣 🔣 🔣 🔣 🔣 🔣 🔣 🔣 🔣
🔣
Nearby Facilities 🔣 🔣 🔣 🔣 🔣
Nearest Town Pwllheli
Directions On the A497, 3 miles from Pwllheli and 7 miles from Porthmadog.
🚃 Pwllheli

PWLLHELI
Hendre Caravan Park, Efailnewydd, Near Pwllheli, Gwynedd, LL53 8TN
Tel: 01758 613416
Email: info@hendrecaravanpark.co.uk
www.hendrecaravanpark.co.uk
Pitches For 🚐 🚎
Open March to Oct
Access Good **Site** Level
Nearest Bus Stop (Miles) ¼
Quiet, secluded site with ¾ of the space for static vans and a ¼ for touring vans and camper vans. Many beaches and lovely walks locally. Close to the old market town of Pwllheli.
Facilities 🔣 🔣 🔣 🔣 🔣 🔣 🔣 🔣 🔣
Nearby Facilities 🔣 🔣 🔣 🔣 🔣 🔣 🔣
Nearest Town Pwllheli
Directions From Pwllheli take the A497 Nefyn road, go across the roundabout to Efailnewydd Village, turn first left and go through the village, take the first left at the bottom of the village.
🚃 Pwllheli

PWLLHELI

Hirdre Fawr Caravan & Camping, Hirdre Fawr Farm, Edern, Pwllheli, Gwynedd, LL53 8YY
Tel: 01758 770309
Email: annwenw@yahoo.com
www.hirdrefawr.co.uk
Pitches For ▲ ⬛ ⬛ **Total** 80
Acreage 7 **Open** End March **to** End Oct
Access Good **Site** Level
Nearest Bus Stop (Miles) Outside
Pebly beach on site which also adjoins the coastal path. Central to the Llyn Peninsula. 2 miles from a golf coarse and beach access. Fishing off the rocks.
Facilities ⬛ ⬛ ⬛ ⬛ ⬛ ⬛ ⬛ ⬛ ⬛
⬛ ⬛ ⬛ ⬛ ⬛ ⬛
Nearby Facilities ⬛ ⬛ ⬛ ⬛ ⬛ ⬛ ⬛ ⬛
Nearest Town Pwllheli
Directions On the B4417, 1½ miles out of Edern towards Tudweiliog.
⇌ Pwllheli

PWLLHELI

Ty Mawr Caravan Park, Bryncroes, Pwllheli, Gwynedd, LL53 8EH
Tel: 01248 351537
Email: rowjones@tiscali.co.uk
www.tymawr-caravan-park.co.uk
Pitches For ▲ ⬛ ⬛ **Total** 30
Acreage 2 **Open** April **to** October
Access Good **Site** Level
Nearest Bus Stop (Miles) ¼
Ideal for touring the beautiful Lleyn Peninsula and near to numerous excellent beaches including Whistling Sands, Penllech Beach and Porth Iago.
Facilities ⬛ ⬛ ⬛ ⬛ ⬛ ⬛ ⬛ ⬛ ⬛
⬛ ⬛ ⬛ ⬛ ⬛ ⬛ ⬛
Nearby Facilities ⬛ ⬛ ⬛ ⬛ ⬛ ⬛ ⬛ ⬛
Nearest Town Pwllheli/Aberdaron
Directions From Pwllheli take the A499 to Llanbedrog, then take the B4413 for approx. 9 miles. Site is signposted.
⇌ Pwllheli

TALSARNAU

Barcdy Touring Caravan & Camping Park, Talsarnau, Gwynedd, LL47 6YG
Tel: 01766 770736
Email: anwen@barcdy.co.uk
www.barcdy.co.uk
Pitches For ▲ ⬛ ⬛ **Total** 98
Acreage 12 **Open** May **to** September
Access Good **Site** Lev/Slope
Nearest Bus Stop (Miles) Outside
Walks from site to nearby mountains and lakes. Ideal touring Snowdonia.
Facilities ⬛ ⬛ ⬛ ⬛ ⬛ ⬛ ⬛ ⬛ ⬛
⬛ ⬛ ⬛ ⬛ ⬛ ⬛ ⬛
Nearby Facilities ⬛ ⬛ ⬛ ⬛ ⬛
Nearest Town Harlech
Directions From Bala A4212 to Trawsfynydd. A487 to Maentwrog. At Maentwrog left onto A496, signposted Harlech. Site 4 miles.
⇌ Talsarnau

TYWYN

Caethle Chalet & Caravan Park, Aberdyfi Road, Tywyn, Gwynedd, LL36 9HS
Tel: 01654 710587
Pitches For ▲ ⬛ ⬛
Acreage 15 **Open** April **to** October
Access Good **Site** Lev/Slope
Nearest Bus Stop (Miles) Outside
Set in the countryside with great views. Near the beach.
Facilities ⬛ ⬛ ⬛ ⬛ ⬛ ⬛ ⬛ ⬛ ⬛
Nearby Facilities ⬛ ⬛ ⬛ ⬛ ⬛ ⬛ ⬛ ⬛
Directions On the A493 coast road, 1½ miles couth of Tywyn.
⇌ Tywyn

TYWYN

Cwmrhwyddfor Campsite, T D Nutting, Talyllyn, Tywyn, Gwynedd, LL36 9AJ
Tel: 01654 761286/761380
Pitches For ▲ ⬛ ⬛ ⬛ **Total** 30
Acreage 6 **Open** All Year
Access Good **Site** Level
Nearest Bus Stop (Miles) Outside
At the foot of Cader Idris and alongside a stream. Very central for Tywyn, Aberdovey and Barmouth. Ideal for the mountains and sea. All kept very clean, excellent reputation. Public telephone, pub and restaurant and a cafe within a 5 minute walk. Prices on application.
Facilities ⬛ ⬛ ⬛ ⬛ ⬛ ⬛ ⬛ ⬛ ⬛
Nearby Facilities ⬛ ⬛ ⬛ ⬛ ⬛
Nearest Town Dolgellau
Directions Situated on the A487 between Dolgellau and Machynlleth, at foot of Cader Idris mountain, right at the bottom of Talyllyn pass, a white house under the rocks.
⇌ Machynlleth

TYWYN

DÃˆI Einion, Tal-y-Llyn, Tywyn, Gwynedd, LL36 9AJ
Tel: 01654 761312
Email: marianrees@tiscali.co.uk
Pitches For ▲ ⬛ ⬛
Acreage 3 **Open** All Year
Access Good **Site** Level
Nearest Bus Stop (Miles) ¼
Flat, grassy site with a stream in Snowdonia National Park. At the start of the popular Minffordd Path to the summit of Cader Idris. Heritage Centre on site with full summer programme on Welsh history, traditions and music. Ideal for walking and touring. Fly fishing ½ mile, narrow gauge railway 3 miles and beach 11 miles. B&B and self catering cottage on site. Hotel restaurant and bar nearby. Public telephone nearby. Good bus service.
Facilities ⬛ ⬛ ⬛ ⬛ ⬛ ⬛ ⬛ ⬛ ⬛
Nearby Facilities ⬛ ⬛ ⬛ ⬛ ⬛
Nearest Town Dolgellau
Directions From Dolgellau take the A470 for 2 miles, turn right onto the A487 and continue for 4 miles. Turn right onto the B4405, site is 300 metres.
⇌ Machynlleth

TYWYN

Erw-Wen Caravan Park, Mill Lane, Bryncrug, Tywyn, Gwynedd, LL36 9NU
Tel: 01654 710374
Pitches For ⬛ ⬛ **Total** 20
Acreage 2
Access Good **Site** Level
Nearest Bus Stop (Miles) ¼
Ideal touring.
Facilities ⬛ ⬛ ⬛ ⬛ ⬛ ⬛ ⬛
Nearby Facilities ⬛ ⬛ ⬛ ⬛ ⬛
Nearest Town Tywyn
Directions 2 miles from Tywyn on the road to Dolgellau in the village of Bryncrug, turn first left after the playing field.
⇌ Tywyn

TYWYN

Glanywern, Dysefin, Llanegryn, Tywyn, Gwynedd, LL36 9TH
Tel: 01654 782247
Pitches For ▲ ⬛ ⬛ **Total** 28
Acreage 4½ **Open** April **to** Oct
Access Good **Site** Level
Nearest Bus Stop (Miles) Outside
½ a mile from Bird Rock, 3 miles from Cader Idris and 5 miles from the beach. Near a Narrow Gauge Railway.

Facilities ⬛ ⬛ ⬛ ⬛ ⬛ ⬛ ⬛ ⬛ ⬛ ⬛
Nearby Facilities ⬛ ⬛ ⬛ ⬛ ⬛ ⬛
Nearest Town Tywyn
Directions From Tywyn take the road to Llanegryn, 3 miles from Llanegryn to Bird Rock.
⇌ Tywyn

TYWYN

Pall Mall Farm Caravan Park, Pall Mall Farm, Tywyn, Gwynedd, LL36 9RU
Tel: 01654 710384
Email: richardmvaughan@gmail.com
www.pallmallfarmcaravanpark.co.uk
Pitches For ▲ ⬛ ⬛ **Total** 50
Open Easter **to** 31-Oct
Nearest Bus Stop (Miles) Entrance
½ a mile to the town and safe sandy beach which is ideal for watersports. Leisure centre in the town plus a cinema, cafes, tennis courts, bowling green and putting green. Tal-y-Llyn Steam Railway nearby.
Facilities ⬛ ⬛ ⬛ ⬛ ⬛ ⬛ ⬛ ⬛ ⬛
⬛ ⬛ ⬛ ⬛ ⬛
Nearby Facilities ⬛ ⬛ ⬛ ⬛ ⬛ ⬛ ⬛ ⬛
Nearest Town Tywyn
Directions Park is the first on the left when leaving Tywyn on the A493 Dolgellau road.
⇌ Tywyn

TYWYN

Waenfach Caravan Site, Waenfach, Llanegryn, Tywyn, Gwynedd, LL36 9SB
Tel: 01654 711052
Email: waenfach@hotmail.co.uk
Pitches For ▲ ⬛ ⬛ **Total** 10
Open Easter **to** October
Access Good
Small site on a working farm. 3 miles from the sea.
Facilities ⬛ ⬛ ⬛ ⬛ ⬛ ⬛ ⬛ ⬛ ⬛
⬛ ⬛ ⬛ ⬛ ⬛
Nearby Facilities ⬛ ⬛ ⬛ ⬛ ⬛ ⬛ ⬛ ⬛
Nearest Town Tywyn
Directions 4 miles north of Tywyn on the A493.
⇌ Tywyn

TYWYN

Ynysymaengwyn Caravan Park, The Lodge, Tywyn, Gwynedd, LL36 9RY
Tel: 01654 710684
Email: rita@ynysy.co.uk
www.ynysy.co.uk
Pitches For ▲ ⬛ ⬛ **Total** 80
Acreage 4 **Open** April **to** October
Access Good **Site** Level
Nearest Bus Stop (Miles) Outside
In the grounds of an old manor house with a river at the bottom of the site for fishing. Near to the beach and shops. Woodland walks open to the public. Superpitches. Walkers and Cyclists Award. Secure storage for cycles. WTB 4 Star Grading and AA 4 Pennants.
Facilities ⬛ ⬛ ⬛ ⬛ ⬛ ⬛ ⬛ ⬛ ⬛
⬛ ⬛ ⬛ ⬛ ⬛
Nearby Facilities ⬛ ⬛ ⬛ ⬛ ⬛ ⬛ ⬛ ⬛
Nearest Town Tywyn
Directions Take the A493 from Tywyn to Dolgellau, we are the second caravan park on the left.
⇌ Tywyn

WALES

MERTHYR TYDFIL
MERTHYR TYDFIL
Grawen Caravan & Camping Park, Cwm-Taf, Cefn Coed, Merthyr Tydfil, CF48 2HS
Tel: 01685 723740
Email: grawen.touring@virgin.net
www.walescaravanandcamping.com
Pitches For ▲ ⚍ 🚐 **Total** 50
Acreage 3½ **Open** April to 30-Oct
Access Good **Site** Level
Nearest Bus Stop (Miles) Outside
Picturesque mountain, forest and reservoir walks inside the Brecon Beacons National Park. A wealth of history can be found in the town of Merthyr Tydfil and the Valleys.
Facilities
Nearby Facilities
Nearest Town Merthyr Tydfil
Directions Easy access along the A470 Brecon Beacons road, 2 miles from Cefn Coed and 4 miles from Merthyr Tydfil. 2 miles off the A465 Heads of the Valleys road, ¼ mile from the reservoir.
⚏ Merthyr Tydfil

MONMOUTHSHIRE
ABERGAVENNY
Pandy Caravan Club Site, Pandy, Abergavenny, Monmouthshire, NP7 8DR
Tel: 01873 890370
www.caravanclub.co.uk
Pitches For ⚍ 🚐 **Total** 53
Acreage 5 **Open** March to Nov
Access Good **Site** Level
Nearest Bus Stop (Miles) ¼
Pleasant site scattered with mature trees and bounded by the River Honddu. Near Offas Dyke Path. 50 yards from the Old Pandy Hotel and there are eight pubs in the vicinity. Close to the Brecon Beacons and Tintern Abbey. Non members welcome. Booking essential.
Facilities
Nearby Facilities
Nearest Town Abergavenny
Directions From the A465, DO NOT go into Abergavenny but continue on the A465 following signs for Hereford. After 6¼ miles turn left by the Pandy Inn into a minor road, site is on the left immediately after passing under the railway bridge.
⚏ Abergavenny

ABERGAVENNY
Pyscodlyn Farm Caravan & Camping Site, Llanwenarth Citra, Abergavenny, Monmouthshire, NP7 7ER
Tel: 01873 853271
Email: pyscodlyn.farm@virgin.net
www.pyscodlyncaravanpark.com
Pitches For ▲ ⚍ 🚐 **Total** 60
Acreage 4½ **Open** 01-Apr to 31-Oct
Access Good **Site** Level
Nearest Bus Stop (Miles) Outside
Ideal for walking, cycling and exploring the Black Mountains and Brecon Beacons National Park.
Facilities
Nearby Facilities
Nearest Town Abergavenny
Directions Situated on A40 (Brecon road), 1½ miles from Nevill Hall Hospital, on the left 50 yards past the telephone box.
⚏ Abergavenny

MONMOUTH
Bridge Caravan Park & Camping Site, Dingestow, Monmouth, Monmouthshire, NP25 4DY
Tel: 01600 740241
Email: info@bridgecaravanpark.co.uk
www.bridgecaravanpark.co.uk
Pitches For ▲ ⚍ 🚐 **Total** 123
Acreage 4 **Open** Easter to October
Access Good **Site** Level
Nearest Bus Stop (Miles) Outside
Riverside site. Easy access.
Facilities
Nearby Facilities
Nearest Town Monmouth
Directions 4 miles west of Monmouth.
⚏ Abergavenny

MONMOUTH
Glen Trothy Caravan Park, Mitchel Troy, Monmouth, Monmouthshire, NP25 4BD
Tel: 01600 712295
Email: enquiries@glentrothy.co.uk
www.glentrothy.co.uk
Pitches For ▲ ⚍ 🚐 **Total** 130
Acreage 6½ **Open** March to October
Access Good **Site** Level
Nearest Bus Stop (Miles) Outside
Quiet level Park set in beautiful countryside on the edge of Forest of Dean and Wye Valley. Alongside a river for fishing. 1½ miles from the historic town of Monmouth. Plenty of castles and attractions nearby. No arrivals before 2pm.
Facilities
Nearby Facilities
Nearest Town Monmouth
Directions From north M5, M50 then A40 taking the left turn after the traffic lights at Monmouth and before reaching road tunnel. From East Gloucester, A40 Ross on Wye, A40 Monmouth. From south and southeast M4 Severn Bridge, A466 Chepstow, Tintern and Monmouth turning left at traffic lights at monmouth on to A40.
⚏ Newport

MONMOUTH
Monmouth Caravan Park, Rockfield Rd, Monmouth, Monmouthshire, NP25 5BA
Tel: 01600 714745
Pitches For ▲ ⚍ 🚐 **Total** 60
Acreage 3½ **Open** 01-Mar to 03-Jan
Access Good **Site** Level
Nearest Bus Stop (Miles) ¼
Flat and level site close to the town. Small bar with bar meals on site.
Facilities
Nearby Facilities
Nearest Town Monmouth
Directions From Monmouth take the B4233, Park is ¼ of a mile towards Rockfield on the right hand side, opposite the fire station.
⚏ Abergavenny

NEWPORT
NEWPORT
Pentre-Tai Farm, Rhiwderin, Newport, NP10 8RQ
Tel: 01633 893284
Email: sue@pentretai.f9.co.uk
www.pentretaifarm.co.uk
Pitches For ▲ ⚍ 🚐 **Total** 5
Acreage 3 **Open** All Year
Access Good **Site** Lev/Slope
Nearest Bus Stop (Miles) ½
Ideal for visiting Cardiff and the Welsh castles. Useful stopover for Irish ferry. Good pub nearby. B&B also available (WTB 4 Star).

Facilities
Nearby Facilities
Nearest Town Newport
Directions Leave the M4 at junction 28 and take the A467, at the next roundabout take the A468 for approx. 1 mile. Turn right immediately after Rhiwderin Inn and go straight through the village and straight down the lane to the Farm. Go past the farmhouse then turn in.
⚏ Newport

NEWPORT
Tredegar House Country Park Caravan Club Site, Coedkernew, Newport, NP10 8TW
Tel: 01633 815600
www.caravanclub.co.uk
Pitches For ⚍ 🚐 **Total** 79
Acreage 7 **Open** All Year
Access Good **Site** Level
Nearest Bus Stop (Miles) ¼
Bordered by an ornamental lake by Tredegar House. Tea rooms on site. Adventure playground adjacent. 7 miles from Cardiff. Non members welcome. Booking essential.
Facilities
Nearby Facilities
Nearest Town Newport
Directions Leave the M4 at junction 28 and take the A48 signposted Tredegar House. At the roundabout turn left into the site entrance and follow site signs.
⚏ Newport

PEMBROKESHIRE
AMROTH
Little Kings Park, Amroth Road, Ludchurch, Narberth, Pembrokeshire, SA67 8PG
Tel: 01834 831330
Email: littlekingspark@btconnect.com
www.littlekings.co.uk
Pitches For ▲ ⚍ 🚐 **Total** 121
Acreage 16 **Open** 01-Mar to 31-Oct
Access Good **Site** Level
Quiet family park in a country setting with an excellent outlook towards the sea. Perfectly placed for easy access to explore all that Pembrokeshire has to offer.
Facilities
Nearby Facilities
Nearest Town Amroth
Directions 5 miles south east of Narberth. From the A477 in Llanteg Village, 2 miles after the petrol station turn left towards Amroth and Wisemans Bridge, turn first right signposted Ludchurch and the Park is 300 metres on the left.
⚏ Kilgetty

AMROTH
Meadow House Holiday Park, Summerhill, Amroth, Pembrokeshire, SA67 8NS
Tel: 01834 812438
Email: enquiries@meadowhouseholidaypark.com
www.meadowhouseholidaypark.com
Pitches For ▲ ⚍ 🚐 **Total** 70
Acreage 16 **Open** March to Oct
Access Good **Site** Level
Nearest Bus Stop (Miles) ¼
Direct access to the Pembrokeshire Coast footpath.
Facilities
Nearby Facilities
Nearest Town Amroth

Directions From the A477, turn left after Llanteg and follow signs for Ludchurch, turn left at sign for Summerhill and the Park is on the left.

AMROTH

Pantglas Farm, Tavernspite, Whitland, Pembrokeshire, SA34 0NS
Tel: 01834 831618
Email: pantglas@btinternet.com
www.pantglasfarm.co.uk
Pitches For 🏕 🚐 🚍 **Total** 86
Acreage 14 **Open** Mid March **to** Mid Oct
Access Good **Site** Lev/Slope
Nearest Bus Stop (Miles) ¼
A family caravan and camping park, quiet and secluded. Super play area for children. High standard toilet and shower facilities, disabled wet room facility. Caravan yearly or weekly storage available from £7.00 per week. Within easy reach of Tenby, Saundersfoot and Amroth. Indoor swimming pool only 1 mile away.
Facilities 🛇 ⚓ 🔼 🔽 🅿 🛈 ⊙ 🍴 🔌 🔲 🍵
🖙 🛒 🎱 ⏰ 🎮 🎣 ➤🚲 🐕 🔺 🎿 🐴 ✗
Nearby Facilities ⚓ ✓ 🔼 🎣 ∪ 🐴 🏇 ✗
Nearest Town Whitland/Narberth
Directions A477 towards Tenby take the B4314 at Red Roses crossroads to Tavernspite 1¼ miles, take the middle road at the village pump. Pantglas is ½ mile down on the left.
🚆 Whitland

ANGLE

Castle Farm Camping Site, Castle Farm, Angle, Nr Pembroke, Pembrokeshire, SA71 5AR
Tel: 01646 641220
Pitches For 🏕 🚐 🚍 **Total** 25
Acreage 2½ **Open** Easter **to** Oct
Access Good **Site** Lev/Slope
Overlooking East Angle Bay and directly behind the church in the village. Approx. 1 mile from a safe, sandy beach. Near to 2 public houses, Beach Cafe, a good shop and childrens play area. Pets are welcome if kept on leads.
Facilities 🔽 🅿 ⊙ 🍵 🖙 🛒 ➤🚲 🔲
Nearby Facilities ⚓ ✓ 🔼 🎣 ∪ 🐴 🏇 ✗
Nearest Town Pembroke
Directions Approx. 10 miles from Pembroke.
🚆 Pembroke

BROAD HAVEN

Creampots Touring Caravan & Camping Park, Broadway, Broad Haven, Haverfordwest, Pembrokeshire, SA62 3TU
Tel: 01437 781776
Email: creampots@btconnect.com
www.creampots.co.uk
Pitches For 🏕 🚐 🚍 **Total** 72
Acreage 7 **Open** March **to** Nov
Access Good **Site** Level
Nearest Bus Stop (Miles) ¼
Family run park thats quiet, peaceful and well maintained. Ideal for couples and families. 1½ miles from safe sandy beach and coastal path at Broad Haven. 21 hardstanding pitches. Near Haverfordwest, Broad Haven and Littlehaven. WTB 5 Star Graded.
Facilities 🛇 🔽 ⚓ 🅿 ⊙ 🍴 🔌 🔲 🍵
🖙 🛒➤🔲 🎿 🔧

Nearby Facilities ⚓ ✓ 🔼 🎣 ∪ 🐴
Nearest Town Broad Haven
Directions Take the B4131 Broad Haven road from Haverfordwest to Broadway (5 miles). Turn left and Creampots is 600 yards on the right.
🚆 Haverfordwest

FISHGUARD

Fishguard Bay Caravan Park, Garn Gelli, Fishguard, Pembrokeshire, SA65 9ET
Tel: 01348 811415
Email: enquiries@fishguardbay.com
www.fishguardbay.com
Pitches For 🏕 🚐 🚍 **Total** 50
Acreage 5 **Open** March **to** December
Access Good **Site** Lev/Slope
Superb cliff top location offering excellent views and walks along this Heritage coast of Pembrokeshire.
Facilities 🔽 🅿 ⚓ 🅿 ⊙ 🍴 🔌 🔲 🍵
🖙 🛒 🎱 🎮 ➤🔲
Nearby Facilities ⚓ ✓ 🔼 🎣 ∪ 🐴 🏇
Nearest Town Fishguard
Directions Take the A487 Cardigan road from Fishguard for 1½ miles, turn left at sign.
🚆 Fishguard

FISHGUARD

Gwaun Vale Touring Park, Llanychaer, Fishguard, Pembrokeshire, SA65 9TA
Tel: 01348 874698
Email: margaret.harries@talk21.com
www.gwaunvale.co.uk
Pitches For 🏕 🚐 🚍 **Total** 29
Acreage 1½ **Open** April **to** Oct
Access Good **Site** Level
Nearest Bus Stop (Miles) 1
Beautiful views of Gwaun Valley. Ideal for walking on Pembrokeshire Coast National Park.
Facilities 🔽 🅿 ⚓ 🅿 ⊙ 🍴 🔌 🍵
🖙 🛒 🎱 🎮 ➤🔲
Nearby Facilities ⚓ ✓ 🔼 🎣 ∪ 🐴
Nearest Town Fishguard
Directions From Fishguard take the B4313, site is 1½ miles on the right hand side.
🚆 Fishguard

FISHGUARD

Rosebush Caravan & Camping Park, Rhoslwyn, Rosebush, Narberth, Pembrokeshire, SA66 7QT
Tel: 01437 532206
Pitches For 🏕 🚐 🚍 **Total** 45
Acreage 15 **Open** March **to** October
Access Good **Site** Level
ADULTS ONLY PARK in the centre of Pembrokeshire, 800ft above sea level. 3 acre lake for coarse fishing. Mountain walks. David Bellamy Gold Award for Conservation.
Facilities 🔽 🅿 ⚓ 🅿 ⊙ 🍴
🖙 🛒 🎱 🎮 ➤🔲 🍵 🔧
Nearby Facilities ⚓ ∪
Nearest Town Fishguard
Directions From the A40 take the B4313 near Narberth to Fishguard. 1 mile from the B4329 Haverfordwest to Cardigan road.
🚆 Clynderwen

HAVERFORDWEST

Brandy Brook Caravan & Camping Site, Roch, Haverfordwest, Pembrokeshire, SA62 6HE
Tel: 01348 840563
Email: a.daye@btopenworld.com
www.brandybrookcampsite.co.uk
Pitches For 🏕 **Total** 40
Acreage 5 **Open** Easter **to** October
Site Lev/Slope
Attractive quiet valley setting with The Brandy Brook flowing alongside. Small motorhomes also accepted.
Facilities 🅿 ⚓ 🅿 ⊙ 🍴 🍵
🖙 🛒 🎱 ⏰ 🎮 ➤🔲
Nearby Facilities ⚓ ✓ 🔼 🎣 ∪ 🐴 🏇
Nearest Town Haverfordwest
Directions From Haverfordwest take the A487 west towards St Davids, turn right at Roch, signposted.
🚆 Haverfordwest

HAVERFORDWEST

Nolton Cross Caravan Park, Nolton, Haverfordwest, Pembrokeshire, SA62 3NP
Tel: 01437 710701
Email: info@noltoncross-holidays.co.uk
www.noltoncross-holidays.co.uk
Pitches For 🏕 🚐 🚍 **Total** 15
Acreage 1½ **Open** March **to** December
Access Good **Site** Level
Nearest Bus Stop (Miles) 1½
Coarse fishing lake on site. 1½ miles from sandy beaches. Central location for touring Pembrokeshire.
Facilities 🔽 🅿 ⚓ 🅿 ⊙ 🍴 🔌 🔲 🍵
🎱 🎮 ➤🔲 🔧 ✓
Nearby Facilities ⚓ ✓ 🔼 🎣 ∪ 🐴
Nearest Town Haverfordwest
Directions Take the A487 from Haverfordwest towards St Davids, after 5 miles at the village of Simpson Cross turn left for Nolton, follow for 1 mile to the next crossroads and turn left, entrance is 100 yards on the right.
🚆 Haverfordwest

HERMON

The Lamb Inn Touring Caravan Park, Hermon, Glogue, Pembrokeshire, SA36 0DS
Tel: 01239 831864
Email: street867@btinternet.com
www.thelambinnhermon.co.uk
Pitches For 🚐 🚍 **Total** 28
Acreage 3 **Open** Easter **to** 03-Jan
Access Good **Site** Level
Nearest Bus Stop (Miles) Entrance
Quiet and secluded ADULTS ONLY Park at the rear of The Lamb Inn Pub. Ideal for walking and cycling. Close to Cardigan.
Facilities 🛇 🔽 🅿 ⚓ 🅿 ⊙ 🍴 🔲 🍵
🖙 🎱 ⚒ ✗ 🅿 🎮 ➤🔲 🎣 🐴 🔺
Nearby Facilities ⚓ ✓ 🔼 🎣 ∪
Nearest Town Cardigan
Directions From Carmarthen take the A40 west, turn right onto the A478 Cardigan road. At Crymmych turn right and follow signs to Hermon for 2 miles.
🚆 Clunderwen

KILGETTY

Ryelands Caravan Park, Ryelands Lane, Kilgetty, Pembrokeshire, SA68 0UY
Tel: 01834 812369
Pitches For Å ⚶ ⚶ **Total** 35
Acreage 9 **Open** March **to** October
Access Poor **Site** Lev/Slope
Nearest Bus Stop (Miles) ¼
2 miles from Saundersfoot beach and 4 miles from Tenby beach. Within walking distance of the town with all its amenities.
Facilities ⌇ ▥⛽⌒⊙♨
Nearby Facilities ┌ ✔ ⚓ ⋎ Ồ ⚲ ⚹
Nearest Town Saundersfoot/Tenby
Directions Drive through Kilgetty, turn at the chip shop/chinese into Ryelands Lane, site entrance is ½ a mile on the right.
⇌ Kilgetty

KILGETTY

Stone Pitt Caravan Park, Begelly, Kilgetty, Pembrokeshire, SA68 0XE
Tel: 01834 811086
Email: info@stonepitt.co.uk
www.stonepitt.co.uk
Pitches For ⚶ ⚶ **Total** 36
Acreage 6 **Open** 01-Mar **to** 09-Jan
Access Good **Site** Lev/Slope
Nearest Bus Stop (Miles) Outside
Quiet, peaceful, family run park. Within easy reach of Pembrokeshires wonderful beaches, Folly Farm, Heatherton, Oakwood, Tenby and Saundersfoot. Ideal touring. All pitches are hardstanding with grey water waste.
Facilities ⌇ ▥⛽⌒⊙♨
Nearby Facilities ┌ ✔ ⚓ ⋎ Ồ
Nearest Town Saundersfoot/Tenby
Directions From St. Clears take the A477, at the next roundabout turn onto the A478 for Narberth. Go over the next roundabout in Begelly Village, site is ½ a mile on the left.
⇌ Kilgetty

LITTLE HAVEN

Redlands Touring Caravan & Camping Park, Hasguard Cross, Nr Little Haven, Haverfordwest, Pembrokeshire, SA62 3SJ
Tel: 01437 781300
Email: info@redlandscamping.co.uk
www.redlandstouring.co.uk
Pitches For Å ⚶ ⚶ ⚶ **Total** 60
Acreage 5 **Open** March **to** December
Access Good **Site** Level
Nearest Bus Stop (Miles) ¼
Small 4 Star Park set in Pembrokeshire National Park, within easy reach of coastal path and superb sandy beaches. Immaculate facilities. Extra large tent pitches. Special Offers for couples in Low Season.
Facilities ⌇ ▥⛽⌒⊙♨
Nearby Facilities ┌ ✔ ⚓ ⋎ Ồ ⚲
Nearest Town Little Haven
Directions 6½ miles southwest of Haverfordwest, on B4327 Dale Road.
⇌ Haverfordwest

LITTLE HAVEN

South Cockett Caravan & Camping Park, Broadway, Little Haven, Haverfordwest, Pembrokeshire, SA62 3TU
Tel: 01437 781296
Email: esmejames@hotmail.co.uk
www.southcockett.co.uk
Pitches For Å ⚶ ⚶ **Total** 73
Acreage 6 **Open** Easter **to** Oct
Access Good **Site** Level
Nearest Bus Stop (Miles) ¼
1 mile from the beach. Ideal for touring.

Facilities ⌇ ▤ ▥⛽⌒⊙♨
Nearby Facilities ┌ ✔ ⚓ ⋎ Ồ ⚲ ⚹
Nearest Town Broad Haven
Directions From Haverfordwest take the B4341 for Broad Haven for about 6 miles, turn left at sign post and the Site is ¼ of a mile.
⇌ Haverfordwest

MANORBIER

Park Farm Holiday Park, Manorbier, Tenby, Pembrokeshire, SA70 7SU
Tel: 01834 871273
Email: info@parkfarmholidaypark.co.uk
www.parkfarmholidaypark.co.uk
Pitches For Å ⚶ ⚶
Open March **to** Oct
Access Good **Site** Lev/Slope
Nearest Bus Stop (Miles) ¼
Just a 10 minute walk from Manorbier Beach along a private foot path.
Facilities ⌇ ▥⛽⌒⊙♨
Nearby Facilities ┌ ✔ ⚓ ⋎ Ồ ⚲ ⚹
Nearest Town Tenby
Directions Take the A4139 from Tenby, take second turn to Manorbier and follow brown tourism signs.
⇌ Manorbier

MILFORD HAVEN

Sandy Haven Caravan Park,
Herbrandston, Nr Milford Haven, Pembrokeshire, SA73 3ST
Tel: 01646 698844
www.sandyhavencamping.co.uk
Pitches For Å ⚶ ⚶ **Total** 26
Open Whitsun **to** September
Access Good **Site** Lev/Slope
Nearest Bus Stop (Miles) ¼
Very quiet and uncommercialised site, alongside a beautiful beach and sea estuary. Ideal for a family holiday.
Facilities ⌒ ⊙♨ ▥⛽
Nearby Facilities ┌ ✔ ⚓ ⋎ Ồ ⚲ ⚹
Nearest Town Milford Haven
Directions Take the Dale Road from Milford Haven, turn left at Herbrandston School and follow the village road down to the beach.
⇌ Milford Haven

NARBERTH

Noble Court Holiday Park, Redstone Road, Narberth, Pembrokeshire, SA67 7ES
Tel: 01834 861908
Email:
enquiries@noblecourtholidaypark.com
www.noblecourtholidaypark.com
Pitches For Å ⚶ ⚶ **Total** 92
Acreage 40 **Open** March **to** October
Access Good **Site** Lev/Slope
Nearest Bus Stop (Miles) ½
Quiet family caravan park with amenities for all ages. Conveniently situated for travel to all Pembrokeshire beaches and countryside, also Pembrokeshire National Park.
Facilities ⌇ ▥⛽⌒⊙♨
Nearby Facilities ┌ ✔ ⚓ ⋎ Ồ ⚲ ⚹
Nearest Town Narberth
Directions On the B4313, ½ a mile north of Narberth and ½ a mile south of the A40.
⇌ Narberth

NARBERTH

Wood Office Caravan & Tent Park, Cold Blow, Narberth, Pembrokeshire, SA67 8RR
Tel: 01834 860565
Email: barbara_morris@btconnect.com
Pitches For ⚶ ⚶
Access Good **Site** Level
Nearest Bus Stop (Miles) Outside
Close to Oakwood Park, Bluestone & Blue Lagoon and Folly Farm. Please telephone prior to bringing a dog.
Facilities ⌇ ▥⛽⌒⊙♨
Nearby Facilities ┌ ✔ ⚓ ⋎ Ồ ⚲
Nearest Town Saundersfoot
Directions Leave the M4 and take the A40, then the A478, at the top of Templeton turn left onto the B4315 to Cold Blow.
⇌ Narberth

NEWPORT

Llwyngwair Manor Holiday Park, Newport, Pembrokeshire, SA42 0LX
Tel: 01239 820498
www.pembrokeshireholidaypark.co.uk
Pitches For Å ⚶ ⚶
Acreage 55 **Open** 01-Mar **to** 02-Jan
Access Good **Site** Level
Nearest Bus Stop (Miles) Entrance
1 mile from a sandy beach. Alongside the River Nevern in 55 acres of wood and parkland in Pembrokeshire Coast National Park.
Facilities ⌇ ▥⛽⌒⊙♨
Nearby Facilities ┌ ✔ ⚓ ⋎ Ồ ⚲
Nearest Town Newport
Directions 1 mile from Newport on the A487 to Cardigan.
⇌ Fishguard

NEWPORT

Morawelon Caravan & Camping Site, Morawelon, The Parrog, Newport, Pembrokeshire, SA42 0RW
Tel: 01239 820565
Email: carreg@morawelon.fsnet.co.uk
Pitches For Å ⚶ ⚶ **Total** 90
Acreage 5 **Open** March **to** October
Access Good **Site** Sloping
Nearest Bus Stop (Miles) ½
Ideal family site. Near to the beach with a slipway for boat launching just outside the entrance. On the Pembrokeshire Coastal Path.
Facilities ⌇ ▥⛽⌒⊙♨ ✗ ⊡
Nearby Facilities ┌ ✔ ⚓ ⋎ Ồ ⚲
Nearest Town Newport
Directions A487 from Fishguard, 7 miles to Newport. A487 from Cardigan, 12 miles to Newport. Turn right after the garage, continue into Newport, turn left down Parrog Road. Go down to the bottom and Morawelon is the house by the slipway.
⇌ Fishguard

NEWPORT

Tycanol Farm Camp Site, Newport, Pembrokeshire, SA42 0ST
Tel: 01239 820264
www.caravancampingsites.co.uk
Pitches For Å ⚶ ⚶ ⚶ **Total** 40
Acreage 6 **Open** All Year
Access Good **Site** Level
Nearest Bus Stop (Miles) ¼
Organic farm, situated on a coastal path with easy access to beaches and the town. FREE barbecue nightly.
Facilities ⌇ ▥⛽⌒⊙♨
Nearby Facilities ┌ ✔ ⚓ ⋎ Ồ ⚲ ⚹
Nearest Town Newport
⇌ Fishguard

WALES

PEMBROKE
Freshwater East Caravan Club Site,
Trewent Hill, Freshwater East, Pembroke,
Pembrokeshire, SA71 5LJ
Tel: 01646 672341
www.caravanclub.co.uk
Pitches For Å ⊕ ⊟ **Total** 130
Acreage 12½ **Open** March **to** Oct
Access Good **Site** Lev/Slope
Nearest Bus Stop (Miles) ¼
Situated at the bottom of a hill in
Pembrokeshire Coast National Park. Just a
few minutes from the beach with clifftop views
and coastal walks. Close to the castles of
Pembroke, Carew and Manorbier. Near Folly
Farm and Oakwood Theme Park. Non
members welcome. Booking essential.
Facilities ⅙ ∤ ⊞ ⊞ ⊓ ⅌ ☺ ☎
⅋ ⊡ ⊜ ▲ ⊠ ⚲ ☂
Nearby Facilities ✔ ⚓ ⅃
Nearest Town Pembroke
Directions From A477 take A4075 sp
Pembroke. Immediately after passing under
railway bridge turn left onto A4139. In
Lamphey at left hand bend continue onto
B4584 sp Freshwater East. After 1¾ miles
turn right sp Stackpole, at the foot of the hill
turn right at Club
⚄ Pembroke

PEMBROKE
Windmill Hill Caravan Park, St Daniels
Hill, Pembroke, Pembrokeshire, SA71 5BT
Tel: 01646 682392
Email: wjgibby@btconnect.com
www.windmillhillcaravanpark.co.uk
Pitches For Å ⊕ ⊟ **Total** 30
Open March **to** December
Access Good **Site** Level
Ideal base for surfing, hiking and rock
climbing.
Facilities ⅙ ∤ ⊞ ⊞ ⊓ ⅌ ☺ ⅃ ☎ ☺⊁⊟
Nearby Facilities ✔ ⚓ ⅃ ⚲ ∪ ✗
Nearest Town Pembroke
Directions From Pembroke take the B4319,
site is ½ a mile on the right hand side.
⚄ Pembroke

REYNALTON
Croft Holiday Park, Reynalton, Kilgetty,
Pembrokeshire, SA68 0PE
Tel: 01834 860315
Email: enquiries@croftholidaypark.com
www.croftholidaypark.com
Pitches For Å ⊕ ⊟ **Total** 55
Open March **to** November
Access Good **Site** Level
Close to the seaside resorts of Tenby and
Saundersfoot, and Pembrokeshire National
Park.
Facilities ⅙ ∤ ⊞ ⊓ ⅌ ☺ ⅃ ▲ ⊠ ☎
⅋ ⅋ ⊡ ⊜ ⊠ ▥⊞⊟ ⚲ ☂
Nearby Facilities ✔ ⚓ ⅃ ⚲ ∪ ⚃ ⅃
Nearest Town Saundersfoot
Directions From Narberth take the A478
following signs for Tenby. In Templeton turn
second right at the Boars Head towards
Yerbeston, turn second left to Reynalton and
the park is ½ mile on the right hand side.
⚄ Kilgetty

SAUNDERSFOOT
Hill Park Caravans, Pentlepoir,
Saundersfoot, Pembrokeshire, SA69 9BH
Tel: 01834 811288
Email: hillpark@btconnect.com
Pitches For ⊕ ⊟
Access Good **Site** Level
Nearest Bus Stop (Miles) Entrance
Situated within a national park near to sandy
beaches and theme parks.

Facilities ⅙ ⚡ ∤ ⊟ ⊞ ⊞ ⅌ ⊓ ⅌ ☺⅃ ⊠ ☎
⅋ ⊡ ⊡ ⚲
Nearby Facilities ✔ ⚓ ⚲
Nearest Town Saundersfoot
Directions On the main A478 Cardigan to
Tenby road, opposite the junction with the
B4316 to Saundersfoot.
⚄ Saundersfoot/Kilgetty

SAUNDERSFOOT
Mill House Caravan Park, Pleasant
Valley, Stepaside, Saundersfoot,
Pembrokeshire, SA67 8LN
Tel: 01834 812069
Email: holiday@millhousecaravan.co.uk
www.millhousecaravan.co.uk
Pitches For Å ⊕ ⊟ **Total** 12
Acreage 2½ **Open** March **to** October
Access Good **Site** Level
Nearest Bus Stop (Miles) Outside
Beautiful and sheltered setting in a wooded
valley, next to an old water mill. 15 minute
walk to the beach and coastal path. Holiday
caravans for hire.
Facilities ∤ ⊞ ⊞ ⊓ ⅌ ☺ ⅃ ▲ ⊠ ☎
⅋ ⊡ ⊜ ▲ ⊠ ⚲
Nearby Facilities ✔ ⚓ ⅃ ⚲ ∪ ⚃ ✗
Directions 13 miles west of St. Clears on
the A477 turn left signposted Stepaside. After
crossing the bridge turn sharp left then
immediately left again signed Pleasant
Valley. Site is approx. 500 metres on the left
hand side.
⚄ Kilgetty

SAUNDERSFOOT
Moreton Farm Leisure Park, Moreton,
Saundersfoot, Pembrokeshire, SA69 9EA
Tel: 01834 812016
Email: moretonfarm@btconnect.com
www.moretonfarm.co.uk
Pitches For Å ⊕ ⊟ **Total** 60
Acreage 12 **Open** March **to** October
Access Good **Site** Level
Nearest Bus Stop (Miles) ½
1 mile of safe golden beach. Castles, theme
park, national park and botanic gardens
nearby. 20 hard standing pitches available.
WTB 4 Star Park.
Facilities ⅙ ∤ ⊞ ⊞ ⊓ ⅌ ☺ ⅃ ▲ ⊠ ☎
⅋ ⅋ ⊡ ⊜ ⊠ ⊓ ⊡ ⊟
Nearby Facilities ✔ ⚓ ⅃ ⚲ ∪ ⚃ ✗
Nearest Town Saundersfoot
Directions From St. Clears on the A477, turn
left onto A478 for Tenby. Site is on left 1¼
miles, opposite Moreton Chapel.
⚄ Tenby

SAUNDERSFOOT
Moysland Farm Camping Site, Narberth
Road, Saundersfoot, Pembrokeshire, SA69
9DS
Tel: 01834 812455
Pitches For Å ⊕ ⊟ **Total** 20
Acreage 3 **Open** June **to** September
Access Good **Site** Level
Nearest Bus Stop (Miles) ¼
1 mile from the beach. Ideal centre for
touring. Please send S.A.E. for details.
Facilities ∤ ⊞ ⊓ ⅌ ☺ ⅃⊞⊟ ⊡
Nearby Facilities ✔ ⚓ ⅃ ⚲ ∪ ⚃ ⅃
Nearest Town Saundersfoot
Directions Leave the M4 and take the A48
and A40 to St. Clears, turn onto the A477 to
Kilgetty then take the A478 to Tenby. Site is
on right hand side of road before New
Hedges roundabout.
⚄ Tenby

ST. DAVIDS
Caerfai Bay Caravan & Tent Park, St
Davids, Pembrokeshire, SA62 6QT
Tel: 01437 720274
Email: info@caerfaibay.co.uk
www.caerfaibay.co.uk
Pitches For Å ⊕ ⊟ **Total** 105
Acreage 10 **Open** March **to** Mid Nov
Site Lev/Slope
Nearest Bus Stop (Miles) 1
A family run park with panoramic coastal
views. Adjacent to the Pembrokeshire
Coastal Path and an award winning beach.
Within walking distance of St Davids,
Europes smallest city. Holiday hire caravans
available. No dogs allowed in the tent fields
during school summer holidays (July/
August).
Facilities ⅙ ∤ ⊞ ⊞ ⊓ ⅌ ☺⅃ ▲ ⊠ ☎
⅋ ⊡ ⊜⊁⊟ ⊡ ☂
Nearby Facilities ✔ ⚓ ⅃ ⚲ ∪ ⅃ ✗
Nearest Town St Davids
Directions Turn off the A487 (Haverfordwest
to St. Davids road) at St. Davids Visitor
Centre signposted Caerfai. At the end of the
road, ¾ miles, turn right into park.
⚄ Haverfordwest

ST. DAVIDS
Camping & Caravanning Club Site, Dwr
Cwmwdig Berea, St Davids,
Haverfordwest, Pembrokeshire, SA62
6DW
Tel: 01348 831376
www.campingandcaravanningclub.co.uk/
stdavids
Pitches For Å ⊕ ⊟ **Total** 40
Acreage 4 **Open** 23-Apr **to** 26-Sep
Access Good **Site** Sloping
Nearest Bus Stop (Miles) Outside
Just 1 mile from the beach. Close to Britains
smallest cathedral city. WTB 3 Star Graded
and AA 2 Pennants. Non members welcome.
You can also call us on 0845 130 7633.
Facilities ∤ ⊞ ⊞ ⊓ ⅌ ☺ ⅃ ⊡ ☎
⅋ ⊡ ⊜⊁⊟
Nearby Facilities ✔ ⚓ ∪ ⅃ ✗
Nearest Town Haverfordwest
Directions Travelling south on the A487, in
Croesgoch turn right at Glyncheryn Farmers
Stores. After approx. 1 mile turn right
signposted Abereiddy, at the crossroads turn
left and the site is 75 yards on the left hand
side.
⚄ Fishguard

ST. DAVIDS
Lleithyr Meadow Caravan Club Site,
Whitesands, St Davids, Pembrokeshire,
SA62 6PR
Tel: 01437 720401
www.caravanclub.co.uk
Pitches For ⊕ ⊟ **Total** 120
Acreage 8 **Open** March **to** Oct
Access Good **Site** Level
Nearest Bus Stop (Miles) ½
Just a short walk to Whitesands Bay. Shop
adjacent. Non members welcome. Booking
essential.
Facilities ⅙ ∤ ⊞ ⊓ ⅌ ☺ ☎
⅋ ⊡ ⊜⊁⊟ ⚲
Nearby Facilities ✔ ⚓ ⅃ ⚲ ∪
Nearest Town St. Davids
Directions From Haverfordwest take A487,
before entering St Davids turn right onto
B4583 sp Whitesands, turn left still on B4583.
At second crossroads (DO NOT follow
Lleithyr Meadow signs at first crossroads)
turn sharp right opposite St Davids Golf Club,
site is 500yds on left.
⚄ St. Davids

WALES

ST. DAVIDS

Nine Wells Caravan & Camping Park,
Nine Wells, Solva, Nr Haverfordwest,
Pembrokeshire, SA62 6UH
Tel: 01437 721809
Email: ocean6@clara.co.uk
www.ninewellscamping.com
Pitches For ▲ ⊞ ➡ **Total** 70
Acreage 4½ **Open** Easter **to** October
Access Good **Site** Lev/Slope
Nearest Bus Stop (Miles) Outside
Sandy beach ¾ mile. Walk the coastal
footpath to Solva. About 5 minute walk to
cove and coastal footpath and Iron Age Fort,
down National Trust Valley. You can also call
us on Mobile 07974 516461.
Facilities ⨍ ▥⬚ ⌐ ☺ ⬝ ▨ 🍴 ⊡ 🖅 🖼 ⬛ ⋇
Nearby Facilities ⌐ ✓ ⬘ ⌇ ∪ ⅃ ✗
Nearest Town Haverfordwest
Directions From Haverfordwest take A487
to Solva. ¼ mile past Solva turn left at Nine
Wells. Site clearly signposted.
🚂 Haverfordwest

ST. DAVIDS

Park Hall Camping Park, Maerdy Farm,
Penycwm, Haverfordwest, Pembrokeshire,
SA62 6LS
Tel: 01437 721606/721282
Pitches For ▲ ⊞ ➡ ➡ **Total** 100
Acreage 7 **Open** March **to** October
Access Good **Site** Level
Near the beach with scenic views. Ideal
touring. Disabled toilet and shower. Dish
washing facilities.
Facilities ⬥ ⨍ ▥⬚ ⌐ ☺ ⬝ ▨ 🍴 ⊡ 🖼 🖅
▥⬚ ⊡ ▨ ⬛ 🖅 ⬛ ⋇
Nearby Facilities ⌐ ✓ ⬘ ⌇ ∪ ⅃ ♔ ✗
Nearest Town Haverfordwest
Directions 12 miles from Haverfordwest on
the A487 and 6 miles from St. Davids. Turn
at the 14th Signal Regiment Brawdy.
🚂 Haverfordwest

TENBY

Hazelbrook Caravan Park, Sageston, Nr
Tenby, Pembrokeshire, SA70 8SY
Tel: 01646 651351
Email: hazbrook12@hotmail.co.uk
www.hazelbrookcaravanpark.co.uk
Pitches For ▲ ⊞ ➡ **Total** 70
Acreage 7½ **Open** 14-Mar **to** 09-Jan
Access Good **Site** Level
Nearest Bus Stop (Miles) ¼
Quiet family site, 1 mile from Carew Castle
and Mill, 2 miles from Dinosaur Park and 7
miles from Oakwood Theme Park.
Facilities ⨍ ▥⬚ ⌐ ☺ ⬝ ▨ 🍴 ⊡ 🖼 🍴
🖾 ⊡ ⬛ ▨ 🖅 ⊡ ⬛ ⋇
Nearby Facilities ⌐ ✓ ⬘ ⌇ ∪ ⅃ ♔ ✗
Nearest Town Tenby

Directions Turn off the A477 at the
roundabout turning onto the B4318 for Tenby.
Caravan park is 20 yards on the right (60
foot entrance).
🚂 Tenby

TENBY

Kiln Park Holiday Centre, Marsh Road,
Tenby, Pembrokeshire, SA70 7RB
Tel: 01834 844121
Email: kilnpark@haven.com
www.haventouring.com/tokilnpark
Pitches For ▲ ⊞ ➡ **Total** 193
Acreage 150 **Open** Mid March **to** End Oct
Access Good **Site** Level
Nearest Bus Stop (Miles) Outside
A lively and popular Holiday Park with direct
access onto Tenbys South Beach. Kids clubs
and family entertainment - day and night.
Many holiday attractions nearby.
Facilities ⬥ ✗ ⨍ ▥⬚ ⌐ ☺ ⬝ ▨ 🍴 ⊡ 🖼 🍴
🖾 ⊡ ⬛ ✗ ▨ ⬝ ✦ 🖅 ⊡ ⬛ ⋇
⬚
Nearby Facilities ⌐ ✓ ⬘ ⌇ ∪ ⅃ ♔ ✗
Nearest Town Tenby
Directions Follow the A478 to Tenby,
signposted from Tenby to Penally and then
Kiln Park.
🚂 Tenby

TENBY

Lodge Farm Holiday Park, New Hedges,
Tenby, Pembrokeshire, SA70 8TN
Tel: 01834 842468
Email: lodgefarm1@hotmail.co.uk
Pitches For ▲ ⊞ ➡ **Total** 65
Acreage 5 **Open** April/Easter **to** Oct
Access Good **Site** Level
Nearest Bus Stop (Miles) Outside
Near the beach and coastal path.
Facilities ⨍ ▥⬚ ⌐ ☺ ⬝ ▨ 🍴
🖾 ⊡ ⬛ ✗ ▨ 🖅 ⊡ ⬛ ✗
Nearby Facilities ⌐ ✓ ⬘ ⌇ ∪ ✗
Nearest Town Tenby/Saundersfoot
Directions Approaching Tenby on the A478,
turn left at New Hedges roundabout, turn first
right, go through the village and Lodge Farm
entrance is opposite the minimarket.
🚂 Tenby/Saundersfoot

TENBY

Manorbier Country Park, Station Road,
Manorbier, Tenby, Pembrokeshire, SA70
7SN
Tel: 01834 871952
Email: enquiries@countrypark.co.uk
www.countrypark.co.uk
Pitches For ▲ ⊞ ➡ **Total** 50
Open March **to** October
Access Good **Site** Level
Nearest Bus Stop (Miles) Entrance

1 miles from the beach and a 20 minute drive
from Oakwood and Folly Farm.
Facilities ⬥ ⨍ ▥⬚ ⌐ ☺ ⬝ ▨ 🍴 ⊡ 🖼 🍴
🖾 ⊡ ⬛ ✗ ▨ 🖾 ⊡ ✦ 🖅 ⊡ ⋇
Nearby Facilities ⌐ ✓ ⬘ ⌇ ∪ ⅃ ✗
Nearest Town Tenby
Directions From Tenby take the A4139
towards Pembroke. After 4½ miles turn right
signposted for Manorbier Train Station. Park
is 300 yards.
🚂 Manorbier

TENBY

Masterland Farm Touring Park,
Broadmoor, Kilgetty, Pembrokeshire, SA68
0RH
Tel: 01834 813298
Email: k.bonser@btconnect.com
www.ukparks.co.uk/masterland
Pitches For ▲ ⊞ ➡ **Total** 38
Open 14-Feb **to** 02-Jan
Access Good **Site** Level
Nearest Bus Stop (Miles) Outside
Facilities ⨍ ▥⬚ ⌐ ☺ ⬝ ▨ 🍴 ⊡ 🖼 🍴
🖾 ✗ ▨ 🖾 ⊡ ⬛ ▨ 🖅 ⊡ ⬛ ⋇ ⋇
Nearby Facilities ⌐ ✓ ⬘ ⌇ ∪ ⅃ ♔ ✗
Nearest Town Tenby
Directions After Carmarthen take the A477
to Broadmoor. Turn right at the Cross Inn
Public House, Masterland is 400 yards on
the right.
🚂 Kilgetty

TENBY

Milton Bridge Caravan Park, Milton, Nr
Tenby, Pembrokeshire, SA70 8PH
Tel: 01646 651204
Email:
enquiries@miltonbridgecaravanpark.co.uk
www.miltonbridgecaravanpark.co.uk
Pitches For ⊞ ➡ **Total** 12
Acreage 3 **Open** March **to** October
Access Good **Site** Lev/Slope
Nearest Bus Stop (Miles) Outside
Small, friendly park situated on a tidal river.
Ideal base for exploring the many attractions
in the area.
Facilities ⨍ ▥⬚ ⌐ ☺ ⬝ ▨ 🍴 ⊡ 🖼 🍴
🖾 ⊡ ⬛ 🖅 ✗ ⬚
Nearby Facilities ⌐ ✓ ⬘ ⌇ ∪ ⅃ ♔ ✗
Nearest Town Tenby
Directions Half way between Kilgetty and
Pembroke Dock on the A477.
🚂 Lamphey

TENBY

Red House Farm, Twy Cross, Tenby,
Pembrokeshire, SA69 9DP
Tel: 01834 813918
Pitches For ▲ ⊞ ➡ **Total** 10
Acreage 2 **Open** May **to** September
Access Good **Site** Lev/Slope

Nearest Bus Stop (Miles) ¼
Very quiet, small, ADULTS ONLY site. Most appreciated by those seeking peace rather than entertainment. Not suitable for small children. Sorry No pets.
Facilities ∤ ⬚ ⎕ ⬚ 🅿 A
Nearby Facilities ⌐ ✓ ⚓ ⤴ U ⋡ ♠ ⚡
Nearest Town Tenby
Directions Situated just off the A478, 1½ miles from both Tenby and Saundersfoot. Regular bus service.
⇌ Tenby

TENBY

Tudor Glen Caravan Park, Jameston, Nr Tenby, Pembrokeshire, SA70 7SS
Tel: 01834 871417
Email: info@tudorglencaravanpark.com
www.tudorglencaravanpark.com
Pitches For Å ⬚ ⬚
Acreage 6 **Open** March **to** October
Access Good **Site** Lev/Slope
Nearest Bus Stop (Miles) ¼
1 mile from Manorbier.
Facilities ∤ ⬚ ⬚ ⌐ ⬚ ⚊ ⬚ ⬚
Ω ⬚ 🅿 ⬚ ⬚ ⬚ ⬚
Nearby Facilities ⌐ ✓ ⚓ ⤴ U ⋡ ♠ ⚡
Nearest Town Tenby
Directions From Tenby take the A4139 Coast Road west for 6 miles. Site is on the right before entering village of Jameston.
⇌ Tenby

TENBY

Well Park Caravans, Tenby, Pembrokeshire, SA70 8TL
Tel: 01834 842179
Email: enquiries@wellparkcaravans.co.uk
www.wellparkcaravans.co.uk
Pitches For Å ⬚ ⬚ ⬚ **Total** 100
Acreage 10 **Open** April **to** October
Access Good **Site** Lev/Slope
Nearest Bus Stop (Miles) Outside
A family run site, situated in pleasant surroundings. Excellent facilities. Very central and convenient for the beautiful beaches and places of interest along the Pembrokeshire coast. WTB 5 Star Graded, AA and Wales in Bloom Award Winning Park.
Facilities ⬚ ∤ ⬚ ⬚ ⌐ ⬚ ⚊ ⬚ ⬚
⬚ ⬚ ⚑ ⬚ ⬚ ⬚ ⬚ ⬚
Nearby Facilities ⌐ ✓ ⚓ ⤴ U ⋡ ♠ ⚡
Nearest Town Tenby
Directions On righthand side of main Tenby (A478) road 1 mile north of Tenby.
⇌ Tenby

TENBY

Windmills Camping Park, Tenby, Pembrokeshire, SA70 8TJ
Tel: 01834 842200
Pitches For Å ⬚ ⬚
Acreage 4 **Open** Easter **to** Oct
Access Good **Site** Level
Nearest Bus Stop (Miles) ½
Situated on a hill overlooking Tenby with sea views. Footpath and cycle track down to the town and north beach.
Facilities ∤ ⬚ ⬚ ⌐ ⬚ ⬚ ⬚ ⬚
Nearby Facilities ⌐ ✓
Nearest Town Tenby
Directions Approaching Tenby turn left up the lane just past New Hedges Village.
⇌ Tenby

TENBY

Wood Park Caravan Park, New Hedges, Tenby, Pembrokeshire, SA70 8TL
Tel: 0845 129 8314 (Lo-call)
Email: info@woodpark.co.uk
www.woodpark.co.uk
Pitches For Å ⬚ ⬚ **Total** 60
Acreage 2 **Open** April **to** October

Access Good **Site** Lev/Slope
Nearest Bus Stop (Miles) Outside
Quiet, family park ideally situated between Tenby and Saundersfoot. Advanced bookings are not taken for Motor Caravans. No Groups permitted. No dogs allowed Bank Holidays and school holidays, one small pet only at all other times. No dogs in hire caravans.
Facilities ∤ ⬚ ⬚ ⌐ ⬚ ⚊ ⬚ ⬚
⬚ ⬚ ⬚ ⬚ ⬚ ⬚
Nearby Facilities ⌐ ✓ ⚓ ⤴ U ⋡ ♠ ⚡
Nearest Town Tenby
Directions At the roundabout 2 miles north of Tenby, take the A478 towards Tenby. Take the second turn right and right again.
⇌ Tenby

POWYS

BRECON

Anchorage Caravan Park, Bronllys, Brecon, Powys, LD3 0LD
Tel: 01874 711246
www.anchoragecp.co.uk
Pitches For Å ⬚ ⬚ **Total** 110
Acreage 8 **Open** All Year
Access Good **Site** Lev/Slope
Nearest Bus Stop (Miles) Outside
Overlooking the Brecon Beacons National Park. Ideally situated for touring and walking mid and South Wales.
Facilities ∤ ⬚ ⬚ ⌐ ⬚ ⚊ ⬚ ⬚
⬚ ⬚ ⬚ ⬚ ⬚ ⬚ ⬚
Nearby Facilities ⌐ ✓ ⚓ ⤴ U ♠
Nearest Town Brecon
Directions 8 miles north east of Brecon in the village of Bronllys.
⇌ Abergavenny

BRECON

Bishops Meadow Caravan Park, Bishops Meadow, Hay Road, Brecon, Powys, LD3 9SW
Tel: 01874 610000
Email: info@bishops-meadow.co.uk
www.bishops-meadow.co.uk
Pitches For Å ⬚ ⬚ **Total** 120
Acreage 7 **Open** March **to** October
Access Good **Site** Lev/Slope
Nearest Bus Stop (Miles) Entrance
Set in idyllic open countryside with spectacular views over the Brecon Beacons. Ideal for walking, cycling, fishing and canoeing on the River Wye.
Facilities ⬚ ∤ ⬚ ⬚ ⌐ ⬚ ⚊ ⬚ ⬚
⬚ ⬚ ⬚ ✗ ⬚ ⬚ ⬚ ⬚ ⬚ ⬚ ⬚
Nearby Facilities ⌐ ✓ ⚓ ⤴ U ⚡
Nearest Town Brecon
Directions On the B4602 1 mile form the town centre.
⇌ Abergavenny

BRECON

Lakeside Caravan Park, Llangorse Lake, Llangorse, Brecon, Powys, LD3 7TR
Tel: 01874 658226
Email: lakesidereception@tiscali.co.uk
www.llangorselake.co.uk
Pitches For Å ⬚ ⬚ **Total** 80
Open 20-Mar **to** 31-Oct
Access Good **Site** Level
Llangorse Lake, mountains and beautiful scenery.
Facilities ∤ ⬚ ⬚ ⌐ ⬚ ⚊ ⬚ ⬚
⬚ ⬚ ✗ ⬚ ⬚ ⬚ ⬚ ⬚ ⬚ ⬚
Nearby Facilities ⌐ ✓ ⚓ ⤴ U ⋡ ♠
Nearest Town Brecon
Directions From Brecon take the B4560 and follow signs to Llyn Lake. 6 miles from Brecon.
⇌ Abergavenny

BRECON

Mill Field Caravan Park, Mill Service Station, Three Cocks, Brecon, Powys, LD3 0SL
Tel: 01497 847381
Pitches For Å ⬚ ⬚ **Total** 40
Acreage 2¼ **Open** All Year
Access Good **Site** Level
Nearest Bus Stop (Miles) ¼
Near to Hay-on-Wye the Town of Books. Easy access to the Black Mountains and Brecon Beacons.
Facilities ∤ ⬚ ⬚ Ω ⬚ ⬚ ⬚ ⬚
Nearby Facilities ⌐ ✓ ⚓ ⤴ U ⋡ ♠ ⚡
Directions On the A438 between Brecon and Hay-on-Wye, 5 miles from Hay-on-Wye.
⇌ Hereford

BRECON

Pencelli Castle Caravan & Camping Park, Pencelli Castle, Pencelli, Brecon, Powys, LD3 7LX
Tel: 01874 665451
Email: pencelli@tiscali.co.uk
www.pencelli-castle.com
Pitches For Å ⬚ ⬚ **Total** 80
Acreage 10 **Open** 01-Feb **to** 28-Nov
Access Good **Site** Level
Nearest Bus Stop (Miles) Entrance
Multi award winning park in the heart of the Brecon Beacons and adjoining Brecon Canal. Plenty of good walking and cycling in the area.
Facilities ⬚ ∤ ⬚ ⬚ ⌐ ⬚ ⚊ ⬚ ⬚
⬚ ⬚ ⬚ ⬚ ⬚ ⬚ ⬚ ⬚ ⬚
Nearby Facilities ⌐ ✓ ⚓ ⤴ U ⋡ ♠
Nearest Town Brecon
Directions Leave Brecon on the A40 heading east, after 2 miles turn onto the B4558 signposted Pencelli and follow brown tourism signs.
⇌ Abergavenny

BUILTH WELLS

Irfon River Caravan Park, Upper Chapel Road, Garth, Builth Wells, Powys, LD4 4BH
Tel: 01591 620310
Email: irfonriver@btinternet.com
Pitches For Å ⬚ ⬚ **Total** 24
Acreage 6½ **Open** Easter **to** October
Access Good **Site** Lev/Slope
Nearest Bus Stop (Miles) ½
Quiet ADULTS ONLY site alongside a river with scenic views. Fly fishing on site. Ideal touring in the beauty of the mountains and forest. Convenient for events at the Royal Welsh Showground. Static holiday vans for sale. You can also contact us on Mobile: 07817 283449.
Facilities ∤ ⬚ ⬚ ⌐ ⬚ ⚊ ⬚ ⬚
⬚ ⬚ ⬚ ⬚ ✓ ⬚ ⬚ ⬚
Nearby Facilities ⌐ ✓ U ♠
Nearest Town Builth Wells
Directions 500 yards along the B4519 on entering Garth (Garth is 6 miles west of Builth Wells along the A483).
⇌ Garth

BUILTH WELLS

White House Campsite, Hay Road, Builth Wells, Powys, LD2 3BP
Tel: 01982 552255
Email: info@whitehousecampsite.co.uk
www.whitehousecampsite.co.uk
Pitches For Å ⬚ ⬚ **Total** 30
Acreage 3 **Open** April **to** Sept
Access Good **Site** Level
Nearest Bus Stop (Miles) ¼
On the banks of the River Wye. Just a ten minute walk from the Royal Welsh Showground. WTB 3 Star Graded.

WALES

POWYS

Facilities ⬡ (symbols)
Nearby Facilities (symbols)
Nearest Town Builth Wells
Directions Adjacent to the A470 at the eastern edge of Builth Wells.
🚃 Builth Road

CLYRO

Borders Hideaway Holiday Home Park, Painscastle Road, Clyro, Hay-on-Wye, Herefordshire, HR3 5SG
Tel: 01497 820156
Email: bhhhp@hotmail.co.uk
www.bhhhp.co.uk
Pitches For ⚑ (symbols)
Acreage 4 **Open** 01-Mar to 07-Jan
Access Good **Site** Lev/Slope
Nearest Bus Stop (Miles) ½
Close to Hay-on-Wye, the second hand book capital of the world! Near to Golden Valley, Brecon Beacons and the Black Mountains.
Facilities (symbols)
Nearby Facilities (symbols)
Nearest Town Hay-on-Wye
Directions Upon entering Clyro on the A438 (Leominster to Brecon road), turn at the brown tourism caravan sign and follow the road and signs for 1 mile.
🚃 Hereford

CRICKHOWELL

Cwmdu Campsite, Cwmdu, Crickhowell, Powys, NP8 1RU
Tel: 01874 730741
Email: cwmducampsite@btconnect.com
www.campingbreconbeacons.com
Pitches For ⚑ **Total** 50
Acreage 4 **Open** Easter (Good Friday) to 31-Oct
Access Good **Site** Lev/Slope
Nearest Bus Stop (Miles) ¾
Quiet, peaceful location at the foot of the Black Mountains in the centre of Brecon Beacons National Park. Perfect for walking.
Facilities (symbols)
Nearby Facilities (symbols)
Nearest Town Crickhowell
Directions Situated 4 miles north of Crickhowell on the A479. Turn off at the Farmers Arms Pub in Cwmdu Village, and the site is 300 metres.
🚃 Abergavenny

CRICKHOWELL

Riverside Caravan & Camping Park New Road, Crickhowell, Powys, NP8 1AY
Tel: 01873 810397
www.riversidecaravanscrickhowell.co.uk
Pitches For ⚑ **Total** 65
Acreage 3 **Open** March to October
Access Good **Site** Level
Nearest Bus Stop (Miles) ¼
ADULTS ONLY site in a National Park. No children under 18 years, over 18 years at owners discretion. Near a river, mountain, canal walks and pony trekking. Just a 5 min walk to the town. New improved toilet and shower block with laundry (inc drying facilities). No hang-gliders and paragliders. AA 3 Pennants.
Facilities (symbols)
Nearby Facilities (symbols)
Nearest Town Crickhowell
Directions Between the A40 and the A4077 at Crickhowell.
🚃 Abergavenny

LLANBRYNMAIR

Cringoed Caravan Park, The Birches, Llanbrynmair, Powys, SY19 7DR
Tel: 01650 521237
Email: enquiries@cringoed.co.uk
www.cringoed.co.uk
Pitches For ⚑ **Total** 72
Acreage 10 **Open** March to November
Access Good **Site** Level
Nearest Bus Stop (Miles) 1
Facilities (symbols)
Nearby Facilities (symbols)
Nearest Town Machynlleth
Directions From Newtown take the A470 towards Llanbrynmair for 18 miles, then turn onto the B4518 in Llanbrynmair, site is 1 mile.
🚃 Machynlleth

LLANBRYNMAIR

Gwern-y-Bwlch Caravan Club Site, Llanbrynmair, Powys, SY19 7EB
Tel: 01650 521351
www.caravanclub.co.uk
Pitches For ⚑ **Total** 37
Acreage 5 **Open** March to Oct
Access Good **Site** Lev/Slope
Lovely setting with views to the mountains across a valley. Bird hide and feeding station on site, watch for Red Kites. Own sanitation required. Non members welcome. Booking essential.
Facilities (symbols)
Nearest Town Llanbrynmair
Directions From the A470, 1 mile past Llanbrynmair turn right at Caravan Club sign, site is 50 yards up the hill on the left.
🚃 Llanbrynmair

LLANDRINDOD WELLS

Bryncrach Farm Caravan Site, Bryncrach, Hundred House, Llandrindod Wells, Powys, LD1 5RY
Tel: 01982 570291
Email: stella@bryncrachcaravans.co.uk
www.bryncrachcaravans.co.uk
Pitches For ⚑ **Total** 15
Acreage 1¾ **Open** All Year
Access Good **Site** Level
Nearest Bus Stop (Miles) ¼
Quiet site with splendid views and walks. Fishing and riding can be arranged. River nearby. You can also contact us on Mobile: 07534 509104.
Facilities (symbols)
Nearby Facilities (symbols)
Nearest Town Builth Wells
Directions Hundred House is on the A481 between Builth Wells and the A44. Turn left signposted Franks Bridge immediately before the public house, after 250 yards turn left into farm road.
🚃 Llandrindod Wells

LLANDRINDOD WELLS

Dalmore Caravan Park, Howey, Llandrindod Wells, Powys, LD1 5RG
Tel: 01597 822483
Pitches For ⚑ **Total** 20
Acreage 2 **Open** March to October
Access Good **Site** Lev/Gentle Slope
Nearest Bus Stop (Miles) Outside
EXCLUSIVELY FOR ADULTS. Ideal base for hiking and touring Mid Wales, scenic views.
Facilities (symbols)
Nearby Facilities (symbols)
Nearest Town Llandrindod Wells
Directions 2½ miles south of Llandrindod Wells, adjoining the main A483, at the top of the hill and towards Builth Wells.
🚃 Llandrindod

LLANDRINDOD WELLS

Disserth Caravan & Camping Park, Howey, Llandrindod Wells, Powys, LD1 6NL
Tel: 01597 860277
Email: disserthcaravan@btconnect.com
www.disserth.biz
Pitches For ⚑ **Total** 30
Acreage 4 **Open** March to Oct
Access Good **Site** Level
Small, tranquil, riverside park with wildlife for neighbours.
Facilities (symbols)
Nearby Facilities (symbols)
Nearest Town Llandrindod Wells
Directions Follow brown tourism signs from the A483 or the A470. Park entrance is by the church.
🚃 Llandrindod Wells

LLANFYLLIN

Henstent Park, Llangynog, Nr Oswestry, Powys, SY10 0EP
Tel: 01691 860479
Email: henstent@mac.com
www.henstent.co.uk
Pitches For ⚑ **Total** 35
Acreage 1½ **Open** All Year
Access Good **Site** Sloping
Nearest Bus Stop (Miles) Outside
Spectacular mountain views with frontage to the River Tanat. Rural location popular with bird watchers and walkers.
Facilities (symbols)
Nearby Facilities (symbols)
Nearest Town Bala
Directions Situated on the B4391. Follow signs for Bala from Oswestry. 18 miles from Oswestry, 12 miles from Bala.
🚃 Gobowen

LLANIDLOES

Dol-Llys Touring Site, Dol-Llys Farm, Llanidloes, Powys, SY18 6JA
Tel: 01686 412694
Pitches For ⚑ (symbols)
Acreage 2 **Open** April to October
Access Good **Site** Level
Nearest Bus Stop (Miles) ½
Alongside the banks of the River Severn. Campers Kitchen for walkers and cyclists.
Facilities (symbols)
Nearby Facilities (symbols)
Nearest Town Llanidloes
Directions From Llanidloes take the B4569, past hospital, fork right onto the Oakley Park Road, Dol-Llys is the first farm on the right.
🚃 Caersws

LLANSANTFFRAID

Bryn-Vyrnwy Caravan Park, Bryn-Vyrnwy, Llansantffraid, Powys, SY22 6AY
Tel: 01691 828252
Pitches For ⚑ (symbols)
Acreage 4 **Open** April to 01-Nov
Access Good **Site** Level
Nearest Bus Stop (Miles) ½
On the banks of the River Vyrnwy. Good eating places close by. ¾ of an hour from seaside resorts.
Facilities (symbols)
Nearby Facilities (symbols)
Nearest Town Oswestry
Directions From Oswestry take the A483 towards Welshpool, at Llynclys take the A495 for 3 miles.
🚃 Welshpool

WALES

WALES

LLANSANTFFRAID

Vyrnwy Caravan Park, Llansantffraid, Powys, SY22 6SY
Tel: 01691 828217
Pitches For 🏕 🚐 🚙 **Total** 40
Acreage 40 **Open** April **to** September
Access Good **Site** Level
Nearest Bus Stop (Miles) Outside
Alongside a river.
Facilities ⚙🚿🚽⬛♿🅿🛒🔌🚮✉🚲
Nearby Facilities ⚓🎣∪
Nearest Town Oswestry
Directions Take the A483 then the B4393 to Llansantffraid.
🚆 Gobowen

MACHYNLLETH

Morben Isaf Holiday Home & Touring Park, Derwenlas, Machynlleth, Powys, SY20 8SR
Tel: 01654 781473
Email: manager@morbenisaf.co.uk
www.morbenisaf.co.uk
Pitches For 🏕 🚐 🚙 **Total** 35
Open Mid March **to** 31-Oct
Access Good **Site** Level
Nearest Bus Stop (Miles) Outside
Next door to Dyfi Osprey Project at Cors Dyfi. 8 miles from Ynyslas Beach and 3 miles from Ynys-Hir Nature Reserve.
Facilities ♿⚙🚿🚽♿🅿🛒🔌🚮✉🚲🚮🔌📶
Nearby Facilities ⚓
Nearest Town Machynlleth
Directions 2½ miles south of Machynlleth on the A487 Aberystwyth road.
🚆 Machynlleth

MIDDLETOWN

Bank Farm Caravan Park, Middletown, Welshpool, Powys, SY21 8EJ
Tel: 01938 570526
Email: bankfarmcaravans@yahoo.co.uk
www.bankfarmcaravans.co.uk
Pitches For 🏕 🚐 🚙 **Total** 20
Acreage 2 **Open** March **to** October
Access Good **Site** Lev/Slope
Nearest Bus Stop (Miles) ¼
Scenic views, ideal touring area.
Facilities ♿⚙🚿🚽♿🅿🛒🔌🚮✉🚲
Nearby Facilities ⚓🎣∪
Nearest Town Welshpool
Directions On A458 5½ miles east of Welshpool and 13¼ miles west of Shrewsbury.
🚆 Welshpool

NEW RADNOR

Old Station Caravan Park, New Radnor, Powys, LD8 2SS
Tel: 01544 350543
Email: info@oldstationcaravanpark.co.uk
www.oldstationcaravanpark.co.uk
Pitches For 🏕 🚐 🚙 **Total** 12
Acreage 1¾ **Open** All Year
Access Good **Site** Level
Nearest Bus Stop (Miles) ¼
Ideal base for walking and cycling. Easy access to Offa's Dyke, Elan Valley Dams and the attractions of Mid Wales. You can also contact us on Mobile: 07917 846508.
Facilities ♿⚙🚿🚽♿🅿🛒🔌🚮✉🚲
Nearby Facilities ⚓🎣🏊∪♟
Nearest Town Kington
Directions 6 miles from Kington on the A44 to Rhayader.
🚆 Leominster

NEWTOWN

Smithy Park, Abermule, Newtown, Montgomery, Powys, SY15 6ND
Tel: 01584 711280
Email: info@westbrookpark.co.uk
www.bestparks.co.uk
Pitches For 🏕 🚐 🚙 **Total** 30
Acreage 5 **Open** March **to** Oct
Access Good **Site** Level
Nearest Bus Stop (Miles) Outside
Set between the River Mule and the River Severn, with a branch of the Shropshire Union Canal nearby.
Facilities ⚙🚿🚽♿🅿🛒🔌🚮✉🚲🔌
Nearby Facilities ⚓🏊🎣∪♟
Nearest Town Newtown
Directions Abermule is off the A483 between Welshpool and Newtown.
🚆 Newtown

PENYBONTFAWR

Parc Farm, Penybontfawr, Powys, SY10 0PD
Tel: 01691 860204
Email: deal@tinyworld.co.uk
www.parcfarm-minafon.co.uk
Pitches For 🚐 🚙 **Total** 12
Open Easter **to** End Oct
Access Good **Site** Level
Nearest Bus Stop (Miles) Outside
River frontage with beautiful scenery.
Facilities ⚙🚿🚽♿🅿🛒🔌🚮
Nearby Facilities ⚓🎣🏊∪♟
Nearest Town Oswestry/Welshpool
Directions On the B4391.
🚆 Welshpool

PRESTEIGNE

Rockbridge Park, Presteigne, Powys, LD8 2NF
Tel: 01568 708326
Email: info@bestparks.co.uk
www.rockbridgepark.co.uk
Pitches For 🏕 🚐 🚙 🚙 **Total** 53
Acreage 13 **Open** March **to** November
Access Good **Site** Level
Nearest Bus Stop (Miles) Entrance
Picturesque and peaceful site alongside the River Lugg.
Facilities ♿⚙🚿🚽♿🅿🔌🚮
Nearby Facilities ⚓🎣∪♟
Nearest Town Presteigne
Directions 1 mile west of Presteigne on the B4356.
🚆 Knighton

PRESTEIGNE

Walton Court Caravan Site, Walton Court, Walton, Presteigne, Powys, LD8 2PY
Tel: 01544 350259
Email: jeanandglyn@hotmail.co.uk
www.waltoncourtcaravanandcampingsite.co.uk
Pitches For 🏕 🚐 🚙 **Total** 30
Acreage 7 **Open** March **to** Oct
Access Good **Site** Level
Nearest Bus Stop (Miles) Outside
Many walks and rides into the hills. The Harp Inn (15 mins walk) serves excellent food.
Facilities ⚙🚿🚽♿🅿🛒🔌🚮🍴✉🚲
Nearby Facilities ⚓🎣∪
Nearest Town Kington
Directions On the A44 Kington to Aberystwyth road, in the village of Walton opposite the Crown Hotel.
🚆 Knighton

RHAYADER

Nantymynach Caravan & Camping Park, Nantmel, Llandrindod Wells, Powys, LD1 6EW
Tel: 01597 810491
Pitches For 🏕 🚐 🚙
Acreage 2 **Open** Easter **to** October
Access Good **Site** Level/Sloping
Nearest Bus Stop (Miles) ½
Near a 17 acre lake for rainbow trout fishing. Ideal for touring.
Facilities 🚿🚽♿🅿🔌🚮
Nearby Facilities ⚓🎣∪♟
Nearest Town Llandrindod Wells
Directions From Rhayader take the A44 east, turn right signposted Nantymynach Caravan Park.
🚆 Llandrindod Wells

RHAYADER

Wyeside Caravan & Camping Park, Llangurig Road, Rhayader, Powys, LD6 5LB
Tel: 01597 810183
Email: info@wyesidecamping.co.uk
www.wyesidecamping.co.uk
Pitches For 🏕 🚐 🚙 **Total** 140
Acreage 8 **Open** February **to** Nov
Access Good **Site** Level
Nearest Bus Stop (Miles) ¼
Set along the banks of the River Wye with excellent facilities. 5 minutes walk to the town centre and 3 miles from Elan Valley.
Facilities ♿⚙🚿🚽♿🅿🛒🔌🚮✉🚲🚮🔌📶
Nearby Facilities ⚓🎣∪♟♟
Nearest Town Rhayader
Directions On the A470 north of Rhayader.
🚆 Llandrindod Wells

WELSHPOOL

Carmel Caravan Park, Tynewydd, Cefncoch, Welshpool, Powys, SY21 0AJ
Tel: 01938 810542
Email: carmelcaravanpk@aol.com
www.carmelcaravanpark.com
Pitches For 🏕 🚐 🚙 🚙 **Total** 120
Open 15-Mar **to** 31-Oct
Access Good **Site** Level
Farm site set alongside a river for walks.
Facilities ♿⚙🚿🚽♿🅿🛒🔌🚮✉🚲🔌
Nearby Facilities ⚓🎣∪
Nearest Town Newtown
Directions From Welshpool take the A458 to Llanfair Caereinion, turn left over the bridge and follow signs for Cefncoch. Turn left at the pub and follow caravan signs.
🚆 Newtown

WELSHPOOL

Henllan Caravan Park, Llangyniew, Welshpool, Powys, SY21 9EJ
Tel: 01938 810554
Email: sue@henllancaravanpark.co.uk
www.henllancaravanpark.co.uk
Pitches For 🏕 🚐 🚙 **Total** 10
Acreage ½ **Open** March **to** December
Access Good **Site** Level
Alongside the River Banwy. Ideal touring, 9 hole golf course and bowling green on site. You can also telephone us on Mobile 07907 531331. Contact Sue Round.
Facilities ⚙🚿🚽♿🅿🛒🔌🚮✉🚲
Nearby Facilities ⚓🎣∪
Nearest Town Welshpool
Directions 6 miles from Welshpool on the A458.
🚆 Welshpool

WELSHPOOL

Rhyd-Y-Groes Touring Caravan & Camping Park, Pont Rhyd-Y-Groes, Marton, Welshpool, Powys, SY21 8JJ
Tel: 01938 561228
Email: hldavies@hotmail.co.uk
www.rhyd-y-groes.co.uk
Pitches For A ⚌ ⚌ ⚌ **Total** 40
Acreage 4½ **Open** All Year
Access Good **Site** Lev/Slope
ADULTS ONLY PARK set among natural beauty with outstanding views. Near Offas Dyke footpath. Ideal for touring and bird watching. Some fully serviced pitches available.
Facilities ⚫⚫ ⚫ ⚫⚫⚫⚫⚫⚫⚫
⚫⚫⚫⚫
Nearby Facilities ⚫ ⚫
Nearest Town Welshpool
Directions From the A490 Welshpool to Churchstoke road, turn left for Marton approx 5 miles from Welshpool.
⚫ Welshpool

WELSHPOOL

Riverbend Caravan Park, Llangadfan, Nr Welshpool, Powys, SY21 0PP
Tel: 01938 820356
Email: riverbend@hillandale.co.uk
www.hillandale.co.uk
Pitches For A ⚌ ⚌ **Total** 50
Acreage 4 **Open** All Year
Access Good **Site** Level
Nearest Bus Stop (Miles) ½
The best of both worlds! - In unspoilt rural Wales, yet close to the Welsh coast. On the River Banwy with 1 mile of private fishing.
Facilities ⚫ ⚫⚫⚫⚫⚫⚫⚫⚫
⚫⚫⚫⚫⚫⚫⚫⚫⚫⚫⚫⚫⚫
Nearby Facilities ⚫ ⚫ ⚫ ⚫ ⚫
Nearest Town Llanfair Caereinion
Directions Take the A458 from Welshpool westbound towards the coast. After 17 miles you enter the village of Llangadfan, turn left at Gann Office (pub), and the Park is 300 metres on the right.
⚫ Welshpool

WELSHPOOL

Severn Caravan Park, Cilcewydd, Welshpool, Powys, SY21 8RT
Tel: 01938 580238
Email: severncp@tiscali.co.uk
www.severncaravans.co.uk
Pitches For A ⚌ ⚌
Open April to October
Access Good **Site** Level
Nearest Bus Stop (Miles) Entrance
On the banks of the River Severn.
Facilities ⚫ ⚫ ⚫⚫⚫⚫⚫⚫⚫
⚫⚫⚫⚫⚫⚫⚫⚫⚫
Nearby Facilities ⚫ ⚫ ⚫
Nearest Town Welshpool
Directions From Welshpool take the A483 towards Newtown, turn onto the A490 sp Forden, then turn first left onto the B4331 for Leighton and site is 500 yards on the left.
⚫ Welshpool

YSTRADGYNLAIS

Dan-Yr-Ogof - The National Showcaves Centre for Wales, Brecon Road, Upper Swansea Valley, Powys, SA9 1GJ
Tel: 01639 730284
Email: ashford@showcaves.co.uk
www.showcaves.co.uk
Pitches For A ⚌ ⚌ ⚌
Acreage 10 **Open** Easter to October
Access Good **Site** Sloping
Nearest Bus Stop (Miles) ¼
Alongside river and forests in the heart of Brecon Beacons National Park. Adult only areas.

Facilities ⚫⚫ ⚫⚫⚫⚫⚫⚫⚫⚫⚫⚫⚫⚫⚫
Nearby Facilities ⚫ ⚫ ⚫
Nearest Town Brecon
Directions Leave the M4 at junction 45 and take the A4067, midway between Brecon and Swansea.
⚫ Swansea

SWANSEA

GOWERTON

Gowerton Caravan Club Site, Pont-y-Cob Road, Gowerton, Swansea, SA4 3QP
Tel: 01792 873050
www.caravanclub.co.uk
Pitches For ⚌ ⚌ **Total** 135
Acreage 17 **Open** March to Nov
Access Good **Site** Level
Nearest Bus Stop (Miles) ½
Easy drive to many safe sandy beaches. Inland theres the Vale of Neath and Aberdulais Falls. Non members welcome. Booking essential.
Facilities ⚫ ⚫⚫⚫⚫⚫⚫⚫⚫
⚫⚫⚫⚫⚫⚫⚫⚫⚫
Nearby Facilities ⚫
Nearest Town Swansea
Directions Leave M4 at junc 47 and take A483 sp Swansea. At rndabt turn right onto A484, at next rndabt go straight over, next rndabt turn left onto B4296 sp Gowerton. After passing under railway bridge at lights turn right, next lights turn right into Pont-y-Cob Road. Site is ¼ mile on right.
⚫ Swansea

HORTON

Bank Farm, Horton, Gower, Swansea, SA3 1LL
Tel: 01792 390228
Email: bankfarmleisure@aol.com
www.bankfarmleisure.co.uk
Pitches For A ⚌ ⚌ **Total** 230
Acreage 80 **Open** March to 13-Nov
Access Good **Site** Sloping
Nearest Bus Stop (Miles) ¼
Overlooking the beach. Heated swimming pool.
Facilities ⚫ ⚫⚫⚫⚫⚫⚫⚫⚫⚫
⚫⚫⚫⚫⚫⚫⚫⚫⚫⚫⚫⚫
Nearby Facilities ⚫ ⚫ ⚫ ⚫ ⚫
Nearest Town Swansea
Directions Take the A4118 from Swansea towards Port Eynon, turn left for Horton 1 mile before Port Eynon, turn right at the site entrance after 200 yards.
⚫ Swansea

LLANGENNITH

Kennexstone Camping & Touring Park, Kennexstone Farm, Llangennith, Gower, Swansea, SA3 1HS
Tel: 01792 386790
Email: gowercamping@btconnect.com
www.gowercamping.co.uk
Pitches For A ⚌ ⚌ **Total** 240
Acreage 10 **Open** April to September
Access Good **Site** Level
Nearest Bus Stop (Miles) ½
Friendly, family run site, ideal for a relaxing holiday. 1½ miles from one of Wales best surfing beaches.
Facilities ⚫ ⚫⚫⚫⚫⚫⚫⚫⚫
⚫⚫⚫⚫⚫⚫⚫⚫⚫
Nearby Facilities ⚫ ⚫ ⚫ ⚫ ⚫ ⚫ ⚫
Nearest Town Swansea
Directions Leave the M4 at junction 47 and take the A483/A484 to Gowerton, then take the B4295 for 8 miles to Llanrhidian. Follow signs to Llangennith for approx. 2½ miles, at T-junction ½ mile after Burry Green turn right, site is 200 yards.
⚫ Gowerton

RHOSSILI

Pitton Cross Caravan & Camping Park, Rhossili, Swansea, SA3 1PH
Tel: 01792 390593
Email: admin@pittoncross.co.uk
www.pittoncross.co.uk
Pitches For A ⚌ ⚌ **Total** 100
Acreage 6 **Open** All Year
Access Good **Site** Level
Nearest Bus Stop (Miles) Outside
Quiet, family friendly park, with a mix of sea views and sheltered areas. Within walking distance of beaches. Ideal for surfing and kiting.
Facilities ⚫ ⚫⚫⚫⚫⚫⚫⚫⚫⚫⚫
⚫⚫⚫⚫⚫⚫⚫⚫⚫⚫⚫
Nearby Facilities ⚫ ⚫ ⚫ ⚫
Nearest Town Swansea
Directions Leave the M4 at junc 42 and take the A483 to Swansea. Follow signs for A4067 to Mumbles, turn right onto the B4436 to South Gower and follow to Kittle, turn right at Pennard Church. Turn left at the T-Junction onto the A4118, go through Scurlage and turn right, park is 2 miles.
⚫ Swansea

VALE OF GLAMORGAN

COWBRIDGE

Llandow Caravan Park, Llandow, Cowbridge, Vale Of Glamorgan, CF71 7PB
Tel: 01446 794527
Email: info@llandowcaravanpark.com
www.llandowcaravanpark.com
Pitches For A ⚌ ⚌ **Total** 100
Acreage 5 **Open** 01-Feb to 01-Dec
Access Good **Site** Level
Heritage Coast, 3 miles from beaches and 20 miles from Cardiff.
Facilities ⚫ ⚫⚫⚫⚫⚫⚫⚫⚫
⚫⚫⚫⚫⚫⚫⚫⚫⚫⚫⚫
Nearby Facilities ⚫ ⚫ ⚫
Nearest Town Cowbridge
Directions From the A48 turn onto the B4268/B4270 and follow brown tourism signs to the caravan park.
⚫ Llantwit Major

LLANTWIT MAJOR

Acorn Camping & Caravanning, Ham Lane South, Llantwit Major, Vale Of Glamorgan, CF61 1RP
Tel: 01446 794024
Email: info@acorncamping.co.uk
www.acorncamping.co.uk
Pitches For A ⚌ ⚌ **Total** 90
Acreage 4½ **Open** 01-Feb to 01-Dec
Access Good **Site** Level
Nearest Bus Stop (Miles) ½
Peaceful country location only 1 mile from the beach and town centre. Marked pitches.
Facilities ⚫ ⚫⚫⚫⚫⚫⚫⚫⚫⚫
⚫⚫⚫⚫⚫⚫⚫⚫⚫⚫⚫
Nearby Facilities ⚫ ⚫ ⚫ ⚫
Nearest Town Cardiff
Directions South east of Llantwit Major.
⚫ Llantwit Major

WREXHAM

WREXHAM

Cae Adar Farm, Bwlchgwyn, Wrexham, LL11 5UE
Tel: 01978 757385
Pitches For A ⚌ ⚌ **Total** 10
Acreage 2 **Open** May to 30-Sep
Access Good **Site** Level
Nearest Bus Stop (Miles) Entrance
2 miles from Llandegla cycle trail. Good walking area. 14 miles from Llangollen and 12 miles from Chester.
Facilities ⚫⚫ ⚫⚫⚫ ⚫⚫⚫⚫
Nearby Facilities ⚫ ⚫

Nearest Town Wrexham
Directions From the A483 Wrexham bypass, take the A525 towards Ruthin. Site is 3½ miles, first left after Bwlchgwyn Village sign.
₪ Wrexham

WREXHAM
Plassey Leisure Park, Eyton, Wrexham, LL13 0SP
Tel: 01978 780277
Email: enquiries@plassey.com
www.plassey.com
Pitches For Å ♥ ♥ **Total** 120
Acreage 10 **Open** All Year
Access Good **Site** Level
Nearest Bus Stop (Miles) ½
On site facilities include a 9 hole golf course, a craft centre with 16 workshops and boutiques, garden centre, hair and beauty studio, restaurant and coffee shop. We even have our own on-site mini real ale brewery!
Facilities
Nearby Facilities
Nearest Town Wrexham
₪ Wrexham

WREXHAM
Trench Farm Touring Caravan Park & Fisheries, Trench Farm, Redhall Lane, Penley, Wrexham, LL13 0NA
Tel: 01978 710098
Email: mail@trenchfarmfisheries.co.uk
www.trenchfarmfisheries.co.uk
Pitches For Å ♥ ♥ **Total** 6
Acreage 5 **Open** March **to** Nov
Access Good **Site** Level
Nearest Bus Stop (Miles) ½
Set in 180 acres of farmland. Lovely long country walks. Fishing on site.
Facilities
Nearby Facilities
Nearest Town Ellesmere
Directions Appeox 3 miles from Ellesmere on the A528 towards Wrexham. On the Shropshire and Wrexham border.
₪ Wrexham

SCOTLAND
ABERDEENSHIRE
ABERDEEN
Deeside Holiday Park, South Deeside Road, Maryculter, Aberdeen, Aberdeenshire, AB12 5FX
Tel: 01224 733860
Email: deeside@holiday-parks.co.uk
www.holiday-parks.co.uk
Pitches For Å ♥ ♥ ♥
Acreage 10 **Open** All Year
Access Good **Site** Level
Nearest Bus Stop (Miles) ¼
A tranquil retreat set in the southern valley of the River Dee, yet only a few miles from the lively city of Aberdeen, and at the gateway to the spectacular scenery of Royal Deeside.
Facilities
Nearby Facilities
Nearest Town Aberdeen
Directions From Aberdeen take the B9077 at Bridge of Dee roundabout for 6 miles. From Stonehaven take the B979.
₪ Aberdeen

ABOYNE
Aboyne Loch Caravan Park, Aboyne, Royal Deeside, Aberdeenshire, AB34 5BR
Tel: 013398 86244
Email: heatherreid24@yahoo.co.uk
Pitches For Å ♥ ♥ **Total** 32
Open March **to** Oct
Access Good **Site** Level
Nearest Bus Stop (Miles) Outside
By Aboyne Loch. Beside two golf courses and within walking distance of two restaurants. Boats available to hire. Good area for walking. Dog walk. Holiday homes for hire. David Bellamy Gold Award.
Facilities
Nearby Facilities
Nearest Town Banchory
Directions Take the A96 to Ballater.

ABOYNE
Camping & Caravanning Club Site, Tarland By Deeside, Tarland By Aboyne, Aberdeenshire, AB34 4UP
Tel: 01339 881388
www.campingandcaravanningclub.co.uk/tarland
Pitches For Å ♥ ♥ **Total** 58
Acreage 8 **Open** 01-Mar **to** 05-Nov
Access Good **Site** Level
Nearest Bus Stop (Miles) ¼
Close to the village of Tarland and approx. 6 miles from Aboyne. STB 5 Star Graded and AA 3 Pennants. Non members welcome. You can also call us on 0845 130 7633.
Facilities
Nearby Facilities
Nearest Town Aboyne
Directions Take the A93 from Aberdeen, in Aboyne turn right at the Struan Hotel onto the B9094. After 6 miles take the next turn right and then fork left before the bridge, site is on the left in 600 yards.
₪ Aberdeen

BANCHORY
Feughside Caravan Park, Mount Battock, Strachan, Banchory, Aberdeenshire, AB31 6NT
Tel: 01330 850669
Email: info@feughsidecaravanpark.co.uk
www.feughsidecaravanpark.co.uk
Pitches For Å ♥ ♥ **Total** 27
Open April **to** October
Access Good **Site** Level
Set in the heart of Royal Deeside. Relax in this beautiful and picturesque part of the Scottish countryside.
Facilities
Nearby Facilities
Nearest Town Banchory
Directions From Banchory take the B974 for 3 miles to Strachan, then take the B976 for 2 miles to the Feughside Inn, turn right and the Park entrance is 100 metres.
₪ Stonehaven

BANFF
Wester Bonnyton Caravan & Camping Park, Wester Bonnyton, Gamrie, Banff, Aberdeenshire, AB45 3EP
Tel: 01261 832470
Email: westerbonnyton@fsmail.net
www.wester-bonnyton.co.uk
Pitches For Å ♥ ♥
Acreage 2 **Open** 31-Mar **to** 31-Oct
Access Good **Site** Lev/Slope
Nearest Bus Stop (Miles) Entrance
Quiet farm site in open countryside with panoramic views of the Moray Firth. Located on the North East Scotland Coastal Trail.

Facilities
Nearby Facilities
Nearest Town Banff/Macduff
Directions 2 miles east of Macduff on the B9031 coastal trail, approx 1 mile from the A98 Banff to Fraserburgh road.
₪ Huntly

BRAEMAR
The Invercauld Caravan Club Site, Glenshee Road, Braemar, Ballater, Aberdeenshire, AB35 5YQ
Tel: 01339 741373
www.caravanclub.co.uk
Pitches For Å ♥ ♥ **Total** 97
Acreage 9½ **Open** Dec **to** Oct
Access Good **Site** Level
Nearest Bus Stop (Miles) ¼
Abundant wildlife can be seen at this gateway to the Cairngorms, ideal for walking and cycling. Near a dry ski slope. Open in December for winter sports. Ski racks, drying room and community room (winter only) on site. Non members welcome. Booking essential.
Facilities
Nearby Facilities
Nearest Town Braemar
Directions Just off the A93 on the outskirts of Braemar Village.

CRUDEN BAY
Craighead Caravan & Camping Park, Cruden Bay, Peterhead, Aberdeenshire, AB42 0PL
Tel: 01779 812251
Email: stephen@craigheadcamping.com
www.craigheadcamping.com
Pitches For Å ♥ ♥ **Total** 17
Acreage 5 **Open** All Year
Access Good **Site** Level
Nearest Bus Stop (Miles) ½
1 mile from the beach. Close to castles and the Whisky Trail.
Facilities
Nearby Facilities
Nearest Town Peterhead
Directions 6 miles south of Peterhead on the A90, signposted from main road.
₪ Aberdeen

KINTORE
Hillhead Caravan Park, Kintore, Aberdeenshire, AB51 0YX
Tel: 01467 632809
Email: enquiries@hillheadcaravan.co.uk
www.hillheadcaravan.co.uk
Pitches For Å ♥ ♥ **Total** 29
Acreage 1½ **Open** All Year
Access Good **Site** Level
Nearest Bus Stop (Miles) Outside
Quiet, sheltered park. Easy access to Castle and Malt Whisky Trails, Aberdeen and Royal Deeside.
Facilities
Nearby Facilities
Nearest Town Kintore
Directions From south leave A96 at Broomhill roundabouts third exit. From north stay on A96 past Kintore (DO NOT enter Kintore), leave at Broomhill roundabouts first exit. Follow brown & white caravan signs onto B994, in ¼ mile turn left onto the B994 sp Kemnay. After 2 miles turn right sp Kintore and Hillhead Caravan Park is 1 mile on the right.
₪ Inverurie

WALES

SCOTLAND

LAURENCEKIRK

Brownmuir Caravan Park, Fordoun, Laurencekirk, Aberdeenshire, AB30 1SJ
Tel: 01561 320786
Email:
brownmuircaravanpark@talk21.com
www.brownmuircaravanpark.co.uk
Pitches For Å ⌂ ⌂ ⌂ **Total** 10
Acreage 7 **Open** April **to** Oct
Access Good **Site** Level
Nearest Bus Stop (Miles) Outside
Quiet site. Ideal for cycling and walking. Golf course in the village.
Facilities
Nearby Facilities
Nearest Town Laurencekirk
Directions On the A90, 4 miles north of Laurencekirk, turn left at the junction marked Fordoun and Auchenblae. After 150 yards turn left and go over the bridge, the Park is 1 mile on the right.
⇄ Stonehaven

LAURENCEKIRK

Dovecot Caravan Park, Northwaterbridge, By Laurencekirk, Aberdeenshire, AB30 1QL
Tel: 01674 840630
Email: adele@dovecotcaravanpark.co.uk
www.dovecotcaravanpark.co.uk
Pitches For Å ⌂ ⌂ **Total** 25
Acreage 6 **Open** 01-Apr **to** 28-Oct
Access Good **Site** Level
Nearest Bus Stop (Miles) ¼
Alongside the River North Esk. 8 miles from a sandy beach and 10 miles from the Angus Glens. Static caravans and a cottage available for hire.
Facilities
Nearby Facilities
Nearest Town Laurencekirk
Directions From the A90 at Northwaterbridge, turn to Edzell Woods and the Site is signposted 300 metres on the left.
⇄ Laurencekirk

PORTSOY

Sandend Caravan Park, Sandend, Portsoy, Aberdeenshire, AB45 2UA
Tel: 01261 842660
Email: sandendholidays@aol.com
www.sandendcaravanpark.co.uk
Pitches For Å ⌂ ⌂ **Total** 52
Acreage 4½ **Open** April **to** 04-Oct
Access Good **Site** Level
Nearest Bus Stop (Miles) ¼
In a conservation village overlooking a sandy beach. Ideal for touring and The Whisky Trail.
Facilities
Nearby Facilities
Nearest Town Portsoy
Directions 3 miles from Portsoy on the A98.
⇄ Keith

ST. CYRUS

East Bowstrips Holiday Park, St Cyrus, Nr Montrose, Aberdeenshire, DD10 0DE
Tel: 01674 850328
Email: tully@bowstrips.freeserve.co.uk
www.ukparks.co.uk/eastbowstrips
Pitches For Å ⌂ ⌂ **Total** 33
Acreage 4 **Open** April **to** October
Access Good **Site** Lev/Slope
Nearest Bus Stop (Miles) ½
Quiet park by the coast. Ideal touring base. Excellent facilities. Beautiful sandy beach and nature reserve approx 1 mile. Tourist Board 4 Star Graded and AA 4 Pennants.

Facilities
Nearby Facilities
Nearest Town Montrose
Directions Approx 6 miles north of Montrose. Follow A92, enter village of St. Cyrus, first left after Hotel, second right.
⇄ Montrose

TURRIFF

East Balthangie Caravan Park, East Balthangie, Cuminestown, Turriff, Aberdeenshire, AB53 5XY
Tel: 01888 544261/544280
Email: ebc@4horse.co.uk
www.eastbalthangie.co.uk
Pitches For Å ⌂ ⌂ **Total** 12
Acreage 5 **Open** March **to** October
Access Good **Site** Gentle Slope
Good base for touring.
Facilities
Nearby Facilities
Nearest Town Turriff
Directions Take the A90 from Aberdeen to Ellon, turn onto the B9107 to Cuminestown. After New Deer turn right to New Byth, caravan park is 3 miles on the left.
⇄ Aberdeen

ANGUS

ARBROATH

Elliot Caravan Park, Dundee Road, Arbroath, Angus, DD11 2PH
Tel: 01241 873466
Pitches For ⌂ ⌂ **Total** 8
Acreage 2 **Open** April **to** September
Access Good **Site** Level
Nearest Bus Stop (Miles) Outside
Near the beach, across from a golf club. Ideal for touring and sea fishing.
Facilities
Nearby Facilities
Nearest Town Arbroath
Directions On the A92, ½ a mile from town.
⇄ Arbroath

ARBROATH

Red Lion Holiday Park, Dundee Road, Arbroath, Angus, DD11 2PT
Tel: 01241 872038
Email: redlion@perthshire-caravans.com
www.perthshire-caravans.com
Pitches For ⌂ ⌂ **Total** 40
Acreage 4 **Open** March **to** October
Access Good **Site** Level
Nearest Bus Stop (Miles) Outside
Adjacent to the seaside and beach.
Facilities
Nearby Facilities
Nearest Town Arbroath
Directions From Dundee take the A92, when entering Arbroath the park is on the left past the first mini roundabout.
⇄ Arbroath

CARNOUSTIE

Woodlands Caravan Site, Newton Road, Carnoustie, Angus, DD7 6GR
Tel: 01241 854430
Email: info@woodlandscaravanpark.net
www.woodlandscaravanpark.net
Pitches For Å ⌂ ⌂ **Total** 46
Open March **to** Oct
Access Good **Site** Level
Nearest Bus Stop (Miles) Outside
Near the beach, leisure centre, golf courses and a bowling green.
Facilities

Nearby Facilities
Nearest Town Carnoustie
Directions Well signposted from all directions of the town.
⇄ Carnoustie

FORFAR

Foresterseat Caravan Park, Arbroath Road, Forfar, Angus, DD8 2RY
Tel: 01307 818880
Email: emma@foresterseat.co.uk
www.foresterseat.co.uk
Pitches For Å ⌂ ⌂ **Total** 76
Acreage 16 **Open** March **to** Nov
Access Good **Site** Level
Nearest Bus Stop (Miles) Outside
Modern Park on the edge of Forfar, with 42 Super Pitches. Ideal base for touring the Angus Glens and scenic coast. 1 mile from a golf course and fishing loch. Walking path networks from the site. Fully licensed restaurant on site.
Facilities
Nearby Facilities
Nearest Town Forfar
Directions From Forfar take the A932 towards Arbroath, Foresterseat is 1 mile after Cunninghill Golf Course on the right.
⇄ Arbroath

KIRRIEMUIR

Drumshademuir Caravan Park, Roundyhill, By Glamis, Forfar, Angus, DD8 1QT
Tel: 01575 573284
Email: info@drumshademuir.com
www.drumshademuir.com
Pitches For Å ⌂ ⌂ **Total** 60
Acreage 15 **Open** All Year
Access Good **Site** Level
Nearest Bus Stop (Miles) Outside
Panoramic views. Central location for towns, cities and Angus Glens.
Facilities
Nearby Facilities
Nearest Town Kirriemuir
Directions From the A94 or the A90 take the A928, park is 3 miles north of Glamis Castle.
⇄ Dundee

MONIFIETH

Tayview Caravan & Camping Park, Marine Drive, Monifieth, Angus, DD5 4NL
Tel: 01382 532837
Email: arlene.tayview@btconnect.com
www.tayview.info
Pitches For Å ⌂ ⌂ **Total** 45
Acreage 9 **Open** Feb **to** Nov
Access Good **Site** Level
Nearest Bus Stop (Miles) ¼
Overlooking the beach with a southerly aspect over the River Tay. Extensive paved walkways and a cycle track along the beach.
Facilities
Nearby Facilities
Nearest Town Monifieth
Directions From Dundee turn right off Monifieth High Street onto Reform Street, at the end turn left, then turn right under the railway bridge and follow signs to TayView.
⇄ Monifieth

ARGYLL & BUTE

CAMPBELTOWN

Peninver Sands Holiday Park, Peninver, By Campbeltown, Argyll & Bute, PA28 6QP
Tel: 01586 552262
Email: info@peninver-sands.com
www.peninver-sands.com
Pitches For ⬛ **Total** 25
Acreage 2¾ **Open** 15-Mar **to** 15-Jan
Access Poor **Site** Lev/Slope
Nearest Bus Stop (Miles) Outside
Situated right on the beach.
Facilities ⬛ ⬛ ⬛ ⬛ ⬛
⬛ ⬛ ⬛ ⬛
Nearby Facilities ⬛ ⬛ ⬛ ⬛ ⬛ ⬛
Nearest Town Campbeltown
Directions From Campbeltown take the B842 north for 4½ miles. Park is on the right as you enter the village of Peninver.
⇥ Oban

CARRADALE

Carradale Bay Caravan Site, Carradale, Campbeltown, Argyll & Bute, PA28 6QG
Tel: 01583 431665
Email: info@carradalebay.com
www.carradalebay.com
Pitches For ⬛ ⬛ ⬛ **Total** 60
Open March **to** Sept
Access Good **Site** Level
Nearest Bus Stop (Miles) ½
Situated facing the Isle of Arran with panoramic views over the surrounding countryside. Alongside the River Carra. Ideal for sea and game fishing, walking, cycling and pony trekking. Shops, bars and restaurants in Carradale.
Facilities ⬛ ⬛ ⬛ ⬛
Nearby Facilities ⬛ ⬛
Nearest Town Carradale
Directions Turn off the A83 at Campbeltown onto the B842. Turn right at the T-Junction onto the B879, after 600 yards at Site sign, turn right into estate road and follow signs to the Site.
⇥ Campbeltown

CONNEL

Oban Camping & Caravanning Club Site, Barcaldine By Connel, Argyll & Bute, PA37 1SG
Tel: 01631 720348
www.campingandcaravanningclub.co.uk/oban
Pitches For ⬛ ⬛ ⬛ **Total** 75
Acreage 4½ **Open** 29-Mar **to** 05-Nov
Access Good **Site** Level
Nearest Bus Stop (Miles) Outside
Set in a delightful walled garden. Superb forest walks are just 5 minutes from the site. A perfect base to explore the Highlands and Islands. STB 4 Star Graded and AA 3 Pennants. Non members welcome. You can also call us on 0845 130 7633.
Facilities ⬛ ⬛ ⬛ ⬛ ⬛ ⬛ ⬛ ⬛ ⬛ ⬛
⬛ ⬛ ⬛ ⬛ ⬛ ⬛ ⬛ ⬛ ⬛ ⬛ ⬛
Nearby Facilities ⬛ ⬛ ⬛ ⬛ ⬛
Nearest Town Loch Linnhe
Directions Heading North on the A828, 7 miles from the Connel bridge turn right at the Camping & Caravanning Club sign opposite the Marine Resource Centre, proceed through the large iron gates.
⇥ Oban

GLENBARR

Killegruer Caravan Site, Woodend, Glenbarr, Tarbert, Argyll & Bute, PA29 6XB
Tel: 01583 421241
Email: anne.littleson@btinternet.com
www.kintyreaccommodation.com
Pitches For ⬛ ⬛ ⬛ **Total** 25
Acreage 1¼ **Open** April **to** October
Access Good **Site** Level
Nearest Bus Stop (Miles) Outside
Overlooking a sandy beach with views of the Inner Hebrides and the Mull of Kintyre. Site facilities have recently been upgraded. Hair dryers available. Close to the ferry link to Arran and Islay Jura & Gigha.
Facilities ⬛ ⬛ ⬛ ⬛ ⬛ ⬛ ⬛
⬛ ⬛ ⬛ ⬛ ⬛ ⬛ ⬛
Nearby Facilities ⬛ ⬛ ⬛ ⬛ ⬛
Nearest Town Campbeltown
Directions 12 miles north of Campbeltown on the A83.
⇥ Oban

ISLE OF COLL

Garden House Camp Site, Garden House, Isle of Coll, Argyll & Bute, PA78 6TB
Tel: 01879 230374
Email: collcampsite@hotmail.com
www.visitcoll.com
Pitches For ⬛ ⬛ ⬛
Acreage 2 **Open** 01-Apr **to** 15-Sep
Access Good **Site** Level
In the middle of a nature reserve and only 5 minutes to the beach.
Facilities ⬛ ⬛ ⬛ ⬛
Nearby Facilities
Nearest Town Arinagour
Directions Take the airport road west and before the airport take the track on the left at Uig to Walled Garden.
⇥ Oban

ISLE OF MULL (CRAIGNURE)

Shieling Holidays, Craignure, Isle of Mull, Argyll & Bute, PA65 6AY
Tel: 01680 812496
Email: info@shielingholidays.co.uk
www.shielingholidays.co.uk
Pitches For ⬛ ⬛ ⬛ **Total** 90
Acreage 6½ **Open** April **to** October
Access Good **Site** Level
Nearest Bus Stop (Miles) ¼
Enchanting location by the sea, great for fishing. Self Catering Shielings and hostel beds. 5 Star Graded.
Facilities ⬛ ⬛ ⬛ ⬛ ⬛ ⬛ ⬛ ⬛ ⬛ ⬛
⬛ ⬛ ⬛ ⬛ ⬛ ⬛ ⬛ ⬛ ⬛ ⬛ ⬛
Nearby Facilities ⬛ ⬛ ⬛
Nearest Town Craignure
Directions From Craignure Ferry turn left on A849 to Iona for 400 metres, then left again at church.
⇥ Oban

LUSS

Camping & Caravanning Club Site, Luss, Loch Lomond, Alexandria, Nr Glasgow, Argyll & Bute, G83 8NT
Tel: 01436 860658
www.campingandcaravanningclub.co.uk/luss
Pitches For ⬛ ⬛ ⬛ **Total** 90
Acreage 12 **Open** 29-Mar **to** 05-Nov
Access Good **Site** Level
Nearest Bus Stop (Miles) ¼
On the banks of Loch Lomond with good views of Ben Lomond. Fishing (permit required) and watersports. STB 4 Star Graded, AA 3 Pennants, Loo of the Year Award and Babychange Winner 2002. CLUB MEMBER CARAVANNERS & MOTORHOMES ONLY. Non member tents welcome. You can also call us on 0845 130 7633.
Facilities ⬛ ⬛ ⬛ ⬛ ⬛ ⬛ ⬛ ⬛ ⬛ ⬛
⬛ ⬛ ⬛ ⬛ ⬛ ⬛ ⬛ ⬛ ⬛ ⬛
Nearby Facilities ⬛ ⬛ ⬛
Nearest Town Luss

Directions Take the A82 from the Erkside Bridge and head north towards Luss. Ignore first signpost for Luss. After the bagpipe and kiltmakers workshop take the next turn right sp Lodge of Loch Lomond and international camping sign, site approx. 200 yards.
⇥ Balloch

MACHRIHANISH

Machrihanish Caravan Park, East Trodigal, Campbeltown, Argyll & Bute, PA28 6PT
Tel: 01586 810366
Email: mail@campkintyre.co.uk
www.campkintyre.co.uk
Pitches For ⬛ ⬛ ⬛ ⬛ **Total** 90
Acreage 6 **Open** March **to** October
Access Good **Site** Level
Nearest Bus Stop (Miles) Entrance
Overlooking the famous Machrihanish Golf Course, and views across the Atlantic Ocean to the islands of Jura and Islay.
Facilities ⬛ ⬛ ⬛ ⬛ ⬛ ⬛ ⬛ ⬛ ⬛ ⬛
⬛ ⬛ ⬛ ⬛ ⬛ ⬛ ⬛
Nearby Facilities ⬛ ⬛ ⬛ ⬛ ⬛
Nearest Town Campbeltown
Directions Take the A82 to Campbeltown then take the B843 to Machrihanish. Site is 200 yards past East Trodigal Farm.
⇥ Oban

MUASDALE

Muasdale Holiday Park, Muasdale, Tarbert, Argyll & Bute, PA29 6XD
Tel: 01583 421207
Email: enquiries@muasdaleholidays.com
www.muasdaleholidays.com
Pitches For ⬛ ⬛ ⬛ **Total** 10
Open 01-Apr **to** 23-Oct
Access Good
Nearest Bus Stop (Miles) 100 Yards
Adjoining the beach with stunning views of Islay, Jura and Gigha. Sea fishing on site (bring your own equipment). Bonfires allowed on the beach. Convenient for ferries to Islay, Jura, Gigha and Arran.
Facilities ⬛ ⬛ ⬛ ⬛ ⬛ ⬛ ⬛ ⬛ ⬛
⬛ ⬛ ⬛ ⬛ ⬛ ⬛ ⬛
Nearby Facilities ⬛ ⬛ ⬛
Nearest Town Campbeltown/Tarbert
Directions On the A83 at the southern end of Muasdale Village, approx. 22 miles from Tarbert.

OBAN

Caravans at Highfield, 3 Kiel Croft, Benderloch, Oban, Argyll & Bute, PA37 1QS
Tel: 01631 720262
Email: elaine.clsite@gmail.com
www.clsite.co.uk
Pitches For ⬛ ⬛ **Total** 10
Acreage 1 **Open** April **to** October
Access Good **Site** Level
Nearest Bus Stop (Miles) ½
Country location only 500 metres from Tralee beach. 1 mile to the village for shop and cafe. Ideal for walking and touring, only 10 miles from Oban. Fort William and Inveraray within 1 hours drive.
Facilities ⬛ ⬛ ⬛ ⬛ ⬛
Nearby Facilities ⬛ ⬛ ⬛ ⬛
Nearest Town Oban
Directions Turn off the A828 in Benderloch signposted Tralee and South Shian. Highfield is approx 800 metres on the right (its the second gate on the right after Hawthorn Cottage Restaurant).
⇥ Oban

OBAN

North Ledaig Caravan Park, Connel, By Oban, Argyll & Bute, PA37 1RU
Tel: 01631 710291
www.northledaigcaravanpark.co.uk
Pitches For ⬤ ⬤ ⬤ **Total** 280
Acreage 28 **Open** 23-Mar **to** 29-Oct
Access Good **Site** Lev/Slope
Nearest Bus Stop (Miles) Entrance
Half mile beach frontage with spectacular views to the islands. 6 miles from the busy ferry port of Oban.
Facilities ⬤ ⬤ ⬤ ⬤ ⬤ ⬤ ⬤ ⬤ ⬤ ⬤ ⬤ ⬤ ⬤ ⬤ ⬤ ⬤ ⬤ ⬤ ⬤
Nearby Facilities ⬤ ⬤ ⬤ ⬤ ⬤ ⬤
Nearest Town Oban
Directions From Oban take the A85 signposted Connel. In Connel turn right onto the A828 signposted Fort William. Park is 1½ miles on the left.
⬤ Oban

OBAN

Roseview Caravan Park, Rose View, Glenshellach Road, Oban, Argyll & Bute, PA34 4QJ
Tel: 01631 562755
Email: info@roseviewoban.co.uk
www.roseviewoban.co.uk
Pitches For ⬤ ⬤ ⬤ **Total** 45
Acreage 4 **Open** Dec **to** Oct
Access Good **Site** Lev/Slope
Nearest Bus Stop (Miles) ½
Quiet, scenic park on different levels with a stream running through. Limited facilities only from Nov to March. Sorry, no commercial vehicles. You can also contact us on Mobile: 07977 807719. STB 4 Star Graded.
Facilities ⬤ ⬤ ⬤ ⬤ ⬤ ⬤ ⬤ ⬤ ⬤ ⬤ ⬤ ⬤
Nearby Facilities ⬤ ⬤ ⬤ ⬤ ⬤ ⬤
Nearest Town Oban
Directions From north go through Oban to the traffic island, take ferry and caravan signs into Albany Street then first or second left. take the first right, then first left sp caravans/ tents. Glenshellach Road is 1½ miles.
⬤ Oban

SOUTHEND

Machribeg Caravan Site, Southend, By Campbeltown, Argyll & Bute, PA28 6RW
Tel: 01586 830249
Pitches For ⬤ ⬤ ⬤ **Total** 80
Acreage 4 **Open** Easter **to** September
Access Good **Site** Level
Nearest Bus Stop (Miles) Outside
Near the beach with good views, very quiet location. 18 hole golf course.
Facilities ⬤ ⬤ ⬤ ⬤ ⬤ ⬤ ⬤
Nearby Facilities ⬤ ⬤ ⬤ ⬤ ⬤
Nearest Town Campbeltown
Directions Take the B843 from Campbeltown for 10 miles. Site is situated 250yds through Southend Village on the left by the beach.

TAYINLOAN

Point Sands Holiday Park, Tayinloan, Argyll & Bute, PA29 6XG
Tel: 01583 441263
Email: info@pointsands.co.uk
www.pointsands.co.uk
Pitches For ⬤ ⬤ ⬤ ⬤
Acreage 14 **Open** April **to** October
Access Good **Site** Level
Peaceful site on a safe sandy beach with terrific scenery. Near to island ferries. Ideal for touring and visiting the Isles of Gigha, Arran and Islay. Holiday homes to let.
Facilities ⬤ ⬤ ⬤ ⬤ ⬤ ⬤ ⬤ ⬤ ⬤ ⬤ ⬤ ⬤ ⬤ ⬤ ⬤
Nearby Facilities ⬤ ⬤ ⬤ ⬤ ⬤ ⬤

Nearest Town Tarbert
Directions On the A83 Glasgow to Campbeltown road, 17 miles south of Tarbert.

TAYVALLICH

Leachive Caravan Site, Leachive Farm, Tayvallich, By Lochgilphead, Argyll & Bute, PA31 8PL
Tel: 01546 870206
Email: fiona@leachive.co.uk
www.leachive.co.uk
Pitches For ⬤ ⬤ ⬤ **Total** 15
Acreage 4 **Open** April **to** October
Access Good **Site** Level
Nearest Bus Stop (Miles) ¼
Set beside a sheltered sea loch, ideal for canoeing and sailing. Near a nature reserve with beautiful scenic walks. Numerous forest walks and trails in the near vacinity.
Facilities ⬤ ⬤ ⬤ ⬤ ⬤ ⬤ ⬤ ⬤ ⬤ ⬤
Nearby Facilities ⬤ ⬤ ⬤ ⬤
Nearest Town Lochgilphead
Directions From Lochgilphead follow signs for Oban for 3 miles, then follow signs for Tayvallich.
⬤ Oban

AYRSHIRE (NORTH)

ISLE OF ARRAN

Lochranza Caravan & Camping Site, Lochranza, Isle of Arran, North Ayrshire, KA27 8HL
Tel: 01770 830273
Email: info@arran-campsite.com
www.arran-campsite.com
Pitches For ⬤ ⬤ ⬤ **Total** 60
Acreage 2½ **Open** March **to** Oct
Access Good **Site** Level
Nearest Bus Stop (Miles) Outside
Beautiful mountain scenery and abundant wildlife. Red Deer and Red Squirrels are often seen on site, aswell as Golden Eagles overhead. Adjacent to a golf course.
Facilities ⬤ ⬤ ⬤ ⬤ ⬤ ⬤ ⬤ ⬤ ⬤ ⬤ ⬤ ⬤ ⬤
Nearby Facilities ⬤ ⬤ ⬤ ⬤ ⬤
Nearest Town Brodick
Directions Follow the road north for 14 miles to the north end of the island. Site entrance is opposite the Isle of Arran Distillery.
⬤ Ardrossan

ISLE OF ARRAN

Middletons Caravan & Camping Park, Cordon, Lamlash, Isle of Arran, North Ayrshire, KA27 8NQ
Tel: 01770 600251/600634
Email: info@middletonscamping.com
www.middletonscamping.com
Pitches For ⬤ ⬤ ⬤ ⬤ **Total** 40
Acreage 3½ **Open** March **to** Oct
Access Good **Site** Level
Nearest Bus Stop (Miles) ¼
Centrally located on the Island, near the beach and village.
Facilities ⬤ ⬤ ⬤ ⬤ ⬤ ⬤ ⬤ ⬤ ⬤ ⬤ ⬤ ⬤
Nearby Facilities ⬤ ⬤ ⬤ ⬤ ⬤ ⬤ ⬤ ⬤
Directions From Brodick ferry terminal turn left onto the A841, 4 miles to Lamlash. Pass the Police Station on the left, go over the bridge then sharp left, site is ¼ of a mile.
⬤ Ardrossan

Isle of Arran

Seal Shore Camping & Touring, Seal Shore, Kildonan, Isle of Arran, North Ayrshire, KA27 8SE
Tel: 01770 820320
Email: enquiries@campingarran.com
www.campingarran.com

Pitches For ⬤ ⬤ ⬤ **Total** 43
Acreage 2¾
Access Good **Site** Sloping
Nearest Bus Stop (Miles) Outside
Situated on our own private beach. Under-cover cooking area.
Facilities ⬤ ⬤ ⬤ ⬤ ⬤ ⬤ ⬤ ⬤ ⬤ ⬤ ⬤ ⬤ ⬤ ⬤ ⬤ ⬤ ⬤ ⬤
Nearby Facilities ⬤ ⬤ ⬤ ⬤ ⬤ ⬤
Nearest Town Brodick
Directions From the ferry turn left, Kildonan is 12 miles.
⬤ Ardrossan

LARGS

South Whittlieburn Farm, Brisbane Glen, Largs, North Ayrshire, KA30 8SN
Tel: 01475 675881
Email:
largsbandb@southwhittlieburnfarm.freeserve.co.uk
www.smoothhound.co.uk/hotels/whittlie
Pitches For ⬤ ⬤ ⬤ **Total** 5
Acreage 5 **Open** All Year
Access Good **Site** Level/Sloping
Nearest Bus Stop (Miles) ½
Situated on a working sheep farm with 4 Star Farmhouse B&B accommodation also available. Great for hill walking. Close to Largs for ferries, shops, restaurants, pubs, swimming pool, putting green and theatre.
Facilities ⬤ ⬤ ⬤ ⬤ ⬤ ⬤ ⬤ ⬤ ⬤
Nearby Facilities ⬤ ⬤ ⬤ ⬤ ⬤ ⬤
Nearest Town Largs
Directions From the A78 in Largs, turn off just past Vikingar Complex (sp Brisbane Glen), Park is approx 2¼ miles on the left.
⬤ Largs

SALTCOATS

Sandylands Holiday Park, Auchenharvie Park, Saltcoats, North Ayrshire, KA21 5JN
Tel: 0843 309 2571
Email: holidaysales.sandylands@park-resorts.com
www.park-resorts.com
Pitches For ⬤ ⬤ ⬤
Open April **to** October
Access Good **Site** Level
Nearest Bus Stop (Miles) ½
Close to the beach in a relaxing seaside destination offering outstanding views. Great location for visiting beautiful Arran and charming Scottish towns.
Facilities ⬤ ⬤ ⬤ ⬤ ⬤ ⬤ ⬤ ⬤ ⬤ ⬤ ⬤ ⬤
Nearby Facilities
Nearest Town Saltcoats
Directions From Glasgow take the M77 and A77 towards Kilmarnock. At Kilmarnock take the A71 towards Irvine, then follow signs to Ardrossan. Join the A78 towards Stevenson, after the leisure centre turn first left, the Park is on the left.
⬤ Saltcoats

AYRSHIRE (SOUTH)

AYR

Craig Tara Holiday Park, Ayr, South Ayrshire, KA7 4LB
Tel: 01292 265141
Email: craigtara@haven.com
www.haventouring.com/tocraigtara
Pitches For ⬤ ⬤ **Total** 39
Open Mid March **to** End Oct
Nearest Bus Stop (Miles) Outside
A large, all-action Holiday Park on the Ayrshire coast. Don't miss the Isle of Arran boat trips nearby. Outstanding range of leisure facilities for the whole family to enjoy on-park.

Facilities ♿ ⚡ 🚿 💶 🛢 📶 🅿 ☺ 🍴 🔌 🛒 🚩
🌙 ⚡ 🏪 ✕ 🍴 ♨ 🏊 🛢 ✈ 🚲 ⛺ 🔌 🎱 ♨ 📶
Nearby Facilities 🚩 ∪
Nearest Town Ayr
Directions From the North take the A77 towards Stranraer, take second right after Bankfield roundabout. At roundabout follow signs for A719, this will lead to the Park on the right hand side. From South leave the M74 at junction 12 and take the A70 towards Cumnock a
⚏ Ayr

AYR

Craigie Gardens Caravan Club Site, Craigie Road, Ayr, South Ayrshire, KA8 0SS
Tel: 01292 264909
www.caravanclub.co.uk
Pitches For 🚐 🚙 **Total** 90
Acreage 7 **Open** 23-Mar **to** 07-Jan
Access Good **Site** Level
Nearest Bus Stop (Miles) ½
Situated in a beautiful park, just a ten minute walk from Ayr seaside resort. Open March then all year. 40 golf courses in the area. Close to Burns Heritage Trail, Culzean Castle, Vikingar and The Tam OShanter Experience. Non members welcome. Booking essential.
Facilities ♿ ⚡ 🚿 💶 🛢 🅿 ☺ 🛢 🛒 🚩
⚡ 🛢 🛒 🍴 🔌 🎱 ♨ 📶
Nearby Facilities 🚩 ✈
Nearest Town Ayr
Directions From the A77 Ayr bypass take the A719 signposted Ayr. Just past the racecourse at the traffic lights turn left into Craigie Road, on right bend turn left into Craigie Gardens, keep right and site is 400 yards.
⚏ Ayr

AYR

Heads of Ayr Caravan Park, Dunure Road, Ayr, South Ayrshire, KA7 4LD
Tel: 01292 442269
Email: stay@headsofayr.com
www.headsofayr.com
Pitches For ⛺ 🚐 🚙 **Total** 25
Acreage 9 **Open** March **to** October
Access Good **Site** Level
Nearest Bus Stop (Miles) Outside
Just a 10 minute walk to the beach.
Facilities ⚡ 🚿 💶 🛢 🅿 ☺ 🛢 🛒 🚩
🌙 ⚡ 🏪 🍴 ♨ 🏊 🛢 ✈ 🚲 ⛺ 🔌
Nearby Facilities 🚩 ✈ ⚓ ∪ ♨
Nearest Town Ayr
Directions 5 miles south of Ayr on the A719.
⚏ Ayr

AYR

Sundrum Castle Holiday Park, By Ayr, South Ayrshire, KA6 5JH
Tel: 0844 335 3731
Email: touringandcamping@parkdeanholidays.com
www.parkdeantouring.com
Pitches For 🚐 🚙 **Total** 45
Acreage 32 **Open** March **to** Oct
Access Good **Site** Level
Nearest Bus Stop (Miles) ½
Four Star Park set in rolling Ayrshire countryside, just 4 miles from the beach. Indoor pool. FREE kids clubs and live family entertainment.
Facilities ⚡ 🚿 💶 🛢 🅿 ☺ 🛢 🛒 🚩
🌙 ⚡ 🏪 ✕ 🍴 ♨ 🏊 🛢 ✈ 🚲 ⛺ 🔌 🎱 📶
Nearby Facilities 🚩 ✈ ♨
Nearest Town Ayr
Directions From Glasgow head south on the A77 to Ayr, then take the A70 to Cumnock. The park is 3 miles along the A70, before Coylton Village.
⚏ Ayr

BARRHILL

Barrhill Holiday Park, Millers Holiday Parks, Barrhill, Girvan, South Ayrshire, KA26 0PZ
Tel: 01465 821355
Email: barrhill@surfree.co.uk
www.barrhillholidaypark.com
Pitches For ⛺ 🚐 🚙 **Total** 30
Acreage 1 **Open** March **to** Jan
Access Good **Site** Level
Nearest Bus Stop (Miles) Outside
Small, sheltered, family run park in rural countryside. Undiscovered part of Scotland offering peace and tranquillity. Ideal for walking, cycling, fishing and golf.
Facilities ♿ ⚡ 🚿 💶 🛢 🅿 ☺ 🛢 🛒 🚩
🌙 ⚡ 🏪 ♨ 🛢 🔌 🎱
Nearby Facilities 🚩 ✈ ∪ ✕
Nearest Town Girvan
Directions Situated on the A714 between Newton Stewart and Girvan, 1 mile north of Barrhill.
⚏ Barrhill

BARRHILL

Queensland Holiday Park, Barrhill, Girvan, South Ayrshire, KA26 0PZ
Tel: 01465 821364
Email: info@queenslandholidaypark.co.uk
www.queenslandholidaypark.co.uk
Pitches For ⛺ 🚐 🚙 **Total** 64
Acreage 9 **Open** March **to** Jan
Access Good **Site** Level
Nearest Bus Stop (Miles) Entrance
Ideal location for walking and cycling in Galloway Forest, or for touring South Scotland. Good local rivers.

Facilities ♿ ⚡ 🚿 💶 🛢 🅿 ☺ 🛢 🛒 🚩
🌙 ⚡ 🏪 🛢 ✈ 🔌 📶
Nearby Facilities 🚩 ✈
Nearest Town Girvan
Directions 10 miles south of Girvan on the A714.
⚏ Barrhill

MAYBOLE

Camping & Caravanning Club Site, Culzean Castle, Maybole, South Ayrshire, KA19 8JX
Tel: 01655 760627
www.campingandcaravanningclub.co.uk
Pitches For ⛺ 🚐 🚙 **Total** 90
Acreage 10 **Open** 29-Mar **to** 05-Nov
Access Good **Site** Lev/Slope
Nearest Bus Stop (Miles) Outside
Set in the grounds of historic Culzean Castle with excellent views and country walks. STB 4 Star Graded and AA 3 Pennants. Non members welcome. You can also call us on 0845 130 7633.
Facilities ♿ ⚡ 🚿 💶 🛢 🅿 ☺ 🛢 🛒 🚩
🛢 🛒 🍴 🔌 🎱 ♨ ⚡ 📶
Nearby Facilities 🚩 ∪
Directions In Maybole turn right onto the B7023 signposted Culzean and Maidens. After 100 yards turn left, site is 4 miles on the right.
⚏ Maybole

TROON

St Meddans Caravan Site, Low St Meddans, Troon, South Ayrshire, KA10 6NS
Tel: 01292 312957
www.ukparks.co.uk/stmeddans
Pitches For 🚐 🚙 **Total** 25
Acreage 1 **Open** 1st Fri March **to** Last Sun Oct
Nearest Bus Stop (Miles) Outside
Just a 5 minute walk from beaches, golf courses and the town centre.
Facilities ⚡ 🚿 💶 🛢 🅿 ☺ 🛢 🛒 🚩
🏪 🛢 🛢 ✈ 🔌 🎱
Nearest Town Troon
⚏ Troon

TURNBERRY

Balkenna Caravan Park, Girvan Road (A77), Turnberry, South Ayrshire, KA26 9LN
Tel: 01655 331692
Email: balkenna@aol.com
www.balkenna.co.uk
Pitches For ⛺ 🚐 🚙 **Total** 15
Acreage 1½ **Open** All Year
Access Good **Site** Level
Nearest Bus Stop (Miles) Outside
Magnificent sea views looking towards the Isle of Arran. Close to Turnberry Golf Course.
Facilities ⚡ 🚿 💶 🛢 🅿 ☺ 🛢
🌙 🛢 ✕ 🍴 🔌 🎱 ♨
Nearby Facilities 🚩 ✈

SCOTLAND

Nearest Town Girvan
Directions From Girvan take the A77 north, site is 5 miles on the right, just before Turnberry Golf Course.
⌁ Girvan

DUMFRIES & GALLOWAY
BORGUE
Brighouse Bay Holiday Park, Borgue, Kirkcudbright, Dumfries & Galloway, DG6 4TS
Tel: 01557 870267
Email: info@gillespie-leisure.co.uk
www.gillespie-leisure.co.uk
Pitches For Å ⊕ ⊕ ⊕ **Total** 180
Acreage 25 **Open** All Year
Access Good **Site** Lev/Slope
Nearest Bus Stop (Miles) At Entrance
Beautifully situated on a quiet peninsula with its own sandy beach, family park with exceptional on-site recreational facilities including an indoor pool complex, jacuzzi, fitness room, family room, bowling green, quad bikes, pony trekking centre, 18 hole par 73 golf course and driving range, 9 hole park 3 golf course, fishing, nature trails, boating, pond canoes and slipway.
Facilities [icons]
Nearby Facilities [icons]
Nearest Town Kirkcudbright
Directions Off the B727 Kirkcudbright to Borgue road. Or take the A755 (Kirkcudbright) off the A75 2 miles west of Twynholm, clear signposting for 8 miles.
⌁ Dumfries

CASTLE DOUGLAS
Lochside Camping & Caravan Park, Lochside, Castle Douglas, Dumfries & Galloway, DG7 1EZ
Tel: 01556 502949
www.dumgal.gov.uk/lochsidecs
Pitches For Å ⊕ ⊕ **Total** 108
Acreage 5 **Open** Easter to Oct
Access Good **Site** Level
Nearest Bus Stop (Miles) ¼
Overlooking Carlingwark Loch. Close to Threave House, Threave Castle. Boating, fishing and putting on site. Two play areas. Swimming pool nearby.
Facilities [icons]
Nearby Facilities [icons]
Nearest Town Castle Douglas
Directions In Castle Douglas at the bottom of the main street by Carlingwark Loch.
⌁ Dumfries

CROCKETFORD
Park of Brandedleys, Crocketford, Dumfries & Galloway, DG2 8RG
Tel: 01387 266700
Email: reception@holgates.com
www.brandedleys.co.uk
Pitches For Å ⊕ ⊕ ⊕ **Total** 47
Acreage 10 **Open** All Year
Access Good **Site** Lev/Slope
Nearest Bus Stop (Miles) Outside
Ideal for touring the south west of Scotland. Tennis on site. Cycle tracks nearby.
Facilities [icons]
Nearby Facilities [icons]
Nearest Town Dumfries
Directions From Dumfries take the A75 west to the village of Crocketford. In the village turn left onto minor road, site is 200 metres on the right.
⌁ Dumfries

DALBEATTIE
Glenearly Caravan Park, Dalbeattie, Dumfries & Galloway, DG5 4NE
Tel: 01556 611393
Email: glenearlycaravan@btconnect.com
Pitches For Å ⊕ ⊕ **Total** 39
Acreage 10 **Open** All Year
Access Good **Site** Level
Nearest Bus Stop (Miles) ¼
Peaceful site situated centrally for all local attractions.
Facilities [icons]
Nearby Facilities [icons]
Nearest Town Dalbeattie
Directions From Dumfries take the A711 towards Dalbeattie. On approaching Dalbeattie see signs for Glenearly on the right hand side.
⌁ Dumfries

DALBEATTIE
Sandyhills Bay Leisure Park, Sandyhills, Dalbeattie, Dumfries & Galloway, DG5 4NY
Tel: 01557 870267
Email: info@gillespie-leisure.co.uk
www.gillespie-leisure.co.uk
Pitches For Å ⊕ ⊕ **Total** 20
Acreage 15 **Open** Easter to Oct
Access Good **Site** Level
Cliff top walk to Rockcliffe from Sandyhills. Adventure play area by the beach, shop and small take-away.
Facilities [icons]
Nearby Facilities [icons]
Nearest Town Dalbeattie
Directions From Dumfries take the A710 Solway Coast road for approx 16 miles. Park is on the left just after signs for Sandyhills.
⌁ Dumfries

DUMFRIES
Barnsoul Farm & Wildlife Area, Barnsoul Farm, Shawhead, Dumfries, Dumfries & Galloway, DG2 9SQ
Tel: 01387 730249
Email: barnsouldg@aol.com
www.barnsoulfarm.co.uk
Pitches For Å ⊕ ⊕ **Total** 50
Acreage 200 **Open** April to Beg Winter
Access Good **Site** Lev/Slope
Nearest Bus Stop (Miles) ½
Walking, cycling and fishing nearby.
Facilities [icons]
Nearby Facilities [icons]
Nearest Town Dumfries
Directions From Dumfries take the A75 towards Stranraer, after 6 miles turn right towards Shawhead, follow signs for Barnsoul Farm for 2½ miles.
⌁ Dumfries

ECCLEFECHAN
Cressfield Caravan Park, Ecclefechan, Lockerbie, Dumfries & Galloway, DG11 3LG
Tel: 01576 300702
Email: info@cressfieldcaravanpark.co.uk
www.cressfieldcaravanpark.co.uk
Pitches For Å ⊕ ⊕ **Total** 40
Acreage 40 **Open** All Year
Access Good **Site** Level
Nearest Bus Stop (Miles) Outside
Quiet rural park. Next to the village and a hotel. Good walking, cycling and motoring area.
Facilities [icons]
Nearby Facilities [icons]
Nearest Town Lockerbie
Directions From the M6 head north on the M74 to junction 19, then follow signs for Cressfield.
⌁ Lockerbie

GATEHOUSE OF FLEET
Anwoth Holiday Park, Garden Street, Gatehouse of Fleet, Castle Douglas, Dumfries & Galloway, DG7 2JU
Tel: 01557 814333
Email: paul@auchenlarie.co.uk
www.anwothholidaypark.co.uk
Pitches For Å ⊕ ⊕ **Total** 28
Open March to Oct
Access Good **Site** Level
Nearest Bus Stop (Miles) ¼
Quiet 5 Star Park in the village of Gatehouse of Fleet.
Facilities [icons]
Nearby Facilities [icons]
Nearest Town Gatehouse of Fleet

SCOTLAND

Directions From Dumfries take the A75 towards Stranraer, 16 miles from Castle Douglas.
⚐ Dumfries

GATEHOUSE OF FLEET
Auchenlarie Holiday Park, Gatehouse of Fleet, Castle Douglas, Dumfries & Galloway, DG7 2EX
Tel: 01556 506200
Email: enquiries@auchenlarie.co.uk
www.swalwellholidaygroup.co.uk
Pitches For 𝗔 ⌂ ⛟ **Total** 109
Acreage 20 **Open** March **to** October
Access Good **Site** Sloping
Nearest Bus Stop (Miles) Outside
Our own sandy cove. Restaurant, 3 bars, Beauty salon and hairdressing on site, as well as a gym, crazy golf and a shop. Good centre for touring.
Facilities
Nearby Facilities
Directions On the main A75 5 miles west of Gatehouse of Fleet heading towards Stranraer, Park is on the left hand side.
⚐ Dumfries

GATEHOUSE OF FLEET
Mossyard Caravan Park, Mossyard, Gatehouse of Fleet, Castle Douglas, Dumfries & Galloway, DG7 2ET
Tel: 01557 840226
Email: enquiry@mossyard.co.uk
www.mossyard.co.uk
Pitches For 𝗔 ⌂ ⛟ **Total** 30
Open April **to** End Oct
Access Good **Site** Level
Nearest Bus Stop (Miles) ½
Situated on a working farm and set in a coastal location with a back drop of the Galloway Hills. Family run business.
Facilities
Nearby Facilities
Nearest Town Gatehouse of Fleet
Directions 4 miles west of Gatehouse of Fleet on the A75, turn left at Mossyard sign and follow for 800 yards to reception.
⚐ Dumfries

GLENLUCE
Glenluce Caravan Park, Balkail Avenue, Glenluce, Dumfries & Galloway, DG8 0QR
Tel: 01581 300412
Email: enquiries@glenlucecaravans.co.uk
www.glenlucecaravans.co.uk
Pitches For 𝗔 ⌂ ⛟
Acreage 4 **Open** All Year
Access Good **Site** Level
Nearest Bus Stop (Miles) ¼
Secluded suntrap in the centre of the village. Set in mature grounds. Ideal for walking, beaches, fishing, mountain biking, UK Dark Skies Park, golfing and watersports.
Facilities
Nearby Facilities
Nearest Town Stranraer
⚐ Stranraer

GLENLUCE
Whitecairn Holiday Park, Glenluce, Newton Stewart, Dumfries & Galloway, DG8 0NZ
Tel: 01581 300267
Email: enquiries@whitecairncaravans.co.uk
www.whitecairncaravans.co.uk
Pitches For 𝗔 ⌂ ⛟
Acreage 22 **Open** All Year
Access Good **Site** Level
Nearest Bus Stop (Miles) ½

Central location for touring Wigtownshire. Very peacful park, away from the main road. Ideal for beaches, walking, fishing, mountain biking, UK Dark Skies Park, golfing and watersports.
Facilities
Nearby Facilities
Nearest Town Stranraer
Directions 1½ miles north of Glenluce Village and 2 miles from the A75.
⚐ Stranraer

GRETNA
Braids Caravan Park, Annan Road, Gretna, Dumfries & Galloway, DG16 5DQ
Tel: 01461 337409
Email: enquiries@thebraidscaravanpark.co.uk
www.thebraidscaravanpark.co.uk
Pitches For ⌂ ⛟ **Total** 84
Acreage 5 **Open** All Year
Access Good **Site** Lev/Slope
Nearest Bus Stop (Miles) ¼
Ideal touring centre. Good area for bird watching. On board tank waste disposal point. Small rallies welcome, rally building available. STB 4 Star Graded Park.
Facilities
Nearby Facilities
Directions From the M6 run straight onto the A74. Take the A75 signposted Dumfries/Stranraer. In 1 mile take the second left for Gretna (B721), park is 600yds on the left.
⚐ Gretna Green

ISLE OF WHITHORN
Burrowhead Holiday Village, Tonderghie Road, Isle of Whithorn, Newton Stewart, Dumfries & Galloway, DG8 8JB
Tel: 01988 500252
Email: burrowheadhv@aol.com
www.burrowheadholidayvillage.co.uk
Pitches For 𝗔 ⌂ ⛟ **Total** 90
Acreage 20 **Open** March **to** 01-Nov
Access Good **Site** Level
Beathtaking views over the Solway Firth and across to the Isle of Man.
Facilities
Nearby Facilities
Nearest Town Newton Stewart
Directions From the A75 at Newton Stewart take the A714 to Wigtown, then take the A746 to Whithorn. Then take the B7004 to the Isle of Whithorn and Burrowhead is signposted.
⚐ Stranraer

KIPPFORD
Kippford Holiday Park, Kippford, Dalbeattie, Kirkcudbrightshire, DG5 4LF
Tel: 01556 620636
Email: info@kippfordholidaypark.co.uk
www.kippfordholidaypark.co.uk
Pitches For 𝗔 ⌂ ⛟ **Total** 50
Acreage 8 **Open** All Year
Access Good **Site** Lev/Slope
Nearest Bus Stop (Miles) Outside
Just ½ a mile from the truly beautiful seaside village and pubs. Level pitches, many separately screened. Enjoy woodland walks to the sea and watch the Red Squirrels. Golf, fishing, biking, childrens play area and a shop on site. No on site entertainment.
Facilities
Nearby Facilities
Directions From Dumfries take the A711 to Dalbeattie, then turn left onto the A710 signposted Colvend Coast. In 3½ miles, just beyond Kippford road end, turn right.
⚐ Dumfries

KIRKCUDBRIGHT
Seaward Caravan Park, Dhoon Bay, Kirkcudbright, Dumfries & Galloway, DG6 4TJ
Tel: 01557 331079
Email: info@gillespie-leisure.co.uk
www.gillespie-leisure.co.uk
Pitches For 𝗔 ⌂ ⛟ **Total** 20
Acreage 23 **Open** March **to** Oct
Access Good **Site** Level
Nearest Bus Stop (Miles) At Entrance
Exceptional panoramic views over the bay. Heated outdoor pool and beach picnic area. Beach and sea angling nearby.
Facilities
Nearby Facilities
Nearest Town Kirkcudbright
Directions From Kirkcudbright take the A755 west, then take the B727 Borgue road. Seaward is on the right after approx 3 miles.
⚐ Dumfries

KIRKCUDBRIGHT
Silvercraigs Caravan & Camping Park, Silvercraigs Road, Kirkcudbright, Dumfries & Galloway, DG6 4BT
Tel: 01557 330123
www.dumgal.gov.uk/silvercraigscs
Pitches For 𝗔 ⌂ ⛟ **Total** 50
Acreage 6 **Open** Easter **to** Oct
Access Good **Site** Sloping
Nearest Bus Stop (Miles) ½
2 miles from the beach. Artists Town, marina, harbour, swimming pool and wildlife park nearby.
Facilities
Nearby Facilities
Nearest Town Kirkcudbright
Directions In Kirkcudbright proceed along St. Marys Road, go past the Parish Church and turn left into Silvercraigs Road, follow signs.
⚐ Dumfries

KIRKPATRICK FLEMING
King Robert the Bruces Cave Caravan & Camping Site, Cove Farm, Kirkpatrick Fleming, By Lockerbie, Dumfries & Galloway, DG11 3AT
Tel: 01461 800285
Email: jan534@btinternet.co.uk
www.brucescave.co.uk
Pitches For 𝗔 ⌂ ⛟ **Total** 40
Acreage 80 **Open** All Year
Access Good **Site** Level
Nearest Bus Stop (Miles) ¼
In the grounds of an 80 acre estate, peaceful, quiet and secluded. Famous ancient monument of King Robert the Bruces cave in the grounds. Free fishing on 3 miles of river for Trout and Salmon, or fish on the pond. Disabled toilet block and family shower rooms. Under 5's park. Holiday apartments available.
Facilities
Nearby Facilities
Nearest Town Gretna
Directions Turn off A74 M74 at Kirkpatrick Fleming, then in Kirkpatrick follow all signs to Bruces Cave.
⚐ Annan

LANGHOLM
Whitshiels Caravan Park, Langholm, Dumfries & Galloway, DG13 0HG
Tel: 01387 380494
Email: whitshielscafe@btconnect.com
Pitches For 𝗔 ⌂ ⛟ **Total** 4
Acreage ½ **Open** All Year
Access Good **Site** Level

SCOTLAND

DUMFRIES & GALLOWAY

Nearest Bus Stop (Miles) Outside
Ideal area for fishing, golf, Hadrians Wall, Gretna Green, Borders region and Armstrong Clan Museum. Scenic route to Edinburgh. 3 x 6 berth holiday caravans available to let.
Facilities ⚡ 🅗 🚿 🛆 🅿 ⊙ 🚻 ✕ 🛒 🌲 🅿
Nearby Facilities ⌐ ✒ ⋡ Ⓤ ✗ ⚲
Nearest Town Langholm
Directions 200 yards north of Langholm on the A7.
🚉 Carlisle

LOCHMABEN

Halleaths Caravan Park, Halleaths, Lochmaben, Lockerbie, Dumfries & Galloway, DG11 1NA
Tel: 01387 810630
Email:
halleathscaravanpark@btopenworld.com
www.caravan-sitefinder.co.uk/sites/2436/
Pitches For 🛆 � ⛺ **Total** 10
Acreage 8 **Open** March **to** November
Access Good **Site** Level
Nearest Bus Stop (Miles) ¼
Bowling, tennis, yachting, boating, golf and both coarse and game fishing, all within 1 mile of park.
Facilities ⚡ 🅗 🚿 🛆 🅿 ⊙ 🚻 🛒 🍴 🅿 🍽
🍴 ⚙ 🛆 🌲 🅿 ⚡ 🔆
Nearby Facilities ⌐ ✒ ⋔ ⋡ Ⓤ ⟑ ℛ
Nearest Town Lochmaben/Lockerbie
Directions From Lockerbie on M74, take A709 to Lochmaben. ½ mile on the right after crossing the River Annan.
🚉 Lockerbie

LOCHMABEN

Kirkloch Caravan & Camping Site, Kirk Loch, Lochmaben, Dumfries & Galloway, DG11 1PZ
Tel: 01556 503806
www.dumgal.gov.uk/kirklochcs
Pitches For 🛆 ♡ ⛺ **Total** 30
Open Easter **to** Oct
Access Good **Site** Level
Situated on the banks of the picturesque Kirk Loch for fishing. Ideal base for touring. Golf course adjacent to the site.
Facilities ⚡ 🅕 🅗 🅤 🅿 ⊙ 🚻 🛒 🅿 🍽
🍴 ⚙ 🛒 🅿 ✒ 🔆
Nearby Facilities ⌐ ✒ ⋔ ⋡
Nearest Town Lochmaben
Directions Turn right off the A709 Dumfries to Lockerbie road in Lochmaben, site is by the loch.
🚉 Lockerbie

MOFFAT

Camping & Caravanning Club Site, Hammerlands Farm, Moffat, Dumfries & Galloway, DG10 9QL
Tel: 01683 220436
www.campingandcaravanningclub.co.uk/moffat
Pitches For 🛆 ♡ ⛺ **Total** 180
Acreage 10 **Open** All Year
Site Level
Nearest Bus Stop (Miles) ¼
Set in the Scottish lowlands, the site is perfect for touring Scotland. The local village of Moffat has won awards for The Best Kept Village in Scotland. STB 4 Star Graded and AA 3 Pennants. Non members welcome. You can also call us on 0845 130 7633.
Facilities ⚙ ⚡ 🅗 🅤 🅿 ⊙ 🚻 🛒 🅿 🍽
🍴 ⚙ 🛆 🛒 🅿 🔆 ⚡ 🔆 📶
Nearby Facilities ⌐ ✒ Ⓤ ℛ
Nearest Town Moffat
Directions Take the Moffat sign off the A74, in 1 mile turn right by the Bank of Scotland, right again in 200 yards, signposted on the right, follow road round to the site.
🚉 Lockerbie

MONREITH

Knock School Caravan Park, Monreith, Newton Stewart, Dumfries & Galloway, DG8 8NJ
Tel: 01988 700414/700409
Email: pauline@knockschool.co.uk
www.knockschool.co.uk
Pitches For 🛆 ♡ ⛺ **Total** 15
Acreage 1 **Open** Easter **to** October
Access Good **Site** Lev/Slope
Nearest Bus Stop (Miles) Outside
Near sandy beaches and golf. Four hard standing pitches available.
Facilities ⚡ 🛆 🅗 🅿 ⊙ 🅢⚡ 🛒 🅿
Nearby Facilities ⌐ ✒ ℛ
Nearest Town Port William
Directions 3 miles south on the A747 at crossroads to golf course.

NEWTON STEWART

Creebridge Caravan Park, Minnigaff, Newton Stewart, Dumfries & Galloway, DG8 6AJ
Tel: 01671 402324
www.creebridgecaravanpark.com
Pitches For 🛆 ♡ ⛺ **Total** 16
Acreage 2 **Open** 01-Mar **to** 01-Nov
Access Good **Site** Level
Nearest Bus Stop (Miles) Outside
Quiet site with lovely walks. Close to a river and Galloway Forest.
Facilities ⚡ 🅗 🅤 🅿 ⊙ 🍴 🛒 🅿 🍽
🍴 ⚙ 🛆 🛒 🅿 🔆 ✒
Nearby Facilities ⌐ ✒ ⋔ ⋡ Ⓤ ⟑ ℛ ✗
Nearest Town Newton Stewart
🚉 Stranraer/Barrhill

NEWTON STEWART

Glentrool Holiday Park, Glentrool, Nr Newton Stewart, Dumfries & Galloway, DG8 6RN
Tel: 01671 840280
Email:
enquiries@glentroolholidaypark.co.uk
www.glentroolholidaypark.co.uk
Pitches For 🛆 ♡ ⛺ **Total** 14
Acreage 7½ **Open** March **to** October
Access Good **Site** Level
Nearest Bus Stop (Miles) Outside
On the edge of a forest, ideal touring.
Facilities ⚡ 🅗 🅤 🅿 ⊙ 🍴 🛒 🅿 🍽
🍴 ⚙ 🛆 🛒 🅿 🔆 ✒
Nearby Facilities ⌐ ✒ Ⓤ ℛ
Nearest Town Newton Stewart
Directions Situated off the A714, 9 miles north of Newton Stewart, ½ mile south of Glentrool Village.
🚉 Barrhill

PALNACKIE

Barlochan Caravan Park, Palnackie, By Castle Douglas, Dumfries & Galloway, DG7 1PF
Tel: 01556 600256
Email: info@gillespie-leisure.co.uk
www.gillespie-leisure.co.uk
Pitches For 🛆 ♡ ⛺ **Total** 20
Acreage 9 **Open** Easter **to** Oct
Access Good **Site** Level
Nearest Bus Stop (Miles) At Entrance
Games and TV rooms, outdoor heated pool, small shop, mini golf and play area. Pub and coarse fishing loch nearby.
Facilities ⚡ 🅤 🅿 🍴 🛒 🅿 🍽
🍴 ⚙ 🛆 🅃 🛒 ⋔ 🔆 Ⓤ
Nearby Facilities ⌐ ✒ ⋔ ⋡ Ⓤ ⟑
Nearest Town Dalbeattie
Directions Barlochan is 2½ miles south west of Dalbeattie on the A711, by the village of Palnackie.
🚉 Dumfries

PARTON

Loch Ken Holiday Park, Parton, Castle Douglas, Dumfries & Galloway, DG7 3NE
Tel: 01644 470282
Email: office@lochkenholidaypark.co.uk
www.lochkenholidaypark.co.uk
Pitches For 🛆 ♡ ⛺ **Total** 90
Acreage 15 **Open** 01-Mar **to** 10-Nov
Access Good **Site** Level
Nearest Bus Stop (Miles) Entrance
On a lochside for excellent fishing, water skiing, boating and sailing. Near an RSPB Nature Reserve.
Facilities ⚙ ⚡ 🅗 🅤 🅿 ⊙ 🍴 🛒 🅿 🍽
🅢⚡ ⚙ 🛆 🛒 ⋔ 🅿 🅿 ✒ 🔆 📶
Nearby Facilities ⌐ ✒ ⋔ ⋡ Ⓤ ⟑ ℛ ✗
Nearest Town Castle Douglas
Directions From Dumfries take the A75 towards Castle Douglas, then take the A713 towards Ayr and continue for 7 miles.
🚉 Dumfries

PORT LOGAN

New England Bay Caravan Club Site, Port Logan, Stranraer, Dumfries & Galloway, DG9 9NX
Tel: 01776 860275
www.caravanclub.co.uk
Pitches For ♡ ⛺ **Total** 159
Acreage 17 **Open** March **to** Nov
Access Good **Site** Level
Set on the edge of Luce Bay with sea views. Direct access to a shingle and sand beach. Boat storage on site. Near a sports centre, bowling green and swimming pool. Close to Mull of Galloway RSPB Sanctuary, Castle Kennedy, Ardwell House and Port Logan Botanic Gardens. Non members welcome. Booking essential.
Facilities ⚡ 🅗 🅤 🅿 ⊙ 🍴 🅿 🍽
🅢⚡ ⚙ 🛆 🛒 ⋔ 🅿 🅿 ✒ 🔆 📶
Nearby Facilities ⌐ ✒ ⋔ ⋡ Ⓤ
Nearest Town Stranraer
Directions Approaching Stranraer on the A77 follow signs for Portpatrick A77, approx. 1½ miles past Stranraer continue on the A716 sp Drummore. Site is 2½ miles past Ardwell on the left.
🚉 Stranraer

PORTPATRICK

Castle Bay Holiday & Residential Park, Portpatrick, Stranraer, Dumfries & Galloway, DG9 9AA
Tel: 01776 810462
Email: castle.bay@btconnect.com
www.lifestylehomesscotland.com
Pitches For 🛆 ♡ ⛺ **Total** 40
Access Good **Site** Lev/Slope
Nearest Bus Stop (Miles) ½
Fine views across the Irish Sea. Coastal walk to nearby Portpatrick.
Facilities ⚙ ⚡ 🅗 🅤 🅿 ⊙ 🍴 🅿 🍽
🅢⚡ ⚙ 🛆 🛒 ⋔ 🅿 🔆
Nearby Facilities ⌐ ✒ ⋔ Ⓤ ℛ
Nearest Town Stranraer
Directions From Stranraer take the A77 south. In Portpatrick turn first left after the 30mph sign, the Park is ¾ miles on the right after the railway bridge.
🚉 Stranraer

PORTPATRICK

Sunnymeade Caravan Park, Portpatrick, Nr Stranraer, Dumfries & Galloway, DG9 8LN
Tel: 01776 810293
Email: info-sunnymeade@btconnect.com
www.sunny-meade.co.uk
Pitches For 🛆 ♡ ⛺
Open May **to** September
Access Good **Site** Lev/Slope
Nearest Bus Stop (Miles) ¼

Near the beach, a golf course, bowling and fishing.
Facilities ⚑ 🅗 📹 🚿 ⌂ 🌅 ⊙ 🍴 🛒 ▦ 🍽
🚲 ⚓ 🚻 ⚖ ✦
Nearby Facilities ⌐ ✍ ⚓ ⚘ ∪ 🏇
Nearest Town Portpatrick
Directions A77 to Portpatrick. First left on entering village, park is ¼ mile on the left.
🚉 Stranraer

SOUTHERNESS

Southerness Holiday Village,
Southerness, By Dumfries, Dumfries & Galloway, DG2 8AZ
Tel: 0844 335 3731
Email:
touringandcamping@parkdeanholidays.com
www.parkdeantouring.com
Pitches For ▲ ⬛ 🚐 **Total** 100
Acreage 58 **Open** March to Oct
Access Good **Site** Level
Nearest Bus Stop (Miles) Outside
Beside 2 miles of sandy beach on the Solway Firth. Superb touring and camping facilities plus a choice of nearby golf courses. Indoor pool. FREE kids clubs and live family entertainment.
Facilities ⚑ 🅗 📹 🚿 ⌂ 🌅 ⊙ 🍴 🛒 ▦ 🍽
🚲 ⚓ 🚻 ✗ ⚖ 🍴 🏪 ⚘ 🕽 🛒 ▦ 🍽 ✦
Nearby Facilities ⌐ ✍ ⚓ ∪
Nearest Town Dumfries
Directions From Dumfries follow the Solway coast road through New Abbey and follow signs to Southerness Holiday Village for 10 miles.
🚉 Dumfries

STRANRAER

Aird Donald Caravan Park, Stranraer, Dumfries & Galloway, DG9 8RN
Tel: 01776 702025
Email: enquiries@aird-donald.co.uk
www.aird-donald.co.uk
Pitches For ▲ ⬛ 🚐 **Total** 75
Acreage 12 **Open** All Year
Access Good **Site** Level
Only 1 mile east of Stranraer town centre. Ideal touring. Tarmac hard standing for touring caravans in wet weather. Ideal site for ferry to Ireland. Good toilets and facilities. Leisure centre nearby.
Facilities ⚖ ⚑ 🅗 📹 🚿 ⌂ 🌅 ⊙ 🍴 🛒 ▦ 🍽
⊙ 🏪 🕽 🛒
Nearby Facilities ⌐ ✍ ⚓ ⚘ ∪ 🏇 🏊 ✗
Nearest Town Stranraer
Directions Off A75 entering Stranraer. Signposted.
🚉 Stranraer

STRANRAER

Ryan Bay Caravan Park, Innermessan, Stranraer, Dumfries & Galloway, DG9 8QP
Tel: 01776 889458
Email: ryanbay@hagansleisure.co.uk
www.hagansleisure.co.uk
Pitches For ⬛ 🚐 🚐 **Total** 40
Acreage 10 **Open** 01-Mar to 01-Nov
Access Good **Site** Level
Nearest Bus Stop (Miles) Entrance
Near the beach and alongside a lough, overlooking Ryan Bay. Great location for exploring Scotland.
Facilities ⚑ 🅗 📹 🚿 ⌂ 🌅 ⊙ 🍴 🛒 ▦ 🍽
⊙ ✗ 🏪 🚻 🏪 🕽 🛒 ▦ 🍽 ✦
Nearby Facilities ⌐ ✍
Nearest Town Stranraer
Directions From Stranraer take the A77 Cairnryan road, the Park is approx 3 miles on the left hand side.
🚉 Stranraer

WHITHORN

Castlewigg Holiday Park, Whithorn, Newton Stewart, Wigtownshire, DG8 8DL
Tel: 01988 500616
Email: mail@castlewiggcaravanpark.co.uk
www.castlewiggcaravanpark.co.uk
Pitches For ▲ ⬛ 🚐 **Total** 12
Acreage 5 **Open** March to October
Access Good **Site** Level
Nearest Bus Stop (Miles) Entrance
Beaches, fishing and golf all within a 10 mile radius. Ideal base for touring the Machars, the Rhins and the Galloway Hills.
Facilities ⚑ 🅗 📹 🚿 ⌂ 🌅 ⊙ 🍴 🛒 ▦ 🍽
🚻 ▦ 🌾
Nearby Facilities ⌐ ✍ ⚓ ✗
Nearest Town Whithorn
Directions 2 miles north of Whithorn on the A714.
🚉 Stranraer

EDINBURGH (City Of)

EDINBURGH

Drum Mohr Caravan Park, Levenhall, Musselburgh, Edinburgh, EH21 8JS
Tel: 0131 665 6867
Email: admin@drummohr.org
www.drummohr.org
Pitches For ▲ ⬛ 🚐 🚐 **Total** 120
Acreage 10 **Open** All Year
Access Good **Site** Lev/Slope
Nearest Bus Stop (Miles) ¼
Camping Bothy and Octolodges now available for hire by the night! Close to Edinburgh with an excellent bus service.
Facilities ⚖ ⚑ 🅗 📹 🚿 ⌂ 🌅 ⊙ 🍴 🛒 ▦ 🍽 ✦
Nearby Facilities ⌐ ✍ ⚓
Directions From south on the A1, take the A199 to Musselburgh then the B1361 and follow park signs. From west on the A1, exit at the Wallyford slip road and follow park signs.
🚉 Wallyford

EDINBURGH

Edinburgh Caravan Club Site, 35-37 Marine Drive, Edinburgh, City Of Edinburgh, EH4 5EN
Tel: 0131 312 6874
www.caravanclub.co.uk
Pitches For ▲ ⬛ 🚐 🚐 **Total** 197
Acreage 12 **Open** All Year
Access Good **Site** Level
Nearest Bus Stop (Miles) Outside
Situated on the Firth of Forth with easy access to Edinburgh. Visit the castle which houses the Scottish Crown Jewels, Holyroodhouse Palace, Princes Street Gardens, Edinburgh Zoo, Whisky Heritage Centre and Deep Sea World. Non members welcome. Booking essential.
Facilities ⚖ ⚑ 🅗 📹 🚿 ⌂ 🌅 ⊙ 🍴 🛒 🍽
🚲 ⊙ 🏪 🏪 🕽 🛒 ▦ 🌾 ✦
Nearby Facilities ⌐ ✍ ⚓ ✗
Nearest Town Edinburgh
Directions At end of M8 turn left onto A720, at Gogar rndbt (end of bypass) turn right sp City Centre A8. After ¼m turn left onto A902, at Barnton junc lights turn right, at Blackhall junc lights fork left into Telford Rd. At Crewe Toll rndbt turn left sp Davidsons Mains, at T junction lights turn right sp Grantown, at next T junction turn left, at rbt turn right in to Marine Drive. Site is ½ mile on left.
🚉 Edinburgh

EDINBURGH

Mortonhall Caravan & Camping Park, 38 Mortonhall Gate, Frogston Road, Edinburgh (City), EH16 6TJ
Tel: 0131 664 1533
Email: mortonhall@meadowhead.co.uk
www.meadowhead.co.uk
Pitches For ▲ ⬛ 🚐 🚐 **Total** 250
Open 13-Mar to 04-Jan
Access Good **Site** Level
Nearest Bus Stop (Miles) Outside
Set in 200 acres of parkland with views to the Pentland Hills. Arboretum with specimen trees. 15 minutes to the city centre.
Facilities ⚖ ⚑ 🅗 📹 🚿 ⌂ 🌅 ⊙ 🍴 🛒 ▦ 🍽
🚲 ⊙ 🏪 ✗ 🍴 🏪 ⚘ 🕽 🛒 ▦ 🍽 ✦
Nearby Facilities ⌐ ✍ ∪
Nearest Town Edinburgh
Directions Five minutes from the A720 city by-pass. Exit the by-pass at Straiton or Lothianburn junctions and follow signs for Mortonhall.
🚉 Edinburgh

FIFE

ELIE

Shell Bay Caravan Park, Elie, Fife, KY9 1HB
Tel: 01333 330283
Email: shellbay@abbeyfordscotland.com
www.abbeyfordscotland.com
Pitches For ▲ ⬛ 🚐 🚐 **Total** 120
Open 21-Mar to 31-Oct
Access Good **Site** Level
Nearest Bus Stop (Miles) Outside
Near the beach. Part of the Fife Coastal Path that also includes the Chain Walk between Shell Bay and Earlsferry.
Facilities ⚖ ⚑ 🅗 📹 🚿 ⌂ 🌅 ⊙ 🍴 🛒 🍽
🚲 ⊙ 🏪 ✗ 🍴 🏪 ⚘ 🕽 🛒 ▦ 🍽 🌾 ⚓
Nearby Facilities ⌐ ✍ ⚓ ⚘ ∪ 🏇 🏊 🏇
Nearest Town Elie
Directions From Leven take the A915 main coastal road, go through Lundin Links and Upper Largo for approx 2½ miles then follow signs for Elie (A917).

GLENROTHES

Balbirnie Park Caravan Club Site, Markinch, Glenrothes, Fife, KY7 6NR
Tel: 01592 759130
www.caravanclub.co.uk
Pitches For ▲ ⬛ 🚐 🚐 **Total** 76
Acreage 8 **Open** March to Nov
Access Good **Site** Lev/Slope
Nearest Bus Stop (Miles) ¼
Set in 400 acres of parkland. Many sporting facilities available in Glenrothes. Near to St. Andrews Golf Course, Royal Palace of Falkland, Deep Sea World Centre, The Secret Bunker, Tarvit House and Anstruther Fisheries Museum. Non members welcome. Booking essential.
Facilities ⚑ 🅗 📹 🍴 ⌂ 🍽
🚲 ⊙ 🏪 🏪 🕽 🛒 🌾
Nearby Facilities ⌐ ⚓ ✗
Directions From south on A90, after crossing bridge continue onto M90, leave at junction 2A and take A92 sp Glenrothes. Follow signs for Tay Road Bridge staying on A92, at end of dual carriageway turn right onto B9130, after ¾ miles turn left into Balbirnie Park.
🚉 Glenrothes

LEVEN

Monturpie Caravan Park, Monturpie, Upper Largo, By Leven, Fife, KY8 5QS
Tel: 01333 360254
Email: enquiries@monturpie.co.uk
www.monturpie.co.uk

Pitches For ⛺ 🚐 🚙 **Total** 28
Open 31-Mar **to** 31-Oct
Access Good **Site** Level
Nearest Bus Stop (Miles) Entrance
ADULTS ONLY SITE ideally situated for access to the East Neuk of Fife. Numerous golf courses in the area. Excellent for the Fife coastal path and St Andrews.
Facilities 🚿 ♿ 🔌 🚻 🅿 📶 ☕ 🍴 🛁 🛒 🍽️
🛗 🗙 🔥 🚮 🖬 🇮 🐕 🔺
Nearby Facilities 🏌️ 🚶 ⚓ 🎣 ∪ ℛ
Nearest Town Leven
Directions From Leven take the A915, when in Upper Largo follow signs for St Andrews, the Park is on the left after approx ¾ miles.
🚃 Markinch

LEVEN

Woodlands Gardens Caravan & Camping Park, Woodland Gardens, Blindwell Road, Lundin Links, Leven, Fife, KY8 5QG
Tel: 01333 360319
Email: enquiries@woodland-gardens.co.uk
www.woodland-gardens.co.uk
Pitches For ⛺ 🚐 🚙 **Total** 20
Acreage 1 **Open** April **to** October
Access Good **Site** Level
Nearest Bus Stop (Miles) ½
Small, exclusive, quiet site. Adults preferred. Ideal for golfing, walking or relaxing around East Fife. Close to a sandy beach. Within easy reach of Edinburgh.
Facilities 🚿 🔌 🚻 🅿 📶 ☕ 🍴 🛁 🛒
🇮 ☐ 🔥 🖬 🔺
Nearby Facilities 🏌️ 🚶 ⚓ 🎣 ∪ ℛ
Nearest Town Leven
Directions On the A915 Kirkcaldy, Leven and St. Andrews road, 3 miles east of Leven at the east end of Lundin Links turn north, signposted.
🚃 Kirkcaldy

ST. ANDREWS

Cairnsmill Caravan Park, Largo Road, St Andrews, Fife, KY16 8NN
Tel: 01334 473604
Email: cairnsmill@aol.com
Pitches For ⛺ 🚐 🚙 🚙 **Total** 40
Open April **to** Oct **Access** Good
Nearest Bus Stop (Miles) Entrance
Ideal for golf and near a beach.
Facilities 🚿 🔌 🚻 🅿 📶 ☕ 🍴 🛁 🛒 🍽️
🇮 ☐ 🛒 🗙 🔥 🇮 🏊 🔺 🖬 🍴 🔺
📶
Nearby Facilities 🏌️ 🚶 ⚓ 🎣 ∪ ℛ
Nearest Town St Andrews
Directions 1 mile west of St Andrews on the A915.
🚃 Leuchars

ST. ANDREWS

Craigtoun Meadows Holiday Park, Mount Melville, St Andrews, Fife, KY16 8PQ
Tel: 01334 475959
Email: craigtoun@aol.com
www.craigtounmeadows.co.uk
Pitches For ⛺ 🚐 🚙 🚙 **Total** 58
Open 15-Mar **to** 31-Oct
Access Good **Site** Level
Nearest Bus Stop (Miles) Outside
Only 1½ miles from beaches and golf course. Large childrens play area also with putting green, football pitch and Flying Fox slide. Woodland walks.
Facilities 🚿 🔌 🚻 🅿 📶 ☕ 🍴 🛁 🛒 🍽️
🇮 ☐ 🛒 🗙 🔥 🇮 🏊 🖬 🔺
Nearby Facilities 🏌️ 🚶 ⚓ 🎣 ∪ 🐕 ℛ 🔺
Nearest Town St Andrews
Directions 1½ miles south west of St Andrews town centre. Head westwards from West Port along Hepburn Gardens.
🚃 Leuchars

ST. MONANS

St. Monans Caravan Park, St Monans, Fife, KY10 2DN
Tel: 01333 730778
Pitches For ⛺ 🚐 🚙 **Total** 18
Acreage 1 **Open** 21-Mar **to** October
Access Good **Site** Level
Nearest Bus Stop (Miles) Outside
Small, quiet park, near the sea and small villages with harbours.
Facilities 🚿 🔌 🚻 🅿 📶 ☕ 🍴 🛁 🛒 🍽️
🇮 🇮 🛒 🔥 🖬 🍴 🔺 🔺
Nearby Facilities 🏌️ 🚶 ⚓ 🎣 ∪ 🐕 ℛ
Nearest Town St Andrews
Directions Park is on the A917 at east end of St. Monans.
🚃 Leuchars

HIGHLAND
ACHARACLE

Resipole Holiday Park, Loch Sunart, Acharacle, Highlands, PH36 4HX
Tel: 01967 431235
Email: info@resipole.co.uk
www.resipole.co.uk
Pitches For ⛺ 🚐 🚙 **Total** 60
Acreage 6 **Open** April **to** October
Access Good **Site** Level
Loch side, roomy site with scenic views. Central for touring the area. On site art gallery, studios and painting holidays.
Facilities 🚿 🔌 🚻 🅿 📶 ☕ 🍴 🛁 🛒 🍽️
🇮 🇮 ☐ 🛒 🔥 🖬 🇮 🔺 🔺 🔧
Nearby Facilities 🚶 ⚓ 🔺
Nearest Town Fort William
Directions From Fort William take the A82 south for 8 miles, across Corran Ferry, then take the A861 to Strontian and Salen. Site is 7¼ miles west of Strontian on the roadside.
🚃 Fort William

BALLACHULISH

Glencoe Camping & Caravanning Club Site, Glencoe, Ballachulish, Argyll, Highlands, PH49 4LA
Tel: 01855 811397
www.campingandcaravanningclub.co.uk/glencoe
Pitches For ⛺ 🚐 🚙 **Total** 120
Acreage 40 **Open** 29-Mar **to** 05-Nov
Access Good **Site** Lev/Slope
Surrounded by mountains, this quiet site is situated next to forests. Non members welcome. You can also call us on 0845 130 7633.
Facilities 🚿 🔌 🚻 🅿 📶 ☕ 🍴 🛁 🛒 🍽️
🇮 ☐ 🛒 🔥 🖬 🔺
Nearby Facilities 🚶 🔺 🔺
Nearest Town Fort William
Directions On the A82, 1 mile south east of Glencoe Village, follow signs for Glencoe Visitor Centre.
🚃 Fort William

BALMACARA

Reraig Caravan Site, Balmacara, Kyle of Lochalsh, Highlands, IV40 8DH
Tel: 01599 566215
Email: warden@reraig.com
www.reraig.com
Pitches For ⛺ 🚐 🚙 **Total** 45
Acreage 2 **Open** May **to** Sept
Access Good **Site** Level
Forest walks and a hotel adjacent to the site. Dishwashing sinks and hairdryers. No bookings. No large tents. Not suitable for units longer than 7½ metres. No awnings during July and August.
Facilities 🔌 🚻 🅿 📶 ☕ 🍴 🛁 🛒 🖬 🍴 🔺 📶
Nearest Town Kyle of Lochalsh

Directions On the A87, 1¾ miles west of junction with A890. 4 miles east of the bridge to the Isle of Skye.
🚃 Kyle of Lochalsh

BETTYHILL

Craigdhu Caravans, Bettyhill, Nr Thurso, Highlands, KW14 7SP
Tel: 01641 521273
Pitches For ⛺ 🚐 🚙 **Total** 90
Acreage 4½ **Open** April **to** October
Access Good **Site** Lev/Slope
Nearest Bus Stop (Miles) ¼
Near beautiful beaches and a river for fishing. Scenic views. Ideal touring. Rare plants. New swimming pool, telephone, cafe/restaurant and licensed club nearby.
Facilities 🔌 🚻 🅿 📶 ☕ 🍴 🛒 🇮 🇮 🔥 🖬
Nearby Facilities 🚶 ⚓ 🐕 🔺
Nearest Town Thurso
Directions Main Thurso/Tongue road.
🚃 Kinbrace

BRORA

Dalchalm Caravan Club Site, Brora, Highlands, KW9 6LP
Tel: 01408 621479
www.caravanclub.co.uk
Pitches For ⛺ 🚐 🚙 **Total** 52
Acreage 5 **Open** April **to** Oct
Access Good **Site** Level
300 yards from a safe, sandy beach where Arctic Tern nest and you can see seals and dolphins. Play golf directly from the site. Many picturesque lochs and mountains nearby. Close to the Clynelish Distillery. Non members welcome. Booking essential.
Facilities 🚿 🔌 🚻 🅿 📶 ☕ 🍴 🛁 🍽️
🇮 ☐ 🛒 🔥 🔺
Nearby Facilities 🏌️ 🚶
Nearest Town Brora
Directions From south on the A9, in Brora 1½ miles past the bridge, ignore Dalchalm sign and turn right at brown caravan sign. After 350 yards at the T-junction turn left, site is 150 yards on the right.
🚃 Brora

BRORA

Green Park Caravan & Camp Site, 58 Dalchalm, Brora, Highlands, KW9 6LP
Tel: 01408 621513
Pitches For ⛺ 🚐 🚙 🚙 **Total** 35
Acreage 2½ **Open** April **to** Oct
Access Good **Site** Sloping
Nearest Bus Stop (Miles) ¼
150 yards from a sandy beach and close to the River Brora which is a popular river with anglers.
Facilities 🔌 🚻 🅿 📶 ☕ 🍴 🍽️
🇮 🇮 🛒 🔥 🖬 🇮 🔺
Nearby Facilities 🏌️ 🚶 ⚓ 🎣 ∪ ℛ 🔺
Nearest Town Brora
Directions From Brora take the A9 north for 1½ miles, turn right at sign for Dalchalm.
🚃 Brora

CANNICH

Cannich Caravan Park, Cannich, By Beauly, Inverness-Shire, IV4 7LN
Tel: 01456 415364
Email: enquiries@highlandcamping.co.uk
www.highlandcamping.co.uk
Pitches For ⛺ 🚐 🚙 **Total** 43
Acreage 6 **Open** March **to** Oct
Access Good **Site** Level
Nearest Bus Stop (Miles) Outside
Set in the heart of Strathglass, at the head of Glen Affric Nature Reserve. Superb highland and lowland, walking and cycling. Disabled shower room. Also open winter by arrangement only.

Facilities ♿ ⚏ 🚻 🆚 🚿 📶 ☉ ⛽ ⚑ 🔌 ⛽
🅿 🛒 🍴 🏕 ♨ ⚓ ✪ 🔌 📶 ⛽ 🔆 📶
Nearby Facilities ⚑ 🚴 ⛵
Nearest Town Drumnadrochit
Directions From Inverness take the A82 towards Fort William, at Drumnadrochit take the A831 signposted Cannich and Strathglass.
🚆 Beauly

CULLODEN

Culloden Moor Caravan Club Site, Newlands, Culloden Moor, Inverness, Highlands, IV2 5EF
Tel: 01463 790625
www.caravanclub.co.uk
Pitches For ⛺ 🚐 🚎 **Total** 97
Acreage 7 **Open** March **to** Jan
Access Good **Site** Lev/Slope
Nearest Bus Stop (Miles) Outside
Breathtaking views over the Nairn Valley. 1 mile from the Culloden battlefield. Only 6 miles from Inverness with its superb shopping, Whisky trails and Loch Ness. Basic provisions available on site. Non members welcome. Booking essential.
Facilities ♿ ⚏ 🚻 🆚 🚿 ☉ ⛽
🅿 🛒 🍴 🔌 ⛽ 🔆
Nearby Facilities 🚴
Nearest Town Inverness/Culloden
Directions From south on the A9 turn off signposted Hilton (ignoring previous signs for Culloden Moor), at roundabout turn left onto the B9006, site is 5¼ miles on the left.
🚆 Inverness

DINGWALL

Camping & Caravanning Club Site, Jubilee Park Road, Dingwall, Highlands, IV15 9QZ
Tel: 01349 862236
www.campingandcaravanningclub.co.uk/dingwall
Pitches For ⛺ 🚐 🚎 **Total** 85
Acreage 6½ **Open** 29-Mar **to** 05-Nov
Access Difficult **Site** Level
Nearest Bus Stop (Miles) ½
Central for touring the Highlands. Train and ferry links to the Isle of Skye. Close to the city of Inverness. STB 4 Star Graded and AA 3 Pennants. Non members welcome. You can also call us on 0845 130 7633.
Facilities ♿ ⚏ 🚻 🆚 🚿 ☉ ⛽ ⚑
🅿 🛒 🍴 🔌 ⛽ 📶
Nearby Facilities ⚑ 🚴
Nearest Town Dingwall
Directions From the northwest on the A862 in Dingwall turn right into Hill Street (past the Shell Filling Station), turn right into High Street then turn first left after the railway bridge, site is ahead.
🚆 Dingwall

DORNIE

Ardelve, Dornie, Kyle, Ross-Shire, IV40 8DY
Tel: 01599 555231
www.ardelvecaravanandcampingpark.co.uk
Pitches For ⛺ 🚐 🚎 **Total** 35
Open Easter **to** October
Access Good **Site** Lev/Slope
Nearest Bus Stop (Miles) ¼
Overlooking a loch with views of Eilean Donan Castle. Static caravans for hire.
Facilities ⚏ 🚻 🆚 🚿 ☉ ⛽ 🔌
Nearby Facilities 🚴 ⚓ 🎣 ⛵
Nearest Town Dornie
Directions Just off the A87.
🚆 Kyle

DORNOCH

Dornoch Caravan & Camping Park, The Links, Dornoch, Highlands, IV25 3LX
Tel: 01862 810423
Email: info@dornochcaravans.co.uk
www.dornochcaravans.co.uk
Pitches For ⛺ 🚐 🚎 **Total** 130
Acreage 25 **Open** April **to** 30-Oct
Access Good **Site** Level
Nearest Bus Stop (Miles) ¼
Beach, championship golf course, cathedral town. Scenic views, ideal touring.
Facilities ♿ ⚏ 🚻 🆚 🚿 ☉ ⛽ ⚑ ⛽
🅿 🛒 🍴 🍴 ♨ ⚓ 🔌 ⛽ 🔆 📶
Nearby Facilities ⚑ 🚴 ⛵ 🎣
Nearest Town Dornoch
Directions From A9, 6 miles north of Tain, turn right into Dornoch. Turn right at the bottom of the square.
🚆 Tain

DORNOCH

Grannie's Heilan' Hame Holiday Park, Embo, Dornoch, Highlands, IV25 3QD
Tel: 0844 335 3731
Email:
touringandcamping@parkdeanholidays.com
www.parkdeantouring.com
Pitches For ⛺ 🚐 🚎 **Total** 160
Acreage 60 **Open** March **to** Oct
Access Good **Site** Level
Nearest Bus Stop (Miles) Outside
Overlooking Embo Beach and close to the village of Dornoch with its Heritage Centre. Dial-A-Bus service. Indoor pool. FREE kids clubs and live family entertainment.
Facilities ⚏ 🆚 🚿 ☉ ⛽ ⚑ ⛽
🅿 🛒 🍴 🍴 🏕 ♨ ⚓ 🔌 ⛽ 🔆 📶
Nearby Facilities ⚑ 🚴 ⛵
Nearest Town Dornoch
Directions Take the A9 north from Inverness. After approx. 45 minutes turn right onto the A949 to Dornoch and Embo, after 3 miles turn right for Embo.
🚆 Tain

DRUMNADROCHIT

Borlum Farm Caravan Park, Borlum Farm, Drumnadrochit, Highlands, IV63 6XN
Tel: 01456 450892
Email: info@borlum.com
www.borlum.com
Pitches For ⛺ 🚐 🚎 **Total** 25
Acreage 2 **Open** All Year
Access Good **Site** Lev/Slope
Nearest Bus Stop (Miles) ½
BHS Approved riding centre on site.
Facilities ⚏ 🚻 🆚 🚿 ☉ ⛽ 🔌 ⛽
🅿 🔌 🔆
Nearby Facilities ⚑ 🚴 ⛵
Nearest Town Inverness
Directions From Inverness take the A82 towards Fort William. The Park is approx. ½ a mile on the right hand side after Lewiston Village.
🚆 Inverness

DUNBEATH

Inver Caravan Park, Houstry Road, Dunbeath, Highlands, KW6 6EH
Tel: 01593 731441
Email: rhonagwillim@yahoo.co.uk
www.inver-caravan-park.co.uk
Pitches For ⛺ 🚐 🚎 **Total** 15
Acreage 1 **Open** All Year
Access Good **Site** Sloping
Nearest Bus Stop (Miles) ½
Quiet small site. Excellent location for exploring the far north of Scotland, walking and cycling.

Facilities ♿ ⚏ 🚻 🆚 🚿 ☉ ⛽ ⚑ ⛽
🅿 🍴 🍴 🔌 ⛽ 📶
Nearby Facilities ⚑ 🚴 🎣 ⛵
Nearest Town Wick
Directions Adjacent to the A9, just north of Dunbeath. Take the turning signposted Houstry 3, Park entrance is 40 metres on the left hand side. 21 miles south west of Wick and 16 miles north east of Helmsdale.
🚆 Helmsdale

DUNDONNELL

Badrallach Bothy & Campsite, Croft 9, Badrallach, Dundonnell, Highlands, IV23 2QP
Tel: 01854 633281
Email: mail@badrallach.com
www.badrallach.com
Pitches For ⛺ 🚐 🚎 **Total** 15
Acreage 1 **Open** All Year
Access Poor **Site** Level
Lochshore site on a working croft, overlooking Anteallach on the Scoraig Peninsular. Bothy, peat stove. Otters, porpoises, Golden Eagles and wild flowers galore. Total peace and quiet - Perfect! Caravans by prior booking only. Airstream for hire. STB 4 Star Graded.
Facilities ⚏ 🚻 🆚 🚿 ☉ ⛽ 🍴 ⚓ 🔌 ⛽ 🔌
Nearby Facilities 🚴 ⚓ 🎣 ⛵
Nearest Town Ullapool/Gairloch
Directions Off the A832, 1 mile east of the Dundonnell Hotel take a left turn onto a single track road to Badrallach, 7 miles to lochshore site.
🚆 Garve/Inverness

DUNDONNELL

Northern Lights Campsite, Croft 9, Badcaul, Dundonnell, Highlands, IV23 2QY
Tel: 01697 371379
Pitches For ⛺ 🚐 🚎 **Total** 12
Acreage 2 **Open** April **to** August
Access Good **Site** Lev/Slope
Nearest Bus Stop (Miles) ½
Overlooking Loch Broom and in close proximity of several Muras.
Facilities ⚏ 🚻 🆚 🚿 ☉ ⛽ 🅿 🔌
Nearby Facilities 🚴 🎣 ⛵
Nearest Town Ullapool
Directions On the A832, 19 miles south west of the junction with the A835 and 12 miles south east of Ullapool.
🚆 Garve

DURNESS

Sango Sands Caravan & Camping Site, Durness, Sutherland, Highlands, IV27 4PP
Tel: 01971 511262/511222
Email: keith.durness@btinternet.com
Pitches For ⛺ 🚐 🚎 **Total** 82
Acreage 12 **Open** April **to** 15-Oct
Access Good **Site** Level
Nearest Bus Stop (Miles) ¼
Overlooking Sango Bay.
Facilities ⚏ 🚻 🆚 🚿 ☉ ⛽ ⚑ ⛽
🅿 🛒 ⚏ ☉ 🍴 🏕 ♨ 🔌 🔆
Nearby Facilities ⚑ 🚴 ⚓ 🎣 ⛵
Nearest Town Durness
Directions On the A838 in the centre of Durness Village.
🚆 Lairg

DUROR

Achindarroch Touring Park, Duror, Highlands, PA38 4BS
Tel: 01631 740329
Email: stay@achindarrochtp.co.uk
www.achindarrochtp.co.uk
Pitches For ⛺ 🚐 🚎
Acreage 5 **Open** 24-Jan **to** 16-Jan
Access Good **Site** Level
Nearest Bus Stop (Miles) ¼

Friendly, family run site in a quiet, well sheltered, picturesque location at the foot of Glen Duror. Camping Pods available for hire.
Facilities ⚅ ℐ ♨ ⌦ ☏ ⌂ ☉ ⛶ ⚐ 🗑 ☎ 🏪 🌀 ⊟ ⊡ 🖵 ☼ ❆ ⚓ 🛜
Nearby Facilities ⌖ ✎ ⚓ ↻ ♪ ♞ ⚑
Nearest Town Fort William
Directions Off the A828 north of Appin and south of Fort William and Ballachulish, signposted.
⚡ Fort William

EDINBANE

Skye Camping & Caravanning Club Site, Borve, Arnisort, Edinbane, Portree, Isle of Skye, Highlands, IV51 9PS
Tel: 01470 582230
www.campingandcaravanningclub.co.uk/skye
Pitches For ▲ ⊞ ⊟ **Total** 105
Acreage 7 **Open** 29-Mar **to** 05-Nov
Access Good **Site** Lev/Slope
Nearest Bus Stop (Miles) Outside
Situated on a working croft with Highland cows, sheep, ducks and chickens. Within easy reach of a variety of attractions including boat trips and a distillery. Restaurants and pubs close by. Camping Pods available for hire. Non members welcome. You can also call us on 0845 130 7633.
Facilities ⚅ ℐ ♨ ⌦ ☏ ⌂ ☉ ⛶ ⚐ 🗑 ☎ 🏪 🌀 ⊟ ⊡ 🖵 ✎ ⚓
Nearby Facilities ✎ ⚓
Nearest Town Inverness
Directions From Inverness head NW on A82 towards Fairfield Lane. At Telford Street roundabout take the third exit onto A82, go over 3 roundabouts and at Longman roundabout take the first exit onto A9. Do a slight left at Millbank, at the roundabout take second exit, turn left, turn left again, then turn left again.
⚡ Kyle of Lochalsh

EVANTON

Black Rock Caravan Park, Balconie Street, Evanton, Highlands, IV16 9UN
Tel: 01349 830917
Email: enquiries@blackrockscotland.co.uk
www.blackrockscotland.co.uk
Pitches For ▲ ⊞ ⊟ **Total** 56
Acreage 4½ **Open** April **to** Oct
Access Good **Site** Level
Nearest Bus Stop (Miles) Outside
Central location with a river beside the site. Ideal for fishing and forest walks.
Facilities ⚅ ℐ ♨ ⌦ ☏ ⌂ ☉ ⛶ ⚐ 🗑 ☎ 🏪 🌀 ⊟ ⊡ 🖵 ☼
Nearby Facilities ⌖ ✎ ↻ ♪ ♞
Nearest Town Dingwall
Directions From Dingwall take the A862 then the A9 to Evanton, approx 5 miles.
⚡ Dingwall

FORT WILLIAM

Glen Nevis Caravan & Camping Park, Glen Nevis, Fort William, Highlands, PH33 6SX
Tel: 01397 702191
Email: holidays@glen-nevis.co.uk
www.glen-nevis.co.uk
Pitches For ▲ ⊞ ⊟ **Total** 380
Acreage 30 **Open** 15-Mar **to** 07-Nov
Access Good **Site** Level
Spectacularly located at the foot of Britains highest mountain, Ben Nevis. Excellent for touring and walking the West Highlands.
Facilities ⚅ ℐ ♨ ⌦ ☏ ⌂ ☉ ⛶ ⚐ 🗑 ☎ 🏪 🌀 ⊟ ⊡ 🖵
Nearby Facilities ⌖ ✎ ⚓ ↻ ♪ ♞
Directions From North or South on the A82, turn at small roundabout signed for Glen Nevis, site is 2 miles into glen.
⚡ Fort William

FORT WILLIAM

Linnhe Lochside Holidays, Corpach, Fort William, Highlands, PH33 7NL
Tel: 01397 772376
Email: relax@linnhe-lochside-holidays.co.uk
www.linnhe-lochside-holidays.co.uk
Pitches For ▲ ⊞ ⊟ **Total** 65
Acreage 14 **Open** Easter **to** 31-Oct
Access Good **Site** Level
Magnificent scenery from this top quality 5 Star Park with a private beach and boat slipway. Mains serviced pitches available. Toddlers play room. Holiday chalets and caravans for hire.
Facilities ℐ ♨ ⌦ ☏ ⌂ ☉ ⛶ ⚐ 🗑 ☎ 🏪 🌀 ⊟ ⊡ 🖵 ☼
Nearby Facilities ⌖ ✎ ⚓ ↻ ♪ ♞
Nearest Town Fort William
Directions On the A830, 1 mile west of Corpach village, 5 miles from Fort William.
⚡ Corpach

FORTROSE

Fortrose Caravan Park, Wester Greengates, Fortrose, Highlands, IV10 8RX
Tel: 01381 621927
Email: fortrosecaravanpark@hotmail.co.uk
Pitches For ▲ ⊞ ⊟ **Total** 50
Acreage 4 **Open** 01-Apr **to** 31-Oct
Access Good **Site** Level
Nearest Bus Stop (Miles) ¼
On the shores of the Black Isle, overlooking Moray Firth. Near to Chanonry Point, one of the best places to view bottlenose dolphins.
Facilities ℐ ♨ ⌦ ☏ ⌂ ☉ ⛶ ⚐ 🗑 ☎ 🏪 🌀 ⊟ ⊡ 🖵 ☼
Nearby Facilities ⌖ ✎ ⚓ ↻ ♪ ♞
Nearest Town Inverness
Directions From the A9 follow signs to Fortrose. Turn right into Academy Street and the Park is on the right hand side.
⚡ Inverness

FORTROSE

Rosemarkie Camping & Caravanning Club Site, Ness Road East, Rosemarkie, Fortrose, Highlands, IV10 8SE
Tel: 01381 621117
www.campingandcaravanningclub.co.uk/rosemarkie
Pitches For ▲ ⊞ ⊟ **Total** 60
Acreage 4 **Open** 29-Mar **to** 05-Nov
Access Good **Site** Level
Nearest Bus Stop (Miles) 1
On the shores of the Black Isle, overlooking Moray and Cromarty Firths. The spectacular coastline is famous for its bottle nosed dolphins. STB 4 Star Graded, AA 3 Pennants and Loo of the Year Award. Non members welcome. You can also call us on 0845 130 7633.
Facilities ⚅ ℐ ♨ ⌦ ☏ ⌂ ☉ ⛶ ⚐ 🗑 ☎ 🏪 🌀 ⊟ ⊡ 🖵
Nearby Facilities ⌖ ✎ ♞ ♪
Nearest Town Rosemarkie
Directions From the A9 at Tore roundabout take the A832 Fortrose to Cromarty road. Go through Avoch, in Fortrose turn right at the Police House into Ness Road signposted golf course and leisure centre. Turn first left and the site is 400 yards.
⚡ Inverness

GAIRLOCH

Gairloch Caravan & Camping Holiday Park, Strath, Gairloch, Highlands, IV21 2BX
Tel: 01445 712373
Email: info@gairlochcaravanpark.com
www.gairlochcaravanpark.com
Pitches For ▲ ⊞ ⊟ **Total** 75
Acreage 6 **Open** April **to** End Oct
Access Good **Site** Level
Near the beach. In the village centre for shops, hotels and restaurants. AA 3 Pennants.
Facilities ℐ ♨ ⌦ ☏ ⌂ ☉ ⛶ ⚐ 🗑 ☎ 🏪 🌀 ⊟ ⊡ 🖵 ☼ 🛜
Nearby Facilities ⌖ ✎ ⚓ ↻ ♪ ♞
Nearest Town Gairloch
Directions Turn off the A832 at Auchtercairn onto the B8021. In approx. ½ mile turn right by Millcroft Hotel then immediately right into the site.
⚡ Achnasheen

GLENCOE

Invercoe Caravan & Camping Park, Glencoe, Ballachulish, Highlands, PH49 4HP
Tel: 01855 811210
Email: holidays@invercoe.co.uk
www.invercoe.co.uk
Pitches For ▲ ⊞ ⊟ **Total** 60
Acreage 5 **Open** All Year

SCOTLAND

Access Good **Site** Level
Nearest Bus Stop (Miles) ¼
Lochside site with beautiful scenery. Slipway access to the loch. Ideal centre for touring West Highlands. Wi-Fi available for a charge.
Facilities ⚓ ⚒ 🅗 🆄🅱 🍴 🏧 ☺🍴 ⚓ 🔋 ⚓ 📶
🍴 🐕 🐾 🗑 🐟 🏕
Nearby Facilities 🐾 ⚓ 🏕
Nearest Town Fort William
Directions Heading north on the A82 turn right at Glencoe crossroads onto the B863.
⚏ Fort William

GLENCOE

Red Squirrel Campsite, Leacantuim Farm, Glencoe, Highlands, PH49 4HX
Tel: 01855 811256
www.redsquirrelcampsite.co.uk
Pitches For ▲
Acreage 20 **Open** All Year **Site** Lev/Slope
Casual and very different Two Star Site in the centre of the mountains. River for swimming and fishing (salmon, permit, must bring your own rods). Meter showers. Kids under 12 years £1, adults £9. Gazebos during July and August for £7 per night. Group discounts available.
Facilities 🅗 🆄🅱 🍴 ☺🍴 🔋 🛒 🍴🐾
Nearby Facilities 🐾 ⚓ 🚤 🎣 🏕 🏕
Nearest Town Fort William
Directions Turn off the main A82 into Glencoe Village, turn up main street, go over the humpback bridge and park is 1½ miles.
⚏ Fort William

GRANTOWN-ON-SPEY

Grantown-on-Spey Caravan Park, Seafield Avenue, Grantown-on-Spey, Highlands, PH26 3JQ
Tel: 01479 872474
Email: warden@caravanscotland.com
www.caravanscotland.com
Pitches For ▲ ⚏ ⚏ ⚏ **Total** 160
Acreage 23 **Open** 05-Jan **to** 31-Oct
Access Good **Site** Lev/Slope
Nearest Bus Stop (Miles) ¼
A bird lovers mecca and a dogs paradise! Easy level walk into town. Salmon fishing on the River Spey. Ideal base for visiting all of Highlands attractions.
Facilities ⚓ ⚒ 🅕 🅗 🆄🅱 🍴 ☺🍴 ⚓ 🔋 ⚓ 📶
🍴 🔋 🛒 🏕 🍴🐾 🗑 🐟 🔆 🐾 📶
Nearby Facilities 🐾 ⚓ 🏕
Nearest Town Grantown-on-Spey
Directions From Aviemore take the A9, approx. 1½ miles past Aviemore turn right onto the A95. When in Grantown high street go through the traffic lights and turn left by the Bank of Scotland, site is ¼ of a mile on the right.
⚏ Aviemore

INVERGARRY

Faichemard Farm Caravan & Camping Park, Faichemard Farm, Invergarry, Highlands, PH35 4HG
Tel: 01809 501314
Email: dgrant@faichemard-caravancamping.co.uk
www.faichemard-caravancamping.co.uk
Pitches For ▲ ⚏ ⚏ **Total** 35
Acreage 10 **Open** April **to** October
Access Good **Site** Lev/Slope
Nearest Bus Stop (Miles) 1
ADULTS ONLY SITE with plenty of space and quiet. Ideal for hill walking and bird watching. Pitch price £6-£12. Every pitch has its own picnic table.
Facilities 🅕 🅗 🆄🅱 🍴 ☺🍴 ⚓ 🔋 ⚓ 🛒🍴🐾🗑🅰
Nearby Facilities 🐾 ⚓ 🚤 🐾 🎣 🏕
Nearest Town Fort William
Directions Take A82 to Invergarry (25 miles) travel west on A87 for 1 mile, take side road on right at sign for Faichem, proceed to the sign for A & D Grant Faichemard Farm.
⚏ Spean Bridge

INVERMORISTON

Loch Ness Holiday Park, Invermoriston, Highlands, IV63 7YE
Tel: 01320 351207
Email: enquiries@lochnessholidaypark.co.uk
www.lochnessholidaypark.co.uk
Pitches For ⚏ ⚏ ⚏ **Total** 50
Open 01-Feb **to** 31-Oct
Access Good **Site** Lev/Slope
Nearest Bus Stop (Miles) 1
Lochside location with a stoney beach and small jetties. Licensed bar during peak season.
Facilities 🅕 🅗 🆄🅱 🍴 ☺🍴 ⚓ 🔋 ⚓
🔋 ☺ 🛒 🍴🐾🗑🅰🔋 🍴
Nearby Facilities 🐾 ⚓ 🚤 🐾 🏕
Nearest Town Fort Augustus
Directions 5 miles west of Fort Augustus on the A82.
⚏ Inverness

INVERNESS

Auchnahillin Caravan & Camping Park, Daviot East, Inverness, Highlands, IV2 5XQ
Tel: 01463 772286
Email: info@auchnahillin.co.uk
www.auchnahillin.co.uk
Pitches For ▲ ⚏ ⚏ **Total** 100
Acreage 10 **Open** April **to** Oct
Access Good **Site** Level
Nearest Bus Stop (Miles) Outside
Ideal touring area for the Highlands, many attractions within easy reach.
Facilities ⚓ ⚒ 🅗 🆄🅱 🍴 ☺🍴 ⚓ 🔋 ⚓ 📶
🍴 🔋 🛒 🏕 🍴🐾 🗑 🐟

Nearest Town Inverness
Directions Approx. 8 miles south of Inverness take the turning onto the B9154 towards Daviot East and Moy.
⚏ Inverness

INVERNESS

MacDonalds Bught Caravan & Tent Park, Bught Lane, Inverness, Highlands, IV3 5SR
Tel: 01463 236920
Email: john@invernesscaravanpark.com
www.invernesscaravanpark.com
Pitches For ▲ ⚏ ⚏ ⚏ **Total** 140
Acreage 4¾ **Open** Easter **to** 01-Oct
Access Good **Site** Level
Nearest Bus Stop (Miles) Outside
Alongside the River Ness and canal, and next to an Aquadome. Just a 20 minute walk into the town centre. Kitchen shed in the tent area. Ice rink and childrens park in the immediate vacinity and two sports stadiums.
Facilities 🅕 🅗 🆄🅱 🍴 ☺🍴 ⚓ 🔋 ⚓ 📶
🔋 🍴🐾 🔋 ☺ 🛒 ✖🍴🗑
Nearby Facilities 🐾 ⚓ 🚤 🐾 🏕 🐾 🏕
Nearest Town Inverness
Directions Situated inside Inverness city limits on the A82 Loch Ness road, beside the canal bridge and Aquadome.
⚏ Inverness

JOHN O'GROATS

John O'Groats Caravan & Camping Site, John O'Groats, Nr Wick, Highlands, KW1 4YR
Tel: 01955 611329
Email: info@johnogroatscampsite.co.uk
www.johnogroatscampsite.co.uk
Pitches For ▲ ⚏ ⚏ **Total** 90
Acreage 4 **Open** April **to** Sept
Access Good **Site** Level
Nearest Bus Stop (Miles) Outside
On sea shore with clear view of Orkney Islands. Day trips to Orkney by passenger ferry, jetty nearby. Hotel and snack bar within 150 yards. Cliff scenery and sea birds 1½ miles. STB 3 Star Graded.
Facilities ⚓ ⚒ 🅗 🆄🅱 🍴 ☺🍴 ⚓ 🔋 ⚓
🔋 🍴🐾 🛒 🗑🅰
Nearby Facilities 🐾 ⚓
Nearest Town John O'Groats
Directions End of A99 beside last house.
⚏ Wick

KINLOCHEWE

Kinlochewe Caravan Club Site, Kinlochewe, Achnasheen, Highlands, IV22 2PA
Tel: 01445 760239
www.caravanclub.co.uk
Pitches For ⚏ ⚏ **Total** 56
Acreage 5 **Open** March **to** Oct

SCOTLAND

Access Good **Site** Level
Peaceful location at the foot of Ben Eighe, surrounded by lochs, woodland and mountains. Close to Victoria Falls and Inverewe Gardens. Butcher calls into site twice a week. Adjacent to a service station and theres a general shop and cafe in the village. Non members welcome. Booking essential.
Facilities
Nearby Facilities
Directions From Inverness take A9, in Tore at roundabout turn onto A835 sp Maryburgh, in Maryburgh at roundabout continue on a A835 sp Ullapool. In Gorstan turn left onto A832, in Achnasheen at roundabout follow signs for Kinlochewe, site is 10 miles on the left.

KINLOCHLEVEN

Caolasnacon Caravan & Camping Park, Caolasnacon, Kinlochleven, Highlands, PH50 4RJ
Tel: 01855 831279
Email:
enquiry@kinlochlevencaravans.com
www.kinlochlevencaravans.com
Pitches For 🏕 🚐 🚍 **Total** 50
Acreage 7½ **Open** April **to** October
Access Good **Site** Lev/Slope
Nearest Bus Stop (Miles) Entrance
Lochside location with breathtaking mountain scenery. Ideal for touring the west coast.
Facilities
Nearby Facilities
Nearest Town Fort William
Directions From Glencoe on the A82, turn onto the B863, Park is 3 miles.
⚞ Fort William

LAIDE

Gruinard Bay Caravan Park, Laide, Ross-Shire, IV22 2ND
Tel: 01445 731225
Email: gruinard@ecosse.net
www.gruinard.scotshost.co.uk
Pitches For 🏕 🚐 🚍 **Total** 35
Acreage 3 **Open** April **to** October
Access Good **Site** Level
Nearest Bus Stop (Miles) ¼
Beach front location.
Facilities
Nearby Facilities
Nearest Town Gairloch
Directions On the A832, 15 miles north of Gairloch.
⚞ Inverness

LAIRG

Dunroamin Caravan Park, Main Street, Lairg, Sutherland, IV27 4AR
Tel: 01549 402447
Email: enquiries@lairgcaravanpark.co.uk
www.lairgcaravanpark.co.uk
Pitches For 🏕 🚐 🚍 **Total** 50
Acreage 5 **Open** April **to** October
Access Good **Site** Level
Nearest Bus Stop (Miles) ¼
Ideal centre for touring, fishing and sight seeing. Close to Loch Shin and all amenities. Secure Storage during Winter only.
Facilities
Nearby Facilities
Nearest Town Lairg
Directions 300 yards east of Loch Shin on the A839 on Main Street Lairg. Site entrance in the village.
⚞ Lairg

LAIRG

Woodend Caravan & Camping Park, Woodend, Achnairn, Lairg, Highlands, IV27 4DN
Tel: 01549 402248
Pitches For 🏕 🚐 🚍 **Total** 45
Acreage 4 **Open** April **to** September
Access Good **Site** Lev/Slope
Overlooking Loch Shin for fishing and scenic views. Campers Kitchen is a small building where campers can take their cooking stores to prepare food, with table, chairs and a dish washing area. Ideal touring centre for north west. AA 3 Pennants and a Gold Award for Quality & Service from International Caravan & Camping Guide.
Facilities
Nearby Facilities
Nearest Town Lairg
Directions From Lairg take the A836, then take the A838 and follow site signs.
⚞ Lairg

LOCHINVER

Clachtoll Campsite, Croft 134, Clachtoll, Lochinver, Highlands, IV27 4JD
Tel: 01571 855377
Email: mail@clachtollbeachcampsite.co.uk
www.clachtollbeachcampsite.co.uk
Pitches For 🏕 🚐 🚍 **Total** 40
Acreage 3 **Open** Easter **to** End Sept
Access Good **Site** Level
200 yards from a sandy beach. Beautiful scenery. Ideal location for hillwalkers and children who enjoy rockpools.
Facilities
Nearby Facilities
Nearest Town Lochinver
Directions 5 miles outside of Lochinver.
⚞ Inverness

MELVICH

Halladale Inn Caravan Park, Halladale Inn, Melvich, Sutherland, KW14 7YJ
Tel: 01641 531282
Email: mazfling@tinyworld.co.uk
www.halladaleinn.co.uk
Pitches For 🏕 🚐 🚍 **Total** 11
Acreage ½ **Open** April **to** October
Access Good **Site** Level
Nearest Bus Stop (Miles) 1
10 minutes walk from a lovely sandy beach. Ideal for surfers. 14 miles from Forsinard RSPB Reserve. Fishing on the Halladale River.
Facilities
Nearby Facilities
Nearest Town Thurso
Directions 16 miles west of Thurso on the A836 following the North Highlands Tourist Route.
⚞ Forsinard

NAIRN

Camping & Caravanning Club Site, Delnies Wood, Nairn, Inverness, Highlands, IV12 5NX
Tel: 01667 455281
www.campingandcaravanningclub.co.uk/nairn
Pitches For 🏕 🚐 🚍 **Total** 75
Acreage 14 **Open** 01-Mar **to** 05-Nov
Access Good **Site** Level
Nearest Bus Stop (Miles) Outside
Wooded setting just 2 miles from the beach, close to the town of Nairn. STB 4 Star Graded and AA 3 Pennants. Non members welcome. You can also call us on 0845 130 7633.
Facilities
Nearby Facilities

NAIRN

Nearest Town Nairn
Directions Off the A96 Inverness to Aberdeen road 2 miles west of Nairn.
⚞ Nairn

NAIRN

Nairn Lochloy Holiday Park, East Beach, Nairn, Highlands, IV12 4PH
Tel: 0844 335 3731
Email:
touringandcamping@parkdeanholidays.com
www.parkdeantouring.com
Pitches For 🏕 🚐 🚍 **Total** 10
Acreage 15 **Open** March **to** Nov
Access Good **Site** Level
Nearest Bus Stop (Miles) ½
Situated next to the harbour, East Nairn Beach and the lovely village of Nairn. Indoor pool. FREE kids clubs and live family entertainment.
Facilities
Nearby Facilities
Nearest Town Nairn
Directions Take the A96 from Inverness or Aberdeen. In Nairn follow signs, adjacent to the harbour.
⚞ Nairn

NEWTONMORE

Invernahavon Caravan Site, Glentruim, Newtonmore, Highlands, PH20 1BE
Tel: 01540 673534/673219
www.caravansite.co.uk
Pitches For 🏕 🚐 🚍 **Total** 67
Acreage 10 **Open** March **to** Oct
Access Good **Site** Level
Tranquil and spacious family run site with spectacular views of the Monarch of the Glen country. Heather covered mountains, ideal for walking and wildlife spotting. Adjacent to the Rivers Spey and Truim, fishing permits available. Booking essential.
Facilities
Nearby Facilities
Nearest Town Newtonmore
Directions 2 miles south of Newtonmore on the A9 turn right onto Glentruim road, site is 400 yards on the right.
⚞ Newtonmore

ONICH

Bunree Caravan Club Site, Onich, Fort William, Highlands, PH33 6SE
Tel: 01855 821283
www.caravanclub.co.uk
Pitches For 🚐 🚍 **Total** 99
Acreage 7 **Open** March **to** Jan
Access Good **Site** Level
Nearest Bus Stop (Miles) ¼
Situated at the edge of Loch Linnhe with mountain views. Visit Ben Nevis or take a cable car 2300 feet to Aonach Mor Mountain for fabulous views of the whole mountain range, the Great Glen and islands of Skye and Rhum. Non members welcome. Booking essential.
Facilities
Nearby Facilities
Nearest Town Onich
Directions From south east on the A82, just past Onich turn left at Caravan Club sign into a narrow track with traffic lights and passing places, site is in ¼ mile.

SCOTLAND

SCOTLAND

POOLEWE
Camping & Caravanning Club Site, Inverewe Gardens, Poolewe, Achnasheen, Highlands, IV22 2LF
Tel: 01445 781249
www.campingandcaravanningclub.co.uk/inverewe
Pitches For Å � ♶ **Total** 55
Acreage 3 **Open** 29-Mar **to** 05-Nov
Site Level
Nearest Bus Stop (Miles) Outside
Close to Inverewe Gardens and Loch Ewe. National Trust Ranger Walks ¼ mile. Diving nearby. STB 4 Star Graded and AA 3 Pennants. Non members welcome. You can also call us on 0845 130 7633.
Facilities ...
Nearby Facilities ...
Directions Site entrance is on the A832, north of the village of Poolewe.
⇌ Achnasheen

PORTREE
Torvaig Caravan & Campsite, 8 Torvaig, Portree, Isle of Skye, Highlands, IV51 9HU
Tel: 01478 611849
Email: torvaigcampsite@aol.com
www.portreecampsite.co.uk
Pitches For Å ♷ ♶ **Total** 90
Acreage 4½ **Open** 01-Apr **to** 20-Oct
Access Good **Site** Sloping
Nearest Bus Stop (Miles) Outside
Ideal for touring the Isle of Skye.
Facilities ...
Nearby Facilities ...
Nearest Town Portree
Directions 1 mile north of Portree on the main A855, on the right.
⇌ Kyle of Lochalsh

ROY BRIDGE
Bunroy Camping & Caravanning Site, Bunroy Park, Roy Bridge, Highlands, PH31 4AG
Tel: 01397 712332
Email: info@bunroycamping.co.uk
www.bunroycamping.co.uk
Pitches For Å ♷ ♶ **Total** 25
Acreage 7 **Open** April **to** October
Access Good **Site** Level
Nearest Bus Stop (Miles) ½
Peaceful, secluded, riverside site. Ideal for touring the Highlands and outdoor pursuits.
Facilities ...
Nearby Facilities ...
Nearest Town Fort William
Directions From the A86 in Roy Bridge, turn off opposite the Stronlossit Inn, go past the school on the left, over the railway bridge and go straight on.
⇌ Roy Bridge

SCOURIE
Scourie Caravan & Camping Park, Harbour Road, Scourie, Highlands, IV27 4TG
Tel: 01971 502060
Pitches For Å ♷ ♶ **Total** 80
Acreage 4 **Open** Mid April **to** Sept
Access Good **Site** Level
Nearest Bus Stop (Miles) ¼
Overlooking Scourie Bay. Ideal for hill walking, bird watching, trout and sea fishing. Please Note, we do not accept advance bookings.
Facilities ...
Nearby Facilities ...
Nearest Town Scourie
Directions Near Scourie Village, at the junction of Harbour Road and the A894. 20 miles south of Cape Wrath.
⇌ Lairg

SHIEL BRIDGE
Morvich Caravan Club Site, Inverinate, Shiel Bridge, Kyle, Highlands, IV40 8HQ
Tel: 01599 511354
www.caravanclub.co.uk
Pitches For Å ♷ ♶ **Total** 106
Acreage 7 **Open** March **to** Nov
Access Good **Site** Level
Set on a valley floor surrounded by hills and mountains on National Trust land. Daily guided walks July and August. Close to Eilean Castle, Dunvegan Castle, Falls of Glomach, Talisker Distillery and Isle of Skye. Non members welcome. Booking essential.
Facilities ...
Nearby Facilities ✓
Nearest Town Shiel Bridge
Directions From the A87, 1½ miles past Shiel Bridge at the head of Loch Duich, turn right by the restaurant into loop road signposted Morvich, after 1 mile turn right into road to the site.

SHIEL BRIDGE
Shiel Bridge Caravan Park, Shiel Bridge, Glenshiel, Kyle of Lochalsh, Ross-Shire, IV40 8HW
Tel: 01599 511221
Email: johnfivesisters@btinternet.com
www.shielbridgecaravanpark.co.uk
Pitches For Å ♷ ♶ **Total** 75
Acreage 3 **Open** 16-Mar **to** 16-Oct
Access Good **Site** Level
Nearest Bus Stop (Miles) ¼
Alongside a river with spectacular scenery. Ideal for walking and touring the Isle of Skye and the North West Highlands.
Facilities ...
Nearby Facilities ...

Nearest Town Kyle of Lochalsh
Directions 16 miles east of Kyle of Lochalsh on the A87.
⇌ Kyle of Lochalsh

SPEAN BRIDGE
Gairlochy Holiday Park, Old Station, Gairlochy Road, Spean Bridge, Highlands, PH34 4EQ
Tel: 01397 712711
Email: theghp@talk21.com
www.theghp.co.uk
Pitches For Å ♷ ♶ **Total** 20
Acreage 1 **Open** April **to** October
Access Good **Site** Level
Self catering also available.
Facilities ...
Nearby Facilities ...
Nearest Town Fort William
Directions 1 mile north of Spean Bridge heading towards Inverness turn onto the B8004 at the Commando Memorial, site is 1 mile.
⇌ Spean Bridge

SPEAN BRIDGE
Stronaba Caravan Camp Site, Stronaba, Spean Bridge, Inverness-Shire, PH34 4DX
Tel: 01397 712259
Pitches For Å ♷ ♶ **Total** 20
Acreage 3 **Open** April **to** October
Access Good **Site** Lev/Slope
Nearest Bus Stop (Miles) Outside
Outdoor activities, mountain bike trails and mountain gondola all nearby.
Facilities ...
Nearby Facilities ...
Nearest Town Fort William
Directions On the main A82, 2 miles north of Spean Bridge, on the left hand side (if travelling north).
⇌ Spean Bridge

STAFFIN
Staffin Caravan & Camping Site, Staffin, Isle of Skye, Highlands, IV51 9JX
Tel: 01470 562213
Email: staffincampsite@btinternet.com
www.staffincampsite.co.uk
Pitches For Å ♷ ♶ **Total** 50
Acreage 2½ **Open** April **to** Oct
Access Good **Site** Lev/Slope
Nearest Bus Stop (Miles) Outside
Near a sandy beach. Ideal for touring the area and the Western Isles. Campers Kitchen and information room on site.
Facilities ...
Nearby Facilities ...
Nearest Town Portree
Directions 16 miles north of Portree on the A855.
⇌ Kyle of Lochalsh

THURSO

Dunnet Bay Caravan Club Site, Dunnet, Thurso, Highlands, KW14 8XD
Tel: 01847 821319
www.caravanclub.co.uk
Pitches For Å ⊕ ⇔ **Total** 57
Acreage 5 **Open** April **to** Oct
Access Good **Site** Level
Nearest Bus Stop (Miles) Outside
Situated on the beach above the sand dunes. Ideal for bird watching, walking, guided walks and day trips to the Orkney Islands. Climb Dunnet Head for magnificent views over Pentland Firth to Orkney and the north coast to Ben Loyal and Ben Hope. Non members welcome. Booking essential.
Facilities ∮ 🖽🖲🖪🗂⌐⊙◎🖳 🖟 ⊖🖈⊟
Nearby Facilities ✒ ⚓🛉∪♪ ⚘
Nearest Town Thurso
Directions From Thurso take the A836, site is on the left approx. 2½ miles past Castletown Village.
➔ Thurso

UIG

Uig Bay Camping & Caravan Site, 10 Idrigill, Uig, Isle of Skye, Highlands, IV51 9XU
Tel: 01470 542714
Email: lisa.madigan@btopenworld.com
www.uig-camping-skye.co.uk
Pitches For Å ⊕ ⇔ **Total** 50
Acreage 2¼ **Open** All Year
Access Good **Site** Level
Nearest Bus Stop (Miles) Outside
Close to a pebble beach. Near ferry terminal to the Western Isles. Ideal for touring the Highlands. Cycle hire locally.
Facilities ⚲ ∮ 🖽🖲🖪🗂⌐⊙◢🖳◎🖴
🖟🖀🖈⊟🅿🎝
Nearby Facilities ✒ ∪ 🛉
Directions From Portree take the A87 to Uig, pass the ferry terminal and turn right just before the pier to the site.
➔ Fort William

ULLAPOOL

Ardmair Point Caravan & Camping Park, Ardmair, Ullapool, Ross-Shire, IV26 2TN
Tel: 01854 612054
Email: sales@ardmair.com
www.ardmair.com
Pitches For Å ⊕ ⇔ **Total** 68
Acreage 3½ **Open** April **to** Sept
Access Good **Site** Lev/Slope
Nearest Bus Stop (Miles) ½
Next to the beach and mountains.
Facilities ⚲ ∮ 🖽🖲🖪🗂⌐⊙◢🖳◎🖴
🖟🖀🖈⊟🅿🎝
Nearby Facilities ⌐ ✒ ⚓🛉♪ 🛉
Nearest Town Ullapool
Directions 3 miles north of Ullapool on the A835.
➔ Inverness

ULLAPOOL

Broomfield Holiday Park, Shore Street, Ullapool, Highlands, IV26 2UT
Tel: 01854 612020
Email: sross@broomfieldhp.com
www.broomfieldhp.com
Pitches For Å ⊕ ⇔ **Total** 140
Acreage 11 **Open** Easter **to** September
Access Good **Site** Level
Nearest Bus Stop (Miles) ¼
On the sea front. Beside a cafe/restaurant and adjacent to a golf course.
Facilities ⚲ ∮ 🖲🖪🗂⌐⊙◢🖳◎🖴
🖟🖀🖈⊟🅿🎝
Nearby Facilities ⌐ ✒ 🛉∪♪ 🛉
Nearest Town Ullapool
Directions Turn right past Ullapool Harbour.
➔ Garve

WICK

Wick Caravan & Camping Site, Riverside Drive, Janetstown, Wick, Highlands, KW1 5SP
Tel: 01955 605420
Email: wickcaravansite@hotmail.co.uk
www.wickcaravansite.co.uk
Pitches For Å ⊕ ⇔ **Total** 90
Acreage 6½ **Open** Mid April **to** Mid Oct
Access Good **Site** Level
Nearest Bus Stop (Miles) ¼
Sheltered site overlooking the River Wick and surrounded by trees. Just a 10 minute walk to the town centre and 3 miles from the beach.
Facilities ∮ 🖽🖲🖪🗂⌐⊙◢ 🖟 🕭🖈⊟
Nearby Facilities ⌐ ✒ ♪
Nearest Town Wick
Directions From the A99, turn left into Thurso Street (A882), after ½ a mile turn right into Riverside Drive.
➔ Wick

LANARKSHIRE (NORTH)

GLASGOW

Craigendmuir Caravan & Camping Site, Red Deer Village Complex, Clayhouse Road, Cardowan, Stepps, Glasgow, North Lanarkshire, G33 6AF
Tel: 0141 779 4159
Email: info@craigendmuir.co.uk
www.craigendmuir.co.uk
Pitches For Å ⊕ ⇔ **Total** 40
Open All Year
Access Good **Site** Level
Nearest Bus Stop (Miles) ½
Ideal for Glasgow (15 mins), Edinburgh, Stirling and Loch Lomond.
Facilities ⚲ ∮ 🖽🖲🖪🗂⌐⊙◢🖳◎🖴
🖟🖀🖈⊟🅿
Nearby Facilities ⌐ ✒ ∪
Nearest Town Glasgow
Directions Leave the M8 (Glasgow North) at junction 11 and take the A80 sp Stepps, Cumbernauld and Stirling. At Buchanaw Business Park turn into Cardowan Road, take the third road on the right (Clayhouse Road) and the Park entrance is at the roundabout.
➔ Stepps

LANARKSHIRE (SOUTH)

ABINGTON

Mount View Caravan Park, Abington, South Lanarkshire, ML12 6RW
Tel: 01864 502808
Email: info@mountviewcaravanpark.co.uk
www.mountviewcaravanpark.co.uk
Pitches For Å ⊕ ⇔ **Total** 50
Acreage 5½ **Open** March **to** October
Access Good **Site** Lev/Slope
Nearest Bus Stop (Miles) ¼
Ideal for walking, touring and a quiet family holiday. Well situated for exploring Clyde Valley. One hour from Glasgow, Edinburgh and the Ayrshire coast.
Facilities ⚲ ∮ 🖽🖲🖪🗂⌐⊙◢🖳◎🖴
🖟🖀🖈⊟🅿
Nearby Facilities ⌐ ✒ ♪
Nearest Town Biggar
Directions Leave the M74 at junction 13 and take the A702 south into Abington Village, then follow signs down Station Road.
➔ Lanark

LOTHIAN (EAST)

ABERLADY

Aberlady Caravan Park, Haddington Road, Aberlady, East Lothian, EH32 0PZ
Tel: 01875 870666
Email:
aberladycaravanpark@hotmail.co.uk
www.aberladycaravanpark.co.uk
Pitches For Å ⊕ ⇔ **Total**
Acreage 2 **Open** March **to** Oct
Access Good **Site** Level
Nearest Bus Stop (Miles) ½
½ a mile from the village. Close to beaches, a nature reserve for bird watching and the Museum of Flight Concorde Experience.
Facilities ∮ 🖽🖲🖪🗂⌐⊙◢🖳◎🖴
🖟🖀🖈⊟🅿🎝⚘
Nearby Facilities ⌐ ✒ ⚓🛉∪♪ ♪
Nearest Town Aberlady
Directions From Haddington take the A6137 to Aberlady, site is approx 4½ miles on the left hand side.
➔ Longniddry

DUNBAR

Belhaven Bay Caravan & Camping Park, Edinburgh Road, Dunbar, East Lothian, EH42 1TS
Tel: 01368 865956
Email: belhaven@meadowhead.co.uk
www.meadowhead.co.uk
Pitches For Å ⊕ ⇔ **Total** 128
Open 13-Mar **to** 31-Oct
Access Good **Site** Level
Nearest Bus Stop (Miles) Outside
Set within the John Muir Country Park, and right on one side of East Lothians beautiful sandy beaches.
Facilities ⚲ ∮ 🖽🖲🖪🗂⌐⊙◢🖳◎🖴
🖟🖀🖈⊟🅿🎝⚘
Nearby Facilities ⌐ ✒ ⚓🛉∪
Nearest Town Dunbar
Directions From the A1 north or south, exit at Thistly Cross roundabout west of Dunbar and take the A1087 towards Dunbar, Park is approx. 1 mile.
➔ Dunbar

DUNBAR

Camping & Caravanning Club Site, Barns Ness, Dunbar, East Lothian, EH42 1WG
Tel: 01368 863536
www.campingandcaravanningclub.co.uk/dunbar
Pitches For Å ⊕ ⇔ **Total** 90
Acreage 10 **Open** 29-Mar **to** 05-Nov
Access Poor **Site** Lev/Slope
Close to the town of Dunbar, on the Scottish coast. STB 3 Star Graded and AA 3 Pennants. Non members welcome. You can also call us on 0845 130 7633.
Facilities ⚲ ∮ 🖲🖪🗂⌐⊙◢🖳◎
🖟🖀🖈⊟🅿🎝⚘
Nearby Facilities ⌐ ✒ ∪
Directions On the A1 approx. 6 miles south of Dunbar (near the Power Station) you will see signs for Barns Ness and Skateraw, turn right at camp site sign towards the lighthouse and take in the views of the sea.
➔ Dunbar

LONGNIDDRY

Seton Sands Holiday Centre, Longniddry, East Lothian, EH32 0QF
Tel: 01875 813333
Email: setonsands@haven.com
www.haventouring.com/tosetonsands
Pitches For Å ⊕ ⇔ **Total** 34
Open Mid March **to** End Oct
Access Good **Site** Level
Nearest Bus Stop (Miles) Outside

SCOTLAND

A relaxed and easy going Holiday Park with lots of green play space. Kids clubs and family entertainment. Situated within easy reach of Edinburgh.
Facilities
Nearby Facilities
Nearest Town Edinburgh
Directions Take the A1 to the A198 at Bankton Junction, from here turn onto the B6371 for Cockenzie, then turn right onto the B1348. The park is 1 mile on the right hand side. Signposted from the A1 north and south.

NORTH BERWICK
Gilsland Caravan Park, Grange Road, North Berwick, East Lothian, EH39 5JA
Tel: 01620 892205
Email: info@gilsland.com
www.gilslandcaravanpark.co.uk
Pitches For Å ⬤ ⬤ **Total** 50
Acreage 8 **Open** April **to** Oct
Access Good **Site** Level
1 mile from the beach and harbour.
Facilities
Nearby Facilities
Nearest Town North Berwick
Directions From the centre of North Berwick find the sports centre and indoor pool on Law Road, turn along Grange Road and travel west for ½ a mile.
⬤ North Berwick

NORTH BERWICK
Tantallon Caravan & Camping Park, Dunbar Road, North Berwick, East Lothian, EH39 5NJ
Tel: 01620 893348
Email: tantallon@meadowhead.co.uk
www.meadowhead.co.uk
Open 03-Mar **to** 31-Oct
Access Good **Site** Level
Nearest Bus Stop (Miles) ¼
Spectacular views over the Firth of Forth to the Bass Rock. Scotlands golfing capital.
Facilities
Nearby Facilities
Nearest Town North Berwick
Directions From the A1, 3 miles west of Dunbar take the A198 and follow to North Berwick. Tantallon Park is on the right.
⬤ North Berwick

NORTH BERWICK
Yellowcraig Caravan Club Site, Dirleton, North Berwick, East Lothian, EH39 5DS
Tel: 01620 850217
www.caravanclub.co.uk
Pitches For ⬤ ⬤ **Total** 116
Acreage 7½ **Open** March **to** Nov
Access Good **Site** Level
Attractive site with grass covered sandy dunes and shrubs. Golden sands and rock pools nearby. Close to the Scottish Seabird Centre, Hailes Castle and East Fortune Museum of Flight. Non members welcome. Booking essential.
Facilities
Nearby Facilities
Nearest Town North Berwick
Directions From A1 approaching East Linton turn right onto A198. After approx. 8¾ miles turn left past railway station, at junction turn left (still on A198). After 2½ miles turn right signposted Dirleton, turn right at site sign, site is 1 mile.
⬤ North Berwick

LOTHIAN (WEST)
BLACKBURN
Mosshall Farm Caravan Park, Mosshall Farm, Blackburn, West Lothian, EH47 7DB
Tel: 01501 762318
Pitches For Å ⬤ ⬤ **Total** 25
Acreage ¾ **Open** All Year
Access Good **Site** Level
Nearest Bus Stop (Miles) ¼
Situated half way between Edinburgh and Glasgow.
Facilities
Nearby Facilities
Directions Leave the M8 at junction 4 and take the road for Whitburn. At T-Junction A705 take a left turn towards Blackburn, we are 300 yards on the right.
⬤ Bathgate

EAST CALDER
Linwater Caravan Park, West Clifton, East Calder, West Lothian, EH53 0HT
Tel: 0131 333 3326
Email: linwater@supanet.com
www.linwater.co.uk
Pitches For Å ⬤ ⬤ **Total** 60
Acreage 5 **Open** 18-Mar **to** 31-Oct
Access Good **Site** Level
Lovely amenities and walks nearby. Ideal for visiting Edinburgh, Royal Highland Showground and Falkirk Wheel.
Facilities
Nearby Facilities
Nearest Town Edinburgh
Directions From junction 1, Newbridge on the M9 or Wilkieston on the A71, park is signposted along the B7030.
⬤ Kirknewton

LINLITHGOW
Beecraigs Caravan & Camping Site, Beecraigs Country Park, Nr Linlithgow, West Lothian, EH49 6PL
Tel: 01506 844516
Email: mail@beecraigs.com
www.beecraigs.com
Pitches For Å ⬤ ⬤ **Total** 48
Acreage 6½ **Open** All Year
Access Good **Site** Level
Within a 913 acre Country Park which offers a wide range of leisure and recreational interests - fly fishing, Go Ape high ropes course, play area, Red Deer attraction, Highland cattle, restaurant and many woodland walks.
Facilities
Nearby Facilities
Nearest Town Linlithgow
Directions From Linlithgow High Street follow signs for Beecraigs Country Park, taking you approx. 2 miles up Preston Road. At the top of the hill turn left and then first right, take the next right into reception within the Beecraigs Restaurant.
⬤ Linlithgow

MORAYSHIRE
ABERLOUR
Aberlour Gardens Caravan Park, Aberlour on Spey, Moray, AB38 9LD
Tel: 01340 871586
Email: info@aberlourgardens.co.uk
www.aberlourgardens.co.uk
Pitches For Å ⬤ ⬤ **Total** 73
Acreage 5 **Open** 01-Mar **to** 28-Dec
Access Good **Site** Level
Nearest Bus Stop (Miles) ¼
In the heart of The Whisky Trail, 500m from the River Spey and salmon fishing. Ideal for touring from Cairngorm National Park to Moray Firth.
Facilities
Nearby Facilities
Nearest Town Charlestown/Aberlour
Directions 1 mile north of Aberlour on the A95, between Aberlour and Craigellachie. Vehicles over 10' 6" must use the A941 (due to bridge) and follow signs.
⬤ Elgin

ABERLOUR
Camping & Caravanning Club Site, Speyside, Archiestown, Aberlour, Moray, AB38 9SL
Tel: 01340 810414
www.campingandcaravanningclub.co.uk/speyside
Pitches For Å ⬤ ⬤ **Total** 75
Acreage 7 **Open** 29-Mar **to** 05-Nov
Access Good **Site** Level
Nearest Bus Stop (Miles) Outside
The surrounding area has historic castles, National Trust properties and gardens to visit. Salmon and Whisky are the specialities of this area of Scotland. STB 4 Star Graded and AA 3 Pennants. Non members welcome. You can also call us on 0845 130 7633.
Facilities
Nearby Facilities
Nearest Town Aberlour
Directions From the A9 at Carrbridge turn onto the A95 to Grantown-on-Spey then on to Aberlour. Take the A941 then turn left onto the B9102 signposted Archiestown, site is on the left after 3 miles.
⬤ Elgin

ELGIN
Riverside Caravan Park, West Road, Elgin, Moray, IV30 8UN
Tel: 01343 542813
Pitches For Å ⬤ ⬤ **Total** 44
Open April **to** Oct
Access Good **Site** Level
Elgin is near to beaches and alongside the River Lossie. Ideal fun touring base. Fishing, golfing and plenty of shops, restaurants and entertainment for children nearby.
Facilities
Nearby Facilities
Nearest Town Elgin
Directions Situated off the A96 Aberdeen to Inverness road. On the western outskirts of Elgin, 3 minutes drive from the town centre.
⬤ Elgin

HOPEMAN
Station Caravan Park, Hopeman, Nr Elgin, Moray, IV30 5RU
Tel: 01343 830880
Email: enquiries@stationcaravanpark.co.uk
www.stationcaravanpark.co.uk
Pitches For Å ⬤ ⬤ **Total** 37
Acreage 13 **Open** March **to** November
Access Good **Site** Level
Nearest Bus Stop (Miles) ¼
On a beach on Moray Firth coast.
Facilities
Nearby Facilities
Nearest Town Elgin
⬤ Elgin

SCOTLAND

LOSSIEMOUTH

Silver Sands Leisure Park, Covesea, West Beach, Lossiemouth, Moray, IV31 6SP
Tel: 01343 813262
Email: enquiries@silver-sands.co.uk
www.silver-sands.co.uk
Pitches For ▲ ⬜ 🚐 🚋 **Total** 140
Acreage 60 **Open** 15-Feb **to** 15-Jan
Access Good **Site** Level
Nearest Bus Stop (Miles) ½
Located adjacent to miles of unspoilt sand dunes and beaches, plus two championship golf courses.
Facilities & ƒ 🔲 🕪 🚿 ⌐ ⊙ ⌐ ⛻ 🔳 🍽
🏋 🛇 🏪 ✕ ♍ 🍴 ♨ 🏊 ⤚🔲 🔳 🎿
Nearby Facilities ┌ ✔ ⚓ 🎣 ∪ ♫
Nearest Town Lossiemouth
Directions Take the A941 to Lossiemouth, after 3¼ miles turn left onto the B9135. After 1¾ miles turn left onto the B9135, Park is 1¼ miles on the right.
⇌ Elgin

SPEY BAY

Spey Bay Caravan Park, Spey Bay, Nr Fochabers, Moray, IV32 7PJ
Tel: 01343 820424
Email: info@speybay.co
www.speybay.co
Pitches For ▲ ⬜ 🚐 🚋
Open April **to** October
Access Good **Site** Level
Nearest Bus Stop (Miles) Entrance
Own golf course on site. Near the beach, historic sites and the Scottish Dolphin Centre.
Facilities & ƒ 🔲 🕪 🚿 ⌐ ⊙ ⌐ ⛻ 🔳 🍽
🛇 ✕ ♍ 🍴 ⤚🔲 🔳 🎿 ♨ 🍺
Nearby Facilities ┌ ✔ ⚓ 🎣 ∪
Nearest Town Elgin
Directions From the A96 Aberdeen to Inverness road, take the B9104, turn off at Baxters Visitor Centre.
⇌ Elgin

ORKNEY ISLES

KIRKWALL

Pickaquoy Caravan & Camping Park, Pickaquoy Road, Kirkwall, Orkney Isles, KW15 1LR
Tel: 01856 888741
Email: enquiries@pickaquoy.com
www.pickaquoy.co.uk
Pitches For ▲ ⬜ 🚐 🚋 **Total** 80
Acreage 5¼ **Open** April **to** October
Access Good **Site** Level
Nearest Bus Stop (Miles) ¼
Within walking distance of Pickaquoy town centre and St Magnus Cathedral. Next to a leisure centre. 10 minutes away from the harbour for ferries to the North Isles.
Facilities & ƒ 🔲 🕪 🚿 ⌐ ⊙ ⌐ ⛻ 🔳 🍽
🏋 🛇 ✕ ♍ 🏊 ⤚🔲
Nearby Facilities ┌ ✔ ⚓ 🎣 ∪ ♫ ♫
Nearest Town Kirkwall
⇌ Thurso (Mainland)

PERTH & KINROSS

ALYTH

Five Roads Caravan Park, Alyth, Blairgowrie, Perth & Kinross, PH11 8NB
Tel: 01828 632255
Email: steven.ewart@btopenworld.com
www.fiveroads-caravan-park.co.uk
Pitches For ▲ ⬜ 🚐 🚋 **Total** 28
Acreage 3 **Open** All Year
Access Good **Site** Level
Nearest Bus Stop (Miles) Outside
Three golf courses within a 1 mile radius.

Facilities & ƒ 🔲 🕪 🚿 ⌐ ⊙ ⌐ ⛻ 🔳 🍽
🏋 🛇 ♍ ⤚🔲 🔳 🎿 🛜
Nearby Facilities ┌ ✔ ⚓ 🎣 ∪ ♫ ♫
Nearest Town Alyth
Directions From Blairgowrie take the A926, after 4½ miles at the Blackbird Inn turn left.
⇌ Dundee

AUCHTERARDER

Auchterarder Caravan & Chalet Park, Auchterarder, Perth & Kinross, PH3 1ET
Tel: 01764 663119
Email: info@prestonpark.co.uk
www.nethercoul.co.uk
Pitches For ▲ ⬜ 🚐 **Total** 25
Acreage 5 **Open** All Year
Access Good **Site** Level
Nearest Bus Stop (Miles) Outside
Two streams within the grounds for private fishing. Ideal touring destination being on the doorstep of the Highlands, with easy access to the Stirling and Perth areas.
Facilities & ƒ 🔲 🕪 🚿 ⌐ ⊙ ⌐ ⛻ 🔳
🛇 ⚑ ♨ ⤚🔲 ✔
Nearby Facilities ┌ ✔ ⚓ 🎣 ∪ ♫ ♫
Nearest Town Auchterarder/Perth
Directions From the A9 take the A824 signposted Auchterarder. Mid way between Auchterarder and Aberuthven turn south onto the B8062, site is 100 yards on the left.
⇌ Gleneagles

BLAIRGOWRIE

Blairgowrie Holiday Park, Rattray, Blairgowrie, Perth & Kinross, PH10 7AL
Tel: 01250 876666
Email: blairgowrie@holiday-parks.co.uk
www.holiday-parks.co.uk
Pitches For ⬜ 🚐
Acreage 15 **Open** All Year
Access Good **Site** Level
Nearest Bus Stop (Miles) Outside
Ideal base for touring the hills, lochs and glens of scenic Perthshire.
Facilities ƒ 🔲 🕪 🚿 ⌐ ⊙ ⌐ ⛻ 🔳 🍽
🏋 🛇 ♍ ⤚🔲 🔳 🎿 ♨ 🛜
Nearby Facilities ┌ ✔ ∪ ♫
Nearest Town Blairgowrie
Directions 1 mile north of Blairgowrie town centre. Turn right off the A93 at caravan sign after ½ a mile on Balmoral Road within the town boundary, Park is 500 yards on the left.
⇌ Perth

BRIDGE OF CALLY

Corriefodly Holiday Park, Bridge of Cally, Perth & Kinross, PH10 7JG
Tel: 01250 876666
Email: corriefodly@holiday-parks.co.uk
www.holiday-parks.co.uk
Pitches For ⬜ 🚐 **Total** 20
Acreage 17½ **Open** All Year
Access Good **Site** Level
Riverside setting with scenic views. Level hardstanding pitches. Lounge bar and TV lounge. Ideal touring base.
Facilities & ƒ 🔲 🕪 🚿 ⌐ ⊙ ⌐ ⛻ 🔳 🍽
🏋 🛇 ♍ ✕ 🍴 ♨ 🏊 ⤚🔲 🔳 ✔ 🎿 🛜
Nearby Facilities ┌ ✔ ∪ ♫
Nearest Town Blairgowrie
Directions From Blairgowrie take A93 north for 6 miles. Turn onto A924 Pitlochry road, site approx 200yds from junction of A93 and A924.
⇌ Perth

COMRIE

Twenty Shilling Wood Caravan Park, St Fillans Road, Comrie, Perth & Kinross, PH6 2JY
Tel: 01764 670411
Email: alowe20@aol.com
www.ukparks.co.uk/twentyshilling

Pitches For 🚐 🚋 **Total** 10
Acreage 10¼ **Open** Late March **to** 20-Oct
Access Good **Site** Level
Nearest Bus Stop (Miles) Outside
Family run, spotless all season, peaceful, sheltered, sunny south facing park set in woodlands that are visited by deer and many woodland birds. Individual pitches. Sorry, NO tents. Pets permitted. David Bellamy Gold Award for Conservation. Booking essential.
Facilities ✗ ƒ 🔲 🕪 🚿 ⌐ ⊙ ⌐ ⛻ 🔳 🍽
🏋 🛇 🏪 ♍ ⤚🔲 🔳 🎿
Nearby Facilities ┌ ✔ ⚓ 🎣 ∪ ♫ ♫
Nearest Town Crieff
Directions ½ mile west of Comrie on A85.
⇌ Perth

COMRIE

West Lodge Caravan Park, Comrie, Perth, Perthshire, PH6 2LS
Tel: 01764 670354
www.westlodgecaravanpark.co.uk
Pitches For ▲ ⬜ 🚐 **Total** 20
Acreage 3 **Open** 01-Apr **to** 31-Oct
Access Good **Site** Level
Nearest Bus Stop (Miles) Outside
Sheltered friendly park, set in beautiful country area. Ideal for touring. Caravans for hire nightly or weekly.
Facilities & ƒ 🕪 🚿 ⌐ ⊙ ⌐ ⛻ 🔳 🍽
🏋 🛇 ♍ ⤚🔲
Nearby Facilities ┌ ✔ ⚓ 🎣 ∪ ♫ ♫
Nearest Town Comrie
Directions On A85, 5 miles from Crieff. 1 mile east of Comrie.
⇌ Perth

DUNKELD

Inver Mill Farm Caravan Park, Inver, Dunkeld, Perth & Kinross, PH8 0JR
Tel: 01350 727477
Email: invermill@talk21.com
www.visitdunkeld.com/perthshire-caravan-park.htm
Pitches For ▲ ⬜ 🚋 **Total** 65
Acreage 5 **Open** End Mar **to** Mid/End Oct
Access Good **Site** Level
Nearest Bus Stop (Miles) ½
Riverside setting. 1 mile from Dunkeld which has many tourist attractions along with walking, fishing, golf and cycling.
Facilities & ƒ 🕪 🚿 ⌐ ⊙ ⌐ ⛻ 🔳 🍽
🛇 ⤚🔲 ✔
Nearby Facilities ┌ ✔ ⚓ 🎣 ∪ ♫ ♫
Nearest Town Dunkeld
Directions From the A9 turn onto the A822 signposted Crieff, turn immediately right following signs to Inver.
⇌ Dunkeld

INCHTURE

Inchmartine Caravan Park, Dundee Road, Inchture, Perth & Kinross, PH14 9QQ
Tel: 01821 670212
Email: enquiries@perthshire-caravans.com
www.perthshire-caravans.com
Pitches For ▲ ⬜ 🚋 **Total** 45
Acreage 8 **Open** April **to** October
Access Good **Site** Level
Nearest Bus Stop (Miles) ¼
A rural setting.
Facilities ƒ 🕪 🚿 ⌐ ⊙ ⌐ 🏋 🛇 ⤚
Nearby Facilities
Nearest Town Dundee
Directions Situated just off the A90 northbound, 12 miles north of Perth and 10 miles south of Dundee.
⇌ Dundee

KINLOCH RANNOCH

Kilvrecht Camping Park, c/o Forestry Commission, Inverpark, Dunkeld, Perth & Kinross, PH8 0JR
Tel: 01350 727284
Email: tay.fd@forestry.gsi.gov.uk
Pitches For 🏕 🚐 🚾 **Total** 60
Open Easter **to** Oct
Access Good **Site** Level
Stunning location close to Loch Rannoch.
Facilities 🚾 🍴 🛒 ☀
Nearby Facilities ┌ ✎ ✗
Nearest Town Pitlochry
Directions From the A9 at Calvine turn left onto the B847. After approx 9½ miles continue onto the B846, go over the bridge and turn right along the south of the loch, after 3 miles turn left into the forest.
⇌ Pitlochry

KINROSS

Gallowhill Caravan & Camping Park, Gallowhill Farmhouse, Kinross, Perth & Kinross, KY13 0RD
Tel: 01577 862364
Email: jpaterson21@hotmail.com
Pitches For 🏕 🚐 🚾 **Total** 50
Acreage 6 **Open** April **to** October
Access Good **Site** Lev/Slope
Nearest Bus Stop (Miles) ½
Situated in central Scotland. Near to a swimming pool, Loch Leven, two golf courses, boat trips to the castle and a walking and cycling track.
Facilities 🚿 🍴 🚾 ☕ ┌ ☉ 🍴 🔲 🍽
🔲 ⌂ ╋🔲 ☀
Nearby Facilities ┌ ✎ ⚓ ⛵ U ♪ ✗
Nearest Town Kinross
Directions Leave the M90 at junction 6 or 7 and head to Kinross following brown tourism signs to the site.
⇌ Inverkeithing

PERTH

Camping & Caravanning Club Site, Scone Palace Caravan Park, Scone, Perth & Kinross, PH2 6BB
Tel: 01738 552323
www.campingandcaravanningclub.co.uk/scone
Pitches For 🏕 🚐 🚾 **Total** 150
Acreage 16 **Open** 01-Mar **to** 05-Nov
Site Lev/Slope
Nearest Bus Stop (Miles) 1
Trout and salmon fishing is available from the nearby River Tay. Just to the north of Perth. Ideal for touring central Scotland. STB 4 Star Graded, David Bellamy Gold Award and AA 3 Pennants. Non members welcome. You can also join us on 0845 130 7633.
Facilities 🚿 🍴 🚾 ☕ ┌ ☉ 🍴 🔲 🍽
🔲 🏧 ☉ 🍴 ╋🔲 ☀ ⚓ 📶

Nearby Facilities ┌ ✎ ✗
Nearest Town Perth
Directions From the Motorway follow signs for Scone Palace, after Scone Palace continue for 2 miles then turn left following camp site signs or signs for Stormontfield. After 1 mile turn left into Racecourse Road, site entrance is through the car park.
⇌ Perth

PITLOCHRY

Milton of Fonab Caravan Site, Bridge Road, Pitlochry, Perth & Kinross, PH16 5NA
Tel: 01796 472882
Email: info@fonab.co.uk
www.fonab.co.uk
Pitches For 🏕 🚐 🚾 **Total** 154
Acreage 15 **Open** End March **to** Beg Oct
Access Good **Site** Level
Nearest Bus Stop (Miles) ¼
On the banks of the River Tummel. 5 minute walk to Pitlochry Festival Theatre and a 10 minute walk to Dam and Fish Ladder.
Facilities 🚿 🚿 🍴 🚾 ☕ ┌ ☉ 🍴 🔲 🍽
🔲 ☉ 🍴╋🔲 ✎ ☀ 📶
Nearby Facilities ┌ ✎ U
Nearest Town Pitlochry
Directions ½ a mile south of Pitlochry, opposite Bells Distillery.
⇌ Pitlochry

ST. FILLANS

Loch Earn Caravan Park, South Shore Road, St Fillans, Perth & Kinross, PH6 2NL
Tel: 01764 685270
Email: lochearn@perthshire-caravans.com
www.perthshire-caravans.com
Pitches For 🚐 🚾 **Total** 40
Acreage 4 **Open** 31-Mar **to** 31-Oct
Access Good **Site** Level
Nearest Bus Stop (Miles) ½
Lochside park with fishing and boating.
Facilities 🚿 🍴 🚾 ☕ ┌ ☉ 🍴 🔲 🍽
🔲 ☉ 🏧 ✗ ☉ 🔲 ⌂ 🔲 ✎ 📶
Nearby Facilities
Directions From Perth take the A85 and turn off signed South Loch Earn. Before entering St Fillans turn left over the hump back bridge, Park is 1 mile.
⇌ Perth

TUMMEL BRIDGE

Tummel Valley Holiday Park, Tummel Bridge, Nr Pitlochry, Perth & Kinross, PH16 5SA
Tel: 0844 355 3731
Email: touringandcamping@parkdeanholidays.com
www.parkdeantouring.com
Pitches For 🚐 🚾 **Total** 34
Acreage 52 **Open** March **to** Nov
Access Good **Site** Lev/Slope
Nearest Bus Stop (Miles) Outside

Set on the banks of the River Tummel in the stunning Perthshire countryside. Indoor pool. FREE kids clubs and live family entertainment.
Facilities 🚿 🍴 🚾 ☕ ┌ ☉ 🍴 🔲 🍽
🔲 ☉ 🏧 ✗ ☉ 🍴 🏧 ☀ ⌂ 🔲 ☀ 📶
Nearby Facilities ┌ ✎ ⚓ U ♪
Nearest Town Pitlochry
Directions From Perth take the A9 to Pitlochry, park is 13 miles along this road.
⇌ Pitlochry

SCOTTISH BORDERS

COLDINGHAM

Scoutscroft Holiday Centre, St Abbs Road, Coldingham, Eyemouth, Borders, TD14 5NB
Tel: 01890 771338
Email: holidays@scoutscroft.co.uk
www.scoutscroft.co.uk
Pitches For 🚐 🚾 **Total** 180
Acreage 16 **Open** March **to** Nov
Access Good **Site** Level
Nearest Bus Stop (Miles) Outside ¾ miles from Coldingham Bay.
Facilities 🚿 🍴 🚾 ☕ ┌ ☉ 🍴 🔲 🍽
🔲 ☉ 🏧 ✗ ☉ 🍴 🏧 ╋🔲 ☀ ⚓ 📶
Nearby Facilities ┌ ✎ ⚓ ⛵ ♪
Nearest Town Eyemouth
⇌ Berwick-on-Tweed

ETTRICK

Honey Cottage Caravan Park, Hope House, Ettrick Valley, Selkirk, Borders, TD7 5HU
Tel: 01750 62246
www.honeycottagecaravanpark.co.uk
Pitches For 🏕 🚐 🚾
Open All Year
Access Good **Site** Level
Alongside a river for fishing. Golf courses within easy reach. Ideal for walking, cycling or just relaxing in open countryside. Pub and restaurant 1 mile.
Facilities 🚿 🍴 🚾 ☕ ┌ ☉ 🍴 🔲 🍽
🔲 ⌂ 🏧 ╋🔲 ✎ ☀
Nearby Facilities ┌ ✎ ⚓
Nearest Town Hawick/Selkirk

EYEMOUTH

Eyemouth Holiday Park, Fort Road, Eyemouth, Scottish Borders, TD14 5BE
Tel: 0843 309 2560
Email: holidaysales.eyemouth@park-resorts.com
www.park-resorts.com
Pitches For 🚐 🚾
Open April **to** October
Access Good **Site** Level
Nearest Bus Stop (Miles) ¼

Cliffside location with superb views of the sea. Just a short walk from the town and near a sandy beach.
Facilities
Nearby Facilities
Nearest Town Eyemouth
Directions From the A1, 6 miles north of Berwick-upon-Tweed, take the A1107 following signs to Eyemouth. On entering the town the Park is signposted.
≠ Berwick-upon-Tweed

HAWICK

Riverside Caravan Park, Hornshole Bridge, Hawick, Borders, TD9 8SY
Tel: 01450 373785
Email: info@bordercaravans.co.uk
www.riversidehawick.co.uk
Pitches For Å ⊕ ⊞ **Total** 40
Open March **to** October
Access Good **Site** Level
Nearest Bus Stop (Miles) Outside
On the banks of a river.
Facilities
Nearby Facilities
Nearest Town Hawick
Directions 1 mile from Hawick on the A698.
≠ Carlisle

JEDBURGH

Camping & Caravanning Club Site, Elliot Park, Jedburgh, Borders, TD8 6EF
Tel: 01835 863393
www.campingandcaravanningclub.co.uk/jedburgh
Pitches For Å ⊕ ⊞ **Total** 60
Acreage 3 **Open** 29-Mar **to** 05-Nov
Access Good **Site** Level
Nearest Bus Stop (Miles) ¼
Quiet, secluded site bounded by the River Jed. Ideal site for picturesque walks. STB 4 Star Graded and AA 3 Pennants. Non members welcome. You can also call us on 0845 130 7633.
Facilities
Nearby Facilities
Nearest Town Jedburgh
Directions On the A68 Newcastle to Edinburgh road, drive to the northern side of Jedburgh and the entrance is opposite the Edinburgh & Jedburgh Woollen Mills.
≠ Berwick-upon-Tweed

JEDBURGH

Lilliardsedge Holiday Park & Golf Course, Jedburgh, Scottish Borders, TD8 6TZ
Tel: 01835 830271
Email: bordercaravans@btconnect.com
www.lilliardsedgepark.co.uk
Pitches For Å ⊕ ⊞ **Total** 40
Open March **to** Oct
Access Good **Site** Level
Nearest Bus Stop (Miles) Outside
On St Cuthberts Way with a 9 hole golf course on site. Fishing available locally.
Facilities
Nearby Facilities
Nearest Town Jedburgh
Directions 5 miles north of Jedburgh on the A68.

KELSO

Springwood Estate, Kelso, Borders, TD5 8LS
Tel: 01573 224596
Email: admin@springwood.biz
www.springwood.biz
Pitches For ⊕ ⊞ **Total** 20

Open 21-Mar **to** 11-Oct
Access Good **Site** Level
Nearest Bus Stop (Miles) Outside
Peaceful site with riverside walks.
Facilities
Nearby Facilities
Nearest Town Kelso
Directions 1 mile west of Kelso on the A699.
≠ Berwick-upon-Tweed

LAUDER

Camping & Caravanning Club Site, Carfraemill, Oxton, Lauder, Borders, TD2 6RA
Tel: 01578 750697
www.campingandcaravanningclub.co.uk/lauder
Pitches For Å ⊕ ⊞ **Total** 60
Acreage 5 **Open** 29-Mar **to** 05-Nov
Access Good **Site** Level
Nearest Bus Stop (Miles) ½
Situated 24 miles south of the vibrant city of Edinburgh. Close to Thirlestane Castle and a good fishing area. Self catering chalets also available to let. STB 4 Star Graded and AA 3 Pennants. Non members welcome. You can also call us on 0845 130 7633.
Facilities
Nearby Facilities
Nearest Town Edinburgh
Directions From Lauder, at the roundabout turn right onto the A697, at the Lodge Hotel turn left and the site is on the right behind Carfraemill Hotel.
≠ Edinburgh

LAUDER

Thirlestane Castle Caravan Park, Thirlestane Castle Park, Lauder, Borders, TD2 6RU
Tel: 01578 718884
Email: thirlestanepark@btconnect.com
www.thirlestanecastlepark.co.uk
Pitches For Å ⊕ ⊞ **Total** 60
Acreage 5 **Open** April **to** End Sept
Access Good **Site** Lev/Slope
Nearest Bus Stop (Miles) ½
Ideal location for exploring the Border towns and Edinburgh.
Facilities
Nearby Facilities
Nearest Town Lauder
Directions Well signposted off the A68.
≠ Edinburgh

MELROSE

Gibson Park Caravan Club Site, High Street, Melrose, Borders, TD6 9RY
Tel: 01896 822969
www.caravanclub.co.uk
Pitches For Å ⊕ ⊞ **Total** 60
Acreage 3 **Open** All Year
Access Good **Site** Level
Nearest Bus Stop (Miles) Outside
Peaceful site overlooked by the three hills which gave rise to its Roman name of Trimontium. Shops, playing fields and tennis adjacent. Close to Melrose Abbey, Priorwood Gardens and Abbotsford House. Non members welcome. Booking essential.
Facilities
Nearby Facilities
Nearest Town Melrose
Directions From the A68 take the A6091 at roundabout turn right onto the B6374 signposted Melrose. Site is on the right at the petrol station and opposite Melrose Rugby Club.
≠ Melrose

PEEBLES

Crossburn Caravan Park, Edinburgh Road, Peebles, Scottish Borders, EH45 8ED
Tel: 01721 720501
Email: enquiries@crossburncaravans.co.uk
www.crossburncaravans.co.uk
Pitches For Å ⊕ ⊞ **Total** 50
Acreage 6 **Open** 1 April/Easter **to** Oct
Access Good **Site** Level
Nearest Bus Stop (Miles) ¼
River nearby. Ideal touring base.
Facilities
Nearby Facilities
Nearest Town Peebles
Directions ½ mile north of Peebles on the A703.
≠ Edinburgh

STIRLINGSHIRE

CALLANDER

Gart Caravan Park, Stirling Road, Callander, Stirling, FK17 8LE
Tel: 01877 330002
Email: enquiries@theholidaypark.co.uk
www.theholidaypark.co.uk
Pitches For ⊕ ⊞ **Total** 131
Acreage 26 **Open** 01-Apr **to** 15-Oct
Access Good **Site** Level
Nearest Bus Stop (Miles) Outside
The ideal centre for walking, golf, fishing and exceptional for off-road cycling. Or you can simply relax and enjoy the scenery.
Facilities
Nearby Facilities
Nearest Town Callander
Directions Situated on the main A84, 1 mile east of Callander.
≠ Stirling

CALLANDER

Keltie Bridge Caravan Park, Callander, Stirling, FK17 8LQ
Tel: 01877 330606
Email: stay@keltiebridge.co.uk
Pitches For Å ⊕ ⊞ **Total** 50
Acreage 12 **Open** April **to** Oct
Access Good **Site** Level
Nearest Bus Stop (Miles) ¼
Well situated for exploring Loch Lomond and Trossachs National Park.
Facilities
Nearby Facilities
Nearest Town Callander
Directions Well signposted just off the A84 from Doune towards Callander, 1 mile before Callander.
≠ Dunblane

CALLANDER

Mains Farm Campsite, Mains Farm, Thornhill, Stirling, FK8 3QR
Tel: 01786 850605
www.mainsfarmwigwams.com
Pitches For Å ⊕ ⊞ ⊞ **Total** 35
Acreage 5 **Open** 15-Mar **to** 31-Oct
Access Good **Site** Lev/Slope
Nearest Bus Stop (Miles) ¼
Near to Loch Lomond National Park. Heated wooden Wigwams and real tepees available for hire.
Facilities
Nearby Facilities
Nearest Town Stirling

SCOTLAND

Directions Leave the M9 at junc 10 and take the A84 sp Callander. After 3¾ miles fork left onto the A873 sp Aberfoyle & Thornhill. After 3¼ miles, in the village, turn left onto the B822 sp Kippen, the Site entrance is 300 yards on the right.
⇥ Stirling

CRIANLARICH

Glen Dochart Holiday Park, Luib, Nr Crianlarich, Stirling, FK20 8QT
Tel: 01567 820637
Email: info@glendochart-caravanpark.co.uk
www.glendochart-caravanpark.co.uk
Pitches For Å ⚏ ⚌
Open March **to** Nov
Access Good **Site** Level
Excellent area for touring.
Facilities ⚬ ∤ 🏕 🖿 ♒ ╭ ⊙ ⟟ 🔲 ☎
🏧 ⦿ ➡🄿 🄳 ☀
Nearby Facilities ╊ ✓ ⚘ ⚓ ⅃ ♒
Nearest Town Stirling
Directions On the A85 Oban to Perth road, 6 miles from Crianlarich and Killin.
⇥ Crianlarich

DOUNE

Blair Drummond Caravan Park, Cuthil Brae, Blair Drummond, Stirling, FK9 4UP
Tel: 01786 841208
Email: bdcaravanpark@btconnect.com
www.blairdrummondcaravanpark.co.uk
Pitches For ⚏ ⚌ **Total** 88
Acreage 8½ **Open** March **to** Jan
Access Good **Site** Level
Nearest Bus Stop (Miles) ½
Set in and around a walled garden with mature trees and shrubs. Childrens play area, dog trail and trout fishing. Safari Park adjacent. Only 1 hour from historic Edinburgh.
Facilities ⚬ ∤ 🏕 🖿 ♒ ╭ ⊙ ⟟ 🔲 ☎
🏧 ⦿ ⛺ ➡🄿 🄳
Nearby Facilities ✓
Nearest Town Stirling
Directions Leave the M9 at junction 10 and take the A84 signposted Crianlarich. After 4 miles (just past the church) turn right at caravan sign into a private road signposted Cuthil Brae Int. Caravan Park, Site is at the end on the right.
⇥ Stirling

DRYMEN

Camping & Caravanning Club Site, Milarrochy Bay, Balmaha, Near Drymen, Stirling, G63 0AL
Tel: 01360 870236
www.campingandcaravanningclub.co.uk/milarrochybay
Pitches For Å ⚏ ⚌ **Total** 150
Acreage 12 **Open** 29-Mar **to** 05-Nov
Access Good **Site** Level
On the east bank of Loch Lomond, in the heart of Rob Roy country. Near Queen Elizabeth Forest Park. Boat launching available from site. STB 4 Star Graded and AA 4 Pennants. Non members welcome. You can also call us on 0845 130 7633.
Facilities ⚬ ∤ 🏕 🖿 ♒ ╭ ⊙ ⟟ 🔲 ☎
🏧 ⦿ 🅰 ➡🄿 🄳 ☀
Nearby Facilities ╊ ✓ ⚘ ⚓ U
Nearest Town Loch Lomond
Directions From the A811 Balloch to Stirling road, take the Drymen turnoff. In Drymen turn onto the B837 (junction is by the War Memorial) to Balmaha. After approx. 5 miles the road turns sharp right up a steep hill, the site is approx. 1½ miles.
⇥ Balloch

FINTRY

Balgair Castle Holiday Park, Overglinns, Fintry, Stirling, G63 0LP
Tel: 01360 860399
Email: balgaircastle@holiday-parks.co.uk
www.holiday-parks.co.uk
Pitches For Å ⚏ ⚌ **Total** 33
Acreage 28 **Open** April **to** October
Access Good **Site** Level
On the banks of the River Endrick. Close to Blair Drummond Safari Park and Stirling Castle.
Facilities ⚬ ∤ 🏕 🖿 ♒ ╭ ⊙ ⟟ 🔲 ☎
🏧 ⦿ ⚓ ⚘ ➡🄿 🄳 ☀
Nearby Facilities ╊ ✓ U
Nearest Town Balfron
Directions From Stirling take the A811 west towards Drymen, then take the B822 south to Fintry. After Balgair Castle Holiday Park sign turn right and follow road down into Park reception, on right hand side as you enter.
⇥ Stirling

KILLIN

Cruachan Caravan Park, Killin, Stirling, FK21 8TY
Tel: 01567 820302
Email: enquiries@cruachanfarm.co.uk
www.cruachanfarm.co.uk
Pitches For Å ⚏ ⚌ **Total** 55
Acreage 10 **Open** 15-Mar **to** End Oct
Access Good **Site** Lev/Slope
Working farm set in countryside. Central location for touring, climbing, golf and fishing.
Facilities ∤ 🏕 🖿 ♒ ╭ ⊙ ⟟ 🔲 ☎
🏧 ⦿ ⛺ ⚘ ➡🄿 🄳 ☀
Nearby Facilities ╊ ✓ ⚘ ⚓ U ⅃ ♒ ✗
Nearest Town Killin
Directions 3 miles east of Killin on the A827.
⇥ Crianlarich

KILLIN

High Creagan Caravan Park, Killin, Stirling, FK21 8TX
Tel: 01567 820449
Pitches For Å ⚏ ⚌ **Total** 30
Acreage 7 **Open** March **to** October
Access Good **Site** Level
Nearest Bus Stop (Miles) Outside
Facilities ∤ 🏕 🖿 ♒ ╭ ⊙ ⟟ 🔲
⦿ ➡🄿 ☀
Nearby Facilities ╊ ✓ ⚘ ⚓ U ⅃ ♒ ✗
Directions 2½ miles east of Killin on the left of the A827.
⇥ Crianlarich

KILLIN

Maragowan Caravan Club Site, Aberfeldy Road, Killin, Stirling, FK21 8TN
Tel: 01567 820245
www.caravanclub.co.uk
Pitches For ⚏ ⚌ **Total** 100
Acreage 8½ **Open** March **to** Nov
Access Good **Site** Level
Nearest Bus Stop (Miles) ½
On the banks of the River Lochay for salmon and trout fishing. Ideal for walkers and wildlife lovers. Close to Archray Forest, Scottish Wool Centre and two Visitor Centres. Non members welcome. Booking essential.
Facilities ⚬ ∤ 🏕 🖿 ♒ ╭ ⊙ 🔲 ☎
🏧 ⦿ ⛺ 🅰 ➡🄿 🄳 ✓ ☀
Nearby Facilities ╊ ✓ ⚘ ⚓ ⅃
Nearest Town Killin
Directions Just off the A827 just outside Killin Village.
⇥ Killin

LOCHEARNHEAD

Balquhidder Braes Holiday Park, Balquhidder Station, Lochearnhead, Stirling, FK19 8NX
Tel: 01567 830293
Email: enquiries@balquhidderbraes.co.uk
www.balquhidderbraes.co.uk
Pitches For Å ⚏ ⚌ **Total** 4
Acreage 2 **Open** March **to** Oct
Access Good **Site** Level
Farm shop and nature trail on site.
Facilities ∤ 🏕 🖿 ♒ ╭ ⊙ ⟟ 🔲 ☎
🏧 🏧 ⦿ ⛺ ⚘ ➡🄿 🄳 ☀
Nearby Facilities ╊ ✓ ⚓ ⅃ ♒
Nearest Town Lochearnhead
Directions From Stirling take the A84 and follow signs for Callander. 1 mile south of Lochearnhead.
⇥ Stirling

STIRLING

Witches Craig Caravan & Camping Park, Blairlogie, Stirling, Stirling, FK9 5PX
Tel: 01786 474947
Email: info@witchescraig.co.uk
www.witchescraig.co.uk
Pitches For Å ⚏ ⚌ **Total** 60
Acreage 5 **Open** April **to** October
Access Good **Site** Level
Nearest Bus Stop (Miles) Outside
Situated at the foot of the Ochil Hills with beautiful scenery and many local historical sites. Good hill walking. Ideal touring centre.
Facilities ⚬ ∤ 🏕 🖿 ♒ ╭ ⊙ ⟟ 🔲 ☎
🏧 ⦿ ⛺ 🅰 ➡🄿 🄳 ☀ ♒ ☎
Nearby Facilities ╊ ✓ U ♒ ✗
Nearest Town Stirling
Directions 3 miles east of Stirling town centre on the A91 Stirling to St. Andrews road.
⇥ Stirling

STRATHYRE

Immervoulin Caravan & Camping Park, Strathyre, Stirling, FK18 8NJ
Tel: 01877 384285
Email: immervoulin@freenetname.co.uk
www.immervoulin.com
Pitches For Å ⚏ ⚌ **Total** 70
Acreage 8 **Open** March **to** October
Access Good **Site** Level
Nearest Bus Stop (Miles) ¼
Alongside the River Balvaig and 300 metres from Strathyre Village. Ideal for touring.
Facilities ⚬ ∤ 🏕 🖿 ♒ ╭ ⊙ ⟟ 🔲 ☎
🏧 ⦿ ⛺ 🅰 ➡🄿 🄳 ☀
Nearby Facilities ╊ ✓ ⚓ ⅃ ♒
Nearest Town Stirling
Directions On the A84, 25 miles north of Stirling.
⇥ Stirling

WESTERN ISLES
HARRIS

Minch View Touring Park, 10 Drinishader, Isle of Harris, Western Isles, HS3 3DX
Tel: 01859 511207
Email: cath.macdonald@btinternet.com
Pitches For Å ⚏ ⚌ **Total** 8
Acreage 3 **Open** April **to** Sept
Access Good **Site** Level
Nearest Bus Stop (Miles) Outside
Friendly, family run site, situated between the sea and a fresh water loch. Beautiful beaches, excellent walking. Central for touring the Western Isles.
Facilities ∤ 🏕 🖿 ♒ ╭ ⟟ ⚌ ☎
🏧 ⛺ ✓ ☀ ☎
Nearby Facilities ╊ ✓ ⚓ ♒ ✗
Nearest Town Tarbert

SCOTLAND

Directions 5 miles south east of Tarbert Ferry Port. Turn off the A859 into Golden Road to Drinishader.

NORTH SHAWBOST
Eilean Fraoich Caravan & Camping Park, North Shawbost, Isle of Lewis, Western Isles, HS2 9BQ
Tel: 01851 710504
Email: eileanfraoich@btinternet.com
www.eileanfraoich.co.uk
Pitches For
Open May **to** October
Access Good **Site** Level
Nearest Bus Stop (Miles) Outside
Nera to beaches and historical sites. Ideal for hill walking.
Facilities
Nearby Facilities
Nearest Town Stornoway
Directions From Stornoway take the A857 to Barvas, turn left onto the A858 for approx. 6 miles, turn left at Shawbost School.

NORTHERN IRELAND
ANTRIM
ANTRIM
Six Mile Water Caravan Park, Lough Road, Antrim, Co. Antrim, BT41 4DG
Tel: 028 9446 4963
Email: sixmilewater@antrim.gov.uk
www.antrim.gov.uk/caravanpark
Pitches For **Total** 67
Open March **to** October
Access Good **Site** Level
Nearest Bus Stop (Miles) ½
Tranquil, rural setting on the scenic shores of Lough Neagh and adjacent to Six Mile Water River. Slipway for boating. Within walking distance of Antrim town and Antrim Forum Leisure Complex. Also OPEN Weekends during February and November.
Facilities
Nearby Facilities
Nearest Town Antrim
Directions From the A26 Dublin road follow signs for Antrim Forum and Lough Shore Park. Turn off for Lough Road passing Antrim Forum (on the right), Park is at the end of the road.
Antrim

BALLYCASTLE
Watertop Farm, 188 Cushendall Road, Ballycastle, Co. Antrim, BT54 6RN
Tel: 028 2076 2576
Email: watertopfarm@aol.com
www.watertopfarm.co.uk
Pitches For **Total** 17
Open 10-Apr **to** 31-Oct
On a working farm (open July and August) with pony trekking, fishing, boating, pedal go-karts, quad train, assault course, museum, small animals and farm tours on the paddiwagon. Opposite Ballypatrick Forest, ideal for walking and birdwatching. Positioned 4th in the Top 50 Campsites in the UK.
Facilities
Nearby Facilities
Directions 18 miles east of Giants Causeway on the A2 between Ballycastle and Cushendall. 6 miles from Ballycastle, signposted.

BALLYMONEY
Drumaheglis Marina & Caravan Park, 36 Glenstall Road, Ballymoney, Co. Antrim, BT53 7QN
Tel: 028 2766 0280/2766 0227
Email: drumaheglis@ballymoney.gov.uk
www.ballymoney.gov.uk
Pitches For **Total** 65
Open 17-Mar **to** 31-Oct
Situated on a boat park and 32 berth marina on the Causeway coastal route. Volley Ball, picnic areas, table tennis and nature walk on site.
Facilities
Nearby Facilities
Directions Off the A26 between Ballymoney and Coleraine. Turn left at Seacon crossroads and follow signs for Drumaheglis Marina.

BUSHMILLS
Ballyness Caravan Park, 40 Castlecatt Road, Bushmills, Co. Antrim, BT57 8TN
Tel: 028 2073 2393
Email: info@ballynesscaravanpark.com
www.ballynesscaravanpark.com
Pitches For **Total** 48
Acreage 16 **Open** March **to** Oct
Access Good **Site** Lev/Slope
Multi award winning Park on the spectacular North Coast. Well maintained, quiet Park in a beautiful location. Close to Giants Causeway and Old Bushmills Distillery. AA 5 Pennants, 5 Stars and David Bellamy Gold Award.
Facilities
Nearby Facilities
Nearest Town Bushmills
Directions On the B66, ½ a mile south of Bushmills.
Coleraine

BUSHMILLS
Bush Caravan Park, 97 Priestland Road, Bushmills, Co. Antrim, BT57 8UJ
Tel: 028 2073 1678/7034 3040
Email: bushcaravanpark@tiscali.co.uk
www.bushcaravanpark.com
Pitches For **Total** 60
Open March **to** 04-Oct
Set in the countryside in an area of exceptional beauty. Large meeting hall available for gatherings, crafts and entertainment. Game shooting can be arranged.
Facilities
Nearby Facilities
Directions Off the B62 Ballymoney to Portrush road, Paark is approx 275 yards on the B17 to Bushmills, signposted.

CUSHENDALL
Cushendall Caravan Park, 62 Coast Road, Cushendall, Co. Antrim, BT44 0QW
Tel: 028 2177 1699
Email: cushendallcp@moyle-council.org
www.moyle-council.org
Pitches For **Total** 24
Open April **to** October
Overlooking the sea and adjacent to Cushendall Boat Club. ¼ mile from the village centre. Boat hire and game shooting can be arranged.
Facilities
Nearby Facilities

CUSHENDUN
Cushendun Caravan Park, 14 Glendun Road, Cushendun, Co. Antrim, BT44 0PX
Tel: 028 2176 1254
Email: cushenduncp@moyle-council.org
www.moyle-council.org
Pitches For **Total** 22
Open April **to** October
Rural location close to the beach and ½ a mile form the village centre. Boat hire and game shooting can be arranged.
Facilities
Nearby Facilities

LARNE
Carnfunnock Country Park, Coast Road, Ballygally, Larne, Co. Antrim, BT40 2QG
Tel: 028 2827 0541/2826 0088
Email: carnfunnock@larne.gov.uk
www.larne.gov.uk/carnfunnock
Pitches For **Total** 39
Open 16-Mar **to** 04-Nov
Set within a country park with a walled garden, a maze, family fun zone (mini golf, bouncy castle, bungee run, laser clay pigeon shooting and miniature railway), outdoor adventure playground, mini cars, trampolines and golfing activities. Picnic and barbecue areas, gift and coffee shop. Regular weekend events.
Facilities
Nearby Facilities
Nearest Town Larne
Directions On the A2 Coast road, 3½ miles north of Larne between Drains Bay and Ballygally.

LARNE
Curran Caravan Park, 131 Curran Road, Larne, Co. Antrim, BT40 1BD
Tel: 028 2827 3797
Pitches For **Total** 47
Open April **to** October
On the edge of Larne town centre and by the harbour (ferry terminal). Next door to a putting and bowling green. Just a 5 minute walk to the leisure centre. Beaches nearby.
Facilities
Nearby Facilities
Directions 400 yards from Main Street on Curran Road towards Larne.

PORTRUSH
Ballymacrea Touring Caravan Park, 220 Ballybogey Road, Portrush, Co. Antrim, BT56 8NE
Tel: 028 7082 4507
Email: info@ballymacreacaravanpark.com
www.ballymacreacaravanpark.com
Pitches For **Total** 45
Open 17-Mar **to** Oct
Family run Park set in the grounds of Ballymacrea House.
Facilities
Nearby Facilities
Directions On the B62 Ballymoney to Portrush road, approx 1½ miles from Portrush, signposted.

PORTRUSH
Bellemont Caravan Park, 10 Islandtasserty Road, Portrush, Co. Antrim, BT52 2PN
Tel: 028 7082 3872
Pitches For **Total** 28
Open April **to** Sept
Facilities
Nearby Facilities
Directions Signposted off the A29 between Coleraine and Portrush.

PORTRUSH

Carrick Dhu Caravan Park, 12 Ballyreagh Road, Portrush, CO. ANTRIM, BT56 8LS
Tel: 028 7082 3712
Email: leisure@colerainebc.gov.uk
www.colerainebc.gov.uk
Pitches For Å 🚲 🚐 **Total** 65
Open April **to** Sept
Situated in an area of natural beauty on the North Antrim Coast. Close to main resorts and plenty of activities.
Facilities ⚡ 📷 🚻 🅟 ⊙ 🔯 👫 🍴 ☺ 🗑
🖬 🛇 ❀ ✦
Nearby Facilities ✦ ✎
Directions On the A2 1 mile west of Portrush.

PORTRUSH

Hilltop Holiday Park, 60 Loguestown Road, Portrush, CO. ANTRIM, BT56 8PD
Tel: 028 7082 3537
Email: info@blairscaravans.com
www.blairscaravans.com
Pitches For Å 🚲 🚐 **Total** 110
Open Feb **to** Oct
1 mile from the town centre. Caravan Holiday Homes also available for hire.
Facilities ⚡ 📷 🚻 🅟 🔯 👫 ☺ 🗑
✕ 🛇 ❀ 🖃 ✦
Nearby Facilities ✦
Directions Off the A29 between Coleraine and Portrush, signposted.

ARMAGH

LURGAN

Kinnego Marina Caravan Park, Kinnego Marina, Oxford Island, Lurgan, CO. ARMAGH, BT66 6WJ
Tel: 028 3832 7573
Email: kinnego.marina@craigavon.gov.uk
www.harbourguides.com
Pitches For Å 🚲 🚐 **Total** 20
Open April **to** Oct
On the shores of Lough Neagh within the National Nature Reserve.
Facilities 📷 🚻 🅟 ⊙ ☺ ✕ 🛇 ❀ 🖃
Nearby Facilities ✦ ⚓ ⋗ ✦
Directions Signposted from the M1 junction 10.

TANDRAGEE

Clare Glen Caravan Park, Markethill Road, Tandragee, CO. ARMAGH, BT62 2DF
Tel: 028 3884 1110
Email: trc@armagh.gov.uk
www.visitarmagh.com
Open All Year
Within a winding river valley in an area of considerable beauty with mature trees and bordering the Cusher River for fishing. Ideal for a relaxing break.
Facilities ⚡ 📷 🚻 🅟 🔯 ☺ ✕ 🖃
Nearby Facilities ✦ ✎
Directions Take the B3 from Tandragee, Park is 1 mile on the left.

BELFAST

BELFAST

Dundonald Touring Caravan Park, Dundonald Leisure Park, 111 Old Dundonald Road, BELFAST, BT16 0XT
Tel: 028 9080 9101
Email: sales@castlereagh.gov.uk
www.theicebowl.com
Pitches For Å 🚲 🚐 **Total** 52
Open 13-Mar **to** 31-Oct
Adjacent to The Ice Bowl with its ice rink, 10 pin bowling alley, adventure playground, pool tables, coffee bar and fast food restaurant. Closest park to Belfast city centre.

Facilities ⚡ 📷 🚻 🅟 🛒 ⊙ 🔯 ☺ ✕ 🛇 ❀
🖃 🖬 📶
Nearby Facilities ✦ ✎ ✎
Directions From Belfast follow directions to City Airport on the M3, then take the A20 to Ulster, at the Hospital turn right and follow past traffic lights, turn right (Ice Bowl is left).

BELFAST

Jordanstown Lough Shore Park, Shore Road, Newtownabbey, BELFAST, BT37 0PY
Tel: 028 9086 3133
www.newtownabbey.gov.uk
Pitches For Å 🚲 🚐 **Total** 8
Open All Year
Close to the Causeway Coast and the Glens of Antrim. Ideal for ferry terminals. Booking essential Oct to March. Maximum stay 2 nights. You can also call us on Mobile: 07775 687356.
Facilities ⚡ 📷 🚻 🅟 ⊙ 🔯 ☺ 🛇 ❀
Nearby Facilities ✦
Directions 5 miles north of Belfast on the A2 (Shore Road).

DOWN

ANNALONG

Annalong Holiday Park, 38 Kilkeel Road, Annalong, CO. DOWN, BT34 4TJ
Tel: 028 4376 8248
Email: info@chestnuttholidayparks.com
www.chestnuttholidayparks.com
Pitches For 🚲 🚐 **Total** 11
Open 1 Mar **to** Oct
On the beachfront. Convenient for the large village of Annalong. Booking is advisable.
Facilities ⚡ 📷 🚻 🅟 ⊙ 🔯 ☺ ✕ 🛇 ❀ 🖃
Nearby Facilities ✦ ✎ ∪ ✎
Directions On the main A2 Newcastle to Kilkeel road.

HILLSBOROUGH

Lakeside View Caravan & Camping Park, 71 Magheraconluce Road, Hillsborough, CO. DOWN, BT26 6PR
Tel: 028 9268 2098
Email: lakeside-view@hotmail.co.uk
www.lakeside-view.8m.com
Pitches For Å 🚲 🚐 **Total** 30
Open Easter **to** Oct
Quiet countryside park with views of lake and mountains. Half hours drive to Belfast. Caravans available for rent.
Facilities ⚡ 📷 🚻 🅟 ⊙ 🔯 ☺ 🛇 ❀ 🖃
Nearby Facilities ✦ ✎ ⋗
Directions From the M1 and A1 travel to Hillsborough Village. Take the B177 Ballynahinch road for 3 miles, signposted.

KILKEEL

Chestnutt Holiday Park, 3 Grange Road, Cranfield West, Kilkeel, CO. DOWN, BT34 4LW
Tel: 028 4176 2653
Email: info@chestnuttholidayparks.com
www.chestnuttholidayparks.com
Pitches For Å 🚲 🚐 **Total** 50
Open Easter **to** Sept
Access Good **Site** Level
Nearest Bus Stop (Miles) Outside
Spacious Park beside Cranfields Blue Flag beach with wonderful views of the Mourne Mountains. NITB 5 Star Park.
Facilities ♿ ⚡ 🖭 🚻 🛒 🅟 ⊙ 🔯 🗑 🖃 ☺
🕍 ⊙ ✕ ☺ 🛇 ❀ 🖃 🖃 ❄ 📶

Nearby Facilities ✦ ✎ ⚓ ⋗ ∪ ✎ ✎ ✦
Nearest Town Kilkeel
Directions From Kilkeel take the Greencastle road, after 2½ miles turn right (at the entrance to Sandilands Holiday Park) and follow signs for Cranfield West, Park is on the left.
⚑ Newry

KILKEEL

Cranfield Caravan Park, 123 Cranfield Road, Kilkeel, CO. DOWN, BT34 4LJ
Tel: 028 4176 2572
Email: jimchestnut@btconnect.com
www.cranfieldcaravanpark.co.uk
Pitches For 🚲 🚐 **Total** 40
Open 17-Mar **to** Oct
Facilities ⚡ 📷 🚻 🅟 ⊙ 🗑 🔯 ☺
☺ ✕ 🛇 ❀ 🖃
Nearby Facilities ✦ ⋗ ∪
Directions Signposted off the A2.

KILKEEL

Sandilands Holiday Park, 30 Cranfield Road, Cranfield East, Kilkeel, CO. DOWN, BT34 4LJ
Tel: 028 4176 3634
Email: info@chestnuttholidayparks.com
www.chestnuttholidayparks.com
Pitches For Å 🚲 🚐 **Total** 32
Open 17-Mar **to** October
Backdrop of the Mourne Mountains and adjacent to a private beach. Booking advisable.
Facilities ⚡ 📷 🚻 🅟 ⊙ 🔯 🗑 ☺ 🛇
❀ ❄ 📶
Nearby Facilities ✦ ✎ ∪
Directions 3 miles south of Kilkeel. From Newry take the A2 signposted Cranfield East.

KILLYLEAGH

Delamont Country Park Camping & Caravanning Club Site, Delamont Country Park, Downpatrick Road, Killyleagh, CO. DOWN, BT30 9TZ
Tel: 028 4482 1833
www.campingandcaravanningclub.co.uk/delamont
Pitches For Å 🚲 🚐 **Total** 63
Acreage 4 **Open** 10-Mar **to** 07-Nov
Access Good **Site** Level
Nearest Bus Stop (Miles) ¼
On the shores of Strangford Lough within a country park (free entry for campers). Many walks, historical sites and cultural landmarks. David Bellamy Silver Award. Non members welcome. You can also call us on 0845 130 7633.
Facilities ♿ ⚡ 🖭 🖭 🚻 🅟 ⊙ 🗑 🖃 ☺
🔯 🗑 ❀ 🖃 🖃 📶
Nearby Facilities ✦ ✎ ∪
Nearest Town Downpatrick
Directions On the A22 1 mile south of Killyleagh and 4 miles north of Downpatrick.

NEWCASTLE

Murlough Cottage Caravan Park, 180182 Dundrum Road, Newcastle, CO. DOWN, BT33 0LN
Tel: 028 4372 2906/4372 3184
Email: info@murloughcottage.com
www.murloughcottage.com
Pitches For 🚲 🚐 **Total** 26
Open March **to** Oct
Idyllic location in an area of outstanding natural beauty. A warm and friendly welcome awaits you!

NORTHERN IRELAND

DOWN, FERMANAGH, LONDONDERRY

Facilities ∮ ▥ ⇄ ⌐ ⊙ ◑ ⅃₤ ◎ ⛱
✕ 㿍 ✿ ⊢
Nearby Facilities ⌐ ∪ ⋏
Directions On the A24 2 miles north of Newcastle. Signposted.

ROSTREVOR

Kilbroney Caravan Park, Shore Road, Rostrevor, CO. DOWN, BT34 3DQ
Tel: 028 4173 8134
Email:
kilbroneypark@newryandmourne.gov.uk
www.visitnewryandmourne.com
Pitches For ⅄ ⊕ ⇔ **Total** 52
Acreage 97 **Open** 13-Apr **to** Oct
Set within Kilbroney Country Park, our landscaped area overlooks Carlingford Lough. Tennis on site.
Facilities ∮ ▥⇄⌐⊙◑ ⅀₤ ◎✕㿍⊢▣
Nearby Facilities ⌐ ⊥ ⋎ ∪ ⋏
Directions Off the A2 Rostrevor to Kilkeel road.

FERMANAGH
BELCOO

Rushin House Caravan Park, Holywell, Belcoo, CO. FERMANAGH, BT93 5DU
Tel: 028 6638 6519
Email: info@rushinhousecaravanpark.com
www.rushinhousecaravanpark.com
Pitches For ⅄ ⊕ ⇔ **Total** 54
Open 13-Mar **to** Oct
On the shores of Lough MacNean with scenic views of the valley and mountains, making a spectacular backdrop. Close to the village. Within easy reach of many attractions, and within walking distance of pubs and restaurants.
Facilities ∮ ▥⇄⌐⊙◑ ⅃₤ ◎ ⛱ ▥
㿍✿⊢▣
Nearby Facilities ⌐ ⋏⋎∪ ⋏ ⋏
Directions From Enniskillen take the A4 west to Belcoo for 13 miles, then take the B52 towards Garrison for 1 mile, signposted.

ENNISKILLEN

Blaney Caravan Park & Camp Site, Blaney, Enniskillen, CO. FERMANAGH, BT93 7ER
Tel: 028 6864 1634
Email: info@blaneycaravanpark.com
www.blaneycaravanpark.com
Pitches For ⅄ ⊕ ⇔ ⇔ **Total** 17
Open 17-Mar **to** Oct
Idyllic, panoramic location where the hills, forests, lakes and islands of the Erne waterway combine with traditional farming landscapes.
Facilities ∮ ▥⇄⌐⊙◑ ◎ ⛱ 㿍⋎ ⏅
Nearby Facilities ⌐ ⋏⋎ ⋏
Directions On the A46, 8 miles west of Enniskillen.

GARRISON

Lough Melvin Holiday Centre, Main Street, Garrison, CO. FERMANAGH, BT93 4ET
Tel: 028 6865 8142
Email: loughmelvin@btconnect.com
www.melvinholidaycentre.com
Pitches For ⅄ ⊕ ⇔ **Total** 18
Open All Year
On the shores of Lough Melvin, ideal for walking and bird watching.
Facilities ∮ ▥⇄⌐⊙◑ ⅃◎ ✕▥ ⛱
✿⋎▣
Nearby Facilities ⌐ ⋏⋎⊥⋎∪ ⋏

KESH

Loan Eden Caravan Park, Muckross Bay, Kesh, CO. FERMANAGH,
Tel: 028 6863 1603
Email: loaneden@aol.com
www.loanedencaravanpark.com
Pitches For ⅄ ⊕ ⇔ **Total** 38
Open Feb **to** End Nov
Facilities ∮ ▥⇄⌐⊙◑ ⅃₤ ◎ ◑ 㿍✿㿍⋏
Nearby Facilities ⌐ ⋏ ⋎ ⋏
Directions Signposted just outside Kesh at Muckross Bay.

LISNARICK

Castle Archdale Caravan Park, Lisnarick, Irvinestown, CO. FERMANAGH, BT94 1PP
Tel: 028 6862 1333
Email: bookings@castlearchdale.com
www.castlearchdale.com
Pitches For ⅄ ⊕ ⇔ **Total** 158
Open April **to** Oct
Situated on the shores of Lough Erne and set amongst thousands of acres of forest park on a former WWII airbase. Close to Donegal and Sligo. Licensed restaurant, takeaway, shop and play park. Seasonal opening times.
Facilities ∮ ▥⇄⌐⊙◑ ⅀₤ ◎ ✕ ⅄
㿍⋎▣
Nearby Facilities ⌐ ⋏⋎⊥⋎ ⋏
Directions Signposted off the B82 Enniskillen to Kesh road, 10 miles north of Enniskillen.

LISNARICK

Drumhoney Caravan Park, Lisnarick, Irvinestown, CO. FERMANAGH, BT94 1NB
Tel: 028 6862 1892
Email: info@drumhoneyholidaypark.com
www.drumhoneyholidaypark.com
Pitches For ⅄ ⊕ ⇔ **Total** 47
Open April **to** Oct
Fun Carts on site. Friendly pubs and restaurants nearby. Caravan holiday homes for hire. You can also contact us on Mobile: 07740 508270.
Facilities ∮ ▥⇄⌐⊙◑ ⅃₤ ◎ ⛱ ▥ ✿
㿍✿⋎▣ ⋏
Nearby Facilities ⌐ ⋏ ⋎ ⋏
Directions Off the B82, 10 miles north of Enniskillen, signposted.

LISNASKEA

Mullynascarthy Caravan Park, Gola Road, Lisnaskea, CO. FERMANAGH, BT92 0NZ
Tel: 028 6772 1040
Pitches For ⅄ ⊕ ⇔ **Total** 68
Open April **to** Oct
Picturesque location on the banks of the Colebrook River. Marble Arch Caves European GeoPark and Crom Estate nearby. Caravans for rent.
Facilities ∮ ▥⇄⌐⊙◑ ⅃₤ ◎ ⛱ ✿㿍▣
Nearby Facilities ⋏⊥⋎∪ ⋏
Directions 1 mile from Lisnaskea on the Carrybridge road.

LISNASKEA

Share Holiday Village, Smiths Strand, Lisnaskea, CO. FERMANAGH, BT92 0EQ
Tel: 028 6772 2122
Email: reception@sharevillage.org
www.sharevillage.org
Pitches For ⅄ ⊕ ⇔ **Total** 34
Open April **to** Sept
Activity Programme available to visitors during peak season, including temporary membership to a leisure suite. Chalets also available for hire.

Facilities ♿ ∮ ▥⇄⌐⊙◑ ⛱ ▥ 㿍✿ ⇔ ⛶ ⌗
Nearby Facilities ⊥ ⋏
Directions On the B127, 3 miles south of Lisnaskea, signposted.

LONDONDERRY
BALLYRONAN

Ballyronan Marina & Caravan Park, 99 Shore Road, Ballyronan, CO. LONDONDERRY, BT45 6JG
Tel: 028 7941 8399
Email: opservices@cookstown.gov.uk
www.cookstown.gov.uk
Pitches For ⅄ ⊕ ⇔ **Total** 15
Open April **to** Sept
Picturesque setting on the shores of Lough Neagh, ideal for watersports. Lovely woodland walks, great for nature lovers and bird watchers.
Facilities ∮ ▥⇄⌐⊙◑ ⅃₤ ◎ ✕㿍 ✿⋏
Nearby Facilities ⌐
Directions 5 miles south east of Magherafelt on the B160. 12 miles north east of Cookstown on the A23/B18. Signposted.

BENONE

Benone Tourist Complex, 53 Benone Avenue, Limavady, CO. LONDONDERRY, BT49 0LQ
Tel: 028 7775 0555
Email: benone.complex@limavady.gov.uk
www.limavady.gov.uk
Pitches For ⅄ ⊕ ⇔ **Total** 106
Open April **to** Sept
Two outside heated splash pools (seasonal), golf practice range, putting and bowling greens (admission fee per activity). Cafe (seasonal).
Facilities ∮ ⌐⊙⌐▣ ⅃₤ ◎ ◑ ✕▥
⋎ ✿㿍▣
Nearby Facilities ⌐ ∪ ⋏
Directions On the A2 coast road, 12 miles from Limavady and 10 miles from Coleraine.

BENONE

Deighan Caravans, 5 Benone Avenue, Benone, CO. LONDONDERRY, BT49 0LQ
Tel: 028 7775 0557
Email: info@deighanscaravans.com
www.deighanscaravans.com
Pitches For ⊕ ⇔ **Total** 50
Open April **to** Sept
Adjacent to 7 miles of sandy beach. Ulster Gliding Club nearby.
Facilities ∮ ▥⇄⌐⊙◑ ⅃₤ ◎ ✕
㿍✿㿍▣
Nearby Facilities ⌐ ∪ ⋏
Directions Off the A2 coast road between Limavady and Coleraine, follow signs for Benone.

BENONE

Golden Sands Caravan Park, 26 Benone Avenue, Benone, CO. LONDONDERRY, BT49 0LQ
Tel: 028 7775 0324
Pitches For ⅄ ⊕ ⇔ **Total** 60
Open 23-Mar **to** Oct
Adjacent to Benones Blue Flag beach. Gliding nearby.
Facilities ∮ ▥⇄⌐⊙◑ ⅃₤ ◎ ✕
㿍✿㿍▣
Nearby Facilities ⌐ ∪ ⋏
Directions Off the A2, 9 miles from both Limavady and Coleraine.

NORTHERN IRELAND

COLERAINE

Ballyleese Town & Country Caravan Park, 34 Agherton Road, Portstewart, CO. LONDONDERRY, BT55 7PJ
Tel: 028 7083 3308
Email: bonalston@btconnect.com
www.bonalstoncaravans.com
Pitches For ⚏ ⚏ **Total** 16
Open March to Oct
Quiet, rural setting on the edge of busy Portstewart. Ideal for enjoying all that the Causeway Coast has to offer.
Facilities
Nearby Facilities
Directions Off the B185, turn left into Agherton Road (approx. 3 miles from Coleraine), Park is 700 metres on the right, signposted.

COLERAINE

Tullans Farm Caravan Park, 46 Newmills Road, Coleraine, CO. LONDONDERRY, BT52 2JB
Tel: 028 7034 2309
Email: tullansfarm@hotmail.com
Pitches For ⚏ ⚏ **Total** 41
Open 17-Mar to Sept
Set on a working farm. Pool table, table tennis and snooker. Game shooting can be arranged.
Facilities
Nearby Facilities
Directions Off the A29 ring road, 1 mile south of Coleraine, midway between Lodge Road and Ballycastle Road roundabouts, follow Windyhall signs.

PORTSTEWART

Juniper Hill Caravan Park, 70 Ballyreagh Road, Portstewart, CO. LONDONDERRY, BT55 7PT
Tel: 028 7083 2023
Email: leisure@colerainebc.gov.uk
www.colerainebc.gov.uk
Pitches For ⚏ ⚏ **Total** 86
Open April to Sept
Splendid views and modern facilities.
Facilities
Nearby Facilities
Directions 1 mile east of Portstewart on the A2 coast road to Portrush.

TYRONE
CLOGHER

Clogher Valley Country Caravan Park, 9 Fardross Road, Clogher, CO. TYRONE, BT76 0HG
Tel: 028 8554 8932
Email: info@caravanpark-northernireland.co.uk
www.cloghervalley.co.uk
Pitches For ⚏ ⚏ **Total** 60
Open All Year
Nestled in 18 acres of Parkland with remarkable scenic beauty, forest walks and lakes. Close to the village with shops. Caravans available for hire.
Facilities
Nearby Facilities
Directions 400 yards off the A4 between Clogher and Fivemiletown, signposted.

DUNGANNON

Dungannon Park, Moy Road, Dungannon, CO. TYRONE, BT71 6DY
Tel: 028 8772
Email: dpreception@dungannon.gov.uk
www.dungannon.gov.uk
Pitches For ⚏ ⚏ **Total** 12
Open 2½ Open March to Oct

Nearest Bus Stop (Miles) ¼
Set within a 70 acre park with tremendous views over a rainbow trout lake. Woodland walks. Modern facilities maintained to a high standard. Tennis, fishing, cricket and football on site.
Facilities
Nearby Facilities
Directions Leave the M1 at junction 15 and take the A29 for Dungannon. Go straight until the second set of traffic lights and turn left sp Dungannon Park.
🚈 Portadown

FIVEMILETOWN

Round Lake Caravan Park, 20 Murley Road, Fivemiletown, CO. TYRONE, BT75 0QS
Tel: 028 8952 1949/8772 7327
Email: dpreception@dungannon.gov.uk
www.dungannon.gov.uk
Pitches For ⚏ ⚏ **Total** 17
Acreage 3¾ **Open** March to Sept
Tranquil Park set amidst the Clogher Valley. Coarse fishing and lakeside walks.
Facilities
Nearby Facilities
Directions Signposted ½ a mile from Fivemiletown on the Fintona road.

OMAGH

Sperrin Mountains Caravan Park, 1 Lisnaharney Road, Omagh, CO. TYRONE, BT79 7UG
Tel: 028 8166 2288
Email: mail@sperrincottages.com
www.sperrincottages.com
Pitches For ⚏ ⚏ **Total** 34
Open Easter to Sept
Adjacent to a forest with 3 graded mountain bike trails. 4 miles from Ulster American Folk Park. Chalet hire available. You can also contact us on Mobile: 07813 957563.
Facilities
Nearby Facilities
Directions On the B48, signposted between Omagh and Gorin.

REPUBLIC OF IRELAND
CAVAN
VIRGINIA

Lough Ramor Caravan & Camping Park, Ryefield, Virginia, Co. Cavan,
Tel: 000 353 87 282 5976
Email: loughramor@eircom.net
Pitches For ⚏ ⚏ **Total** 22
Acreage 5½ **Open** 19-Jun to 01-Sep
On the shores of the scenic Lough Ramor for fishing and boating (boat hire on site). Pubs, restaurants and shops close by. Historical Newgrange, Loughcrew and Hill of Tara nearby.
Facilities
Nearby Facilities
Directions Just off the N3 south of Virginia.

CLARE
COROFIN

Corofin Village, Main Street, Corofin, Co. Clare,
Tel: 000 353 65 683 7683
Email: corohost@iol.ie
www.corofincamping.com
Pitches For ⚏ ⚏ **Total** 20
Acreage 1¼ **Open** 10-Apr to Sept

Family run, sheltered site near to Burren and the Cliffs of Moher. 7 fishing lakes in the area, also good walking and cycling.
Facilities
Directions From Shannon Airport take the N18, N85 and R476.

DOOLIN

Nagles Doolin Camping & Caravan Park, Doolin, Co. Clare,
Tel: 000 353 65 707 4458
Email: ken@doolincamping.com
www.doolincamping.com
Pitches For ⚏ ⚏ **Total** 99
Acreage 9¾ **Open** Mid March to Mid Oct
Situated on the edge of the Atlantic between the Cliffs of Moher and the Burren. Only 100 metres from Doolin Pier, ferry port for boats to Aran Islands. Shop only open from June BH weekend to the end of August. Lovely coastal walks and pot holing in the area.
Facilities
Nearby Facilities
Directions From Lisdoonvarna go towards Cliffs of Moher, turn right for Doolin and follow signs to Doolin Pier. Park is situated 100m from Doolin Pier.

DOOLIN

O'Connors Riverside Camping & Caravan Park, Doolin, Co. Clare,
Tel: 000 353 65 707 4498
Email: joan@oconnorsdoolin.com
www.oconnorsdoolin.com
Pitches For ⚏ ⚏ **Total** 100
Acreage 6¼ **Open** April to Sept
In the heart of Doolin in a unique setting overlooking the Aille River. Small and friendly family run Park on a farm. 3 Star Graded Park. Guesthouse on site (3 Stars).
Facilities
Nearby Facilities
Directions From the N67 turn for Doolin, go straight across the main crossroads (Hotal Doolin on the right), go over the Aille River Bridge and the Park is on the left behind O'Connors Guesthouse.

KILKEE

Green Acres Caravan & Camping Park, Doonaha, Kilkee, Co. Clare,
Tel: 000 353 65 905 7011
Pitches For ⚏ ⚏ **Total** 40
Acreage 17 **Open** April to Sept
Delightful setting on the shores of the River Shannon, with lovely beaches and spectacular coastal views. Dolphin watch at Carrigaholt (5 minutes drive).
Facilities
Nearby Facilities
Directions From Kilrush take the N67 to Kilkee, then follow signs from the R487.

MOUNTSHANNON

Lakeside Holiday Park, Dooras, Mountshannon, Co. Clare,
Tel: 000 353 61 927225
Email: lakesidecamping@eircom.net
www.lakesideireland.com
Pitches For ⚏ ⚏ **Total** 45
Acreage 17¾ **Open** May to 01-Oct
Unique, spacious Park situated on the shores of Lough Derg, Irelands finest lake. Motor boats, rowing boats, kayaks, swimming, fishing, tennis, soccer and table tennis on site. NO dogs during July and August.
Facilities
Nearby Facilities
Directions On the R352, go through Mountshannon Village and take the first turn right (signposted).

CORK

BANTRY

Dunbeacon Camping Site, Durrus, Bantry, Co. Cork,
Tel: 000 353 27 62851
Email: julaclem@gmail.com
Pitches For 🛖 ⛺ 🚐 **Total** 20
Acreage 2½ **Open** June **to** Sept
Overlooking Dunmanus Bay. Trees and shrubs create individual private pitches. Ideal for exploring Mizen and Sheep's Head Peninsulas.
Facilities ✦ 🕮 🅿 🛆 🐾
Nearby Facilities 🏕 🚣 ⚓
Directions From Bantry take the R591 through Durras Village. Site is 3 miles on the left hand side.

BANTRY

Eagle Point Camping, Ballylickey, Bantry, West Cork, Co. Cork,
Tel: 000 353 27 50630
Email: eaglepointcamping@eircom.net
www.eaglepointcamping.com
Pitches For 🛖 ⛺ 🚐 **Total** 125
Acreage 19¾ **Open** 24-Apr **to** 28-Sep
On a peninsula with a safe and sheltered coastline. Pebbled beaches suitable for watersports, swimming and fishing. Tennis on site. Shop and petrol station at park entrance. No commercial vehicles. Booking essential.
Facilities ✦ 🕮 🅿 🛆 🍴 🛜
🏊 🏕 🕮 🔥 ✦ 🛜
Nearby Facilities 🏕 ⛵
Directions Take the N71 from Cork towards Bandon to Glengarriff, then take the R586 to Bantry. Opposite Cronins Petrol Station.

BEARA

Hungry Hill Camping Site, Adrigole Harbour, Beara, Co. Cork,
Tel: 000 353 27 60228
Email: info@hungryhilllodge.com
www.hungryhilllodge.com
Pitches For 🛖 ⛺ 🚐 **Total** 23
Acreage 7½ **Open** March **to** Oct
At the foot of Healy Pass in a rural setting at Adrigole, the jewel of Beara Peninsula. Pub on site, shop adjacent.
Facilities ✦ 🕮 🅿 🛆 🍴 🐾 ✦
Nearby Facilities
Directions West of Glengarriff on the R572.

BLARNEY

Blarney Caravan & Camping Park, Stone View, Blarney, Co. Cork,
Tel: 000 353 21 451 6519
Email: conquill@camping-ireland.ie
www.blarneycaravanpark.com
Pitches For 🛖 ⛺ 🚐 **Total** 40
Acreage 3 **Open** 01-Apr **to** 29-Oct
Award winning Park only 5 miles from the city of Cork. Sheltered, secluded and gently sloping family run park with views towards the famous Blarney Castle. 18 hole pitch 'n' putt on site. Plenty of attractions nearby. NO commercial vehicles.
Facilities ✦ 🏠 🕮 🅿 🅿 🛆
🏊 🛝 🕮 🔥 ✦ 🔲
Nearby Facilities
Directions From the N25 take the N8 towards Cork. Turn onto the N20 and then turn right onto the R617.

CARRIGTWOHILL

Jasmine Villa Caravan & Camping Park, Carrigtwohill, Co. Cork,
Tel: 000 353 21 488 3234
Pitches For 🛖 ⛺ 🚐 **Total** 17
Acreage 1¼ **Open** All Year
Close to all amenities and beaches.

Facilities ✦ 🚾
Nearby Facilities 🏕 🚣
Directions On the N25 Cork to Rosslare road, 1 mile from Carrigtwohill and 4 miles from Midleton.

CASTLETOWNBERE

Berehaven Camper & Amenity Park, Filane, Castletownbere, Co. Cork,
Tel: 000 353 27 71957/70700
Email: info@berehavengolf.com
www.berehavengolf.com
Pitches For 🛖 ⛺ 🚐 **Total** 22
Acreage 2½ **Open** All Year
Set amidst mountain scenery on the shores of Bantry Bay, breathtakingly beautiful. Ideal for fishing, hill walking, canoeing and golf. Very short walk to the ferry on Bere Island.
Facilities 🕮 🅿 🅿 🛆 🏊 🛝 🛆 ✕ 🐾 ✦
Nearby Facilities

CLONAKILTY

Desert House Caravan & Camping Park, Coast Road, Clonakilty, Co. Cork,
Tel: 000 353 23 883 3331
Email: deserthouse@eircom.net
Pitches For 🛖 ⛺ 🚐 **Total** 36
Acreage 4 **Open** May **to** Sept
Small, family run Park on a dairy farm overlooking Clonakilty Bay. Sandy beaches and model railway village nearby. Take-away food available.
Facilities ✦ 🕮 🅿 🛆 🕮 🔥 🔲
Nearby Facilities 🏕 🚣 ⚓
Directions Take the N71 from Cork and follow signs.

FERMOY

Blackwater Valley Caravan & Camping Park, Mallow Road, Fermoy, Co. Cork,
Tel: 000 353 25 32147
Email: blackwatervalleycaravanpark@gmail.com
www.blackwatervalleycaravanpark.ie
Pitches For 🛖 ⛺ 🚐 **Total** 30
Acreage 2 **Open** 15-Mar **to** Oct
Adjacent to Fermoy Town Park with its swimming pool and childrens play area. Fishing on site. No commercial vehicles.
Facilities ✦ 🕮 🅿 🛆 🏊 🕮 🔥 ✦ 🚣
Nearby Facilities
Directions From the M8/N8 take the R639 to Fermoy Town. Park is 100 metres from the town on the N72.

GLANDORE

The Meadow Camping Park, Glandore, Co. Cork,
Tel: 000 353 28 33280
Email: meadowcamping@eircom.net
Pitches For 🛖 ⛺ 🚐 **Total** 19
Acreage 2½ **Open** Easter **to** 15-Sep
Family run park providing peace and tranquility, yet only 1 mile from the village. Three environmental awards. Near the beach. 10 minute drive to Union Hall for fresh fish, fishing or a whale watching trip.
Facilities ✦ 🏠 🕮 🅿 🅿 🛆 🐾 ✦
Nearby Facilities 🚣 ⛆ 🏖
Directions From the N71 take the R597 to Glandore.

GLENGARRIFF

Dowlings Caravan & Camping Park, Castletownbere Road, Glengarriff, Co. Cork,
Tel: 000 353 27 63154
Email: nickydee@eircom.net
Pitches For 🛖 ⛺ 🚐 **Total** 90
Acreage 12 **Open** April **to** Oct
Spacious, well maintained Park situated between mountains and the sea. Top standard amenities. Take-away food

available. Abundant leisure pursuits in the area. Ideal for touring West Cork and South Kerry.
Facilities ✦ 🏠 🕮 🅿 🅿 🛆
🏊 🛝 🛆 🍴 🕮 🔥 🐾 ✦ 🛜
Nearby Facilities 🏕 🚣 ⛆ 🏖 U
Directions Leave Glengarriff on the R572 towards Castletownbere, Park is 1 mile.

KINSALE

Garrettstown House Holiday Park, Kinsale, Co. Cork,
Tel: 000 353 21 477 8156
Email: info@garrettstownhouse.com
www.garrettstownhouse.com
Pitches For 🛖 ⛺ 🚐 **Total** 60
Acreage 19¾ **Open** May **to** 06-Sep
Set within the grounds of an 18th Century Estate with top class facilities. Childrens Club and family discos. Crazy golf, snooker and tennis on site. Close to two Blue Flag beaches. Take-away food available. Seal, dolphin and whale watching locally. 6 miles from Kinsale with its numerous attractions
Facilities ✦ 🕮 🅿 🅿 🛆
🏊 🛝 🛆 🍴 🕮 🔥 🐾 ✦
Nearby Facilities 🏕 🚣 ⛆ U
Directions 6 miles from Kinsale on the R600.

ROSSCARBERY

O'Riordans Caravan Park, Owenahincha, Rosscarbery, Co. Cork,
Tel: 000 353 21 454 1825
Pitches For 🛖 ⛺ 🚐 **Total** 16
Acreage 3¾ **Open** All Year
Family run Park beside a sandy beach. Adjacent to Castlefreke Woods. Modern mobile home available for hire.
Facilities ✦ 🕮 🅿 🅿 🛆 🐾
Nearby Facilities 🏕 U
Directions Take the N71 to Clonakilty then to Rosscarbery.

SKIBBEREEN

The Hideaway Camping & Caravan Park, Skibbereen, Co. Cork,
Tel: 000 353 28 22254/28 33280
Email: skibbereencamping@eircom.net
Pitches For 🛖 ⛺ 🚐 **Total** 60
Acreage 5 **Open** Easter **to** 15-Sep
Rural setting, just a 10 minute walk to the market town of Skibbereen.
Facilities ✦ 🕮 🅿 🅿 🛆 🏊 🕮 🔥 🐾 ✦ 🛜
Nearby Facilities
Directions ½ a mile from Skibbereen town centre on the R596 towards Castletownsend.

TIMOLEAGUE

Sexton's Caravan & Camping Park, R600 Clonakilty Road, Timoleague, Co. Cork,
Tel: 000 353 88 46347/87 220 8088
Email: fb.sextons@gmail.com
www.sextonscamping.com
Pitches For 🛖 ⛺ 🚐 **Total** 30
Acreage 4 **Open** 15-Mar **to** 30-Oct
Situated in countryside, yet only a 5 minute drive to beaches and family activities. Dog friendly site. Breakfast available. Free Wi-Fi. Groups welcome. Find us on Facebook.
Facilities ✦ 🎏 🏠 🕮 🅿 🅿 🛆
🏊 🛝 🛆 🕮 🔥 🐾 ✦ 🔲 🛜 ⛆ 🍴 🛜
Nearby Facilities 🏕 🚣 ⛆ 🏖 U ⚓ 🎣 🏇
Directions Just off the R600.

DONEGAL
CARRIGART
Caseys Caravan Site, Downings, Letterkenny, Carrigart, Co. Donegal,
Tel: 000 353 74 915 5376
Pitches For Å ⚏ 🚐 🚗 **Total** 78
Acreage 19¾ **Open** April **to** Sept
On the edge of Sheephaven Bay in the fishing village of Downings. Bordered by a safe sandy beach. 200 yards from shops, pubs and a hotel. Two 18 hole links championship golf courses in ¼ mile. Interesting walks and drives.
Facilities ♿ ∮ 🔟 🕍 ⌂ ⊙ 🚿 🍴 🛒 🖂 ⛺ 🏧
Nearby Facilities ┣ ✓ ⚓ 🛝 U ⚑ ⌖ ⚘

DUNGLOE
Dungloe Touring Caravan Park,
Carnmore Road, Dungloe, Co. Donegal,
Tel: 000 353 74 95 21021
Email: chasg14@gmail.com
www.dungloecaravanpark.com
Pitches For ⚏ 🚗 **Total** 25
Acreage 2 **Open** Easter Weekend **to** Mid Sept
Access Good **Site** Level
Nearest Bus Stop (Miles) ¼
In the village of Dungloe with pubs, restaurants and supermarkets all just a ten minute walk away. Dungloe is on a coastal bay with beaches within 5km.
Facilities ∮ 🔟 🕍 ⌂ ⊙ 🖂 ⛽🍴 🖂 🛜
Nearby Facilities ┣ ✓ ⚘
Nearest Town Dungloe
Directions In the town, at the N56 roundabout junction, 200 metres from Main Street.

DUBLIN
CLONDALKIN
Camac Valley Tourist Caravan & Camping Park, Green Isle Road, Clondalkin, Co. Dublin,
Tel: 000 353 1464 0644
Email: info@camacvalley.com
www.camacvalley.com
Pitches For Å ⚏ 🚐 🚗 **Total** 163
Acreage 37 **Open** All Year
Spacious premier park with top class facilities. Adjoining Corkagh Park with 300 acres of fishing lakes and playgrounds, and is ideal for walking.
Facilities ∮ 🔟 🕍 ⌂ 🖂 🛒 ⚿ 🍴 🚿 🖂 🛜
Nearby Facilities
Directions Off the N7 beside Corkagh Park near Clondalkin Village.

RUSH
North Beach Caravan & Camping Park,
North Beach, Rush, Co. Dublin,
Tel: 000 353 1843 7131
Email: info@northbeach.ie
www.northbeach.ie
Pitches For Å ⚏ 🚐 🚗 **Total** 64
Acreage 4½ **Open** April **to** Sept
Plenty of amenities in the village. Ideal base for visiting Dublin.
Facilities ∮ 🕍 ⌂ 🖂 ⊙ ✕
Nearby Facilities
Directions Leave the M1 signposted Rush. Leave the R132 at the Esso, drive along Rush main street and at the third set of traffic lights turn left, after 100 metres turn right.

GALWAY
CLIFDEN
Shanaheever Campsite & Caravan Park,
Shanaheever, Westport Road, Clifden, Co. Galway,
Tel: 000 353 95 22150/95 21078
Email: info@clifdencamping.com
www.clifdencamping.com
Pitches For Å ⚏ 🚐 🚗 **Total** 42
Acreage 2½ **Open** 14-Apr **to** Sept
In a sheltered valley at the foot of Twelve Bens but within a few minutes drive of the sea. 15 minute walk to Clifden, the capital of Connemara.
Facilities ∮ 🕍 ⌂ 🖂 🛒 🖂 🍴 ⛺ 🏧 ✕
Nearby Facilities
Directions From Galway take the N59 through Clifden to Westport. Turn right at the AIB Bank (on the left), Park is first turn right after the lake.

GALWAY CITY
Galway City East Caravan & Camping Park, Ballyloughane Beach, Renmore, Co. Galway,
Tel: 000 353 91 752029
Email: galwcamp@iol.ie
Pitches For Å ⚏ 🚐 🚗 **Total** 45
Acreage 4 **Open** 15-May **to** 01-Sep
Quiet, family run park with a high standard of cleanliness and security. Beside a sandy beach with scenic walks and panoramic views of Galway Bay. Close to the city centre and all amenities.
Facilities ∮ 🕍 ⌂ 🖂 🛒 🖂 🍴 ⛺ ✕
Nearby Facilities
Directions Approaching the city, at the first roundabout take exit for 'Galway City East - Merlin Park'. At Skerritt roundabout follow city centre route and take next turn left at Dawn Dairies.

LEENANE CONNEMARA
Connemara Caravan & Camping Park,
Lettergesh Renvyle, Leenane, Connemara, Co. Galway,
Tel: 000 353 95 43406
Pitches For Å ⚏ 🚗 **Total** 36
Acreage 5 **Open** May **to** Sept
Dolphins often seen from the site. Sandy beaches. National Park & Adventure Centre and a diving centre close by.
Facilities 🕍 ⌂ 🖂 🛒 🖂 🍴 ⛺ 🖂 ✕
Nearby Facilities ┣ ✓ ⚓ 🛝 U ⚘
Directions 5 miles south of Leenane, turn right off the main Westport to Clifden road.

RENVYLE
Renvyle Beach Caravan & Camping Park, Renvyle Peninsula, Connemara, Co. Galway,
Tel: 000 353 95 43462
Email:
renvylebeachcaravanpark@gmail.com
www.renvylebeachcaravanpark.com
Pitches For Å ⚏ 🚗 **Total** 36
Acreage 6¼ **Open** April **to** Sept
Scenic park with direct access to the beach. High standard of cleanliness. 10 minute walk to shops, pubs and restaurants. Holiday Cottages available for hire. NO Dogs July and August.
Facilities ∮ 🕍 ⌂ 🖂 🛒 ⊙ ✕
Directions Signposted in Tullycross.

SALTHILL
Salthill Caravan Park, Salthill, Co. Galway,
Tel: 000 353 91 523972
Email: info@salthillcaravanpark.com
www.salthillcaravanpark.com
Pitches For Å ⚏ 🚐 🚗 **Total** 70
Acreage 19¾ **Open** Easter **to** Sept
Family run Park on the shores of Galway Bay with stunning views of of the Burren and Clare Hills. 1½ miles from Galway City. NO Commercial vehicles.
Facilities ∮ 🕍 ⌂ 🖂 🛒 🖂 ⊙ 🐕 ✕
Nearby Facilities ✓ U ⚑
Directions Approaching Galway on the N17, to avoid the city centre stay on the N6 which will take you to Dunnes Stores and onto Bodkin roundabout, turn right and continue straight on the N6 to Deane roundabout, just past at the traffic lights turn right onto the R3

KERRY
ARDFERT
Sir Rogers Caravan Park, Banna, Ardfert, Tralee, Co. Kerry,
Tel: 000 353 66 713 4730
Email: sirrogerscaravanpark@eircom.net
www.sirrogerscaravanpark.com
Pitches For Å ⚏ 🚐 🚗 **Total** 56
Acreage 3½ **Open** Feb **to** Dec
Modern family run park with state of the art childrens playground. Pleasant, safe and secure for families. 200 metres from the beach.
Facilities ∮ 🕍 ⌂ 🖂 🛒 ⊙ 🛒 Å 🐕 ✕ 🖂
Nearby Facilities
Directions Approx 6 miles north west of Tralee on the R551.

CAHERDANIEL
Wave Crest Caravan & Camping Park,
Caherdaniel, Co. Kerry,
Tel: 000 353 66 947 5188
Email: wavecrest@eircom.net
www.wavecrestcamping.com
Pitches For Å ⚏ 🚐 🚗 **Total** 100
Acreage 5½ **Open** 15-Mar **to** 15-Oct
Elevated, landscaped Park with views of beaches, coves and the majestic mountains of the Beara Peninsula. Dolphins and basking sharks are familiar sights. A haven for outdoor enthusiasts. Take-away food available. NO commercial vehicles.
Facilities ∮ 🕍 ⌂ 🖂
🖂 🛒 ⊙ 🛒 ⚿ ⛺ 🍴 🐕 ✕ 🖂
Nearby Facilities ┣ ✓ ⚓ 🛝 U ⚑ ⌖

CAHIRCIVEEN
Mannix Point Camping & Caravan Park,
Cahirciveen, Ring of Kerry Coast, Co. Kerry,
Tel: 000 353 66 947 2806
Email: mortimer@campinginkerry.com
www.campinginkerry.com
Pitches For Å ⚏ 🚐 🚗 **Total** 42
Acreage 6¼ **Open** 15-Mar **to** 15-Oct
On the waterfront in the spectacular Gulf Stream coast of South West Kerry with wonderful views in every direction. 15 minute walk to the town and amenities. Ideal for hill, mountain and foreshore walks. Pre-booking is essential for the music festival and there is a minimum of a 3 night stay for that weekend (first weekend in August).
Facilities ∮ 🕍 ⌂ 🖂 🛒 ⊙ 🛒 🐕 ✕ 🛜
Nearby Facilities U ⚑
Directions 300 metres from the N70, just west of Cahirciveen.

REPUBLIC OF IRELAND

CASTLEGREGORY

Anchor Caravan Park, Castlegregory,
Tralee, Co. Kerry,
Tel: 000 353 66 713 9157
Email: anchorcaravanpark@eircom.net
www.anchorcaravanpark.com
Pitches For 🚐 🚓 **Total** 30
Acreage 5 **Open** Easter **to** Sept
Sheltered Park with direct access to sandy
beach for safe bathing. Ideal for the Dingle
Peninsula, Killarney and the Ring of Kerry.
Facilities 🏊♿️🅿️🏕 📲 🛒 🍽 🔥 🎮⊣
Nearby Facilities ↾ ✈ ≀
Directions 12 miles from Tralee on the coast
road to Dingle, signposted.

DINGLE

Campail Teach an Aragail, Gallarus, Baile
na Gall, Dingle, Co. Kerry,
Tel: 000 353 66 915 5143
Email: info@gaeilgebeo.com
www.gaeilgebeo.com
Pitches For ⛺ 🚐 🚓 **Total** 42
Acreage 3 **Open** April **to** 20-Sep
On the tranquil, pure and beautiful Dingle
Peninsula, a Gaelic speaking area. Ideal for
walking with the Way of the Saints to Mount
Brandon, or the Dingle Way to visit the
Blasket Islands. Pub and restaurant in the
nearby village.
Facilities ♿️🏊⚡️🅿️ 🛒 📲 🍽 🕹 🎮
Nearby Facilities
Directions From Dingle (An Daingean) take
the R559 to Baile an Fheirtearaigh and follow
signs.

GLENBEIGH

Glenross Caravan & Camping Park,
Glenbeigh Village, Ring of Kerry, Co. Kerry,
Tel: 000 353 66 976 8451 (April -
Email: glenross@eircom.net
www.campingkerry.com
Pitches For ⛺ 🚐 🚓 **Total** 40
Acreage 4½ **Open** 06-Apr **to** 24-Sep
On the spectacular Ring of Kerry with fine
views of Rossbeigh Strand. 5 minutes from
the beach. Telephone number for Oct to April:
00 353 87 137 6865.
Facilities 🏊♿️🅿️⚡️🕐⊙⊣ 🛒 🍽
🏕 💻 🚿 🔥 🎮 🛒 ♿️ 🛍 🌲
Nearby Facilities ↾ 🚣 ⚓ ⬆ 🏊 U ≀ ✈
Directions From Killarney take the N70, park
is on the right just before the village.

KILLARNEY

Beech Grove Caravan & Camping Park,
Fossa, Killarney, Co. Kerry,
Tel: 000 353 64 663 1727
www.beechgrovecamping.net
Pitches For ⛺ 🚐 🚓 **Total** 46
Acreage 3½ **Open** 04-Apr **to** 03-Oct
Family run site with a woodland background
and panoramic views overlloking Killarneys
lower lake.
Facilities 🏊♿️🅿️ 🛒 📲 🍽 🛍 🎮⊣
Nearby Facilities
Directions On the N72, 3 miles west of
Killarney, right after the Golden Nugget Pub.

KILLARNEY

**Donoghues White Villa Farm Caravan &
Camping Park,** Lissivigeen, Killarney-Cork
Road (N22, Killarney, Co. Kerry,
Tel: 000 353 64 662 0671
Email: killarneycamping@eircom.net
www.killarneycaravanpark.com
Pitches For ⛺ 🚐 🚓 **Total** 24
Acreage 11 **Open** Easter **to** 01-Oct
Award winning, well landscaped, sheltered
Park in the countryside, yet only minutes from
Killarney town. The River Flesk runs through

the farm for fishing. Coach trips from the
Park. Self catering holiday apartments
available for hire.
Facilities ♿️🏊⚡️🅿️🕐⊙⊣ 🛒 📲
🕹 🛒 📲 🍽 🛍 📲 🛍 🎮 🚿 🌲 🛜
Nearby Facilities ↾ 🚣 ⬆ U ≀
Directions 2 miles east of Killarney on the
N22, 300 metres from the N22/N72
roundabout.

KILLARNEY

**Fleming's White Bridge Caravan &
Camping Park,** White Bridge,
Ballycasheen Road, Killarney, Co. Kerry,
Tel: 000 353 64 663 1590
Email: info@killarneycamping.com
www.killarneycamping.com
Pitches For ⛺ 🚐 🚓 **Total** 92
Acreage 24½ **Open** 09-Apr **to** 05-Oct
Multi award winning riverside Park, in a prime
location away from all the busy road, yet only
a short walk to the town. Coach trips from
the site. Pool, gym and fitness centre nearby.
Fishing and cycle hire on site.
Facilities 🏊♿️🅿️ 🛒
🍽 🕹 🛒 🍽 🛍 🔥 🛒⊣ 🛍 🌲 🛜
Directions 300 metres off the N22 south east
of Killarney.

KILLARNEY

Fossa Caravan & Camping Park, Fossa,
Killarney, Co. Kerry,
Tel: 000 353 64 663 1497
www.fossacampingkillarney.com
Pitches For ⛺ 🚐 🚓 **Total** 120
Acreage 8 **Open** April **to** Sept
Nearest Bus Stop (Miles) Outside
Beautiful wooded area overlooking the
famous MacGillycuddy Reeks and only a 5
minute walk to Lough Leane. Ideal for touring
the Kingdom of Kerry, and only 7 miles from
Carrantuohill which is Irelands highest
mountain. Tennis and take-away food on site.
Mobile homes available for hire.
Facilities 🏊♿️🅿️ 🛒
🍽 🕹 🛒 🍽 ♉ 🔥 🛒⊣🍽
Directions On the N72 3 miles west of
Killarney.

KILLARNEY

**Killarney Flesk Caravan & Camping
Park,** Flesk, Muckross Road, Killarney, Co.
Kerry,
Tel: 000 353 64 31704
Email: info@campingkillarney.com
www.campingkillarney.com
Pitches For ⛺ 🚐 🚓 **Total** 72
Acreage 5 **Open** April **to** Sept
Situated at the gateway to the National Park
and lakes. At the start of the Kerry Walk for
enjoying the magnificent woodlands and
mountains, and our native deer!
Entertainment in high season. Cycle hire and
take-away food available.
Facilities ♿️🏊⚡️🅿️ 🛒
🍽 🛒 🚿 ♉ 🍽 🛒 🛜
Nearby Facilities ↾ ≀
Directions From Killarney take the N71,
adjacent to Irelands National Events Centre.

KILLORGLIN

West's Caravan Park, Killarney Road,
Killorglin, Ring of Kerry, Co. Kerry,
Tel: 000 353 66 976 1240
Email: enquiries@westcaravans.com
www.westcaravans.com
Pitches For ⛺ 🚐 🚓 **Total** 60
Acreage 3½ **Open** Easter **to** Oct
Access Good **Site** Level
Alongside a river and overlooked by Irelands
highest mountain. Only 1 mile from the town.
Close to Killarney National Park, Skellig Rock
and Dingle. Mobile home sales and hire.

Facilities 🏊♿️🅿️🕐⊙⊣ 🛒
🛒 🍽 🛒 🛍 🍽 🚿 🌙
Nearby Facilities ↾ 🚣 U ≀ ✈
Nearest Town Killorglin
Directions Take the Ring of Kerry road from
Killarney to Killorglin, 1 mile from Killorglin
town.
➤ Killarney

LAURAGH

Creveen Lodge Caravan Park, Healy
Pass Road, Lauragh Village, Co. Kerry,
Tel: 000 353 64 668 3131
Email: info@creveenlodge.com
www.creveenlodge.com
Pitches For ⛺ 🚐 🚓 **Total** 20
Acreage 4 **Open** Easter **to** Oct
Small, well sheltered Park in the beautiful
Ring of Beara with excellent amenities. The
perfect place for a quiet holiday. Cottages
and caravans available to hire.
Facilities 🏊♿️🅿️ 🛒 📲 🍽 🛍 🎮⊣
Nearby Facilities 🚣
Directions From the R571 in Lauragh, take
the R574 Healy Pass Road and look for
signs.

TRALEE

Woodlands Park, Dan Spring Road,
Tralee, Co. Kerry,
Tel: 000 353 66 712 1235
Email: wdlands@eircom.net
www.kingdomcamping.com
Pitches For ⛺ 🚐 🚓 **Total** 135
Acreage 15 **Open** Mid March **to** Sept
Multi award winning Park situated in a quiet
parkland setting at the gateway to Dingle
Peninsula. Just a short walk through a rose
garden to Tralee town centre. Close to a
greyhound stadium, Aqua Dome, Aqua Golf,
a museum, the National Folk Theatre and a
cinema.
Facilities 🏊♿️🅿️ 🛒
🛒 🍽 🕹 🛒 📲 🍽 🛍 🔥 🛒⊣🍽 🛜
Nearby Facilities ≀
Directions From the N21, N22 or N70, follow
signs for Dingle N86.

KILKENNY

BENNETTSBRIDGE

Nore Valley Park, Annamult,
Bennettsbridge, Kilkenny, Co. Kilkenny,
Tel: 000 353 56 772 7229
Email: norevalleypark@eircom.net
www.norevalleypark.com
Pitches For ⛺ 🚐 🚓 **Total** 60
Acreage 5 **Open** March **to** Oct
Quiet, family run Park in a peaceful, rural
setting on a farm where children can feed
the animals. Lovely walks in the area. High
standard of cleanliness. Delicious home
baked food available. Fly fishing (extra
charge), crazy golf, pedal go-karts, 3D maze,
trailer rides and pool table on site.
Facilities 🏊♿️🅿️ 🛒
🛒 🍽 🕹 🛒 📲 🍽 🛍 🔥 🛒⊣🍽 🛒
Nearby Facilities ↾ 🚣 U
Directions From Kilkenny take the R700 to
Bennettsbridge. Just before the bridge turn
right at the sign, then after approx 3km turn
left at the sign.

KILKENNY

Tree Grove Caravan & Camping Park,
Danville House, New Ross Road, Kilkenny,
Co. Kilkenny,
Tel: 000 353 56 777 0302
Email: treecc@iol.ie
www.treegrovecamping.com
Pitches For ⛺ 🚐 🚓 **Total** 30
Acreage 4¼ **Open** March **to** Mid Nov

Perfectly situated for Medieval Kilkenny and South East. 25 minute easy walk along a river pathway to Kilkenny. Cycle hire on site. Also open weekends from Nov to March by prior arrangement only.
Facilities ⌶ ⌷ ⌐ ⌐ ⌐
⌷ ⌷ ⌷ ⌷ ⌷ ⌷ ⌷ ⌷
Nearby Facilities ⌐ ⌐ U
Directions Approx 1 mile from Kilkenny, after the roundabout on the R700 in the direction of New Ross.

LEITRIM
CARRICK-ON-SHANNON
Battlebridge Caravan & Camping Park, Leitrim Village, Carrick-on-Shannon, Co. Leitrim,
Tel: 000 353 71 965 0824
Email: battlebridge@eircom.net
www.beirnesofbattlebridge.com
Pitches For ⌂ ⌗ ⌗ **Total** 20
Acreage 2 **Open** All Year
On the banks of the River Shannon with a traditional Irish pub on site serving food. Cast a fishing line from your pitch or enjoy our private marina with slipway for boating. Miles of forest and canal walks in the area, good bird watching. Take-away food available.
Facilities ⌶ ⌷ ⌐ ⌷ ⌷ ⌷ ⌷ ⌷ ⌷ ⌷
Nearby Facilities ⌐ ⌐ ⌐
Directions From Carrick-on-Shannon take the R280 to Leitrim, turn left onto the R284 to Keadue, Park is ½ a mile.

MOHILL
Lough Rynn Caravan & Camping Park, Lough Rynn, Mohill, Co. Leitrim,
Tel: 000 353 86 825 4428
Email: cbohan@leitrimcoco.ie
www.leitrimcoco.ie
Pitches For ⌂ ⌗ ⌗ **Total** 20
Acreage 19 **Open** 08-Apr to Sept
On the shores of Lough Rynn and adjacent to Lough Rynn House & Gardens. Host of friendly pubs and restaurants and a childrens play area close by.
Facilities ⌶ ⌷ ⌐ ⌐ ⌐
Nearby Facilities U
Directions 1¼ miles south of Mohill on the road to Drumlish.

LIMERICK
ADARE
Adare Camping & Caravan Park, Adare, Co. Limerick,
Tel: 000 353 61 395376
Email: dohertycampingadare@eircom.net
www.adarecamping.com
Pitches For ⌂ ⌗ ⌗ **Total** 28
Acreage 5 **Open** 12-Mar to Sept
Family run Park with a high standard throughout. Newly developed farm walk. Outdoor hot tub on site.
Facilities ⌶ ⌷ ⌐ ⌐ ⌷ ⌷ ⌷ ⌷
Nearby Facilities ⌐ ⌐ U
Directions From Limerick take the N21 for Tralee and continue through Adare, turn left onto the R519 to Balingarry and follow signs.

KILCORNAN
Curragh Chase Caravan & Camping, Coillte Forest Park, Kilcornan, Co. Limerick,
Tel: 000 353 61 396349
Email: eileen.okeeffe@coillte.ie
www.coillteoutdoors.ie
Pitches For ⌂ ⌗ ⌗ **Total** 80
Acreage 8½ **Open** Easter then May to Sept
Located within the 773 acres of Coillte Forest Park with its arboretum, picnic sites, childrens

playground, forest walks and cycle trails, as well as multi-use trails which are suitable for all users.
Facilities ⌶ ⌷ ⌐ ⌐ ⌐ ⌐ ⌷ ⌷ ⌶
Nearby Facilities
Directions Take the N69 from Limerick for Foynes, in Kilcornan Village turn left and the Site is 2 miles.

LOUTH
DUNDALK
Gyles Quay Caravan Park, Riverstown, Dundalk, Co. Louth,
Tel: 000 353 42 937 6262
Pitches For ⌂ ⌗ ⌗ **Total** 139
Open 31-May to 01-Sep
Licensed pub on site with live entertainment.
Facilities ⌶ ⌷ ⌐ ⌐
⌷ ⌷ ⌷ ⌷ ⌷ ⌷ ⌷ ⌷
Nearby Facilities ⌐ ⌐ ⌐ ⌷ ⌷ ⌷
Directions From the M1 take the R173 for Dundalk. Follow signs for Carlingford for approx 7 miles then turn right for Gyles Quay. The Park is towards the end of the road on the right.

MAYO
ACHILL
Lavelles Golden Strand Caravan & Camping Park, Golden Strand, Dugort, Achill, Co. Mayo,
Tel: 000 353 86 231 4596/87 616 5
Pitches For ⌂ ⌗ ⌗ **Total** 37
Acreage 3¾ **Open** April to Oct
Set beside one of Mayos finest Blue Flag beaches (direct access form the Park). Scenic walks in the area.
Facilities ⌶ ⌷ ⌐ ⌐ ⌐ ⌐ ⌷ ⌷ ⌶
Nearby Facilities ⌐ ⌐ U
Directions From Achill Sound take the R319 to Bunnacurry T-Junction, turn right onto the crossroads at the valley, turn left and the Park is 1 mile.

ACHILL ISLAND
Keel Sandybanks Caravan & Camping Park, Achill Island, Keel, Co. Mayo,
Tel: 000 353 98 43211
Email: info@achillcamping.com
www.achillcamping.com
Pitches For ⌂ ⌗ ⌗ **Total** 100
Acreage 15 **Open** Mid May to Mid Sept
Set spectacularly between Slievemore Mountain, the Minaun Cliffs and Keel beach on Achill Island. Plenty of activities locally. Tennis on site.
Facilities ⌶ ⌷ ⌐ ⌐
⌷ ⌷ ⌷ ⌷ ⌐ ⌐ ⌐ ⌐
Nearby Facilities ⌐ ⌐ ⌷ ⌷ ⌷

BALLINA
Belleek Park Caravan & Camping, Belleek, Ballina, Co. Mayo,
Tel: 000 353 96 71533
Email: lenahan@belleekpark.com
www.belleekpark.com
Pitches For ⌂ ⌗ ⌗ **Total** 58
Acreage 9¾ **Open** March to Oct
Award winning park in a tranquil and sheltered location with excellent facilities and high standards. Close to the town and the River Moy (one of Europes most prolific salmon rivers). Ten minute walk to a forest park and riverside walks.
Facilities ⌷ ⌐ ⌐ ⌷ ⌷ ⌐ ⌐ ⌐ ⌐ ⌐ ⌐ ⌐
⌷ ⌷ ⌷ ⌷ ⌷ ⌷ ⌷ ⌷ ⌐ ⌐ ⌐ ⌐ ⌐
Nearby Facilities ⌐ ⌐ ⌷ ⌷ ⌷ U ⌐ ⌷ ⌷
Directions Take the R314 from Ballina towards Ballycastle, Park is just outside the town boundary, look for signs to Belleek on your right, turn right and the Park entrance is 300 metres on the right.

CASTLEBAR
Carra Caravan & Camping Park, Belcarra, Castlebar, Co. Mayo,
Tel: 000 353 94 903 2054
Email: post@mayoholidays.com
www.horsedrawncaravan.com
Pitches For ⌂ ⌗ ⌗ **Total** 20
Acreage 1¾ **Open** May to Late Sept
Village centre site. Horsedrawn holidays and country walks are a speciality from this site. Close to all amenities and attractions.
Facilities ⌶ ⌷ ⌐ ⌐ ⌷ ⌷ ⌷ ⌷ ⌷ ⌶
Nearby Facilities ⌐
Directions Take the N84 from Castlebar towards Ballinrobe, immediately turn left for Ballycarra (Belcarra).

CASTLEBAR
Carrowkeel Camping & Caravan Park, Ballyvary, Castlebar, Co. Mayo,
Tel: 000 353 94 903 1264
Email: mail@carrowkeelpark.ie
www.carrowkeelpark.ie
Pitches For ⌂ ⌗ ⌗ **Total** 58
Acreage 5 **Open** April to Sept
Well maintained Park in the heart of Mayo. Clubhouse with live entertainment in high season. Small shop with basic food supplies. Take-away food available. Just a few miles from the famous River Moy for salmon fishing.
Facilities ⌶ ⌷ ⌐ ⌐
⌷ ⌷ ⌷ ⌷ ⌷ ⌷ ⌷ ⌷ ⌷ ⌶
Nearby Facilities ⌐ ⌐ U ⌷
Directions 5 miles from Castlebar, just off the N5.

CASTLEBAR
Lough Lannagh Caravan Park, Castlebar, Co. Mayo,
Tel: 000 353 94 902 7111
Email: info@loughlannagh.ie
www.loughlannagh.ie
Pitches For ⌂ ⌗ ⌗ **Total** 20
Acreage 2½ **Open** Mid April to Sept
Lakeside setting just a 10 minute walk from Castlebar. Kids activities July and August. Breakfast caf, B&B, tennis and table tennis on site. Also for the over 18's, gym, sauna and steam rooms.
Facilities ⌶ ⌷ ⌐ ⌐ ⌷ ⌷
Nearby Facilities ⌐ ⌷ ⌷
Directions On the N5 at the edge of Castlebar going towards Westport, straight over two roundabouts, at the third take the second exit then turn immediately left.

CONG
Cong Caravan & Camping Park, Lisloughrey, Quay Road, Cong, Co. Mayo,
Tel: 000 353 94 954 6089
Email: info@quietman-cong.com
www.quietman-cong.com
Pitches For ⌂ ⌗ ⌗ **Total** 40
Acreage 3 **Open** All Year
Situated between Lough Mask and Lough Corrib, 1 mile from the fascinating Cong Village. Fisherman and boatsmans paradise! Lakeside and forest walks. Bike and boat rental on site.
Facilities ⌶ ⌷ ⌐ ⌐
⌷ ⌷ ⌷ ⌷ ⌷ ⌷ ⌷ ⌷ ⌷
Nearby Facilities ⌐ U
Directions From Cong head out on the Galway road, go past Ashford Castle entrance and take the next turn right, the Park is on your right after the cemetery.

REPUBLIC OF IRELAND

KNOCK

Knock Caravan & Camping Park, Main Street, Knock, Co. Mayo,
Tel: 000 353 94 938 8100
Email: info@knock-shrine.ie
www.knock-shrine.ie
Pitches For ▲ ⊕ ⊟ **Total** 88
Acreage 7¼ **Open** March **to** Oct
Sheltered, landscaped park. 5 minute walk from Our Lady's Shrine and Knock Museum. Ideal base for touring Mayo and the West of Ireland. Mobile homes for hire.
Facilities ╤ ▥ ♠ ⌐
🏴 ⊠ ⚲ ⊓ ♨ ➤ ⏚ ⊞
Nearby Facilities
Directions At Knock roundabout take Main Street for 1 mile, Park is on the left.

WESTPORT

Westport House Parkland Caravan & Camping Park, Westport House & Adventure Pk, Westport, Co. Mayo,
Tel: 000 353 98 27766/98 27780
Email: camping@westporthouse.ie
www.westporthouse.ie
Pitches For ▲ ⊕ ⊟ **Total** 95
Acreage 9¾ **Open** May **to** 06-Sep
Situated in the grounds of Westport House & Gardens with tennis, pitch n putt, fishing, swan pedaloes, mini railway, log flume ride, bouncy castle, Pirate Queen Ships Galleon, and indoor Jungle World (soft play). Easy drive to beaches.
Facilities ╤ ▥ ♠ ⌐ ⊠ ♀ ⊓ ⏚ ⊞
Nearby Facilities ⌐ ✔ ⚓ ⚲
Directions On the R335 2 miles from Westport, turn right at Westport Quay.

ROSCOMMON
ATHLONE

Hodson Bay Caravan & Camping Park, Kiltoom, Athlone, Co. Roscommon,
Tel: 000 353 90 649 2448
Pitches For ▲ ⊕ ⊟ **Total** 34
Acreage 2½ **Open** June **to** August
Quiet lakeside location beside a hotel, marina and golf course.
Facilities ╤ ▥ ♠ ⌐ ⊠ ⚲
Nearby Facilities
Directions From Athlone take the N61 Roscommon road for 3 miles, turn right for Hodson Bay and the Park is ½ a mile past the Hotel.

BALLAGHADERREEN

Willowbrook Caravan & Camping Park, Killtybranks, Ballaghaderreen, Co. Roscommon,
Tel: 000 353 94 986 1307
Email: info@willowbrookpark.com
www.willowbrookpark.com
Pitches For ▲ ⊕ ⊟ ⊟ **Total** 29
Acreage 2 **Open** All Year
Warm and friendly atmosphere in the Lung Valley, an unspoilt and beautiful landscaped area. Walking, archery and course fishing on site. We also offer the relaxing techniques of meditation, Tai Chi and Chi Kung.
Facilities ╤ ▥ ♠ ⌐ ⊠ ⚲ ✕ ⊓ ➤ ⚲
Nearby Facilities ⌐ ✔ ♪
Directions Take the R293 towards Castlerea, then take the R325. Go over the bridge and turn left, after approx ½ a mile turn right at Park sign and continue for 500 metres, Park is on the left.

BOYLE

Lough Key Forest & Activity Park, Caravan & Camping Dept., Boyle, Co. Roscommon,
Tel: 000 353 71 966 2212
www.loughkey.ie
Pitches For ▲ ⊕ ⊟ **Total** 72
Acreage 13½
Situated in Lough Key Forest Park with a legendary backdrop of water, parkland and forest encompassing a landmark cluster of unique attractions offering gentle pursuits or energetic activities. Boda Borg Technology House and Adventure Play Kingdom.
Facilities ╤ ▥ ♠ ⌐ ⊠ ⚲ ✕ ⊓ ♨
Directions On the N4, approx 2½ miles east of Boyle.

GAILEY BAY

Gailey Bay Caravan & Camping Park, Gailey Bay, Knockcroghery, Co. Roscommon,
Tel: 000 353 90 666 1058
Email: gaileybay@hotmail.com
www.gaileybay.com
Pitches For ▲ ⊕ ⊟ ⊟ **Total** 27
Acreage 2¾ **Open** Mid April **to** Oct
Fishing tackle and boat hire on site.
Facilities ╤ ▥ ♠ ⌐ ⊠ ⊓ ♨ ➤ ⚲
Directions Take the N61 from Roscommon towards Athlone. After Knockcroghery Village turn right the immediately left after the railway crossing, at first crossroads turn right.

SLIGO
BOYLE

Lough Arrow Touring Park, Ballynarry, Riverstown, Boyle, Co. Sligo,
Tel: 000 353 71 966 6018
Email: latp@eircom.net
www.homepage.eircom.net/~latp
Pitches For ▲ ⊕ ⊟ **Total** 30
Acreage 8½ **Open** Mid March **to** Oct
Award winning, landscaped site in a conservation area of stunning natural beauty overlooking Lough Arrow. Boules pitch, golf practice nets and boat hire on site.
Facilities ╤ ▥ ♠ ⌐ ⊠ ⚲
Nearby Facilities ⌐ ✔
Directions Take the N4 north, pass Boyle and turn first right sp Ballyfarnon and follow signs.

ROSSES POINT

Greenlands Caravan & Camping Park, Rosses Point, Co. Sligo,
Tel: 000 353 71 917 7113
Pitches For ▲ ⊕ ⊟ ⊟ **Total** 120
Acreage 6¼ **Open** Mid April **to** Mid Sept
Overlooking the Atlantic Ocean with magnificent views of Coney Island, Oyster Island, Blackrock Lighthouse and Benbulben and Knocknarea Mountains. Two bathing beaches. Adjacent to s golf club.
Facilities ♿ ╤ ▥ ♠ ⌐ ⊠ ⚲
🏴 ⊠ ♠ ⏚ ⊞
Nearby Facilities ⌐ ✔ ⚓ ⚲
Directions On the R29, 5 miles west of Sligo.

STRANDHILL

Strandhill Caravan & Camping Park, Strandhill, Co. Sligo,
Tel: 000 353 71 916 8111
Pitches For ⊕ ⊟ ⊟ **Total** 100
Acreage 14¾ **Open** Mid April **to** Sept
Beside Strandhill beach.
Facilities ╤ ▥ ♠ ⌐ ⊠ ⊓ ♠ ➤ ⊞
Nearby Facilities ⌐
Directions 5 miles west of Sligo City on the R292, on Airport Road.

TIPPERARY
AHERLOW

Ballinacourty House Caravan & Camping Park, Glen of Aherlow, Co. Tipperary,
Tel: 000 353 62 56559
Email: info@camping.ie
www.camping.ie
Pitches For ▲ ⊕ ⊟ **Total** 50
Acreage 5 **Open** Mid April **to** End Sept
Quiet and unique family run Park set in the beautiful Glen of Aherlow in the grounds of an 18th Century estate with the restored stable block as our main building. Wonderful views of the Galtee Mountains and the Sliebh na Much Hills. Tennis on site.
Facilities ╤ ▥ ♠ ⌐ ☉ ⚲ ☎
⊠ ⚲ ♠ ⊓ ♨ ➤ ⏚ ⊞
Nearby Facilities ⌐ ✔ ⋃
Directions Take the N24 from Cahir roundabout towards Tipperary, after 4 miles turn left to Glen of Aherlow Scenic Route, turn next right over the railway crossing and follow road through Rossadrehid Village, after approx 8½ miles turn right and follow signs to the

CAHIR

The Apple Camping & Caravan Park, Moorstown, Cahir, Co. Tipperary,
Tel: 000 353 52 744 1459
Email: con@theapplefarm.com
www.theapplefarm.com
Pitches For ▲ ⊕ ⊟ **Total** 32
Acreage 3½ **Open** May **to** Sept
Well maintained, nicely landscaped, unique park on a fruit farm. Succession of fruits to try all summer from strawberries and raspberries to apples and plums. Tennis on site.
Facilities ♿ ╤ ▥ ♠ ⌐ ☉ ⚲ ☎
⊠ ⚲ ♠ ⏚ ⊞ ⊠
Nearby Facilities ⌐ ✔ ⋃ ⚲ ⚲
Directions On the N24 between Cahir and Clonmel.

CLOGHEEN

Parson's Green, Clogheen, Co. Tipperary,
Tel: 000 353 52 65290
Email: kathleennoonan@oceanfree.net
www.clogheen.com
Pitches For ▲ ⊕ ⊟ **Total** 40
Acreage 27 **Open** All Year
Small family run Park with excellent facilities including coffee shop and take-away, farm museum, indoor and outdoor playgrounds, pet field, pony and pony n trap rides, boat rides and tennis court. Garden and river walks. Close to many places of interest.
Facilities ╤ ▥ ♠ ⌐ ⊠ ⚲ ♀ ⊓ ♠ ➤ ⊞
Nearby Facilities
Directions From Cahir take the R668.

CLONMEL

Powers The Pot Camping & Caravan Park, Harneys Cross, Clonmel, Co. Tipperary,
Tel: 000 353 52 612 3085
Email: info@powersthepot.net
www.powersthepot.net
Pitches For ▲ ⊕ ⊟ **Total** 20
Acreage 3¾ **Open** May **to** Sept
A beautiful spot on the side of the Comeragh Mountains with a wonderful ambiance and breathtaking views on a clear day. Ideal for walking with Munster Way passing by the site. Take-away food available.
Facilities ╤ ▥ ♠ ⌐ ⊠ ⚲
⊠ ☎ ☉ ⊠ ⚲ ♀ ⊓ ♠ ⊞
Nearby Facilities
Directions From the East on the N24, in Clonmel turn left at the first set of traffic lights, go straight and continue past the golf club.

ROSCREA

Streamstown Caravan & Camping Park, Roscrea, Co. Tipperary,
Tel: 000 353 50 521519
Email: streamstowncaravanpark@eircom.net
www.tipperarycaravanpark.com
Pitches For 🏕 ⚕ 🚐 🚍 **Total** 30
Acreage 2½ **Open** Easter **to** Sept
Beautifully landscaped family run Park on a dairy farm in quiet surroundings. Ideal for walking the Slieve Bloom Mountains. Mobile homes for hire.
Facilities ♿ ✦ ⓦ🅿 ⌐ ⌂
⌧ ⓘ ⚙ 🛁 Ⓦ ♠ ➡🄴
Nearby Facilities 🏌 🚣 ⋃
Directions Just off the N7. From Roscrea take the R491 to Shinrone for 1½ miles, signposted.

WATERFORD

DUNGARVAN

Bayview Caravan & Camping Park, Gold Coast Golf Resort, Dungarvan, Co. Waterford,
Tel: 000 353 58 45100/58 45050
Email: info@bayviewcaravancamping.com
www.bayviewcaravancamping.com
Pitches For 🏕 ⚕ 🚐 🚍 **Total** 32
Acreage 6 **Open** Feb **to** Nov
Award winning Park adjacent to The Gold Coast Golf Hotel & Leisure Centre with its 18 hole golf course which overlooks Dungarvan Bay. Bike hire and ten pin bowling. 1 mile from Clonea Beach.
Facilities ✦ ⓦ🅿 ⌐ ⌂
⌧ ✗ ♈ ♒ ⚓ ✕➡🄴 ⊡ ✐ 🛜
Nearby Facilities 🏌 🚣 ⚓ ⋃ ⫧ ♺
Directions Turn south off the N25 or the R675 onto the Gold Coast road and follow signs.

DUNGARVAN

Casey's Caravan & Camping Park, Clonea, Dungarvan, Co. Waterford,
Tel: 000 353 58 41919
Pitches For 🏕 ⚕ 🚐 🚍 **Total** 284
Acreage 19¾ **Open** 09-Apr **to** 13-Sep
Award winning Park with direct access to a golden sandy beach. Crazy golf on site. Wet World Kids Club during July and August. Hotel with leisure centre adjacent. Whilst here why not visit the famous Waterford Crystal Factory.
Facilities ✦ ⓦ🅿 ⌐ ⌂
⌧ ⓘ ⚙ 🛁 Ⓦ ♠ ➡🄴
Nearby Facilities 🏌 🚣 ⚓
Directions From Waterford take the N25 towards Dungarvan, turn left after the Clonea Strand & Gold Coast Amenity sign. Pass Dungarvan Golf Club and turn first left, go straight over crossroads and roundabout onto Clonea.

TRAMORE

Newtown Cove Caravan & Camping Park, Newtown Road, Tramore, Co. Waterford,
Tel: 000 353 51 381979/51 381121
Email: info@newtowncove.com
www.newtowncove.com
Pitches For 🏕 ⚕ 🚐 🚍 **Total** 40
Acreage 5½ **Open** 11-Apr **to** 28-Sep
Superbly kept, multi award winning, family run Park in a peaceful setting. Short distance from Tramore with its sandy beach, and just

a 5 minute walk from the picturesque cove of Newtown. Plenty of attractions nearby. Mobile homes for hire. No commercial vehicles. Booking is advisable.
Facilities ✦ ⓦ🅿 ⌐ ⌂
⌧ ⓢ ⓘ ⚙ 🛁 Ⓦ ♠ 🛗➡🄴 🛜
Nearby Facilities 🏌 🚴 ⚓ ⋃ ♺

WESTMEATH

ATHLONE

Lough Ree (East) Caravan & Camping Park, Ballykeeran, Athlone, Co. Westmeath,
Tel: 000 353 90 647 8561
Email: athlonecamping@eircom.net
Pitches For 🏕 ⚕ 🚐 🚍 **Total** 40
Acreage 5 **Open** April **to** Sept
Set on wonderful countryside on the shores of Lough Ree and bordered by the Breensford trout river. Ideal for fishing, canoeing, boating, windsurfing and sailing. Jetty and boat slip. Beside a pub and 2 miles from Athlone.
Facilities ✦ ⓦ🅿 ⌐ ⌂ ⓘ ⚙ ♠ 🛗➡
Nearby Facilities 🏌 ⚓ ⋃
Directions Take the N55 off the Athlone Bypass and head north for 1¾ miles. Park is directly behind the srone clad house in Ballykeeran Village.

WEXFORD

FETHARD-ON-SEA

Ocean Island, Fethard-on-Sea, New Ross, Co. Wexford,
Tel: 000 353 51 397148
Pitches For 🏕 ⚕ 🚐 🚍 **Total** 42
Acreage 3 **Open** Mid April **to** Sept
1¼ miles to the beach.
Facilities ✦ ⓦ🅿 ⌐ ⌂ ⓢ ⓢ ⚙ ♠ ➡🄴
Nearby Facilities 🏌 🚣 ⋃
Directions From Wexford take the R733 to Duncannon Road roundabout and turn left sp Wellington Bridge. Follow signs for Fethard-on-Sea.

KILMUCKRIDGE

Morriscastle Strand Caravan & Camping Park, Morriscastle, Kilmuckridge, Co. Wexford,
Tel: 000 353 53 913 0124
Email: info@morriscastlestrand.com
www.morriscastlestrand.com
Pitches For 🏕 ⚕ 🚐 🚍 **Total** 100
Acreage 39½ **Open** Mid March **to** Sept
Beside the soft sand dunes with 12 miles of Blue Flag beach. Close to many attractions.
Facilities ✦ ⓦ🅿 ⌐ ⌂ ⓢ ⓢ ⚙ ♠ 🛗➡🄴
Nearby Facilities
Directions From Wexford take the R741 and follow signs for Kilmuckridge Village. Park is clearly signposted.

ROSSLARE

St Margarets Beach, Lady's Island, Rosslare Harbour, Co. Wexford,
Tel: 000 353 53 913 1169
Email: stmarg@eircom.net
Pitches For 🏕 ⚕ 🚐 🚍 **Total** 38
Acreage 5 **Open** Mid March **to** Sept
Quiet, rural park in an area of natural beauty. 500 metres from a sandy beach. 15 minutes from Rosslare Ferry Port.
Facilities ✦ ⓦ🅿 ⌐ ⌂ ⓢ ⓢ ⚙ 🛗➡🄴 🛜
Nearby Facilities
Directions From Rosslare take the N25, approaching Tagoat, turn left just after the roundabout towards Lady's Island and Carne. Continue past Butlers Bar on the left and turn next left. Signposted from the N25.

WEXFORD

Ferrybank Caravan & Camping, Ferrybank, Wexford, Co. Wexford,
Tel: 000 353 53 918 5256
Email: info@wexfordswimmingpool.ie
www.wexfordswimmingpool.ie
Pitches For 🏕 ⚕ 🚐 🚍 **Total** 97
Acreage 10 **Open** All Year
Overlooking Wexford Harbour. Within 9 miles of Blue Flag beaches, heritage sites and nature reserves. Booking essential for May and September.
Facilities ✦ ⓦ🅿 ⌐ ⌂ ⌧ ⓢ ⚙ 🛁 Ⓦ ♠ 🐴 ➡🄴
Nearby Facilities
Directions ½ a mile east of Wexford Town on the R741 (over the bridge).

WEXFORD

The Trading Post, Ballaghkeen, Co. Wexford,
Tel: 000 353 53 912 7368
Email: info@wexfordcamping.com
www.wexfordcamping.com
Pitches For 🏕 ⚕ 🚐 🚍 **Total** 21
Acreage 3 **Open** April **to** Sept
4 Star family run Park. Beside a traditional thatched pub, a shop and a service station (open 24 hours for fuel). 5km from the beach and only 25km from Rosslarf Ferry Port.
Facilities ♿ ✦ ⓦ🅿 ⌐ ⌂ ⚙ ⌧ ⊡ ⌂
ⓢ ⓘ ⚙ 🛁 Ⓦ 🛗➡🄴 ✳ ⚘ ♦ 🛜
Nearby Facilities 🏌 🚣 ⚓ ⋃ ⫧ ♺
Directions From Enniscorthy take the Blackwater/Oulart road for approx 4km then turn right onto the R744. Go through Ballaghkeen and at the R741 intersection turn right, Park is approx 2km beside the Emo petrol station. ENTRANCE FROM THE FORECOURT.

WICKLOW

DONARD

Moat Farm Caravan & Camping Park, Donard, Co. Wicklow,
Tel: 000 353 45 404727
Email: moatfarm@ireland.com
Pitches For 🏕 ⚕ 🚐 🚍 **Total** 40
Acreage 2½ **Open** Mid March **to** Sept
Small, quiet and secluded family run Park set in a tranquil, rural area in the foothills of Wicklow Mountains. Short stroll to Donard Village. Painters, walkers and photographers paradise. No commercial vehicles.
Facilities ✦ ⓦ🅿 ⌐ ⌂ ⓢ ⚙ 🛁 Ⓦ ➡
Nearby Facilities 🏌 🚣 ⋃ ♦
Directions From the N81 in Doinard, turn at The Old Toll House Pub and follow signs.

RATHDRUM

Hidden Valley Caravan & Camping Park, Rathdrum, Co. Wicklow,
Tel: 000 353 86 727 2872
Email: info@irelandholidaypark.com
www.irelandholidaypark.com
Pitches For 🏕 ⚕ 🚐 🚍 **Total** 60
Acreage 18 **Open** 09-Apr **to** 20-Sep
Serene haven of tranquility and relaxation. Set in a beautiful valley overlooking the cascading waters of the Avonmore River and our very own lake for fishing, swimming, kayaking and rowboats. Abundance of wildlife. NEW fun park on site. 10 minute walk to Rathdrum and its amenities. Numerous walks in the Wicklow Mountains and Clara Vale National Park.
Facilities ✦ ⊟ ⓗ ⓦ🅿 ⌐ ⌂ ⚙ 🛗➡🄴 ✐
Nearby Facilities 🏌 🚣 ⚓ ⋃ ♦
Directions From Dublin take the N11/M50 South to the R752 exit and go into Rathnew. Follow signs to Rathdrum and on passing Glanbia (on the left) take the next right turn.

REPUBLIC OF IRELAND

INDEX TO PARKS OPEN ALL YEAR

Look for the County in which you wish to stay, then choose a Town. The park name is shown alongside. Then simply refer to the main section of the guide to read more on the park you have selected.

ENGLAND
BRISTOL (COUNTY OF)
BRISTOL, Baltic Wharf Caravan Club Site,

CAMBRIDGESHIRE
CAMBRIDGE, Appleacre Park,
CAMBRIDGE, Cherry Hinton Caravan Club Site,
ELY, Riverside C & C P,
GRAFHAM, Grafham Water Caravan Club Site,
HUNTINGDON, Burliegh Hill Farm,
HUNTINGDON, Stroud Hill Park,
HUNTINGDON, The Willows Caravan Park,
MARCH, Floods Ferry Marina Park,
PETERBOROUGH, Ferry Meadows C Club Site,
WISBECH, Virginia Lake Caravan Park,

CHESHIRE
CHESTER, Chester Southerly Holiday Park,
CHESTER, Chester Fairoaks C Club Site,
CHESTER, Manor Wood Country Caravan Park,
NORTHWICH, Delamere Forest C & C Club Site,

CORNWALL
BODMIN, Ruthern Valley Holidays,
BUDE, Budemeadows Touring Park,
HAYLE, Sunny Meadow Holiday Park,
HAYLE, Lavender Fields Touring Park,
LANDS END, Cardinney C & C Park,
LISKEARD, Pine Valley Park,
LISKEARD, Colliford Tavern Camp Site,
LIZARD, Henrys Campsite,
LOOE, Tregoad Park,
LOOE, Tencreek Holiday Park,
LOOE, Polborder House C & C Park,
LOOE, Camping Caradon Touring Park,
LOOE, Bay View Farm,
NEWQUAY, Trekenning Tourist Park,
NEWQUAY, Carvynick Country Club
NEWQUAY, Perran-Quay Touring Park,
PADSTOW, Old MacDonalds Farm,
PADSTOW, Padstow Touring Park,
PENZANCE, Bone Valley C & C Park,
REDRUTH, St Day Touring Park,
REDRUTH, Lakeside Camping,
REDRUTH, Globe Vale Holiday Park,
SALTASH, Dolbeare Park,
SENNEN, Seaview Holiday Park,
ST. IVES, Ayr Holiday Park,

ST. JUST, Kelynack C & C P,
ST. JUST, Roselands Caravan Park,
TORPOINT, Whitsand Bay Holiday Park,
TRURO, Carnon Downs C & C Park,
TRURO, Cosawes Park,

CUMBRIA
APPLEBY, Silverband Park,
APPLEBY, Wild Rose Park,
ARNSIDE/SILVERDALE, Fell End C P,
DENT, Ewegales Farm,
GRANGE-OVER-SANDS, Meathop Fell C C Site,
KESWICK, Scotgate Holiday Park,
LONGTOWN, High Gaitle Caravan Park,
SILLOTH, Stanwix Park Holiday Centre,
ULLSWATER, The Quiet Site,
ULLSWATER, Sykeside Camping Park,
ULVERSTON, Bardsea Leisure,
WASDALE, Wasdale National Trust Campsite,

DERBYSHIRE
BAKEWELL, Chatsworth Park Cara Club Site,
BUXTON, Endon Cottage,
BUXTON, Beech Croft Farm,
CASTLETON, Losehill Caravan Club Site,
DERBY, Beechwood Park,
DOVERIDGE, Cavendish Caravan Site,
EDALE, Fieldhead Campsite,
EDALE, Cooper's Camp & Caravan Site,
MATLOCK, Holly Bush C & C Site,
MATLOCK, Packhorse Farm Bungalow,
MATLOCK, Lickpenny Caravan Park,
RIPLEY, Golden Valley C & C Park,
SWADLINCOTE, Conkers C & C Club Site,

DEVON
BUCKFASTLEIGH, Beara Farm Camping Site,
CHAGFORD, Woodland Springs Adult T P,
COMBE MARTIN, Stowford Farm Meadows,
DAWLISH, Cofton Country Holidays,
EXETER, Kennford International Caravan Park,
HARTLAND, Hartland C & C P,
HOLSWORTHY, Hedley Wood C & C P,
HOLSWORTHY, Noteworthy C & C,
ILFRACOMBE, Hidden Valley T & C Park,
KINGSBRIDGE, Parkland,
NEWTON ABBOT, Lemonford Caravan Park,
NEWTON ABBOT, The Dartmoor Halfway Inn C P,

OKEHAMPTON, Bundu C & C P,
PLYMOUTH, Riverside Caravan Park,
SOUTH MOLTON, Riverside C & C P,
TAVISTOCK, Harford Bridge Holiday Park,
TAVISTOCK, Tavistock C & C Club Site,
TIVERTON, West Middlewick Farm C & C,
WOOLACOMBE, Europa Park,

DORSET
BOURNEMOUTH, Charris C & C P,
CHARMOUTH, Manor Farm Holiday Centre,
CHRISTCHURCH, Mount Pleasant T Pk,
CHRISTCHURCH, Longfield Caravan Park,
DORCHESTER, Lyons Gate Caravan Park,
SHAFTESBURY, Blackmore Vale C & C P,
WAREHAM, Manor Farm C & C P,
WAREHAM, Lookout Holiday Park,
WAREHAM, Wareham Forest Tourist Park,
WEYMOUTH, Bagwell Farm Touring Park,

DURHAM
DURHAM, Finchale Abbey Caravan Park,
DURHAM, Grange Caravan Club Site,

ESSEX
COLCHESTER, Colchester Holiday Park Ltd.,

GLOUCESTERSHIRE
CHELTENHAM, Briarfields Motel & T P,
CIRENCESTER, Mayfield Touring Park,
COLEFORD, Woodlands View Caravan Park,
DURSLEY, Hogsdown Farm C & C,
MORETON-IN-MARSH, Moreton-In-Marsh C C Site,
SLIMBRIDGE, Tudor C & C Park,

HAMPSHIRE
ANDOVER, Wyke Down Touring C & C P,
FAREHAM, Dibles Park,

HEREFORDSHIRE
HEREFORD, Cuckoos Corner,
LEOMINSTER, Home Farm Caravan Site,
PETERCHURCH, Poston Mill Park,
CHORLEYWOOD, North Hill Farm,
HERTFORD, C & C Club Site,

ISLE OF WIGHT
COWES, Waverley Park Holiday Centre,
SANDOWN, Village Way C & C P,
ST. HELENS, Carpenters Farm Campsite,

KENT
ASHFORD, Broadhembury C & C P,
CANTERBURY, C & C Club Site,
FOLKESTONE, Black Horse Farm C C Site,
MAIDSTONE, Coldblow Camping,

MARDEN, Tanner Farm Touring C & C P,
RAMSGATE, Nethercourt Touring Park,
ROCHESTER, Woolmans Wood Tourist Caravan Park,
SEVENOAKS, Thriftwood Holiday Park,

LANCASHIRE
CROSTON, Royal Umpire Caravan Park,
HEYWOOD, Gelderwood Country Park,
LANCASTER, Wyreside Lakes Fishery,
MORECAMBE, Venture Caravan Park,

LEICESTERSHIRE
LEICESTER, Hill Top Caravan Park,
LUTTERWORTH, Stanford Hall Caravan Park,

LINCOLNSHIRE
BOSTON, Pilgrims Way C & C P,
BOSTON, Orchard Park,
CROWLAND, The Bridge Caravan Park,
GRANTHAM, Woodland Waters Ltd.,
LINCOLN, Oakhill Leisure,
LINCOLN, Shortferry Caravan Park,
MARKET DEEPING, The Deepings C P,
MARKET RASEN, Lincolnshire Lanes C & C Site,
SCUNTHORPE, Brookside C & C P,
SKEGNESS, Ronam Cottage,
SPALDING, Delph Bank Touring Caravan Park,
SPILSBY, Meadowlands,
STAMFORD, Road End Farm Caravan Site,

LONDON
ABBEY WOOD, Abbey Wood C C Site,

MANCHESTER
LITTLEBOROUGH, Hollingworth Lake C P,

NORFOLK
BURGH ST. PETER, Waveney River Centre,
CLIPPESBY, Clippesby Hall,
FAKENHAM, Fakenham Racecourse C C Site,
GREAT HOCKHAM, Thetford Forest C & C C Site,
GREAT YARMOUTH, Rose Farm T & C Park,
KINGS LYNN, Pentney Park,
KINGS LYNN, Kings Lynn C & C P,
NORWICH, Swans Harbour C & C P,
SANDRINGHAM, Sandringham Estate C C Site,
SWAFFHAM, Breckland Meadows Touring Park,
THETFORD, Lowe Caravan Park,

NORTHAMPTONSHIRE
KETTERING, Kestrel Caravans,
ALNWICK, Railway Inn Caravan Park,
BERWICK-UPON-TWEED, Ord House C Park,
OTTERBURN, Border Forest Caravan P,
WOOLER, Riverside Country Park,

NOTTINGHAMSHIRE
HOLME PIERREPONT, N W S, C & C P,
MANSFIELD, Tall Trees Park,
NEWARK, Robin Hood Retreat,
NOTTINGHAM, Manor Farm Caravan Site,
NOTTINGHAM, Thorntons Holt Camping Park,
RATCLIFFE ON SOAR, Red Hill Marina,
SUTTON-IN-ASHFIELD, Teversal C & C C Site,
WORKSOP, Clumber Park Caravan Club Site,
WORKSOP, Riverside Caravan Park,

OXFORDSHIRE
BANBURY, Barnstones C & C Site,
BLETCHINGDON, Greenhill Leisure Park,
BLETCHINGDON, Diamond C & C P,
OXFORD, C & C Club Site,

SHROPSHIRE
BISHOPS CASTLE, Daisy Bank Caravan Park,
BRIDGNORTH, Woodend Farm,
MARKET DRAYTON, Wharf Caravan Park,
OSWESTRY, Oswestry C & C Club Site,
SHREWSBURY, Beaconsfield Farm H P,
WEM, Lower Lacon Caravan Park,
WHITCHURCH, Roden View C & C,

SOMERSET
BATH, Bath Chew Valley Caravan Park,
BATH, Bury View Farm,
BATH, Newton Mill Holiday Park,
BRIDGWATER, Fairways International C & C P,
BRIDGWATER, Mill Farm C & C P,
CHARD, Barleymows Farm Shop & Restaurant,
CROWCOMBE, Quantock Orchard C P,
EXFORD, Westermill Farm,
LANGPORT, Bowdens Crest C & C P,
MARTOCK, Southfork Caravan Park,
SPARKFORD, Long Hazel Park,
TAUNTON, Holly Bush Park,
TAUNTON, Cornish Farm Touring Park,
TAUNTON, Waterrow Touring Park,
WELLINGTON, Cadeside Caravan Club Site,
WESTON-SUPER-MARE, West End Farm C P,
WILLITON, Home Farm Holiday Centre,

STAFFORDSHIRE
BURTON-ON-TRENT, Willowbrook Farm,
LEEK, C & C Club Site,
LICHFIELD, Cathedral Grange T C Park,

SUFFOLK
BURY ST EDMUNDS, The Dell Touring Park,
IPSWICH, Low House Touring Caravan Centre,
STOWMARKET, Stonham Barns C & C P,
WOODBRIDGE, Run Cottage Touring Park,

SURREY
CHERTSEY, C & C Club Site,
LINGFIELD, Long Acres C & C P,
REDHILL, Alderstead Heath C Club Site,

SUSSEX (EAST)
BEXHILL-ON-SEA, Kloofs Caravan Park,
BRIGHTON, Sheepcote Valley C Club Site,
SEAFORD, Buckle Holiday Park,
UCKFIELD, Heaven Farm,

SUSSEX (WEST)
ARUNDEL, Maynards C & C P,
CHICHESTER, Stubcroft Farm Campsite,
HORSHAM, Honeybridge Park,
HORSHAM, Sumners Ponds Fishery & Campsite,
LITTLEHAMPTON, Daisyfields Touring Park,

WARWICKSHIRE
STRATFORD-UPON-AVON, Dodwell Park,
WOLVEY, Wolvey C & C P,

WEST MIDLANDS
MERIDEN, Somers Wood Caravan Park,
SUTTON COLDFIELD, C & C Club Site,

WILTSHIRE
CALNE, Blackland Lakes,
DEVIZES, C & C Club Site,
ORCHESTON, Stonehenge Touring Park,
SALISBURY, Green Hill Farm C & C P,
TILSHEAD, Brades Acre,
WESTBURY, Brokerswood Country Park,

WORCESTERSHIRE
BEWDLEY, Bank Farm Holiday Parks Ltd.,
GREAT MALVERN, C & C Club Site,
STOURPORT-ON-SEVERN, Lickhill Manor C P,
WYTHALL, Chapel Lane Caravan Club Site,

YORK (COUNTY OF)
YORK, Rowntree Park Caravan Club Site,
YORK, York Touring Caravan Site,
YORK, Acomb Grange,

YORKSHIRE (EAST)
GOOLE, Dobella Lane Farm,

YORKSHIRE (NORTH)
BOROUGHBRIDGE, C & C Club Site,
HARROGATE, Shaws Trailer Park,
KNARESBOROUGH, Spen House Caravan Site,
MUKER, Usha Gap Caravan & Camp Site,
SKIPTON, Eshton Road Caravan Site,
THORNABY-ON-TEES, White Water C C Site,

YORK (Near), The Ponderosa Caravan Park,
YORK (Near), Willow House Caravan Park,
YORK (Near), Cawood Park,

YORKSHIRE (SOUTH)
ROTHERHAM, Thrybergh Country Park,
THORNE, Elder House Touring Park,

YORKSHIRE (WEST)
HOLMFIRTH, Holme Valley C & C P,
LEEDS, Moor Lodge Caravan Park,
LEEDS, Glenfield Caravan Park,
WETHERBY, Haighfield Caravan Park,

SCOTLAND
ABERDEENSHIRE
ABERDEEN, Deeside Holiday Park,
CRUDEN BAY, Craighead C & C P,
KINTORE, Hillhead Caravan Park,

ANGUS
KIRRIEMUIR, Drumshademuir Caravan Park,

AYRSHIRE (NORTH)
LARGS, South Whittlieburn Farm,

AYRSHIRE (SOUTH)
TURNBERRY, Balkenna Caravan Park,

CLACKMANNAN
ALLOA, The Woods Caravan Park,

DUMFRIES & GALLOWAY
BORGUE, Brighouse Bay Holiday Park,
CROCKETFORD, Park of Brandedleys,
DALBEATTIE, Glenearly Caravan Park,
ECCLEFECHAN, Cressfield Caravan Park,
GLENLUCE, Whitecairn Holiday Park,
GLENLUCE, Glenluce Caravan Park,
GRETNA, Braids Caravan Park,
KIPPFORD, Kippford Holiday Park,
KIRKPATRICK FLEMING, King Robert the
        Bruces Cave Caravan & Camping Site,
LANGHOLM, Whitshiels Caravan Park,
MOFFAT, C & C Club Site,
STRANRAER, Aird Donald Caravan Park,

EDINBURGH (CITY)
EDINBURGH, Drum Mohr Caravan Park,
EDINBURGH, Edinburgh Caravan Club Site,

HIGHLANDS
DRUMNADROCHIT, Borlum Farm C P,
DUNBEATH, Inver Caravan Park,
DUNDONNELL, Badrallach Bothy & Campsite,

GLENCOE, Invercoe C & C P,
GLENCOE, Red Squirrel Campsite,
UIG, Uig Bay Camping & Caravan Site,

LANARKSHIRE (NORTH)
GLASGOW, Craigendmuir C & C Site,

LOTHIAN (WEST)
BLACKBURN, Mosshall Farm Caravan Park,
LINLITHGOW, Beecraigs C & C Site,

PERTH & KINROSS
ALYTH, Five Roads Caravan Park,
AUCHTERARDER, Auchterarder C & C P,
BLAIRGOWRIE, Blairgowrie Holiday Park,
BRIDGE OF CALLY, Corriefodly Holiday Park,

SCOTTISH BORDERS
ETTRICK, Honey Cottage Caravan Park,
MELROSE, Gibson Park Caravan Club Site,

WALES
ANGLESEY
RHOSNEIGR, Tyn Llidiart Camping Site,

CAERPHILLY
BLACKWOOD, Penyfan C & L Park,

CARMARTHENSHIRE
LLANDDEUSANT, Black Mountain C P,
LLANDOVERY, Erwlon C & C P,

CEREDIGION
ABERYSTWYTH, Bryncarnedd Caravan Park,

CONWY
BETWS-Y-COED, Rynys Farm Camping Site,
BETWS-Y-COED, Y Giler Arms,
COLWYN BAY, Bron-Y-Wendon T C P,

GWYNEDD
ARTHOG, Garthyfog Camping Site,
DOLGELLAU, Pant-y-Cae,
DOLGELLAU, Tyddyn Farm,
MORFA NEFYN, Graeanfryn Farm,
TYWYN, DÃ´I Einion,
TYWYN, Cwmrhwyddfor Campsite,

NEWPORT
NEWPORT, Tredegar House Country Park C C Site,
NEWPORT, Pentre-Tai Farm,

PEMBROKESHIRE
NEWPORT, Tycanol Farm Camp Site,

POWYS
BRECON, Anchorage Caravan Park,
BRECON, Mill Field Caravan Park,
LLANDRINDOD WELLS, Bryncrach Farm C S,
LLANFYLLIN, Henstent Park,
NEW RADNOR, Old Station Caravan Park,
WELSHPOOL, Rhyd-Y-Groes Touring C & C P,
WELSHPOOL, Riverbend Caravan Park,

SWANSEA
RHOSSILI, Pitton Cross C & C P,

WREXHAM
WREXHAM, Plassey Leisure Park,

NORTHERN IRELAND
BELFAST
BELFAST, Jordanstown Lough Shore Park,

CO. ARMAGH
TANDRAGEE, Clare Glen Caravan Park,

CO. FERMANAGH
GARRISON, Lough Melvin Holiday Centre,

CO. TYRONE
CLOGHER, Clogher Valley Country C P,

REPUBLIC OF IRELAND
CO. CORK
CARRIGTWOHILL, Jasmine Villa C & C P,
CASTLETOWNBERE, Berehaven C & A Park,
ROSSCARBERY, O'Riordans Caravan Park,

CO. DUBLIN
CLONDALKIN, Camac Valley Tourist C & C P,

CO. LEITRIM
CARRICK-ON-SHANNON, Battlebridge C & C P,

CO. MAYO
CONG, Cong C & C P,

CO. ROSCOMMON
BALLAGHADERREEN, Willowbrook C & C P,

CO. TIPPERARY
CLOGHEEN, Parson's Green,

CO. WEXFORD
WEXFORD, Ferrybank Caravan & Camping,

INDEX TO PARKS ACCEPTING ADULTS ONLY

Look for the County in which you wish to stay, then choose a Town. The park name is shown alongside. Then simply refer to the main section of the guide to read more on the park you have selected.

ENGLAND
CAMBRIDGESHIRE
ELY, Riverside Caravan & Camping Park,
HUNTINGDON, Stroud Hill Park,
HUNTINGDON, Wyton Lakes Holiday Park,
MARCH, Floods Ferry Marina Park,

CHESHIRE
CHESTER, Netherwood Touring Site,
KNUTSFORD, Royal Vale Caravan Park,
WINSFORD, Lamb Cottage Caravan Park

CORNWALL
NEWQUAY, Rosecliston Park,
PENZANCE, Wayfarers C & C Park,
REDRUTH, St Day Touring Park,
TRURO, Chacewater Camping & Caravan Park,

CUMBRIA
CARLISLE, Green Acres Caravan Park,

CUMBRIA (continued)
KENDAL, Ashes Exclusively Adult Caravan Park,
MEALSGATE, The Larches Caravan Park,

DERBYSHIRE
MATLOCK, Packhorse Farm Bungalow,

DEVON
CHAGFORD, Woodland Springs Adult T P,
LYDFORD, Lydford Caravan & Camping Park,
TIVERTON, Zeacombe House Caravan Park,
TORQUAY, Widdicombe Farm Touring Park,

DORSET
BRIDPORT, Bingham Grange T C P,
ST. LEONARDS, Back-of-Beyond Touring Park,

VISIT **www.cades.co.uk** TO SEE OUR MONTHLY COMPETITION

DURHAM
DURHAM, Finchale Abbey Caravan Park,

HEREFORDSHIRE
HEREFORD, Cuckoos Corner,
LEOMINSTER, Arrow Bank Holiday Park,

KENT
ROCHESTER, Woolmans Wood Tourist
Caravan Park,
TENTERDEN, Spill Land Farm Holiday Park,

LANCASHIRE
HEYWOOD, Gelderwood Country Park,

LEICESTERSHIRE
LEICESTER, Hill Top Caravan Park,

LINCOLNSHIRE
BOSTON, Long Acres (Adult Only) C Park,
BOSTON, Orchard Park,
BOSTON, Walnut Lake Lodges & Camping,
HUTTOFT, Jolly Common Adult Only C P,
SPALDING, Delph Bank Touring Caravan Park,
SPILSBY, Meadowlands,
STAMFORD, Road End Farm Caravan Site,
SUTTON-ON-SEA, Cherry Tree Site,

NORFOLK
DOWNHAM MARKET, Grange Farm T P,
MUNDESLEY, Sandy Gulls Cliff Top T P,
NORTH WALSHAM, Two Mills Touring Park,
STANHOE, The Rickels C & C Park,
SWAFFHAM, Breckland Meadows Touring Park,

SHROPSHIRE
BISHOPS CASTLE, Daisy Bank Caravan Park,
SHREWSBURY, Beaconsfield Farm H P,

SOMERSET
BATH, Bath Chew Valley Caravan Park,
CHEDDAR, Cheddar Bridge Touring Park,
CHEDDAR, Rodney Stoke Inn,
DULVERTON, Exe Valley Caravan Site,
GLASTONBURY, The Old Oaks Touring Park,
HIGHBRIDGE, Greenacre Place Touring
Caravan Park,
SPARKFORD, Long Hazel Park,
STREET, Bramble Hill C & C Park,
TAUNTON, Waterrow Touring Park,
WELLINGTON, Greenacres Touring Park,
WELLS, Homestead Park,

STAFFORDSHIRE
LONGNOR, Longnor Wood Holiday Park,

SUFFOLK
SHOTLEY, Shotley Caravan Park,
THEBERTON, Cakes & Ale,

WEST MIDLANDS
MERIDEN, Somers Wood Caravan Park,

WILTSHIRE
CHIPPENHAM, Plough Lane Caravan Site,

WORCESTERSHIRE
STOURPORT-ON-SEVERN, Lincomb Lock C P,

YORK (COUNTY OF)
YORK, Moorside Caravan Park,

YORKSHIRE (NORTH)
HARROGATE, Shaws Trailer Park,
HARROGATE, Maustin Park,
HELMSLEY, Foxholme Touring C & C Park,
PICKERING, Overbrook Caravan Park,
RICHMOND, Tavern House Caravan Park,
YORK (Near), Willow House Caravan Park,

YORKSHIRE (WEST)
LEEDS, Moor Lodge Caravan Park,
WETHERBY, Haighfield Caravan Park,

SCOTLAND
FIFE
LEVEN, Monturpie Caravan Park,

HIGHLANDS
INVERGARRY, Faichemard Farm C & C Park,

WALES
CARMARTHENSHIRE
CARMARTHEN, Pant Farm C & C Park,

CONWY
PENMAENMAWR, Tyddyn Du Touring Park,

DENBIGHSHIRE
RUTHIN, Dyffryn Ial Caravan Site,

PEMBROKESHIRE
FISHGUARD, Rosebush C & C Park,
HERMON, The Lamb Inn T C P,
TENBY, Red House Farm,

POWYS
BUILTH WELLS, Irfon River Caravan Park,
CRICKHOWELL, Riverside C & C Park
LLANDRINDOD WELLS, Dalmore C P,
WELSHPOOL, Rhyd-Y-Groes T C & C Park,

INDEX TO PARKS WITH FISHING ON SITE

Look for the County in which you wish to stay, then choose a Town. The park name is shown alongside. Then simply refer to the main section of the guide to read more on the park you have selected.

ENGLAND

BUCKINGHAMSHIRE
STONY STRATFORD, Cosgrove Park,

CAMBRIDGESHIRE
EARITH, Westview Marina,
HUNTINGDON, Quiet Waters Caravan Park,
HUNTINGDON, Wyton Lakes Holiday Park,
HUNTINGDON, Stroud Hill Park,
HUNTINGDON, Huntingdon Boathaven & C P,
MARCH, Floods Ferry Marina Park,
ST. IVES, Crystal Lakes Leisure Park,
ST. NEOTS, Camping & Caravanning Club Site,
WISBECH, Virginia Lake Caravan Park,

CHESHIRE
CHESTER, Chester Southerly Holiday Park,
CHESTER, Manor Wood Country Caravan Park,
CHESTER, Netherwood Touring Site,
MACCLESFIELD, Strawberry Wood C P,

CORNWALL
BODMIN, South Penquite Farm,
BOSCASTLE, St. Tinney Farm Holidays,
BUDE, Wooda Farm Holiday Park,
CRANTOCK, Treago Farm C & C Site,
HAYLE, Beachside Holiday Park,
ISLES OF SCILLY, Troytown Farm Campsite,
LOOE, Tregoad Park,
NEWQUAY, Trevornick Holiday Park,
NEWQUAY, Trethiggey Touring Park,
NEWQUAY, Trencreek Holiday Park,
NEWQUAY, Monkey Tree Holiday Park,
PADSTOW, Mother Ivey's Bay Holiday Park,
PERRANPORTH, Perran Springs Holiday Park,
POLZEATH, Tristram Camping & Caravan Park,
REDRUTH, Stithians Lake Country Park,
ST. IVES, St Ives Bay Holiday Park,
TRURO, Cosawes Park,
WADEBRIDGE, Trewince Farm Holiday Park,

CUMBRIA
AMBLESIDE, Low Wray National Trust Campsite,
ARNSIDE/SILVERDALE, Hall More C P,
CARLISLE, Dalston Hall Caravan Park,
CONISTON, Pier Cottage Caravan Park,
CONISTON, Coniston Hall Camping Site,
DENT, Ewegales Farm,

EGREMONT, Tarnside Caravan Park,
KENDAL, Waters Edge Caravan Park,
KESWICK, Burns Farm Caravan Site,
PENRITH, Lowther Holiday Park,
PENRITH, Waterside House Campsite,
PENRITH, Park Foot Caravan & Camping Park,
ULVERSTON, Bardsea Leisure,
WINDERMERE, Hill of Oaks Caravan Estate,

DERBYSHIRE
ASHBOURNE, Callow Top Holiday Park,
ASHBOURNE, Rivendale C & L Park,
BAMFORD, Swallowholme C & C Park,
DERBY, Shardlow Marina Caravan Park,
DERBY, Beechwood Park,
RIPLEY, Golden Valley C & C Park,

DEVON
ASHBURTON, River Dart Country Park,
BUDLEIGH SALTERTON, Ladram Bay H P,
COMBE MARTIN, Newberry Valley Park,
CREDITON, Yeatheridge Farm C & C Park,
CROYDE BAY, Ruda Holiday Park,
DAWLISH, Cofton Country Holidays,
DAWLISH WARREN, Peppermint Park,
EXETER, Springfield Holiday Park,
HARTLAND, Hartland Caravan & Camping Park,
ILFRACOMBE, Watermouth Cove Holiday Park,
MORTEHOE, Twitchen House Holiday Village,
MORTEHOE, Warcombe Farm Camping Park,
PUTSBOROUGH, Putsborough Sands C P,
SOUTH MOLTON, Riverside C & C Park,
TAVISTOCK, Harford Bridge Holiday Park,
UMBERLEIGH, C & C Club Site,
WOOLACOMBE, Woolacombe Bay H Village,
WOOLACOMBE, Golden Coast Holiday Village,

DORSET
BRIDPORT, Britt Valley Campground,
BRIDPORT, Freshwater Beach Holiday Park,
CHARMOUTH, Manor Farm Holiday Centre,
CHARMOUTH, Wood Farm C & C Park,
CHIDEOCK, Golden Cap Holiday Park,
DORCHESTER, Lyons Gate Caravan Park,
POOLE, Beacon Hill Touring Park,
SHAFTESBURY, Blackmore Vale C & C Park,
ST. LEONARDS, Back-of-Beyond Touring Park,
THREE LEGGED CROSS, Woolsbridge Manor,
WAREHAM, East Creech C & C Site,

DURHAM
DARLINGTON, Doe Park Caravan Site,
DURHAM, Finchale Abbey Caravan Park,
MIDDLETON-IN-TEESDALE, Mickleton Mill C P,

ESSEX
CLACTON-ON-SEA, Orchards Holiday Village,
HALSTEAD, Gosfield Lake Resort,
HARWICH, Dovercourt Caravan Park,
MERSEA ISLAND, Waldegraves H & L Park,
SOUTHEND-ON-SEA, Riverside Village H P,
WEELEY, Homestead Lake Park,

GLOUCESTERSHIRE
CIRENCESTER, Second Chance Caravan Park,
CIRENCESTER, Hoburne Cotswold,
GLOUCESTER, The Red Lion Inn C & C Park,
TEWKESBURY, Winchcombe Camping &
Caravanning Club Site,
TEWKESBURY, Mill Avon Holiday Park,
TEWKESBURY, Croft Farm L & W Park,

HAMPSHIRE
BRANSGORE, Harrow Wood Farm Caravan
Park,
FORDINGBRIDGE, Hill Cottage Farm C & C P,
HAYLING ISLAND, Fleet Park,

HEREFORDSHIRE
BROMYARD, Boyce Caravan Park,
HEREFORD, Hereford C & C Club Site,
HEREFORD, Lucksall C & C Park,
LEOMINSTER, Arrow Bank Holiday Park,
LEOMINSTER, Pearl Lake Leisure Park,
LEOMINSTER, Nicholson Farm,
PETERCHURCH, Poston Mill Park,
ROSS-ON-WYE, Broadmeadow Caravan Park,

ISLE OF WIGHT
FRESHWATER, Compton Farm,
SANDOWN, Adgestone Camping &
Caravanning Club Site,
SANDOWN, Village Way C & C Park,
SHANKLIN, Ninham Country Holidays,

KENT
MARDEN, Tanner Farm Touring C & C Park,

LANCASHIRE
BENTHAM, Riverside Caravan Park,
BLACKPOOL, Windy Harbour Holiday Park,
CARNFORTH, The Villa Fishery & C P,
GARSTANG, Claylands Caravan Park,
LANCASTER, Wyreside Lakes Fishery,
SOUTHPORT, Riverside Holiday Park,

LINCOLNSHIRE
ALFORD, Woodthorpe Hall Leisure Park,
BOSTON, Walnut Lake Lodges & Camping,
BOSTON, Orchard Park,
BOSTON, The Moorings,
CLEETHORPES, Thorpe Park Holiday Centre,
GRANTHAM, Woodland Waters Ltd.,
HORNCASTLE, Ashby Park,
HUTTOFT, Jolly Common Adult Only C P,
INGOLDMELLS, Hardy's Touring Site,
LINCOLN, Shortferry Caravan Park,
LINCOLN, Hartsholme Country Park,
LINCOLN, Oakhill Leisure,
MARKET DEEPING, The Deepings C P,
MARKET DEEPING/STAMFORD, Tallington Lakes,
NORTH SOMERCOTES, Lakeside Park,
SKEGNESS, Pine Trees Leisure Park,
SKEGNESS, Southview Holiday Park,
SKEGNESS, Country Meadows Holiday Park,
SKEGNESS, Skegness Water Leisure Park,
SPALDING, Ashleigh Caravan Park,
SPALDING, Foremans Bridge Caravan Park,
SUTTON-ON-SEA, Lakeside Caravan Park,
TATTERSHALL, Orchard Caravan Park,
TATTERSHALL, Willow Holt C & C Park,
WAINFLEET, Holly Tree Pub & Caravan Park,

NORFOLK
BURGH ST. PETER, Waveney River Centre,
DISS, The Willows Camping & Caravan Park,
DOWNHAM MARKET, Grange Farm T P,
FAKENHAM, The Old Brick Kilns,
GREAT HOCKHAM, Thetford Forest C & C Site,
HARLESTON, Little Lakeland Caravan Park,
HEMSBY, Long Beach Caravan Park,
HOLT, Kelling Heath Holiday Park,
HUNSTANTON, Searles Leisure Resort,
MUNDESLEY, Sandy Gulls Cliff Top T P,
NORWICH, Swans Harbour C & C P,
NORWICH, Camping & Caravanning Club Site,
REEDHAM, Reedham Ferry Complex Ltd.,
SHERINGHAM, Beeston Regis Caravan Park,

NORTHAMPTONSHIRE
NORTHAMPTON, Billing Aquadrome,

NORTHUMBERLAND
HALTWHISTLE, Seldom Seen Caravan Park,
HALTWHISTLE, C & C Club Site,
HAYDON BRIDGE, Poplars Riverside C P,
OTTERBURN, Border Forest Caravan Park,
OVINGHAM, High Hermitage Caravan Park,
WOOLER, Riverside Country Park,

NOTTINGHAMSHIRE
MANSFIELD, Tall Trees Park,
TUXFORD, Marnham Meadows Holiday Park,

OXFORDSHIRE
BLETCHINGDON, Greenhill Leisure Park,
HENLEY-ON-THAMES, Swiss Farm International,
WITNEY, Hardwick Parks,

SHROPSHIRE
BISHOPS CASTLE, The Green Caravan Park,
BRIDGNORTH, Woodend Farm,
BRIDGNORTH, The Riverside Caravan Park,
ELLESMERE, Fernwood Caravan Park,
LUDLOW, Westbrook Park,
SHREWSBURY, Severn House,
SHREWSBURY, Beaconsfield Farm H P,
SHREWSBURY, Ebury Hill C & C Club Site,
WHITCHURCH, Roden View C & C,

SOMERSET
BREAN SANDS, Northam Farm Holiday Park,
BREAN SANDS, Warren Farm Holiday Centre,
BREAN SANDS, Holiday Resort Unity
BRUTON, Batcombe Vale C & C Park,
BURNHAM-ON-SEA, B-on-S Holiday Village,
BURNHAM-ON-SEA, Diamond Farm C & T P,
BURNHAM-ON-SEA, Home Farm Holiday Park,
DULVERTON, Exe Valley Caravan Site,
DULVERTON, Lakeside Caravan Club Site,
EXFORD, Westermill Farm,
GLASTONBURY, The Old Oaks Touring Park,
LANGPORT, Thorney Lakes Caravan Site,
TAUNTON, Waterrow Touring Park,
WELLINGTON, Gamlins Farm Caravan Park,
WILLITON, Home Farm Holiday Centre,

STAFFORDSHIRE
CHEADLE, Hales Hall C & C Park,
LEEK, Glencote Caravan Park,

SUFFOLK
BUNGAY, Outney Meadow Caravan Park,
EYE, Honeypot Caravan & Camping Park,
LOWESTOFT, Heathland Beach C P,
NAYLAND, Rushbanks Farm,
SAXMUNDHAM, Carlton Meres Country Park,
SAXMUNDHAM, Whitearch Touring Park,
STOWMARKET, Stonham Barns C & C Park,
SUDBURY, Willowmere Caravan Park,

SURREY
CHERTSEY, Camping & Caravanning Club Site,
HORSLEY, Camping & Caravanning Club Site,

SUSSEX (EAST)
BATTLE, Brakes Coppice Park,
EASTBOURNE, Fairfields Farm C & C Park,
SEAFORD, Buckle Holiday Park,
UCKFIELD, Honeys Green Caravan Park,
UCKFIELD, Heaven Farm,

SUSSEX (WEST)
CHICHESTER, Chichester Lakeside H P,
HORSHAM, Sumners Ponds

WARWICKSHIRE
STRATFORD-UPON-AVON, Island Meadow C P,
STRATFORD-UPON-AVON, Riverside C P,
WOLVEY, Wolvey Caravan & Camping Park,

WILTSHIRE
CALNE, Blackland Lakes,
MALMESBURY, Burton Hill Caravan Park,
SALISBURY, Green Hill Farm C & C Park,
TROWBRIDGE, Stowford Manor Farm,
WESTBURY, Brokerswood Country Park,

WORCESTERSHIRE
BEWDLEY, Bank Farm Holiday Parks Ltd.,
MALVERN, Kingsgreen Caravan Park,
STOURPORT-ON-SEVERN, Lickhill Manor C P,
STOURPORT-ON-SEVERN, Lincomb Lock C P,
WORCESTER, Ketch Caravan Park,
WORCESTER, Mill House C & C Site,
WORCESTER, Peachley Leisure,

YORK (COUNTY OF)
YORK, Acomb Grange,
YORK, Moorside Caravan Park,

YORKSHIRE (EAST)
BRIDLINGTON, Thorpe Hall C & C Site,
HULL, Sand-le-Mere Caravan Park,
STAMFORD BRIDGE, Weir Caravan Park,
WITHERNSEA, Willows Holiday Park,

YORKSHIRE (NORTH)
BENTHAM, Riverside Caravan Park,
BOROUGHBRIDGE, C & C Club Site,
FILEY, Orchard Farm Holiday Village,
FILEY, Primrose Valley Holiday Park,
HARROGATE, Bilton Park,
HARROGATE, High Moor Farm Caravan Park,
KNARESBOROUGH, Kingfisher C & C Park,
LEYBURN, Akebar Park,
PATELEY BRIDGE, Riverside Caravan Park,
RIPON, Sleningford Watermill,
RIPON, River Laver Holiday Park,
SCARBOROUGH, Blue Dolphin Holiday Centre,
SELBY, Oakmere Caravan Park,

SKIPTON, Eshton Road Caravan Site,
YORK (Near), Willow House Caravan Park,
YORK (Near), Home Farm C & C Park,
YORK (Near), Cawood Park,
YORK (Near), Goosewood Holiday Park,

YORKSHIRE (SOUTH)
ROTHERHAM, Thrybergh Country Park,

YORKSHIRE (WEST)
HOLMFIRTH, Holme Valley C & C Park,

SCOTLAND
ABERDEENSHIRE
ABOYNE, Aboyne Loch Caravan Park,

ARGYLL & BUTE
ISLE OF MULL (CRAIGNURE), Shieling Holidays,
MACHRIHANISH, Machrihanish Caravan Park,
MUASDALE, Muasdale Holiday Park,
OBAN, North Ledaig Caravan Park,
SOUTHEND, Machribeg Caravan Site,

DUMFRIES & GALLOWAY
BORGUE, Brighouse Bay Holiday Park,
CASTLE DOUGLAS, Lochside C & C Park,
DUMFRIES, Barnsoul Farm & Wildlife Area,
GATEHOUSE OF FLEET, Mossyard C P,
GLENLUCE, Whitecairn Holiday Park,
ISLE OF WHITHORN, Burrowhead H Village,
KIRKPATRICK FLEMING, King Robert the
Bruces Cave Caravan & Camping Site,
LOCHMABEN, Kirkloch C & C Site,
PARTON, Loch Ken Holiday Park,
PORT LOGAN, New England Bay C Club Site,
PORTPATRICK, Sunnymeade Caravan Park,

FIFE
ST. ANDREWS, Cairnsmill Caravan Park,

HIGHLANDS
ACHARACLE, Resipole Holiday Park,
DUNDONNELL, Badrallach Bothy & Campsite,
EDINBANE, Skye C & C Club Site,
FORT WILLIAM, Glen Nevis C & C Park,
FORT WILLIAM, Linnhe Lochside Holidays,
GLENCOE, Red Squirrel Campsite,
GLENCOE, Invercoe Caravan & Camping Park,
INVERMORISTON, Loch Ness Holiday Park,
KINLOCHLEVEN, Caolasnacon C & C Park,
LOCHINVER, Clachtoll Campsite,
ROY BRIDGE, Bunroy C & C Site,
UIG, Uig Bay Camping & Caravan Site,
ULLAPOOL, Ardmair Point C & C Park,

LOTHIAN (WEST)
LINLITHGOW, Beecraigs C & C Site,

MORAY
ELGIN, Riverside Caravan Park,

PERTH & KINROSS
AUCHTERARDER, Auchterarder C & C Park,
BRIDGE OF CALLY, Corriefodly Holiday Park,
DUNKELD, Inver Mill Farm Caravan Park,
PITLOCHRY, Milton of Fonab Caravan Site,
ST. FILLANS, Loch Earn Caravan Park,

SCOTTISH BORDERS
ETTRICK, Honey Cottage Caravan Park,
HAWICK, Riverside Caravan Park,
KELSO, Springwood Estate,

STIRLING
CALLANDER, Gart Caravan Park,
KILLIN, Maragowan Caravan Club Site,
STRATHYRE, Immervoulin C & C Park,

WESTERN ISLES
HARRIS, Minch View Touring Park,

WALES
ANGLESEY
LLANFWROG, Penrhyn Bay Caravan Park,

CAERPHILLY
ABERCARN, Cwmcarn Forest Campsite,

CARMARTHENSHIRE
LLANDOVERY, Erwlon C & C Park,
LLANGADOG, Pont Aber,
NEWCASTLE EMLYN, Afon Teifi C & C Park,

CEREDIGION
ABERYSTWYTH, Morfa Bychan Holiday Park,
LLANRHYSTUD, Pengarreg Caravan Park,
NEW QUAY, Pencnwc Holiday Park,

CONWY
BETWS-Y-COED, Y Giler Arms,
TY-NANT, Glan Ceirw Caravan Park,

DENBIGHSHIRE
CORWEN, Hendwr Caravan Park,
LLANGOLLEN, Ddol Hir Caravan Park,
RUTHIN, Dyffryn Ial Caravan Site,

GWYNEDD
ABERSOCH, Nant-Y-Big,
ABERSOCH, Tyn-y-Mur T & C Park,

GWYNEDD (continued)
BALA, Tyn Cornel Camping & Caravan Park,
BALA, Bryn Gwyn Caravan & Camping Park,
BALA, Glanllyn-Lakeside C & C Park,
BALA, Ty-Isaf Camping Site,
BANGOR, Dinas Farm Camping & Touring Site,
BARMOUTH, Sunnysands Caravan Park,
CAERNARFON, Bryn Gloch C & C Park,
CAERNARFON, Riverside Camping,
CAERNARFON, Talymignedd Campsite,
CLYNNOG FAWR, Aberafon Camping &
Caravan Site,
CRICCIETH, Eisteddfa C & C Site,
DINAS MAWDDWY, Tynypwll C & C Site,
DOLGELLAU, Dolgamedd C & C Site,
PWLLHELI, Hafan Y Mor,
PWLLHELI, Hirdre Fawr Caravan & Camping,

MONMOUTHSHIRE
MONMOUTH, Glen Trothy Caravan Park,
MONMOUTH, Bridge C P & C Site,

PEMBROKESHIRE
FISHGUARD, Rosebush C & C Park,
HAVERFORDWEST, Nolton Cross C P,
MILFORD HAVEN, Sandy Haven Caravan Park,
NARBERTH, Noble Court Holiday Park,
NEWPORT, Llwyngwair Manor Holiday Park,
NEWPORT, Tycanol Farm Camp Site,
TENBY, Milton Bridge Caravan Park,

POWYS
BRECON, Lakeside Caravan Park,
BUILTH WELLS, Irfon River Caravan Park,
LLANDRINDOD WELLS, Disserth C & C Park,
LLANFYLLIN, Henstent Park,
LLANIDLOES, Dol-Llys Touring Site,
LLANSANTFFRAID, Vyrnwy Caravan Park,
LLANSANTFFRAID, Bryn-Vyrnwy Caravan Park,
MACHYNLLETH, Morben Isaf H H & T P,
MIDDLETOWN, Bank Farm Caravan Park,
PENYBONTFAWR, Parc Farm,
PRESTEIGNE, Rockbridge Park,
RHAYADER, Wyeside C & C Park,
RHAYADER, Nantymynach C & C Park,
WELSHPOOL, Henllan Caravan Park,
WELSHPOOL, Riverbend Caravan Park,
WELSHPOOL, Severn Caravan Park,
WELSHPOOL, Carmel Caravan Park,

WREXHAM
WREXHAM, Trench Farm T C P & Fisheries,
WREXHAM, Plassey Leisure Park,

NORTHERN IRELAND
FERMANAGH
BELCOO, Rushin House Caravan Park,
KESH, LoanEden Caravan Park,
LISNARICK, Drumhoney Caravan Park,

TYRONE
DUNGANNON, Dungannon Park,

REPUBLIC OF IRELAND
CLARE
DOOLIN, O'Connors Riverside C & C Park,
KILKEE, Green Acres Caravan & Camping Park,

CORK
BANTRY, Eagle Point Camping,
FERMOY, Blackwater Valley C & C Park,

KERRY
KILLARNEY, Fleming's White Bridge C & C P,
KILLARNEY, Donoghues White Villa Farm,
KILLORGLIN, West's Caravan Park,

KILKENNY
BENNETTSBRIDGE, Nore Valley Park,

ROSCOMMON
BALLAGHADERREEN, Willowbrook C & C P,

WATERFORD
DUNGARVAN, Bayview C & C Park,

WICKLOW
RATHDRUM, Hidden Valley C & C Park,

Thank you for choosing Cade's Guide to help you find the right Touring Park for you.

Do please help us to continue providing this information by informing any park you contact of where you found their details.

NOTES

If you have a favourite park that is currently not included in Cade's, do let us know. Email us enquiries@cades.co.uk.

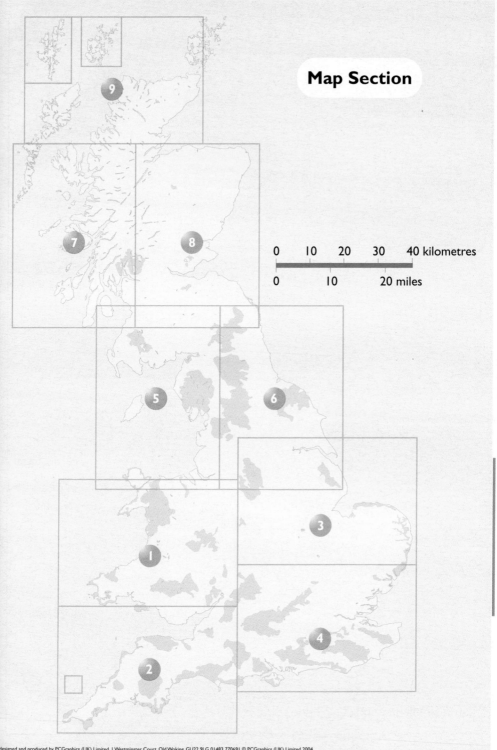

Map Section

0   10   20   30   40 kilometres

0   10   20 miles

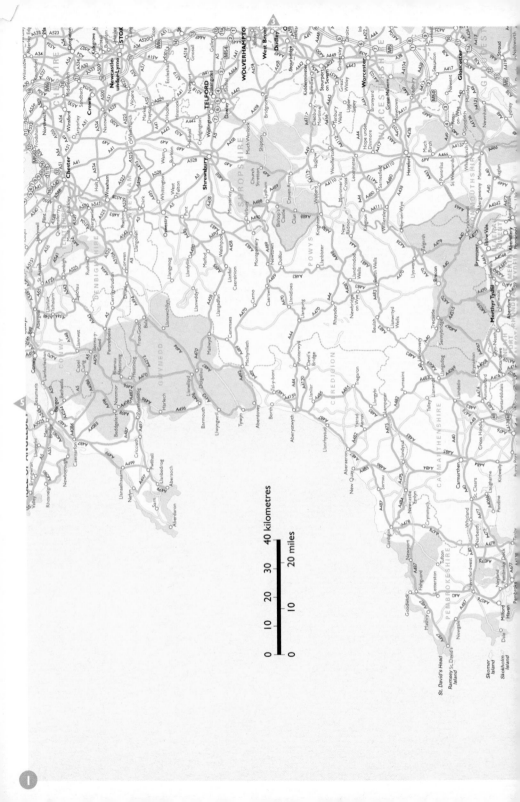

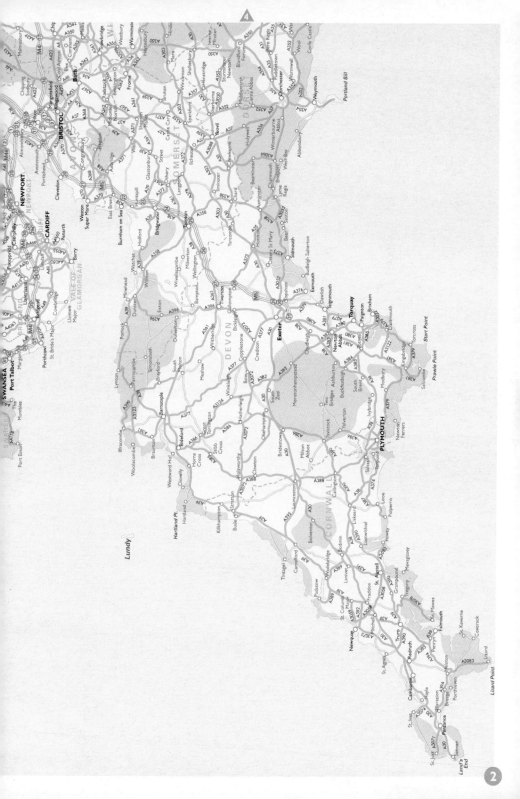

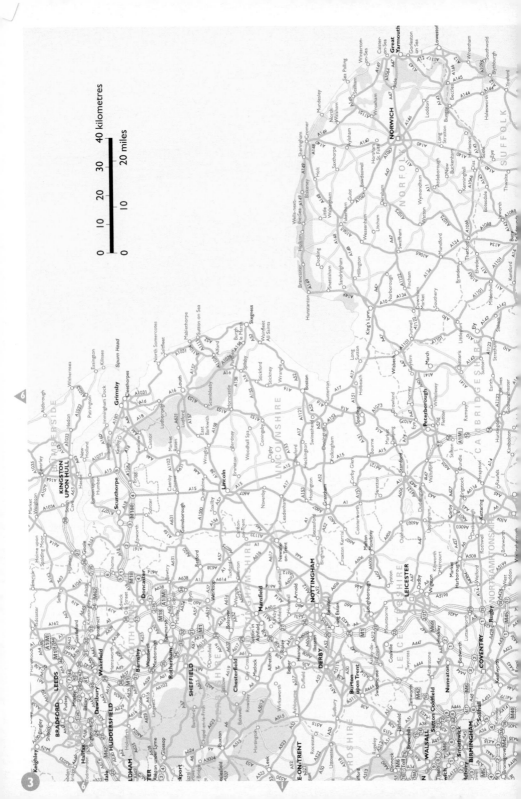

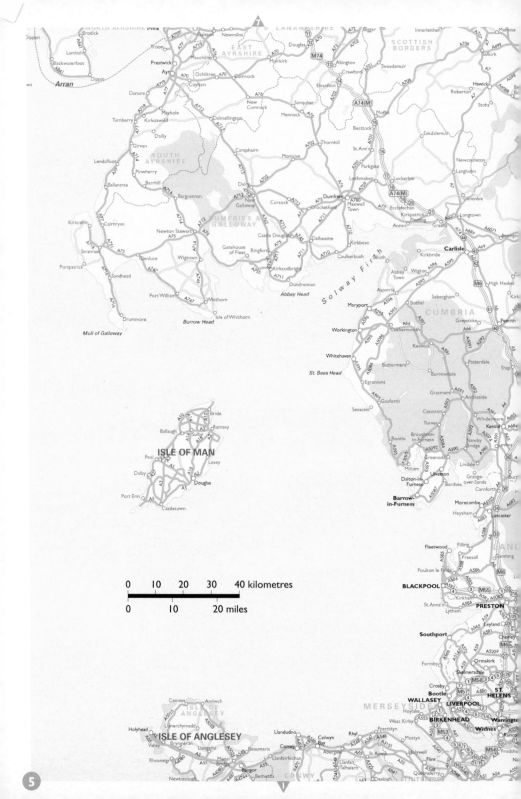

NORTH AYRSHIRE
Irvine
Brodick
Lamlash
Blackwaterfoot
Dippin
Arran
Troon
Prestwick
Ayr
Dunure
Maybole
Turnberry
Kirkoswald
Dalry
Girvan
Daily
Lendalfoot
Pinwherry
Ballantrae
Barrhill
Bargrennan
Kirkcolm
Cairnryan
Newton Stewart
Stranraer
Glenluce
Wigtown
Portpatrick
Sandhead
Port William
Whithorn
Drummore
Burrow Head
Isle of Whithorn
Mull of Galloway

EAST AYRSHIRE
Balsten
Newmilns
Mauchline
Muirkirk
Ochiltree
Cumnock
New Cumnock
Sanquhar
Mennock
Carsphairn
Monaive
Thornhill
St. Ann's
Parkgate
Lochmaben
Dalry
New Galloway
Corsock
Crocketford
Dumfries
Maxwell Town
Castle Douglas
Dalbeattie
Gatehouse of Fleet
Ringford
Kirkcudbright
Caulkerbush
Dundrennan
Abbey Head

Douglas
Abington
Crawford
Elvanfoot
Moffat
Beattock
Eskdalemuir
Newcastleton
Langholm
Ecclefechan
Kirkpatrick-Fleming
Annan
Gretna
Longtown

SCOTTISH BORDERS
Biggar
Innerleithen
Melrose
Tweedsmuir
Selkirk
Hawick
Roberton
Stobs
Carlisle
Kirkbride
Silloth
Abbey Town
Wigton
Aspatria
Seberham
Maryport
Bothel
Workington
Cockermouth
Keswick
Whitehaven
Buttermere
Borrowdale
St. Bees Head
Egremont
Grasmere
Ambleside
Seascale
Gosforth
Coniston
Windermere
Kendal
Torver
Bootle
Broughton-in-Furness
Newby Bridge
Greenodd
Lindale
Millom
Liverston
Grange-over-Sands
Dalton-in-Furness
Bardsea
Carnforth
Barrow-in-Furness
Morecambe
Heysham
Lancaster

Solway Firth

CUMBRIA
High Hesket
Greystoke
Penrith
Patterdale
Shap

ISLE OF MAN
Bride
Ballaugh
Sulby
Ramsey
Peel
Laxey
Dalby
Douglas
Port Erin
Castletown

0 10 20 30 40 kilometres
0 10 20 miles

Fleetwood
Pilling
Preesall
Garstang
Poulton le Fylde
BLACKPOOL
St. Anne's
Kirkham
Lytham
PRESTON
Southport
Leyland
Chorley
Formby
Ormskirk
Skelmersdale
Crosby
Bootle
ST. HELENS
WALLASEY
LIVERPOOL
MERSEYSIDE
Hoylake
BIRKENHEAD
Warrington
West Kirby
Widnes
Runcorn
Frodsham

ISLE OF ANGLESEY
Cemaes
Amlwch
Holyhead
Llanerchymedd
Valley
Brynpwran
Llangefni
Llandudno
Conwy
Colwyn Bay
Rhyl
Prestatyn
Rhosneigr
Menai
Besumaris
Llanfairfechan
Abergele
St. Asaph
Mostyn
Holywell
Flint
Bangor
Bethesda
Newborough
Denbigh
Queensferry
CONWY

8

Kelso
Belford
Bamburgh
Town Yetholm
Wooler
Embleton
Alnwick
Lesbury
Newton-on-the-Moor
Amble
Rothbury
Rochester
Otterburn
Longhorsley
Newbiggin-by-the-Sea
NORTHUMBERLAND
Morpeth
Ashington
Cambo
Bellingham
Ridsdale
Bedlington
Blyth
Wark
Belsay
Whitley Bay
Simonburn
Chollerton
Ponteland
Gosforth
Wallsend
North Shields
Haydon Bridge
NEWCASTLE
SOUTH SHIELDS
Haltwhistle
Hexham
Corbridge
Hebburn
Jarrow
TYNE AND WEAR
Broomhaugh
GATESHEAD
Boldon
Washington
SUNDERLAND
Allendale
Consett
Stanley
Houghton-le-Spring
Edmundbyers
Chester-le-Street
Seaham
Castleside
Lanchester
Alston
Easington
Durham
Peterlee
Wearhead
Stanhope
Tow Law
St. John's Chapel
Crook
Spennymoor
CLEVELAND
DURHAM
Bishop Auckland
Sedgefield
Hartlepool
Middleton-in-Teesdale
Newton Aycliffe
Billingham
Redcar
West Auckland
Marske-by-the-Sea
Saltburn-by-the-Sea
Appleby-in-Westmorland
Stockton-on-Tees
Eston
Brotton
Barnard Castle
MIDDLESBROUGH
Brough
Darlington
Thornaby on Tees
Guisborough
Loftus
Bowes
Yarm
Whitby
Kirkby Stephen
Stokesley
Sleights
Robin Hood's Bay
Scotch Corner
Great Smeaton
Reeth
Richmond
Catterick
Muker
Northallerton
Sedbergh
Hawes
Aysgarth
Leyburn
Lockton
Scalby
Scarborough
Middleham
Bedale
Leeming Bar
Kirkbymoorside
Thirsk
Helmsley
Pickering
Seamer
Masham
Staxton
Filey
Buckden
Hovingham
Reighton
NORTH YORKSHIRE
Ingleton
Ripon
Malton
Norton
Rillington
Foxholes
Flamborough
Flamborough Head
Clapham
Easingwold
Pateley Bridge
Boroughbridge
Sledmere
Langtoft
Bridlington
Settle
Grassington
Long Preston
Ripley
Shipton
Fridaythorpe
Driffield
Lissett
Blubberhouses
Harrogate
Knaresborough
Stamford Bridge
Skipsea
Gisburn
Skipton
Bolton Bridge
YORK
Pocklington
Bainton
Earby
Wetherby
Hornsea
Ilkley
Leven
Clitheroe
Keighley
Otley
Harewood
Tadcaster
Escrick
Market Weighton
Holme upon Spalding Moor
Beverley
Aldbrough
Colne
Bingley
Shipley
Whalley
Nelson
Burnley
BRADFORD
LEEDS
Selby
HUMBERSIDE
KINGSTON UPON HULL
Accrington
Hebden Bridge
Pudsey
South Cave
Hedon
Withernsea
Morley
Castleford
Howden
BLACKBURN
Halifax
Batley
Hessle
Darwen
Rawtenstall
Bacup
Todmorden
Brighouse
Snaith
Goole
New Holland
Patrington
Knottingley
Ramsbottom
Dewsbury
Wakefield
Pontefract
Barton upon Humber
Easington
Kilnsea
Rochdale
HUDDERSFIELD
Immingham Dock
Immingham
Heywood
Hemsworth
Thorne
Bury
Scunthorpe
Grimsby
Spurn Head
Holmfirth
Adwick le Street
Keelby
BOLTON
OLDHAM
Cleethorpes
Barnsley
SOUTH YORKS.
Epworth
Brigg
Penistone
Wombwell
Doncaster
Swallow
Eccles
MANCHESTER
Caistor
Langsett
Mexborough
Scotter
Salford
Ashton under Lyme
North Somercotes
Saltfleet
Glossop
Rawmarsh
Bawtry
Ludborough
Sale
Rotherham
Tickhill
Caenby Corner
Market Rasen
Stockport
Maltby
Gainsborough
Louth
Cheadle
Hazel Grove
Bamford
SHEFFIELD
Blyth
Ludford
Wilmslow
Whaley Bridge
Chapel-en-le-Frith
Retford
Dunholme
Wragby
East Barkwith
Alderley Edge
Dronfield
Worksop
Saxilby
Scamblesby
Knutsford
DERBYSHIRE
Alford
Macclesfield
Buxton
Baslow
Bolsover
Tuxford
Lincoln
Chesterfield
Warsop
Ollerton
Horncastle
Bakewell
Branston
Bardney
Partney
M1
M18
M62
M180
M60
M65
M66
M56
A1(M)
A66(M)

3

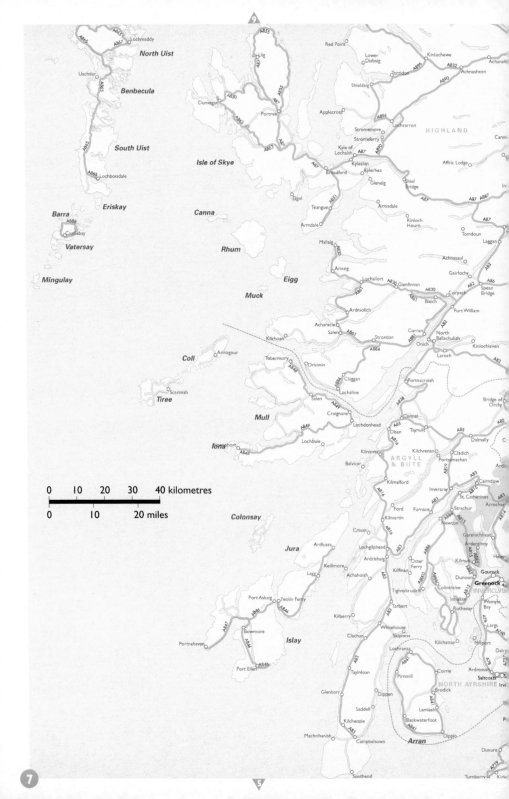

North Uist

Lochmaddy

Uig

Uachdar

Benbecula

Dunvegan

Portree

Red Point

Lower
Diabaig

Kinlochewe

Achanalt

Torridon

A832

Achnasheen

Shieldaig

HIGHLAND

Canni

South Uist

Isle of Skye

Applecross

Stromemore

Lochcarron

Strome ferry

Affric Lodge

Lochboisdale

Elgol

Kyle of
Lochalsh

Broadford

Kyleakin

Kylerhea

Glenelg

Shiel
Bridge

Eriskay

Canna

Teangue

Armisdale

Barra

Castlebay

Armdale

Kinloch
Hourn

Tomdoun

Laggan

Vatersay

Rhum

Mallaig

Achnasaul

Mingulay

Eigg

Arisaig

Lochailort

Glenfinnan

Gairlochy

Spean
Bridge

Muck

Corpach

Blaich

Fort William

Ardmolich

Coll

Arinagour

Acharacle

Salen

Strontian

Corran

North
Ballachulish

Onich

Kinlochleven

Kilchoan

Laroch

Tobermory

Drimnin

Portnacroish

Bridge of
Orchy

Scarinish

Tiree

Claggan

Lochaline

Salen

Connel

Craignure

Lochdonhead

Oban

Taynuilt

A85

Dalmally

Mull

Lochbuie

Kilninver

Kilchrenan

Cladich

Portsonachan

Ardh

Iona

Balvicar

ARGYLL
& BUTE

Cairndow

Kilmelford

Inveraray

St. Catherines

Arrochar

Ford

Furnace

Strachur

Garelochhead

Kilmartin

Newton

Ardentinny

Helen

Colonsay

Crinan

Lochgilphead

Otter
Ferry

Kilmun

Jura

Ardlussa

Ardrishaig

Kilfinan

Dunoon

Gourock

Keillmore

Achahoish

Colintraive

Greenock

Lagg

Tighnabruaich

Inniallan

INVERCLYD

Tarbert

Rothesay

Wemyss
Bay

Port Askaig

Feolin Ferry

Kilberry

Whitehouse

Skipness

Kilchattan

Millport

Dalry

Portnahaven

Bowmore

Islay

Clachan

Lochranza

Largs

Port Ellen

Taynloan

Pirnmill

Corrie

Ardrossan

Saltcoats

Irv

NORTH AYRSHIRE

Brodick

Glenbarr

Dippen

Lamlash

Saddell

Kilchenzie

Blackwaterfoot

Machrihanish

Campbeltown

Arran

Dippie

Dunure

P

Southend

Turnberry

0   10   20   30   40 kilometres

0   10   20 miles

9

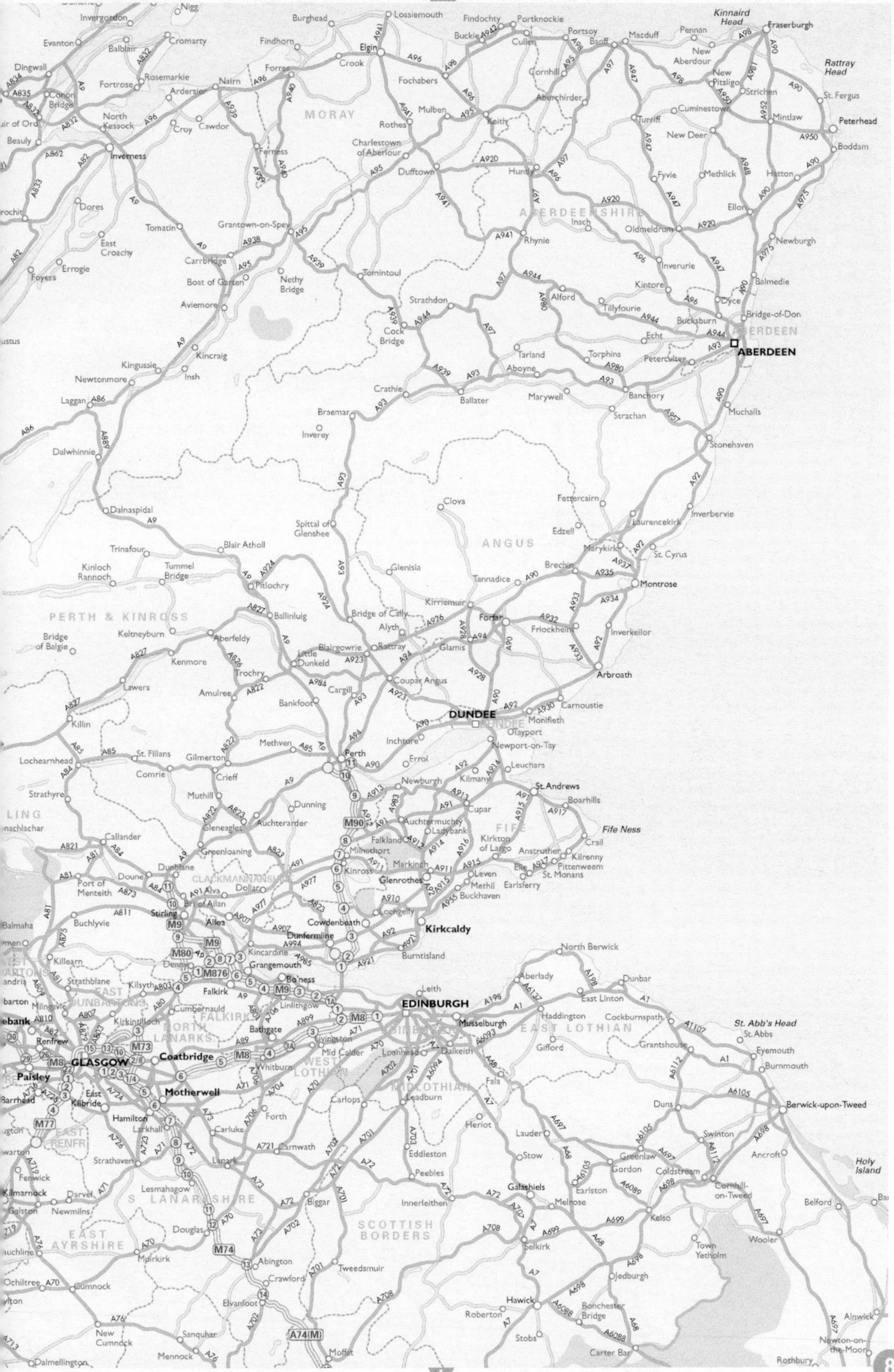
Invergordon
Nigg
Evanton
Balblair
Cromarty
Dingwall
Fortrose
Rosemarkie
Conon Bridge
North Kessock
Beauly
Inverness
Ardersier
Nairn
Croy
Cawdor
Dores
Tomatin
East Croachy
Errogie
Foyers
Burghead
Findhorn
Forres
Lossiemouth
Elgin
Crook
MORAY
Ferness
Grantown-on-Spey
Carrbridge
Boat of Garten
Nethy Bridge
Aviemore
Kincraig
Kingussie
Insh
Newtonmore
Laggan
Dalwhinnie
Findochty
Portknockie
Buckie
Cullen
Portsoy
Banff
Macduff
Pennan
Kinnaird Head
Fraserburgh
New Aberdour
New Pitsligo
Strichen
Rattray Head
St. Fergus
Mintlaw
Peterhead
Boddam
Fochabers
Mulben
Rothes
Keith
Cornhill
Aberchirder
Turriff
Cuminestown
New Deer
Charlestown of Aberlour
Dufftown
Huntly
Fyvie
Methlick
Hatton
ABERDEENSHIRE
Insch
Rhynie
Oldmeldrum
Ellon
Newburgh
Inverurie
Balmedie
Tomintoul
Kintore
Dyce
Alford
Tillyfourie
Bucksburn
Bridge-of-Don
ABERDEEN
Strathdon
Cock Bridge
Echt
Tarland
Torphins
Peterculter
Aboyne
Crathie
Ballater
Marywell
Banchory
Braemar
Inverey
Strachan
Muchalls
Stonehaven
Dalnaspidal
Clova
Fettercairn
Inverbervie
Laurencekirk
Edzell
Spittal of Glenshee
ANGUS
Marykirk
St. Cyrus
Blair Atholl
Trinafour
Kinloch Rannoch
Tummel Bridge
Pitlochry
Glenisla
Brechin
Tannadice
Montrose
PERTH & KINROSS
Ballinluig
Kirriemuir
Bridge of Cally
Alyth
Forfar
Friockheim
Inverkeilor
Keltneyburn
Aberfeldy
Bridge of Balgie
Kenmore
Blairgowrie
Rattray
Little Dunkeld
Glamis
Trochry
Lawers
Coupar Angus
Arbroath
Amulree
Cargill
Bankfoot
Carnoustie
DUNDEE
Monifieth
Tayport
Newport-on-Tay
Killin
Methven
Inchture
Lochearnhead
St. Fillans
Gilmerton
Perth
Errol
Leuchars
Comrie
Crieff
Kilmany
Newburgh
St. Andrews
Strathyre
Muthill
Dunning
Cupar
Boarhills
Auchtermuchty
Ladybank
FIFE
Fife Ness
Gleneagles
Auchterarder
Callander
Falkland
Kirkton of Largo
Crail
Milnathort
Anstruther
Kilrenny
Greenloaning
Kinross
Markinch
Pittenweem
Elie
St. Monans
Dunblane
Doune
Port of Menteith
CLACKMANNANSHIRE
Alva
Dollar
Glenrothes
Leven
Methil
Earlsferry
Buckhaven
Bridge of Allan
Stirling
Alloa
Lochgelly
Cowdenbeath
Kirkcaldy
Buchlyvie
Balmaha
Dunfermline
Kincardine
Burntisland
Killearn
Denny
Grangemouth
North Berwick
Strathblane
EAST DUNBARTONSHIRE
Kilsyth
Bo'ness
Falkirk
Aberlady
Dunbar
Leith
East Linton
EDINBURGH
Linlithgow
FALKIRK
Cumbernauld
Kirkintilloch
NORTH LANARKSHIRE
Bathgate
Musselburgh
Haddington
Cockburnspath
EAST LOTHIAN
St. Abb's Head
St. Abbs
Renfrew
Livingston
Mid Calder
Loanhead
Dalkeith
Gifford
Grantshouse
Eyemouth
GLASGOW
Coatbridge
Whitburn
WEST LOTHIAN
Burnmouth
Paisley
Barrhead
East Kilbride
Motherwell
MIDLOTHIAN
Fala
Hamilton
Carlops
Leadburn
Duns
Berwick-upon-Tweed
Larkhall
Forth
Heriot
EAST RENFREWSHIRE
Carluke
Lauder
Swinton
Strathaven
Carnwath
Eddleston
Stow
Greenlaw
Ancroft
Holy Island
Fenwick
Lanark
Peebles
Gordon
Coldstream
Kilmarnock
Darvel
Lesmahagow
Galashiels
Earlston
Cornhill-on-Tweed
Galston
Newmilns
S LANARKSHIRE
Biggar
Innerleithen
Melrose
Belford
Douglas
SCOTTISH BORDERS
Kelso
EAST AYRSHIRE
Muirkirk
Selkirk
Town Yetholm
Wooler
Abington
Tweedsmuir
Crawford
Ochiltree
Cumnock
Jedburgh
Elvanfoot
Hawick
Bonchester Bridge
Roberton
Alnwick
New Cumnock
Sanquhar
Stobs
Newton-on-the-Moor
Mennock
Moffat
Carter Bar
Rothbury
Dalmellington

6

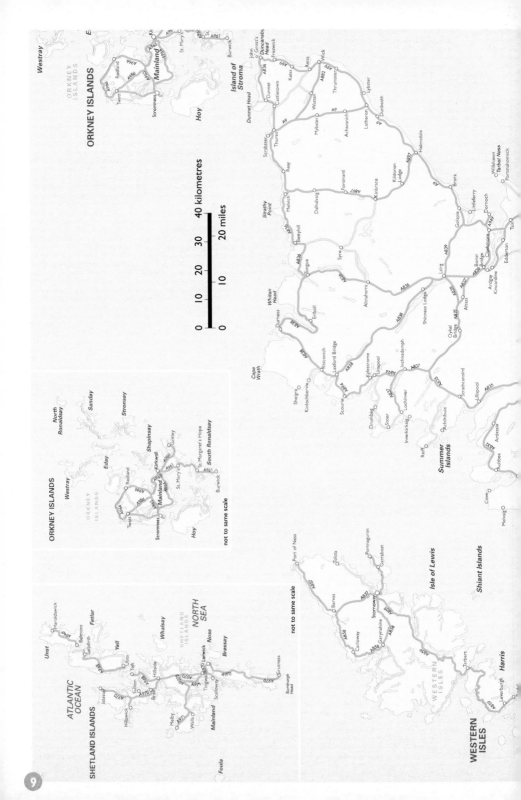

SHETLAND ISLANDS

ATLANTIC OCEAN

Unst
Haroldswick
Fetlar
Belmont
Gutcher
Sellafirth
Yell
Ulsta
Toft
Hillswick
Sullom
Brae
Whalsay
Voe
Vidlin
Noss
NORTH SEA
SHETLAND ISLANDS
Hesta
Lerwick
Bressay
Walls
Tingwall
Scalloway
Mainland
Melby
Sumburgh Head

Foula

ORKNEY ISLANDS

ORKNEY ISLANDS

North Ronaldsay
Sanday
Westray
Stronsay
Eday
Shapinsay
Twatt
Redland
Kirkwall
Stromness
Mainland
Hoy
St. Margaret's Hope
South Ronaldsay
Burwick

not to same scale

ORKNEY ISLANDS

Westray
ORKNEY ISLANDS
Twatt
Redland
Mainland
Kirkwall
St. Mary's
Stromness
Hoy
Burwick

Island of Stroma
Dunnet Head

John O'Groat's
Duncansby Head
Freswick
Keiss
Reiss
Wick
Castletown
Dunnet
Watten
Thrumster
Lybster
Scrabster
Thurso
Mybster
Achavanich
Latheron
Dunbeath
Reay
Forsinard
Kinbrace
Kildonan Lodge
Helmsdale
Strathy Point
Melvich
Dalhalvig
Brora
Golspie
Littleferry
Whiten Head
Bettyhill
Syre
Dornoch
Tain
Durness
Tongue
Altnaharra
Lairg
Bonar Bridge
Clashmore
Cape Wrath
Eriboll
Shinness Lodge
Ardgay
Edderton
Kincardine
Sheigra
Rhiconich
Laxford Bridge
Oykel Bridge
Altass
Kinlochbervie
Scourie
Kylestrome
Inchnadamph
Strathcanaird
Drumbeg
Unapool
Lochinver
Ullapool
Stoer
Inverkirkaig
Achiltibuie
Reiff
Summer Islands
Aultbea
Cove
Melvaig
Gairloch
Poolewe

WESTERN ISLES

Port of Ness
not to same scale
Tolsta
Portnaguran
Garrabost
Barvas
Stornoway
Carloway
Garrynahine
Isle of Lewis
Shiant Islands
WESTERN ISLES
Tarbert
Leverburgh
Harris

40 kilometres

0   10   20   30   40

0   10   20 miles

CADE'S ONE POUND	CADE'S ONE POUND
CAMPING, TOURING & MOTOR CARAVAN SITE GUIDE 2012	**CAMPING, TOURING & MOTOR CARAVAN SITE GUIDE 2012**
PRESENT THIS VOUCHER TO THE SITE OPERATOR WHEN PAYING TO RECEIVE ONE POUND DISCOUNT PER VOUCHER, PER NIGHT. SEE CONDITIONS OVERLEAF. VALID UNTIL 31-12-12	PRESENT THIS VOUCHER TO THE SITE OPERATOR WHEN PAYING TO RECEIVE ONE POUND DISCOUNT PER VOUCHER, PER NIGHT. SEE CONDITIONS OVERLEAF. VALID UNTIL 31-12-12
CADE'S ONE POUND	CADE'S ONE POUND
CAMPING, TOURING & MOTOR CARAVAN SITE GUIDE 2012	**CAMPING, TOURING & MOTOR CARAVAN SITE GUIDE 2012**
PRESENT THIS VOUCHER TO THE SITE OPERATOR WHEN PAYING TO RECEIVE ONE POUND DISCOUNT PER VOUCHER, PER NIGHT. SEE CONDITIONS OVERLEAF. VALID UNTIL 31-12-12	PRESENT THIS VOUCHER TO THE SITE OPERATOR WHEN PAYING TO RECEIVE ONE POUND DISCOUNT PER VOUCHER, PER NIGHT. SEE CONDITIONS OVERLEAF. VALID UNTIL 31-12-12
CADE'S ONE POUND	CADE'S ONE POUND
CAMPING, TOURING & MOTOR CARAVAN SITE GUIDE 2012	**CAMPING, TOURING & MOTOR CARAVAN SITE GUIDE 2012**
PRESENT THIS VOUCHER TO THE SITE OPERATOR WHEN PAYING TO RECEIVE ONE POUND DISCOUNT PER VOUCHER, PER NIGHT. SEE CONDITIONS OVERLEAF. VALID UNTIL 31-12-12	PRESENT THIS VOUCHER TO THE SITE OPERATOR WHEN PAYING TO RECEIVE ONE POUND DISCOUNT PER VOUCHER, PER NIGHT. SEE CONDITIONS OVERLEAF. VALID UNTIL 31-12-12
CADE'S ONE POUND	CADE'S ONE POUND
CAMPING, TOURING & MOTOR CARAVAN SITE GUIDE 2012	**CAMPING, TOURING & MOTOR CARAVAN SITE GUIDE 2012**
PRESENT THIS VOUCHER TO THE SITE OPERATOR WHEN PAYING TO RECEIVE ONE POUND DISCOUNT PER VOUCHER, PER NIGHT. SEE CONDITIONS OVERLEAF. VALID UNTIL 31-12-12	PRESENT THIS VOUCHER TO THE SITE OPERATOR WHEN PAYING TO RECEIVE ONE POUND DISCOUNT PER VOUCHER, PER NIGHT. SEE CONDITIONS OVERLEAF. VALID UNTIL 31-12-12
CADE'S ONE POUND	CADE'S ONE POUND
CAMPING, TOURING & MOTOR CARAVAN SITE GUIDE 2012	**CAMPING, TOURING & MOTOR CARAVAN SITE GUIDE 2011**
PRESENT THIS VOUCHER TO THE SITE OPERATOR WHEN PAYING TO RECEIVE ONE POUND DISCOUNT PER VOUCHER, PER NIGHT. SEE CONDITIONS OVERLEAF. VALID UNTIL 31-12-12	PRESENT THIS VOUCHER TO THE SITE OPERATOR WHEN PAYING TO RECEIVE ONE POUND DISCOUNT PER VOUCHER, PER NIGHT. SEE CONDITIONS OVERLEAF. VALID UNTIL 31-12-12

VISIT **www.cades.co.uk** TO SEE OUR MONTHLY COMPETITION

CONDITIONS OF USE

Vouchers will only be redeemed by those sites featuring a ▣ symbol in the *facilities* line of their County entry. Presentation of this voucher to the Site Operator at the time of paying your balance will entitle you to a one pound discount per voucher, per night. (Only one voucher per night). Vouchers may be used in multiples i.e. five vouchers presented for a five night stay will entitle you to a discount of £5.00.

A **CADE'S CAMPING, TOURING & MOTOR CARAVAN SITE GUIDE 2012 EDITION** must be presented at the time of payment. Vouchers are valid for accommodation only. Vouchers may not be exchanged for cash. Not to be used with any other offer. Valid until 31-12-12.

CONDITIONS OF USE

Vouchers will only be redeemed by those sites featuring a ▣ symbol in the *facilities* line of their County entry. Presentation of this voucher to the Site Operator at the time of paying your balance will entitle you to a one pound discount per voucher, per night. (Only one voucher per night). Vouchers may be used in multiples i.e. five vouchers presented for a five night stay will entitle you to a discount of £5.00.

A **CADE'S CAMPING, TOURING & MOTOR CARAVAN SITE GUIDE 2012 EDITION** must be presented at the time of payment. Vouchers are valid for accommodation only. Vouchers may not be exchanged for cash. Not to be used with any other offer. Valid until 31-12-12.

CONDITIONS OF USE

Vouchers will only be redeemed by those sites featuring a ▣ symbol in the *facilities* line of their County entry. Presentation of this voucher to the Site Operator at the time of paying your balance will entitle you to a one pound discount per voucher, per night. (Only one voucher per night). Vouchers may be used in multiples i.e. five vouchers presented for a five night stay will entitle you to a discount of £5.00.

A **CADE'S CAMPING, TOURING & MOTOR CARAVAN SITE GUIDE 2012 EDITION** must be presented at the time of payment. Vouchers are valid for accommodation only. Vouchers may not be exchanged for cash. Not to be used with any other offer. Valid until 31-12-12.

CONDITIONS OF USE

Vouchers will only be redeemed by those sites featuring a ▣ symbol in the *facilities* line of their County entry. Presentation of this voucher to the Site Operator at the time of paying your balance will entitle you to a one pound discount per voucher, per night. (Only one voucher per night). Vouchers may be used in multiples i.e. five vouchers presented for a five night stay will entitle you to a discount of £5.00.

A **CADE'S CAMPING, TOURING & MOTOR CARAVAN SITE GUIDE 2012 EDITION** must be presented at the time of payment. Vouchers are valid for accommodation only. Vouchers may not be exchanged for cash. Not to be used with any other offer. Valid until 31-12-12.

CONDITIONS OF USE

Vouchers will only be redeemed by those sites featuring a ▣ symbol in the *facilities* line of their County entry. Presentation of this voucher to the Site Operator at the time of paying your balance will entitle you to a one pound discount per voucher, per night. (Only one voucher per night). Vouchers may be used in multiples i.e. five vouchers presented for a five night stay will entitle you to a discount of £5.00.

A **CADE'S CAMPING, TOURING & MOTOR CARAVAN SITE GUIDE 2012 EDITION** must be presented at the time of payment. Vouchers are valid for accommodation only. Vouchers may not be exchanged for cash. Not to be used with any other offer. Valid until 31-12-12.

CONDITIONS OF USE

Vouchers will only be redeemed by those sites featuring a ▣ symbol in the *facilities* line of their County entry. Presentation of this voucher to the Site Operator at the time of paying your balance will entitle you to a one pound discount per voucher, per night. (Only one voucher per night). Vouchers may be used in multiples i.e. five vouchers presented for a five night stay will entitle you to a discount of £5.00.

A **CADE'S CAMPING, TOURING & MOTOR CARAVAN SITE GUIDE 2012 EDITION** must be presented at the time of payment. Vouchers are valid for accommodation only. Vouchers may not be exchanged for cash. Not to be used with any other offer. Valid until 31-12-12.

CONDITIONS OF USE

Vouchers will only be redeemed by those sites featuring a ▣ symbol in the *facilities* line of their County entry. Presentation of this voucher to the Site Operator at the time of paying your balance will entitle you to a one pound discount per voucher, per night. (Only one voucher per night). Vouchers may be used in multiples i.e. five vouchers presented for a five night stay will entitle you to a discount of £5.00.

A **CADE'S CAMPING, TOURING & MOTOR CARAVAN SITE GUIDE 2012 EDITION** must be presented at the time of payment. Vouchers are valid for accommodation only. Vouchers may not be exchanged for cash. Not to be used with any other offer. Valid until 31-12-12.

CONDITIONS OF USE

Vouchers will only be redeemed by those sites featuring a ▣ symbol in the *facilities* line of their County entry. Presentation of this voucher to the Site Operator at the time of paying your balance will entitle you to a one pound discount per voucher, per night. (Only one voucher per night). Vouchers may be used in multiples i.e. five vouchers presented for a five night stay will entitle you to a discount of £5.00.

A **CADE'S CAMPING, TOURING & MOTOR CARAVAN SITE GUIDE 2012 EDITION** must be presented at the time of payment. Vouchers are valid for accommodation only. Vouchers may not be exchanged for cash. Not to be used with any other offer. Valid until 31-12-12.

CADE'S　　　ONE POUND **CAMPING, TOURING &** **MOTOR CARAVAN SITE** **GUIDE 2012** PRESENT THIS VOUCHER TO THE SITE OPERATOR WHEN PAYING TO RECEIVE ONE POUND DISCOUNT PER VOUCHER, PER NIGHT. SEE CONDITIONS OVERLEAF. VALID UNTIL 31-12-12	CADE'S　　　ONE POUND **CAMPING, TOURING &** **MOTOR CARAVAN SITE** **GUIDE 2012** PRESENT THIS VOUCHER TO THE SITE OPERATOR WHEN PAYING TO RECEIVE ONE POUND DISCOUNT PER VOUCHER, PER NIGHT. SEE CONDITIONS OVERLEAF. VALID UNTIL 31-12-12
CADE'S　　　ONE POUND **CAMPING, TOURING &** **MOTOR CARAVAN SITE** **GUIDE 2012** PRESENT THIS VOUCHER TO THE SITE OPERATOR WHEN PAYING TO RECEIVE ONE POUND DISCOUNT PER VOUCHER, PER NIGHT. SEE CONDITIONS OVERLEAF. VALID UNTIL 31-12-12	CADE'S　　　ONE POUND **CAMPING, TOURING &** **MOTOR CARAVAN SITE** **GUIDE 2012** PRESENT THIS VOUCHER TO THE SITE OPERATOR WHEN PAYING TO RECEIVE ONE POUND DISCOUNT PER VOUCHER, PER NIGHT. SEE CONDITIONS OVERLEAF. VALID UNTIL 31-12-12
CADE'S　　　ONE POUND **CAMPING, TOURING &** **MOTOR CARAVAN SITE** **GUIDE 2012** PRESENT THIS VOUCHER TO THE SITE OPERATOR WHEN PAYING TO RECEIVE ONE POUND DISCOUNT PER VOUCHER, PER NIGHT. SEE CONDITIONS OVERLEAF. VALID UNTIL 31-12-12	CADE'S　　　ONE POUND **CAMPING, TOURING &** **MOTOR CARAVAN SITE** **GUIDE 2012** PRESENT THIS VOUCHER TO THE SITE OPERATOR WHEN PAYING TO RECEIVE ONE POUND DISCOUNT PER VOUCHER, PER NIGHT. SEE CONDITIONS OVERLEAF. VALID UNTIL 31-12-12
CADE'S　　　ONE POUND **CAMPING, TOURING &** **MOTOR CARAVAN SITE** **GUIDE 2012** PRESENT THIS VOUCHER TO THE SITE OPERATOR WHEN PAYING TO RECEIVE ONE POUND DISCOUNT PER VOUCHER, PER NIGHT. SEE CONDITIONS OVERLEAF. VALID UNTIL 31-12-12	CADE'S　　　ONE POUND **CAMPING, TOURING &** **MOTOR CARAVAN SITE** **GUIDE 2012** PRESENT THIS VOUCHER TO THE SITE OPERATOR WHEN PAYING TO RECEIVE ONE POUND DISCOUNT PER VOUCHER, PER NIGHT. SEE CONDITIONS OVERLEAF. VALID UNTIL 31-12-12
CADE'S　　　ONE POUND **CAMPING, TOURING &** **MOTOR CARAVAN SITE** **GUIDE 2012** PRESENT THIS VOUCHER TO THE SITE OPERATOR WHEN PAYING TO RECEIVE ONE POUND DISCOUNT PER VOUCHER, PER NIGHT. SEE CONDITIONS OVERLEAF. VALID UNTIL 31-12-12	CADE'S　　　ONE POUND **CAMPING, TOURING &** **MOTOR CARAVAN SITE** **GUIDE 2011** PRESENT THIS VOUCHER TO THE SITE OPERATOR WHEN PAYING TO RECEIVE ONE POUND DISCOUNT PER VOUCHER, PER NIGHT. SEE CONDITIONS OVERLEAF. VALID UNTIL 31-12-12

VISIT **www.cades.co.uk** TO SEE OUR MONTHLY COMPETITION

CONDITIONS OF USE

Vouchers will only be redeemed by those sites featuring a ⬛ symbol in the *facilities* line of their County entry. Presentation of this voucher to the Site Operator at the time of paying your balance will entitle you to a one pound discount per voucher, per night. (Only one voucher per night). Vouchers may be used in multiples i.e. five vouchers presented for a five night stay will entitle you to a discount of £5.00.

A **CADE'S CAMPING, TOURING & MOTOR CARAVAN SITE GUIDE 2012 EDITION** must be presented at the time of payment. Vouchers are valid for accommodation only. Vouchers may not be exchanged for cash. Not to be used with any other offer. Valid until 31-12-12.

CONDITIONS OF USE

Vouchers will only be redeemed by those sites featuring a ⬛ symbol in the *facilities* line of their County entry. Presentation of this voucher to the Site Operator at the time of paying your balance will entitle you to a one pound discount per voucher, per night. (Only one voucher per night). Vouchers may be used in multiples i.e. five vouchers presented for a five night stay will entitle you to a discount of £5.00.

A **CADE'S CAMPING, TOURING & MOTOR CARAVAN SITE GUIDE 2012 EDITION** must be presented at the time of payment. Vouchers are valid for accommodation only. Vouchers may not be exchanged for cash. Not to be used with any other offer. Valid until 31-12-12.

CONDITIONS OF USE

Vouchers will only be redeemed by those sites featuring a ⬛ symbol in the *facilities* line of their County entry. Presentation of this voucher to the Site Operator at the time of paying your balance will entitle you to a one pound discount per voucher, per night. (Only one voucher per night). Vouchers may be used in multiples i.e. five vouchers presented for a five night stay will entitle you to a discount of £5.00.

A **CADE'S CAMPING, TOURING & MOTOR CARAVAN SITE GUIDE 2012 EDITION** must be presented at the time of payment. Vouchers are valid for accommodation only. Vouchers may not be exchanged for cash. Not to be used with any other offer. Valid until 31-12-12.

CONDITIONS OF USE

Vouchers will only be redeemed by those sites featuring a ⬛ symbol in the *facilities* line of their County entry. Presentation of this voucher to the Site Operator at the time of paying your balance will entitle you to a one pound discount per voucher, per night. (Only one voucher per night). Vouchers may be used in multiples i.e. five vouchers presented for a five night stay will entitle you to a discount of £5.00.

A **CADE'S CAMPING, TOURING & MOTOR CARAVAN SITE GUIDE 2012 EDITION** must be presented at the time of payment. Vouchers are valid for accommodation only. Vouchers may not be exchanged for cash. Not to be used with any other offer. Valid until 31-12-12.

CONDITIONS OF USE

Vouchers will only be redeemed by those sites featuring a ⬛ symbol in the *facilities* line of their County entry. Presentation of this voucher to the Site Operator at the time of paying your balance will entitle you to a one pound discount per voucher, per night. (Only one voucher per night). Vouchers may be used in multiples i.e. five vouchers presented for a five night stay will entitle you to a discount of £5.00.

A **CADE'S CAMPING, TOURING & MOTOR CARAVAN SITE GUIDE 2012 EDITION** must be presented at the time of payment. Vouchers are valid for accommodation only. Vouchers may not be exchanged for cash. Not to be used with any other offer. Valid until 31-12-12.

CONDITIONS OF USE

Vouchers will only be redeemed by those sites featuring a ⬛ symbol in the *facilities* line of their County entry. Presentation of this voucher to the Site Operator at the time of paying your balance will entitle you to a one pound discount per voucher, per night. (Only one voucher per night). Vouchers may be used in multiples i.e. five vouchers presented for a five night stay will entitle you to a discount of £5.00.

A **CADE'S CAMPING, TOURING & MOTOR CARAVAN SITE GUIDE 2012 EDITION** must be presented at the time of payment. Vouchers are valid for accommodation only. Vouchers may not be exchanged for cash. Not to be used with any other offer. Valid until 31-12-12.

CONDITIONS OF USE

Vouchers will only be redeemed by those sites featuring a ⬛ symbol in the *facilities* line of their County entry. Presentation of this voucher to the Site Operator at the time of paying your balance will entitle you to a one pound discount per voucher, per night. (Only one voucher per night). Vouchers may be used in multiples i.e. five vouchers presented for a five night stay will entitle you to a discount of £5.00.

A **CADE'S CAMPING, TOURING & MOTOR CARAVAN SITE GUIDE 2012 EDITION** must be presented at the time of payment. Vouchers are valid for accommodation only. Vouchers may not be exchanged for cash. Not to be used with any other offer. Valid until 31-12-12.

CONDITIONS OF USE

Vouchers will only be redeemed by those sites featuring a ⬛ symbol in the *facilities* line of their County entry. Presentation of this voucher to the Site Operator at the time of paying your balance will entitle you to a one pound discount per voucher, per night. (Only one voucher per night). Vouchers may be used in multiples i.e. five vouchers presented for a five night stay will entitle you to a discount of £5.00.

A **CADE'S CAMPING, TOURING & MOTOR CARAVAN SITE GUIDE 2012 EDITION** must be presented at the time of payment. Vouchers are valid for accommodation only. Vouchers may not be exchanged for cash. Not to be used with any other offer. Valid until 31-12-12.

CONDITIONS OF USE

Vouchers will only be redeemed by those sites featuring a ⬛ symbol in the *facilities* line of their County entry. Presentation of this voucher to the Site Operator at the time of paying your balance will entitle you to a one pound discount per voucher, per night. (Only one voucher per night). Vouchers may be used in multiples i.e. five vouchers presented for a five night stay will entitle you to a discount of £5.00.

A **CADE'S CAMPING, TOURING & MOTOR CARAVAN SITE GUIDE 2012 EDITION** must be presented at the time of payment. Vouchers are valid for accommodation only. Vouchers may not be exchanged for cash. Not to be used with any other offer. Valid until 31-12-12.

CONDITIONS OF USE

Vouchers will only be redeemed by those sites featuring a ⬛ symbol in the *facilities* line of their County entry. Presentation of this voucher to the Site Operator at the time of paying your balance will entitle you to a one pound discount per voucher, per night. (Only one voucher per night). Vouchers may be used in multiples i.e. five vouchers presented for a five night stay will entitle you to a discount of £5.00.

A **CADE'S CAMPING, TOURING & MOTOR CARAVAN SITE GUIDE 2012 EDITION** must be presented at the time of payment. Vouchers are valid for accommodation only. Vouchers may not be exchanged for cash. Not to be used with any other offer. Valid until 31-12-12.

CONDITIONS OF USE

Vouchers will only be redeemed by those sites featuring a ⬛ symbol in the *facilities* line of their County entry. Presentation of this voucher to the Site Operator at the time of paying your balance will entitle you to a one pound discount per voucher, per night. (Only one voucher per night). Vouchers may be used in multiples i.e. five vouchers presented for a five night stay will entitle you to a discount of £5.00.

A **CADE'S CAMPING, TOURING & MOTOR CARAVAN SITE GUIDE 2012 EDITION** must be presented at the time of payment. Vouchers are valid for accommodation only. Vouchers may not be exchanged for cash. Not to be used with any other offer. Valid until 31-12-12.

CONDITIONS OF USE

Vouchers will only be redeemed by those sites featuring a ⬛ symbol in the *facilities* line of their County entry. Presentation of this voucher to the Site Operator at the time of paying your balance will entitle you to a one pound discount per voucher, per night. (Only one voucher per night). Vouchers may be used in multiples i.e. five vouchers presented for a five night stay will entitle you to a discount of £5.00.

A **CADE'S CAMPING, TOURING & MOTOR CARAVAN SITE GUIDE 2012 EDITION** must be presented at the time of payment. Vouchers are valid for accommodation only. Vouchers may not be exchanged for cash. Not to be used with any other offer. Valid until 31-12-12.

CADE'S **ONE POUND** *CAMPING, TOURING &* *MOTOR CARAVAN SITE* *GUIDE 2012* PRESENT THIS VOUCHER TO THE SITE OPERATOR WHEN PAYING TO RECEIVE ONE POUND DISCOUNT PER VOUCHER, PER NIGHT. SEE CONDITIONS OVERLEAF. VALID UNTIL 31-12-12	**CADE'S** **ONE POUND** *CAMPING, TOURING &* *MOTOR CARAVAN SITE* *GUIDE 2012* PRESENT THIS VOUCHER TO THE SITE OPERATOR WHEN PAYING TO RECEIVE ONE POUND DISCOUNT PER VOUCHER, PER NIGHT. SEE CONDITIONS OVERLEAF. VALID UNTIL 31-12-12
CADE'S **ONE POUND** *CAMPING, TOURING &* *MOTOR CARAVAN SITE* *GUIDE 2012* PRESENT THIS VOUCHER TO THE SITE OPERATOR WHEN PAYING TO RECEIVE ONE POUND DISCOUNT PER VOUCHER, PER NIGHT. SEE CONDITIONS OVERLEAF. VALID UNTIL 31-12-12	**CADE'S** **ONE POUND** *CAMPING, TOURING &* *MOTOR CARAVAN SITE* *GUIDE 2012* PRESENT THIS VOUCHER TO THE SITE OPERATOR WHEN PAYING TO RECEIVE ONE POUND DISCOUNT PER VOUCHER, PER NIGHT. SEE CONDITIONS OVERLEAF. VALID UNTIL 31-12-12
CADE'S **ONE POUND** *CAMPING, TOURING &* *MOTOR CARAVAN SITE* *GUIDE 2012* PRESENT THIS VOUCHER TO THE SITE OPERATOR WHEN PAYING TO RECEIVE ONE POUND DISCOUNT PER VOUCHER, PER NIGHT. SEE CONDITIONS OVERLEAF. VALID UNTIL 31-12-12	**CADE'S** **ONE POUND** *CAMPING, TOURING &* *MOTOR CARAVAN SITE* *GUIDE 2012* PRESENT THIS VOUCHER TO THE SITE OPERATOR WHEN PAYING TO RECEIVE ONE POUND DISCOUNT PER VOUCHER, PER NIGHT. SEE CONDITIONS OVERLEAF. VALID UNTIL 31-12-12
CADE'S **ONE POUND** *CAMPING, TOURING &* *MOTOR CARAVAN SITE* *GUIDE 2012* PRESENT THIS VOUCHER TO THE SITE OPERATOR WHEN PAYING TO RECEIVE ONE POUND DISCOUNT PER VOUCHER, PER NIGHT. SEE CONDITIONS OVERLEAF. VALID UNTIL 31-12-12	**CADE'S** **ONE POUND** *CAMPING, TOURING &* *MOTOR CARAVAN SITE* *GUIDE 2012* PRESENT THIS VOUCHER TO THE SITE OPERATOR WHEN PAYING TO RECEIVE ONE POUND DISCOUNT PER VOUCHER, PER NIGHT. SEE CONDITIONS OVERLEAF. VALID UNTIL 31-12-12
CADE'S **ONE POUND** *CAMPING, TOURING &* *MOTOR CARAVAN SITE* *GUIDE 2012* PRESENT THIS VOUCHER TO THE SITE OPERATOR WHEN PAYING TO RECEIVE ONE POUND DISCOUNT PER VOUCHER, PER NIGHT. SEE CONDITIONS OVERLEAF. VALID UNTIL 31-12-12	**CADE'S** **ONE POUND** *CAMPING, TOURING &* *MOTOR CARAVAN SITE* *GUIDE 2011* PRESENT THIS VOUCHER TO THE SITE OPERATOR WHEN PAYING TO RECEIVE ONE POUND DISCOUNT PER VOUCHER, PER NIGHT. SEE CONDITIONS OVERLEAF. VALID UNTIL 31-12-12

VISIT **www.cades.co.uk** TO SEE OUR MONTHLY COMPETITION

CONDITIONS OF USE

Vouchers will only be redeemed by those sites featuring a ◩ symbol in the *facilities* line of their County entry. Presentation of this voucher to the Site Operator at the time of paying your balance will entitle you to a one pound discount per voucher, per night. (Only one voucher per night). Vouchers may be used in multiples i.e. five vouchers presented for a five night stay will entitle you to a discount of £5.00.

A **CADE'S CAMPING, TOURING & MOTOR CARAVAN SITE GUIDE 2012 EDITION** must be presented at the time of payment. Vouchers are valid for accommodation only. Vouchers may not be exchanged for cash. Not to be used with any other offer. Valid until 31-12-12.

CONDITIONS OF USE

Vouchers will only be redeemed by those sites featuring a ◩ symbol in the *facilities* line of their County entry. Presentation of this voucher to the Site Operator at the time of paying your balance will entitle you to a one pound discount per voucher, per night. (Only one voucher per night). Vouchers may be used in multiples i.e. five vouchers presented for a five night stay will entitle you to a discount of £5.00.

A **CADE'S CAMPING, TOURING & MOTOR CARAVAN SITE GUIDE 2012 EDITION** must be presented at the time of payment. Vouchers are valid for accommodation only. Vouchers may not be exchanged for cash. Not to be used with any other offer. Valid until 31-12-12.

CONDITIONS OF USE

Vouchers will only be redeemed by those sites featuring a ◩ symbol in the *facilities* line of their County entry. Presentation of this voucher to the Site Operator at the time of paying your balance will entitle you to a one pound discount per voucher, per night. (Only one voucher per night). Vouchers may be used in multiples i.e. five vouchers presented for a five night stay will entitle you to a discount of £5.00.

A **CADE'S CAMPING, TOURING & MOTOR CARAVAN SITE GUIDE 2012 EDITION** must be presented at the time of payment. Vouchers are valid for accommodation only. Vouchers may not be exchanged for cash. Not to be used with any other offer. Valid until 31-12-12.

CONDITIONS OF USE

Vouchers will only be redeemed by those sites featuring a ◩ symbol in the *facilities* line of their County entry. Presentation of this voucher to the Site Operator at the time of paying your balance will entitle you to a one pound discount per voucher, per night. (Only one voucher per night). Vouchers may be used in multiples i.e. five vouchers presented for a five night stay will entitle you to a discount of £5.00.

A **CADE'S CAMPING, TOURING & MOTOR CARAVAN SITE GUIDE 2012 EDITION** must be presented at the time of payment. Vouchers are valid for accommodation only. Vouchers may not be exchanged for cash. Not to be used with any other offer. Valid until 31-12-12.

CONDITIONS OF USE

Vouchers will only be redeemed by those sites featuring a ◩ symbol in the *facilities* line of their County entry. Presentation of this voucher to the Site Operator at the time of paying your balance will entitle you to a one pound discount per voucher, per night. (Only one voucher per night). Vouchers may be used in multiples i.e. five vouchers presented for a five night stay will entitle you to a discount of £5.00.

A **CADE'S CAMPING, TOURING & MOTOR CARAVAN SITE GUIDE 2012 EDITION** must be presented at the time of payment. Vouchers are valid for accommodation only. Vouchers may not be exchanged for cash. Not to be used with any other offer. Valid until 31-12-12.

CONDITIONS OF USE

Vouchers will only be redeemed by those sites featuring a ◩ symbol in the *facilities* line of their County entry. Presentation of this voucher to the Site Operator at the time of paying your balance will entitle you to a one pound discount per voucher, per night. (Only one voucher per night). Vouchers may be used in multiples i.e. five vouchers presented for a five night stay will entitle you to a discount of £5.00.

A **CADE'S CAMPING, TOURING & MOTOR CARAVAN SITE GUIDE 2012 EDITION** must be presented at the time of payment. Vouchers are valid for accommodation only. Vouchers may not be exchanged for cash. Not to be used with any other offer. Valid until 31-12-12.

CONDITIONS OF USE

Vouchers will only be redeemed by those sites featuring a ◩ symbol in the *facilities* line of their County entry. Presentation of this voucher to the Site Operator at the time of paying your balance will entitle you to a one pound discount per voucher, per night. (Only one voucher per night). Vouchers may be used in multiples i.e. five vouchers presented for a five night stay will entitle you to a discount of £5.00.

A **CADE'S CAMPING, TOURING & MOTOR CARAVAN SITE GUIDE 2012 EDITION** must be presented at the time of payment. Vouchers are valid for accommodation only. Vouchers may not be exchanged for cash. Not to be used with any other offer. Valid until 31-12-12.

CONDITIONS OF USE

Vouchers will only be redeemed by those sites featuring a ◩ symbol in the *facilities* line of their County entry. Presentation of this voucher to the Site Operator at the time of paying your balance will entitle you to a one pound discount per voucher, per night. (Only one voucher per night). Vouchers may be used in multiples i.e. five vouchers presented for a five night stay will entitle you to a discount of £5.00.

A **CADE'S CAMPING, TOURING & MOTOR CARAVAN SITE GUIDE 2012 EDITION** must be presented at the time of payment. Vouchers are valid for accommodation only. Vouchers may not be exchanged for cash. Not to be used with any other offer. Valid until 31-12-12.

CONDITIONS OF USE

Vouchers will only be redeemed by those sites featuring a ◩ symbol in the *facilities* line of their County entry. Presentation of this voucher to the Site Operator at the time of paying your balance will entitle you to a one pound discount per voucher, per night. (Only one voucher per night). Vouchers may be used in multiples i.e. five vouchers presented for a five night stay will entitle you to a discount of £5.00.

A **CADE'S CAMPING, TOURING & MOTOR CARAVAN SITE GUIDE 2012 EDITION** must be presented at the time of payment. Vouchers are valid for accommodation only. Vouchers may not be exchanged for cash. Not to be used with any other offer. Valid until 31-12-12.

CONDITIONS OF USE

Vouchers will only be redeemed by those sites featuring a ◩ symbol in the *facilities* line of their County entry. Presentation of this voucher to the Site Operator at the time of paying your balance will entitle you to a one pound discount per voucher, per night. (Only one voucher per night). Vouchers may be used in multiples i.e. five vouchers presented for a five night stay will entitle you to a discount of £5.00.

A **CADE'S CAMPING, TOURING & MOTOR CARAVAN SITE GUIDE 2012 EDITION** must be presented at the time of payment. Vouchers are valid for accommodation only. Vouchers may not be exchanged for cash. Not to be used with any other offer. Valid until 31-12-12.

CADE'S **ONE POUND** *CAMPING, TOURING &* *MOTOR CARAVAN SITE* *GUIDE 2012* PRESENT THIS VOUCHER TO THE SITE OPERATOR WHEN PAYING TO RECEIVE ONE POUND DISCOUNT PER VOUCHER, PER NIGHT. SEE CONDITIONS OVERLEAF. VALID UNTIL 31-12-12	**CADE'S** **ONE POUND** *CAMPING, TOURING &* *MOTOR CARAVAN SITE* *GUIDE 2012* PRESENT THIS VOUCHER TO THE SITE OPERATOR WHEN PAYING TO RECEIVE ONE POUND DISCOUNT PER VOUCHER, PER NIGHT. SEE CONDITIONS OVERLEAF. VALID UNTIL 31-12-12
CADE'S **ONE POUND** *CAMPING, TOURING &* *MOTOR CARAVAN SITE* *GUIDE 2012* PRESENT THIS VOUCHER TO THE SITE OPERATOR WHEN PAYING TO RECEIVE ONE POUND DISCOUNT PER VOUCHER, PER NIGHT. SEE CONDITIONS OVERLEAF. VALID UNTIL 31-12-12	**CADE'S** **ONE POUND** *CAMPING, TOURING &* *MOTOR CARAVAN SITE* *GUIDE 2012* PRESENT THIS VOUCHER TO THE SITE OPERATOR WHEN PAYING TO RECEIVE ONE POUND DISCOUNT PER VOUCHER, PER NIGHT. SEE CONDITIONS OVERLEAF. VALID UNTIL 31-12-12
CADE'S **ONE POUND** *CAMPING, TOURING &* *MOTOR CARAVAN SITE* *GUIDE 2012* PRESENT THIS VOUCHER TO THE SITE OPERATOR WHEN PAYING TO RECEIVE ONE POUND DISCOUNT PER VOUCHER, PER NIGHT. SEE CONDITIONS OVERLEAF. VALID UNTIL 31-12-12	**CADE'S** **ONE POUND** *CAMPING, TOURING &* *MOTOR CARAVAN SITE* *GUIDE 2012* PRESENT THIS VOUCHER TO THE SITE OPERATOR WHEN PAYING TO RECEIVE ONE POUND DISCOUNT PER VOUCHER, PER NIGHT. SEE CONDITIONS OVERLEAF. VALID UNTIL 31-12-12
CADE'S **ONE POUND** *CAMPING, TOURING &* *MOTOR CARAVAN SITE* *GUIDE 2012* PRESENT THIS VOUCHER TO THE SITE OPERATOR WHEN PAYING TO RECEIVE ONE POUND DISCOUNT PER VOUCHER, PER NIGHT. SEE CONDITIONS OVERLEAF. VALID UNTIL 31-12-12	**CADE'S** **ONE POUND** *CAMPING, TOURING &* *MOTOR CARAVAN SITE* *GUIDE 2012* PRESENT THIS VOUCHER TO THE SITE OPERATOR WHEN PAYING TO RECEIVE ONE POUND DISCOUNT PER VOUCHER, PER NIGHT. SEE CONDITIONS OVERLEAF. VALID UNTIL 31-12-12
CADE'S **ONE POUND** *CAMPING, TOURING &* *MOTOR CARAVAN SITE* *GUIDE 2012* PRESENT THIS VOUCHER TO THE SITE OPERATOR WHEN PAYING TO RECEIVE ONE POUND DISCOUNT PER VOUCHER, PER NIGHT. SEE CONDITIONS OVERLEAF. VALID UNTIL 31-12-12	**CADE'S** **ONE POUND** *CAMPING, TOURING &* *MOTOR CARAVAN SITE* *GUIDE 2011* PRESENT THIS VOUCHER TO THE SITE OPERATOR WHEN PAYING TO RECEIVE ONE POUND DISCOUNT PER VOUCHER, PER NIGHT. SEE CONDITIONS OVERLEAF. VALID UNTIL 31-12-12

VISIT **www.cades.co.uk** TO SEE OUR MONTHLY COMPETITION

CONDITIONS OF USE

Vouchers will only be redeemed by those sites featuring a ⬛ symbol in the *facilities* line of their County entry. Presentation of this voucher to the Site Operator at the time of paying your balance will entitle you to a one pound discount per voucher, per night. (Only one voucher per night). Vouchers may be used in multiples i.e. five vouchers presented for a five night stay will entitle you to a discount of £5.00.

A **CADE'S CAMPING, TOURING & MOTOR CARAVAN SITE GUIDE 2012 EDITION** must be presented at the time of payment. Vouchers are valid for accommodation only. Vouchers may not be exchanged for cash. Not to be used with any other offer. Valid until 31-12-12.

CONDITIONS OF USE

Vouchers will only be redeemed by those sites featuring a ⬛ symbol in the *facilities* line of their County entry. Presentation of this voucher to the Site Operator at the time of paying your balance will entitle you to a one pound discount per voucher, per night. (Only one voucher per night). Vouchers may be used in multiples i.e. five vouchers presented for a five night stay will entitle you to a discount of £5.00.

A **CADE'S CAMPING, TOURING & MOTOR CARAVAN SITE GUIDE 2012 EDITION** must be presented at the time of payment. Vouchers are valid for accommodation only. Vouchers may not be exchanged for cash. Not to be used with any other offer. Valid until 31-12-12.

CONDITIONS OF USE

Vouchers will only be redeemed by those sites featuring a ⬛ symbol in the *facilities* line of their County entry. Presentation of this voucher to the Site Operator at the time of paying your balance will entitle you to a one pound discount per voucher, per night. (Only one voucher per night). Vouchers may be used in multiples i.e. five vouchers presented for a five night stay will entitle you to a discount of £5.00.

A **CADE'S CAMPING, TOURING & MOTOR CARAVAN SITE GUIDE 2012 EDITION** must be presented at the time of payment. Vouchers are valid for accommodation only. Vouchers may not be exchanged for cash. Not to be used with any other offer. Valid until 31-12-12.

CONDITIONS OF USE

Vouchers will only be redeemed by those sites featuring a ⬛ symbol in the *facilities* line of their County entry. Presentation of this voucher to the Site Operator at the time of paying your balance will entitle you to a one pound discount per voucher, per night. (Only one voucher per night). Vouchers may be used in multiples i.e. five vouchers presented for a five night stay will entitle you to a discount of £5.00.

A **CADE'S CAMPING, TOURING & MOTOR CARAVAN SITE GUIDE 2012 EDITION** must be presented at the time of payment. Vouchers are valid for accommodation only. Vouchers may not be exchanged for cash. Not to be used with any other offer. Valid until 31-12-12.

CONDITIONS OF USE

Vouchers will only be redeemed by those sites featuring a ⬛ symbol in the *facilities* line of their County entry. Presentation of this voucher to the Site Operator at the time of paying your balance will entitle you to a one pound discount per voucher, per night. (Only one voucher per night). Vouchers may be used in multiples i.e. five vouchers presented for a five night stay will entitle you to a discount of £5.00.

A **CADE'S CAMPING, TOURING & MOTOR CARAVAN SITE GUIDE 2012 EDITION** must be presented at the time of payment. Vouchers are valid for accommodation only. Vouchers may not be exchanged for cash. Not to be used with any other offer. Valid until 31-12-12.

CONDITIONS OF USE

Vouchers will only be redeemed by those sites featuring a ⬛ symbol in the *facilities* line of their County entry. Presentation of this voucher to the Site Operator at the time of paying your balance will entitle you to a one pound discount per voucher, per night. (Only one voucher per night). Vouchers may be used in multiples i.e. five vouchers presented for a five night stay will entitle you to a discount of £5.00.

A **CADE'S CAMPING, TOURING & MOTOR CARAVAN SITE GUIDE 2012 EDITION** must be presented at the time of payment. Vouchers are valid for accommodation only. Vouchers may not be exchanged for cash. Not to be used with any other offer. Valid until 31-12-12.

CONDITIONS OF USE

Vouchers will only be redeemed by those sites featuring a ⬛ symbol in the *facilities* line of their County entry. Presentation of this voucher to the Site Operator at the time of paying your balance will entitle you to a one pound discount per voucher, per night. (Only one voucher per night). Vouchers may be used in multiples i.e. five vouchers presented for a five night stay will entitle you to a discount of £5.00.

A **CADE'S CAMPING, TOURING & MOTOR CARAVAN SITE GUIDE 2012 EDITION** must be presented at the time of payment. Vouchers are valid for accommodation only. Vouchers may not be exchanged for cash. Not to be used with any other offer. Valid until 31-12-12.

CONDITIONS OF USE

Vouchers will only be redeemed by those sites featuring a ⬛ symbol in the *facilities* line of their County entry. Presentation of this voucher to the Site Operator at the time of paying your balance will entitle you to a one pound discount per voucher, per night. (Only one voucher per night). Vouchers may be used in multiples i.e. five vouchers presented for a five night stay will entitle you to a discount of £5.00.

A **CADE'S CAMPING, TOURING & MOTOR CARAVAN SITE GUIDE 2012 EDITION** must be presented at the time of payment. Vouchers are valid for accommodation only. Vouchers may not be exchanged for cash. Not to be used with any other offer. Valid until 31-12-12.

CONDITIONS OF USE

Vouchers will only be redeemed by those sites featuring a ⬛ symbol in the *facilities* line of their County entry. Presentation of this voucher to the Site Operator at the time of paying your balance will entitle you to a one pound discount per voucher, per night. (Only one voucher per night). Vouchers may be used in multiples i.e. five vouchers presented for a five night stay will entitle you to a discount of £5.00.

A **CADE'S CAMPING, TOURING & MOTOR CARAVAN SITE GUIDE 2012 EDITION** must be presented at the time of payment. Vouchers are valid for accommodation only. Vouchers may not be exchanged for cash. Not to be used with any other offer. Valid until 31-12-12.

CONDITIONS OF USE

Vouchers will only be redeemed by those sites featuring a ⬛ symbol in the *facilities* line of their County entry. Presentation of this voucher to the Site Operator at the time of paying your balance will entitle you to a one pound discount per voucher, per night. (Only one voucher per night). Vouchers may be used in multiples i.e. five vouchers presented for a five night stay will entitle you to a discount of £5.00.

A **CADE'S CAMPING, TOURING & MOTOR CARAVAN SITE GUIDE 2012 EDITION** must be presented at the time of payment. Vouchers are valid for accommodation only. Vouchers may not be exchanged for cash. Not to be used with any other offer. Valid until 31-12-12.

CONDITIONS OF USE

Vouchers will only be redeemed by those sites featuring a ⬛ symbol in the *facilities* line of their County entry. Presentation of this voucher to the Site Operator at the time of paying your balance will entitle you to a one pound discount per voucher, per night. (Only one voucher per night). Vouchers may be used in multiples i.e. five vouchers presented for a five night stay will entitle you to a discount of £5.00.

A **CADE'S CAMPING, TOURING & MOTOR CARAVAN SITE GUIDE 2012 EDITION** must be presented at the time of payment. Vouchers are valid for accommodation only. Vouchers may not be exchanged for cash. Not to be used with any other offer. Valid until 31-12-12.

CONDITIONS OF USE

Vouchers will only be redeemed by those sites featuring a ⬛ symbol in the *facilities* line of their County entry. Presentation of this voucher to the Site Operator at the time of paying your balance will entitle you to a one pound discount per voucher, per night. (Only one voucher per night). Vouchers may be used in multiples i.e. five vouchers presented for a five night stay will entitle you to a discount of £5.00.

A **CADE'S CAMPING, TOURING & MOTOR CARAVAN SITE GUIDE 2012 EDITION** must be presented at the time of payment. Vouchers are valid for accommodation only. Vouchers may not be exchanged for cash. Not to be used with any other offer. Valid until 31-12-12.